INSTRUCTOR'S SOLUTIONS MANUAL

DANIEL S. MILLER
Niagara County Community College

THINKING MATHEMATICALLY
FIFTH EDITION

Robert Blitzer
Miami Dade College

**Prentice Hall**
is an imprint of

PEARSON

The author and publisher of this book have used their best efforts in preparing this book. These efforts include the development, research, and testing of the theories and programs to determine their effectiveness. The author and publisher make no warranty of any kind, expressed or implied, with regard to these programs or the documentation contained in this book. The author and publisher shall not be liable in any event for incidental or consequential damages in connection with, or arising out of, the furnishing, performance, or use of these programs.

Reproduced by Pearson Addison-Wesley from electronic files supplied by the author.

Copyright © 2011, 2008, 2005 Pearson Education, Inc.
Publishing as Prentice Hall, 75 Arlington Street, Boston, MA 02116.

ISBN-13: 978-0-321-64638-5
ISBN-10: 0-321-64638-X

2 3 4 5 6 BRR 14 13 12 11 10

Prentice Hall
is an imprint of

www.pearsonhighered.com

Contents

Chapter 1
Problem Solving and Critical Thinking

Check Points 1.1

1. Counterexamples will vary. Example: $40 \times 40 = 1600$

2. **a.** Add 6 each time.
   $3 + 6 = 9$
   $9 + 6 = 15$
   $15 + 6 = 21$
   $21 + 6 = 27$
   $27 + 6 = 33$
   3, 9, 15, 21, 27, <u>33</u>

   b. Multiply by 5 each time.
   $2 \times 5 = 10$
   $10 \times 5 = 50$
   $50 \times 5 = 250$
   $250 \times 5 = 1250$
   2, 10, 50, 250, <u>1250</u>

   c. Cycle multiplying by 2, 3, 4.
   $3 \times 2 = 6$
   $6 \times 3 = 18$
   $18 \times 4 = 72$
   $72 \times 2 = 144$
   $144 \times 3 = 432$
   $432 \times 4 = 1728$
   $1728 \times 2 = 3456$
   6, 18, 72, 144, 432, 1728, <u>3456</u>

   d. Cycle adding 8, adding 8, subtracting 14.
   $1 + 8 = 9$
   $9 + 8 = 17$
   $17 - 14 = 3$
   $3 + 8 = 11$
   $11 + 8 = 19$
   $19 - 14 = 5$
   $5 + 8 = 13$
   $13 + 8 = 21$
   $21 - 14 = 7$
   9, 17, 3, 11, 19, 5, 13, 21, <u>7</u>

3. **a.** Starting with the third number, each number is the sum of the previous two numbers, $29 + 47 = 76$

   b. Starting with the second number, each number one less than twice the previous number, $2(129) - 1 = 257$

4. The shapes alternate between rectangle and triangle.
   The number of little legs cycles from 1 to 2 to 3 and then back to 1.
   Therefore the next figure will be a rectangle with 2 little legs.

5. **a.** Conjecture based on results: The original number is doubled.

Select a number.	4	10	0	3
Multiply the number by 4.	$4 \times 4 = 16$	$10 \times 4 = 40$	$0 \times 4 = 0$	$3 \times 4 = 12$
Add 6 to the product.	$16 + 6 = 22$	$40 + 6 = 46$	$0 + 6 = 6$	$12 + 6 = 18$
Divide this sum by 2.	$22 \div 2 = 11$	$46 \div 2 = 23$	$6 \div 2 = 3$	$18 \div 2 = 9$
Subtract 3 from the quotient.	$11 - 3 = 8$	$23 - 3 = 20$	$3 - 3 = 0$	$9 - 3 = 6$
Summary of results:	4 → 8	10 → 20	0 → 0	3 → 6

   b. Select a number: n
   Multiply the number by 4: $4n$
   Add 6 to the product: $4n + 6$
   Divide this sum by 2: $\dfrac{4n + 6}{2} = \dfrac{4n}{2} + \dfrac{6}{2} = 2n + 3$
   Subtract 3 from the quotient: $2n + 3 - 3 = 2n$

Exercise Set 1.1

1. Counterexamples will vary. Example: President Obama was younger than 65 at the time of his inauguration.

2. Counterexamples will vary. Example: Beyoncé Knowles is a singer who appears in movies.

3. Counterexamples will vary. Example: 3 multiplied by itself is 9, which is not even.

4. Counterexamples will vary. Example: 100 is a three-digit number and $100 + 100 = 200$, which is not a four-digit number.

5. Counterexamples will vary. Example: Adding 1 to the numerator and denominator of $\frac{1}{2}$ results in $\frac{2}{3}$ which is not equal to $\frac{1}{2}$.

6. Counterexamples will vary. Example: $8 - 3 = 5$, which is odd, but 8 and 3 are not both odd.

7. Counterexamples will vary. Example: When -1 is added to itself, the result is -2, which is less than -1.

8. Counterexamples will vary. Example: When 1 is divided by -2, the result is $-\frac{1}{2}$, which is greater than -2.

9. Pattern: Add 4
   $24 + 4 = 28$
   8, 12, 16, 20, 24, $\underline{28}$

10. Pattern: Add 5
    $39 + 5 = 44$
    19, 24, 29, 34, 39, $\underline{44}$

11. Pattern: Subtract 5
    $17 - 5 = 12$
    37, 32, 27, 22, 17, $\underline{12}$

12. Pattern: Subtract 4
    $17 - 4 = 13$
    33, 29, 25, 21, 17, $\underline{13}$

13. Pattern: Multiply by 3
    $243 \times 3 = 729$
    3, 9, 27, 81, 243, $\underline{729}$

14. Pattern: Multiply by 4
    $512 \times 4 = 2048$
    2, 8, 32, 128, 512, $\underline{2048}$

15. Pattern: Multiply by 2
    $16 \times 2 = 32$
    1, 2, 4, 8, 16, $\underline{32}$

16. Pattern: Multiply by 5
    $125 \times 5 = 625$
    1, 5, 25, 125, $\underline{625}$

17. Pattern: 1 alternates with numbers that are multiplied by 2
    $16 \times 2 = 32$
    1, 4, 1, 8, 1, 16, 1, $\underline{32}$

18. Pattern: 1 alternates with numbers that are increased by 3
    $10 + 3 = 13$
    1, 4, 1, 7, 1, 10, 1, $\underline{13}$

19. Pattern: Subtract 2
    $-4 - 2 = -6$
    4, 2, 0, -2, -4, $\underline{-6}$

20. Pattern: Subtract 3
    $-6 - 3 = -9$
    6, 3, 0, -3, -6, $\underline{-9}$

21. Pattern: Add 4 to the denominator
    $\frac{1}{18+4} = \frac{1}{22}$
    $\frac{1}{2}, \frac{1}{6}, \frac{1}{10}, \frac{1}{14}, \frac{1}{18}, \underline{\frac{1}{22}}$

22. Pattern: Add 1 to the denominator
    $\frac{1}{5+1} = \frac{1}{6}$
    $1, \frac{1}{2}, \frac{1}{3}, \frac{1}{4}, \frac{1}{5}, \underline{\frac{1}{6}}$

23. Pattern: Multiply the denominator by 3
    $\frac{1}{27 \times 3} = \frac{1}{81}$
    $1, \frac{1}{3}, \frac{1}{9}, \frac{1}{27}, \underline{\frac{1}{81}}$

24. Pattern: Multiply the denominator by 2
    $\frac{1}{8 \times 2} = \frac{1}{16}$
    $1, \frac{1}{2}, \frac{1}{4}, \frac{1}{8}, \underline{\frac{1}{16}}$

25. Pattern: The second number is obtained by adding 4 to the first number. The third number is obtained by adding 5 to the second number. The number being added to the previous number increases by 1 each time. $33 + 9 = \underline{42}$

26. Pattern: The second number is obtained by adding 3 to the first number. The third number is obtained by adding 4 to the second number. The number being added to the previous number increases by 1 each time. $27 + 8 = \underline{35}$

27. Pattern: The second number is obtained by adding 3 to the first number. The third number is obtained by adding 5 to the second number. The number being added to the previous number increases by 2 each time. $38 + 13 = \underline{51}$

28. Pattern: The second number is obtained by adding 3 to the first number. The third number is obtained by adding 5 to the second number. The number being added to the previous number increases by 2 each time. $37 + 13 = \underline{50}$

29. Pattern: Starting with the third number, each number is the sum of the previous two numbers. $27 + 44 = \underline{71}$

30. Pattern: Starting with the third number, each number is the sum of the previous two numbers. $19 + 31 = \underline{50}$

31. Pattern: Cycle by adding 5, adding 5, then subtracting 7. $13 + 5 = \underline{18}$

32. Pattern: Cycle by adding 6, adding 6, then subtracting 10. $13 + 6 = \underline{19}$

33. Pattern: The second number is obtained by multiplying the first number by 2. The third number is obtained by subtracting 1 from the second number. Then multiply by 2 and then subtract 1, repeatedly. $34 - 1 = \underline{33}$

34. Pattern: The second number is obtained by multiplying the first number by 3. The third number is obtained by subtracting 1 from the second number. Then multiply by 3 and then subtract 1, repeatedly. $123 - 1 = \underline{122}$

35. Pattern: Divide by -4

$$-1 \div (-4) = \frac{1}{4}$$

$$64, \ -16, \ 4, \ -1, \ \frac{1}{\underline{4}}$$

36. Pattern: Divide by -5

$$-1 \div (-4) = \frac{1}{5}$$

$$125, \ -25, \ 5, \ -1, \ \frac{1}{\underline{5}}$$

37. Pattern: The second value of each pair is 4 less than the first.
$3 - 4 = -1$
$(6,2), \ (0,-4), \ (7\frac{1}{2}, 3\frac{1}{2}), \ (2,-2), \ (3, \underline{-1})$

38. Pattern: The second value of each pair is the square of the first.
$$\left(-\frac{4}{7}\right)^2 = \frac{16}{49}$$
$$\left(\frac{2}{3}, \frac{4}{9}\right), \left(\frac{1}{5}, \frac{1}{25}\right), (7, 49), \left(-\frac{5}{6}, \frac{25}{36}\right), \left(-\frac{4}{7}, \frac{16}{\underline{49}}\right)$$

39. The figure cycles from square to triangle to circle and then repeats. So the next figure is

40. The figure rotates 90° counterclockwise. So the next figure is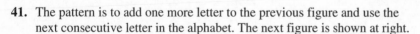

41. The pattern is to add one more letter to the previous figure and use the next consecutive letter in the alphabet. The next figure is shown at right.

d	d	d
d	d	

42. The figure alternates from triangle to square and gains one line on the bottom. The next figure is ⊿.

43. a. Conjecture based on results: The original number is doubled.

Select a number.	4	10	0	3
Multiply the number by 4.	$4 \times 4 = 16$	$10 \times 4 = 40$	$0 \times 4 = 0$	$3 \times 4 = 12$
Add 8 to the product.	$16 + 8 = 24$	$40 + 8 = 48$	$0 + 8 = 8$	$12 + 8 = 20$
Divide this sum by 2.	$24 \div 2 = 12$	$48 \div 2 = 24$	$8 \div 2 = 4$	$20 \div 2 = 10$
Subtract 4 from the quotient.	$12 - 4 = 8$	$24 - 4 = 20$	$4 - 4 = 0$	$10 - 4 = 6$
Summary of results:	$4 \rightarrow 8$	$10 \rightarrow 20$	$0 \rightarrow 0$	$3 \rightarrow 6$

b. $4n$

$4n + 8$

$\dfrac{4n + 8}{2} = \dfrac{4n}{2} + \dfrac{8}{2} = 2n + 4$

$2n + 4 - 4 = 2n$

44. a. Conjecture based on results: The result is always 2.

Select a number.	4	10	0	3
Multiply the number by 3.	$4 \times 3 = 12$	$10 \times 3 = 30$	$0 \times 3 = 0$	$3 \times 3 = 9$
Add 6 to the product.	$12 + 6 = 18$	$30 + 6 = 36$	$0 + 6 = 6$	$9 + 6 = 15$
Divide this sum by 3.	$18 \div 3 = 6$	$36 \div 3 = 12$	$6 \div 3 = 2$	$15 \div 3 = 5$
Subtract the original from the quotient.	$6 - 4 = 2$	$12 - 10 - 2$	$2 - 0 = 2$	$5 - 3 = 2$
Summary of results:	$4 \rightarrow 2$	$10 \rightarrow 2$	$0 \rightarrow 2$	$3 \rightarrow 2$

b. $3n$

$3n + 6$

$\dfrac{3n + 6}{3} = \dfrac{3n}{3} + \dfrac{6}{3} = n + 2$

$n + 2 - n = 2$

45. a. Conjecture based on results: The result is always 3.

Select a number.	4	10	0	3
Add 5 to the number.	$4 + 5 = 9$	$10 + 5 = 15$	$0 + 5 = 5$	$3 + 5 = 8$
Double the result.	$9 \times 2 = 18$	$15 \times 2 = 30$	$5 \times 2 = 10$	$8 \times 2 = 16$
Subtract 4.	$18 - 4 = 14$	$30 - 4 = 26$	$10 - 4 = 6$	$16 - 4 = 12$
Divide the result by 2.	$14 \div 2 = 7$	$26 \div 2 = 13$	$6 \div 2 = 3$	$12 \div 2 = 6$
Subtract the original number.	$7 - 4 = 3$	$13 - 10 = 3$	$3 - 0 = 3$	$6 - 3 = 3$
Summary of results:	$4 \rightarrow 3$	$10 \rightarrow 3$	$0 \rightarrow 3$	$3 \rightarrow 3$

b. $n + 5$

$2(n + 5) = 2n + 10$

$2n + 10 - 4 = 2n + 6$

$\dfrac{2n + 6}{2} = \dfrac{2n}{2} + \dfrac{6}{2} = n + 3$

$n + 3 - n = 3$

46. a. Conjecture based on results: The result is always 5.

Select a number.	4	10	0	3
Add 3 to the number.	$4+3=7$	$10+3=13$	$0+3=3$	$3+3=6$
Double the result.	$7\times2=14$	$13\times2=26$	$3\times2=6$	$6\times2=12$
Add 4.	$14+4=18$	$26+4=30$	$6+4=10$	$12+4=16$
Divide the result by 2.	$18\div2=9$	$30\div2=15$	$10\div2=5$	$16\div2=8$
Subtract the original number.	$9-4=5$	$15-10=5$	$5-0=5$	$8-3=5$
Summary of results:	$4\rightarrow5$	$10\rightarrow5$	$0\rightarrow5$	$3\rightarrow5$

   b. $n+3$

   $2(n+3)=2n+6$

   $2n+6+4=2n+10$

   $\dfrac{2n+10}{2}=\dfrac{2n}{2}+\dfrac{10}{2}=n+5$

   $n+5-n=5$

47. Using inductive reasoning we predict $1+2+3+4+5+6=\dfrac{6\times7}{2}$.

   Arithmetic verifies this result: $21=21$

48. Using inductive reasoning we predict $3+6+9+12+15+18=\dfrac{18\times7}{2}$.

   Arithmetic verifies this result: $63=63$

49. Using inductive reasoning we predict $1+3+5+7+9+11=6\times6$.

   Arithmetic verifies this result: $36=36$

50. Using inductive reasoning we predict $\dfrac{1}{1\times2}+\dfrac{1}{2\times3}+\dfrac{1}{3\times4}+\dfrac{1}{4\times5}+\dfrac{1}{5\times6}=\dfrac{5}{6}$.

   Arithmetic verifies this result:

   $$\dfrac{1}{1\times2}+\dfrac{1}{2\times3}+\dfrac{1}{3\times4}+\dfrac{1}{4\times5}+\dfrac{1}{5\times6}=\dfrac{5}{6}$$

   $$\dfrac{1}{2}+\dfrac{1}{6}+\dfrac{1}{12}+\dfrac{1}{20}+\dfrac{1}{30}=\dfrac{5}{6}$$

   $$\dfrac{30}{60}+\dfrac{10}{60}+\dfrac{5}{60}+\dfrac{3}{60}+\dfrac{2}{60}=\dfrac{5}{6}$$

   $$\dfrac{50}{60}=\dfrac{5}{6}$$

   $$\dfrac{5}{6}=\dfrac{5}{6}$$

51. Using inductive reasoning we predict $98765\times9+3=888,888$.

   Arithmetic verifies this result:

   $98765\times9+3=888,888$

   $888,885+3=888,888$

   $888,888=888,888$

52. Using inductive reasoning we predict
$54321 \times 9 - 1 = 488,888$.
Arithmetic verifies this result:
$54321 \times 9 - 1 = 488,888$
$488,889 - 1 = 488,888$
$488,888 = 488,888$

53. The first multiplier increases by 33.
$132 + 33 = 165$
The second multiplier is 3367.
The product increases by 111,111.
$165 \times 3367 = 555,555$ is correct.

54. The pattern implies we should attach a 6 to the right of the first multiplier. The second multiplier is always 8. The pattern implies we should add 6 to that product to obtain 987,654.
$123,456 \times 8 + 6 = 987,654$ is correct.

55. b; The resulting exponent is always the first exponent added to twice the second exponent.

56. c; The resulting exponent is always half the sum of the three exponents.

57. deductive; The specific value was based on a general formula.

58. inductive; The general conclusion for all HMO patients was based on specific observations.

59. inductive; The general conclusion for all full-time four-year colleges was based on specific observations.

60. deductive; The specific grade was based on a general course policy.

61. **a.**   1, 3, 6, 10, 15, and 21 are followed by
$21 + 7 = 28$
$28 + 8 = 36$
$36 + 9 = 45$
$45 + 10 = 55$
$55 + 11 = 66$
1, 3, 6, 10, 15, 21, 28, 36, 45, 55, and 66.

   b. $4 - 1 = 3$
$9 - 4 = 5$
$16 - 9 = 7$
$25 - 16 = 9$
The successive differences increase by 2.
$25 + 11 = 36$
$36 + 13 = 49$
$49 + 15 = 64$
$64 + 17 = 81$
$81 + 19 = 100$

c.   The successive differences are 4, 7, and 10. Since these differences are increasing by 3 each time. The next five numbers will be found by using differences of 13, 16, 19, 22, and 25.
$22 + 13 = 35$
$35 + 16 = 51$
$51 + 19 = 70$
$70 + 22 = 92$
$92 + 25 = 117$

d.   If a triangular number is multiplied by 8 and then 1 is added to the product, a <u>square</u> number is obtained.

62. Each row begins and ends with 1. Other numbers are the sum of the two values that are diagonally above.

```
              1
           1     1
        1     2     1
     1     3     3     1
  1     4     6     4     1
1     5    10    10     5     1
```

66. does not make sense; Explanations will vary. Sample explanation: Such conclusions would be certain.

67. makes sense

68. does not make sense; Explanations will vary. Sample explanation: Though this sample was 51%, it is not certain that this exact percentage will hold for the entire population.

69. makes sense

70. The pattern suggests that the compatible expression is the square of the first number minus twice the product of the two numbers, plus the square of the second number.
$(11 - 7)^2 = 121 - 154 + 49$

71. **a.**   The sums are all 30:

16	3	11
5	10	15
9	17	4

b.   The sums are all 36:

17	5	14
9	12	15
10	19	7

c.   For any values of a, b, and c, the sums of all rows, all columns, and both diagonals are the same.

d. The sums of the expressions in each row, each column, and each diagonal is $3a$.

e. Finding each sum verifies the conjecture that they are all $3a$.
First row: $(a+b)+(a-b-c)+(a+c)=3a$
Second row: $(a-b+c)+(a)+(a+b-c)=3a$
Third row: $(a-c)+(a+b+c)+(a-b)=3a$
First Column: $(a+b)+(a-b+c)+(a-c)=3a$
Second Column:
$(a-b-c)+(a)+(a+b+c)=3a$
Third Column:
$(a+c)+(a+b-c)+(a-b)=3a$
First Diagonal: $(a+b)+(a)+(a-b)=3a$
Second Diagonal: $(a-c)+(a)+(a+c)=3a$

72. Answers will vary. Possible answer: 5, 10, 15 or 5, 10, 20.

$5 \times 1 = 5$ $5 \times 2^0 = 5$
$5 \times 2 = 10$ $5 \times 2^1 = 10$
$5 \times 3 = 15$ $5 \times 2^2 = 20$

73. a. The result is a three- or four- digit number in which the thousands and hundreds places represent the month of the birthday and the tens and ones places represent the day of the birthday.

b. $5[4(5M+6)+9]+D-165$
$= 5[20M+24+9]+D-165$
$= 5[20M+33]+D-165$
$= 100M+165+D-165$
$= 100M+D$

74. a. $6 \times 6 = 36$
$66 \times 66 = 4356$
$666 \times 666 = 443{,}556$
$6666 \times 6666 = 44{,}435{,}556$

b. An additional digit of 6 is attached to the numbers being multiplied. An additional digit of 4 is attached to the left of the result and an additional digit of 5 is placed between the 3 and the 6.

c. $66666 \times 66666 = 4{,}444{,}355{,}556$
$666{,}666 \times 666{,}666 = 444{,}443{,}555{,}556$

d. Inductive reasoning; it uses an observed pattern and draws conclusions from that pattern.

75. a. $3367 \times 3 = 10101$
$3367 \times 6 = 20202$
$3367 \times 9 = 30303$
$3367 \times 12 = 40404$

b. The first multiplier is always 3367. The second multipliers are successive multiples of 3. The product increases by 10101.

c. $3367 \times 15 = 50505$
$3367 \times 18 = 60606$

d. Inductive reasoning; it uses an observed pattern and draws conclusions from that pattern.

Check Points 1.2

1. a. The digit to the right of the billions digit is greater than 5. Thus, add 1 to the digit to be rounded and replace all the digits to the right with zeroes. 6,751,593,103 rounded to the nearest billion is 7,000,000,000.

b. The digit to the right of the hundred millions is 5. Thus, add 1 to the digit to be rounded and replace all the digits to the right with zeroes. 6,751,593,103 rounded to the nearest hundred million is 6,800,000,000.

c. The digit to the right of the ten thousands digit is less than 5. Thus, replace all the digits to the right with zeroes. 6,751,593,103 rounded to the nearest hundred thousand is 6,751,590,000.

2. a. The digit to the right of the tenths digit is less than 5. Thus, 3.141593 rounded to the nearest tenth is 3.1.

b. The digit to the right of the ten-thousandths digit is greater than 5. Thus, 3.141593 rounded to the nearest ten-thousandth is 3.1416.

3. a.

$\$2.40+\$1.25+\$4.60+\$4.40+\$1.40+\$1.85+2.95$
$\approx \$2+\$1+\$5+\$4+\$1+\$2+3$
$\approx \$18$

b. The bill of $21.85 is not reasonable. It is too high.

4. a. Round \$52 per hour to \$50 per hour and assume 40 hours per week.

$$\frac{40 \text{ hours}}{\text{week}} \times \frac{\$50}{\text{hour}} = \frac{\$2000}{\text{week}}$$

The architect's salary is $\approx \$2000$ per week.

b. Round 52 weeks per year to 50 weeks per year.

$$\frac{\$2000}{\text{week}} \times \frac{50 \text{ weeks}}{\text{year}} = \frac{\$100,000}{\text{year}}$$

The architect's salary is $\approx \$100,000$ per year.

5. a. $0.32 \times 21,728,978$

b. $0.3 \times 22,000,000 = 6,600,000$ defined old age in this way.

6. a. The yearly increase in life expectancy can be approximated by dividing the change in life expectancy by the change in time from 1960 to 2005. $\dfrac{80.4 - 73.1}{2005 - 1960} = \dfrac{7.3}{45} \approx 0.16$ yr for each subsequent birth year.

b.
$$\overset{\substack{\text{life expectancy} \\ \text{in 1950}}}{\overbrace{73.1}} + \overset{\substack{\text{yearly} \\ \text{increase}}}{\overbrace{0.16}} (\overset{\substack{\text{number of years} \\ \text{from 1960 to 2050}}}{\overbrace{2050 - 1960}})$$
$$= 73.1 + 0.16(90)$$
$$= 73.1 + 14.4$$
$$= 87.5 \text{ yr}$$

Exercise Set 1.2

1. a. 55,444,600

b. 55,445,000

c. 55,440,000

d. 55,400,000

e. 55,000,000

f. 60,000,000

2. a. 1,528,000

b. 1,528,000

c. 1,530,000

d. 1,500,000

e. 2,000,000

3. 2.718

7. a. about 66% of seniors

b. The percentage of seniors who used marijuana decreased at the slowest rate can be found by identifying the portion of the graph with the smallest downward slope. This occurs between 2000 and 2005.

c. Approximately 57% of seniors used alcohol in 1990.

8. a. The yearly increase in tuition and fees can be approximated by dividing the change in tuition and fees by the change in time from 2000 to 2008. $\dfrac{\$23,712 - \$15,518}{2008 - 2000} = \dfrac{\$8194}{8} \approx \$1024$

b. $T = \overset{\substack{\text{Cost in} \\ 2000}}{\overbrace{15,518}} + \overset{\substack{\text{yearly} \\ \text{increase}}}{\overbrace{1024}} x$

c. 2012 is 12 years after 2000. Thus,
$$T = 15,518 + 1024x$$
$$= 15,518 + 1024(12)$$
$$= \$27,806$$

4. 2.7183

5. 2.71828

6. 2.718282

7. 2.718281828

8. 2.7182818285

9. $350 + 600 = 950$
Actual answer of 955 compares reasonably well

10. $250 + 800 = 1050$
Actual answer of 1045 compares reasonably well

11. $9 + 1 + 19 = 29$
Actual answer of 29.23 compares quite well

12. $8 + 3 + 24 = 35$
Actual answer of 35.34 compares quite well

13. $32 - 11 = 21$
Actual answer of 20.911 compares quite well

14. $46 - 15 = 31$
Actual answer of 30.893 compares quite well

15. $40 \times 6 = 240$
Actual answer of 218.185 compares not so well

16. $80 \times 7 = 560$
Actual answer of 512.98 compares not so well

17. $0.8 \times 400 = 320$
Actual answer of 327.06 compares reasonably well

18. $0.7 \times 200 = 140$
Actual answer of 141.37 compares quite well

19. $48 \div 3 = 16$
Actual answer of 16.49 compares quite well

20. $55 \div 5 = 11$
Actual answer of 11.62 compares quite well

21. 30% of 200,000 is 60,000
Actual answer of 59,920.96 compares quite well

22. 40% of 300,000 is 120,000
Actual answer of 122,432.52 compares reasonably well

23. $\$3.47 + \$5.89 + \$19.98 + \$2.03 + \$11.85 + \$0.23$
$\approx \$3 + \$6 + \$20 + \$2 + \$12 + \$0$
$\approx \$43$

24. $\$4 + \$8 + \$29 + \$4 + \$13 + \$1 = \$59$

25. Round \$19.50 to \$20 per hour.
40 hours per week
(40 × \$20) per week = \$800/week
Round 52 weeks to 50 weeks per year.
50 weeks per year
(50 × \$800) per year = \$40,000
\$19.50 per hour ≈ \$40,000 per year

26. $\$30 \times 40 \times 50 = \$60,000$ per year

27. Round the \$605 monthly payment to \$600.
3 years is 36 months.
Round the 36 months to 40 months.
\$600 × 40 months = \$24,000 total cost.
\$605 monthly payment for 3 years ≈ \$24,000 total cost.

28. Round the \$415 monthly payment to \$400.
4 years is 48 months.
Round the 48 months to 50 months.
\$400 × 50 months = \$20,000 total cost.
\$415 monthly payment for 3 years ≈ \$20,000 total cost.

29. Round the raise of \$310,000 to \$300,000.
Round the 294 professors to 300.
\$300,000 ÷ 300 professors = \$1000 per professor.
\$310,000 raise ≈ \$1000 per professor.

30. Round the raise of \$310,000 to \$300,000.
Round the 196 professors to 200.
\$300,000 ÷ 200 professors = \$1500 per professor.
\$310,000 raise ≈ \$1500 per professor.

31. Round \$61,500 to \$60,000 per year.
Round 52 weeks per year to 50 weeks per year.
50 weeks × 40 hours per week = 2000 hours
\$60,000 ÷ 2000 hours = \$30 per hour
\$61,500 per year ≈ \$30 per hour

32. Round \$38,950 to \$40,000 per year.
Round 52 weeks per year to 50 weeks per year.
50 weeks × 40 hours per week = 2000 hours
\$40,000 ÷ 2000 hours = \$20 per hour
\$38,950 per year ≈ \$20 per hour

33. $80 \times 365 \times 24 = 700,800$ hr

34. $40 \times 365 \times 24 = 350,400$ hr

35. $\dfrac{0.2 \times 100}{0.5} = \dfrac{20}{0.5} = 40$
Actual answer of 42.03 compares quite reasonable.

36. $\dfrac{0.5 \times 90}{0.25} = \dfrac{45}{0.25} = 180$
Actual answer of 169.62 compares somewhat reasonable.

37. The given information suggests \$30 would be a good estimate per calculator.
$\$30 \times 10 = \$300$ which is closest to choice b.

38. The given information suggests \$7 would be a good estimate per calculator.
$\$7 \times 10 = \$70$ which is closest to choice c.

39. The given information suggests 65 mph would be a good rate estimate and 3.5 would be a good time estimate.
$65 \times 3.5 = 227.5$ which is closest to choice c.

40. The given information suggests 45 mph would be a good rate estimate and 3.5 would be a good time estimate.
$45 \times 3.5 = 157.5$ which is closest to choice b.

41. The given information suggests you can count 1 number per second.

$$\frac{10000}{60 \times 60} \approx 2.77 \text{ or } 3 \text{ hours}$$

42. The given information suggests you can count 1 number per second.

$$\frac{1,000,000}{60 \times 60 \times 24} \approx 11.57 \text{ or } 12 \text{ days}$$

43. 50% of 200,000,000 is 100,000,000 American adults.

44. 25% of 200,000,000 is 50,000,000 American adults.

45. a. about 85 people per 100

b. $(85 - 23) \times 87 \approx 5400$

46. a. about 66 people per 100

b. $(66 - 27) \times 72 \approx 2800$

47. a. $\frac{57.4 - 33.1}{2006 - 1980} = \frac{24.3}{26} \approx 0.9$

The annual increase is about 0.9%.

b. $33.1 + 0.9(2010 - 1980) = 33.1 + 0.9(30)$
$$= 33.1 + 27$$
$$= 60.1$$

In 2010 the percentage will be approximately 60.1%.

48. a. $\frac{43.1 - 20.9}{2006 - 1980} = \frac{22.2}{26} \approx 0.9$

The annual increase is about 0.9%.

b. $20.9 + 0.9(2010 - 1980) = 20.9 + 0.9(30)$
$$= 20.9 + 27$$
$$= 47.9$$

In 2010 the percentage will be approximately 47.9%.

49. a. The maximum was reached in 2000. The percentage was about 69% or 70%.

b. The greatest rate of increase was from 1965 to 1970.

c. 1965

50. a. The minimum was reached in 1960. The percentage was about 18% or 19%..

b. The greatest rate of decrease was from 2000 to 2005.

c. 1995

51. a. $\frac{153 - 122}{2007 - 1985} = \frac{31}{22} \approx 1.4$ million per year

b. $F = 122 + 1.4x$

c. 2020 is 35 years after 1985.
$F = 122 + 1.4(35) = 171$ million

52. a. $\frac{149 - 116}{2007 - 1985} = \frac{33}{22} = 1.5$ million per year

b. $M = 116 + 1.5x$

c. 2020 is 35 years after 1985.
$M = 116 + 1.5(35) = 168.5$ million

66. makes sense

67. does not make sense; Explanations will vary. Sample explanation: Very large numbers and very small numbers often must be estimated when using a calculator.

68. makes sense

69. does not make sense; Explanations will vary. Sample explanation: Some mathematical models can break down over time.

70. Since there are infinitely many digits, the digits can not be reversed.

71. a

72. d

73. b

74. c

75. $20 \times 16 \times 50 = 16,000$ hours .

$$\frac{16,000}{24} \approx 667 \text{ days}$$

$$\frac{667}{365} \approx 1.8 \text{ yr}$$

76. Round days in a year to 400.

$$\frac{\$1,000,000,000}{\$1000/\text{day}} = 1,000,000 \text{ days}$$

$$\approx \frac{1,000,000 \text{ days}}{400 \text{ days/year}}$$

$$\approx 2500 \text{ years}$$

Check Points 1.3

1. The amount of money given to the cashier is unknown.

2. Step 1: Understand the problem.
    Bottles: 128 ounces costs $5.39
    Boxes: a 9-pack of 6.75 ounce boxes costs $3.15
    We must determine whether bottles or boxes are the better value.
    Step 2: Devise a plan.
    Dividing the cost by the number of ounces will give us the cost per ounce. We will need to multiply 9 by 6.75 to determine the total number of ounces the boxes contain. The lower cost per ounce is the best value.
    Step 3: Carry out the plan and solve the problem.

    Unit price for the bottles: $\dfrac{\$5.39}{128 \text{ ounces}} \approx \$0.042$ per ounce

    Unit price for the boxes: $\dfrac{\$3.15}{9 \times 6.75 \text{ ounces}} = \dfrac{\$3.15}{60.75 \text{ ounces}} \approx \$0.052$ per ounce

    Bottles have a lower price per ounce and are the better value.
    Step 4: Look back and check the answer.
    This answer satisfies the conditions of the problem.

3. Step 1: Understand the problem.
    We are given the cost of the computer, the amount of cash paid up front, and the amount paid each month. We must determine the number of months it will take to finish paying for the computer.
    Step 2: Devise a plan.
    Subtract the amount paid in cash from the cost of the computer. This results in the amount still to be paid. Because the monthly payments are $45, divide the amount still to be paid by 45. This will give the number of months required to pay for the computer.
    Step 3: Carry out the plan and solve the problem.
    The balance is $980 - \$350 = \$630.$ Now divide the $630 balance by $45, the monthly payment.

    $$\$630 \div \frac{\$45}{\text{month}} = \$630 \times \frac{\text{month}}{\$45} = \frac{630 \text{ months}}{45} = 14 \text{ months}.$$

    Step 4: Look back and check the answer.
    This answer satisfies the conditions of the problem. 14 monthly payments at $45 each gives $14 \times \$45 = \$630$. Adding in the up front cash payment of $350 gives us $\$630 + \$350 = \$980.$ $980 is the cost of the computer.

4. Step 1: Understand the problem.
   Step 2: Devise a plan.
   Make a list of all possible coin combinations. Begin with the coins of larger value and work toward the coins of smaller value.

   Step 3: Carry out the plan and solve the problem.

Quarters	Dimes	Nickels
1	0	1
0	3	0
0	2	2
0	1	4
0	0	6

   There are 5 combinations.
   Step 4: Look back and check the answer.
   Check to see that no combinations are omitted, and that those given total 30 cents. Also double-check the count.

5. Step 1: Understand the problem.
   We must determine the number of jeans/T-shirt combinations that we can make.
   For example, one such combination would be to wear the blue jeans with the beige shirt.
   Step 2: Devise a plan.
   Each pair of jeans could be matched with any of the three shirts. We will make a tree diagram to show all combinations.
   Step 3: Carry out the plan and solve the problem.

JEANS	T-SHIRT	COMBINATIONS
Blue jeans	Beige shirt	Blue jeans-Beige shirt
	Yellow shirt	Blue jeans-Yellow shirt
	Blue shirt	Blue jeans-Blue shirt
Black jeans	Beige shirt	Black jeans-Beige shirt
	Yellow shirt	Black jeans-Yellow shirt
	Blue shirt	Black jeans-Blue shirt

   There are 6 different outfits possible.
   Step 4: Look back and check the answer.
   Check to see that no combinations are omitted, and double-check the count.

6. Step 1: Understand the problem.
   There are many possible ways to visit each city once and then return home. We must find a route that costs less than $1460.
   Step 2: Devise a plan.
   From city A fly to the city with the cheapest available flight. Repeat this until all cities have been visited and then fly home. If this cost is above $1460 then use trial and error to find other alternative routes.
   Step 3: Carry out the plan and solve the problem.
   A to D costs $185, D to E costs $302, E to C costs $165, C to B costs $305, B back to A costs $500
    $185 + $302 + $165 + $305 + $500 = $1457
   The route A, D, E, C, B, A costs less than $1460
   Step 4: Look back and check the answer.
   This answer satisfies the conditions of the problem.

Trick Questions 1.3

1. The farmer has 12 sheep left since all but 12 sheep died.

2. All 12 months have [at least] 28 days.

3. The doctor and brother are brother and sister.

4. You should light the match first.

Exercise Set 1.3

1. The price of the computer is needed.

2. The weight of the steak is needed.

3. The number of words per page is needed.

4. The amount of the payments is needed.

5. Weekly salary is unnecessary information.
   $212 - 200 = 12$ items sold in excess of 200
   $12 \times \$15 = \$180$ extra is received.

6. Tire weight is unnecessary information.
   $4 \times (\$42 + \$2.50) = 4 \times \$44.50 = \$178.00$
   $\$250 - \$178 = \$72$ remaining after purchase.

7. How much the attendant was given is not necessary.
   There were 5 hours of parking.
   1st hour is $2.50
   4 hours at $0.50/hr
   $\$2.50 + (4 \times \$0.50) = \$2.50 + \$2.00$
   $$= \$4.50$$
   $4.50 was charged.

8. The width of the house is not necessary.
   $90 \text{ feet} = 15 \times 6 \text{ feet}$
   The line representing the length is 15 inches.

9. a. Step 1: Understand the problem.
       Box #1: 15.3 ounces costs $3.37
       Box #2: 24 ounces costs $4.59
       We must determine whether Box #1 or Box #2 is the better value.
       Step 2: Devise a plan.
       Dividing the cost by the number of ounces will give us the cost per ounce. The lower cost per ounce is the best value.
       Step 3: Carry out the plan and solve the problem.
       Unit price for Box #1: $\dfrac{\$3.37}{15.3 \text{ ounces}} \approx \$0.22$ per ounce
       Unit price for Box #2: $\dfrac{\$4.59}{24 \text{ ounces}} \approx \$0.19$ per ounce
       The cereal that is 24 ounces for $4.59 is the better value.
       Step 4: Look back and check the answer.
       This answer satisfies the conditions of the problem.

   b.   Unit price for Box #1: $0.22 per ounce

        Unit price for Box #2: $\dfrac{\$4.59}{24 \text{ ounces}} \times \dfrac{16 \text{ ounces}}{\text{pound}} \approx \$3.06$ per pound

   c.   No, explanations will vary.

10. a.   Step 1: Understand the problem.
        Jar #1: 12 ounces costs $2.25
        Jar #2: 18 ounces costs $3.24
        We must determine whether Jar #1 or Jar #2 is the better value.
        Step 2: Devise a plan.
        Dividing the cost by the number of ounces will give us the cost per ounce. The lower cost per ounce is the best value.
        Step 3: Carry out the plan and solve the problem.

        Unit price for Jar #1: $\dfrac{\$2.25}{12 \text{ ounces}} \approx \$0.19$ per ounce

        Unit price for Jar #2: $\dfrac{\$3.24}{18 \text{ ounces}} \approx \$0.18$ per ounce

        The honey that is 18 ounces for $3.24 is the better value.
        Step 4: Look back and check the answer.
        This answer satisfies the conditions of the problem.

   b.   Unit price for Jar #1: $0.19 per ounce

        Unit price for Jar #2: $\dfrac{\$3.24}{18 \text{ ounces}} \times \dfrac{32 \text{ ounces}}{\text{quart}} \approx \$5.76$ per quart

   c.   No, explanations will vary.

11.   Step 1: Comparing two yearly salaries
     Step 2:
     Convert the second person's wages to yearly salary.
     Step 3:
     The person that earns $3750/month earns
     $12 \times \$3750 = \$45,000$/year. The person that earns $48,000/year gets $3000 more per year.
     Step 4:
     It appears to satisfy the conditions of the problem.

12.   Step 1:
     Find the car's mileage for one year, and gas usage.
     Step 2:
     Subtract beginning odometer reading from ending reading.
     Step 3:
     $37,364$ miles $- 25,124$ miles $= 12,240$ miles

     $\dfrac{12,240 \text{ miles}}{24 \text{ mpg}} = 510$ gallons

     Step 4:
     It satisfies the conditions of the problem.

13. Step 1:
    Find the difference between two methods of payment.
    Step 2:
    Compute total costs and compare two figures.
    Step 3:
    By spreading purchase out, the total comes to:
    $100 + 14($50) = $100 + $700 = $800
    $800 – $750 = $50 saved by paying all at once
    Step 4:
    It satisfies the conditions of problem.

14. Step 1: Determine which team won.
    Step 2: Compile point totals and compare.
    Step 3:
    Bulldogs: $34 \times 2 + 13 = 68 + 13 = 81$ points
    Panthers: $38 \times 2 + 8 = 76 + 8 = 84$ points
    Panthers won by 3 points
    Step 4:
    It satisfies the conditions of the problem.

15. Step 1:
    Determine profit on goods sold.
    Step 2:
    Find total cost of buying product and comparing with gross sales.
    Step 3:
    Purchased: ($65 per dozen)(6 dozen) = $390
    Sold: 6 dozen = 72 calculators
    $\frac{72}{3} = 24$ groups of 3 at $20 per group.
    $24 \times $20 = 480
    $480 – $390 = $90 profit
    Step 4:
    It satisfies the conditions of the problem.

16. Step 1: Determine profit.
    Step 2:
    Determine cost of purchase and compare with gross sales.
    Step 3:
    Bought:
    ($0.95/dozen)(15 dozen) = $14.25
    Sold:
    15 dozen = 180 pens
    $\frac{180}{4} = 45$ packs
    45 packs $\times$ $2.25 = $101.25
    Profit = $101.25 – $14.25 = $87
    Step 4:
    It satisfies the conditions of the problem.

17. Step 1: Determine profit for ten-day period.
    Step 2: Compare totals.
    Step 3:
    (200 slices)($1.50) = $300 for pizza
    (85 sandwiches)($2.50) = $212.50 for sandwiches
    For 10 day period:
    Gross: $10($300) + 10($212.50) = $3000 + 2125.00
    $= 5125.00
    Expenses: 10($60) = $600
    Profit: $5125.00 – $600 = $4525
    Step 4:
    It satisfies the conditions of the problem.

18. Step 1: Determine how much was earned over two-week period.
    Step 2: Compute each week's earnings and total.
    Step 3:
    1st week:
    (40 hours)($5.15 per hour) + (2 hours)($5.15 + $1.20)
    = $206 + (2 hours)($6.35)
    = $206 + $12.70
    = $218.70
    2nd week:
    (40 hours)($ 5.15 per hour) + (5 hours)($ 6.35)
    = $206 + $31.75
    = $237.75
    Total is $218.70 + $237.75 = $456.45
    Step 4:
    It satisfies the conditions of problem.

19. Step 1:
    Compute total rental cost.
    Step 2:
    Add rental cost and mileage cost to get total cost.
    Step 3:
    Rental costs:
    (2 weeks)($220 per week) = $440
    Mileage: (500 miles)($0.25) = $125
    Total: $440 + $125 = $565
    Step 4:
    It satisfies the conditions of problem.

20. Step 1:
We are trying to figure out an annual budget and see how much is left to buy stock and how many shares of stock.
Step 2:
Determine annual earnings and compare with budget.
Step 3:
Salary:
(12 months/year)($2750/month) = $33,000
Expenses:
$4800 + $8200 + $3750 + $4250 + $3000
= $24,000
Available to buy stocks:
$33,000 – $24,000 = $9000
Number of stocks: $\dfrac{\$9000}{\$375/\text{share}} = 24$ shares
Step 4:
It satisfies the conditions of problem.

21. Step 1:
A round trip was made; we need to determine how much was walked or ridden.
Step 2:
Add up the totals walked and ridden and compare.
Step 3:
It is 5 miles between the homes or a 10 mile round trip. The first 3 were covered with the bicycle, leaving 7 miles covered by walking.
7 miles – 3 miles = 4 miles more that was walked.
Step 4:
It satisfies the conditions of the problem.

22. Step 1:
Determine the profit on goods sold.
Step 2:
Determine the cost of obtaining product and compare with gross sales.
Step 3:
Cost:
200 containers at $0.75 apiece = $150
Cost = $150
Gross sales: (150 containers)($1.25) = $187.50
50 containers returned for $0.50 refund:
50($0.50) = $25.00
Total received: $187.50 + $25.00 = $212.50
Total Profit: $212.50 – $150.00 = $62.50
Step 4:
It satisfies the conditions of the problem.

23. Step 1:
Determine profit by comparing expenses with gross sales.
Step 2:
Calculate expenses and gross sales and compare.
Step 3:
Expense:
(25 calculators)($30) = $750
Gross Sales:
(22 calculators)($35.00) = $770
The storeowner receives $30 – $2 = $28 for each returned calculator.
(3 calculators)($28) = $84

Total Income:
$770 + $84 = $854
Profit=Income–Expenses
=$854–$750
=$104
Step 4:
It satisfies the conditions of the problem.

24. When the drivers meet for lunch they have been traveling for 2 hours and 24 minutes or 2.4 hours.
The car from New York City has traveled
(2.4 hours)(55 miles per hour) = 132 miles.
The car from D.C. has traveled
(2.4 hours)(45 miles per hour) = 108 miles.

25. The car depreciates at
$\dfrac{23,000 - 2700}{7} = \$2900$ per year.
$23,000 - 3(2900) = \$14,300$

26. The car depreciates at
$\dfrac{34,800 - 8550}{7} = \$3750$ per year.
$34,800 - 3(3750) = \$23,550$

27. Use a list.

2 Quarters	3 Dimes	5 Nickels
1	2	0
1	1	2
1	0	4
0	3	3
0	2	5

There are 5 ways.

28. Use a list.

Pennies	Nickels	Dimes
25	0	0
20	1	0
15	2	0
15	0	1
10	3	0
10	1	1
5	4	0
5	2	1
5	0	2
0	5	0
0	3	1
0	1	2

There are 12 ways.

29. Make a list of all possible selections:
Depp/Foxx, Depp/Stewart, Depp/Hilary,
Foxx/Stewart, Foxx/Hilary,
Stewart/Hilary
There are 6 ways.

30. Make a list of all possible selections:
Clinton/Combs, Clinton/Trump, Clinton/Winfrey,
Clinton/Woods,
Combs/Trump, Combs/Winfrey, Combs/Woods,
Trump /Winfrey, Trump /Woods,
Winfrey/Woods,
There are 10 ways.

31. Use a list.

Pennies	Nickels	Dimes
21	0	0
16	1	0
11	2	0
11	0	1
6	3	0
6	1	1
1	4	0
1	2	1
1	0	2

There are 9 ways.

32. Use a list.

Pennies	Nickels	Dimes	Quarters
26	0	0	0
21	1	0	0
16	2	0	0
16	0	1	0
11	3	0	0
11	1	1	0
6	4	0	0
6	2	1	0
6	0	2	0
1	5	0	0
1	3	1	0
1	1	2	0
1	0	0	1

There are 13 ways.

33. Use a list.

1 pt	5 pt	10-pt	Total
3	0	0	3
2	1	0	7
1	2	0	11
2	0	1	12
0	3	0	15
1	1	1	16
0	2	1	20
1	0	2	21
0	1	2	25
0	0	3	30

There are 10 different totals.

34. Answers will vary. An example is 61, 9, 7, 23.

35. The average expense is $\dfrac{42+10+26+32+30}{5} = \$28$

Thus, B owes \$18 and C owes \$2, A is owed \$14, D is owed \$4, and E is owed \$2.
To resolve these discrepancies, B should give A \$14 and give D \$4, while C should give E \$2.

36. At 5 minutes between houses, it will take 30 minutes to walk all the way around.

37. Make a list of all possible orders:
TFFF, FTFF, FFTF, FFFT
The "True" could be written 1st, 2nd, 3rd, or 4th.
There are 4 ways.

38. Represent the 5 people as A, B, C, D, and E and make a list of all possible handshakes:
AB, AC, AD, AE, BC, BD, BE, CD, CE and DE.
There are 10 handshakes exchanged.

39. The order the racers finished was; Andy, Darnell, Caleb, Beth, Ella.

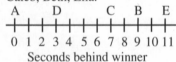

Seconds behind winner

40. To determine a winner, seven teams must be eliminated. Since each game eliminates one team, this tournament will take seven games.

41. Home→Bank→Post Office→Dry Cleaners→Home will take 11.5 miles.

42. Home→Post Office→Dry Cleaners→Bank→Home will take 12.5 miles.

43. CO→WY→UT→AZ→NM→CO→UT

44. One possible route is indicated:

45. The problem states that the psychology major knocks on Jose's wall, and Jose's dorm is adjacent to Bob's dorm but not Tony's. Therefore Bob is the psychology major.

46. A minimum of 4 colors are needed.

47. a.

5	22	18
28	15	2
12	8	25

b.

4	9	8
11	7	3
6	5	10

48. a.

96	64	37	45
39	43	98	62
84	76	25	57
23	59	82	78

b.

69	46	73	54
93	34	89	26
48	67	52	75
32	95	28	87

49.

9	6	7
0	1	4
3	2	5

50.

2	3	3	6
4	1	4	6
1	1	4	8
9	8	2	5

51.

$$
\begin{array}{r}
156 \\
28\overline{)4368} \\
\underline{28} \\
156 \\
\underline{140} \\
168 \\
\underline{168} \\
0
\end{array}
$$

56. does not make sense; Explanations will vary. Sample explanation: Polya's four steps are a guide. They will not necessarily make the solution quick and/or easy.

57. makes sense

58. makes sense

59. does not make sense; Explanations will vary. Sample explanation: When you are bogged down with a problem, it can often be helpful to stop working on it and return to it later.

60. A total of twenty 7s are needed.
Possible solution: Notice that the digit 7 will occur 10 times in the tens digit and 10 times in the ones digit.
An alternative solution would be to make a list of every instance of a seven; 7, 17, 27, 37, 47, 57, 67, 70, 71, 72, 73, 74, 75, 76, 77, 78, 79, 87, 97; and then count the occurrences of the digit 7.

61. You should choose the dentist whose teeth show the effects of poor dental work because he took good care of the other dentist's teeth.

62. Use one plank diagonally across one corner of the square. Use the other plank to go from the first plank to the stone.

63. It is Friday. The first person is lying (as expected) because he told the truth on Thursday. The second is truthfully admitting that he lied the previous day.

64. The farmer can use the following strategy: Take the goat to the other side of the stream and return to get either the wolf or cabbage. The farmer should take that across the stream and bring the goat back to the original side. He then takes across the cabbage or wolf, whichever remains, and leaves it on the other side while he returns to get the goat.

65. Answers will vary.

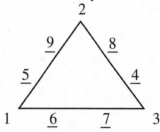

66. Sudoku Puzzle solution:

2	3	1	4	9	5	6	7	8
4	5	7	6	3	8	9	2	1
8	9	6	7	1	2	3	5	4
5	7	2	3	8	6	1	4	9
3	6	4	1	7	9	2	8	5
9	1	8	5	2	4	7	3	6
1	8	3	9	4	7	5	6	2
6	2	9	8	5	3	4	1	7
7	4	5	2	6	1	8	9	3

67. There is no missing dollar; in the end the customers paid a total of $27 of which $25 went to the restaurant and $2 was stolen by the waiter.

68. From the middle rung the firefighter went up 4, down 6, up 7, and up 4 to reach the top rung. This is a net climb of up 9. Since there are 9 rungs above the middle rung, there must also be 9 rungs below. 9 above + 9 below + 1 middle = 19 rungs.

69. Answers will vary. One method is to start by multiplying 30 by each state's fraction of the population.

State A: $30 \times \dfrac{275}{1890} \approx 4.365$ or 4

State B: $30 \times \dfrac{383}{1890} \approx 6.079$ or 6

State C: $30 \times \dfrac{465}{1890} \approx 7.381$ or 7

State D: $30 \times \dfrac{767}{1890} \approx 12.175$ or 12

Notice that 4, 6, 7, and 12 add to 29, so there is 1 more representative to be allocated. We could give this extra representative to state C because it had the largest decimal part (0.381). This leads to an allocation of state A: 4, state B: 6, state C: 8, and state D: 12.

Chapter 1 Review Exercises

1. Deductive; the specific conclusion about *Carrie* was based on a general statement about all Stephen King books.

2. Inductive; the general conclusion for this next book was based on past specific observations.

3. Pattern: Add 5
$19 + 5 = 24$
4, 9, 14, 19, <u>24</u>

4. Pattern: Multiply by 2
$56 \times 2 = 112$
7, 14, 28, 56, <u>112</u>

5. Pattern: Numbers added increase by 1
$1 + 2 = 3$
$3 + 3 = 6$
$6 + 4 = 10$
$10 + 5 = 15$
$15 + 6 = 21$
1, 3, 6, 10, 15, <u>21</u>

6. Notice that $\dfrac{1}{2} = \dfrac{3}{6}$

Pattern: Add 1 to the denominator

$\dfrac{3}{7+1} = \dfrac{3}{8}$

$\dfrac{3}{4}, \dfrac{3}{5}, \dfrac{3}{6}, \dfrac{3}{7}, \dfrac{3}{8}$ or

$\dfrac{3}{4}, \dfrac{3}{5}, \dfrac{1}{2}, \dfrac{3}{7}, \underline{\dfrac{3}{8}}$

7. Pattern: Divide by -2

$-5 \div (-2) = \dfrac{-5}{-2} = \dfrac{5}{2}$ or $2\dfrac{1}{2}$

$40, -20, 10, -5, \underline{\dfrac{5}{2}}$

8. Pattern: Subtract 60
$-140 - 60 = -200$
$40, -20, -80, -140, \underline{-200}$

9. Each number beginning with the third number is the sum of the previous two numbers. $16 + 26 = \underline{42}$

10. To get the second number, multiply the first number by 3. Then multiply the second number by 2 to get the third number. Then multiply by 3 and then by 2, repeatedly. $216 \times 2 = \underline{432}$

11. The pattern is alternating between square and circle while the line rotates $90°$ clockwise. The next figure is shown at right.

12. Using inductive reasoning we predict
$2 + 4 + 8 + 16 + 32 = 64 - 2$.
Arithmetic verifies this result:
$2 + 4 + 8 + 16 + 32 = 64 - 2$
$62 = 62$

13. Using inductive reasoning we predict
$444 \div 12 = 37$.
Arithmetic verifies this result: $444 \div 12 = 37$
$37 = 37$

14. a. Conjecture based on results: The result is the original number.

Select a number.	4	10	0	3
Double the number.	$4 \times 2 = 8$	$10 \times 2 = 20$	$0 \times 2 = 0$	$3 \times 2 = 6$
Add 4 to the product.	$8 + 4 = 12$	$20 + 4 = 24$	$0 + 4 = 4$	$6 + 4 = 10$
Divide this sum by 2.	$12 \div 2 = 6$	$24 \div 2 = 12$	$4 \div 2 = 2$	$10 \div 2 = 5$
Subtract 2 from the quotient.	$6 - 2 = 4$	$12 - 2 = 10$	$2 - 2 = 0$	$5 - 2 = 3$
Summary of results:	$4 \to 4$	$10 \to 10$	$0 \to 0$	$3 \to 3$

b. $2n$

$2n + 4$

$\dfrac{2n+4}{2} = \dfrac{2n}{2} + \dfrac{4}{2} = n + 2$

$n + 2 - 2 = n$

15. a. 4,266,000

b. 4,266,000

c. 4,300,000

d. 4,000,000

16. a. 1.5

b. 1.51

c. 1.507

d. 1.5065917

17. $2 + 4 + 10 = 16$
Actual answer: 15.71
quite reasonable

18. $9 \times 50 = 450$
Actual answer: 432.67
somewhat reasonable

19. $20 \div 4 = 5$
Actual answer: 4.79
quite reasonable

20. $0.60 \times 4000 = 2400$
Actual answer: 2397.0548
quite reasonable

21. $8.47 + $0.89 + $2.79 + $0.14 + $1.19 + $4.76
$\approx$ $8 + $1 + $3 + $0 + $1 + $5
$\approx$ $18

22. Round 78 hours to 80, round $6.85 to $7.00. $78 \times \$6.85 \approx 80 \times \$7.00 \approx \$560$

23. Round book price to $1.00 each.
    Round chair price to $12.00 each.
    Round plate price to $15.00.
    $(21 \times \$0.85) + (2 \times \$11.95) + \$14.65$
    $\approx (21 \times \$1) + (2 \times \$12) + \$15$
    $\approx \$21 + \$24 + \$15$
    $\approx \$60$

24. 29% of 1,585,326 can be estimated as 30% of 1,600,000.
    $0.3 \times 1,600,000 = 480,000$ students

25. The given information suggests $900 would be a good estimate for weekly salary.
    $\$900 \times 10 \times 4 = \$36,000$ which is choice b.

26. $60 \times 60 \times 24 = 86,400$ which is closest to choice c.

27. **a.** The Asian group exceeds 100. They have a population of about 122.

    b. 30×33 million $= 990$ million

28. **a.** $\dfrac{28.0 - 6.0}{2006 - 1950} = \dfrac{22.0}{56} = 0.4$ per year

    b. $6.0 + 0.4(2020 - 1950) = 6.0 + 0.4(70) = 34$
    About 34% of people 25 years of age and older will be college graduates in 2020.

29. **a.** The woman's maximum heart rate was about 115 beats per minute. This occurred after about 10 minutes.

    b. The woman's minimum heart rate was about 64 beats per minute. This occurred after about 8 minutes.

    c. between 9 and 10 minutes

    d. 9 minutes

30. **a.** $\dfrac{104 - 61}{2006 - 2000} = \dfrac{43}{6} \approx 7$ channels per year

    b. $T = 61 + 7x$

    c. $T = 61 + 7(2014 - 2000) = 159$ channels

31. The weight of the child is needed.

32. The unnecessary information is the customer giving the driver a $20 bill.
    For a 6 mile trip, the first mile is $3.00, and the next 5 miles are $0.50/half-mile or $1.00/mile. The cost is
    $\$3.00 + (5 \times \$1.00) = \$3.00 + \$5.00$
    $\qquad\qquad\qquad\qquad\quad = \$8.00.$

33. Total of $28 \times 2 = 56$ frankfurters would be needed. $\dfrac{56}{7} = 8$. Therefore, 8 pounds would be needed.

34. Rental for 3 weeks at $175 per week is
    $3 \times \$175 = \$525$. Mileage for 1200 miles at $0.30 per mile is $1200 \times \$0.30 = \$360$. Total cost is $\$525 + \$360 = \$885$.

35.. Plan A is $90 better.

Cost under Plan A: $100 + 0.80(1500) = \$1300$

Cost under Plan B: $40 + 0.90(1500) = \$1390$

36. The flight leaves Miami at 7:00 A.M. Pacific Standard Time. With a lay-over of 45 minutes, it arrives in San Francisco at 1:30 P.M. Pacific Standard Time, 6 hrs 30 min. – 45 min = 5 hours 45 minutes.

37. At steady decrease in value: $\dfrac{\$37,000 - \$2600}{8 \text{ years}} = \dfrac{\$34,400}{8 \text{ years}} = \$4300/\text{year}$

After 5 years: $\$4300 \times 5 = \$21,500$ decrease in value

Value of car: $\$37,000 - \$21,500 = \$15,500$

38. The machine will accept nickels, dimes, quarters.

nickels	dimes	quarters
7	0	0
5	1	0
3	2	0
2	0	1
1	3	0
0	1	1

There are 6 combinations.

Chapter 1 Test

1. deductive

2. inductive

3. $0 + 5 = 5$
$5 + 5 = 10$
$10 + 5 = 15$
$15 + 5 = 20$
0, 5, 10, 15, <u>20</u>

4. $\dfrac{1}{6 \times 2} = \dfrac{1}{12}$

$\dfrac{1}{12 \times 2} = \dfrac{1}{24}$

$\dfrac{1}{24 \times 2} = \dfrac{1}{48}$

$\dfrac{1}{48 \times 2} = \dfrac{1}{96}$

$\dfrac{1}{6}, \dfrac{1}{12}, \dfrac{1}{24}, \dfrac{1}{48}, \dfrac{1}{\underline{96}}$

5. $3367 \times 15 = 50,505$

6.   The outer figure is always a square. The inner figure appears to cycle from triangle to circle to square. The line segments at the bottom alternate from two to one. The next shape is shown at right.

7. **a.** Conjecture based on results: The original number is doubled.

Select a number.	4	10	3
Multiply the number by 4.	$4 \times 4 = 16$	$10 \times 4 = 40$	$3 \times 4 = 12$
Add 8 to the product.	$16 + 8 = 24$	$40 + 8 = 48$	$12 + 8 = 20$
Divide this sum by 2.	$24 \div 2 = 12$	$48 \div 2 = 24$	$20 \div 2 = 10$
Subtract 4 from the quotient.	$12 - 4 = 8$	$24 - 4 = 20$	$10 - 4 = 6$
Summary of results:	$4 \rightarrow 8$	$10 \rightarrow 20$	$3 \rightarrow 6$

    b. $4n$

        $4n + 8$

        $\dfrac{4n + 8}{2} = \dfrac{4n}{2} + \dfrac{8}{2} = 2n + 4$

        $2n + 4 - 4 = 2n$

8. 3,300,000

9. 706.38

10. Round $47.00 to $50.00.
     Round $311.00 to $310.00.
     Round $405.00 to $410.00.
     Round $681.79 to $680.00.
     Total needed for expenses:
     $47.00 + $311.00 + $405.00
     $\approx$ $50.00 + $310.00 + $410.00
     $\approx$ $770.00
     Additional money needed:
     $770.00 − $681.79 $\approx$ $770.00 − $680.00
                          $\approx$ $90

11. Round $485,000 to $500,000.
     Round number of people to 20.
     $\dfrac{\$485,000}{19 \text{ people}} \approx \dfrac{\$500,000}{20 \text{ people}}$
             $\approx$ $25,000 per person

12. $0.48992 \times 120 \approx 0.5 \times 120 \approx 60$

13. 11% of 512 billion can be estimated by 10% of 500 billion.
     0.10×500 billion $= 50$ billion

14. $72,000 \div 30 = 2400$ which is choice a.

15. **a.** 2001; about 1275 discharges

    b. 2006; about 610 discharges

    b. They decreased at the greatest rate where the graph has the steepest downward slope. This occurred between 2001 and 2002

    c. There were about 1000 discharges in 1997 under this policy.

16. **a.** $\dfrac{381-310}{2007-1950} = \dfrac{71}{57} = 1.25$ ppm per year

    b. $C = 310 + 1.25x$

    c. $C = 310 + 1.25(2050 - 1950) = 435$ ppm

17. For 3 hours:

    Estes: \$9 per $\dfrac{1}{4}$ hour

    $3 \times 4 = 12$ quarter-hours $\rightarrow 12 \times \$9 = \$108$

    Ship and Shore: \$20 per $\dfrac{1}{2}$ hour

    $3 \times 2 = 6$ half-hours $\rightarrow 6 \times \$20 = \$120$
    Estes is a better deal by
    $\$120 - \$108 = \$12.00$.

18. 20 round trips mean 40 one-way trips at \$11/trip.
    (40 trips)(32 passengers)(\$11)
    = \$14,080 in one day

19. $\$960 - \$50 = \$910$ remaining to pay
    $\dfrac{\$910}{\$35 \text{ per week}} = 26$ weeks

20. Belgium will have 160,000 more.
    Greece: $10,600,000 - 28,000(35) = 9,620,000$
    Belgium: $10,200,000 - 12,000(35) = 9,780,000$

Chapter 2
Set Theory

Check Points 2.1

1. Set L is the set of the first six lowercase letters in the English alphabet.

2. $M = \{$April, August$\}$

3. $O = \{1, 3, 5, 7, 9\}$

4. **a.** not the empty set; Many numbers meet the criteria to belong to this set.

   b. the empty set; No numbers meet the criteria, thus this set is empty

   c. not the empty set; "nothing" is not a set.

   d. not the empty set; This is a set that contains one element, that element is a set.

5. **a.** True; 8 is an element of the given set.

   b. True; r is not an element of the given set.

   c. False; {Monday} is a set and the set {Monday} is not an element of the given set.

6. **a.** $A = \{1, 2, 3\}$

   b. $B = \{15, 16, 17, \ldots\}$

   c. $O = \{1, 3, 5, \ldots\}$

7. **a.** $\{1, 2, 3, 4, \ldots, 199\}$

   b. $\{51, 52, 53, 54, \ldots, 200\}$

8. **a.** $n(A) = 5$; the set has 5 elements

   b. $n(B) = 1$; the set has only 1 element

   c. $n(C) = 8$; Though this set lists only five elements, the three dots indicate 12, 13, and 14 are also elements.

   d. $n(D) = 0$ because the set has no elements.

9. No, the sets are not equivalent. Set A has 5 elements yet set B has only 4 elements.

10. **a.** true; {O, L, D} = {D, O, L} because the sets contain exactly the same elements.

    b. false; The two sets do not contain exactly the same elements.

Exercise Set 2.1

1. This is well defined and therefore it is a set.

2. This is well defined and therefore it is a set.

3. This is a matter of opinion and not well defined, thus it is not a set.

4. This is a matter of opinion and not well defined, thus it is not a set.

5. This is well defined and therefore it is a set.

6. This is well defined and therefore it is a set.

7. The set of known planets in our Solar System.
Note to student: This exercise did not forget Pluto.
In 2006, based on the requirement that a planet must
dominate its own orbit, the International
Astronomical Union removed Pluto from the list of
planets.

8. The set of weekend days.

9. The set of months that begin with J.

10. The set of months that begin with A.

11. The set of natural numbers greater than 5.

12. The set of natural numbers greater than 8.

13. The set of natural numbers between 6 and 20,
inclusive.

14. The set of natural numbers between 9 and 25,
inclusive.

15. {winter, spring, summer, fall}

16. {April, June, September, November}

17. {September, October, November, December}

18. {e, f, g, h, i}

19. {1, 2, 3}

20. {1, 2, 3, 4, 5, 6}

21. {1, 3, 5, 7, 9, 11}

22. {2, 4, 6, 8}

23. {1, 2, 3, 4, 5}

24. {1, 2, 3, 4}

25. {6, 7, 8, 9, …}

26. {5, 6, 7, 8, …}

27. {7, 8, 9, 10}

28. {8, 9, 10, 11}

29. {10, 11, 12, 13, …, 79}

30. {15, 16, 17, 18, …, 59}}

31. {2}

32. {6}

33. not the empty set

34. not the empty set

35. empty set

36. empty set

37. not the empty set
Note that the number of women who served as U.S.
president before 2000 is 0. Thus the number 0 is an
element of the set.

38. not the empty set
Note that the number of living U.S. presidents born
before 1700 is 0. Thus the number 0 is an element
of the set.

39. empty set

40. empty set

41. empty set

42. empty set

43. not the empty set

44. not the empty set

45. not the empty set

46. not the empty set

47. True
3 is a member of the set.

48. True
6 is a member of the set.

49. True
12 is a member of the set.

50. True
10 is a member of the set.

51. False
5 is *not* a member of the set.

52. False
8 is *not* a member of the set.

53. True
11 is *not* a member of the set.

54. True.
17 is *not* a member of the set.

55. False
37 is a member of the set.

56. False
26 is a member of the set.

57. False
4 is a member of the set.

58. False
2 is *not* a member of the set.

59. True
13 is *not* a member of the set.

60. True
20 is *not* a member of the set.

61. False
16 is a member of the set.

62. False
19 is a member of the set.

63. False
The set {3} is *not* a member of the set.

64. False
The set {7} is *not* a member of the set.

65. True
−1 is *not* a natural number.

66. True
−2 is *not* a natural number.

67. $n(A) = 5$; There are 5 elements in the set.

68. $n(A) = 6$; There are 6 elements in the set.

69. $n(B) = 15$; There are 15 elements in the set.

70. $n(B) = 11$; There are 11 elements in the set.

71. $n(C) = 0$; There are *no* days of the week beginning with A.

72. $n(C) = 0$; There are no such months.

73. $n(D) = 1$; There is 1 element in the set.

74. $n(D) = 1$; There is 1 element in the set.

75. $n(A) = 4$; There is 4 elements in the set.

76. $n(A) = 3$; There is 3 elements in the set.

77. $n(B) = 5$; There is 5 elements in the set.

78. $n(B) = 7$; There is 7 elements in the set.

79. $n(C) = 0$; There are no elements in the set.

80. $n(C) = 0$; There are no elements in the set.

81. a. Not equivalent
The number of elements is not the same.

    b. Not equal
The two sets contain different elements.

82. a. Equivalent
The number of elements is the same.

    b. Not equal
The two sets contain different elements.

83. a. Equivalent
The number of elements is the same.

    b. Not equal
The elements are not exactly the same.

84. a. Equivalent
The number of elements is the same.

    b. Not equal
The elements are not exactly the same.

85. a. Equivalent
The number of elements is the same.

    b. Equal
The elements are exactly the same.

86. a. Equivalent
Number of elements is the same.

    b. Equal
The elements are exactly the same.

87. a. Equivalent
Number of elements is the same.

    b. Not equal
The two sets contain different elements.

88. a. Equivalent
Number of elements is the same.

    b. Not equal
The two sets contain different elements.

89. a. Equivalent
Number of elements is the same.

    b. Equal
The elements are exactly the same.

90. a. Equivalent
Number of elements is the same.

b. Equal
The elements are exactly the same.

91. infinite

92. infinite

93. finite

94. finite

95. finite

96. finite

97. $\left\{ x \middle| x \in \mathbb{N} \text{ and } x \geq 61 \right\}$

98. $\left\{ x \middle| x \in \mathbb{N} \text{ and } x \geq 36 \right\}$

99. $\left\{ x \middle| x \in \mathbb{N} \text{ and } 61 \leq x \leq 89 \right\}$

100. $\left\{ x \middle| x \in \mathbb{N} \text{ and } 36 \leq x \leq 59 \right\}$

101. Answers will vary; an example is: $\left\{ 0, 1, 2, 3 \right\}$ and $\left\{ 1, 2, 3, 4 \right\}$.

102. Answers will vary; an example is: $\left\{ x \middle| x \in \mathbb{N} \text{ and } x < 5 \right\}$ and $\left\{ 1, 2, 3, 4 \right\}$.

103. Impossible. Equal sets have exactly the same elements. This would require that there also must be the same number of elements.

104. Answers will vary; an example is: $\left\{ 1 \right\}$ and $\left\{ 1, 2 \right\}$.

105. {New Zealand, Australia, United States}

106. {New Zealand, Australia, United States}

107. {Australia, United States, United Kingdom, Switzerland, Ireland}

108. {Australia, United States, United Kingdom, Switzerland}

109. {United Kingdom, Switzerland, Ireland}

110. {Switzerland, Ireland, Spain}

111. { }

112. {New Zealand}

113. {12, 19}

114. {10, 14, 16}

115. {20, 21}

116. {20, 21, 22}

117. There is not a one-to-one correspondence. These sets are not equivalent.

124. makes sense

125. does not make sense; Explanations will vary. Sample explanation: The natural numbers do not include negative numbers. Since the temperature will be below zero, a set that includes negative numbers would be necessary.

126. does not make sense; Explanations will vary. Sample explanation: There is not a one-to-one correspondence for men because two ages sleep for 8.3 hours.

127. makes sense

128. false; Changes to make the statement true will vary. A sample change is: If two sets are equal, they must be equivalent.

129. false; Changes to make the statement true will vary. A sample change is: If a roster set contains three dots, it is finite if there is an ending value after the three dots.

130. false; Changes to make the statement true will vary. A sample change is: The cardinality of the empty set is 0.

131. true

132. true

133. false; Changes to make the statement true will vary. A sample change is: Though that set has many values, it is still a finite set.

134. false; Changes to make the statement true will vary. A sample change is: Some finite sets could have so many elements that it would take longer than a trillion years to count them.

135. false; Changes to make the statement true will vary. A sample change is: If 0 is removed from a set, it will lower the cardinality of that set by one.

136. This question contains a paradox. Sweeney Todd cannot shave himself because he does not shave any men who shave themselves. That suggests that $s \notin A$ which implies $s \in B$. However, if Sweeney Todd does not shave himself, the question states he shaves all such men who do not shave themselves. That suggests that he does shave himself, giving $s \in A$ which implies $s \notin B$. Therefore, paradoxically, s belongs and does not belong in both sets.

   a. no

   b. no

Check Points 2.2

1. a. $\not\subseteq$; because 6, 9, and 11 are not in set B.

   b. $\subseteq$; because all elements in set A are also in set B.

   c. $\subseteq$; because all elements in set A are also in set B.

2. a. Both $\subseteq$ and $\subset$ are correct.

   b. Both $\subseteq$ and $\subset$ are correct.

3. Yes, the empty set is a subset of any set.

4. a. 16 subsets, 15 proper subsets
There are 4 elements, which means there are 2^4 or 16 subsets. There are $2^4 - 1$ proper subsets or 15.

   b. 64 subsets, 63 proper subsets
There are 6 elements, which means there are 2^6 or 64 subsets. There are $2^6 - 1$ proper subsets or 63.

Exercise Set 2.2

1. $\subseteq$
2. $\subseteq$
3. $\not\subseteq$
4. $\not\subseteq$
5. $\not\subseteq$

6. $\not\subseteq$
7. $\not\subseteq$
Subset cannot be larger than the set.
8. $\not\subseteq$
Subset cannot be larger than the set.
9. $\subseteq$
10. $\subseteq$
11. $\not\subseteq$
12. $\not\subseteq$
13. $\subseteq$
14. $\subseteq$
15. $\not\subseteq$
16. $\not\subseteq$
17. $\subseteq$
18. $\subseteq$
19. $\subseteq$ or $\subset$
20. $\subseteq$ or $\subset$
21. $\subseteq$
22. $\subseteq$
23. neither
24. neither
25. both
26. both
27. $\subseteq$
28. $\subseteq$
29. $\subseteq$
30. $\subseteq$
31. both
32. both

33. both

34. neither

35. both

36. both

37. neither

38. neither

39. $\subseteq$

40. $\subseteq$

41. True

42. True

43. False
{Ralph} is a subset, not Ralph.

44. False
{Canada} is a subset, not Canada.

45. True

46. True

47. False
The symbol " $\varnothing$ " is not a member of the set.

48. True

49. True

50. True

51. False
All elements of {1, 4} are members of {4, 1}

52. True

53. True

54. True

55. { } {Border Collie} {Poodle} {Border Collie, Poodle}

56. { } {Romeo} {Juliet} {Romeo, Juliet}

57. { } {t} {a} {b} {t, a} {t, b} {a, b} {t, a, b}

58. { } {I} {II} {III} {I, II} {I, III} {II, III} {I, II, III }

59. { } {0}

60. $\varnothing$

61. 16 subsets, 15 proper subsets
There are 4 elements, which means there are 2^4 or 16 subsets. There are $2^4 - 1$ proper subsets or 15.

62. 16 subsets, 15 proper subsets
There are 4 elements, which means there are 2^4 or 16 subsets. There are $2^4 - 1$ proper subsets or 15.

63. 64 subsets, 63 proper subsets
There are 6 elements, which means there are 2^6 or 64 subsets. There are $2^6 - 1$ proper subsets or 63.

64. 64 subsets, 63 proper subsets
There are 6 elements, which means there are 2^6 or 64 subsets. There are $2^6 - 1$ proper subsets or 63.

65. 128 subsets, 127 proper subsets
There are 7 elements, which means there are 2^7 or 128 subsets. There are $2^7 - 1$ proper subsets or 127.

66. 32 subsets, 31 proper subsets
There are 5 elements, which means there are 2^5 or 32 subsets. There are $2^5 - 1$ proper subsets or 31.

67. 8 subsets, 7 proper subsets
There are 3 elements, which means there are 2^3 or 8 subsets. There are $2^3 - 1$ proper subsets or 7.

68. 32 subsets, 31 proper subsets
There are 5 elements, which means there are 2^5 or 32 subsets. There are $2^5 - 1$ proper subsets or 31.

69. false; The set $\{1, 2, 3, ..., 1000\}$ has $2^{1000} - 1$ proper subsets.

70. false; The set $\{1, 2, 3, ..., 10,000\}$ has $2^{10,000} - 1$ proper subsets.

71. true

72. true

73. false; $\varnothing \subseteq \{\varnothing, \{\varnothing\}\}$

74. false; $\{\varnothing\} \subseteq \{\varnothing, \{\varnothing\}\}$

75. true

76. true

77. true

78. true

79. true

80. true

81. false; The set of subsets of {a, e, i, o, u} contains 2^5 or 32 elements.

82. false; The set of subsets of {a, b, c, d, e, f} contains 2^6 or 64 elements.

83. false; $D \subseteq T$

84. false; $R \subseteq T$

85. true

86. true

87. false; If $x \in W$, then $x \in D$.

88. false; If $x \in M$, then $x \in D$.

89. true

90. true

91. true

92. true

93. $2^5 = 32$ option combinations

94. $2^9 = 512$ topping combinations

95. $2^6 = 64$ viewing combinations

96. $2^4 = 16$ response options

97. $2^8 = 256$ city combinations

98. $2^7 = 128$ viewing combinations

105. does not make sense; Explanations will vary. Sample explanation: The set's elements are not members of the other set.

106. makes sense

107. does not make sense; Explanations will vary. Sample explanation: The same formulas are used for each of the mentioned problems.

108. makes sense

109. false; Changes to make the statement true will vary. A sample change is: The set has one element and has $2^1 = 2$ subsets.

110. true

111. false; Changes to make the statement true will vary. A sample change is: The empty set does not have a proper subset.

112. false; Changes to make the statement true will vary. A sample change is: The set has two elements and has $2^2 = 4$ subsets.

113. 0, 5¢, 10¢, 25¢, 40¢, 15¢, 30¢, 35¢
Since there are 3 elements or coins, there are 2^3 or 8 different coin combinations.

114. Number of proper subsets is $2^n - 1$, which means there are 128 total subsets (127 + 1). 128 is 2^7, so there are 7 elements.

Check Points 2.3

1. a. {1, 5, 6, 7, 9}

   b. {1, 5, 6}

   c. {7, 9}

2. a. {a, b, c, d}

   b. {e}

   c. {e, f, g}

   d. {f, g}

3. $A' = \{b, c, e\}$; those are the elements in U but not in A.

4. a. {1, 3, 5, <u>7</u>, <u>10</u>} ∩ {6, <u>7</u>, <u>10</u>, 11} = {7, 10}

   b. {1, 2, 3} ∩ {4, 5, 6, 7} = ∅

   c. {1, 2, 3} ∩ ∅ = ∅

5. a. {1, 3, 5, 7, 10} ∪ {6, 7, 10, 11}
   = {1, 3, 5, 6, 7, 10, 11}

   b. {1, 2, 3} ∪ {4, 5, 6, 7} = {1, 2, 3, 4, 5, 6, 7}

   c. {1, 2, 3} ∪ ∅ = {1, 2, 3}

6. a. $A \cup B = \{b, c, e\}$

$(A \cup B)' = \{a, d\}$

b. $A' = \{a, d, e\}$

$B' = \{a, d\}$

$A' \cap B' = \{a, d\}$

7. a. $\{5\}$; region II

b. $\{2, 3, 7, 11, 13, 17, 19\}$; the complement of region II

c. $\{2, 3, 5, 7, 11, 13\}$; regions I, II, and III

d. $\{17, 19\}$; the complement of regions I, II, and III

e. $\{5, 7, 11, 13, 17, 19\}$; the complement of A united with B

f. $\{2, 3\}$; A intersected with the complement of B

8. $n(A \cup B) = n(A) + n(B) - n(A \cap B)$

$= 244 + 230 - 89$

$= 385$

Exercise Set 2.3

1. U is the set of all composers.

2. U is the set of all writers.

3. U is the set of all brands of soft drinks.

4. U is the set of all models of automobiles.

5. $A' = \{c, d, e\}$

6. $B' = \{a, b, f, g\}$

7. $C' = \{b, c, d, e, f\}$

8. $D' = \{g\}$

9. $A' = \{6, 7, 8, \ldots, 20\}$

10. $B' = \{1, 2, 3, 4, 5, 10, 11, 12, 13, 14, 15, 16, 17, 18, 19, 20\}$

11. $C' = \{2, 4, 6, 8, \ldots, 20\}$

12. $D' = \{1, 3, 5, 7, \ldots, 19\}$

13. $A' = \{21, 22, 23, 24, \ldots\}$

14. $B' = \{51, 52, 53, 54, \ldots\}$

15. $C' = \{1, 3, 5, 7, \ldots\}$

16. $D' = \{2, 4, 6, 8, \ldots\}$

17. $A = \{1, 3, 5, 7\}$

$B = \{1, 2, 3\}$

$A \cap B = \{1, 3\}$

18. $B = \{1, 2, 3\}$

$C = \{2, 3, 4, 5, 6\}$

$B \cap C = \{2, 3\}$

19. $A = \{1, 3, 5, 7\}$

$B = \{1, 2, 3\}$

$A \cup B = \{1, 2, 3, 5, 7\}$

20. $B = \{1, 2, 3\}$

$C = \{2, 3, 4, 5, 6\}$

$B \cup C = \{1, 2, 3, 4, 5, 6\}$

21. $A = \{1, 3, 5, 7\}$

$U = \{1, 2, 3, 4, 5, 6, 7\}$

$A' = \{2, 4, 6\}$

22. $B = \{1, 2, 3\}$

$U = \{1, 2, 3, 4, 5, 6, 7\}$

$B' = \{4, 5, 6, 7\}$

23. $A' = \{2, 4, 6\}$

$B' = \{4, 5, 6, 7\}$

$A' \cap B' = \{4, 6\}$

24. $B' = \{4, 5, 6, 7\}$

$C = \{2, 3, 4, 5, 6\}$

$B' \cap C = \{4, 5, 6\}$

25. $A = \{1, 3, 5, 7\}$

$C' = \{1, 7\}$

$A \cup C' = \{1, 3, 5, 7\}$

26. $B = \{1, 2, 3\}$

$C' = \{1, 7\}$

$B \cup C' = \{1, 2, 3, 7\}$

27. $A = \{1, 3, 5, 7\}$

$C = \{2, 3, 4, 5, 6\}$

$A \cap C = \{3, 5\}$

$(A \cap C)' = \{1, 2, 4, 6, 7\}$

28. $A = \{1, 3, 5, 7\}$
$B = \{1, 2, 3\}$
$A \cap B = \{1, 3\}$
$(A \cap B)' = \{2, 4, 5, 6, 7\}$

29. $A = \{1, 3, 5, 7\}$ $\quad C = \{2, 3, 4, 5, 6\}$
$A' = \{2, 4, 6\}$ $\quad\quad C' = \{1, 7\}$
$A' \cup C' = \{1, 2, 4, 6, 7\}$

30. $A = \{1, 3, 5, 7\}$
$B = \{1, 2, 3\}$
$A' = \{2, 4, 6\}$
$B' = \{4, 5, 6, 7\}$
$A' \cup B' = \{2, 4, 5, 6, 7\}$

31. $A = \{1, 3, 5, 7\}$ $B = \{1, 2, 3\}$
$(A \cup B) = \{1, 2, 3, 5, 7\}$
$(A \cup B)' = \{4, 6\}$

32. $A = \{1, 3, 5, 7\}$
$C = \{2, 3, 4, 5, 6\}$
$A \cup C = \{1, 2, 3, 4, 5, 6, 7\}$
$(A \cup C)' = \varnothing$

33. $A = \{1, 3, 5, 7\}$
$A \cup \varnothing = \{1, 3, 5, 7\}$

34. $C = \{2, 3, 4, 5, 6\}$
$C \cup \varnothing = \{2, 3, 4, 5, 6\}$

35. $A \cap \varnothing = \varnothing$

36. $C \cap \varnothing = \varnothing$

37. $A \cup U = U$
$U = \{1, 2, 3, 4, 5, 6, 7\}$

38. $B \cup U = U$
$U = \{1, 2, 3, 4, 5, 6, 7\}$

39. $A \cap U = A$
$A = \{1, 3, 5, 7\}$

40. $B \cap U = B$
$B = \{1, 2, 3\}$

41. $A = \{a, g, h\}$
$B = \{b, g, h\}$
$A \cap B = \{g, h\}$

42. $B = \{b, g, h\}$
$C = \{b, c, d, e, f\}$
$B \cap C = \{b\}$

43. $A = \{a, g, h\}$
$B = \{b, g, h\}$
$A \cup B = \{a, b, g, h\}$

44. $B = \{b, g, h\}$
$C = \{b, c, d, e, f\}$
$B \cup C = \{b, c, d, e, f, g, h\}$

45. $A = \{a, g, h\}$
$U = \{a, b, c, d, e, f, g, h\}$
$A' = \{b, c, d, e, f\}$

46. $B = \{b, g, h\}$
$U = \{a, b, c, d, e, f, g, h\}$
$B' = \{a, c, d, e, f\}$

47. $A' = \{b, c, d, e, f\}$
$B' = \{a, c, d, e, f\}$
$A' \cap B' = \{c, d, e, f\}$

48. $B' = \{a, c, d, e, f\}$
$C = \{b, c, d, e, f\}$
$B' \cap C = \{c, d, e, f\}$

49. $A = \{a, g, h\}$
$C' = \{a, g, h\}$
$A \cup C' = \{a, g, h\}$

50. $B = \{b, g, h\}$
$C = \{b, c, d, e, f\}$
$C' = \{a, g, h\}$
$B \cup C' = \{a, b, g, h\}$

51. $A = \{a, g, h\}$
$C = \{b, c, d, e, f\}$
$A \cap C = \varnothing$
$(A \cap C)' = \{a, b, c, d, e, f, g, h\}$

52. $A = \{a, g, h\}$
$B = \{b, g, h\}$
$A \cap B = \{g, h\}$
$(A \cap B)' = \{a, b, c, d, e, f\}$

53. $A' = \{b, c, d, e, f\}$
$C' = \{a, g, h\}$
$A' \cup C' = \{a, b, c, d, e, f, g, h\}$

54. $A' = \{b, c, d, e, f\}$
$B' = \{a, c, d, e, f\}$
$A' \cup B' = \{a, b, c, d, e, f\}$

55. $A = \{a, g, h\}$
$B = \{b, g, h\}$
$A \cup B = \{a, b, g, h\}$
$(A \cup B)' = \{c, d, e, f\}$

56. $A = \{a, g, h\}$
$C = \{b, c, d, e, f\}$
$A \cup C = \{a, b, c, d, e, f, g, h\}$
$(A \cup C)' = \varnothing$

57. $A \cup \varnothing = A$
$A = \{a, g, h\}$

58. $C \cup \varnothing = C$
$C = \{b, c, d, e, f\}$

59. $A \cap \varnothing = \varnothing$

60. $C \cap \varnothing = \varnothing$

61. $A = \{a, g, h\}$
$U = \{a, b, c, d, e, f, g, h\}$
$A \cup U = \{a, b, c, d, e, f, g, h\}$

62. $B = \{b, g, h\}$
$U = \{a, b, c, d, e, f, g, h\}$
$B \cup U = \{a, b, c, d, e, f, g, h\}$

63. $A = \{a, g, h\}$
$U = \{a, b, c, d, e, f, g, h\}$
$A \cap U = \{a, g, h\}$

64. $B = \{b, g, h\}$
$U = \{a, b, c, d, e, f, g, h\}$
$B \cap U = \{b, g, h\}$

65. $A = \{a, g, h\}$
$B = \{b, g, h\}$
$B' = \{a, c, d, e, f\}$
$A \cap B = \{g, h\}$
$(A \cap B) \cup B' = \{a, c, d, e, f, g, h\}$

66. $A = \{a, g, h\}$
$B = \{b, g, h\}$
$B' = \{a, c, d, e, f\}$
$A \cup B = \{a, b, g, h\}$
$(A \cup B) \cap B' = \{a\}$

67. $A = \{1, 3, 4, 7\}$

68. $B = \{2, 3, 5, 6, 7\}$

69. $U = \{1, 2, 3, 4, 5, 6, 7, 8, 9\}$

70. $A \cup B = \{1, 2, 3, 4, 5, 6, 7\}$

71. $A \cap B = \{3, 7\}$

72. $A' = \{2, 5, 6, 8, 9\}$

73. $B' = \{1, 4, 8, 9\}$

74. $(A \cap B)' = \{1, 2, 4, 5, 6, 8, 9\}$

75. $(A \cup B)' = \{8, 9\}$

76. $A' = \{2, 5, 6, 8, 9\}$
$B = \{2, 3, 5, 6, 7\}$
$A' \cap B = \{2, 5, 6\}$

77. $A = \{1, 3, 4, 7\}$
$B' = \{1, 4, 8, 9\}$
$A \cap B' = \{1, 4\}$

78. $A = \{1, 3, 4, 7\}$
$B' = \{1, 4, 8, 9\}$
$A \cup B' = \{1, 3, 4, 7, 8, 9\}$

79. $B = \{\triangle, \text{two, four, six}\}$

80. $A = \{\triangle, \#, \$\}$

81. $A \cup B = \{\triangle, \#, \$, \text{two, four, six}\}$

82. $A \cap B = \{\triangle\}$

83. $n(A \cup B) = n(\{\triangle, \#, \$, \text{two, four, six}\}) = 6$

84. $n(A \cap B) = n(\{\triangle\}) = 1$

85. $n(A') = 5$

86. $n(B') = 4$

87. $(A \cap B)' = \{\#, \$, \text{two, four, six}, 10, 01\}$

88. $(A \cup B)' = \{10, 01\}$

89. $A' \cap B = \{\text{two, four, six}\}$

90. $A \cap B' = \{\#, \$\}$

91. $n(U) - n(B) = 8 - 4 = 4$

92. $n(U) - n(A) = 8 - 3 = 5$

93. $n(A \cup B) = n(A) + n(B) - n(A \cap B)$
$$= 17 + 20 - 6$$
$$= 31$$

94. $n(A \cup B) = n(A) + n(B) - n(A \cap B)$
$$= 30 + 18 - 5$$
$$= 43$$

95. $n(A \cup B) = n(A) + n(B) - n(A \cap B)$
$$= 17 + 17 - 7$$
$$= 27$$

96. $n(A \cup B) = n(A) + n(B) - n(A \cap B)$
$$= 30 + 24 - 7$$
$$= 47$$

97. $A = \{1, 3, 5, 7\}$
$B = \{2, 4, 6, 8\}$
$A \cup B = \{1, 2, 3, 4, 5, 6, 7, 8\}$

98. $B = \{2, 4, 6, 8\}$
$C = \{2, 3, 4, 5\}$
$B \cup C = \{2, 3, 4, 5, 6, 8\}$

99. $U = \{1, 2, 3, 4, 5, 6, 7, 8\}$
$A = \{1, 3, 5, 7\}$
$A \cap U = \{1, 3, 5, 7\}$

100. $U = \{1, 2, 3, 4, 5, 6, 7, 8\}$
$A = \{1, 3, 5, 7\}$
$A \cup U = \{1, 2, 3, 4, 5, 6, 7, 8\}$

101. $A = \{1, 3, 5, 7\}$
$C' = \{1, 6, 7, 8\}$
$A \cap C' = \{1, 7\}$

102. $A = \{1, 3, 5, 7\}$
$B' = \{1, 3, 5, 7\}$
$A \cap B' = \{1, 3, 5, 7\}$

103. $U = \{1, 2, 3, 4, 5, 6, 7, 8\}$
$B = \{2, 4, 6, 8\}$
$C = \{2, 3, 4, 5\}$
$B \cap C = \{2, 4\}$
$(B \cap C)' = \{1, 3, 5, 6, 7, 8\}$

104. $U = \{1, 2, 3, 4, 5, 6, 7, 8\}$
$A = \{1, 3, 5, 7\}$
$C = \{2, 3, 4, 5\}$
$A \cap C = \{3, 5\}$
$(A \cap C)' = \{1, 2, 4, 6, 7, 8\}$

105. $A \cup (A \cup B)'$
$$= \{23, 29, 31, 37, 41, 43, 53, 59, 61, 67, 71\}$$

106. $(A' \cap B) \cup (A \cap B) = \{41, 43, 47\}$

107. $n(U)\left[n(A \cup B) - n(A \cap B) \right] = 12[7 - 2]$
$$= 12(5) = 60$$

108. $n(A \cap B)\left[n(A \cup B) - n(A') \right] = 2[7 - 6] = 2(1) = 2$

109. {Ashley, Mike, Josh}

110. {Mike, Josh, Emily, Hannah, Ethan}

111. {Ashley, Mike, Josh, Emily, Hannah, Ethan}

112. {Mike, Josh}

113. {Ashley}

114. {Emily, Hannah, Ethan}

115. {Jacob}

116. {Ashley, Mike, Josh, Emily, Hannah, Ethan, Jacob}

117. Region III, *elementary school teacher* is in set B but not set A.

118. Region I, *police officer* is in set A but not set B.

119. Region I, *surgeon* is in set A but not set B.

120. Region III, *banker* is in set B but not set A.

121. Region II, *family doctor* is in set A and set B.

122. Region II, *lawyer* is in set A and set B.

123. Region I, 11 is in set A but not set B.

124. Region II, 22 is in set *A* and set *B*.

125. Region IV, 15 is in neither set *A* nor set *B*.

126. Region IV, 17 is in neither set *A* nor set *B*.

127. Region II, 454 is in set *A* and set *B*.

128. Region I, 101 is in set *A* but not set *B*.

129. Region III, 9558 is in set *B* but not set *A*.

130. Region III, 9778 is in set *B* but not set *A*.

131. Region I, 9559 is in set *A* but not set *B*.

132. Region I, 9779 is in set *A* but not set *B*.

133. {spatial-temporal, sports equipment, toy cars and trucks} ∩ {dollhouses, spatial-temporal, sports equipment, toy cars and trucks}
= {spatial-temporal, sports equipment, toy cars and trucks}

134. {dollhouses, domestic accessories, dolls} ∩ {dollhouses, spatial-temporal, sports equipment, toy cars and trucks}
= {dollhouses}

135. {spatial-temporal, sports equipment, toy cars and trucks} ∪ {dollhouses, spatial-temporal, sports equipment, toy cars and trucks}
= {dollhouses, spatial-temporal, sports equipment, toy cars and trucks}

136. {dollhouses, domestic accessories, dolls} ∪ {dollhouses, spatial-temporal, sports equipment, toy cars and trucks}
= {dollhouses, domestic accessories, dolls, spatial-temporal, sports equipment, toy cars and trucks}

137. {toy cars and trucks } ∩ {dollhouses, domestic accessories, dolls, spatial-temporal, sports equipment}
= ∅

138. {toy cars and trucks } ∪ {dollhouses, domestic accessories, dolls, spatial-temporal, sports equipment}
= {dollhouses, domestic accessories, dolls, spatial-temporal, sports equipment, toy cars and trucks}

139. $n(A \cup B) = n(A) + n(B) - n(A \cap B)$
$= 178 + 154 - 49$
$= 283$ people

140. $n(A \cup B) = n(A) + n(B) - n(A \cap B)$
$= 96 + 97 - 29$
$= 164$ people

152. makes sense

153. does not make sense; Explanations will vary. Sample explanation: Even with only one common element, the sets intersection will be shown by overlapping circles.

154. makes sense

155. does not make sense; Explanations will vary. Sample explanation: The given expression indicates that you should find the union of set *A* and set *B*, and then find the complement of the resulting set.

156. false; Changes to make the statement true will vary. A sample change is:
$n(A \cup B) = n(A) + n(B) - n(A \cap B)$

157. true

158. false; Changes to make the statement true will vary. A sample change is: $A \subseteq (A \cup B)$

159. false; Changes to make the statement true will vary. A sample change is: If $A \subseteq B$, then $A \cup B = B$.

160. false; Changes to make the statement true will vary. A sample change is: $A \cup U = U$

161. false; Changes to make the statement true will vary. A sample change is: $A \cap \varnothing = \varnothing$

162. false; Changes to make the statement true will vary. A sample change is: If $A \subseteq B$, then $A \cap B = A$.

163. true

164.

165.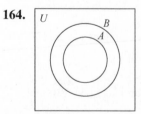

166.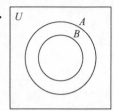

167.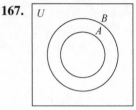

Check Points 2.4

1. a. $A \cup (B \cap C) = \{a, b, c, d\} \cup \{b, f\}$
             $= \{a, b, c, d, f\}$

   b.

   $(A \cup B) \cap (A \cup C) = \{a, b, c, d, f\} \cap \{a, b, c, d, f\}$
                     $= \{a, b, c, d, f\}$

   c.

   $A \cap (B \cup C') = \{a, b, c, d\} \cap (\{a, b, d, f\} \cup \{a, d, e\})$
               $= \{a, b, c, d\} \cap \{a, b, d, e, f\}$
               $= \{a, b, d\}$

2. a. C is represented by regions IV, V, VI, and VII.
            Thus, $C = \{5, 6, 7, 8, 9\}$

   b. $B \cup C$ is represented by regions II, III, IV, V,
            VI, and VII.
            Thus, $B \cup C = \{1, 2, 5, 6, 7, 8, 9, 10, 12\}$

   c. $A \cap C$ is represented by regions IV and V.
            Thus, $A \cap C = \{5, 6, 7\}$

   d. B' is represented by regions I, IV, VII, and
            VIII.
            Thus, $B' = \{3, 4, 6, 8, 11\}$

e. $A \cup B \cup C$ is represented by regions I, II, III,
         IV, V, VI, and VII.
         Thus,
         $A \cup B \cup C = \{1, 2, 3, 5, 6, 7, 8, 9, 10, 11, 12\}$

3.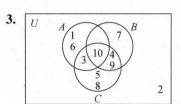

4. a. $A \cup B$ is represented by regions I, II, and III.
            Therefore $(A \cup B)'$ is represented by region
            IV.

   b. A' is represented by regions III and IV.
            B' is represented by regions I and IV.
            Therefore $A' \cap B'$ is represented by region IV.

   c. $(A \cup B)' = A' \cap B'$ because they both represent
            region IV.

5. a. $B \cup C$ is represented by regions II, III, IV, V,
            VI, and VII.
            Therefore $A \cap (B \cup C)$ is represented by
            regions II, IV, and V.

   b. $A \cap B$ is represented by regions II and V.
            $A \cap C$ is represented by regions IV and V.
            Therefore $(A \cap B) \cup (A \cap C)$ is represented by
            regions II, IV, and V.

   c. $A \cap (B \cup C) = (A \cap B) \cup (A \cap C)$ because they
            both represent region IV.

Exercises 2.4

1. $B \cap C = \{2, 3\}$
        $A \cup (B \cap C) = \{1, 2, 3, 5, 7\}$

2. $B \cup C = \{1, 2, 3, 4, 5, 6\}$
        $A \cap (B \cup C) = \{1, 3, 5\}$

3. $A \cup B = \{1, 2, 3, 5, 7\}$
        $A \cup C = \{1, 2, 3, 4, 5, 6, 7\}$
        $(A \cup B) \cap (A \cup C) = \{1, 2, 3, 5, 7\}$

4. $(A \cap B) = \{1, 3\}$
        $(A \cap C) = \{3, 5\}$
        $(A \cap B) \cup (A \cap C) = \{1, 3, 5\}$

5. $A' = \{2, 4, 6\}$ $C' = \{1, 7\}$
    $B \cup C' = \{1, 2, 3, 7\}$
    $A' \cap (B \cup C') = \{2\}$

6. $B' = \{4, 5, 6, 7\}$
    $C' = \{1, 7\}$
    $A \cup B' = \{1, 3, 4, 5, 6, 7\}$
    $C' \cap (A \cup B') = \{1, 7\}$

7. $A' = \{2, 4, 6\}$ $C' = \{1, 7\}$
    $A' \cap B = \{2\}$
    $A' \cap C' = \emptyset$
    $(A' \cap B) \cup (A' \cap C') = \{2\}$

8. $B' = \{4, 5, 6, 7\}$
    $C' = \{1, 7\}$
    $(C' \cap A) = \{1, 7\}$
    $(C' \cap B') = \{7\}$
    $(C' \cap A) \cup (C' \cap B') = \{1, 7\}$

9. $A = \{1, 3, 5, 7\}$
    $B = \{1, 2, 3\}$
    $C = \{2, 3, 4, 5, 6\}$
    $A \cup B \cup C = \{1, 2, 3, 4, 5, 6, 7\}$
    $(A \cup B \cup C)' = \emptyset$

10. $A = \{1, 3, 5, 7\}$
    $B = \{1, 2, 3\}$
    $C = \{2, 3, 4, 5, 6\}$
    $A \cap B \cap C = \{3\}$
    $(A \cap B \cap C)' = \{1, 2, 4, 5, 6, 7\}$

11. $A = \{1, 3, 5, 7\}$
    $B = \{1, 2, 3\}$
    $A \cup B = \{1, 2, 3, 5, 7\}$
    $(A \cup B)' = \{4, 6\}$
    $C = \{2, 3, 4, 5, 6\}$
    $(A \cup B)' \cap C = \{4, 6\}$

12. $B \cup C = \{1, 2, 3, 4, 5, 6\}$
    $(B \cup C)' = \{7\}$
    $(B \cup C)' \cap A = \{7\}$

13. $B \cap C = \{b\}$
    $A \cup (B \cap C) = \{a, b, g, h\}$

14. $B \cup C = \{b, c, d, e, f, g, h\}$
    $A \cap (B \cup C) = \{g, h\}$

15. $A \cup B = \{a, b, g, h\}$
    $A \cup C = \{a, b, c, d, e, f, g, h\}$
    $(A \cup B) \cap (A \cup C) = \{a, b, g, h\}$

16. $A \cap B = \{g, h\}$
    $A \cap C = \emptyset$
    $(A \cap B) \cup (A \cap C) = \{g, h\}$

17. $A' = \{b, c, d, e, f\}$
    $C' = \{a, g, h\}$
    $B \cup C' = \{a, b, g, h\}$
    $A' \cap (B \cup C') = \{b\}$

18. $C' = \{a, g, h\}$
    $B' = \{a, c, d, e, f\}$
    $A \cup B' = \{a, c, d, e, f, g, h\}$
    $C' \cap (A \cup B') = \{a, g, h\}$

19. $A' = \{b, c, d, e, f\}$
    $A' \cap B = \{b\}$
    $C' = \{a, g, h\}$
    $A' \cap C' = \emptyset$
    $(A' \cap B) \cup (A' \cap C') = \{b\}$

20. $C' = \{a, g, h\}$
    $B' = \{a, c, d, e, f\}$
    $C' \cap A = \{a, g, h\}$
    $C' \cap B' = \{a\}$
    $(C' \cap A) \cup (C' \cap B') = \{a, g, h\}$

21. $A \cup B \cup C = \{a, b, c, d, e, f, g, h\}$
    $(A \cup B \cup C)' = \emptyset$

22. $A \cap B \cap C = \emptyset$
    $(A \cap B \cap C)' = \{a, b, c, d, e, f, g, h\}$

23. $A \cup B = \{a, b, g, h\}$
    $(A \cup B)' = \{c, d, e, f\}$
    $(A \cup B)' \cap C = \{c, d, e, f\}$

24. $B \cup C = \{b, c, d, e, f, g, h\}$
    $(B \cup C)' = \{a\}$
    $(B \cup C)' \cap A = \{a\}$

25. II, III, V, VI

26. IV, V, VI, VII

27. I, II, IV, V, VI, VII

28. II, III, IV, V, VI, VII

29. II, V

30. IV, V

31. I, IV, VII, VIII

32. I, II, III, VIII

33. $A = \{1, 2, 3, 4, 5, 6, 7, 8\}$

34. $B = \{4, 5, 6, 9, 10, 11\}$

35. $A \cup B = \{1, 2, 3, 4, 5, 6, 7, 8, 9, 10, 11\}$

36. $B = \{4, 5, 6, 9, 10, 11\}$
$C = \{6, 7, 8, 9, 12\}$
$B \cup C = \{4, 5, 6, 7, 8, 9, 10, 11, 12\}$

37. $A = \{1, 2, 3, 4, 5, 6, 7, 8\}$
$B = \{4, 5, 6, 9, 10, 11\}$
$A \cup B = \{1, 2, 3, 4, 5, 6, 7, 8, 9, 10, 11\}$
$(A \cup B)' = \{12, 13\}$

38. $B = \{4, 5, 6, 9, 10, 11\}$
$C = \{6, 7, 8, 9, 12\}$
$B \cup C = \{4, 5, 6, 7, 8, 9, 10, 11, 12\}$
$(B \cup C)' = \{1, 2, 3, 13\}$

39. The set contains the elements in the two regions where the circles representing sets A and B overlap.
$A \cap B = \{4, 5, 6\}$

40. The set contains the elements in the two regions where the circles representing sets A and C overlap.
$A \cap C = \{6, 7, 8\}$

41. The set contains the element in the center region where the circles representing sets A, B, and C overlap.
$A \cap B \cap C = \{6\}$

42. The set contains the elements in the seven regions of the circles representing sets A, B, and C. Only element 13 lies outside these regions.
$A \cup B \cup C = \{1, 2, 3, 4, 5, 6, 7, 8, 9, 10, 11, 12\}$

43. $A \cap B \cap C = \{6\}$
$(A \cap B \cap C)' = \{1, 2, 3, 4, 5, 7, 8, 9, 10, 11, 12, 13\}$

44. $A \cup B \cup C = \{1, 2, 3, 4, 5, 6, 7, 8, 9, 10, 11, 12\}$
$(A \cup B \cup C)' = \{13\}$

45.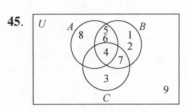

46.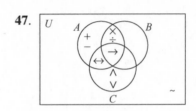

47.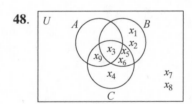

48.

49. a. II

b. II

c. $A \cap B = B \cap A$

50. a. I, II, III

b. I, II, III

c. $A \cup B = B \cup A$

51. a. I, III, IV

b. IV

c. No, $(A \cap B)' \neq A' \cap B'$

52. a. IV

b. I, III, IV

c. No, $(A \cup B)' \neq A' \cup B'$

53. Set A is represented by regions I and II.
Set A' is represented by regions III and IV.
Set B is represented by regions II and III.
Set B' is represented by regions I and IV.
$A' \cup B$ is represented by regions II, III, and IV.
$A \cap B'$ is represented by region I.
Thus, $A' \cup B$ and $A \cap B'$ are not equal for all sets A and B.

54. Set A is represented by regions I and II.
Set A' is represented by regions III and IV.
Set B is represented by regions II and III.
Set B' is represented by regions I and IV.
$A' \cap B$ is represented by region III.
$A \cup B'$ is represented by regions I, II, and IV.
Thus, $A' \cap B$ and $A \cup B'$ are not equal for all sets A and B.

55. Set A is represented by regions I and II.
Set B is represented by regions II and III.

$(A \cup B)'$ is represented by region IV.

$(A \cap B)'$ is represented by regions I, III, and IV.

Thus, $(A \cup B)'$ and $(A \cap B)'$ are not equal for all sets A and B.

56. Set A is represented by regions I and II.
Set B is represented by regions II and III.

$(A \cup B)'$ is represented by region IV.

$A' \cap B$ is represented by region III.

Thus, $(A \cup B)'$ and $A' \cap B$ are not equal for all sets A and B.

57. Set A is represented by regions I and II.
Set A' is represented by regions III and IV.
Set B is represented by regions II and III.
Set B' is represented by regions I and IV.

$(A' \cap B)'$ is represented by regions I, II, and IV.

$A \cup B'$ is represented by regions I, II, and IV.
Thus, $A' \cap B$ and $A \cup B'$ are equal for all sets A and B.

58. Set A is represented by regions I and II.
Set A' is represented by regions III and IV.
Set B is represented by regions II and III.
Set B' is represented by regions I and IV.

$(A \cup B')'$ is represented by region III.

$A' \cap B$ is represented by region III.
Thus, $A' \cap B$ and $A \cup B'$ are equal for all sets A and B.

59. a. II, IV, V, VI, VII

b. II, IV, V, VI, VII

c. $(A \cap B) \cup C = (A \cup C) \cap (B \cup C)$

60. a. IV, V, VI

b. IV, V, VI

c. $(A \cup B) \cap C = (A \cap C) \cup (B \cap C)$

61. a. II, IV, V

b. I, II, IV, V, VI

c. No
The results in **a** and **b** show
$A \cap (B \cup C) \neq A \cup (B \cap C)$ because of the different regions represented.

62. a. II, IV, V, VI, VII

b. IV, V, VI

c. No
The results in **a** and **b** show
$C \cup (B \cap A) \neq C \cap (B \cup A)$ because of the different regions represented.

63. The left expression is represented by regions II, IV, and V. The right expression is represented by regions II, IV, V, VI, and VII. Thus this statement is not true.

64. The left expression is represented by regions I, II, IV, V, and VI. The right expression is represented by regions IV, V, and VI. Thus this statement is not true.

65. Both expressions are represented by regions II, III, IV, V, and VI. Thus this statement is true and is a theorem.

66. Both expressions are represented by regions II, V, and VI. Thus this statement is true and is a theorem.

67. Both expressions are represented by region I. Thus this statement is true and is a theorem.

68. Both expressions are represented by regions I, II, III, IV, V, VII, and VIII. Thus this statement is true and is a theorem.

69. a. $A \cup (B' \cap C') = \{c, e, f\}$

$(A \cup B') \cap (A \cup C') = \{c, e, f\}$

b. $A \cup (B' \cap C') = \{1, 3, 5, 7, 8\}$

$(A \cup B') \cap (A \cup C') = \{1, 3, 5, 7, 8\}$

c. $A \cup (B' \cap C') = (A \cup B') \cap (A \cup C')$

d. $A \cup (B' \cap C')$ and $(A \cup B') \cap (A \cup C')$ are both represented by regions I, II, IV, V, and VIII. Thus, the conjecture in part c is a theorem.

70. a. $(A \cup B)' \cap C = \{4\}$

$A' \cap (B' \cap C) = \{4\}$

b. $(A \cup B)' \cap C = \{e\}$

$A' \cap (B' \cap C) = \{e\}$

c. $(A \cup B)' \cap C = A' \cap (B' \cap C)$

d. $(A \cup B)' \cap C$ and $A' \cap (B' \cap C)$ are both represented by regions IV, V, and VI. Thus, the conjecture in part c is a theorem.

71. $(A \cap B') \cap (A \cup B)$

72. $(A \cup B)'$

73. $A' \cup B$

74. $A' \cap B$

75. $(A \cap B) \cup C$

76. $A \cap (B \cup C)$

77. $A' \cap (B \cup C)$

78. $(A \cup B)' \cap C$

79. {Ann, Jose, Al, Gavin, Amy, Ron, Grace}

80. {Jose, Ron, Grace, Lee, Maria}

81. {Jose}

82. {Ann, Jose}

83. {Lily, Emma}

84. {Ron, Grace, Lee, Maria}

85. {Lily, Emma, Ann, Jose, Lee, Maria, Fred, Ben, Sheila, Ellen, Gary}

86. {Jose, Ron, Grace, Lee, Maria, Al, Gavin, Amy, Fred, Ben, Sheila, Ellen, Gary}

87. {Lily, Emma, Al, Gavin, Amy, Lee, Maria}

88. {Ann, Jose, Ron, Grace}

89. {Al, Gavin, Amy}

90. {Lily, Emma}

91. The set of students who scored 90% or above on exam 1 and exam 3 but not on exam 2 is the empty set.

92. The set of students who did not score 90% or higher on any of the exams.

93. Region II

94. Region VII

95. Region V

96. Region V

97. Region III

98. Region VIII

99. Region III

100. Region VI

101. Region V

102. Region IV

103. Region VII

104. Region IV

105.

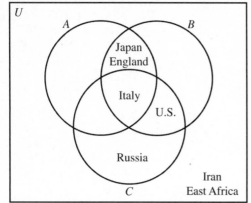

106.

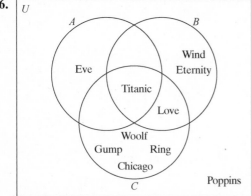

109. does not make sense; Explanations will vary. Sample explanation: You should begin by placing elements in the innermost region.

110. makes sense

111. makes sense

112. does not make sense; Explanations will vary. Sample explanation: Finding examples, even many examples, is not enough to prove a conjecture.

113. AB^+

114. O^-

115. no

116. yes

Check Points 2.5

1. **a.** $55 + 20 = 75$

    b. $20 + 70 = 90$

    c. 20

    d. $55 + 20 + 70 = 145$

    e. 55

    f. 70

    g. 30

    h. $55 + 20 + 70 + 30 = 175$

2. Start by placing 700 in region II.
    Next place $1190 - 700$ or 490 in region III.
    Since half of those surveyed were women, place $1000 - 700$ or 300 in region I.
    Finally, place $2000 - 300 - 700 - 490$ or 510 in region IV.

    a. 490 men agreed with the statement and are represented by region III.

    b. 510 men disagreed with the statement and are represented by region IV.

3. Since 2 people collect all three items, begin by placing a 2 in region V.
    Since 29 people collect baseball cards and comic books, $29 - 2$ or 27 should be placed in region II.
    Since 5 people collect baseball cards and stamps, $5 - 2$ or 3 should be placed in region IV.
    Since 2 people collect comic books and stamps, $2 - 2$ or 0 should be placed in region VI.
    Since 108 people collect baseball cards, $108 - 27 - 3 - 2$ or 76 should be placed in region I.
    Since 92 people collect comic books, $92 - 27 - 2 - 0$ or 63 should be placed in region III.
    Since 62 people collect stamps, $62 - 3 - 2 - 0$ or 57 should be placed in region VII.
    Since there were 250 people surveyed, place $250 - 76 - 27 - 63 - 3 - 2 - 0 - 57 = 22$ in region VIII.

    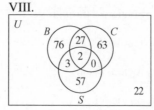

4. **a.** 63 as represented by region III.

   b. 3 as represented by region IV.

   c. 136 as represented by regions I, IV, and VII.

   d. 30 as represented by regions II, IV, and VI.

   e. 228 as represented by regions I through VII.

   f. 22 as represented by region VIII.

Exercise Set 2.5

   1. 26

   2. 20

   3. 17

   4. 11

   5. 37

   6. 9

   7. 7

   8. 44

   9. Region I has 21 – 7 or 14 elements.
   Region III has 29 – 7 or 22 elements.
   Region IV has 48 – 14 – 7– 22 or 5 elements.

   10. Region I has 23 – 7 or 16 elements.
   Region III has 27 – 7 or 20 elements.
   Region IV has 53 – 16 – 7– 20 or 10 elements.

   11. 17 as represented by regions II, III, V, and VI.

   12. 15 as represented by regions I, II, IV, and V.

   13. 6 as represented by regions I and II.

   14. 9 as represented by regions III and VI.

   15. 28 as represented by regions I, II, IV, V, VI, and VII.

   16. 24 as represented by regions I through VI.

   17. 9 as represented by regions IV and V.

   18. 8 as represented by regions II and V.

   19. 3 as represented by region VI.

   20. 2 as represented by region IV.

21. 19 as represented by regions III, VI, and VII.

22. 17 as represented by regions I, IV, and VII.

23. 21 as represented by regions I, III, and VII.

24. 6 as represented by regions II, IV, and VI.

25. 34 as represented by regions I through VII.

26. 13 as represented by regions II, IV, V, and VI.

27. Since $n(A \cap B) = 3$, there is 1 element in region II.

Since $n(A \cap C) = 5$, there are 3 elements in region IV.

Since $n(B \cap C) = 3$, there is 1 element in region VI.

Since $n(A) = 11$, there are 5 elements in region I.

Since $n(B) = 8$, there are 4 elements in region III.

Since $n(C) = 14$, there are 8 elements in region VII.

Since $n(U) = 30$, there are 6 elements in region VIII.

28. Since $n(A \cap B) = 6$, there are 4 elements in region II.

Since $n(A \cap C) = 7$, there are 5 elements in region IV.

Since $n(B \cap C) = 8$, there are 6 elements in region VI.

Since $n(A) = 21$, there are 10 elements in region I.

Since $n(B) = 15$, there are 3 elements in region III.

Since $n(C) = 14$, there is 1 element in region VII.

Since $n(U) = 32$, there is 1 element in region VIII.

29. Since $n(A \cap B \cap C) = 7$, there are 7 elements in region V.

Since $n(A \cap B) = 17$, there are 10 elements in region II.

Since $n(A \cap C) = 11$, there are 4 elements in region IV.

Since $n(B \cap C) = 8$, there is 1 element in region VI.

Since $n(A) = 26$, there are 5 elements in region I.

Since $n(B) = 21$, there are 3 elements in region III.

Since $n(C) = 18$, there are 6 elements in region VII.

Since $n(U) = 38$, there are 2 elements in region VIII.

30. Since $n(A \cap B \cap C) = 5$, there are 5 elements in region V.

Since $n(A \cap B) = 17$, there are 12 elements in region II.

Since $n(A \cap C) = 11$, there are 6 elements in region IV.

Since $n(B \cap C) = 9$, there are 4 elements in region VI.

Since $n(A) = 26$, there are 3 elements in region I.

Since $n(B) = 22$, there is 1 element in region III.

Since $n(C) = 25$, there are 10 elements in region VII.

Since $n(U) = 42$, there is 1 element in region VIII.

31. Since $n(A \cap B \cap C) = 2$, there are 2 elements in region V.

Since $n(A \cap B) = 6$, there are 4 elements in region II.

Since $n(A \cap C) = 9$, there are 7 elements in region IV.

Regions II, IV, and V contain a total of 13 elements, yet set A is stated to contain a total of only 10 elements. That is impossible.

32. Since $n(A \cap B \cap C) = 5$, there are 5 elements in region V.

Since $n(A \cap B) = 6$, there is 1 element in region II.

Since $n(A \cap C) = 9$, there are 4 elements in region IV.

Regions II, IV, and V contain a total of 10 elements, yet set A is stated to contain a total of only 8 elements. That is impossible.

33. $4 + 5 + 2 + 7 = 18$ respondents agreed with the statement.

34. $8 + 2 + 3 + 9 = 22$ respondents disagreed with the statement.

35. $2 + 7 = 9$ women agreed with the statement.

36. $4 + 2 = 6$ people who are not African American agreed with the statement.

37. 9 women who are not African American disagreed with the statement.

38. 8 men who are not African American agreed with the statement.

39. Parts b, c, and d are labeled.

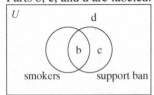

40. Parts b, c, and d are labeled.

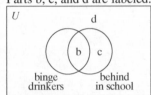

41. Parts b, c, and d are labeled.

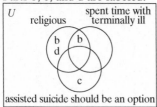

Answers for part e will vary.

42. Parts b, c, and d are labeled.

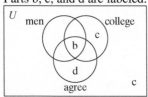

Answers for part e will vary.

43. Begin by placing 7 in the region that represents both newspapers and television.

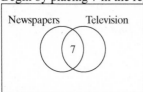

    a.   Since 29 students got news from newspapers, $29 - 7 = 22$ got news from only newspapers.

    b.   Since 43 students got news from television, $43 - 7 = 36$ got news from only television.

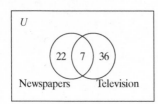

    c. $22 + 7 + 36 = 65$ students who got news from newspapers or television.

    d.   Since 75 students were surveyed, $75 - 65 = 10$ students who did not get news from either.

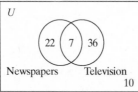

44. Begin by placing 40 in the region that represents both math and English.

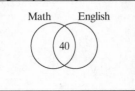

a. Since 75 students registered for math, $75 - 40 = 35$ registered for only math.

b. Since 65 students registered for English, $65 - 40 = 25$ registered for only English.

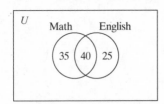

c. $35 + 40 + 25 = 100$ students who registered for math or English.

d. Since 120 students were surveyed, $120 - 100 = 20$ students who did not register for either.

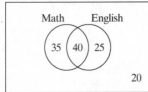

45. Construct a Venn diagram.

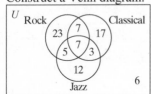

a. 23

b. 3

c. $17 + 3 + 12 = 32$

d. $23 + 17 + 12 = 52$

e. $7 + 3 + 5 + 7 = 22$

f. 6

46. Construct a Venn diagram.

   a. 30

   b. 8

   c. $23+8+30=61$

   d. $23+30+14=67$

   e. $8+7+9+5=29$

   f. 84

47. Construct a Venn diagram.

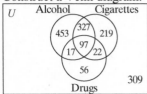

   a. 1500 (all eight regions)

   b. 1135 (the six regions of sets A and C)

   c. 56 (region VII)

   d. 327 (region II)

   e. 526 (regions I, IV, and VII)

   f. 366 (regions II, IV, and VI)

   g. 1191 (regions I through VII)

48. Construct a Venn diagram.

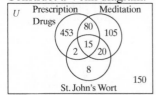

   a. 833 (all eight regions)

   b. 675 (the six regions of sets A and C)

   c. 8 (region VII)

   d. 80 (region II)

   e. 463 (regions I, IV, and VII)

   f. 102 (regions II, IV, and VI)

   g. 683 (regions I through VII)

51. does not make sense; Explanations will vary. Sample explanation: A survey problem could present the information in any order.

52. makes sense

53. does not make sense; Explanations will vary. Sample explanation: Since there is a circle to represent smokers, then nonsmokers are represented by being placed outside that circle, not in a separate circle.

54. does not make sense; Explanations will vary. Sample explanation: The bar graph does not indicate how the various ailments intersect.

55. false; Changes to make the statement true will vary. A sample change is: It is possible that some students are taking more than one of these courses. If so, then the number surveyed is less than 220.

56. true

57. false; Changes to make the statement true will vary. A sample change is: Then innermost region is the first region to be filled in.

58. true

59. a. 0; This would assume none of the psychology students were taking mathematics.

   b. 30; This would assume all 30 students taking psychology were taking mathematics.

   c. 60; $U=150$ so with 90 taking mathematics, if we assume all the psychology students are taking mathematics courses, $U-90=60$.

60. Under the conditions given concerning enrollment in math, chemistry, and psychology courses, the total number of students is 100, not 90

Chapter 2 Review Exercises

1. the set of days of the week beginning with the letter T.

2. the set of natural numbers between 1 and 10, inclusive.

3. {m, i, s}

4. {8, 9, 10, 11, 12}

5. {1, 2, 3, …, 30}

6. not empty

7. empty set

8. $\in$
   93 is an element of the set.

9. $\notin$
   {d} is a subset, not a member; "d" would be a member.

10. 12
    12 months in the year.

11. 15

12. $\neq$
    The two sets do not contain exactly the same elements.

13. $\neq$
    One set is infinite. The other is finite.

14. Equivalent
    Same number of elements, but different elements.

15. Equal and equivalent
    The two sets have exactly the same elements.

16. finite

17. infinite

18. $\subseteq$

19. $\nsubseteq$

20. $\subseteq$

21. $\subseteq$

22. both

23. false; Texas is not a member of the set.

24. false; 4 is not a subset. {4} is a subset.

25. true

26. false; It is a subset but not a proper subset.

27. true

28. false; The set {six} has only one element so it has $2^1 = 2$ subsets.

29. true

30. $\varnothing$ {1} {5} {1, 5}
    {1, 5} is not a proper subset.

31. There are 5 elements. This means there are $2^5 = 32$ subsets.
    There are $2^5 - 1 = 31$ proper subsets.

32. {January, June, July}
    There are 3 elements. This means there are $2^3 = 8$ subsets.
    There are $2^3 - 1 = 7$ proper subsets.

33. $A \cap B = \{1, 2, 4\}$

34. $A \cup B' = \{1, 2, 3, 4, 6, 7, 8\}$

35. $A' \cap B = \{5\}$

36. $(A \cup B)' = \{6, 7, 8\}$

37. $A' \cap B' = \{6, 7, 8\}$

38. {4, 5, 6}

39. {2, 3, 6, 7}

40. {1, 4, 5, 6, 8, 9}

41. {4, 5}

42. {1, 2, 3, 6, 7, 8, 9}

43. {2, 3, 7}

44. {6}

45. {1, 2, 3, 4, 5, 6, 7, 8, 9}

46. $n(A \cup B) = n(A) + n(B) - n(A \cap B)$
    $$= 25 + 17 - 9$$
    $$= 33$$

47. $B \cap C = \{1, 5\}$
    $A \cup (B \cap C) = \{1, 2, 3, 4, 5\}$

48. $A \cap C = \{1\}$
    $(A \cap C)' = (2, 3, 4, 5, 6, 7, 8)$
    $(A \cap C)' \cup B = \{1, 2, 3, 4, 5, 6, 7, 8\}$

49. {c, d, e, f, k, p, r}

50. {f, p}

51. {c, d, f, k, p, r}

52. {c, d, e}

53. {a, b, c, d, e, g, h, p, r}

54. {f}

55.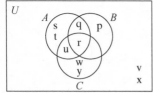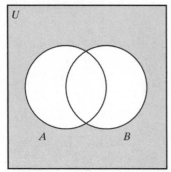

56. The shaded regions are the same for $(A \cup B)'$ and $A' \cap B'$. Therefore $(A \cup B)' = A' \cap B'$

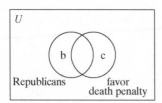

57. The statement is false because the shaded regions are different.

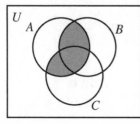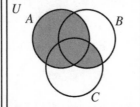

58. United States is in V; Italy is in IV; Turkey is in VIII; Norway is in V; Pakistan is in VIII; Iceland is in V; Mexico is in I

59. a. Parts b and c are labeled.

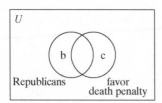

60. Begin by placing 400 in the region that represents both stocks and bonds.

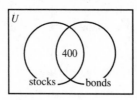

a. Since 650 respondents invested in stocks, $650 - 400 = 250$ invested in only stocks.

Furthermore, since 550 respondents invested in bonds, $550 - 400 = 150$ invested in only bonds. Place this data in the Venn diagram.

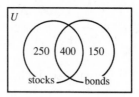

b. $250 + 400 + 150 = 800$ respondents invested in stocks or bonds.

c. Since 1000 people were surveyed, $1000 - 800 = 200$ respondents who did not invest in either.

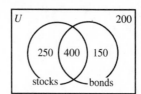

61. Construct a Venn diagram.

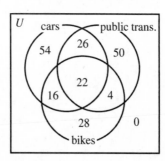

a. 50

b. 26

c. $54 + 26 + 50 = 130$

d. $26 + 16 + 4 = 46$

e. 0

Chapter 2 Test

1. {18, 19, 20, 21, 22, 23, 24}

2. False, {6} is not an element of the set, but 6 is an element.

3. True, both sets have seven elements.

4. True

5. False, *g* is not an element in the larger set.

6. True

7. False, 14 is an element of the set.

8. False, Number of subsets: 2^N where *N* is the number of elements. There are 5 elements. $2^5 = 32$ subsets

9. False, $\varnothing$ is *not* a proper subset of itself.

10. $\varnothing$ {6} {9} {6, 9}
    {6, 9} is not a proper subset.

11. {a, b, c, d, e, f}

12. $B \cap C = \{e\}$
    $(B \cap C)' = \{a, b, c, d, f, g\}$

13. $C' = \{b, c, d, f\}$
    $A \cap C' = \{b, c, d\}$

14. $A \cup B = \{a, b, c, d, e, f\}$
    $(A \cup B) \cap C = \{a, e\}$

15. $B' = \{a, b, g\}$
    $A \cup B' = \{a, b, c, d, g\}$
    $n(A \cup B') = 5$

16. {b, c, d, i, j, k}

17. {a}

18. {a, f, h}

19.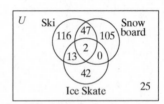

20. Both expressions are represented by regions III, VI, and VII. Thus this statement is true and is a theorem.

21. a. region V

    b. region VII

    c. region IV

    d. region I

    e. region VI

22. a.
    ```
    U   Ski              Snow
              116  47  105 board
                    2
                 13   0
                   42
              Ice Skate     25
    ```

    b. 263 (regions I, III, and VII)

    c. 25 (region VIII)

    d. 62 (regions II, IV, V, and VI)

    e. 0 (region VI)

    f. 147 (regions III, VI, and VII)

    g. 116 (region I)

Chapter 3
Logic

Check Points 3.1

1. **a.** Paris is not the capital of Spain.

    b. July is a month.

2. **a.** ~*p*

    b. ~*q*

3. Chicago O'Hare is not the world's busiest airport.

4. Some new tax dollars will not be used to improve education.
    At least one new tax dollar will not be used to improve education.

Exercise Set 3.1

1. statement

2. statement

3. statement

4. statement

5. not a statement

6. not a statement

7. statement

8. statement

9. not a statement

10. not a statement

11. statement

12. statement

13. statement

14. not a statement

15. It is not raining.

16. It is not snowing.

17. The Dallas Cowboys are the team with the most Super Bowl wins.

18. The New York Yankees are the team with the most World Series wins.

19. Chocolate in moderation is good for the heart.

20. Albert Einstein was offered the presidency of Israel.

21. ~*p*

22. ~*q*

23. ~*r*

24. ~*s*

25. Listening to classical music does not make infants smarter.

26. Subliminal advertising does not make you buy things.

27. Sigmund Freud's father was 20 years older than his mother.

28. Humans and bananas share approximately 60% of the same DNA structure.

29. **a.** There are no whales that are not mammals.

    b. Some whales are not mammals.

30. **a.** There are no journalists who are not writers.

    b. Some journalists are not writers.

31. **a.** At least one student is a business major.

    b. No students are business majors.

32. **a.** At least one movie is a comedy.

    b. No movies are comedies.

33. **a.** At least one thief is not a criminal.

    b. All thieves are criminals.

34. **a.** At least one pianist is not a keyboard player.

    b. All pianists are keyboard players.

35. a. All Democratic presidents have not been impeached.

b. Some Democratic presidents have been impeached.

36. a. All women have not served as Supreme Court justices.

b. Some women have served as Supreme Court justices.

37. a. All seniors graduated.

b. Some seniors did not graduate.

38. a. All applicants were hired.

b. Some applicants were not hired.

39. a. Some parrots are not pets.

b. All parrots are pets.

40. a. Some dogs are not playful.

b. All dogs are playful.

41. a. No atheist is a churchgoer.

b. Some atheists are churchgoers.

42. a. No burnt muffin is edible.

b. Some burnt muffins are edible

43. Some Africans have Jewish ancestry.

44. Some religious traditions recognize sexuality as central to their understanding of the sacred.

45. Some rap is not hip-hop.

46. All hip-hop is rap.

47. a. All birds are parrots.

b. false; Some birds are not parrots.

48. a. All mammals are humans.

b. false; Some mammals are not humans.

49. a. No college students are business majors.

b. false; Some college students are business majors.

50. a. No college students are athletes.

b. false; Some college students are athletes.

51. a. All people like Sara Lee.

b. Some people don't like Sara Lee.

52. a. All well stated problems are half solved.

b. Some well stated problems are not half solved.

53. a. No safe thing is exciting.

b. Some safe things are exciting.

54. a. Some people live to regret a misspent youth.

b. No people live to regret a misspent youth.

55. a. Some great actors are not Tom Hanks.

b. All great actors are Tom Hanks.

56. a. Some generous philanthropists are not Bill Gates.

b. All generous philanthropists are Bill Gates.

57. b

58. c

59. true

60. true

61. false; Some college students in the United States are willing to marry without romantic love.

62. false; Some college students in Pakistan are not willing to marry without romantic love.

63. true

64. true

65. false; The sentence "5% of college students in Australia are willing to marry without romantic love" is a statement.

66. false; The sentence "12% of college students in the Philippines are willing to marry without romantic love" is a statement.

74. does not make sense; Explanations will vary. Sample explanation: A statement is a sentence that is either true or false, but not both simultaneously. Knowing, or not knowing, the statement's truth value is not relevant.

75. does not make sense; Explanations will vary. Sample explanation: Statements that have opposite truth values are not necessarily negations of each other.

76. makes sense

77. does not make sense; Explanations will vary. Sample explanation: The correctness of the spelling is not relevant.

78. Answers will vary. Possible answer: Everything I say or write is false.

79. Answers will vary. Possible answer: Some mammals are not cats (true). Some cats are not mammals (false).

80. The statement could mean that she *is* dating him, but that his muscularity is *not* the reason. The statement could also mean that she *is not* dating him because she does not like the fact that he is muscular.

Check Points 3.2

1. a. $q \wedge p$ **b.** $\sim p \wedge q$

2. a. $p \vee q$ **b.** $q \vee \sim p$

3. a. $\sim p \rightarrow \sim q$ **b.** $q \rightarrow \sim p$

4. $\sim q \rightarrow p$

5. a. $q \leftrightarrow p$ **b.** $\sim p \leftrightarrow \sim q$

6. a. It is not true that he earns $105,000 yearly and that he is often happy.

  b. He is not often happy and he earns $105,000 yearly.

  c. It is not true that if he is often happy then he earns $105,000 yearly.

7. a. If the plant is fertilized and watered, then the plant does not wilt.

  b. The plant is fertilized, and if the plant is watered then it does not wilt.

8. p: There is too much homework.; q: A teacher is boring.; r: I take the class.

  a. $(p \vee q) \rightarrow \sim r$ **b.** $p \vee (q \rightarrow \sim r)$

Exercise Set 3.2

1. $p \wedge q$

2. $q \wedge p$

3. $q \wedge \sim p$

4. $p \wedge \sim q$

5. $\sim q \wedge p$

6. $\sim p \wedge q$

7. $p \vee q$; $\underset{p}{\underline{\text{I study}}}$ $\underset{\vee}{\underline{\text{or}}}$ $\underset{q}{\underline{\text{I pass the course.}}}$

8. $q \vee p$; $\underset{q}{\underline{\text{I pass the course}}}$ $\underset{\vee}{\underline{\text{or}}}$ $\underset{p}{\underline{\text{I study.}}}$

9. $p \vee \sim q$; $\underset{p}{\underline{\text{I study}}}$ $\underset{\vee}{\underline{\text{or}}}$ $\underset{\sim q}{\underline{\text{I do not pass the course.}}}$

10. $\sim p \vee \sim q$;
  $\underset{\sim p}{\underline{\text{I do not study}}}$ $\underset{\vee}{\underline{\text{or}}}$ $\underset{\sim q}{\underline{\text{I do not pass the course.}}}$

11. $p \rightarrow q$;
  $\underline{\text{If}}$ $\underset{p}{\underline{\text{this is an alligator,}}}$ $\underset{\rightarrow}{\underline{\text{then}}}$ $\underset{q}{\underline{\text{this is a reptile.}}}$

12. $q \rightarrow p$;
  $\underline{\text{If}}$ $\underset{q}{\underline{\text{this is a reptile,}}}$ $\underset{\rightarrow}{\underline{\text{then}}}$ $\underset{p}{\underline{\text{this is an alligator.}}}$

13. $\sim p \rightarrow \sim q$;

$$\underbrace{\text{If}} \quad \underbrace{\text{this is not an alligator,}}_{\sim p} \quad \underbrace{\text{then}}_{\rightarrow}$$

$$\underbrace{\text{this is not a reptile.}}_{\sim q}$$

14. $\sim q \rightarrow \sim p$;

$$\underbrace{\text{If}} \quad \underbrace{\text{this is not a reptile,}}_{\sim q} \quad \underbrace{\text{then}}_{\rightarrow}$$

$$\underbrace{\text{this is not an alligator.}}_{\sim p}$$

15. $\sim q \rightarrow \sim p$

16. $p \rightarrow q$

17. $p \rightarrow q$

18. $p \rightarrow q$

19. $p \rightarrow \sim q$

20. $q \rightarrow \sim p$

21. $q \rightarrow \sim p$

22. $p \rightarrow \sim q$

23. $p \rightarrow \sim q$

24. $q \rightarrow \sim p$

25. $q \rightarrow \sim p$

26. $p \rightarrow \sim q$

27. $p \leftrightarrow q$;

$$\underbrace{\text{The campus is closed}}_{p} \quad \underbrace{\text{if and only if}}_{\leftrightarrow} \quad \underbrace{\text{it is Sunday.}}_{q}$$

28. $q \leftrightarrow p$;

$$\underbrace{\text{It is Sunday}}_{q} \quad \underbrace{\text{if and only if}}_{\leftrightarrow} \quad \underbrace{\text{the campus is closed.}}_{p}$$

29. $\sim q \leftrightarrow \sim p$;

$$\underbrace{\text{It is not Sunday}}_{\sim q} \quad \underbrace{\text{if and only if}}_{\leftrightarrow}$$

$$\underbrace{\text{the campus is not closed.}}_{\sim p}$$

30. $\sim p \leftrightarrow \sim q$;

$$\underbrace{\text{The campus is not closed}}_{\sim p} \quad \underbrace{\text{if and only if}}_{\leftrightarrow}$$

$$\underbrace{\text{it is not Sunday.}}_{\sim q}$$

31. $q \leftrightarrow p$

32. $p \leftrightarrow q$

33. The heater is not working and the house is cold.

34. The heater is working and the house is not cold.

35. The heater is working or the house is not cold.

36. The heater is not working or the house is cold.

37. If the heater is working then the house is not cold.

38. If the house is cold then the heater is not working.

39. The heater is working if and only if the house is not cold.

40. The heater is not working if and only if the house is cold.

41. It is July 4th and we are not having a barbeque.

42. It is not July 4th and we are having a barbeque.

43. It is not July 4th or we are having a barbeque.

44. It is July 4th or we are not having a barbeque.

45. If we are having a barbeque, then it is not July 4th.

46. If it is July 4th, then we are not having a barbeque.

47. It is not July 4th if and only if we are having a barbeque.

48. It is July 4th if and only if we are not having a barbeque.

49. It is not true that Romeo loves Juliet and Juliet loves Romeo.

50. It is not true that Juliet loves Romeo and Romeo loves Juliet.

51. Romeo does not love Juliet and Juliet loves Romeo.

52. Juliet does not love Romeo and Romeo loves Juliet.

53. Neither Juliet loves Romeo nor Romeo loves Juliet.

54. Neither Romeo loves Juliet nor Juliet loves Romeo.

55. Juliet does not love Romeo or Romeo loves Juliet.

56. Romeo does not love Juliet or Juliet loves Romeo.

57. Romeo does not love Juliet and Juliet does not love Romeo.

58. Juliet does not love Romeo and Romeo does not love Juliet.

59. $(p \wedge q) \vee r$; $\left(\underset{p}{\text{The temperature outside is freezing}} \underset{\wedge}{\text{ and }} \underset{q}{\text{the heater is working,}} \right) \underset{\vee}{\text{ or }} \underset{r}{\text{the house is cold.}}$

60. $p \rightarrow (q \vee \sim r)$; $\underset{p}{\text{If the temperature outside is freezing,}} \underset{\rightarrow}{\text{ then }} \left(\underset{q}{\text{the heater is working}} \underset{\vee}{\text{ or }} \underset{\sim r}{\text{the house is not cold.}} \right)$

61. $(p \vee \sim q) \rightarrow r$; $\left(\underset{p}{\text{If the temperature outside is freezing}} \underset{\vee}{\text{ or }} \underset{\sim q}{\text{the heater is not working,}} \right) \underset{\rightarrow}{\text{ then }} \underset{r}{\text{the house is cold.}}$

62. $\sim (r \rightarrow \sim q)$; $\underset{\sim}{\text{It is not the case that}} \left(\underset{r}{\text{if the house is cold}} \underset{\rightarrow}{\text{ then }} \underset{\sim q}{\text{the heater is not working.}} \right)$

63. $r \leftrightarrow (p \wedge \sim q)$; $\underset{r}{\text{The house is cold}} \underset{\leftrightarrow}{\text{ if and only if }} \left(\underset{p}{\text{the temperature outside is freezing}} \underset{\wedge}{\text{ and }} \underset{\sim q}{\text{the heater isn't working.}} \right)$

64. $q \rightarrow (p \leftrightarrow r)$; $\underset{q}{\text{If the heater is working,}} \underset{\rightarrow}{\text{ then }} \left(\underset{p}{\text{the temperature outside is freezing}} \underset{\leftrightarrow}{\text{ if and only if }} \underset{r}{\text{the house is cold.}} \right)$

65. $(p \wedge \sim q) \rightarrow r$;

$\left(\underset{p}{\text{The temperature outside is freezing}} \underset{\wedge}{\text{ and }} \underset{\sim q}{\text{the heater isn't working}} \right) \underset{\rightarrow}{\text{ is a sufficient condition for }} \underset{r}{\text{the house being cold.}}$

66. $p \leftrightarrow (\sim q \rightarrow r)$;

$\underset{p}{\text{A freezing outside temperature}} \underset{\leftrightarrow}{\text{ is necessary and sufficient for }} \left(\underset{\sim q}{\text{the heater not working}} \underset{\rightarrow}{\text{ implying }} \underset{r}{\text{the house is cold.}} \right)$

67. If the temperature is above 85° and we have finished studying, then we go to the beach.

68. If we finished studying and we go to the beach, then the temperature is above 85°.

69. The temperature is above 85°, and if we finished studying then we go to the beach.

70. The temperature is above 85°, and if we go to the beach then we have finished studying.

71. $\sim r \rightarrow (\sim p \vee \sim q)$; If we do not go to the beach, then the temperature is not above 85° or we have not finished studying.

72. $\sim p \rightarrow (q \vee r)$; If the temperature is not above 85°, then we have finished studying or we will go to the beach.

73. If we do not go to the beach then we have not finished studying, or the temperature is above 85°.

74. If the temperature is not above 85° then we will not go to the beach, or we have finished studying.

75. $r \leftrightarrow (p \wedge q)$; We will go to the beach if and only if the temperature is above 85° and we have finished studying.

76. $r \leftrightarrow (q \wedge p)$; We will go to the beach if and only if we have finished studying and the temperature is above 85°.

77. The temperature is above 85° if and only if we have finished studying, and we go to the beach.

78. If we have finished studying, then we will go to the beach if and only if the temperature is above 85°.

79. If we do not go to the beach, then it is not true that both the temperature is above 85° and we have finished studying.

80. If it is not true that both the temperature is above 85° and we have finished studying, then we will not go to the beach.

81. p: I like the teacher.; q: The course is interesting.; r: I miss class.; $(p \vee q) \rightarrow \sim r$

82. p: The lines go down.; q: The transformer blows.; r: We have power.; $(p \vee q) \rightarrow \sim r$

83. p: I like the teacher.; q: The course is interesting.; r: I miss class.; $p \vee (q \rightarrow \sim r)$

84. p: The lines go down.; q: The transformer blows.; r: We have power.; $p \vee (q \rightarrow \sim r)$

85. p: I like the teacher.; q: The course is interesting.; r: I miss class.; $r \leftrightarrow \sim (p \wedge q)$

86. p: The lines go down.; q: The transformer blows.; r: We have power.; $r \leftrightarrow \sim (p \wedge q)$

87. p: I like the teacher.; q: The course is interesting.; r: I miss class.; $p \rightarrow (\sim r \leftrightarrow q)$

88. p: The lines go down.; q: The transformer blows.; r: We have power.; $p \rightarrow (\sim r \leftrightarrow q)$

89. p: I like the teacher.; q: The course is interesting.; r: I miss class.; s: I spend extra time reading the book.;
     $(\sim p \wedge r) \rightarrow (\sim q \vee s)$

90. p: The lines go down.; q: The transformer blows.; r: We have power.; s: There is an increase in the cost of electricity.;
     $(\sim p \wedge r) \rightarrow (\sim q \vee s)$

91. p: Being French is necessary for being a Parisian.; q: Being German is necessary for being a Berliner.; $\sim p \rightarrow \sim q$

92. p: Being English is necessary for being a Londoner.; q: Being American is necessary for being a New Yorker.;
     $\sim p \rightarrow \sim q$

93. p: You file an income tax report.; q: You file a complete statement of earnings.; r: You are a taxpayer.; s: You are an
     authorized tax preparer.; $(r \vee s) \rightarrow (p \wedge q)$

94. p: You fall in love with someone in your class.; q: You pick someone to hate.; r: You show up to vent your emotions.; s:
     You skip.; $(p \vee q) \rightarrow (r \wedge \sim s)$

95. p: You are wealthy.; q: You are happy.; r: You live contentedly.; $\sim (p \rightarrow (q \wedge r))$

96. p: You are wealthy.; q: You are happy.; r: You live contentedly.; $\sim (p \rightarrow (q \wedge r))$

97. $[p \rightarrow (q \vee r)] \leftrightarrow (p \wedge r)$

98. $[(p \wedge q) \to r] \leftrightarrow (p \vee r)$

99. $(p \to p) \leftrightarrow [(p \wedge p) \to \sim p]$

100. $(p \to p) \leftrightarrow [(p \vee p) \to \sim p]$

101. p: You can get rid of the family skeleton.
q: You may as well make it dance.
$\sim p \to q$

102. p: I did have all the old-fashioned values to rebel against.
q: I would turn out the way I did.
$\sim p \to \sim q$

103. p: You know what you believe.
q: I can answer your questions.
$(p \to q) \wedge \sim q$

104. p: You do like what you are doing.
q: You can always pick up your needle.
r: You can move to another groove.
$\sim p \to (q \wedge r)$

105. p: I am an intellectual.
q: I would be pessimistic about America.
$((p \to q) \wedge \sim p) \to \sim q$

106. p: You can be a good socializer.
q: You can be a good writer.
$\sim (p \wedge q)$

115. makes sense

116. does not make sense; Explanations will vary. Sample explanation: Because the word *and* comes before the word *or*, it takes precedence. Therefore the statement is false and no conclusion can be made about chemistry.

117. does not make sense; Explanations will vary. Sample explanation: Wearing red is necessary (not sufficient) for being a Chinese bride.

118. makes sense

119. $\left(\left(\underbrace{\text{Shooting unarmed civilians is morally justifiable}}_{p} \underbrace{\text{ if and only if }}_{\leftrightarrow} \underbrace{\text{bombing unarmed civilians is morally justifiable,}}_{q} \right. \right.$
$\left. \underbrace{\text{and}}_{\wedge} \underbrace{\text{as the former is not morally justifiable,}}_{\sim p} \right) \to \left(\underbrace{\text{neither is the latter.}}_{\sim q} \right)$

Check Points 3.3

1. p: $3 + 5 = 8$ is true
   q: $2 \times 7 = 20$ is false

   a. $p \wedge q$

   $T \wedge F$

   F

   b. $p \wedge \sim q$

   $T \wedge \sim F$

   $T \wedge T$

   T

   c. $\sim p \vee q$

   $\sim T \vee F$

   $F \vee F$

   F

   d. $\sim p \vee \sim q$

   $\sim T \vee \sim F$

   $F \vee T$

   T

2. $\sim (p \vee q)$

p	q	$p \vee q$	$\sim (p \vee q)$
T	T	T	F
T	F	T	F
F	T	T	F
F	F	F	T

3. $\sim p \wedge \sim q$

p	q	$\sim p$	$\sim q$	$\sim p \wedge \sim q$
T	T	F	F	F
T	F	F	T	F
F	T	T	F	F
F	F	T	T	T

4. $(p \wedge \sim q) \vee \sim p$

p	q	$\sim p$	$\sim q$	$p \wedge \sim q$	$(p \wedge \sim q) \vee \sim p$
T	T	F	F	F	F
T	F	F	T	T	T
F	T	T	F	F	T
F	F	T	T	F	T

5. $p \wedge \sim p$ is false in all cases.

p	$\sim p$	$p \wedge \sim p$
T	F	F
F	T	F

6. p: I study hard.; q: I ace the final.; r: I fail the course.

   a.

p	q	r	$q \vee r$	$p \wedge (q \vee r)$
T	T	T	T	T
T	T	F	T	T
T	F	T	T	T
T	F	F	F	F
F	T	T	T	F
F	T	F	T	F
F	F	T	T	F
F	F	F	F	F

   b. false

7. $(p \vee q) \wedge \sim r$

   $(T \vee F) \wedge \sim F$

   $T \wedge T$

   T

Exercise Set 3.3

1. $\sim q$

   $\sim F$

   T

2. $\sim p$

   $\sim T$

   F

3. $p \wedge q$

   $T \wedge F$

   F

4. $q \wedge p$

   $F \wedge T$

   F

5. $\sim p \wedge q$

   $\sim T \wedge F$

   $F \wedge F$

   F

6. $p \wedge \sim q$

   $T \wedge \sim F$

   $T \wedge T$

   T

7. $\sim p \wedge \sim q$

   $\sim T \wedge \sim F$

   $F \wedge T$

   F

8. $q \wedge \sim q$

   $F \wedge \sim F$

   $F \wedge T$

   F

9. $q \vee p$

   $F \vee T$

   T

10. $p \vee q$

   $T \vee F$

   T

11. $p \vee \sim q$

   $T \vee \sim F$

   $T \vee T$

   T

12. $\sim p \vee q$

   $\sim T \vee F$

   $F \vee F$

   F

13. $p \vee \sim p$

   $T \vee \sim T$

   $T \vee F$

   T

14. $q \vee \sim q$

   $F \vee \sim F$

   $F \vee T$

   T

15. $\sim p \vee \sim q$

   $\sim T \vee \sim F$

   $F \vee T$

   T

16. $\sim q \vee \sim p$

   $\sim F \vee \sim T$

   $T \vee F$

   T

17. $\sim p \wedge p$

p	$\sim p$	$\sim p \wedge p$
T	F	F
F	T	F

18. $\sim(\sim p)$

p	$\sim p$	$\sim(\sim p)$
T	F	T
F	T	F

19. $\sim p \wedge q$

p	q	$\sim p$	$\sim p \wedge q$
T	T	F	F
T	F	F	F
F	T	T	T
F	F	T	F

20. $\sim p \vee q$

p	q	$\sim p$	$\sim p \vee q$
T	T	F	T
T	F	F	F
F	T	T	T
F	F	T	T

21. $\sim(p \vee q)$

p	q	$p \vee q$	$\sim(p \vee q)$
T	T	T	F
T	F	T	F
F	T	T	F
F	F	F	T

22. $\sim(p \vee \sim q)$

p	q	$\sim q$	$p \vee \sim q$	$\sim(p \vee \sim q)$
T	T	F	T	F
T	F	T	T	F
F	T	F	F	T
F	F	T	T	F

23. $\sim p \wedge \sim q$

p	q	$\sim p$	$\sim q$	$\sim p \wedge \sim q$
T	T	F	F	F
T	F	F	T	F
F	T	T	F	F
F	F	T	T	T

24. $p \wedge \sim q$

p	q	$\sim q$	$p \wedge \sim q$
T	T	F	F
T	F	T	T
F	T	F	F
F	F	T	F

25. $p \vee \sim q$

p	q	$\sim q$	$p \vee \sim q$
T	T	F	T
T	F	T	T
F	T	F	F
F	F	T	T

26. $\sim q \wedge p$

p	q	$\sim q$	$\sim q \wedge p$
T	T	F	F
T	F	T	T
F	T	F	F
F	F	T	F

27. $\sim(\sim p \vee q)$

p	q	$\sim p$	$\sim p \vee q$	$\sim(\sim p \vee q)$
T	T	F	T	F
T	F	F	F	T
F	T	T	T	F
F	F	T	T	F

28. $\sim(p \wedge \sim q)$

p	q	$\sim q$	$p \wedge \sim q$	$\sim(p \wedge \sim q)$
T	T	F	F	T
T	F	T	T	F
F	T	F	F	T
F	F	T	F	T

29. $(p \vee q) \wedge \sim p$

p	q	$\sim p$	$p \vee q$	$(p \vee q) \wedge \sim p$
T	T	F	T	F
T	F	F	T	F
F	T	T	T	T
F	F	T	F	F

30. $(p \wedge q) \vee \sim p$

p	q	$\sim p$	$p \wedge q$	$(p \wedge q) \vee \sim p$
T	T	F	T	T
T	F	F	F	F
F	T	T	F	T
F	F	T	F	T

31. $\sim p \vee (p \wedge \sim q)$

p	q	$\sim p$	$\sim q$	$p \wedge \sim q$	$\sim p \vee (p \wedge \sim q)$
T	T	F	F	F	F
T	F	F	T	T	T
F	T	T	F	F	T
F	F	T	T	F	T

32. $\sim p \wedge (p \vee \sim q)$

p	q	$\sim p$	$\sim q$	$p \vee \sim q$	$\sim p \wedge (p \vee \sim q)$
T	T	F	F	T	F
T	F	F	T	T	F
F	T	T	F	F	F
F	F	T	T	T	T

33. $(p \vee q) \wedge (\sim p \vee \sim q)$

p	q	$\sim p$	$\sim q$	$p \vee q$	$\sim p \vee \sim q$	$(p \vee q) \wedge (\sim p \vee \sim q)$
T	T	F	F	T	F	F
T	F	F	T	T	T	T
F	T	T	F	T	T	T
F	F	T	T	F	T	F

34. $(p \wedge \sim q) \vee (\sim p \wedge q)$

p	q	$\sim p$	$\sim q$	$p \wedge \sim q$	$\sim p \wedge q$	$(p \wedge \sim q) \vee (\sim p \wedge q)$
T	T	F	F	F	F	F
T	F	F	T	T	F	T
F	T	T	F	F	T	T
F	F	T	T	F	F	F

35. $(p \wedge \sim q) \vee (p \wedge q)$

p	q	$\sim q$	$p \wedge \sim q$	$p \wedge q$	$(p \wedge \sim q) \vee (p \wedge q)$
T	T	F	F	T	T
T	F	T	T	F	T
F	T	F	F	F	F
F	F	T	F	F	F

36. $(p \vee \sim q) \wedge (p \vee q)$

p	q	$\sim q$	$p \vee \sim q$	$p \vee q$	$(p \vee \sim q) \wedge (p \vee q)$
T	T	F	T	T	T
T	F	T	T	T	T
F	T	F	F	T	F
F	F	T	T	F	F

37. $p \wedge (\sim q \vee r)$

p	q	r	$\sim q$	$\sim q \vee r$	$p \wedge (\sim q \vee r)$
T	T	T	F	T	T
T	T	F	F	F	F
T	F	T	T	T	T
T	F	F	T	T	T
F	T	T	F	T	F
F	T	F	F	F	F
F	F	T	T	T	F
F	F	F	T	T	F

38. $p \vee (\sim q \wedge r)$

p	q	r	$\sim q$	$\sim q \wedge r$	$p \vee (\sim q \wedge r)$
T	T	T	F	F	T
T	T	F	F	F	T
T	F	T	T	T	T
T	F	F	T	F	T
F	T	T	F	F	F
F	T	F	F	F	F
F	F	T	T	T	T
F	F	F	T	F	F

39. $(r \wedge \sim p) \vee \sim q$

p	q	r	$\sim p$	$\sim q$	$r \wedge \sim p$	$(r \wedge \sim p) \vee \sim q$
T	T	T	F	F	F	F
T	T	F	F	F	F	F
T	F	T	F	T	F	T
T	F	F	F	T	F	T
F	T	T	T	F	T	T
F	T	F	T	F	F	F
F	F	T	T	T	T	T
F	F	F	T	T	F	T

40. $(r \vee \sim p) \wedge \sim q$

p	q	r	$\sim p$	$\sim q$	$r \vee \sim p$	$(r \vee \sim p) \wedge \sim q$
T	T	T	F	F	T	F
T	T	F	F	F	F	F
T	F	T	F	T	T	T
T	F	F	F	T	F	F
F	T	T	T	F	T	F
F	T	F	T	F	T	F
F	F	T	T	T	T	T
F	F	F	T	T	T	T

41. $\sim (p \vee q) \wedge \sim r$

p	q	r	$p \vee q$	$\sim (p \vee q)$	$\sim r$	$\sim (p \vee q) \wedge \sim r$
T	T	T	T	F	F	F
T	T	F	T	F	T	F
T	F	T	T	F	F	F
T	F	F	T	F	T	F
F	T	T	T	F	F	F
F	T	F	T	F	T	F
F	F	T	F	T	F	F
F	F	F	F	T	T	T

42. $\sim (p \wedge q) \vee \sim r$

p	q	r	$p \wedge q$	$\sim (p \wedge q)$	$\sim r$	$\sim (p \wedge q) \vee \sim r$
T	T	T	T	F	F	F
T	T	F	T	F	T	T
T	F	T	F	T	F	T
T	F	F	F	T	T	T
F	T	T	F	T	F	T
F	T	F	F	T	T	T
F	F	T	F	T	F	T
F	F	F	F	T	T	T

43. a. p: You did the dishes.; q: You left the room a mess.; $\sim p \wedge q$

b. See truth table for Exercise 19.

c. The statement is true when p is false and q is true.

44. a. p: You did the dishes.; q: You left the room a mess.; $\sim p \wedge \sim q$

b. See truth table for Exercise 23.

c. The statement is true when both p and q are false.

45. a. p: I bought a meal ticket.; q: I used it.; $\sim (p \wedge \sim q)$

b. $\sim(p \wedge \sim q)$

p	q	$\sim q$	$p \wedge \sim q$	$\sim(p \wedge \sim q)$
T	T	F	F	T
T	F	T	T	F
F	T	F	F	T
F	F	T	F	T

c. Answers will vary; an example is: The statement is true when p and q are true.

46. a. p: I ordered pizza while watching late-night TV.; q: I gained weight.; $\sim (p \wedge \sim q)$

b. See truth table for Exercise 45.

c. Answers will vary; an example is: The statement is true when both p and q are true.

47. a. p: The student is intelligent.; q: The student is an overachiever.; $(p \vee q) \wedge \sim q$

b.

p	q	$\sim q$	$p \vee q$	$(p \vee q) \wedge \sim q$
T	T	F	T	F
T	F	T	T	T
F	T	F	T	F
F	F	T	F	F

c. The statement is true when p is true and q is false.

48. a. p: You are blushing.; q: You are sunburned.; $(p \vee q) \wedge \sim q$

    b. See truth table for Exercise 47.

    c. The statement is true when p is true and q is false.

49. a. p: Married people are healthier than single people.; q: Married people are more economically stable than single people.; r: Children of married people do better on a variety of indicators.; $(p \wedge q) \wedge r$

    b.

p	q	r	$p \wedge q$	$(p \wedge q) \wedge r$
T	T	T	T	T
T	T	F	T	F
T	F	T	F	F
T	F	F	F	F
F	T	T	F	F
F	T	F	F	F
F	F	T	F	F
F	F	F	F	F

    c. The statement is true when p, q, and r are all true.

50. a. p: You walk.; q: You jog.; r: You engage in something physical.; $(p \vee q) \vee r$

    b.

p	q	r	$p \vee q$	$(p \vee q) \vee r$
T	T	T	T	T
T	T	F	T	T
T	F	T	T	T
T	F	F	T	T
F	T	T	T	T
F	T	F	T	T
F	F	T	F	T
F	F	F	F	F

    c. Answers will vary; an example is: The statement is true when p, q, and r are all true.

51. a. p: I go to office hours.; q: I ask questions.; r: My professor remembers me.; $(p \wedge q) \vee \sim r$

    b.

p	q	r	$\sim r$	$p \wedge q$	$(p \wedge q) \vee \sim r$
T	T	T	F	T	T
T	T	F	T	T	T
T	F	T	F	F	F
T	F	F	T	F	T
F	T	T	F	F	F
F	T	F	T	F	T
F	F	T	F	F	F
F	F	F	T	F	T

    c. Answers will vary; an example is: The statement is true when p, q, and r are all true.

52. a. *p*: You marry the person you love.; *q*: You always love that person.; *r*: You always have a successful marriage.;
$p \wedge (\sim q \vee \sim r)$

b.

p	*q*	*r*	$\sim q$	$\sim r$	$\sim q \vee \sim r$	$p \wedge (\sim q \vee \sim r)$
T	T	T	F	F	F	F
T	T	F	F	T	T	T
T	F	T	T	F	F	T
T	F	F	T	T	T	T
F	T	T	F	F	F	F
F	T	F	F	T	T	F
F	F	T	T	F	F	F
F	F	F	T	T	T	F

c. Answers will vary; an example is: The statement is true when *p* is true and *q* and *r* are false.

53. $p \wedge (q \vee r)$
$F \wedge (T \vee F)$
$F \wedge T$
F

54. $p \vee (q \wedge r)$
$F \vee (T \wedge F)$
$F \vee F$
F

55. $\sim p \vee (q \wedge \sim r)$
$\sim F \vee (T \wedge \sim F)$
$T \vee (T \wedge T)$
$T \vee T$
T

56. $\sim p \wedge (\sim q \wedge r)$
$\sim F \wedge (\sim T \wedge F)$
$T \wedge (F \wedge F)$
$T \wedge F$
F

57. $\sim (p \wedge q) \vee r$
$\sim (F \wedge T) \vee F$
$\sim (F) \vee F$
$T \vee F$
T

59. $\sim(p \vee q) \wedge \sim(p \wedge r)$

$\sim(F \vee T) \wedge \sim(F \wedge F)$

$\sim(T) \wedge \sim(F)$

$F \wedge T$

F

60. $\sim(p \wedge q) \vee \sim(p \vee r)$

$\sim(F \wedge T) \vee \sim(F \vee F)$

$\sim(F) \vee \sim(F)$

$T \vee T$

T

61. $(\sim p \wedge q) \vee (\sim r \wedge p)$

$(\sim F \wedge T) \vee (\sim F \wedge F)$

$(T \wedge T) \vee (T \wedge F)$

$T \vee F$

T

62. $(\sim p \vee q) \wedge (\sim r \vee p)$

$(\sim F \vee T) \wedge (\sim F \vee F)$

$(T \vee T) \wedge (T \vee F)$

$T \wedge T$

T

63. $\sim[\sim(p \wedge \sim q) \vee \sim(\sim p \vee q)]$

p	q	$\sim[\sim(p \wedge \sim q) \vee \sim(\sim p \vee q)]$
T	T	F
T	F	F
F	T	F
F	F	F

64. $\sim[\sim(p \vee \sim q) \wedge \sim(\sim p \wedge q)]$

p	q	$\sim[\sim(p \vee \sim q) \wedge \sim(\sim p \wedge q)]$
T	T	T
T	F	T
F	T	T
F	F	T

65. $[(p \wedge \sim r) \vee (q \wedge \sim r)] \wedge \sim(\sim p \vee r)$

p	q	r	$[(p \wedge \sim r) \vee (q \wedge \sim r)] \wedge \sim(\sim p \vee r)$
T	T	T	F
T	T	F	T
T	F	T	F
T	F	F	T
F	T	T	F
F	T	F	F
F	F	T	F
F	F	F	F

66. $[(p \vee \sim r) \wedge (q \vee \sim r)] \vee \sim(\sim p \vee r)$

p	q	r	$[(p \vee \sim r) \wedge (q \vee \sim r)] \vee \sim(\sim p \vee r)$
T	T	T	T
T	T	F	T
T	F	T	F
T	F	F	T
F	T	T	F
F	T	F	T
F	F	T	F
F	F	F	T

67. p: You notice this notice.; q: You notice this notice is not worth noticing.; $(p \vee \sim p) \wedge q$

p	q	$\sim p$	$p \vee \sim p$	$(p \vee \sim p) \wedge q$
T	T	F	T	T
T	F	F	T	F
F	T	T	T	T
F	F	T	T	F

The statement is true when q is true.

68. p: You notice this notice.; q: You notice this notice is not worth noticing.; $(p \wedge q) \vee \sim p$;

See truth table for Exercise 30.; The statement is true when p is false or q is true.

69. p: $x \leq 3$; q: $x \geq 7$; $\sim (p \vee q) \wedge (\sim p \wedge \sim q)$

p	q	$\sim p$	$\sim q$	$p \vee q$	$\sim (p \vee q)$	$\sim p \wedge \sim q$	$\sim (p \vee q) \wedge \sim (p \wedge \sim q)$
T	T	F	F	T	F	F	F
T	F	F	T	T	F	F	F
F	T	T	F	T	F	F	F
F	F	T	T	F	T	T	T

The statement is true when both p and q are false.

70. p: $x < 5$; q: $x > 8$; $\sim (p \vee q) \wedge (\sim p \wedge \sim q)$; See truth table for Exercise 69.; The statement is true when both p and q are false.

71. The percent body fat in women peaks at age 55 and the percent body fat in men does not peak at age 65. This statement is false.

72. The percent body fat in women peaks at age 55 and men do not have more than 24% body fat at age 25. This statement is true.

73. The percent body fat in women does not peak at age 55 and men have more than 24% body fat at age 25. This statement is false.

74. The percent body fat in men peaks at age 65 and the percent body fat in women does not peak at age 55. This statement is false.

75. The percent body fat in women peaks at age 55 or the percent body fat in men does not peak at age 65. This statement is true.

76. The percent body fat in women peaks at age 55 or men do not have more than 24% body fat at age 25. This statement is true.

77. The percent body fat in women does not peak at age 55 or men have more than 24% body fat at age 25. This statement is false.

78. The percent body fat in men peaks at age 65 or the percent body fat in women does not peak at age 55. This statement is true.

79. The percent body fat in women peaks at age 55 and the percent body fat in men peaks at age 65, or men have more than 24% body fat at age 25. This statement is true.

80. The percent body fat in women peaks at age 55, and the percent body fat in men peaks at age 65 or men have more than 24% body fat at age 25. This statement is true.

81. p: In 2000, 2% of 20-year-old men had completed the transition to adulthood.; q: In 2000, 46% of 30-year-old men had completed the transition to adulthood.; $\sim (p \wedge q)$; true

82. p: In 2000, 2% of 20-year-old women had completed the transition to adulthood.; q: In 2000, 46% of 30-year-old women had completed the transition to adulthood.; $\sim (p \wedge q)$; true

83. p: From 1960 to 2000 the percentage of 20-year-old women making the transition to adulthood decreased.; q: From 1960 to 2000 the percentage of 30-year-old women making the transition to adulthood increased.; r: From 1960 to 2000 the percentage of 30-year-old men making the transition to adulthood decreased.; $(p \vee q) \wedge \sim r$; false

84. *p*: From 1960 to 2000 the percentage of 20-year-old men making the transition to adulthood decreased.; *q*: From 1960 to 2000 the percentage of 30-year-old men making the transition to adulthood decreased.; *r*: From 1960 to 2000 the percentage of 20-year-old women making the transition to adulthood increased.; $p \wedge (\sim q \vee r)$; false

85. a.   Hora Gershwin

   b.   Bolera Mozart does not have a master's degree in music. Cha-Cha Bach does not either play three instruments or have five years experience playing with a symphony orchestra.

86. a.   Rondo Seurat

   b.   Adagio Picasso does not have a master's degree in art. Yodel Van Gogh does not have either a body of work judged as excellent by two working artists or have at least two works on public display in the United States.

95. does not make sense; Explanations will vary. Sample explanation: When filling in the truth values for a column of a truth table, only one or two previous columns are necessary.

96. does not make sense; Explanations will vary. Sample explanation: The most efficient way is to substitute the truth values directly into the expression.

97. does not make sense; Explanations will vary. Sample explanation: Since there is only one simple statement, there are only two possible truth values.

98. makes sense

100. *p* and *q* are both false when $\sim(p \vee q)$ is true.

$\sim(p \vee q)$

p	*q*	$p \vee q$	$\sim(p \vee q)$
T	T	T	F
T	F	T	F
F	T	T	F
F	F	F	T

101. $p \veebar q$

p	*q*	$p \veebar q$
T	T	F
T	F	T
F	T	T
F	F	F

Check Points 3.4

1. $\sim p \rightarrow \sim q$

p	*q*	$\sim p$	$\sim q$	$\sim p \rightarrow \sim q$
T	T	F	F	T
T	F	F	T	T
F	T	T	F	F
F	F	T	T	T

The rightmost column shows that the statement is false when *p* is false and *q* is true; otherwise the statement is true.

2. $[(p \to q) \wedge \sim q] \to \sim p$ is a tautology because the final column is always true.

p	q	$\sim p$	$\sim q$	$p \to q$	$(p \to q) \wedge \sim q$	$[(p \to q) \wedge \sim q] \to \sim p$
T	T	F	F	T	F	T
T	F	F	T	F	F	T
F	T	T	F	T	F	T
F	F	T	T	T	T	T

3. a. p: You use Hair Grow.; q: You apply it daily.; r: You go bald.

p	q	r	$\sim r$	$p \wedge q$	$(p \wedge q) \to \sim r$
T	T	T	F	T	F
T	T	F	T	T	T
T	F	T	F	F	T
T	F	F	T	F	T
F	T	T	F	F	T
F	T	F	T	F	T
F	F	T	F	F	T
F	F	F	T	F	T

b. No, the claim is not false under these conditions as shown by the third row resulting in a T.

4. $(p \vee q) \leftrightarrow (\sim p \to q)$ is a tautology because all cases are true.

p	q	$\sim p$	$p \vee q$	$\sim p \to q$	$(p \vee q) \leftrightarrow (\sim p \to q)$
T	T	F	T	T	T
T	F	F	T	T	T
F	T	T	T	T	T
F	F	T	F	F	T

5. $(p \wedge q) \to r$

$(T \wedge F) \to F$

$\quad F \to F$

$\quad\quad T$

Under these conditions, the claim is true.

Exercise Set 3.4

1. $p \to \sim q$

p	q	$\sim q$	$p \to \sim q$
T	T	F	F
T	F	T	T
F	T	F	T
F	F	T	T

2. $\sim p \to q$

p	q	$\sim p$	$\sim p \to q$
T	T	F	T
T	F	F	T
F	T	T	T
F	F	T	F

3. $\sim(q \to p)$

p	q	$q \to p$	$\sim(q \to p)$
T	T	T	F
T	F	T	F
F	T	F	T
F	F	T	F

4. $\sim(p \to q)$

p	q	$p \to q$	$\sim(p \to q)$
T	T	T	F
T	F	F	T
F	T	T	F
F	F	T	F

5. $(p \wedge q) \to (p \vee q)$

p	q	$p \wedge q$	$p \vee q$	$(p \wedge q) \to (p \vee q)$
T	T	T	T	T
T	F	F	T	T
F	T	F	T	T
F	F	F	F	T

6. $(p \vee q) \to (p \wedge q)$

p	q	$p \vee q$	$p \wedge q$	$(p \vee q) \to (p \wedge q)$
T	T	T	T	T
T	F	T	F	F
F	T	T	F	F
F	F	F	F	T

7. $(p \to q) \wedge \sim q$

p	q	$p \to q$	$\sim q$	$(p \to q) \wedge \sim q$
T	T	T	F	F
T	F	F	T	F
F	T	T	F	F
F	F	T	T	T

8. $(p \to q) \wedge \sim p$

p	q	$p \to q$	$\sim p$	$(p \to q) \wedge \sim p$
T	T	T	F	F
T	F	F	F	F
F	T	T	T	T
F	F	T	T	T

9. $(p \vee q) \to r$

p	q	r	$p \vee q$	$(p \vee q) \to r$
T	T	T	T	T
T	T	F	T	F
T	F	T	T	T
T	F	F	T	F
F	T	T	T	T
F	T	F	T	F
F	F	T	F	T
F	F	F	F	T

10. $p \to (q \vee r)$

p	q	r	$q \vee r$	$p \to (q \vee r)$
T	T	T	T	T
T	T	F	T	T
T	F	T	T	T
T	F	F	F	F
F	T	T	T	T
F	T	F	T	T
F	F	T	T	T
F	F	F	F	T

11. $r \to (p \wedge q)$

p	q	r	$p \wedge q$	$r \to (p \wedge q)$
T	T	T	T	T
T	T	F	T	T
T	F	T	F	F
T	F	F	F	T
F	T	T	F	F
F	T	F	F	T
F	F	T	F	F
F	F	F	F	T

12. $r \to (p \vee q)$

p	q	r	$p \vee q$	$r \to (p \vee q)$
T	T	T	T	T
T	T	F	T	T
T	F	T	T	T
T	F	F	T	T
F	T	T	T	T
F	T	F	T	T
F	F	T	F	F
F	F	F	F	T

13. $\sim r \wedge (\sim q \rightarrow p)$

p	q	r	$\sim q$	$\sim r$	$\sim q \rightarrow p$	$\sim r \wedge (\sim q \rightarrow p)$
T	T	T	F	F	T	F
T	T	F	F	T	T	T
T	F	T	T	F	T	F
T	F	F	T	T	T	T
F	T	T	F	F	T	F
F	T	F	F	T	T	T
F	F	T	T	F	F	F
F	F	F	T	T	F	T

14. $\sim r \wedge (q \rightarrow \sim p)$

p	q	r	$\sim p$	$\sim r$	$q \rightarrow \sim p$	$\sim r \wedge (q \rightarrow \sim p)$
T	T	T	F	F	F	F
T	T	F	F	T	F	F
T	F	T	F	F	T	F
T	F	F	F	T	T	T
F	T	T	T	F	T	F
F	T	F	T	T	T	T
F	F	T	T	F	T	F
F	F	F	T	T	T	T

15. $\sim (p \wedge r) \rightarrow (\sim q \vee r)$

p	q	r	$\sim q$	$p \wedge r$	$\sim (p \wedge r)$	$\sim q \vee r$	$\sim (p \wedge r) \rightarrow (\sim q \vee r)$
T	T	T	F	T	F	T	T
T	T	F	F	F	T	F	F
T	F	T	T	T	F	T	T
T	F	F	T	F	T	T	T
F	T	T	F	F	T	T	T
F	T	F	F	F	T	F	F
F	F	T	T	F	T	T	T
F	F	F	T	F	T	T	T

16. $\sim (p \vee r) \rightarrow (\sim q \wedge r)$

p	q	r	$\sim q$	$p \vee r$	$\sim (p \vee r)$	$\sim q \wedge r$	$\sim (p \vee r) \rightarrow (\sim q \wedge r)$
T	T	T	F	T	F	F	T
T	T	F	F	T	F	F	T
T	F	T	T	T	F	T	T
T	F	F	T	T	F	F	T
F	T	T	F	T	F	F	T
F	T	F	F	F	T	F	F
F	F	T	T	T	F	T	T
F	F	F	T	F	T	F	F

17. $p \leftrightarrow \sim q$

p	q	$\sim q$	$p \leftrightarrow \sim q$
T	T	F	F
T	F	T	T
F	T	F	T
F	F	T	F

18. $\sim p \leftrightarrow q$

p	q	$\sim p$	$\sim p \leftrightarrow q$
T	T	F	F
T	F	F	T
F	T	T	T
F	F	T	F

19. $\sim(p \leftrightarrow q)$

p	q	$p \leftrightarrow q$	$\sim(p \leftrightarrow q)$
T	T	T	F
T	F	F	T
F	T	F	T
F	F	T	F

20. $\sim(q \leftrightarrow p)$

p	q	$q \leftrightarrow p$	$\sim(q \leftrightarrow p)$
T	T	T	F
T	F	F	T
F	T	F	T
F	F	T	F

21. $(p \leftrightarrow q) \rightarrow p$

p	q	$p \leftrightarrow q$	$(p \leftrightarrow q) \rightarrow p$
T	T	T	T
T	F	F	T
F	T	F	T
F	F	T	F

22. $(p \leftrightarrow q) \rightarrow q$

p	q	$p \leftrightarrow q$	$(p \leftrightarrow q) \rightarrow q$
T	T	T	T
T	F	F	T
F	T	F	T
F	F	T	F

23. $(\sim p \leftrightarrow q) \rightarrow (\sim p \rightarrow q)$

p	q	$\sim p$	$\sim p \leftrightarrow q$	$\sim p \rightarrow q$	$(\sim p \leftrightarrow q) \rightarrow (\sim p \rightarrow q)$
T	T	F	F	T	T
T	F	F	T	T	T
F	T	T	T	T	T
F	F	T	F	F	T

24. $(p \leftrightarrow \sim q) \rightarrow (q \rightarrow \sim p)$

p	q	$\sim p$	$\sim q$	$p \leftrightarrow \sim q$	$q \rightarrow \sim p$	$(p \leftrightarrow \sim q) \rightarrow (q \rightarrow \sim p)$
T	T	F	F	F	F	T
T	F	F	T	T	T	T
F	T	T	F	T	T	T
F	F	T	T	F	T	T

25. $\left[(p \wedge q) \wedge (q \rightarrow p)\right] \leftrightarrow (p \wedge q)$

p	q	$p \wedge q$	$q \rightarrow p$	$(p \wedge q) \wedge (q \rightarrow p)$	$\left[(p \wedge q) \wedge (q \rightarrow p)\right] \leftrightarrow (p \wedge q)$
T	T	T	T	T	T
T	F	F	T	F	T
F	T	F	F	F	T
F	F	F	T	F	T

26. $\left[(p \rightarrow q) \vee (p \wedge \sim p)\right] \leftrightarrow (\sim q \rightarrow \sim p)$

p	q	$\sim p$	$\sim q$	$p \rightarrow q$	$p \wedge \sim p$	$(p \rightarrow q) \vee (p \wedge \sim p)$	$\sim q \rightarrow \sim p$	$\left[(p \rightarrow q) \vee (p \wedge \sim p)\right] \leftrightarrow (\sim q \rightarrow \sim p)$
T	T	F	F	T	F	T	T	T
T	F	F	T	F	F	F	F	T
F	T	T	F	T	F	T	T	T
F	F	T	T	T	F	T	T	T

27. $(p \leftrightarrow q) \rightarrow \sim r$

p	q	r	$\sim r$	$p \leftrightarrow q$	$(p \leftrightarrow q) \rightarrow \sim r$
T	T	T	F	T	F
T	T	F	T	T	T
T	F	T	F	F	T
T	F	F	T	F	T
F	T	T	F	F	T
F	T	F	T	F	T
F	F	T	F	T	F
F	F	F	T	T	T

28. $(p \rightarrow q) \leftrightarrow \sim r$

p	q	r	$\sim r$	$p \rightarrow q$	$(p \rightarrow q) \leftrightarrow \sim r$
T	T	T	F	T	F
T	T	F	T	T	T
T	F	T	F	F	T
T	F	F	T	F	F
F	T	T	F	T	F
F	T	F	T	T	T
F	F	T	F	T	F
F	F	F	T	T	T

29. $(p \wedge r) \leftrightarrow \sim (q \vee r)$

p	q	r	$p \wedge r$	$q \vee r$	$\sim (q \vee r)$	$(p \wedge r) \leftrightarrow \sim (q \vee r)$
T	T	T	T	T	F	F
T	T	F	F	T	F	T
T	F	T	T	T	F	F
T	F	F	F	F	T	F
F	T	T	F	T	F	T
F	T	F	F	T	F	T
F	F	T	F	T	F	T
F	F	F	F	F	T	F

30. $(p \vee r) \leftrightarrow \sim (q \wedge r)$

p	q	r	$p \vee r$	$q \wedge r$	$\sim (q \wedge r)$	$(p \vee r) \leftrightarrow \sim (q \wedge r)$
T	T	T	T	T	F	F
T	T	F	T	F	T	T
T	F	T	T	F	T	T
T	F	F	T	F	T	T
F	T	T	T	T	F	F
F	T	F	F	F	T	F
F	F	T	T	F	T	T
F	F	F	F	F	T	F

31. $\left[r \vee (\sim q \wedge p) \right] \leftrightarrow \sim p$

p	q	r	$\sim q$	$\sim q \wedge p$	$r \vee (\sim q \wedge p)$	$\sim p$	$\left[r \vee (\sim q \wedge p) \right] \leftrightarrow \sim p$
T	T	T	F	F	T	F	F
T	T	F	F	F	F	F	T
T	F	T	T	T	T	F	F
T	F	F	T	T	T	F	F
F	T	T	F	F	T	T	T
F	T	F	F	F	F	T	F
F	F	T	F	F	T	T	T
F	F	F	F	F	F	T	F

32. $\left[r \wedge (q \vee \sim p) \right] \leftrightarrow \sim q$

p	q	r	$\sim p$	$q \vee \sim p$	$r \wedge (q \vee \sim p)$	$\sim q$	$\left[r \wedge (q \vee \sim p) \right] \leftrightarrow \sim q$
T	T	T	F	T	T	F	F
T	T	F	F	T	F	F	T
T	F	T	F	F	F	T	F
T	F	F	F	F	F	T	F
F	T	T	T	T	T	F	F
F	T	F	T	T	F	F	T
F	F	T	T	T	T	T	T
F	F	F	T	T	F	T	F

33. $[(p \rightarrow q) \wedge q] \rightarrow p$ is neither.

p	q	$p \rightarrow q$	$(p \rightarrow q) \wedge q$	$\left[(p \rightarrow q) \wedge q\right] \rightarrow p$
T	T	T	T	T
T	F	F	F	T
F	T	T	T	F
F	F	T	F	T

34. $\left[(p \rightarrow q) \wedge p \right] \rightarrow q$ is a tautology.

p	q	$p \rightarrow q$	$(p \rightarrow q) \wedge p$	$\left[(p \rightarrow q) \wedge p \right] \rightarrow q$
T	T	T	T	T
T	F	F	F	T
F	T	T	F	T
F	F	T	F	T

35. $\left[(p \to q) \wedge \sim q\right] \to \sim p$ is a tautology.

p	q	$\sim p$	$\sim q$	$p \to q$	$(p \to q) \wedge \sim q$	$\left[(p \to q) \wedge \sim q\right] \to \sim p$
T	T	F	F	T	F	T
T	F	F	T	F	F	T
F	T	T	F	T	F	T
F	F	T	T	T	T	T

36. $\left[(p \to q) \wedge \sim p\right] \to \sim q$ is neither.

p	q	$\sim p$	$\sim q$	$p \to q$	$(p \to q) \wedge \sim p$	$\left[(p \to q) \wedge \sim p\right] \to \sim q$
T	T	F	F	T	F	T
T	F	F	T	F	F	T
F	T	T	F	T	T	F
F	F	T	T	T	T	T

37. $\left[(p \vee q) \wedge p\right] \to \sim q$ is neither.

p	q	$\sim q$	$p \vee q$	$(p \vee q) \wedge p$	$\left[(p \vee q) \wedge p\right] \to \sim q$
T	T	F	T	T	F
T	F	T	T	T	T
F	T	F	T	F	T
F	F	T	F	F	T

38. $\left[(p \vee q) \wedge \sim q\right] \to p$ is a tautology.

p	q	$\sim q$	$p \vee q$	$(p \vee q) \wedge \sim q$	$\left[(p \vee q) \wedge \sim q\right] \to p$
T	T	F	T	F	T
T	F	T	T	T	T
F	T	F	T	F	T
F	F	T	F	F	T

39. $(p \to q) \to (\sim p \vee q)$ is a tautology.

p	q	$\sim p$	$p \to q$	$\sim p \vee q$	$(p \to q) \to (\sim p \vee q)$
T	T	F	T	T	T
T	F	F	F	F	T
F	T	T	T	T	T
F	F	T	T	T	T

40. $(q \to p) \to (p \vee \sim q)$ is a tautology.

p	q	$\sim q$	$q \to p$	$p \vee \sim q$	$(q \to p) \to (p \vee \sim q)$
T	T	F	T	T	T
T	F	T	T	T	T
F	T	F	F	F	T
F	F	T	T	T	T

41. $(p \wedge q) \wedge (\sim p \vee \sim q)$ is a self-contradiction.

p	q	$\sim p$	$\sim q$	$p \wedge q$	$\sim p \vee \sim q$	$(p \wedge q) \wedge (\sim p \vee \sim q)$
T	T	F	F	T	F	F
T	F	F	T	F	T	F
F	T	T	F	F	T	F
F	F	T	T	F	T	F

42. $(p \vee q) \wedge (\sim p \wedge \sim q)$ is a self-contradiction.

p	q	$\sim p$	$\sim q$	$p \vee q$	$\sim p \wedge \sim q$	$(p \vee q) \wedge (\sim p \wedge \sim q)$
T	T	F	F	T	F	F
T	F	F	T	T	F	F
F	T	T	F	T	F	F
F	F	T	T	F	T	F

43. $\sim(p \wedge q) \leftrightarrow (\sim p \wedge \sim q)$ is neither.

p	q	$\sim p$	$\sim q$	$p \wedge q$	$\sim(p \wedge q)$	$\sim p \wedge \sim q$	$\sim(p \wedge q) \leftrightarrow (\sim p \wedge \sim q)$
T	T	F	F	T	F	F	T
T	F	F	T	F	T	F	F
F	T	T	F	F	T	F	F
F	F	T	T	F	T	T	T

44. $\sim(p \vee q) \leftrightarrow (\sim p \wedge \sim q)$ is a tautology.

p	q	$\sim p$	$\sim q$	$p \vee q$	$\sim(p \vee q)$	$\sim p \wedge \sim q$	$\sim(p \vee q) \leftrightarrow (\sim p \wedge \sim q)$
T	T	F	F	T	F	F	T
T	F	F	T	T	F	F	T
F	T	T	F	T	F	F	T
F	F	T	T	F	T	T	T

45. $(p \rightarrow q) \leftrightarrow (q \rightarrow p)$ is neither.

p	q	$p \rightarrow q$	$q \rightarrow p$	$(p \rightarrow q) \leftrightarrow (q \rightarrow p)$
T	T	T	T	T
T	F	F	T	F
F	T	T	F	F
F	F	T	T	T

46. $(p \rightarrow q) \leftrightarrow (\sim p \rightarrow \sim q)$ is neither.

p	q	$\sim p$	$\sim q$	$p \rightarrow q$	$\sim p \rightarrow \sim q$	$(p \rightarrow q) \leftrightarrow (\sim p \rightarrow \sim q)$
T	T	F	F	T	T	T
T	F	F	T	F	T	F
F	T	T	F	T	F	F
F	F	T	T	T	T	T

47. $(p \to q) \leftrightarrow (\sim p \vee q)$ is a tautology.

p	q	$\sim p$	$p \to q$	$\sim p \vee q$	$(p \to q) \leftrightarrow (\sim p \vee q)$
T	T	F	T	T	T
T	F	F	F	F	T
F	T	T	T	T	T
F	F	T	T	T	T

48. $(p \to q) \leftrightarrow (p \vee \sim q)$ is neither.

p	q	$\sim q$	$p \to q$	$p \vee \sim q$	$(p \to q) \leftrightarrow (p \vee \sim q)$
T	T	F	T	T	T
T	F	T	F	T	F
F	T	F	T	F	F
F	F	T	T	T	T

49. $(p \leftrightarrow q) \leftrightarrow \left[(q \to p) \wedge (p \to q)\right]$ is a tautology.

p	q	$q \to p$	$p \to q$	$p \leftrightarrow q$	$(q \to p) \wedge (p \to q)$	$(p \leftrightarrow q) \leftrightarrow \left[(q \to p) \wedge (p \to q)\right]$
T	T	T	T	T	T	T
T	F	T	F	F	F	T
F	T	F	T	F	F	T
F	F	T	T	T	T	T

50. $(q \leftrightarrow p) \leftrightarrow \left[(p \to q) \wedge (q \to p)\right]$ is a tautology.

p	q	$q \leftrightarrow p$	$p \to q$	$q \to p$	$(p \to q) \wedge (q \to p)$	$(q \leftrightarrow p) \leftrightarrow \left[(p \to q) \wedge (q \to p)\right]$
T	T	T	T	T	T	T
T	F	F	F	T	F	T
F	T	F	T	F	F	T
F	F	T	T	T	T	T

51. $(p \wedge q) \leftrightarrow (\sim p \vee r)$ is neither

p	q	r	$\sim p$	$p \wedge q$	$\sim p \vee r$	$(p \wedge q) \leftrightarrow (\sim p \vee r)$
T	T	T	F	T	T	T
T	T	F	F	T	F	F
T	F	T	F	F	T	F
T	F	F	F	F	F	T
F	T	T	T	F	T	F
F	T	F	T	F	T	F
F	F	T	T	F	T	F
F	F	F	T	F	T	F

52. $(p \wedge q) \to (\sim q \vee r)$ is neither

p	q	r	$\sim q$	$p \wedge q$	$\sim q \vee r$	$(p \wedge q) \to (\sim q \vee r)$
T	T	T	F	T	T	T
T	T	F	F	T	F	F
T	F	T	T	F	T	T
T	F	F	T	F	T	T
F	T	T	F	F	T	T
F	T	F	F	F	F	T
F	F	T	T	F	T	T
F	F	F	T	F	T	T

53. $[(p \to q) \land (q \to r)] \to (p \to r)$ is a tautology.

p	q	r	$p \to q$	$q \to r$	$(p \to q) \land (q \to r)$	$p \to r$	$[(p \to q) \land (q \to r)] \to (p \to r)$
T	T	T	T	T	T	T	T
T	T	F	T	F	F	F	T
T	F	T	F	T	F	T	T
T	F	F	F	T	F	F	T
F	T	T	T	T	T	T	T
F	T	F	T	F	F	T	T
F	F	T	T	T	T	T	T
F	F	F	T	T	T	T	T

54. $[(p \to q) \land (q \to r)] \to (\sim r \to \sim p)$ is a tautology.

p	q	r	$\sim p$	$\sim r$	$p \to q$	$q \to r$	$(p \to q) \land (q \to r)$	$\sim r \to \sim p$	$[(p \to q) \land (q \to r)] \to (\sim r \to \sim p)$
T	T	T	F	F	T	T	T	T	T
T	T	F	F	T	T	F	F	F	T
T	F	T	F	F	F	T	F	T	T
T	F	F	F	T	F	T	F	F	T
F	T	T	T	F	T	T	T	T	T
F	T	F	T	T	T	F	F	T	T
F	F	T	T	F	T	T	T	T	T
F	F	F	T	T	T	T	T	T	T

55. $[(q \to r) \land (r \to \sim p)] \leftrightarrow (q \land p)$ is neither.

p	q	r	$[(q \to r) \land (r \to \sim p)] \leftrightarrow (q \land p)$
T	T	T	F
T	T	F	F
T	F	T	T
T	F	F	F
F	T	T	F
F	T	F	T
F	F	T	F
F	F	F	F

56. $[(q \to \sim r) \land (\sim r \to p)] \leftrightarrow (q \land \sim p)$ is neither.

p	q	r	$[(q \to \sim r) \land (\sim r \to p)] \leftrightarrow (q \land \sim p)$
T	T	T	T
T	T	F	F
T	F	T	F
T	F	F	F
F	T	T	F
F	T	F	F
F	F	T	F
F	F	F	T

57. a. p: You do homework right after class.; q: You fall behind.; $(p \rightarrow \sim q) \wedge (\sim p \rightarrow q)$

b.

p	q	$\sim p$	$\sim q$	$p \rightarrow \sim q$	$\sim p \rightarrow q$	$(p \rightarrow \sim q) \wedge (\sim p \rightarrow q)$
T	T	F	F	F	T	F
T	F	F	T	T	T	T
F	T	T	F	T	T	T
F	F	T	T	T	F	F

c.   Answers will vary; an example is: The statement is true when p and q have opposite truth values.

58. a. p: You do a little bit each day.; q: You get by.; $(p \rightarrow q) \wedge (\sim p \rightarrow \sim q)$

b.

p	q	$\sim p$	$\sim q$	$p \rightarrow q$	$\sim p \rightarrow \sim q$	$(p \rightarrow q) \wedge (\sim p \rightarrow \sim q)$
T	T	F	F	T	T	T
T	F	F	T	F	T	F
F	T	T	F	T	F	F
F	F	T	T	T	T	T

c.   Answers will vary; an example is: The statement is true when p and q have the same truth values.

59. a. p: You cut and paste from the Internet.; q: You cite the source.; r: You are charged with plagiarism.; $(p \wedge \sim q) \rightarrow r$

b.

p	q	r	$\sim q$	$p \wedge \sim q$	$(p \wedge \sim q) \rightarrow r$
T	T	T	F	F	T
T	T	F	F	F	T
T	F	T	T	T	T
T	F	F	T	T	F
F	T	T	F	F	T
F	T	F	F	F	T
F	F	T	T	F	T
F	F	F	T	F	T

c.   Answers will vary; an example is: The statement is true when p, q, and r are all true.

60. a. p: You take more than one class with a lot of reading.; q: You have free time.; r: You are in the library until 1 A.M.; $p \rightarrow (\sim q \wedge r)$

b.

p	q	r	$\sim q$	$\sim q \wedge r$	$p \rightarrow r(\sim q \wedge r)$
T	T	T	F	F	F
T	T	F	F	F	F
T	F	T	T	T	T
T	F	F	T	F	F
F	T	T	F	F	T
F	T	F	F	F	T
F	F	T	T	T	T
F	F	F	T	F	T

c.   Answers will vary; an example is: The statement is true when p, q, and r are all false.

61. a.　*p*: You are comfortable in your room.; *q*: You are honest with your roommate.; *r*: You enjoy the college experience.; $(p \leftrightarrow q) \vee \sim r$

b.

p	*q*	*r*	*∼ r*	*p ↔ q*	*(p ↔ q)∨ ∼ r*
T	T	T	F	T	T
T	T	F	T	T	T
T	F	T	F	F	F
T	F	F	T	F	T
F	T	T	F	F	F
F	T	F	T	F	T
F	F	T	F	T	T
F	F	F	T	T	T

c.　Answers will vary; an example is: The statement is true when *p*, *q*, and *r* are all true.

62. a.　*p*: I fail the course.; *q*: I rely on a used book with highlightings by an idiot.; *r*: I buy a used book.; $(p \leftrightarrow q) \vee \sim r$

b.　See truth table for Exercise 61.

c.　Answers will vary; an example is: The statement is true when *p*, *q*, and *r* are all true.

63. a.　*p*: I enjoy the course.; *q*: I choose the class based on the professor.; *r*: I choose the class based on the course description.; $p \leftrightarrow (q \wedge \sim r)$

b.

p	*q*	*r*	*∼ r*	*q∧ ∼ r*	*p ↔ (q∧ ∼ r)*
T	T	T	F	F	F
T	T	F	T	T	T
T	F	T	F	F	F
T	F	F	T	F	F
F	T	T	F	F	T
F	T	F	T	T	F
F	F	T	F	F	T
F	F	F	T	F	T

c.　Answers will vary; an example is: The statement is true when *p*, *q*, and *r* are all false.

64. a.　*p*: I miss class.; *q*: They take attendance.; *r*: There is a pop quiz.; $\sim p \leftrightarrow (q \vee r)$

b.

p	*q*	*r*	*∼ p*	*q ∨ r*	*∼ p ↔ (q ∨ r)*
T	T	T	F	T	F
T	T	F	F	T	F
T	F	T	F	T	F
T	F	F	F	F	T
F	T	T	T	T	T
F	T	F	T	T	T
F	F	T	T	T	T
F	F	F	T	F	F

c.　Answers will vary; an example is: The statement is true when *p* is true and *q* and *r* are false.

65. $\sim(p \to q)$

$\sim(F \to T)$

$\sim T$

F

66. $\sim(p \leftrightarrow q)$

$\sim(F \leftrightarrow T)$

$\sim F$

T

67. $\sim p \leftrightarrow q$

$\sim F \leftrightarrow T$

$T \leftrightarrow T$

T

68. $\sim p \to q$

$\sim F \to T$

$T \to T$

T

69. $q \to (p \wedge r)$

$T \to (F \wedge F)$

$T \to F$

F

70. $(p \wedge r) \to q$

$(F \wedge F) \to T$

$F \to T$

T

71. $(\sim p \wedge q) \leftrightarrow \sim r$

$(\sim F \wedge T) \leftrightarrow \sim F$

$(T \wedge T) \leftrightarrow T$

$T \leftrightarrow T$

T

72. $\sim p \leftrightarrow (\sim q \wedge r)$

$\sim F \leftrightarrow (\sim T \wedge F)$

$T \leftrightarrow (F \wedge F)$

$T \leftrightarrow F$

F

73. $\sim\big[(p \to \sim r) \leftrightarrow (r \wedge \sim p)\big]$

$\sim\big[(F \to \sim F) \leftrightarrow (F \wedge \sim F)\big]$

$\sim\big[(F \to T) \leftrightarrow (F \wedge T)\big]$

$\sim[T \leftrightarrow F]$

$\sim F$

T

74. $\sim\big[(\sim p \to r) \leftrightarrow (p \vee \sim q)\big]$

$\sim\big[(\sim F \to F) \leftrightarrow (F \vee \sim T)\big]$

$\sim\big[(T \to F) \leftrightarrow (F \vee F)\big]$

$\sim[F \leftrightarrow F]$

$\sim T$

F

75. $(p \to q) \leftrightarrow \big[(p \wedge q) \to \sim p\big]$

p	q	$(p \to q) \leftrightarrow \big[(p \wedge q) \to \sim p\big]$
T	T	F
T	F	F
F	T	T
F	F	T

76. $(q \to p) \leftrightarrow \big[(p \vee q) \to \sim p\big]$

p	q	$(p \to q) \leftrightarrow \big[(p \wedge q) \to \sim p\big]$
T	T	F
T	F	F
F	T	F
F	F	T

77. $\big[p \to (\sim q \vee r)\big] \leftrightarrow (p \wedge r)$

p	q	r	$\big[p \to (\sim q \vee r)\big] \leftrightarrow (p \wedge r)$
T	T	T	T
T	T	F	T
T	F	T	T
T	F	F	F
F	T	T	F
F	T	F	F
F	F	T	F
F	F	F	F

78. $\left[\sim p \to (q \wedge r)\right] \leftrightarrow (p \vee r)$

p	q	r	$\left[\sim p \to (q \wedge r)\right] \leftrightarrow (p \vee r)$
T	T	T	T
T	T	F	T
T	F	T	T
T	F	F	T
F	T	T	T
F	T	F	T
F	F	T	F
F	F	F	T

79. p: You love a person.; q: You marry that person.; $(q \to p) \wedge (\sim p \to \sim q)$

p	q	$\sim p$	$\sim q$	$q \to p$	$\sim p \to \sim q$	$(q \to p) \wedge (\sim p \to \sim q)$
T	T	F	F	T	T	T
T	F	F	T	T	T	T
F	T	T	F	F	F	F
F	F	T	T	T	T	T

Answers will vary; an example is: The statement is true when both p and q are true.

80. p: You study hard.; q: You get an A.; $(q \to p) \wedge (\sim p \to \sim q)$

p	q	$\sim p$	$\sim q$	$q \to p$	$\sim p \to \sim q$	$(q \to p) \wedge (\sim p \to \sim q)$
T	T	F	F	T	T	T
T	F	F	T	T	T	T
F	T	T	F	F	F	F
F	F	T	T	T	T	T

Answers will vary; an example is: The statement is true when both p and q are true.

81. p: You are happy.; q: You live contentedly.; r: You are wealthy.; $\sim [r \to (p \wedge q)]$

p	q	r	$p \wedge q$	$r \to (p \wedge q)$	$\sim [r \to (p \wedge q)]$
T	T	T	T	T	F
T	T	F	T	T	F
T	F	T	F	F	T
T	F	F	F	T	F
F	T	T	F	F	T
F	T	F	F	T	F
F	F	T	F	F	T
F	F	F	F	T	F

Answers will vary; an example is: The statement is true when p is false and both q and r are true.

82. p: You are happy.; q: You live contentedly.; r: You are wealthy.; $\sim [r \to (p \wedge q)]$; See truth table for Exercise 81.;
Answers will vary; an example is: The statement is true when p is false and both q and r are true.

83. p: There was an increase in the percentage who believed in God.; q: There was a decrease in the percentage who believed in Heaven.; r: There was an increase in the percentage who believed in the devil.; The statement is of the form $(p \wedge q) \rightarrow r$ with p false, q true, and r false.

$(p \wedge q) \rightarrow r$

$(F \wedge T) \rightarrow F$

$\quad F \rightarrow F$

$\quad\quad T$

Therefore the statement is true.

84. p: There was a decrease in the percentage who believed in God.; q: There was an increase in the percentage who believed in the devil.; r: There was an increase in the percentage who believed in Hell.; The statement is of the form $p \rightarrow \sim (q \vee r)$ with p true, q false, and r false.

$p \rightarrow \sim (q \vee r)$

$T \rightarrow \sim (F \vee F)$

$\quad T \rightarrow \sim F$

$\quad T \rightarrow T$

$\quad\quad T$

Therefore the statement is true.

85. p: There was a decrease in the percentage who believed in God.; q: There was an increase in the percentage who believed in Heaven.; r: The percentage believing in the devil decreased.; The statement is of the form $(p \leftrightarrow q) \vee r$ with p true, q false, and r true.

$(p \leftrightarrow q) \vee r$

$(T \leftrightarrow F) \vee T$

$\quad F \vee T$

$\quad\quad T$

Therefore the statement is true.

86. p: There was an increase in the percentage who believed in God.; q: There was an increase in the percentage who believed in Heaven.; r: The percentage believing in Hell decreased.; The statement is of the form $(p \leftrightarrow q) \wedge r$ with p false, q false, and r true.

$(p \leftrightarrow q) \wedge r$

$(F \leftrightarrow F) \wedge T$

$\quad T \wedge T$

$\quad\quad T$

Therefore the statement is true.

87. p: Fifteen percent are capitalists.; q: Thirty-four percent are members of the upper middle class.; r: The number of working poor exceeds the number belonging to the working class.; The statement is of the form $(p \vee \sim q) \leftrightarrow r$ with p false, q false, and r false.

$(p \vee \sim q) \leftrightarrow r$

$(F \vee \sim F) \leftrightarrow F$

$(F \vee T) \leftrightarrow F$

$\quad T \leftrightarrow F$

$\quad\quad F$

88. *p*: Fifteen percent are capitalists.; *q*: Thirty-four percent are members of the upper middle class.; *r*: The number of working poor exceeds the number belonging to the working class.; The statement is of the form $(p \land \sim q) \leftrightarrow r$ with *p* false, *q* false, and *r* false.

$$(p \land \sim q) \leftrightarrow r$$
$$(F \land \sim F) \leftrightarrow F$$
$$(F \land T) \leftrightarrow F$$
$$F \leftrightarrow F$$
$$T$$

Therefore the statement is true.

89. *p*: There are more people in the lower-middle class than in the capitalist and upper-middle classes combined.; *q*: One percent are capitalists.; *r*: Thirty-four percent belong to the upper-middle class.; The statement is of the form $p \to (q \land r)$ with *p* true, *q* true, and *r* false.

$$p \to (q \land r)$$
$$T \to (T \land F)$$
$$T \to F$$
$$F$$

Therefore the statement is false.

90. *p*: There are more people in the lower-middle class than in the capitalist and upper-middle classes combined.; *q*: One percent are capitalists.; *r*: Thirty-four percent belong to the upper-middle class.; The statement is of the form $p \to (q \lor r)$ with *p* true, *q* true, and *r* false.

$$p \to (q \lor r)$$
$$F \to (T \lor F)$$
$$F \to T$$
$$T$$

Therefore the statement is true.

104. No, you cannot conclude you got an A. The person could still take you out to dinner if you received a different grade. That would be an example of an *if-then* statement with a false antecedent and a true consequent.

105. Answers will vary. Possible column headings:

p	q	$p \to q$	$\sim p$	$(p \to q) \lor \sim p$	$p \to [(p \to q) \lor \sim p]$

106. Answers will vary. Possible column headings:

p	q	$p \lor q$	$p \land q$	$\sim(p \land q)$	$(p \lor q) \to \sim(p \land q)$

Check Points 3.5

1. a. $p \vee q$ and $\sim q \to p$ are equivalent.

p	q	$\sim q$	$p \vee q$	$\sim q \to p$
T	T	F	T	T
T	F	T	T	T
F	T	F	T	T
F	F	T	F	F

The statements are equivalent since their truth values are the same.

b. $$\underline{ p } \vee \underline{ q }$$
I attend classes or I lose my scholarship.

…is equivalent to… $\underline{ \sim q } \to \underline{ p }$
If I do not lose my scholarship, then I attend classes.

2. $\sim p$ and $\sim[\sim(\sim p)]$ are equivalent.

p	$\sim p$	$\sim(\sim p)$	$\sim[\sim(\sim p)]$
T	F	T	F
F	T	F	T

The statements are equivalent since their truth values are the same.

3.   Given: If it's raining, then I need a jacket.
p: It's raining.
q: I need a jacket.
a: It's not raining or I need a jacket.
b: I need a jacket or it's not raining.
c: If I need a jacket, then it's raining.
d: If I do not need a jacket, then it's not raining.

The given is *not* equivalent to statement (**c**)

				Given	**a**	**b**	**c**	**d**
p	q	$\sim p$	$\sim q$	$p \to q$	$\sim p \vee q$	$q \vee \sim p$	$q \to p$	$\sim q \to \sim p$
T	T	F	F	T	T	T	T	T
T	F	F	T	F	F	F	T	F
F	T	T	F	T	T	T	F	T
F	F	T	T	T	T	T	T	T

4. a.   If you're not driving too closely, then you can't read this.

b.   If it's not time to do the laundry, then you have clean underwear.

c.   If supervision during exams is required, then some students are not honest.

d. $q \to (p \vee r)$

5.   Converse: If you don't see a Club Med, then you are in Iran.; Inverse: If you are not in Iran, then you see a Club Med.; Contrapositive: If you see a Club Med, then you are not in Iran.

Exercise Set 3.5

1. **a.** $\sim p \to q$ and $p \vee q$ are equivalent.

p	q	$\sim p$	$\sim p \to q$	$p \vee q$
T	T	F	T	T
T	F	F	T	T
F	T	T	T	T
F	F	T	F	F

   b. The United States supports the development of solar-powered cars or it will suffer increasing atmospheric pollution.

2. **a.** $p \to q$ and $\sim p \vee q$ are equivalent.

p	q	$\sim p$	$p \to q$	$\sim p \vee q$
T	T	F	T	T
T	F	F	F	F
F	T	T	T	T
F	F	T	T	T

   b. $\underset{p}{\underline{\text{If a number is even,}}} \quad \underset{\to}{\underline{\text{then}}} \quad \underset{q}{\underline{\text{it is divisible by 2.}}}$

   …is equivalent to…

   $\underset{\sim p}{\underline{}} \quad \underset{\vee}{\underline{}} \quad \underset{q}{\underline{}}$
   A number is not even or it is divisible by 2.

3. not equivalent

4. not equivalent

5. equivalent

6. equivalent

7. equivalent

8. equivalent

9. not equivalent

10. not equivalent

11. not equivalent

12. not equivalent

13. equivalent

14. equivalent

15. Given: I saw the original *King Kong* or the 2005 version.
    p: I saw the original *King Kong*.
    q: I saw the 2005 version.
    a: If I did not see the original King Kong, I saw the 2005 version.
    b: I saw both the original *King Kong* and the 2005 version.
    c: If I saw the original *King Kong*, I did not see the 2005 version
    d: If I saw the 2005 version, I did not see the original *King Kong*.

The given is equivalent to statement (**a**)

p	q	Given $p \vee q$	a $\sim p \to q$	b $p \wedge q$	c $p \to \sim q$	d $q \to \sim p$
T	T	T	T	T	F	F
T	F	T	T	F	T	T
F	T	T	T	F	T	T
F	F	F	F	F	T	T

16. Given: *Citizen Kane* or *Howard the Duck* appear in a list of greatest U.S. movies.
   p: *Citizen Kane* appears in a list of greatest U.S. movies.
   q: *Howard the Duck* appears in a list of greatest U.S. movies.
   a: If *Citizen Kane* appears in the list of greatest U.S. movies, *Howard the Duck* does not.
   b: If *Howard the Duck* does not appear in the list of greatest U.S. movies, then *Citizen Kane* does.
   c: Both *Citizen Kane* and *Howard the Duck* appear in a list of greatest U.S. movies.
   d: If *Howard the Duck* appears in the list of greatest U.S. movies, *Citizen Kane* does not.

The given is equivalent to statement (**b**)

p	q	Given $p \vee q$	a $p \to \sim q$	b $\sim q \to p$	c $p \wedge q$	d $q \to \sim p$
T	T	T	F	T	T	F
T	F	T	T	T	F	T
F	T	T	T	T	F	T
F	F	F	T	F	F	T

17. Given: It is not true that Sondheim and Picasso are both musicians.
   p: Sondheim is a musician.
   q: Picasso is a musician.
   a: Sondheim is not a musician or Picasso is not a musician.
   b: If Sondheim is a musician, then Picasso is not a musician.
   c: Sondheim is not a musician and Picasso is not a musician.
   d: If Picasso is a musician, then Sondheim is not a musician.

The given is *not* equivalent to statement (**c**)

p	q	Given $\sim(p \wedge q)$	a $\sim p \vee \sim q$	b $p \to \sim q$	c $\sim p \wedge \sim q$	d $q \to \sim p$
T	T	F	F	F	F	F
T	F	T	T	T	F	T
F	T	T	T	T	F	T
F	F	T	T	T	T	T

18. Given: It is not true that England and Africa are both countries.
   p: England is a country.
   q: Africa is a country.
   a: If England is a country, then Africa is not a country.
   b: England is not a country and Africa is not a country.
   c: England is not a country or Africa is not a country.
   d: If Africa is a country, then England is not a country.

The given is *not* equivalent to statement (**b**)

p	q	Given $\sim(p \wedge q)$	a $p \to \sim q$	b $\sim p \wedge \sim q$	c $\sim p \vee \sim q$	d $p \to \sim q$
T	T	F	F	F	F	F
T	F	T	T	F	T	T
F	T	T	T	F	T	T
F	F	T	T	T	T	T

19. Converse: If I am in Illinois, then I am in Chicago.
Inverse: If I am not in Chicago, then I am not in Illinois.
Contrapositive: If I am not in Illinois, I am not in Chicago.

20. Converse: If I am in the South, then I am in Birmingham.
Inverse: If I am not in Birmingham, then I am not in the South.
Contrapositive: If I am not in the South, I am not in Birmingham.

21. Converse: If I cannot hear you, then the stereo is playing.
Inverse: If the stereo is not playing, then I can hear you.
Contrapositive: If I can hear you, then the stereo is not playing.

22. Converse: If it is not an apple, then it is blue.
Inverse: If it is not blue, then it is an apple.
Contrapositive: If it is an apple, it is not blue.

23. Converse: If you die, you don't laugh.
Inverse: If you laugh, you don't die.
Contrapositive: If you don't die, you laugh.

24. Converse: If you must acquit, it doesn't fit.
Inverse: If it fits, you must not acquit. Contrapositive: If you do not acquit, then it fits.

25. Converse: If all troops were withdrawn, then the president is telling the truth.
Inverse: If the president is not telling the truth, then some troops were not withdrawn.
Contrapositive: If some troops were not withdrawn, then the president was not telling the truth.

26. Converse: If no students fail the test, then the review session is successful.
Inverse: If the review session is not successful, then some students fail the test.
Contrapositive: If some students fail the test, then the review session was not successful.

27. Converse: If some people suffer, then all institutions place profit above human need.
Inverse: If some institutions do not place profit above human need, then no people suffer.
Contrapositive: If no people suffer, then some institutions do not place profit above human need.

28. Converse: If some people are not hard workers, then all hard workers are successful.
Inverse: If some hard workers are not successful, then all people are hard workers.
Contrapositive: If all people are hard workers, then some hard workers are not successful.

29. Converse: $\sim r \rightarrow \sim q$; Inverse: $q \rightarrow r$; Contrapositive: $r \rightarrow q$

30. Converse: $r \rightarrow \sim p$; Inverse: $p \rightarrow \sim r$; Contrapositive: $\sim r \rightarrow p$

31. If a person diets, then he or she loses weight.
Converse: If a person loses weight, then he or she is dieting.
Inverse: If a person is not dieting, then he or she is not losing weight.
Contrapositive: If a person is not losing weight, then he or she is not dieting.

32. If a person is a senator, then he or she is a politician.
Converse: If a person is a politician, then he or she is a senator.
Inverse: If a person is not a senator, then he or she is not a politician.
Contrapositive: If a person is not a politician, then he or she is not a senator.

33. If a vehicle has no flashing light on top, then it is not an ambulance.
Converse: If a vehicle is not an ambulance, then it has no flashing light on top.
Inverse: If a vehicle has a flashing light on top, then it is an ambulance.
Contrapositive: If a vehicle is an ambulance, then it has a flashing light on top.

34. If a person is not fearful, then he or she is crazy.
Converse: If a person is crazy, then he or she is not fearful.
Inverse: If a person is fearful, then he or she is not crazy.
Contrapositive: If a person is not crazy, then he or she is fearful.

35. If a person is an attorney, then he or she has passed the bar exam.
Converse: If a person has passed the bar exam, then he or she is an attorney.
Inverse: If a person is not an attorney, then he or she has not passed the bar exam.
Contrapositive: If a person has not passed the bar exam, then he or she is not an attorney.

36. If a person votes, then he or she is a citizen.
Converse: If a person is a citizen, then he or she votes.
Inverse: If a person does not vote, then he or she is not a citizen.
Contrapositive: If a person is not a citizen, then he or she does not vote.

37. If a person is a pacifist, then he or she is not a warmonger.
Converse: If a person is not a warmonger, then he or she is a pacifist.
Inverse: If a person is not a pacifist, then he or she is a warmonger.
Contrapositive: If a person is a warmonger, then he or she is not a pacifist.

38. If a person is a writer, then he or she is not illiterate.
Converse: If a person is not illiterate, then he or she is a writer.
Inverse: If a person is not a writer, then he or she is illiterate.
Contrapositive: If a person is illiterate, then he or she is not a writer.

39. a. The conditional statement is true.

    b. Converse: If the corruption rating is 9.6, then the country is Finland.
Inverse: If the country is not Finland, then the corruption rating is not 9.6.
Contrapositive: If the corruption rating is not 9.6, then the country is not Finland.
The contrapositive is true.
The converse and inverse are not necessarily true.

40. a. The conditional statement is true.

    b. Converse: If the corruption rating is 1.8, then the country is Haiti
Inverse: If the country is not Haiti, then the corruption rating is not 1.8
Contrapositive: If the corruption rating is not 1.8, then the country is not Haiti
The contrapositive is true.
The converse and inverse are not necessarily true.

47. does not make sense; Explanations will vary. Sample explanation: A conditional statement and its contrapositive always have the same truth value.

48. does not make sense; Explanations will vary. Sample explanation: A conditional statement and its converse can have different truth values.

49. makes sense

50. makes sense

Check Points 3.6

1. You do not have a fever and you have the flu.

2. Bart Simpson is not a cartoon character or Tony Soprano is not a cartoon character.

3. You do not leave by 5 P.M. and you arrive home on time.

4. **a.** Some horror movies are not scary or none are funny.

   b. Your workouts are not strenuous and you get stronger.

5. p: It is windy.
   q: We can swim.
   r: We can sail.
   The statement can be represented symbolically as $\sim p \rightarrow (q \wedge \sim r)$.
   Next write the contrapositive and simplify.
   $$\sim(q \wedge \sim r) \rightarrow \sim(\sim p)$$
   $$\left[\sim q \vee \sim(\sim r)\right] \rightarrow p$$
   $$(\sim q \vee r) \rightarrow p$$
   Thus, $\sim p \rightarrow (q \wedge \sim r) \equiv (\sim q \vee r) \rightarrow p$.
   The original statement is equivalent to "If we cannot swim or we can sail, then it is windy."

Exercise Set 3.6

1. The negation of $p \rightarrow q$ is $p \wedge \sim q$: I am in Los Angeles and not in California.

2. The negation of $p \rightarrow q$ is $p \wedge \sim q$: I am in Houston and not in Texas.

3. The negation of $p \rightarrow q$ is $p \wedge \sim q$: It is purple and it is a carrot.

4. The negation of $p \rightarrow q$ is $p \wedge \sim q$: The TV is playing and I can concentrate.

5. The negation of $p \rightarrow q$ is $p \wedge \sim q$: He doesn't, and I won't.

6. The negation of $p \rightarrow q$ is $p \wedge \sim q$: She says "yes," and he does not say "no."

7. The negation of $p \rightarrow q$ is $p \wedge \sim q$: There is a blizzard, and some schools are not closed.

8. The negation of $p \rightarrow q$ is $p \wedge \sim q$: There is a tax cut and some people do not have extra spending money.

9. The negation of $\sim q \rightarrow \sim r$ is $\sim q \wedge r$

10. The negation of $\sim p \rightarrow r$ is $\sim p \wedge \sim r$

11. Australia is not an island or China is not an island.

12. Florida is not a peninsula or California is not a peninsula.

13. My high school did not encourage creativity or did not encourage diversity.

14. The course does not cover logic or does not cover dream analysis.

15. Jewish scripture does not give a clear indication of a heaven and it does not give a clear indication of an afterlife.

16. Martin Luther King supported neither violent protests nor the Vietnam War.

17. The United States has eradicated neither poverty nor racism.

18. The movie was neither interesting nor entertaining.

19. $\sim(\sim p \wedge q)$

$\sim(\sim p) \vee \sim q$

$p \vee \sim q$

20. $\sim(p \vee \sim q)$

$\sim p \wedge \sim(\sim q)$

$\sim p \wedge q$

21. p: You attend lecture.
    q: You study.
    r: You succeed.
    The statement can be represented symbolically as $(p \wedge q) \rightarrow r$.

    Next write the contrapositive and simplify.

    $\sim r \rightarrow \sim(p \wedge q)$

    $\sim r \rightarrow (\sim p \vee \sim q)$

    Thus, $(p \wedge q) \rightarrow r \equiv \sim r \rightarrow (\sim p \vee \sim q)$.

    The original statement is equivalent to "If you do not succeed, then you did not attend lecture or did not study."

22. If you can not taste music or you can not smell colors, then you do not suffer from synesthesia.

23. p: He cooks.
    q: His wife cooks.
    r: His child cooks.
    The statement can be represented symbolically as $\sim p \rightarrow (q \vee r)$.

    Next write the contrapositive and simplify.

    $\sim(q \vee r) \rightarrow \sim(\sim p)$

    $(\sim q \wedge \sim r) \rightarrow p$

    Thus, $\sim p \rightarrow (q \vee r) \equiv (\sim q \wedge \sim r) \rightarrow p$.

    The original statement is equivalent to "If his wife does not cook and his child does not cook, then he does."

24. p: It is Saturday.
    q: It is Sunday.
    r: I work.
    The statement can be represented symbolically as $(p \vee q) \rightarrow \sim r$.

    Next write the contrapositive and simplify.

    $\sim(\sim r) \rightarrow \sim(p \vee q)$

    $r \rightarrow (\sim p \wedge \sim q)$

    Thus, $(p \vee q) \rightarrow \sim r \equiv r \rightarrow (\sim p \wedge \sim q)$.

    The original statement is equivalent to "If I work, then it is not Saturday and it is not Sunday."

25. Write the contrapositive of $p \to (q \vee \sim r)$ and simplify.

$\sim(q \vee \sim r) \to \sim p$

$\left[\sim q \wedge \sim(\sim r)\right] \to \sim p$

$(\sim q \wedge r) \to \sim p$

Thus, $p \to (q \vee \sim r) \equiv (\sim q \wedge r) \to \sim p$.

26. Write the contrapositive of $p \to (\sim q \wedge \sim r)$ and simplify.

$\sim(\sim q \wedge \sim r) \to \sim p$

$\left[q \vee \sim(\sim r)\right] \to \sim p$

$(q \vee r) \to \sim p$

Thus, $p \to (\sim q \wedge \sim r) \equiv (q \vee r) \to \sim p$.

27. I'm going to neither Seattle nor San Francisco.

28. This course covers neither logic nor statistics.

29. I do not study and I pass.

30. I don't give up tobacco and I am healthy.

31. I am going or he is not going.

32. I apply myself or I do not succeed.

33. A bill does not become law or it receives majority approval.

34. They do not see the show or they have tickets.

35. Write the negation of $p \vee \sim q$ and simplify.

$\sim(p \vee \sim q)$

$\sim p \wedge \sim(\sim q)$

$\sim p \wedge q$

Thus the negation of $p \vee \sim q$ is $\sim p \wedge q$.

36. Write the negation of $\sim p \vee q$ and simplify.

$\sim(\sim p \vee q)$

$\sim(\sim p) \wedge \sim q$

$p \wedge \sim q$

Thus the negation of $\sim p \vee q$ is $p \wedge \sim q$.

37. Write the negation of $p \wedge (q \vee r)$ and simplify.

$\sim\left[p \wedge (q \vee r)\right]$

$\sim p \vee \sim(q \vee r)$

$\sim p \vee (\sim q \wedge \sim r)$

Thus the negation of $p \wedge (q \vee r)$ is $\sim p \vee (\sim q \wedge \sim r)$.

38. Write the negation of $p \vee (q \wedge r)$ and simplify.

$\sim \left[p \vee (q \wedge r) \right]$

$\sim p \wedge \sim (q \wedge r)$

$\sim p \wedge (\sim q \vee \sim r)$

Thus the negation of $p \vee (q \wedge r)$ is $\sim p \wedge (\sim q \vee \sim r)$.

39. None are equivalent.

		a	b	c
p	q	$p \rightarrow \sim q$	$\sim p \vee q$	$\sim p \rightarrow q$
T	T	F	T	T
T	F	T	T	F
F	T	T	T	T
F	F	T	F	T

40. a and c are equivalent.

		a	b	c
p	q	$p \rightarrow \sim q$	$p \vee q$	$q \rightarrow \sim p$
T	T	F	T	F
T	F	T	T	T
F	T	T	T	T
F	F	T	F	T

41. None are equivalent.

		a	b	c
p	q	$\sim (p \wedge \sim q)$	$\sim p \wedge q$	$p \vee \sim q$
T	T	T	F	T
T	F	F	F	T
F	T	T	T	F
F	F	T	F	T

42. a and b are equivalent.

		a	b	c
p	q	$p \vee \sim q$	$\sim (\sim p \wedge q)$	$\sim p \wedge q$
T	T	T	T	F
T	F	T	T	F
F	T	F	F	T
F	F	T	T	F

43. None are equivalent.

			a	b	c
p	q	r	$p \rightarrow \sim (q \vee r)$	$(q \wedge r) \rightarrow \sim p$	$\sim p \rightarrow (q \wedge r)$
T	T	T	F	F	T
T	T	F	F	T	T
T	F	T	F	T	T
T	F	F	T	T	T
F	T	T	T	T	T
F	T	F	T	T	F
F	F	T	T	T	F
F	F	F	T	T	F

44. None are equivalent.

p	q	r	a $(\sim p \vee q) \to r$	b $(p \wedge \sim q) \to \sim r$	c $\sim r \to (p \vee \sim q)$
T	T	T	T	T	T
T	T	F	F	T	T
T	F	T	T	F	T
T	F	F	T	T	T
F	T	T	T	T	T
F	T	F	F	T	F
F	F	T	T	T	T
F	F	F	F	T	T

45. a and b are equivalent.

p	q	r	a $p \wedge (q \vee r)$	b $p \wedge \sim (\sim q \wedge \sim r)$	c $p \to (q \vee r)$
T	T	T	T	T	T
T	T	F	T	T	T
T	F	T	T	T	T
T	F	F	F	F	F
F	T	T	F	F	T
F	T	F	F	F	T
F	F	T	F	F	T
F	F	F	F	F	T

46. a and c are equivalent.

p	q	r	a $p \wedge (q \to r)$	b $r \leftrightarrow (q \wedge p)$	c $p \wedge (\sim r \to \sim q)$
T	T	T	T	T	T
T	T	F	F	F	F
T	F	T	T	F	T
T	F	F	T	T	T
F	T	T	F	F	F
F	T	F	F	T	F
F	F	T	F	F	F
F	F	F	F	T	F

47. If there is no pain, there is no gain.; Converse: If there is no gain, then there is no pain.; Inverse: If there is pain, then there is gain.; Contrapositive: If there is gain, then there is pain.; Negation: There is no pain and there is gain.

48. If you get a speeding ticket, then you are not observing the speed limit.; Converse: If you are not observing the speed limit, then you get a speeding ticket.; Inverse: If you do not get a speeding ticket, then you are observing the speed limit.; Contrapositive: If you are observing the speed limit, then you do not get a speeding ticket.; Negation: You get a speeding ticket and you are observing the speed limit.

49. If you follow Buddha's "Middle Way," then you are neither hedonistic nor ascetic.; Converse: If you are neither hedonistic nor ascetic, then you follow Buddha's "Middle Way."; Inverse: If you do not follow Buddha's "Middle Way," then you are either hedonistic or ascetic.; Contrapositive: If you are either hedonistic or ascetic, then you do not follow Buddha's "Middle Way."; Negation: You follow Buddha's "Middle Way" and you are either hedonistic or ascetic.

50. If a female ferret goes into heat and does not find a mate, then she dies.; Converse: If a female ferret dies, then she went into heat and did not find a mate.; Inverse: If a female ferret does not go into heat or finds a mate, then she does not die.; Contrapositive: If a female ferret doesn't die, then she did not go into heat or she found a mate.; Negation: A female ferret goes into heat and does not find a mate, and she doesn't die.

51. $p \wedge (\sim r \vee s)$

52. $p \wedge (r \wedge \sim s)$

53. $\sim p \vee (r \wedge s)$

54. $\sim p \wedge (\sim r \wedge \sim s)$

55. **a.** false

    b. Smoking does not reduce life expectancy by 2370 days or heart disease does not reduce life expectancy by 1247 days.

    c. true

56. **a.** false

    b. Cancer does not reduce life expectancy by 1607 days or being overweight does not reduce life expectancy by 777 days.

    c. true

57. **a.** true

    b. Homicide does not reduce life expectancy by 74 days and fire reduces life expectancy by 25 days.

    c. false

58. **a.** true

    b. Automobile accidents do not reduce life expectancy by 500 days and drowning reduces life expectancy by 30 days.

    c. false

59. **a.** true

    b. Drowning reduces life expectancy by ten times the number of days as airplane accidents and drowning reduces life expectancy by 24 days.

    c. false

60. **a.** true

    b. Fire reduces life expectancy by ten times the number of days as airplane accidents and fire reduces life expectancy by 20 days.

    c. false

64. does not make sense; Explanations will vary. Sample explanation: Negations of these compound statements involves more than merely negating the simple statements,

65. makes sense

66. does not make sense; Explanations will vary. Sample explanation: The contrapositive of $\sim q \rightarrow (p \wedge r)$ is $\sim(p \wedge r) \rightarrow q$.

67. makes sense

68. We will replace or repair the roof, *or* we will not sell the house.

69. Contrapositive: If no one is eating turkey, then it is not Thanksgiving.
Negation: It is thanksgiving and no one is eating turkey.

Check Points 3.7

1. The argument is valid. *p*: The U.S. must energetically support the development of solar-powered cars.
q: The U.S. must suffer increasing atmospheric pollution.

$p \vee q$

$\sim q$
_____

$\therefore p$

p	q	$\sim q$	$p \vee q$	$(p \vee q) \wedge \sim q$	$[(p \vee q) \wedge \sim p] \rightarrow p$
T	T	F	T	F	T
T	F	T	T	T	T
F	T	F	T	F	T
F	F	T	F	F	T

2. The argument is valid. *p*: I study for 5 hours. *q*: I fail.

$p \vee q$

$\sim p$
_____

$\therefore q$

p	q	$\sim p$	$p \vee q$	$(p \vee q) \wedge \sim p$	$[(p \vee q) \wedge p] \rightarrow q$
T	T	F	T	F	T
T	F	F	T	F	T
F	T	T	T	T	T
F	F	T	F	F	T

3. The argument is invalid. *p*: You lower the fat in your diet. *q*: You lower your cholesterol. *r*: You reduce your risk of heart disease.

$p \rightarrow q$

$q \rightarrow r$
_____

$\therefore \sim p \rightarrow \sim r$

p	q	r	$p \rightarrow q$	$q \rightarrow r$	$\sim p \rightarrow \sim r$	$[(p \rightarrow q) \wedge (q \rightarrow r)] \rightarrow (\sim p \rightarrow \sim r)$
T	T	T	T	T	T	T
T	T	F	T	F	T	T
T	F	T	F	T	T	T
T	F	F	F	T	T	T
F	T	T	T	T	F	F
F	T	F	T	F	T	T
F	F	T	T	T	F	F
F	F	F	T	T	T	T

4. a. $p \vee q$

$\sim q$
_____

$\therefore p$

This argument is valid by Disjunctive Reasoning.

b. $p \rightarrow q$

$\dfrac{q}{\therefore p}$

This argument is invalid by Fallacy of the Converse.

c. $p \rightarrow q$

$\dfrac{q \rightarrow r}{\therefore p \rightarrow r}$

This argument is valid by Transitive Reasoning.

5. The argument is valid. **p:** people are good.   **q:** laws are needed to prevent wrongdoing.   **r:** laws will succeed in preventing wrongdoing.

$p \rightarrow \sim q$ $\sim p \rightarrow \sim r$ $\therefore \sim q \vee \sim r$	p	q	r	$p \rightarrow \sim q$	$\sim p \rightarrow \sim r$	$\sim q \vee \sim r$	$[(p \rightarrow \sim q) \wedge (\sim p \rightarrow \sim r)] \rightarrow (\sim q \vee \sim r)$
	T	T	T	F	T	F	T
	T	T	F	F	T	T	T
	T	F	T	T	T	T	T
	T	F	F	T	T	T	T
	F	T	T	T	F	F	T
	F	T	F	T	T	T	T
	F	F	T	T	F	T	T
	F	F	F	T	T	T	T

6. Let p be: all people lead
Let q be: no people follow
This is an argument of the form $p \rightarrow q$

$\dfrac{\sim q}{\therefore \sim p}$

The conclusion, $\sim p$, in words would be: Some people do not lead.

Exercise Set 3.7

1. This is an invalid argument.

p	q	$\sim p$	$\sim q$	$p \rightarrow q$	$(p \rightarrow q) \wedge \sim p$	$[(p \rightarrow q) \wedge \sim p] \rightarrow \sim q$
T	T	F	F	T	F	T
T	F	F	T	F	F	T
F	T	T	F	T	T	F
F	F	T	T	T	T	T

2. This is an invalid argument.

p	q	$\sim p$	$p \rightarrow q$	$(p \rightarrow q) \wedge \sim p$	$[(p \rightarrow q) \wedge \sim p] \rightarrow q$
T	T	F	T	F	T
T	F	F	F	F	T
F	T	T	T	T	T
F	F	T	T	T	F

3. This is a valid argument.

p	q	$\sim p$	$\sim q$	$p \to \sim q$	$(p \to \sim q) \land q$	$[(p \to \sim q) \land q] \to \sim p$
T	T	F	F	F	F	T
T	F	F	T	T	F	T
F	T	T	F	T	T	T
F	F	T	T	T	F	T

4. This is a valid argument.

p	q	$\sim p$	$\sim q$	$\sim p \to q$	$(\sim p \to q) \land \sim q$	$[(\sim p \to q) \land \sim q] \to p$
T	T	F	F	T	F	T
T	F	F	T	T	T	T
F	T	T	F	T	F	T
F	F	T	T	F	F	T

5. This is a valid argument.

p	q	$\sim q$	$p \land \sim q$	$(p \land \sim q) \land p$	$[(p \land \sim q) \land p] \to \sim q$
T	T	F	F	F	T
T	F	T	T	T	T
F	T	F	F	F	T
F	F	T	F	F	T

6. This is a valid argument.

p	q	$\sim p$	$\sim p \lor q$	$(\sim p \lor q) \land p$	$[(\sim p \lor q) \land p] \to q$
T	T	F	T	T	T
T	F	F	F	F	T
F	T	T	T	F	T
F	F	T	T	F	T

7. This is an invalid argument.

p	q	$p \to q$	$q \to p$	$p \land q$	$[(p \to q) \land (q \to p)]$	$[(p \to q) \land (q \to p)] \to (p \land q)$
T	T	T	T	T	T	T
T	F	F	T	F	F	T
F	T	T	F	F	F	T
F	F	T	T	F	T	F

8. This is a valid argument.

p	q	$p \to q$	$q \to p$	$(p \to q) \land (q \to p)$	$[(p \to q) \land (q \to p)] \land p$	$p \lor q$
T	T	T	T	T	T	T
T	F	F	T	F	F	T
F	T	T	F	F	F	T
F	F	T	T	T	F	F

$[[(p \to q) \land (q \to p)] \land p] \to (p \lor q)$
T
T
T
T

9. This is an invalid argument.

p	q	r	$p \to q$	$q \to r$	$r \to p$	$(p \to q) \land (q \to r)$	$[(p \to q) \land (q \to r)] \to (r \to p)$
T	T	T	T	T	T	T	T
T	T	F	T	F	T	F	T
T	F	T	F	T	T	F	T
T	F	F	F	T	T	F	T
F	T	T	T	T	F	T	F
F	T	F	T	F	T	F	T
F	F	T	T	T	F	T	F
F	F	F	T	T	T	T	T

10. This is an invalid argument.

p	q	r	$\sim p$	$\sim r$	$p \to q$	$q \to r$	$\sim p \to \sim r$	$(p \to q) \land (q \to r)$	$[(p \to q) \land (q \to r)] \to (\sim p \to \sim r)$
T	T	T	F	F	T	T	T	T	T
T	T	F	F	T	T	F	T	F	T
T	F	T	F	F	F	T	T	F	T
T	F	F	F	T	F	T	T	F	T
F	T	T	T	F	T	T	F	T	F
F	T	F	T	T	T	F	T	F	T
F	F	T	T	F	T	T	F	T	F
F	F	F	T	T	T	T	T	T	T

11. This is a valid argument.

p	q	r	$p \to q$	$q \land r$	$p \lor r$	$(p \to q) \land (q \land r)$	$[(p \to q) \land (q \land r)] \to (p \lor r)$
T	T	T	T	T	T	T	T
T	T	F	T	F	T	F	T
T	F	T	F	F	T	F	T
T	F	F	F	F	T	F	T
F	T	T	T	T	T	T	T
F	T	F	T	F	F	F	T
F	F	T	T	F	T	F	T
F	F	F	T	F	F	F	T

12. This is an invalid argument.

p	q	r	$\sim p$	$\sim p \land q$	$p \to r$	$r \to p$	$p \leftrightarrow r$	$p \land r$	$(\sim p \land q) \land (p \leftrightarrow r)$	$[(\sim p \land q) \land (p \leftrightarrow r)] \to (p \land r)$
T	T	T	F	F	T	T	T	T	F	T
T	T	F	F	F	F	T	F	F	F	T
T	F	T	F	F	T	T	T	T	F	T
T	F	F	F	F	F	T	F	F	F	T
F	T	T	T	T	T	F	F	F	F	T
F	T	F	T	T	T	T	T	F	T	F
F	F	T	T	F	T	F	F	F	F	T
F	F	F	T	F	T	T	T	F	F	T

13. This is a valid argument.

p	q	r	$\sim p$	$\sim r$	$p \leftrightarrow q$	$q \rightarrow r$	$\sim r \rightarrow \sim p$	$(p \leftrightarrow q) \wedge (q \rightarrow r)$	$\big[(p \leftrightarrow q) \wedge (q \rightarrow r)\big] \rightarrow (\sim r \rightarrow \sim p)$
T	T	T	F	F	T	T	T	T	T
T	T	F	F	T	T	F	F	F	T
T	F	T	F	F	F	T	T	F	T
T	F	F	F	T	F	T	F	F	T
F	T	T	T	F	F	T	T	F	T
F	T	F	T	T	F	F	T	F	T
F	F	T	T	F	T	T	T	T	T
F	F	F	T	T	T	T	T	T	T

14. This is an invalid argument.

p	q	r	$\sim p$	$q \rightarrow \sim p$	$q \wedge r$	$r \rightarrow p$	$(q \rightarrow \sim p) \wedge (q \wedge r)$	$\big[(q \rightarrow \sim p) \wedge (q \wedge r)\big] \rightarrow (r \rightarrow p)$
T	T	T	F	F	T	T	F	T
T	T	F	F	F	F	T	F	T
T	F	T	F	T	F	T	F	T
T	F	F	F	T	F	T	F	T
F	T	T	T	T	T	F	T	F
F	T	F	T	T	F	T	F	T
F	F	T	T	T	F	F	F	T
F	F	F	T	T	F	T	F	T

15. This is a valid argument. p: It is cold. q: Motorcycle started.

$p \rightarrow \sim q$

q
_____

$\therefore \sim p$

p	q	$\sim p$	$\sim q$	$p \rightarrow \sim q$	$(p \rightarrow \sim q) \wedge q$	$\big[(p \rightarrow \sim q) \wedge q \rightarrow \sim p\big]$
T	T	F	F	F	F	T
T	F	F	T	T	F	T
F	T	T	F	T	T	T
F	F	T	T	T	F	T

16. This is a valid argument. p: Metrorail system is in operation. q: There are traffic delays.

$\sim p \rightarrow q$

$\sim q$
_____

$\therefore p$

p	q	$\sim p$	$\sim q$	$\sim p \rightarrow q$	$(\sim p \rightarrow q) \wedge \sim q$	$\big[(\sim p \rightarrow q) \wedge \sim q\big] \rightarrow p$
T	T	F	F	T	F	T
T	F	F	T	T	T	T
F	T	T	F	T	F	T
F	F	T	T	F	F	T

17. This an invalid argument. p: There is a dam. q: There is flooding.

$p \vee q$

q
_____

$\therefore \sim p$

p	q	$\sim p$	$p \vee q$	$(p \vee q) \wedge q$	$\big[(p \vee q) \wedge q\big] \rightarrow \sim p$
T	T	F	T	T	F
T	F	F	T	F	T
F	T	T	T	T	T
F	F	T	F	F	T

18. This is an invalid argument. ***p:*** You eat well. ***q:*** You are healthy.

$p \vee \sim q$

p

$\therefore q$

p	q	$\sim q$	$p \vee \sim q$	$(p \vee \sim q) \wedge p$	$[(p \vee \sim q) \wedge p] \rightarrow q$
T	T	F	T	T	T
T	F	T	T	T	F
F	T	F	F	F	T
F	F	T	T	F	T

19. p: We close the door.
q: There is less noise.

$p \rightarrow q$

q

$\therefore p$

Invalid, by fallacy of the converse.

20. $p \rightarrow q$

q

$\therefore p$

invalid

21. $p \rightarrow q$

$\sim p \rightarrow q$

$\therefore q$

valid

22. $p \rightarrow q$

$\sim p \rightarrow q$

$\therefore q$

valid

23. p: We criminalize drugs.
q: We damage the future of young people.

$p \vee q$

$\sim q$

$\therefore p$

Valid, by disjunctive reasoning.

24. $p \vee q$

$\sim p$

$\therefore q$

valid

25. This is an invalid argument. **p:** All people obey the law. **q:** No jails are needed.

$p \to q$

$\dfrac{\sim p}{}$

$\therefore \sim q$

p	q	$\sim p$	$\sim q$	$p \to q$	$(p \to q) \wedge \sim p$	$[(p \to q) \wedge \sim p] \to \sim q$
T	T	F	F	T	F	T
T	F	F	T	F	F	T
F	T	T	F	T	T	F
F	F	T	T	T	T	T

26. This is a valid argument. **p:** All people obey the law. **q:** No jails are needed.

$p \to q$

$\dfrac{\sim q}{}$

$\therefore \sim p$

p	q	$\sim p$	$\sim q$	$p \to q$	$(p \to q) \wedge \sim q$	$[(p \to q) \wedge \sim q] \to \sim p$
T	T	F	F	T	F	T
T	F	F	T	F	F	T
F	T	T	F	T	F	T
F	F	T	T	T	T	T

27. $p \to q$

$\dfrac{q \to r}{}$

$\therefore p \to r$

valid

28. p: I am at the beach.
q: I swim in the ocean.
r: I feel refreshed.

$p \to q$

$\dfrac{q \to r}{}$

$\therefore p \to r$

Valid, by transitive reasoning.

29. $p \to q$

$\dfrac{q \to r}{}$

$\therefore r \to p$

invalid

30. p: I'm at the beach.
q: I swim in the ocean.
r: I feel refreshed.

$p \to q$

$\dfrac{q \to r}{}$

$\therefore \sim p \to \sim r$

Invalid, by misuse of transitive reasoning.

31. This is a valid argument.   *p*: Tim plays   *q*: Janet plays   *r*: Team wins

$(p \wedge q) \rightarrow r$

$\underline{p \wedge \sim r}$

$\therefore \sim q$

p	*q*	*r*	~*q*	~*r*	$p \wedge q$	$p \wedge \sim r$	$(p \wedge q) \rightarrow r$
T	T	T	F	F	T	F	T
T	T	F	F	T	T	T	F
T	F	T	T	F	F	F	T
T	F	F	T	T	F	T	T
F	T	T	F	F	F	F	T
F	T	F	F	T	F	F	T
F	F	T	T	F	F	F	T
F	F	F	T	T	F	F	T

$[(p \wedge q) \rightarrow r] \wedge (p \wedge \sim r)$	$[[(p \wedge q) \rightarrow r] \wedge (p \wedge \sim r)] \rightarrow \sim q$
F	T
F	T
F	T
T	T
F	T
F	T
F	T
F	T

32. This is a valid argument.

    p: *The Graduate* was shown   *q*: *Midnight Cowboy* was shown   *r*: performance was sold out

$(p \wedge q) \rightarrow r$

$\underline{q \wedge \sim r}$

$\therefore \sim p$

p	*q*	*r*	~*p*	~*r*	$p \wedge q$	$(p \wedge q) \rightarrow r$	$q \wedge \sim r$
T	T	T	F	F	T	T	F
T	T	F	F	T	T	F	T
T	F	T	F	F	F	T	F
T	F	F	F	T	F	T	F
F	T	T	T	F	F	T	F
F	T	F	T	T	F	T	T
F	F	T	T	F	F	T	T
F	F	F	T	T	F	T	F

$[(p \wedge q) \rightarrow r] \wedge (q \wedge \sim r)$	$[[(p \wedge q) \rightarrow r] \wedge (q \wedge \sim r)] \rightarrow \sim p$
F	T
F	T
F	T
F	T
F	T
T	T
F	F
F	T

33. This is a valid argument. *p*: It rains   *q*: It snows   *r*: I read

$(p \vee q) \rightarrow r$

$\sim r$

$\therefore \sim(p \vee q)$

p	q	r	~r	$p \vee q$	$\sim(p \vee q)$	$(p \vee q) \rightarrow r$
T	T	T	F	T	F	T
T	T	F	T	T	F	F
T	F	T	F	T	F	T
T	F	F	T	T	F	F
F	T	T	F	T	F	T
F	T	F	T	T	F	F
F	F	T	F	F	T	T
F	F	F	T	F	T	T

$[(p \vee q) \rightarrow r] \wedge \sim r$	$[[(p \vee q) \rightarrow r] \wedge \sim r] \rightarrow \sim(p \vee q)$
F	T
F	T
F	T
F	T
F	T
F	T
F	T
T	T

34. This is a valid argument. *p*: I am tired.   *q*: I am hungry.   *r*: I can't concentrate.

$(p \vee q) \rightarrow r$

$\sim r$

$\therefore \sim(p \vee q)$

p	q	r	~r	$p \vee q$	$\sim(p \vee q)$	$(p \vee q) \rightarrow r$
T	T	T	F	T	F	T
T	T	F	T	T	F	F
T	F	T	F	T	F	T
T	F	F	T	T	F	F
F	T	T	F	T	F	T
F	T	F	T	T	F	F
F	F	T	F	F	T	T
F	F	F	T	F	T	T

$[(p \vee q) \rightarrow r] \wedge \sim r$	$[[(p \vee q) \rightarrow r] \wedge \sim r] \rightarrow \sim(p \vee q)$
F	T
F	T
F	T
F	T
F	T
F	T
F	T
T	T

35. This is an invalid argument. *p*: It rains *q*: It snows *r*: I read

$(p \vee q) \to r$

r

$\therefore p \vee q$

p	*q*	*r*	$p \vee q$	$(p \vee q) \to r$	$[(p \vee q) \to r] \wedge r$	$[[(p \vee q) \to r] \wedge r] \to (p \vee q)$
T	T	T	T	T	T	T
T	T	F	T	F	F	T
T	F	T	T	T	T	T
T	F	F	T	F	F	T
F	T	T	T	T	T	T
F	T	F	T	F	F	T
F	F	T	F	T	T	F
F	F	F	F	T	F	T

36. This is an invalid argument. *p*: I am tired. *q*: I am hungry. *r*: I can't concentrate.

$(p \vee q) \to r$

r

$\therefore p \vee q$

p	*q*	*r*	$p \vee q$	$(p \vee q) \to r$	$[(p \vee q) \to r] \wedge r$	$[[(p \vee q) \to r] \wedge r] \to (p \vee q)$
T	T	T	T	T	T	T
T	T	F	T	F	F	T
T	F	T	T	T	T	T
T	F	F	T	F	F	T
F	T	T	T	T	T	T
F	T	F	T	F	F	T
F	F	T	F	T	T	F
F	F	F	F	T	F	T

37. This is an invalid argument. *p*: It's hot. *q*: It's humid. *r*: I complain.

$(p \wedge q) \rightarrow r$

$\sim p \vee \sim q$
_____
$\therefore \sim r$

p	q	r	$\sim p$	$\sim q$	$\sim r$	$p \wedge q$	$\sim p \vee \sim q$	$(p \wedge q) \rightarrow r$
T	T	T	F	F	F	T	F	T
T	T	F	F	F	T	T	F	F
T	F	T	F	T	F	F	T	T
T	F	F	F	T	T	F	T	T
F	T	T	T	F	F	F	T	T
F	T	F	T	F	T	F	T	T
F	F	T	T	T	F	F	T	T
F	F	F	T	T	T	F	T	T

$[(p \wedge q) \rightarrow r] \wedge (\sim p \vee \sim q)$	$\left[[(p \wedge q) \rightarrow r] \wedge (\sim p \vee \sim q)\right] \rightarrow \sim r$
F	T
F	T
T	F
T	T
T	F
T	T
T	F
T	T

38. This is an invalid argument.
   p: I watch *Schindler's List*
   q: I watch *Milk*
   r: I am aware of the destructive nature of intolerance.

$(p \wedge q) \rightarrow r$

$\sim p \vee \sim q$
_____
$\therefore \sim r$

p	q	r	$\sim p$	$\sim q$	$\sim r$	$p \wedge q$	$\sim p \vee \sim q$	$(p \wedge q) \rightarrow r$
T	T	T	F	F	F	T	F	T
T	T	F	F	F	T	T	F	F
T	F	T	F	T	F	F	T	T
T	F	F	F	T	T	F	T	T
F	T	T	T	F	F	F	T	T
F	T	F	T	F	T	F	T	T
F	F	T	T	T	F	F	T	T
F	F	F	T	T	T	F	T	T

$[(p \wedge q) \rightarrow r] \wedge (\sim p \vee \sim q)$	$\left[[(p \wedge q) \rightarrow r] \wedge (\sim p \vee \sim q)\right] \rightarrow \sim r$
F	T
F	T
T	F
T	T
T	F
T	T
T	F
T	T

39. $p \rightarrow q$

$\underline{\sim p \rightarrow r}$

$\therefore q \vee r$

valid

40. $p \rightarrow \sim q$

$\underline{r \rightarrow q}$

$\therefore \sim p \wedge \sim r$

invalid

41. $p \rightarrow q$

$q \rightarrow \sim r$

$\underline{r}$

$\therefore \sim p$

valid

42. $p \rightarrow q$

$q \rightarrow \sim r$

$\underline{\sim p}$

$\therefore r$

invalid

43. p: A person is a chemist.

q: A person has a college degree.

$p \rightarrow q$

$\underline{\sim q}$

$\therefore \sim p$

My best friend is not a chemist. By contrapositive reasoning.

44. p: Expressway is not in operation.

q: Traffic is bad.

$p \rightarrow q$

$\underline{p}$

$\therefore q$

Traffic is bad. By direct reasoning. i.e. On June 2nd, the Eastside Expressway looked like a parking lot.

45. p: Writers improve.

q: "My Mother the Car" dropped from primetime.

$p \vee q$

$\underline{\sim p}$

$\therefore q$

"My Mother the Car" was dropped from primetime. By disjunctive reasoning.

46. *p*: I exercise.
   q: I do not feel energized.

   $p \lor q$

   $\underline{\sim p}$

   $\therefore q$

   I do not feel energized. By disjunctive reasoning.

47. *p*: All electricity off.
   q: No lights work.

   $p \rightarrow q$

   $\underline{\sim q}$

   $\therefore \sim p$

   Some electricity is not off. By contrapositive reasoning.

48. *p*: All houses meet the hurricane code.
   q: None are destroyed by category 4 hurricane.
   $p \rightarrow q$

   $\underline{\sim q}$

   $\therefore \sim p$

   Some houses did not meet the hurricane code. By contrapositive reasoning.

49. *p*: I vacation in Paris.
   q: I eat French pastries.
   r: I gain weight.

   $p \rightarrow q$

   $\underline{q \rightarrow r}$

   $\therefore p \rightarrow r$

   If I vacation in Paris I gain weight. By transitive reasoning.

50. *p*: I am a full-time student.
   q: I cannot work.
   r: I cannot afford a rental apartment costing more than $500 per month.

   $p \rightarrow q$

   $\underline{q \rightarrow r}$

   $\therefore p \rightarrow r$

   If I am a full-time student, I cannot afford a rental apartment costing more than $500 per month. By transitive reasoning.

51. This is an invalid argument.

$p \rightarrow q$

$\underline{\sim p}$

$\therefore \sim q$

p	q	$\sim p$	$\sim q$	$p \rightarrow q$	$(p \rightarrow q) \land \sim p$	$[(p \rightarrow q) \land \sim p] \rightarrow \sim q$
T	T	F	F	T	F	T
T	F	F	T	F	F	T
F	T	T	F	T	T	F
F	F	T	T	T	T	T

52. $p \rightarrow q$

$\dfrac{q}{\therefore p}$

Invalid, by fallacy of the converse.

53. $\dfrac{\begin{array}{c} p \vee q \\ \sim p \end{array}}{\therefore q}$

valid

54. $p \vee q$

$\dfrac{\sim q}{\therefore p}$

Valid, by disjunctive reasoning.

55. $p \rightarrow q$

$\dfrac{q}{\therefore p}$

Invalid.

56. This is an invalid argument.

$p \rightarrow q$

$\sim p$

$\therefore \sim q$

p	q	$\sim p$	$\sim q$	$p \rightarrow q$	$(p \rightarrow q) \wedge \sim p$	$[(p \rightarrow q) \wedge \sim p] \rightarrow \sim q$
T	T	F	F	T	F	T
T	F	F	T	F	F	T
F	T	T	F	T	T	F
F	F	T	T	T	T	T

57. This is a valid argument.

$p \rightarrow q$

$\sim q$

$\therefore \sim p$

p	q	$\sim p$	$\sim q$	$p \rightarrow q$	$(p \rightarrow q) \wedge \sim q$	$[(p \rightarrow q) \wedge \sim q] \rightarrow \sim p$
T	T	F	F	T	F	T
T	F	F	T	F	F	T
F	T	T	F	T	F	T
F	F	T	T	T	T	T

58. p: An argument is valid.; q: An argument produces truth.; r: An argument is sound.;

$\sim p \rightarrow \sim q$

$(p \wedge \sim r) \rightarrow \sim q$

$\dfrac{\sim p \vee (p \wedge \sim r)}{\therefore \sim q}$

valid but not sound

59. $p \rightarrow q$

$\dfrac{q \rightarrow r}{\therefore p \rightarrow r}$

valid

60. $p \rightarrow\ \sim p$

$\dfrac{p}{\therefore \sim p}$

valid

61. p: Poverty causes crime.
q: Crime sweeps American cities during the Great Depression.

$p \rightarrow q$

$\dfrac{\sim q}{\therefore \sim p}$

Valid. By contrapositive reasoning.

62. p: Segregation statutes damage personality.; q: Segregation statutes are unjust;

$p \rightarrow q$

$\dfrac{p}{\therefore q}$

valid but not sound

63. h

64. b

65. i

66. f

67. c

68. l

69. a

70. g

71. j

72. e

73. d

74. k

82. does not make sense; Explanations will vary. Sample explanation: If one of the premises is false, then the validity of the conclusion can not be determined.

83. does not make sense; Explanations will vary. Sample explanation: Conclusions must be based on logic, not based on personal feelings.

84. makes sense

85. does not make sense; Explanations will vary. Sample explanation: The argument is valid.

87. *p*: You only spoke when spoken to, and
I only speak when spoken to.
q: Nobody would ever say anything.

$p \rightarrow q$

$\sim q$

$\therefore \sim p$

People sometimes speak without being spoken to.

p	*q*	*~p*	*~q*	$p \rightarrow q$	$(p \rightarrow q) \wedge \sim q$	$[(p \rightarrow q) \wedge \sim q] \rightarrow \sim p$
T	T	F	F	T	F	T
T	F	F	T	F	F	T
F	T	T	F	T	F	T
F	F	T	T	T	T	T

88. This is a valid argument.
p: Secondary cigarette smoke is a health threat.
q: It's wrong to smoke in public.
r: The ALA says that secondary cigarette smoke is a health threat.

$p \rightarrow q$

$\sim p \rightarrow \sim r$

r

$\therefore q$

p	*q*	*r*	*~p*	*~r*	$p \rightarrow q$	$\sim p \rightarrow \sim r$	$[(p \rightarrow q) \wedge (\sim p \rightarrow \sim r)] \wedge r$	$[[(p \rightarrow q) \wedge (\sim p \rightarrow \sim r)] \wedge r] \rightarrow q$
T	T	T	F	F	T	T	T	T
T	T	F	F	T	T	T	F	T
T	F	T	F	F	F	T	F	T
T	F	F	F	T	F	T	F	T
F	T	T	T	F	T	F	F	T
F	T	F	T	T	T	T	F	T
F	F	T	T	F	T	F	F	T
F	F	F	T	T	T	T	F	T

89. The doctor either destroys the base on which the placebo rests or jeopardizes a relationship built on trust.

Check Points 3.8

1. The argument is valid.

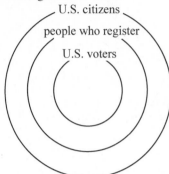

2. The argument is invalid.

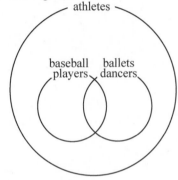

3. The argument is valid.

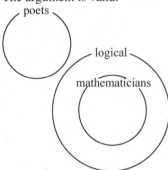

4. The argument is invalid.

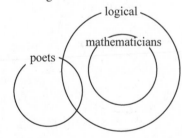

5. The argument is invalid.

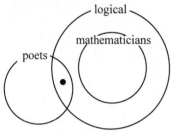

6. The argument is invalid.
The ● is Euclid.

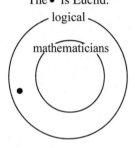

Exercise Set 3.8

1. Valid.

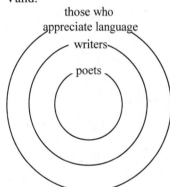

2. Valid.

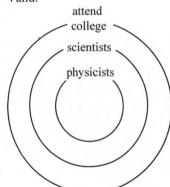

3. Invalid.

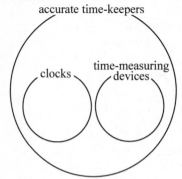

4. Invalid.

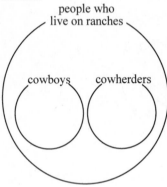

5. Valid.

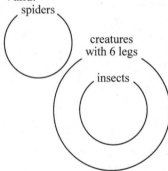

6. Valid.

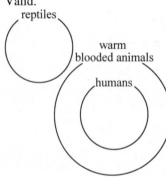

7. Invalid.

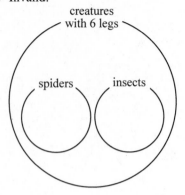

8. Invalid.

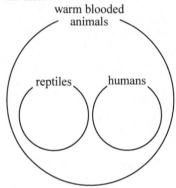

9. Invalid.

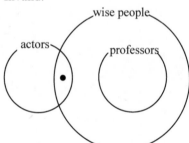

10. Invalid.

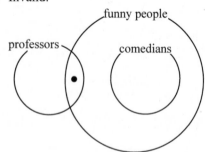

11. Valid.

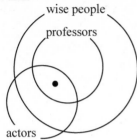

12. Valid.

13. Valid. The • is Savion Glover.

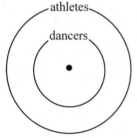

14. Valid. The • is Kim Basinger.

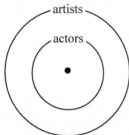

15. Invalid. The • is Savion Glover.

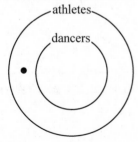

16. Invalid. The • is Kim Basinger.

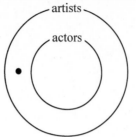

17. Invalid.

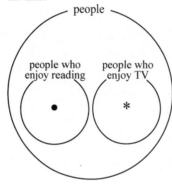

18. Valid.

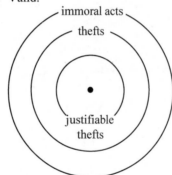

19. Valid.

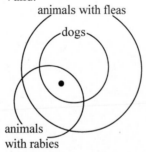

~p **20.**   Invalid.

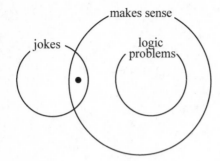

21. Valid.

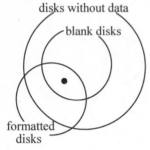

22. Invalid.

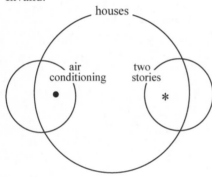

23. Valid. The • is 8.

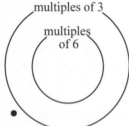

24. Invalid. The • is 8.

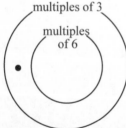

25. Invalid.

26. Valid.

27. Invalid.

28. Invalid.

29. Valid.

30. Valid.

31. Invalid.

32. Valid.

33. Invalid.

34. Invalid.

35. Invalid.

36. Invalid.

37. Valid.

38. Valid.

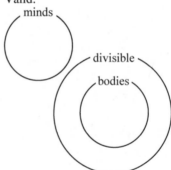

39. Valid.

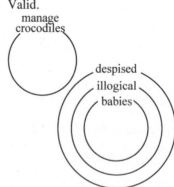

42. does not make sense; Explanations will vary.
Sample explanation: To be valid, it must always be
true.

43. makes sense

44. makes sense

45. does not make sense; Explanations will vary. Sample explanation: Euler diagrams can be used for this purpose.

47. b is true.

48. All opera singers take voice lessons.

49. Some teachers are amusing people.

Chapter 3 Review Exercises

1. $(p \wedge q) \to r$; If the temperature is below 32° and we have finished studying, then we go to the movies.

2. $\sim r \to (\sim p \vee \sim q)$; If we do not go to the movies, then the temperature is not below 32° or we have not finished studying.

3. The temperature is below 32°, and if we finished studying, we go to the movies.

4. We will go to the movies if and only if the temperature is below 32° and we have finished studying.

5. It is not true that both the temperature is below 32° and we have finished studying.

6. We will not go to the movies if and only if the temperature is not below 32° or we have not finished studying.

7. $(p \wedge q) \vee r$

8. $(p \vee \sim q) \to r$

9.

10. $r \leftrightarrow (p \wedge \sim q)$

11. $p \to r$

12. $q \to \sim r$

13. Some houses are not made with wood.

14. Some students major in business.

15. No crimes are motivated by passion.

16. All Democrats are registered voters.

17. Some new taxes will not be used for education.

18. neither

p	q	$\sim p$	$\sim p \wedge q$	$p \vee (\sim p \wedge q)$
T	T	F	F	T
T	F	F	F	T
F	T	T	T	T
F	F	T	F	F

19. neither

p	q	$\sim p$	$\sim q$	$\sim p \vee \sim q$
T	T	F	F	F
T	F	F	T	T
F	T	T	F	T
F	F	T	T	T

20. neither

p	q	$\sim p$	$\sim p \vee q$	$p \to (\sim p \vee q)$
T	T	F	T	T
T	F	F	F	F
F	T	T	T	T
F	F	T	T	T

21. neither

p	q	$\sim q$	$p \leftrightarrow \sim q$
T	T	F	F
T	F	T	T
F	T	F	T
F	F	T	F

22. tautology

p	q	$\sim p$	$\sim q$	$p \vee q$	$\sim(p \vee q)$	$\sim p \wedge \sim q$	$\sim(p \vee q) \to (\sim p \wedge \sim q)$
T	T	F	F	T	F	F	T
T	F	F	T	T	F	F	T
F	T	T	F	T	F	F	T
F	F	T	T	F	T	T	T

23. neither

p	q	r	$\sim r$	$p \vee q$	$(p \vee q) \to \sim r$
T	T	T	F	T	F
T	T	F	T	T	T
T	F	T	F	T	F
T	F	F	T	T	T
F	T	T	F	T	F
F	T	F	T	T	T
F	F	T	F	F	T
F	F	F	T	F	T

24. neither

p	q	r	$p \wedge q$	$p \wedge r$	$(p \wedge q) \leftrightarrow (p \wedge r)$
T	T	T	T	T	T
T	T	F	T	F	F
T	F	T	F	T	F
T	F	F	F	F	T
F	T	T	F	F	T
F	T	F	F	F	T
F	F	T	F	F	T
F	F	F	F	F	T

25. neither

p	q	r	$r \rightarrow p$	$q \vee (r \rightarrow p)$	$p \wedge [q \vee (r \rightarrow p)]$
T	T	T	T	T	T
T	T	F	T	T	T
T	F	T	T	T	T
T	F	F	T	T	T
F	T	T	F	T	F
F	T	F	T	T	F
F	F	T	F	F	F
F	F	F	T	T	F

26. a. p: I'm in class.; q: I'm studying.; $(p \vee q) \wedge \sim p$

b. $(p \vee q) \wedge \sim p$

p	q	$\sim p$	$p \vee q$	$(p \vee q) \wedge \sim p$
T	T	F	T	F
T	F	F	T	F
F	T	T	T	T
F	F	T	F	F

c. The statement is true when p is false and q is true.

27. a. p: You spit from a truck.; q: It's legal.; r: You spit from a car.; $(p \rightarrow q) \wedge (r \rightarrow \sim q)$

b.

p	q	r	$\sim q$	$p \rightarrow q$	$r \rightarrow \sim q$	$(p \rightarrow q) \wedge (r \rightarrow \sim q)$
T	T	T	F	T	F	F
T	T	F	F	T	T	T
T	F	T	T	F	T	F
T	F	F	T	F	T	F
F	T	T	F	T	F	F
F	T	F	F	T	T	T
F	F	T	T	T	T	T
F	F	F	T	T	T	T

c. The statement is true when p and q are both false.

28. $\sim (q \leftrightarrow r)$

$\sim (F \leftrightarrow F)$

$\sim T$

F

29. $(p \wedge q) \rightarrow (p \vee r)$

$(T \wedge F) \rightarrow (T \vee F)$

$F \rightarrow T$

T

30. $(\sim q \to p) \vee (r \wedge \sim p)$

$\quad (\sim F \to T) \vee (F \wedge \sim T)$

$\quad\quad (T \to T) \vee (F \wedge F)$

$\quad\quad\quad\quad T \vee F$

$\quad\quad\quad\quad\quad T$

31. $\sim \left[(\sim p \vee r) \to (q \wedge r) \right]$

$\quad \sim \left[(\sim T \vee F) \to (F \wedge F) \right]$

$\quad\quad \sim \left[(F \vee F) \to F \right]$

$\quad\quad\quad \sim \left[F \to F \right]$

$\quad\quad\quad\quad \sim T$

$\quad\quad\quad\quad\quad F$

32. p: 29% consider religion the most taboo topic.; q: 14% consider politics the most taboo topic.
$p \wedge \sim q$ is false.

33. p: A greater percentage of people consider money a more taboo topic than personal life.; q: 16% consider money the most taboo topic.; r: 14% consider personal life the most taboo topic.
$p \to (q \wedge r)$ is true.

34. p: 14% consider money the most taboo topic.; q: 14% consider politics the most taboo topic.; r: The greatest percentage consider religion the most taboo topic.
$(p \leftrightarrow q) \vee \sim r$ is true.

35. a. $\sim p \vee q \equiv p \to q$

p	q	$\sim p$	$\sim p \vee q$	$p \to q$
T	T	F	T	T
T	F	F	F	F
F	T	T	T	T
F	F	T	T	T

    b. If the triangle is isosceles, then it has two equal sides.

36. c

37. not equivalent

p	q	$\sim(p \leftrightarrow q)$	$\sim p \vee \sim q$
T	T	F	F
T	F	T	T
F	T	T	T
F	F	F	T

38. equivalent

p	q	r	$\sim p \wedge (q \vee r)$	$(\sim p \wedge q) \vee (\sim p \wedge r)$
T	T	T	F	F
T	T	F	F	F
T	F	T	F	F
T	F	F	F	F
F	T	T	T	T
F	T	F	T	T
F	F	T	T	T
F	F	F	F	F

39. Converse: If I am in the South, then I am in Atlanta.
Inverse: If I am not in Atlanta, then I am not in the South.
Contrapositive: If I am not in the South, then I am not in Atlanta.

40. Converse: If today is not a holiday, then I am in class.
Inverse: If I am not in class, then today is a holiday.
Contrapositive: If today is a holiday, then I'm not in class.

41. Converse: If I pass all courses, then I worked hard.
Inverse: If I don't work hard, then I don't pass some courses.
Contrapositive: If I do not pass some course, then I did not work hard.

42. Converse: $\sim q \to \sim p$; Inverse: $p \to q$; Contrapositive: $q \to p$

43. An argument is sound and it is not valid.

44. I do not work hard and I succeed.

45. $\sim r \wedge \sim p$

46. Chicago is not a city or Maine is not a city.

47. Ernest Hemingway was neither a musician nor an actor.

48. p: the number is positive.
q: the number is negative.
r: the number is zero.
The statement can be represented symbolically as $(\sim p \wedge \sim q) \to r$.
Next write the contrapositive and simplify.
$$\sim (r) \to \sim (\sim p \wedge \sim q)$$
$$\sim r \to (p \vee q)$$
Thus, $(\sim p \wedge \sim q) \to r \equiv \sim r \to (p \vee q)$.
The original statement is equivalent to "If a number is not zero, then the number is positive or negative."

49. I do not work hard and I succeed.

50. She is using her car or she is not taking a bus.

51. Write the negation of $\sim p \vee q$ and simplify.

$\sim(\sim p \vee q)$

$\sim(\sim p) \wedge \sim q$

$p \wedge \sim q$

52. **a** and **c** are equivalent.

		a	b	c
p	q	$p \rightarrow q$	$\sim p \rightarrow \sim q$	$\sim p \vee q$
T	T	T	T	T
T	F	F	T	F
F	T	T	F	T
F	F	T	T	T

53. **a** and **b** are equivalent.

		a	b	c
p	q	$\sim p \rightarrow q$	$\sim q \rightarrow p$	$\sim p \wedge \sim q$
T	T	T	T	F
T	F	T	T	F
F	T	T	T	F
F	F	F	F	T

54. **a** and **c** are equivalent.

		a	b	c
p	q	$p \vee \sim q$	$\sim q \rightarrow p$	$\sim(\sim p \wedge q)$
T	T	T	T	T
T	F	T	T	T
F	T	F	T	F
F	F	T	F	T

55. none

56. The argument is invalid.

p	q	$\sim q$	$p \rightarrow q$	$(p \rightarrow q) \wedge \sim q$	$[(p \rightarrow q) \wedge \sim q] \rightarrow p$
T	T	F	T	F	T
T	F	T	F	F	T
F	T	F	T	F	T
F	F	T	T	T	F

57. The argument is valid.

p	q	r	$p \wedge q$	$q \rightarrow r$	$p \rightarrow r$	$(p \wedge q) \wedge (q \rightarrow r)$	$[(p \wedge q) \wedge (q \rightarrow r)] \rightarrow (p \rightarrow r)$
T	T	T	T	T	T	T	T
T	T	F	T	F	F	F	T
T	F	T	F	T	T	F	T
T	F	F	F	T	F	F	T
F	T	T	F	T	T	F	T
F	T	F	F	F	T	F	T
F	F	T	F	T	T	F	T
F	F	F	F	T	T	F	T

58. The argument is invalid. **p:** Tony plays. **q:** Team wins.

$p \rightarrow q$

q
_____

$\therefore p$

p	q	$p \rightarrow q$	$(p \rightarrow q) \wedge q$	$[(p \rightarrow q) \wedge q] \rightarrow p$
T	T	T	T	T
T	F	F	F	T
F	T	T	T	F
F	F	T	F	T

59. The argument is invalid. **p:** Plant is fertilized. **q:** Plant turns yellow.

$p \vee q$

q
_____

$\therefore \sim p$

p	q	$\sim p$	$p \vee q$	$(p \vee q) \wedge q$	$[(p \vee q) \wedge q] \rightarrow \sim p$
T	T	F	T	T	F
T	F	F	T	F	T
F	T	T	T	T	T
F	F	T	F	F	T

60. The argument is valid. **p:** A majority of legislators vote for a bill. **q:** Bill does not become law.

$p \vee q$

$\sim p$
_____

$\therefore q$

p	q	$\sim p$	$p \vee q$	$(p \vee q) \wedge \sim p$	$[(p \vee q) \wedge \sim p] \rightarrow q$
T	T	F	T	F	T
T	F	F	T	F	T
F	T	T	T	T	T
F	F	T	F	F	T

61. The argument is valid. **p:** Good baseball player. **q:** Good hand–eye coordination.

$p \rightarrow q$

$\sim q$
_____

$\therefore \sim p$

p	q	$\sim p$	$\sim q$	$p \rightarrow q$	$(p \rightarrow q) \wedge \sim q$	$[(p \rightarrow q) \wedge \sim q] \rightarrow \sim p$
T	T	F	F	T	F	T
T	F	F	T	F	F	T
F	T	T	F	T	F	T
F	F	T	T	T	T	T

62. $p \rightarrow \sim q$

     $\sim p \rightarrow q$
_____

    $\therefore p \leftrightarrow \sim q$

    valid

63. $p \rightarrow \sim q$

     $r \rightarrow q$
_____

    $\therefore \sim r \rightarrow p$

    invalid

64. Invalid.

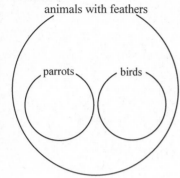

65. Valid.

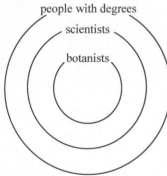

66. Valid.

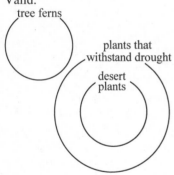

67. Invalid.

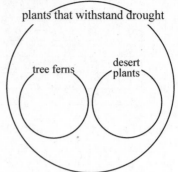

68. Invalid.

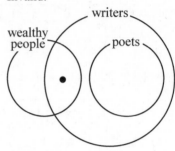

69. Valid.

Chapter 3 Test

1. If I'm registered and I'm a citizen, then I vote.

2. I don't vote if and only if I'm not registered or I'm not a citizen.

3. I'm neither registered nor a citizen.

4. $(p \wedge q) \vee \sim r$

5. $(\sim p \vee \sim q) \rightarrow \sim r$

6. $r \rightarrow q$

7. Some numbers are not divisible by 5.

8. No people wear glasses.

9. $p \wedge (\sim p \vee q)$

p	q	$\sim p$	$\sim p \vee q$	$p \wedge (\sim p \vee q)$
T	T	F	T	T
T	F	F	F	F
F	T	T	T	F
F	F	T	T	F

10. $\sim(p \wedge q) \leftrightarrow (\sim p \vee \sim q)$

p	q	$\sim p$	$\sim q$	$p \wedge q$	$\sim(p \wedge q)$	$(\sim p \vee \sim q)$	$\sim(p \wedge q) \leftrightarrow (\sim p \vee \sim q)$
T	T	F	F	T	F	F	T
T	F	F	T	F	T	T	T
F	T	T	F	F	T	T	T
F	F	T	T	F	T	T	T

11. $p \leftrightarrow (q \vee r)$

p	q	r	$q \vee r$	$p \leftrightarrow (q \vee r)$
T	T	T	T	T
T	T	F	T	T
T	F	T	T	T
T	F	F	F	F
F	T	T	T	F
F	T	F	T	F
F	F	T	T	F
F	F	F	F	T

12. p: You break the law.; q: You change the law.; $(p \wedge q) \rightarrow \sim p$

p	q	$\sim p$	$p \wedge q$	$(p \wedge q) \rightarrow \sim p$
T	T	F	T	F
T	F	F	F	T
F	T	T	F	T
F	F	T	F	T

Answers will vary; an example is: The statement is true when p is false.

13. $\sim(q \to r)$

$\sim(T \to F)$

$\sim F$

T

14. $(p \vee r) \leftrightarrow (\sim r \wedge p)$

$(F \vee F) \leftrightarrow (\sim F \wedge F)$

$F \leftrightarrow (T \wedge F)$

$F \leftrightarrow F$

T

15. **a.** *p*: There was no increase in the percentage of Americans who supported the death penalty.
q: There was an increase in the percentage of Americans who opposed the death penalty.
r: There was an increase in the percentage of Americans who were not sure about the death penalty.
$p \vee (q \wedge r)$

b. $p \vee (q \wedge r)$

$T \vee (T \wedge T)$

$T \vee T$

T

The statement is true.

16. b

17. If it snows, then it is not August.

18. Converse: If I cannot concentrate, then the radio is playing.
Inverse: If the radio is not playing, then I can concentrate.

19. It is cold and we use the pool.

20. The test is not today and the party is not tonight.

21. The banana is not green or it is ready to eat.

22. a and b are equivalent.

		a	b	c
p	*q*	$\sim p \to q$	$p \vee q$	$p \to \sim q$
T	T	T	T	F
T	F	T	T	T
F	T	T	T	T
F	F	F	F	T

23. a and c are equivalent.

		a	b	c
p	*q*	$\sim(p \vee q)$	$\sim p \to \sim q$	$\sim p \wedge \sim q$
T	T	F	T	F
T	F	F	T	F
F	T	F	F	F
F	F	T	T	T

24. The argument is invalid. **p**: Parrot talks. **q**: It is intelligent.

$p \to q$

$\underline{q}$

$\therefore p$

25. The argument is valid. **p**: I am sick. **q**: I am tired.

$p \vee q$

$\underline{\sim q}$

$\therefore p$

26. The argument is invalid. **p**: I am going. **q**: You are going.

$p \leftrightarrow \sim q$

$\underline{q}$

$\therefore p$

27. Invalid.

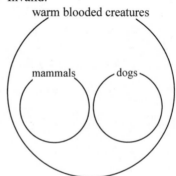

28. Valid.

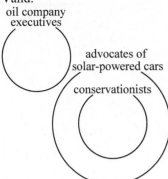
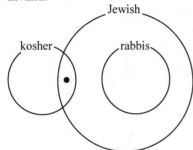

29. Invalid.

Chapter 4
Number Representation and Calculation

Check Points 4.1

1. **a.** $7^2 = 7 \times 7 = 49$

   b. $5^3 = 5 \times 5 \times 5 = 125$

   c. $1^4 = 1 \times 1 \times 1 \times 1 = 1$

   d. $10^5 = 10 \times 10 \times 10 \times 10 \times 10 = 100,000$

   e. $10^6 = 10 \times 10 \times 10 \times 10 \times 10 \times 10 = 1,000,000$

   f. $18^1 = 18$

2. **a.** $4026 = (4 \times 10^3) + (0 \times 10^2) + (2 \times 10^1) + (6 \times 1) = (4 \times 1000) + (0 \times 100) + (2 \times 10) + (6 \times 1)$

   b. $24,232 = (2 \times 10^4) + (4 \times 10^3) + (2 \times 10^2) + (3 \times 10^1) + (2 \times 1)$
   $$= (2 \times 10,000) + (4 \times 1000) + (2 \times 100) + (3 \times 10) + (2 \times 1)$$

3. **a.** $6000 + 70 + 3 = 6073$ **b.** $80,000 + 900 = 80,900$

4. **a.** First, represent the numeral in each place value as a Hindu-Arabic numeral. Then multiply them by their place values and find the sum.

   $$\text{vvv} \qquad \text{<<} \qquad \text{<<< v}$$
   $$\downarrow \qquad\quad \downarrow \qquad\quad \downarrow$$

   $$(3 \times 60^2) + (20 \times 60) + (31 \times 1)$$
   $$= (3 \times 3600) + (20 \times 60) + (31 \times 1)$$
   $$= 10,800 + 1200 + 31$$
   $$= 12,031$$

   b. First, represent the numeral in each place value as a Hindu-Arabic numeral. Then multiply them by their place values and find the sum.

   $$\text{vv} \qquad \text{<} \qquad \text{< vv} \qquad \text{v}$$
   $$\downarrow \qquad\quad \downarrow \qquad\quad \downarrow \qquad\quad \downarrow$$

   $$(2 \times 60^3) + (10 \times 60^2) + (12 \times 60) + (1 \times 1)$$
   $$= (2 \times 216,000) + (10 \times 3600) + (12 \times 60) + (1 \times 1)$$
   $$= 432,000 + 36,000 + 720 + 1$$
   $$= 468,721$$

5. a. First, represent the numeral in each place value as a Hindu-Arabic numeral. Then multiply them by their place values and find the sum.

$$
\begin{aligned}
11 \; &\times \; 18 \times 20^2 = \; 11 \; \times \; 7200 = \; 79,200 \\
3 \; &\times \; 18 \times 20^1 = \; 3 \; \times \; 360 = \; 1080 \\
0 \; &\times \; \qquad 20 = \; 0 \; \times \; 20 = \; 0 \\
13 \; &\times \; \qquad 1 = \; 13 \; \times \; 1 = \; \underline{\quad 13} \\
& \qquad\qquad\qquad\qquad\qquad\qquad 80,293
\end{aligned}
$$

b. First, represent the numeral in each place value as a Hindu-Arabic numeral. Then multiply them by their place values and find the sum.

$$
\begin{aligned}
2 \; &\times \; 18 \times 20^3 = \; 2 \; \times \; 144,000 = \; 288,000 \\
0 \; &\times \; 18 \times 20^2 = \; 0 \; \times \; 7200 = \; 0 \\
6 \; &\times \; 18 \times 20^1 = \; 6 \; \times \; 360 = \; 2160 \\
16 \; &\times \; \qquad 20 = \; 16 \; \times \; 20 = \; 320 \\
10 \; &\times \; \qquad 1 = \; 10 \; \times \; 1 = \; \underline{\quad 10} \\
& \qquad\qquad\qquad\qquad\qquad\qquad 290,490
\end{aligned}
$$

Exercise Set 4.1

1. $5^2 = 5 \times 5 = 25$

2. $6^2 = 6 \times 6 = 36$

3. $2^3 = 2 \times 2 \times 2 = 8$

4. $4^3 = 4 \times 4 \times 4 = 64$

5. $3^4 = 3 \times 3 \times 3 \times 3 = 81$

6. $2^4 = 2 \times 2 \times 2 \times 2 = 16$

7. $10^5 = 10 \times 10 \times 10 \times 10 \times 10 = 100,000$

8. $10^6 = 10 \times 10 \times 10 \times 10 \times 10 \times 10 = 1,000,000$

9. $36 = (3 \times 10^1) + (6 \times 1) = (3 \times 10) + (6 \times 1)$

10. $65 = (6 \times 10^1) + (5 \times 1) = (6 \times 10) + (5 \times 1)$

11. $249 = (2 \times 10^2) + (4 \times 10^1) + (9 \times 1) = (2 \times 100) + (4 \times 10) + (9 \times 1)$

12. $698 = (6 \times 10^2) + (9 \times 10^1) + (8 \times 1) = (6 \times 100) + (9 \times 10) + (8 \times 1)$

13. $703 = (7 \times 10^2) + (0 \times 10^1) + (3 \times 1) = (7 \times 100) + (0 \times 10) + (3 \times 1)$

14. $902 = (9 \times 10^2) + (0 \times 10^1) + (2 \times 1) = (9 \times 100) + (0 \times 10) + (2 \times 1)$

15. $4856 = (4 \times 10^3) + (8 \times 10^2) + (5 \times 10^1) + (6 \times 1) = (4 \times 1000) + (8 \times 100) + (5 \times 10) + (6 \times 1)$

16. $5749 = (5 \times 10^3) + (7 \times 10^2) + (4 \times 10^1) + (9 \times 1) = (5 \times 1000) + (7 \times 100) + (4 \times 10) + (9 \times 1)$

17. $3070 = (3 \times 10^3) + (0 \times 10^2) + (7 \times 10^1) + (0 \times 1) = (3 \times 1000) + (0 \times 100) + (7 \times 10) + (0 \times 1)$

18. $9007 = (9 \times 10^3) + (0 \times 10^2) + (0 \times 10^1) + (7 \times 1) = (9 \times 1000) + (0 \times 100) + (0 \times 10) + (7 \times 1)$

19. $34,569 = (3 \times 10^4) + (4 \times 10^3) + (5 \times 10^2) + (6 \times 10^1) + (9 \times 1)$
$= (3 \times 10,000) + (4 \times 1000) + (5 \times 100) + (6 \times 10) + (9 \times 1)$

20. $67,943 = (6 \times 10^4) + (7 \times 10^3) + (9 \times 10^2) + (4 \times 10^1) + (3 \times 1)$
$= (6 \times 10,000) + (7 \times 1000) + (9 \times 100) + (4 \times 10) + (3 \times 1)$

21. $230,007,004 = (2 \times 10^8) + (3 \times 10^7) + (0 \times 10^6) + (0 \times 10^5) + (0 \times 10^4) + (7 \times 10^3) + (0 \times 10^2) + (0 \times 10^1) + (4 \times 1)$
$= (2 \times 100,000,000) + (3 \times 10,000,000) + (0 \times 1,000,000) + (0 \times 100,000)$
$+ (0 \times 10,000) + (7 \times 1000) + (0 \times 100) + (0 \times 10) + (4 \times 1)$

22. $909,006,070$
$= (9 \times 10^8) + (0 \times 10^7) + (9 \times 10^6) + (0 \times 10^5) + (0 \times 10^4) + (6 \times 10^3) + (0 \times 10^2) + (7 \times 10^1) + (0 \times 1)$
$= (9 \times 100,000,000) + (0 \times 10,000,000) + (9 \times 1,000,000) + (0 \times 100,000) + (0 \times 10,000) + (6 \times 1000)$
$+ (0 \times 100) + (7 \times 10) + (0 \times 1)$

23. $70 + 3 = 73$

24. $90 + 4 = 94$

25. $300 + 80 + 5 = 385$

26. $700 + 50 + 3 = 753$

27. $500,000 + 20,000 + 8000 + 700 + 40 + 3 = 528,743$

28. $7,000,000 + 400,000 + 20,000 + 3000 + 100 + 90 + 6 = 7,423,196$

29. $7000 + 2 = 7002$

30. $90,000 + 40 + 5 = 90,045$

31. $600,000,000 + 2000 + 7 = 600,002,007$

32. $300,000,000 + 50,000 + 4 = 300,050,004$

33. $(10 + 10 + 1 + 1 + 1) \times 1 = 23 \times 1 = 23$

34. $(10 + 10 + 10 + 1 + 1) \times 1 = 32 \times 1 = 32$

35. $(10 + 10 + 1) \times 60^1 + (1 + 1) \times 1 = (21 \times 60) + 2 = 1260 + 2 = 1262$

36. $(10 + 10) \times 60^1 + (10 + 1 + 1) \times 1 = (20 \times 60) + 12 = 1200 + 12 = 1212$

37. $(10+10+10)\times 60^1 + (10+10+10+1+1+1)\times 1 = (30\times 60) + 33 = 1800+33 = 1833$

38. $(10+10+1)\times 60^1 + (10+10+1+1+1+1)\times 1 = (21\times 60) + 24 = 1260+24 = 1284$

39. $(1+1+1)\times 60^2 + (10+1+1)\times 60^1 + (1+1+1)\times 1 = (3\times 3600) + (12\times 60) + 3 = 10,800 + 720 + 3 = 11,523$

40. $(1+1)\times 60^2 + (10+1)\times 60^1 + (10+10+1+1)\times 1 = (2\times 3600) + (11\times 60) + (22\times 1)$
$$= 7200 + 660 + 22$$
$$= 7882$$

41. $(10+10+1)\times 60^2 + (1+1+1+1)\times 60^1 + (10+1)\times 1$
$$= (21\times 60^2) + (4\times 60^1) + (11\times 1)$$
$$= (21\times 3600) + (4\times 60) + 11$$
$$= 75,600 + 240 + 11$$
$$= 75,851$$

42. $(10+1+1)\times 60^2 + (10+1+1+1+1)\times 60^1 + (10+10)\times 1$
$$= (12\times 60^2) + (14\times 60^1) + (20\times 1)$$
$$= (12\times 3600) + (14\times 60) + 20$$
$$= 43,200 + 840 + 20$$
$$= 44,060$$

43. $(10+1)\times 60^3 + (10+1)\times 60^2 + (10+1)\times 60^1 + (10+1)\times 1$
$$= (11\times 60^3) + (11\times 60^2) + (11\times 60^1) + (11\times 1)$$
$$= (11\times 216,000) + (11\times 3600) + (11\times 60) + 11$$
$$= 2,376,000 + 39,600 + 660 + 11$$
$$= 2,416,271$$

44. $(10+10)\times 60^3 + (10+10)\times 60^2 + (10+1+1)\times 60^1 + (10+1+1)\times 1$
$$= (20\times 216,000) + (20\times 3600) + (12\times 60) + (12\times 1)$$
$$= 4,320,000 + 72,000 + 720 + 12$$
$$= 4,392,732$$

45. $(1+1+1)\times 60^3 + (1+1)\times 60^2 + (1)\times 60^1 + (1)\times 1$
$$= (3\times 216,000) + (2\times 3600) + (1\times 60) + (1\times 1)$$
$$= 648,000 + 7200 + 60 + 1$$
$$= 655,261$$

46. $(1)\times 60^3 + (1)\times 60^2 + (1+1)\times 60^1 + (1+1+1)\times 1$
$$= (1\times 216,000) + (1\times 3600) + (2\times 60) + (3\times 1)$$
$$= 216,000 + 3600 + 120 + 3$$
$$= 219,723$$

47. $14\times 1 = 14$

48. $13\times 1 = 13$

49.

$$
\begin{array}{r}
19 \times 18 \times 20^1 = 19 \times 360 = 6840 \\
0 \times 20 = 0 \times 20 = 0 \\
6 \times 1 = 6 \times 1 = \underline{6} \\
6846
\end{array}
$$

50.

$$
\begin{array}{r}
19 \times 18 \times 20^1 = 19 \times 360 = 6840 \\
0 \times 20 = 0 \times 20 = 0 \\
5 \times 1 = 5 \times 1 = \underline{5} \\
6845
\end{array}
$$

51.

$$
\begin{array}{r}
8 \times 18 \times 20^1 = 8 \times 360 = 2880 \\
8 \times 20 = 8 \times 20 = 160 \\
8 \times 1 = 8 \times 1 = \underline{8} \\
3048
\end{array}
$$

52.

$$
\begin{array}{r}
6 \times 18 \times 20^1 = 6 \times 360 = 2160 \\
6 \times 20 = 6 \times 20 = 120 \\
6 \times 1 = 6 \times 1 = \underline{6} \\
2286
\end{array}
$$

53.

$$
\begin{array}{r}
2 \times 18 \times 20^2 = 2 \times 7200 = 14,400 \\
0 \times 18 \times 20^1 = 0 \times 360 = 0 \\
0 \times 20 = 0 \times 20 = 0 \\
11 \times 1 = 11 \times 1 = \underline{11} \\
14,411
\end{array}
$$

54.

$$
\begin{array}{r}
3 \times 18 \times 20^2 = 3 \times 7200 = 21,600 \\
10 \times 18 \times 20^1 = 10 \times 360 = 3,600 \\
0 \times 20 = 0 \times 20 = 0 \\
0 \times 1 = 0 \times 1 = \underline{0} \\
25,200
\end{array}
$$

55.

$$
\begin{array}{r}
10 \times 18 \times 20^2 = 10 \times 7200 = 72,000 \\
10 \times 18 \times 20^1 = 10 \times 360 = 3,600 \\
0 \times 20 = 0 \times 20 = 0 \\
10 \times 1 = 10 \times 1 = \underline{10} \\
75,610
\end{array}
$$

56.

$$
\begin{array}{r}
10 \times 18 \times 20^2 = 10 \times 7200 = 72,000 \\
0 \times 18 \times 20^1 = 0 \times 360 = 0 \\
10 \times 20 = 10 \times 20 = 200 \\
10 \times 1 = 10 \times 1 = \underline{10} \\
72,210
\end{array}
$$

57.

5	$\times$	$18\times20^4 =$	5 $\times$ 2,880,000 $=$	14,400,000
10	$\times$	$18\times20^3 =$	10 $\times$ 144,000 $=$	1,440,000
0	$\times$	$18\times20^2 =$	0 $\times$ 7200 $=$	0
6	$\times$	$18\times20^1 =$	6 $\times$ 360 $=$	2160
2	$\times$	$20 =$	2 $\times$ 20 $=$	40
3	$\times$	$1 =$	3 $\times$ 1 $=$	3
				15,842,203

58.

5	$\times$	$18\times20^4 =$	5 $\times$ 2,880,000 $=$	14,400,000
0	$\times$	$18\times20^3 =$	0 $\times$ 144,000 $=$	0
10	$\times$	$18\times20^2 =$	10 $\times$ 7200 $=$	72,000
2	$\times$	$18\times20^1 =$	2 $\times$ 360 $=$	720
6	$\times$	$20 =$	6 $\times$ 20 $=$	120
4	$\times$	$1 =$	4 $\times$ 1 $=$	4
				14,472,844

59.

10	$\times$	$18\times20^4 =$	10 $\times$ 2,880,000 $=$	28,800,000
5	$\times$	$18\times20^3 =$	5 $\times$ 144,000 $=$	720,000
0	$\times$	$18\times20^2 =$	0 $\times$ 7200 $=$	0
0	$\times$	$18\times20^1 =$	0 $\times$ 360 $=$	0
11	$\times$	$20 =$	11 $\times$ 20 $=$	220
4	$\times$	$1 =$	4 $\times$ 1 $=$	4
				29,520,224

60.

10	$\times$	$18\times20^4 =$	10 $\times$ 2,880,000 $=$	28,800,000
3	$\times$	$18\times20^3 =$	3 $\times$ 144,000 $=$	432,000
0	$\times$	$18\times20^2 =$	0 $\times$ 7200 $=$	0
0	$\times$	$18\times20^1 =$	0 $\times$ 360 $=$	0
12	$\times$	$20 =$	12 $\times$ 20 $=$	240
2	$\times$	$1 =$	2 $\times$ 1 $=$	2
				29,232,242

61. $\left[(1)\times60^2 + (10+10)\times60^1 + (10+10+1)\times1\right] + \left[(10+1)\times60^2 + (10+10+10)\times60^1 + (1+1+1+1)\times1\right]$

$= \left[(1)\times60^2 + (20)\times60^1 + (21)\times1\right] + \left[(11)\times60^2 + (30)\times60^1 + (4)\times1\right]$

$= [3600 + 1200 + 21] + [39,600 + 1800 + 4]$

$= 4821 + 41,404$

$= 46,225$

$= (4\times10^4) + (6\times10^3) + (2\times10^2) + (2\times10^1) + (5\times1)$

62. $\left[(10+1)\times 60^2 + (10)\times 60^1 + (10+1+1+1)\times 1\right] + \left[(1+1+1)\times 60^2 + (10+10)\times 60^1 + (1+1)\times 1\right]$

$= \left[(11)\times 60^2 + (10)\times 60^1 + (13)\times 1\right] + \left[(3)\times 60^2 + (20)\times 60^1 + (2)\times 1\right]$

$= \left[39,600+600+13\right] + \left[10,800+1200+2\right]$

$= 40,213+12,002$

$= 52,215$

$= (5\times 10^4)+(2\times 10^3)+(2\times 10^2)+(1\times 10^1)+(5\times 1)$

63. $\left[(1\times 360)+(6\times 20)+(6\times 1)\right]+\left[(5\times 360)+(0\times 20)+(13\times 1)\right]$

$= \left[360+120+6\right]+\left[1800+0+13\right]$

$= 486+1813$

$= 2299$

$= (2\times 10^3)+(2\times 10^2)+(9\times 10^1)+(9\times 1)$

64. $\left[(2\times 360)+(5\times 20)+(7\times 1)\right]+\left[(6\times 360)+(10\times 20)+(0\times 1)\right]$

$= \left[720+100+7\right]+\left[2160+200+0\right]$

$= 827+2360$

$= 3187$

$= (3\times 10^3)+(1\times 10^2)+(8\times 10^1)+(7\times 1)$

65. 0.4759

66. 0.6812

67. 0.700203

68. 0.800307

69. 5000.03

70. 70,000.005

71. 30,700.05809

72. 700,300.20201

73. 9734

74. 8625

75. 8097

76. 7802

77. $10^2 + 11^2 + 12^2 = 13^2 + 14^2$

$100+121+144=169+196$

$365 = 365$

365 is the number of days in a non-leap year.

86. does not make sense; Explanations will vary. Sample explanation: $10^4 = 10,000$

87. does not make sense; Explanations will vary. Sample explanation: The numeral will need zeroes as place holders: 4,000,300.

88. makes sense

89. makes sense

90. Change to Hindu-Arabic:

$(1 \times 60^2) + (10 + 1 + 1) \times 60^1 + (10 + 1) \times 1$

$= 3600 + (12 \times 60) + 11$

$= 3600 + 720 + 11 = 4331$

Change to Mayan:

$12 \times 360 = 4320$

$0 \times 20 = 0$

$11 \times 1 = \underline{11}$

4331

91. Change to Hindu-Arabic:

$7 \times 360 = 2520$

$7 \times 20 = 140$

$7 \times 1 = \underline{7}$

2667

Change to Babylonian:

$= 2667$

$= 2640 + 27$

$= (44 \times 60) + 27$

$= (10 + 10 + 10 + 10 + 1 + 1 + 1 + 1) \times 60 + (10 + 10 + 1 + 1 + 1 + 1 + 1 + 1 + 1) \times 1$

< < < < ∨ ∨ ∨ ∨   < < ∨ ∨ ∨ ∨ ∨ ∨ ∨

92. *Writing the numeral that precedes:*

Subtract 1 or ∨ from the numeral on the right:

< ∨   <<<<< ∨ ∨ ∨ ∨ ∨ ∨ ∨ ∨

Writing the numeral that follows:

First, add 1, or ∨, to the numeral on the right:

< ∨   <<<<< ∨ ∨ ∨ ∨ ∨ ∨ ∨ ∨ ∨ ∨

Next, change the 10 ∨'s to a < :

< ∨   <<<<<<

Since <<<<<< has a value of 60 it

can be carried as a ∨ in the next higher place:

< ∨ ∨ (note the missing place value)

The missing place value is indicated by <
                                       <

giving a final answer of: < ∨ ∨   <
                                  <

Check Points 4.2

1. $3422_{\text{five}} = (3 \times 5^3) + (4 \times 5^2) + (2 \times 5^1) + (2 \times 1)$
    $= (3 \times 5 \times 5 \times 5) + (4 \times 5 \times 5) + (2 \times 5) + (2 \times 1)$
    $= 375 + 100 + 10 + 2$
    $= 487$

2. $110011_{\text{two}} = (1 \times 2^5) + (1 \times 2^4) + (0 \times 2^3) + (0 \times 2^2) + (1 \times 2^1) + (1 \times 1)$
    $= (1 \times 32) + (1 \times 16) + (0 \times 8) + (0 \times 4) + (1 \times 2) + (1 \times 1)$
    $= 32 + 16 + 2 + 1$
    $= 51$

3. $AD4_{\text{sixteen}} = (10 \times 16^2) + (13 \times 16^1) + (4 \times 1)$
    $= (10 \times 16 \times 16) + (13 \times 16) + (4 \times 1)$
    $= 2560 + 208 + 4$
    $= 2772$

4. $6_{\text{ten}} = (1 \times 5) + (1 \times 1) = 11_{\text{five}}$

5. The place values in base 7 are $\ldots 7^4$, 7^3, 7^2, 7^1, 1 or $\ldots 2401$, 343, 49, 7, 1

    $$\begin{array}{r} 1 \\ 343\overline{)365} \\ \underline{343} \\ 22 \end{array} \qquad \begin{array}{r} 0 \\ 49\overline{)22} \\ \underline{0} \\ 22 \end{array} \qquad \begin{array}{r} 3 \\ 7\overline{)22} \\ \underline{21} \\ 1 \end{array}$$

    $365_{\text{ten}} = (1 \times 343) + (0 \times 49) + (3 \times 7) + (1 \times 1)$
    $= (1 \times 7^3) + (0 \times 7^2) + (3 \times 7^1) + (1 \times 1)$
    $= 1031_{\text{seven}}$

6. The place values in base 2 are $\ldots 2^5$, 2^4, 2^3, 2^2, 2^1, 1 or $\ldots 32$, 16, 8, 4, 2, 1

    $$\begin{array}{r} 1 \\ 32\overline{)51} \\ \underline{32} \\ 19 \end{array} \quad \begin{array}{r} 1 \\ 16\overline{)19} \\ \underline{16} \\ 3 \end{array} \quad \begin{array}{r} 0 \\ 8\overline{)3} \\ \underline{0} \\ 3 \end{array} \quad \begin{array}{r} 0 \\ 4\overline{)3} \\ \underline{0} \\ 3 \end{array} \quad \begin{array}{r} 1 \\ 2\overline{)3} \\ \underline{2} \\ 1 \end{array}$$

    Use the five quotients and the final remainder to write the answer.
    $51_{\text{ten}} = 110011_{\text{two}}$

7. The place values in base 5 are $\ldots 5^4$, 5^3, 5^2, 5^1, 1 or $\ldots 3125$, 625, 125, 25, 5, 1

    $$\begin{array}{r} 4 \\ 625\overline{)2763} \\ \underline{2500} \\ 263 \end{array} \quad \begin{array}{r} 2 \\ 125\overline{)263} \\ \underline{250} \\ 13 \end{array} \quad \begin{array}{r} 0 \\ 25\overline{)13} \\ \underline{0} \\ 13 \end{array} \quad \begin{array}{r} 2 \\ 5\overline{)13} \\ \underline{10} \\ 3 \end{array}$$

    Use the four quotients and the final remainder to write the answer.
    $2763_{\text{ten}} = (4 \times 625) + (2 \times 125) + (0 \times 25) + (2 \times 5) + (3 \times 1)$
    $= (4 \times 5^4) + (2 \times 5^3) + (0 \times 5^2) + (2 \times 5^1) + (3 \times 1)$
    $= 42023_{\text{five}}$

Exercise Set 4.2

1. $(4 \times 5^1) + (3 \times 1)$
    $= 20 + 3$
    $= 23$

2. $(3 \times 5^1) + (4 \times 1) = 15 + 4 = 19$

3. $(5 \times 8^1) + (2 \times 1)$
    $= 40 + 2$
    $= 42$

4. $(6 \times 8^1) + (7 \times 1) = 48 + 7 = 55$

5. $(1 \times 4^2) + (3 \times 4^1) + (2 \times 1)$
    $= 16 + 12 + 2$
    $= 30$

6. $(3 \times 4^2) + (2 \times 4^1) + (1 \times 1) = 48 + 8 + 1 = 57$

7. $(1 \times 2^3) + (0 \times 2^2) + (1 \times 2^1) + (1 \times 1)$
    $= 8 + 0 + 2 + 1 = 11$

8. $(1 \times 2^3) + (1 \times 2^2) + (0 \times 2^1) + (1 \times 1) = 8 + 4 + 0 + 1$
    $= 13$

9. $(2 \times 6^3) + (0 \times 6^2) + (3 \times 6^1) + (5 \times 1) = 432 + 0 + 18 + 5$
    $= 455$

10. $(2 \times 9^3) + (0 \times 9^2) + (7 \times 9^1) + (3 \times 1) = 1458 + 0 + 63 + 3$
    $= 1524$

11. $(7 \times 8^4) + (0 \times 8^3) + (3 \times 8^2) + (5 \times 8^1) + (5 \times 1) = 28,672 + 0 + 192 + 40 + 5$
    $= 28,909$

12. $(4 \times 6^4) + (1 \times 6^3) + (5 \times 6^2) + (0 \times 6^1) + (2 \times 1) = 5184 + 216 + 180 + 0 + 2$
    $= 5582$

13. $(2 \times 16^3) + (0 \times 16^2) + (9 \times 16^1) + (6 \times 1) = 8192 + 0 + 144 + 6$
    $= 8342$

14. $(3 \times 15^3) + (1 \times 15^2) + (0 \times 15^1) + (4 \times 1) = 10,125 + 225 + 0 + 4$
    $= 10,354$

15. $(1 \times 2^5) + (1 \times 2^4) + (0 \times 2^3) + (1 \times 2^2) + (0 \times 2^1) + (1 \times 1) = 32 + 16 + 0 + 4 + 0 + 1$
    $= 53$

16. $(1 \times 2^5) + (0 \times 2^4) + (1 \times 2^3) + (1 \times 2^2) + (0 \times 2^1) + (1 \times 1) = 32 + 0 + 8 + 4 + 0 + 1$
$$= 45$$

17. $(10 \times 16^3) + (12 \times 16^2) + (14 \times 16^1) + (5 \times 1) = 40,960 + 3072 + 224 + 5$
$$= 44,261$$

18. $(14 \times 16^3) + (13 \times 16^2) + (15 \times 16^1) + (7 \times 1) = 57,344 + 3328 + 240 + 7$
$$= 60,919$$

19. 12_{five}

20. 14_{five}

21. 14_{seven}

22. 15_{seven}

23. 10_{two}

24. 11_{two}

25. 101_{two}

26. 110_{two}

27. 1000_{two}

28. 1001_{two}

29. 31_{four}

30. 103_{four}

31. 101_{six}

32. 41_{six}

33.
$$25\overline{)87}^{\;3} \quad 5\overline{)12}^{\;2}$$
$$\underline{75} \qquad \underline{10}$$
$$12 \qquad\; 2$$
$$87 = 322_{\text{five}}$$

34.
$$49\overline{)85}^{\;1} \quad 7\overline{)36}^{\;5}$$
$$\underline{49} \qquad \underline{35}$$
$$36 \qquad\; 1$$
$$85 = 151_{\text{seven}}$$

35. $\begin{array}{r}1\\64\overline{)108}\\\underline{64}\\44\end{array}$ $\begin{array}{r}2\\16\overline{)44}\\\underline{32}\\12\end{array}$ $\begin{array}{r}3\\4\overline{)12}\\\underline{12}\\0\end{array}$

$108 = 1230_{\text{four}}$

36. $\begin{array}{r}3\\64\overline{)199}\\\underline{192}\\7\end{array}$ $\begin{array}{r}0\\16\overline{)7}\\\underline{0}\\7\end{array}$ $\begin{array}{r}1\\4\overline{)7}\\\underline{4}\\3\end{array}$

$199 = 3013_{\text{four}}$

37. $\begin{array}{r}1\\16\overline{)19}\\\underline{16}\\3\end{array}$ $\begin{array}{r}0\\8\overline{)3}\\\underline{0}\\3\end{array}$ $\begin{array}{r}0\\4\overline{)3}\\\underline{0}\\3\end{array}$ $\begin{array}{r}1\\2\overline{)3}\\\underline{2}\\1\end{array}$

$19 = 10011_{\text{two}}$

38. $\begin{array}{r}1\\16\overline{)23}\\\underline{16}\\7\end{array}$ $\begin{array}{r}0\\8\overline{)7}\\\underline{0}\\7\end{array}$ $\begin{array}{r}1\\4\overline{)7}\\\underline{4}\\3\end{array}$ $\begin{array}{r}1\\2\overline{)3}\\\underline{2}\\1\end{array}$

$23 = 10111_{\text{two}}$

39. $\begin{array}{r}1\\32\overline{)57}\\\underline{32}\\25\end{array}$ $\begin{array}{r}1\\16\overline{)25}\\\underline{16}\\9\end{array}$ $\begin{array}{r}1\\8\overline{)9}\\\underline{8}\\1\end{array}$ $\begin{array}{r}0\\4\overline{)1}\\\underline{0}\\1\end{array}$ $\begin{array}{r}0\\2\overline{)1}\\\underline{0}\\1\end{array}$

$57 = 111001_{\text{two}}$

40. $\begin{array}{r}1\\32\overline{)63}\\\underline{32}\\31\end{array}$ $\begin{array}{r}1\\16\overline{)31}\\\underline{16}\\15\end{array}$ $\begin{array}{r}1\\8\overline{)15}\\\underline{8}\\7\end{array}$ $\begin{array}{r}1\\4\overline{)7}\\\underline{4}\\3\end{array}$ $\begin{array}{r}1\\2\overline{)3}\\\underline{2}\\1\end{array}$

$63 = 111111_{\text{two}}$

41. $\begin{array}{r}1\\64\overline{)90}\\\underline{64}\\26\end{array}$ $\begin{array}{r}0\\32\overline{)26}\\\underline{0}\\26\end{array}$ $\begin{array}{r}1\\16\overline{)26}\\\underline{16}\\10\end{array}$ $\begin{array}{r}1\\8\overline{)10}\\\underline{8}\\2\end{array}$ $\begin{array}{r}0\\4\overline{)2}\\\underline{0}\\2\end{array}$ $\begin{array}{r}1\\2\overline{)2}\\\underline{2}\\0\end{array}$

$90 = 1011010_{\text{two}}$

42. $\begin{array}{r}1\\64\overline{)87}\\\underline{64}\\23\end{array}$ $\begin{array}{r}0\\32\overline{)23}\\\underline{0}\\23\end{array}$ $\begin{array}{r}1\\16\overline{)23}\\\underline{16}\\7\end{array}$ $\begin{array}{r}0\\8\overline{)7}\\\underline{0}\\7\end{array}$ $\begin{array}{r}1\\4\overline{)7}\\\underline{4}\\3\end{array}$ $\begin{array}{r}1\\2\overline{)3}\\\underline{2}\\1\end{array}$

$87 = 1010111_{\text{two}}$

43.
$$81\overline{)138} \quad 27\overline{)57} \quad 9\overline{)3} \quad 3\overline{)3}$$

with quotients 1, 2, 0, 1

$$\begin{array}{cccc} \underline{81} & \underline{54} & \underline{0} & \underline{3} \\ 57 & 3 & 3 & 0 \end{array}$$

$138 = 12010_{three}$

44.
$$81\overline{)129} \quad 27\overline{)48} \quad 9\overline{)21} \quad 3\overline{)3}$$

with quotients 1, 1, 2, 1

$$\begin{array}{cccc} \underline{81} & \underline{27} & \underline{18} & \underline{3} \\ 48 & 21 & 3 & 0 \end{array}$$

$129 = 11210_{three}$

45.
$$216\overline{)386} \quad 36\overline{)170} \quad 6\overline{)26}$$

with quotients 1, 4, 4

$$\begin{array}{ccc} \underline{216} & \underline{144} & \underline{24} \\ 170 & 26 & 2 \end{array}$$

$386 = 1442_{six}$

46.
$$81\overline{)428} \quad 9\overline{)23}$$

with quotients 5, 2

$$\begin{array}{cc} \underline{405} & \underline{18} \\ 23 & 5 \end{array}$$

$428 = 525_{nine}$

47.
$$343\overline{)1599} \quad 49\overline{)227} \quad 7\overline{)31}$$

with quotients 4, 4, 4

$$\begin{array}{ccc} \underline{1372} & \underline{196} & \underline{28} \\ 227 & 31 & 3 \end{array}$$

$1599 = 4443_{seven}$

48.
$$512\overline{)1346} \quad 64\overline{)322} \quad 8\overline{)2}$$

with quotients 2, 5, 0

$$\begin{array}{ccc} \underline{1024} & \underline{320} & \underline{0} \\ 322 & 2 & 2 \end{array}$$

$1346 = 2502_{eight}$

49. $3052 = 3000 + 52$

$= (50 \times 60^1) + (52 \times 1)$

$= \quad \text{<<<<<} \quad \text{<<<<< ∨ ∨}$

50. $6704 = 3600 + 3060 + 44$

$= (1 \times 60^2) + (51 \times 60^1) + (44 \times 1)$

$= \quad \text{∨} \quad \text{<<<<< ∨} \quad \text{<<<< ∨ ∨ ∨ ∨}$

51. $23,546 = 21,600 + 1920 + 26$

$= (6 \times 60^2) + (32 \times 60^1) + (26 \times 1)$

$= \lor\lor\lor\lor\lor\lor \quad <<<\lor\lor \quad <<\lor\lor\lor\lor\lor\lor$

52. $41,265 = 39,600 + 1620 + 45$

$= (11 \times 60^2) + (27 \times 60^1) + (45 \times 1)$

$= <\lor \quad <<\lor\lor\lor\lor\lor\lor\lor \quad <<<<\lor\lor\lor\lor\lor$

53. 9307

$= 7200 + 1800 + 300 + 7$

$= (1 \times 7200) + (5 \times 360) + (15 \times 20) + (7 \times 1)$

54. 8703

$= 7200 + 1440 + 60 + 3$

$= (1 \times 7200) + (4 \times 360) + (3 \times 20) + (3 \times 1)$

55. $28,704$

$= 21,600 + 6840 + 260 + 4$

$= (3 \times 7200) + (19 \times 360) + (13 \times 20) + (4 \times 1)$

56. $34,847$

$= 28,800 + 5760 + 280 + 7$

$= (4 \times 7200) + (16 \times 360) + (14 \times 20) + (7 \times 1)$

57. $34_{\text{five}} = (3 \times 5^1) + (4 \times 1)$

$= 15 + 4$

$= 19_{\text{ten}}$

$19_{\text{ten}} = 14 + 5$

$= (2 \times 7^1) + (5 \times 1)$

$= 25_{\text{seven}}$

58. $46_{\text{eight}} = (4 \times 8^1) + (6 \times 1)$

$= 32 + 6$

$= 38_{\text{ten}}$

$38_{\text{ten}} = 25 + 10 + 3$

$= (1 \times 5^2) + (2 \times 5^1) + (3 \times 1)$

$= 123_{\text{five}}$

59. $110010011_{\text{two}} = 403_{\text{ten}}$

$403_{\text{ten}} = 384 + 16 + 3$

$= (6 \times 8^2) + (2 \times 8^1) + (3 \times 1)$

$= 623_{\text{eight}}$

60. $101110001_{\text{two}} = 369_{\text{ten}}$

$369_{\text{ten}} = 320 + 48 + 1$

$= (5 \times 8^2) + (6 \times 8^1) + (1 \times 1)$

$= 561_{\text{eight}}$

61. Since A = 65, F = 70

$70 = 64 + 0 + 0 + 0 + 4 + 2 + 0$

$= 1 \cdot 2^6 + 0 \cdot 2^5 + 0 \cdot 2^4 + 0 \cdot 2^3 + 1 \cdot 2^2 + 1 \cdot 2^1 + 0 \cdot 1$

$= 1000110_{\text{two}}$

62. Since A = 65, Y = 89

$89 = 64 + 0 + 16 + 8 + 0 + 0 + 1$

$= 1 \cdot 2^6 + 0 \cdot 2^5 + 1 \cdot 2^4 + 1 \cdot 2^3 + 0 \cdot 2^2 + 0 \cdot 2^1 + 1 \cdot 1$

$= 1011001_{\text{two}}$

63. Since a = 97, m = 109

$109 = 64 + 32 + 0 + 8 + 4 + 0 + 1$

$= 1 \cdot 2^6 + 1 \cdot 2^5 + 0 \cdot 2^4 + 1 \cdot 2^3 + 1 \cdot 2^2 + 0 \cdot 2^1 + 1 \cdot 1$

$= 1101101_{\text{two}}$

64. Since a = 97, p = 112

$112 = 64 + 32 + 16 + 0 + 0 + 0 + 0$

$= 1 \cdot 2^6 + 1 \cdot 2^5 + 1 \cdot 2^4 + 0 \cdot 2^3 + 0 \cdot 2^2 + 0 \cdot 2^1 + 0 \cdot 1$

$= 1110000_{\text{two}}$

65. 1010000_{two} 1000001_{two} 1001100_{two}

    $64 + 16$ $64 + 1$ $64 + 8 + 4$

      80   65   76

      P   A   L

The word is PAL.

66. 1001100_{two} 1010101_{two} 1000011_{two} 1001011_{two}

$64+8+4$ $64+16+4+1$ $64+2+1$ $64+8+2+1$

76 85 67 75

L U C K

The word is LUCK.

67.   M   o   m

77   111   109

$64+8+4+1$ $64+32+8+4+2+1$ $64+32+8+4+1$

1001101_{two} 1101111_{two} 1101101_{two}

The sequence is 100110111011111101101

68.   D   a   d

68   97   100

$64+4$ $64+32+1$ $64+32+4$

1000100_{two} 1100001_{two} 1100100_{two}

The sequence is 100010011000011100100

72. does not make sense; Explanations will vary. Sample explanation: Base b contains b digits.

73. does not make sense; Explanations will vary. Sample explanation: For bases greater than 10 we can use letters of the alphabet to represent digits.

74. makes sense

75. does not make sense; Explanations will vary. Sample explanation: Since $2^5 = 32,$ and 32 is greater than 28, you should start with $2^4 = 16$.

76. Preceding: Following:

888_{nine} 888_{nine}

$-\ 1_{nine}$ $+\ 1_{nine}$

887_{nine} 1000_{nine}

77. Preceding: Following:

$EC5_{sixteen}$ $EC5_{sixteen}$

$-\ 1_{sixteen}$ $+\ 1_{sixteen}$

$EC4_{sixteen}$ $EC6_{sixteen}$

78. 11111011_{two}

$(1\times 2^7)+(1\times 2^6)+(1\times 2^5)+(1\times 2^4)+(1\times 2^3)+(0\times 2^2)+(1\times 2^1)+(1\times 1)$

$=128+64+32+16+8+0+2+1$

$=251$

$3A6_{twelve}$

$(3\times 12^2)+(10\times 12^1)+(6\times 1)=432+120+6=558$

673_{eight}

$(6\times 8^2)+(7\times 8^1)+(3\times 1)=384+56+3=443$

$11111011_{two},\ 673_{eight},\ 3A6_{twelve}$

Check Points 4.3

1.
$$\overset{1}{3}2_{\text{five}}$$
$$+44_{\text{five}}$$
$$\overline{131_{\text{five}}}$$

$$2+4 = 6 = (1 \times 5^1) + (1 \times 1) = 11_{\text{five}}$$
$$1+3+4 = 8 = (1 \times 5^1) + (3 \times 1) = 13_{\text{five}}$$

2.
$$\overset{11}{1}11_{\text{two}}$$
$$+111_{\text{two}}$$
$$\overline{1110_{\text{two}}}$$

$$1+1 = 2 = (1 \times 2^1) + (0 \times 1) = 10_{\text{two}}$$
$$1+1+1 = 3 = (1 \times 2^1) + (1 \times 1) = 11_{\text{two}}$$

3.
$$\overset{3\,6}{4}1_{\text{five}}$$
$$-23_{\text{five}}$$
$$\overline{13_{\text{five}}}$$

4.
$$\overset{4\,8\,3\,11}{5}144_{\text{seven}}$$
$$-3236_{\text{seven}}$$
$$\overline{1605_{\text{seven}}}$$

5.
$$\overset{2}{4}5_{\text{seven}}$$
$$\times\ 3_{\text{seven}}$$
$$\overline{201_{\text{seven}}}$$

$$3 \times 5 = 15 = (2 \times 7^1) + (1 \times 1) = 21_{\text{seven}}$$
$$(3 \times 4) + 2 = 14 = (2 \times 7^1) + (0 \times 1) = 20_{\text{seven}}$$

6.
$$2_{\text{four}} \overline{)112_{\text{four}}}$$
with quotient 23
$$\underline{10}$$
$$12$$
$$\underline{12}$$
$$0$$
$$23_{\text{four}}$$

Exercise Set 4.3

Note: Numbers with no base specified are base 10.

1.
$$\overset{1}{2}3_{\text{four}}$$
$$+13_{\text{four}}$$
$$\overline{102_{\text{four}}}$$

$$3+3 = 6 = (1 \times 4^1) + (2 \times 1) = 12_{\text{four}}$$
$$1+2+1 = 4 = (1 \times 4^1) + (0 \times 1) = 10_{\text{four}}$$

2.
$$31_{\text{four}}$$
$$+22_{\text{four}}$$
$$\overline{113_{\text{four}}}$$

$$3+2 = 5 = (1 \times 4^1) + (1 \times 1) = 11_{\text{four}}$$

3.
$$\overset{1}{1}1_{\text{two}}$$
$$+11_{\text{two}}$$
$$\overline{110_{\text{two}}}$$

$$1+1+1 = 3 = (1 \times 2^1) + (1 \times 1) = 11_{\text{two}}$$

4.
$$\overset{1\ 1}{1}01_{\text{two}}$$
$$+\ 11_{\text{two}}$$
$$\overline{1000_{\text{two}}}$$

5.
$$\overset{1\ 1}{3}42_{\text{five}}$$
$$+413_{\text{five}}$$
$$\overline{1310_{\text{five}}}$$

$$2+3 = 5 = (1 \times 5^1) + (0 \times 1) = 10_{\text{five}}$$
$$1+4+1 = 6 = (1 \times 5^1) + (1 \times 1) = 11_{\text{five}}$$
$$1+3+4 = 8 = (1 \times 5^1) + (3 \times 1) = 13_{\text{five}}$$

6.
$$323_{\text{five}}$$
$$+421_{\text{five}}$$
$$\overline{1244_{\text{five}}}$$

$$3+4 = 7 = (1 \times 5^1) + (2 \times 1) = 12_{\text{five}}$$

7.
$$\overset{1\ 1}{645}_{\text{seven}}$$
$$+324_{\text{seven}}$$
$$\overline{1302_{\text{seven}}}$$

$5+4=9=(1\times 7^{1})+(2\times 1)=12_{\text{seven}}$

$1+4+2=7=(1\times 7^{1})+(0\times 1)=10_{\text{seven}}$

$1+6+3=10=(1\times 7^{1})+(3\times 1)=13_{\text{seven}}$

8.
$$\overset{1}{632}_{\text{seven}}$$
$$+\ 564_{\text{seven}}$$
$$\overline{1526_{\text{seven}}}$$

$3+6=9=(1\times 7^{1})+(2\times 1)=12_{\text{seven}}$

$1+6+5=12=(1\times 7^{1})+(5\times 1)=15_{\text{seven}}$

9.
$$\overset{1\ 1\ 1}{6784}_{\text{nine}}$$
$$+7865_{\text{nine}}$$
$$\overline{15760_{\text{nine}}}$$

$4+5=9=(1\times 9^{1})+(0\times 1)=10_{\text{nine}}$

$1+8+6=15=(1\times 9^{1})+(6\times 1)=16_{\text{nine}}$

$1+7+8=16=(1\times 9^{1})+(7\times 1)=17_{\text{nine}}$

$1+6+7=14=(1\times 9^{1})+(5\times 1)=15_{\text{nine}}$

10.
$$\overset{1}{1021}_{\text{three}}$$
$$+2011_{\text{three}}$$
$$\overline{10102_{\text{three}}}$$

$2+1=3=(1\times 3^{1})+(0\times 1)=10_{\text{three}}$

11.
$$\overset{1\ 1}{14632}_{\text{seven}}$$
$$+5604_{\text{seven}}$$
$$\overline{23536_{\text{seven}}}$$

$6+6=12=(1\times 7^{1})+(5\times 1)=15_{\text{seven}}$

$1+4+5=10=(1\times 7^{1})+(3\times 1)=13_{\text{seven}}$

12.
$$53B_{\text{sixteen}}$$
$$+\ 694_{\text{sixteen}}$$
$$\overline{BCF_{\text{sixteen}}}$$

$B+4=11+4=15=F_{\text{sixteen}}$

$3+9=12=C_{\text{sixteen}}$

$5+6=11=B_{\text{sixteen}}$

13.
$$\overset{2\ 6}{\cancel{3}\cancel{2}}_{\text{four}}$$
$$-13_{\text{four}}$$
$$\overline{13_{\text{four}}}$$

14.
$$\overset{1\ 5}{2\cancel{1}}_{\text{four}}$$
$$-12_{\text{four}}$$
$$\overline{3_{\text{four}}}$$

15.
$$\overset{1\ 8}{2\cancel{3}}_{\text{five}}$$
$$-14_{\text{five}}$$
$$\overline{4_{\text{five}}}$$

16.
$$\overset{2\ 9}{\cancel{3}\cancel{2}}_{\text{seven}}$$
$$-16_{\text{seven}}$$
$$\overline{13_{\text{seven}}}$$

17.
$$\overset{6\ 13}{47\cancel{5}}_{\text{eight}}$$
$$-267_{\text{eight}}$$
$$\overline{206_{\text{eight}}}$$

18.
$$\overset{6\ 9\ 11}{7\cancel{1}\cancel{2}}_{\text{nine}}$$
$$-483_{\text{nine}}$$
$$\overline{218_{\text{nine}}}$$

19.
$$\overset{4\ 12\quad 10}{\cancel{5}\ \cancel{6}\ \cancel{3}}_{\text{seven}}$$
$$-1\ 64_{\text{seven}}$$
$$\overline{366_{\text{seven}}}$$

20.
$$\overset{\quad 13}{\overset{3\ \cancel{5}\ 10}{4\cancel{5}\ 2}}_{\text{eight}}$$
$$-\ 177_{\text{eight}}$$
$$\overline{263_{\text{eight}}}$$

21.
$$\overset{0\ 1\ 2}{10\cancel{0}1}_{\text{two}}$$
$$-111_{\text{two}}$$
$$\overline{10_{\text{two}}}$$

22.
$$\overset{0\ 1\ 1\ 2}{1\cancel{0}\cancel{0}0}_{\text{two}}$$
$$-\ 101_{\text{two}}$$
$$\overline{11_{\text{two}}}$$

23. $\overset{1\ 2\ 3}{12\cancel{0}\cancel{0}}_{\text{three}}$
$\underline{-1012_{\text{three}}}$
111_{three}

24. $\overset{\text{B}\quad 22}{4C6}_{\text{sixteen}}$
$\underline{-1\,9\,8_{\text{sixteen}}}$
$3\,2\,E_{\text{sixteen}}$

25. $\overset{3}{25}_{\text{six}}$
$\underline{\times 4_{\text{six}}}$
152_{six}
$(2_{\text{six}} \times 4_{\text{six}}) + 3_{\text{six}} = 8_{\text{ten}} + 3_{\text{six}}$
$= 12_{\text{six}} + 3_{\text{six}}$
$= 15_{\text{six}}$

26. $\overset{2}{34}_{\text{five}}$
$\underline{\times\ \ 3_{\text{five}}}$
212_{five}
$(3_{\text{five}} \times 3_{\text{five}}) + 2_{\text{five}} = 9_{\text{ten}} + 2_{\text{five}}$
$= (1\times 5^1 + 4\times 5^0) + 2_{\text{five}}$
$= 14_{\text{five}} + 2_{\text{five}}$
$= 21_{\text{five}}$

27. 11_{two}
$\underline{\times\ 1_{\text{two}}}$
11_{two}

28. 21_{four}
$\underline{\times\ \ 3_{\text{four}}}$
123_{four}
$2_{\text{four}} \times 3_{\text{four}} = 6_{\text{ten}}$
$= (1\times 4^1) + (2\times 1)$
$= 12_{\text{four}}$

29. $\overset{3\ 2}{543}_{\text{seven}}$
$\underline{\times\ \ 5_{\text{seven}}}$
4011_{seven}
$3\times 5 = 15 = (2\times 7^1) + (1\times 1) = 21_{\text{seven}}$
$(4\times 5) + 2 = 22 = (3\times 7^1) + (1\times 1) = 31_{\text{seven}}$
$(5\times 5) + 3 = 28 = (4\times 7^1) + (0\times 1) = 40_{\text{seven}}$

30. $\overset{2\ 2}{243}_{\text{nine}}$
$\underline{\times\ \ 6_{\text{nine}}}$
1580_{nine}
$3\times 6 = 18 = (2\times 9^1) + (0\times 1) = 20_{\text{nine}}$
$(4\times 6) + 2 = 26 = (2\times 9^1) + (8\times 1) = 28_{\text{nine}}$
$(2\times 6) + 2 = 14 = (1\times 9^1) + (5\times 1) = 15_{\text{nine}}$

31. $\overset{1\ 1}{623}_{\text{eight}}$
$\underline{\times\ \ 4_{\text{eight}}}$
3114_{eight}
$(3_{\text{eight}} \times 4_{\text{eight}}) = 12_{\text{ten}}$
$= (1\times 8^1) + (4\times 1)$
$= 14_{\text{eight}}$
$(2_{\text{eight}} \times 4_{\text{eight}}) + 1_{\text{eight}} = 8_{\text{ten}} + 1_{\text{ten}}$
$= 9_{\text{ten}}$
$= (1\times 8^1) + (1\times 1)$
$= 11_{\text{eight}}$
$(6_{\text{eight}} \times 4_{\text{eight}}) + 1_{\text{eight}} = 24_{\text{ten}} + 1_{\text{ten}}$
$= 25_{\text{ten}}$
$= (3\times 8^1) + (1\times 1)$
$= 31_{\text{eight}}$

32. $\overset{3\ 2}{543}_{\text{six}}$
$\underline{\times\ \ 5_{\text{six}}}$
4443_{six}
$3_{\text{six}} \times 5_{\text{six}} = 15_{\text{ten}} = (2\times 6^1) + (3\times 1)$
$= 23_{\text{six}}$
$(4_{\text{six}} \times 5_{\text{six}}) + 2_{\text{six}} = 20_{\text{ten}} + 2_{\text{ten}}$
$= 22_{\text{ten}}$
$= (3\times 6^1) + (4\times 1)$
$= 34_{\text{six}}$
$(5_{\text{six}} \times 5_{\text{six}}) + 3_{\text{six}} = 25_{\text{ten}} + 3_{\text{ten}}$
$= 28_{\text{ten}}$
$= (4\times 6^1) + (4\times 1)$
$= 44_{\text{six}}$

33. 21_{four}
$$\times 12_{\text{four}}$$

102

$\underline{210}$

312_{four}

$21_{\text{four}} \times 2_{\text{four}} = 9_{\text{ten}} \times 2_{\text{ten}}$

$\phantom{21_{\text{four}} \times 2_{\text{four}}} = 18$

$\phantom{21_{\text{four}} \times 2_{\text{four}}} = (1 \times 4^2) + (0 \times 4) + (2 \times 1)$

$\phantom{21_{\text{four}} \times 2_{\text{four}}} = 102_{\text{four}}$

$21_{\text{four}} \times 1_{\text{four}} = 21_{\text{four}}$

34. $\overset{1}{3}2_{\text{four}}$
$$\times\ 23_{\text{four}}$$

222_{four}

$\underline{1300}_{\text{four}}$

2122_{four}

$32_{\text{four}} \times 3_{\text{four}} = 14_{\text{ten}} \times 3_{\text{ten}}$

$\phantom{32_{\text{four}} \times 3_{\text{four}}} = 42$

$\phantom{32_{\text{four}} \times 3_{\text{four}}} = (2 \times 4^2) + (2 \times 4^1) + (2 \times 1)$

$\phantom{32_{\text{four}} \times 3_{\text{four}}} = 222_{\text{four}}$

$32_{\text{four}} \times 2_{\text{four}} = 14_{\text{ten}} \times 2_{\text{ten}}$

$\phantom{32_{\text{four}} \times 2_{\text{four}}} = 28$

$\phantom{32_{\text{four}} \times 2_{\text{four}}} = (1 \times 4^2) + (3 \times 4^1) + (0 \times 1)$

$\phantom{32_{\text{four}} \times 2_{\text{four}}} = 130_{\text{four}}$

35. $2_{\text{four}} \overline{)100_{\text{four}}}$ with quotient 20

$\phantom{2_{\text{four}})}\underline{10}$

$\phantom{2_{\text{four}})}00$

$\phantom{2_{\text{four}})}20_{\text{four}}$

36. 130_{four} remainder of 1

$2_{\text{four}} \overline{)321_{\text{four}}}$ with quotient 130

$\phantom{2_{\text{four}})}\underline{2}$

$\phantom{2_{\text{four}})}12$

$\phantom{2_{\text{four}})}\underline{12}$

$\phantom{2_{\text{four}})}01$

$\phantom{2_{\text{four}})}\underline{0}$

$\phantom{2_{\text{four}})}1$

37. 41_{five} remainder of 1

$3_{\text{five}} \overline{)224_{\text{five}}}$ with quotient 41

$\phantom{3_{\text{five}})}\underline{22}$

$\phantom{3_{\text{five}})}04$

$\phantom{3_{\text{five}})}\underline{3}$

$\phantom{3_{\text{five}})}1$

38. 21_{five}

$4_{\text{five}} \overline{)134_{\text{five}}}$ with quotient 21

$\phantom{4_{\text{five}})}\underline{13}$

$\phantom{4_{\text{five}})}04$

$\phantom{4_{\text{five}})}\underline{4}$

$\phantom{4_{\text{five}})}0$

39. $\overset{1\ 1}{}$
$$10110_{\text{two}}$$
$$\underline{+\ 10100_{\text{two}}}$$
$$1000110_{\text{two}}$$

40. $\overset{1\,0\,1\,0\,1\,1}{}$
$$11100_{\text{two}}$$
$$11111_{\text{two}}$$
$$\underline{+\ 10111_{\text{two}}}$$
$$1010010_{\text{two}}$$

41. $\overset{1\ 1\ 1}{}$
$$11111_{\text{two}}$$
$$\underline{+\ 10110_{\text{two}}}$$
$$110101_{\text{two}}$$

$$110101_{\text{two}}$$
$$\underline{-\ 101_{\text{two}}}$$
$$110000_{\text{two}}$$

42. $\overset{1\ 1\ 1}{}$
$$10111_{\text{two}}$$
$$\underline{+\ 11110_{\text{two}}}$$
$$110101_{\text{two}}$$

$$110101_{\text{two}}$$
$$\underline{-\ 111_{\text{two}}}$$
$$101110_{\text{two}}$$

43. 1011_{two}
$$\underline{\times\ 101_{\text{two}}}$$
$$1011_{\text{two}}$$
$$\underline{+\ 101100_{\text{two}}}$$
$$110111_{\text{two}}$$

44. 1101_{two}
    $\times\quad 110_{two}$
    —————
    11010_{two}
    $+\,110100_{two}$
    —————
    1001110_{two}

45. $D3_{sixteen}$
    $\times\quad 8A_{sixteen}$
    —————
    $83E_{sixteen}$
    $+\,6980_{sixteen}$
    —————
    $71BE_{sixteen}$

46. $B5_{sixteen}$
    $\times\quad 2C_{sixteen}$
    —————
    $87C_{sixteen}$
    $+\,16A0_{sixteen}$
    —————
    $1F1C_{sixteen}$

47.

10011

11001

01100

11101

48.

10011

11001

01100

01000

49.

10011

11001

10001

11001

50.

10011

11001

11011

11001

51.

10011

11001

01100

00110

00100

11011

52.

10011

11001

01100

00110

01110

10001

53. The circuit in Exercise 47 is a conditional gate.

57. makes sense

58. makes sense

59. makes sense

60. makes sense

61.

	4 hours,	26 minutes,	57 seconds
+	3 hours,	46 minutes,	39 seconds
	7 hours,	72 minutes,	96 seconds
	↓	↓	↓
	7 hours,	73 minutes,	36 seconds
	↓	↓	↓
	8 hours,	13 minutes,	36 seconds

62.

$$\overset{7}{\cancel{8}} \text{ hours,} \quad \overset{104}{\cancel{45}} \text{ minutes,} \quad \overset{88}{\cancel{28}} \text{ seconds}$$
$$- \quad 2 \text{ hours,} \quad 47 \text{ minutes,} \quad 53 \text{ seconds}$$
$$\overline{\quad 5 \text{ hours,} \quad 57 \text{ minutes,} \quad 35 \text{ seconds}}$$

63.

$$\begin{array}{r} 56_{\text{seven}} \\ 31_{\text{seven}}) \overline{2426_{\text{seven}}} \\ \underline{215} \\ 246 \\ \underline{246} \\ 0 \end{array}$$

64.

$$\frac{\bullet}{\begin{array}{c} \bullet\ \bullet \\ \hline \bigcirc \end{array}}$$

Check Points 4.4

1. $100,000 + 100,000 + 100,000 + 100 + 100 + 10 + 10 + 1 + 1 = 300,222$

2. $2563 = 1000 + 1000 + 100 + 100 + 100 + 100 + 100 + 10 + 10 + 10 + 10 + 10 + 10 + 1 + 1 + 1$

3. MCCCLXI $= 1000 + 100 + 100 + 100 + 50 + 10 + 1 = 1361$

4. MCDXLVII $= \overset{M}{\overbrace{1000}} + \overset{CD}{\overbrace{(500-100)}} + \overset{XL}{\overbrace{(50-10)}} + \overset{V}{5} + \overset{I}{1} + \overset{I}{1} = 1000 + 400 + 40 + 5 + 1 + 1 = 1447$

5. $399 = 100 + 100 + 100 + 90 + 9 = \overset{C}{\overbrace{100}} + \overset{C}{\overbrace{100}} + \overset{C}{\overbrace{100}} + \overset{XC}{\overbrace{(100-10)}} + \overset{IX}{\overbrace{(10-1)}} = \text{CCCXCIX}$

6. $2693 = 2000 + 600 + 90 + 3$

千

六

百

九

十

三

7. $\omega\pi\varepsilon = 800 + 80 + 5 = 885$

Exercise Set 4.4

1. 322

2. 3,040,214

3. 300,423

4. 200,213

5. 132

6. 121,302

7. $423 = (4 \times 100) + (2 \times 10) + (3 \times 1)$

ꝊꝊꝊꝊ∩∩|||

8. $825 = (8 \times 100) + (2 \times 10) + (5 \times 1)$

ꝊꝊꝊꝊꝊꝊꝊꝊ∩∩|||||

9. $1846 = (1 \times 1000) + (8 \times 100) + (4 \times 10) + (6 \times 1)$

⚇ꝊꝊꝊꝊꝊꝊꝊꝊ∩∩∩∩||||||

10. $1425 = (1 \times 1000) + (4 \times 100) + (2 \times 10) + (5 \times 1)$

⚇ꝊꝊꝊꝊ∩∩|||||

11. $23,547 = (2 \times 10,000) + (3 \times 1000) + (5 \times 100) + (4 \times 10) + (7 \times 1)$

⌒⌒⚇⚇⚇ꝊꝊꝊꝊꝊ∩∩∩∩|||||||

12. $2,346,031 = (2 \times 1,000,000) + (3 \times 100,000) + (4 \times 10,000) + (6 \times 1000) + (0 \times 100) + (3 \times 10) + (1 \times 1)$

𓀀𓀀 ⌒⌒⌒⌒ ⌒⌒⌒⌒⌒ ⚇⚇⚇⚇⚇⚇ ∩∩∩|

13. XI = 11

14. CL = 150

15. XVI = 16

16. LVII = 57

17. XL = 40

18. CM = 900

19. LIX = 59

20. XLIV = 44

21. CXLVI = 146

22. CLXI = 161

23. MDCXXI = 1621

24. MMCDXLV = 2445

25. MMDCLXXVII = 2677

26. MDCXXVI = 1626

27. $\overline{\text{IX}}$CDLXVI = 9466

28. $\overline{\text{V}}$MCCXI = 6211

29. 43 = XLIII

30. 96 = XCVI

31. 129 = CXXIX

32. 469 = CDLXIX

33. 1896 = MDCCCXCVI

34. 4578 = $\overline{\text{IV}}$DLXXVIII

35. 6892 = $\overline{\text{VI}}$DCCCXCII

36. 5847 = $\overline{\text{V}}$DCCCXLVII

37. $80 + 8 = 88$

$$\left.\begin{array}{r}8\\10\end{array}\right\}80$$

$$8\}8$$

38. $700 + 5 = 705$

$$\left.\begin{array}{r}7\\100\end{array}\right\}700$$

$$5\}5$$

39. $500 + 20 + 7 = 527$

$$\left.\begin{array}{r}5\\100\end{array}\right\}500$$

$$\left.\begin{array}{r}2\\10\end{array}\right\}20$$

$$7\}7$$

40. $3000+80+1=3081$

$$\left.\begin{array}{r}3\\1000\end{array}\right\}3000$$

$$\left.\begin{array}{r}8\\10\end{array}\right\}80$$

$$1\}1$$

41. $2000+700+70+6=2776$

$$\left.\begin{array}{r}2\\1000\end{array}\right\}2000$$

$$\left.\begin{array}{r}7\\100\end{array}\right\}700$$

$$\left.\begin{array}{r}7\\10\end{array}\right\}70$$

$$6\}6$$

42. $8000 + 200 + 30 + 6 = 8236$

$$\left.\begin{array}{r}8\\1000\end{array}\right\}8000$$

$$\left.\begin{array}{r}2\\100\end{array}\right\}200$$

$$\left.\begin{array}{r}3\\10\end{array}\right\}30$$

$$6\}6$$

43.

$\boxdot$

$+$

$=$

44.

二
百
六
十
九

45.

五
百
八
十
三

46.

二
千
九
百
六
十
五

47.

四
千
八
百
七
十
七

48.

七
千
六
百
五

49. $\iota\beta = 12$

50. $\varphi\varepsilon = 505$

51. $\sigma\lambda\delta = 234$

52. $\psi o\theta = 779$

53. $43 = \mu\gamma$

54. $257 = \sigma\nu\zeta$

55. $483 = \upsilon\pi\gamma$

56. $895 = \omega\mathsf{Q}\varepsilon$

57. The value of this numeral is 2324.
Roman numeral: MMCCCXXIV
Chinese numeral:

二
千
三
百
二
十
四

58. The value of this numeral is 3413.
Roman numeral: MMMCDXIII
Chinese numeral:

三
千
四
百
一
十
三

59. The value of this numeral is 1741.
Egyptian numeral: 𓆼𓏲𓏲𓏲𓏲𓏲𓏲𓏲𓎢𓎢𓎢𓏤
Chinese numeral:

一
千
七
百
四
十
一

60. The value of this numeral is 2245.
Egyptian numeral: 𓆼𓆼𓏲𓏲𓎢𓎢𓎢𓏦𓏦
Chinese numeral:

二
千
二
百
四
十
五

61. The value of this numeral is 404.
$404 = 3104_{\text{five}}$

62. The value of this numeral is 332.
$332 = 2312_{\text{five}}$

63. The value of this numeral is 192.
$192 = 1232_{\text{five}}$

64. The value of this numeral is 974.
$974 = 12344_{\text{five}}$

65. ∩∩∩∩∩∩∩∩∩|||||||

66. ∩∩∩∩∩∩∩∩∩|||||||||

67. 1776 is the date the Declaration of Independence was signed.

68. The crew expected the number to be the year the old building was built. They were surprised that the number represented 1989, a fairly recent year.

69. Hindu-Arabic: 4,640,224
Roman numeral: MMMMDCXLCCXXIV

70. Hindu-Arabic: 4,647,700
Roman numeral: MMMMDCXLVIIDCC

76. does not make sense; Explanations will vary. Sample explanation: It is possible to understand the concepts without memorizing the symbols.

77. does not make sense; Explanations will vary. Sample explanation: The Egyptian numeration system does not use the same subtraction rule as the Roman numeral system.

78. does not make sense; Explanations will vary. Sample explanation: The Egyptian numeration system often takes more space because the Roman numeral system has a subtraction rule.

79. makes sense

80. 428, 431, 449 or

⊡
ฬ
=
十
八, ⊚⊚⊚⊚∩∩∩|, CCCCXLIX

81. Preceding: ⊚⊚∩∩∩∩∩∩∩∩∩|||||||||

Following: ⊚⊚⊚

82. Roman: XLVI = 46
Egyptian: = 32
Chinese: = 20
Greek: $200 - 46 - 32 - 20 = 102 = \rho\beta$

Chapter 4 Review Exercises

1. $11^2 = 11 \times 11 = 121$

2. $7^3 = 7 \times 7 \times 7 = 343$

3. $472 = (4 \times 10^2) + (7 \times 10^1) + (2 \times 1) = (4 \times 100) + (7 \times 10) + (2 \times 1)$

4. $8076 = (8 \times 10^3) + (0 \times 10^2) + (7 \times 10^1) + (6 \times 1) = (8 \times 1000) + (0 \times 100) + (7 \times 10) + (6 \times 1)$

5. $70,329 = (7 \times 10^4) + (0 \times 10^3) + (3 \times 10^2) + (2 \times 10^1) + (9 \times 1)$
$= (7 \times 10,000) + (0 \times 1000) + (3 \times 100) + (2 \times 10) + (9 \times 1)$

6. $706,953$

7. $740,000,306$

8. $<\vee \quad <\vee \vee\vee = (10+1) \times 60^1 + (10+1+1+1) \times 1$
$= (11 \times 60^1) + (13 \times 1)$
$= 660 + 13$
$= 673$

9. $\vee\vee \quad << \quad <<<$
$= (1+1) \times 60^2 + (10+10) \times 60^1 + (10+10+10) \times 1$
$= (2 \times 60^2) + (20 \times 60) + (30 \times 1)$
$= (2 \times 3600) + 1200 + 30$
$= 7200 + 1230$
$= 8430$

10.
$6 \times 360 = 2160$
$8 \times 20 = 160$
$11 \times 1 = \underline{\quad 11}$
$\qquad\qquad 2331$

11.
$9 \times 7200 = 64,800$
$2 \times 360 = 720$
$0 \times 20 = 0$
$16 \times 1 = \underline{\quad 16}$
$\qquad\qquad 65,536$

12. Each position represents a particular value. The symbol in each position tells how many of that value are represented.

13. $34_{\text{five}} = (3 \times 5^1) + (4 \times 1)$
$= 15 + 4$
$= 19$

14. $110_{\text{two}} = (1 \times 2^2) + (1 \times 2^1) + (0 \times 1)$
$= 4 + 2 + 0$
$= 6$

15. $643_{\text{seven}} = (6 \times 7^2) + (4 \times 7^1) + (3 \times 1)$
$= 294 + 28 + 3$
$= 325$

16. $1084_{\text{nine}} = (1 \times 9^3) + (0 \times 9^2) + (8 \times 9^1) + (4 \times 1)$
$= 729 + 0 + 72 + 4$
$= 805$

17. $FD3_{\text{sixteen}} = (15 \times 16^2) + (13 \times 16^1) + (3 \times 1)$
$= 3840 + 208 + 3$
$= 4051$

18. $202202_{\text{three}} = (2 \times 3^5) + (0 \times 3^4) + (2 \times 3^3) + (2 \times 3^2) + (0 \times 3^1) + (2 \times 1)$
$= 486 + 0 + 54 + 18 + 0 + 2$
$= 560$

19. $89 = (3 \times 5^2) + (2 \times 5^1) + (4 \times 1)$
$= 324_{\text{five}}$

20. $21 = (1 \times 2^4) + (0 \times 2^3) + (1 \times 2^2) + (0 \times 2^1) + (1 \times 1)$
$= 10101_{\text{two}}$

21. $473 = (1 \times 3^5) + (2 \times 3^4) + (2 \times 3^3) + (1 \times 3^2) + (1 \times 3^1) + (2 \times 1)$
$= 243 + 162 + 54 + 9 + 3 + 2$
$= 122112_{\text{three}}$

22. $7093 = (2 \times 7^4) + (6 \times 7^3) + (4 \times 7^2) + (5 \times 7^1) + (2 \times 1)$
$= 4802 + 2058 + 196 + 35 + 2$
$= 26452_{\text{seven}}$

23. $9348 = (1 \times 6^5) + (1 \times 6^4) + (1 \times 6^3) + (1 \times 6^2) + (4 \times 6^1) + (0 \times 1)$
$= 7776 + 1296 + 216 + 36 + 24$
$= 111140_{\text{six}}$

24. $554 = (3 \times 12^2) + (A \times 12^1) + (2 \times 1)$
$= 3A2_{\text{twelve}}$

25.
$$\begin{array}{r} \overset{1}{}46_{\text{seven}} \\ + 53_{\text{seven}} \\ \hline 132_{\text{seven}} \end{array}$$

26.
$$\begin{array}{r} \overset{1\ 1}{}574_{\text{eight}} \\ + 605_{\text{eight}} \\ \hline 1401_{\text{eight}} \end{array}$$

27.
$$\begin{array}{r} {}^{1\,1\,1\,1} \\ 11011_{two} \\ \underline{10101_{two}} \\ 110000_{two} \end{array}$$

28.
$$\begin{array}{r} {}^{1} \\ 43C_{sixteen} \\ \underline{+694_{sixteen}} \\ AD0_{sixteen} \end{array}$$

29.
$$\begin{array}{r} {}^{2\ 10} \\ \cancel{3}\cancel{4}_{six} \\ \underline{25_{six}} \\ 5_{six} \end{array}$$

30.
$$\begin{array}{r} {}^{5\ 8\ 11} \\ \cancel{6}\cancel{2}\cancel{4}_{seven} \\ \underline{-246_{seven}} \\ 345_{seven} \end{array}$$

31.
$$\begin{array}{r} {}^{0\ 1\ 2} \\ 1\cancel{0}\cancel{0}1_{two} \\ \underline{-110_{two}} \\ 11_{two} \end{array}$$

32.
$$\begin{array}{r} {}^{3\ 6\ 1\ 6} \\ \cancel{4}\cancel{1}\cancel{2}\cancel{1}_{five} \\ \underline{-1312_{five}} \\ 2304_{five} \end{array}$$

33.
$$\begin{array}{r} {}^{1} \\ 32_{four} \\ \underline{\times\ \ 3_{four}} \\ 222_{four} \end{array}$$

34.
$$\begin{array}{r} {}^{2} \\ 43_{seven} \\ \underline{\times\ \ 6_{seven}} \\ 354_{seven} \end{array}$$

35.
$$\begin{array}{r} {}^{2\ 2} \\ 123_{five} \\ \underline{\quad\ 4_{five}} \\ 1102_{five} \end{array}$$

36.

$$
\begin{array}{r}
133 \\
2_{\text{four}} \overline{) 332_{\text{four}}} \\
\underline{2} \\
13 \\
\underline{12} \\
12 \\
\underline{12} \\
0
\end{array}
$$

133_{four}

37.

$$
\begin{array}{r}
12 \\
4_{\text{five}} \overline{) 103_{\text{five}}} \\
\underline{4} \\
13 \\
\underline{13} \\
0
\end{array}
$$

12_{five}

38. 1246

39. 12,432

40. $2486 = (2 \times 1000) + (4 \times 100) + (8 \times 10) + (6 \times 1)$

41. $34{,}573 = (3 \times 10{,}000) + (4 \times 1000) + (5 \times 100) + (7 \times 10) + (3 \times 1)$

42. DDCCCBAAAA = 2314

43. 5492 = DDDDDCCCCBBBBBBBBBAA

44. Answers will vary.

45. CLXIII = 163

46. MXXXIV = 1034

47. MCMXC = 1990

48. 49 = XLIX

49. 2965 = MMCMLXV

50. If symbols increase in value from left to right, subtract the value of the symbol on the left from the symbol on the right.

51. $500 + 50 + 4 = 554$

$\left.\begin{array}{c}5\\100\end{array}\right\}500$

$\left.\begin{array}{c}5\\10\end{array}\right\}50$

$\left.4\right\}4$

52. $8000 + 200 + 50 + 3 = 8253$

$\left.\begin{array}{c}8\\1000\end{array}\right\}8000$

$\left.\begin{array}{c}2\\100\end{array}\right\}200$

$\left.\begin{array}{c}5\\10\end{array}\right\}50$

$\left.3\right\}3$

53.
二
百
七
十
四

54.
三
千
五
百
八
十
七

55. 365

56. 4520

57. G
Y
I
X
C

58. F
Z
H
Y
E
X
D

59. Answers will vary.

60. $\chi\nu\gamma = 653$

61. $\chi o\eta = 678$

62. $453 = \nu\nu\gamma$

63. $902 = \pi\beta$

64. UNG = 357

65. mhZRD = 37,894

66. rXJH = 80,618

67. 597 = WRG

68. $25,483 = $ lfVQC

Chapter 4 Test

1. $9 \times 9 \times 9 = 729$

2. $567 = (5 \times 10^2) + (6 \times 10^1) + (7 \times 1)$
$\qquad = (5 \times 100) + (6 \times 10) + (7 \times 1)$

3. $63,028 = (6 \times 10^4) + (3 \times 10^3) + (0 \times 10^2) + (2 \times 10^1) + (8 \times 1)$
$\qquad\qquad = (6 \times 10,000) + (3 \times 1000) + (0 \times 100) + (2 \times 10) + (8 \times 1)$

4. $7000 + 400 + 90 + 3 = 7493$

5. $400,000 + 200 + 6 = 400,206$

6. A number represents, "How many?" whereas a numeral is a symbol used to write a number

7. A symbol for zero is needed as a place holder when there are no values for a position.

8. $<<\ <\vee\vee\ <\vee = (10+10) \times 60^2 + (10+1+1) \times 60^1 + (10+1) \times 1$
$\qquad = (20 \times 60^2) + (12 \times 60) + (11 \times 1) = 72,000 + 720 + 11 = 72,731$

9. $\begin{aligned} 4 \times 360 &= 1440 \\ 6 \times 20 &=\ \ 120 \\ 0 \times 1 &=\ \ \underline{\quad 0} \\ & \quad\ \ 1560 \end{aligned}$

10. $423_{\text{five}} = (4 \times 5^2) + (2 \times 5^1) + (3 \times 1) = 4 \times 25 + 10 + 3 = 100 + 10 + 3 = 113$

11. $267_{\text{nine}} = (2 \times 9^2) + (6 \times 9^1) + (7 \times 1) = 2 \times 81 + 54 + 7 = 162 + 54 + 7 = 223$

12. $110101_{\text{two}} = (1 \times 2^5) + (1 \times 2^4) + (0 \times 2^3) + (1 \times 2^2) + (0 \times 2^1) + (1 \times 1) = 32 + 16 + 0 + 4 + 0 + 1 = 53$

13. $77 = (2 \times 3^3) + (2 \times 3^2) + (1 \times 3^1) + (2 \times 1) = 2212_{\text{three}}$

14. $56 = (1 \times 2^5) + (1 \times 2^4) + (1 \times 2^3) + (0 \times 2^2) + (0 \times 2^1) + (0 \times 1) = 111000_{\text{two}}$

15. $1844 = (2 \times 5^4) + (4 \times 5^3) + (3 \times 5^2) + (3 \times 5^1) + (4 \times 1) = 1250 + 500 + 75 + 15 + 4 = 24334_{\text{five}}$

16. $$\begin{array}{r} \overset{1\ 1}{234_{\text{five}}} \\ +423_{\text{five}} \\ \hline 1212_{\text{five}} \end{array}$$

17. $$\begin{array}{r} \overset{5\ 9}{56\!\!\not{2}_{\text{seven}}} \\ -145_{\text{seven}} \\ \hline 414_{\text{seven}} \end{array}$$

18. $$\begin{array}{r} \overset{2}{5}4_{\text{six}} \\ \times\ \ 3_{\text{six}} \\ \hline 250_{\text{six}} \end{array}$$

19. $$\begin{array}{r} 221 \\ 3_{\text{five}} \overline{)1213_{\text{five}}} \\ \underline{11} \\ 11 \\ \underline{11} \\ 03 \\ \underline{3} \\ 0 \end{array}$$

    221_{five}

20. 20,303

21. $32,634 = (3 \times 10,000) + (2 \times 1000) + (6 \times 100) + (3 \times 10) + (4 \times 1)$

    ⦅⦅⦅𓏢𓏢𓎖𓎖999999999∩∩∩|||||

22. $\text{MCMXCIV} = \underset{M}{\overbrace{1000}} + \underset{CM}{\overbrace{(1000-100)}} + \underset{XC}{\overbrace{(100-10)}} + \underset{IV}{\overbrace{(5-1)}} = 1000 + 900 + 90 + 4 = 1994$

23. $459 = \underset{CD}{\overbrace{(500-100)}} + \underset{L}{\overbrace{50}} + \underset{IX}{\overbrace{(10-1)}} = \text{CDLIX}$

24. Answers will vary.

Chapter 5
Number Theory and the Real Number System

Check Points 5.1

1. The statement given in part (b) is true.

   a. False, 8 does not divide 48,324 because 8 does not divide 324.

   b. True, 6 divides 48,324 because both 2 and 3 divide 48,324. 2 divides 48,324 because the last digit is 4. 3 divides 48,324 because the sum of the digits, 21, is divisible by 3.

   c. False, 4 *does* divide 48,324 because the last two digits form 24 which is divisible by 4.

2.
```
        120
        / \
      (2)  60
           / \
         (2)  30
              / \
            (2)  15
                 / \
               (3) (5)
```
   $120 = 2^3 \cdot 3 \cdot 5$

3. $225 = 3^2 \cdot 5^2$
   $825 = 3 \cdot 5^2 \cdot 11$
   Greatest Common Divisor: $3 \cdot 5^2 = 75$

4. $192 = 2^6 \cdot 3$
   $288 = 2^5 \cdot 3^2$
   Greatest Common Divisor: $2^5 \cdot 3 = 96$
   The largest number of people that can be placed in each singing group is 96.

5. $18 = 2 \cdot 3^2$
   $30 = 2 \cdot 3 \cdot 5$
   Least common multiple is: $90 = 2 \cdot 3^2 \cdot 5$

6. $40 = 2^3 \cdot 5$
   $60 = 2^2 \cdot 3 \cdot 5$
   Least common multiple is: $120 = 2^3 \cdot 3 \cdot 5$
   It will be 120 minutes, or 2 hours, until both movies begin again at the same time.
   The time will be 5:00 PM.

Exercise Set 5.1

1. 6944

   a. Yes. The last digit is four.

   b. No. The sum of the digits is 23, which is not divisible by 3.

   c. Yes. The last two digits form 44, which is divisible by 4.

   d. No. The number does not end in 0 or 5.

   e. No. The number is not divisible by both 2 and 3.

   f. Yes. The last three digits form 944, which is divisible by 8.

   g. No. The sum of the digits is 23, which is not divisible by 9.

   h. No. The number does not end in 0.

   i. No. The number is not divisible by both 3 and 4.

2. 7245

   a. No. The last digit is five.

   b. Yes. The sum of the digits is 18, which is divisible by 3.

   c. No. The last two digits form 45, which is not divisible by 4.

   d. Yes. The number ends with 5.

   e. No. The number is not divisible by both 2 and 3.

   f. No. The last 3 digits form 245, which is not divisible by 8.

   g. Yes. The sum of the digits is 18, which is divisible by 9.

   h. No. The number does not end in 0.

   i. No. The number is not divisible by both 3 and 4.

3. 21,408

    a. Yes. The last digit is eight.

    b. Yes. The sum of the digits is 15, which is divisible by 3.

    c. Yes. The last two digits form 08, which is divisible by 4.

    d. No. The number does not end in 0 or 5.

    e. Yes. The number is divisible by both 2 and 3.

    f. Yes. The last three digits form 408, which is divisible by 8.

    g. No. The sum of the digits is 15, which is not divisible by 9.

    h. No. The number does not end in 0.

    i. Yes. The number is divisible by both 3 and 4.

4. 25,025

    a. No. The last digit is 5.

    b. No. The sum of the digits is 14, which is not divisible by 3.

    c. No. The last two digits form 25 which is not divisible by 4.

    d. Yes. The last digit is 5.

    e. No. The number is not divisible by 2 and 3.

    f. No. The last three digits form 025 which is not divisible by 8.

    g. No. The sum of the digits is 14, which is not divisible by 9.

    h. No. The number does not end in 0.

    i. No. The number is not divisible by 3 and 4.

5. 26,428

    a. Yes. The last digit is 8.

    b. No. The sum of the digits is 22, which is not divisible by 3.

    c. Yes. The last 2 digits form 28, which is divisible by 4.

    d. No. The last digit is eight.

    e. No. The number is not divisible by both two and three.

    f. No. The last three digits form 428, which is not divisible by 8.

    g. No. The sum of the digits is 22, which is not divisible by 9.

    h. No. The number does not end in 0.

    i. No. The number is not divisible by 3 and 4.

6. 89,001

    a. No. The last digit is one.

    b. Yes. The sum of the digits is 18, which is divisible by 3.

    c. No. The last two digits form 01, which is not divisible by 4.

    d. No. The last digit is one.

    e. No. The number is not divisible by two and three.

    f. No. The last three digits form 001, which is not divisible by 8.

    g. Yes. The sum of the digits is 18, which is divisible by 9.

    h. No. The number does not end in 0.

    i. No. The number is not divisible by 3 and 4.

7. 374,832

    a. Yes. The last digit is 2.

    b. Yes. The sum of the digits is 27, which is divisible by 3.

    c. Yes. The last two digits form 32, which is divisible by 4.

    d. No. The last digit is two.

    e. Yes. The number is divisible by 2 and 3.

    f. Yes. The last 3 digits form 832, which is divisible by 8.

    g. Yes. The sum of the digits is 27, which is divisible by 9.

    h. No. The last digit is 2.

    i. Yes. The number is divisible by both 3 and 4.

8. 347,712

   a. Yes. The last digit is 2.

   b. Yes. The sum of the digits is 24, which is divisible by 3.

   c. Yes. The last two digits form 12, which is divisible by 4.

   d. No. The last digit is 2.

   e. Yes. The number is divisible by both 2 and 3.

   f. Yes. The last 3 digits form 712, which is divisible by 8.

   g. No. The sum of the digits is 24, which is not divisible by 9.

   h. No. The last digit is 2.

   i. Yes. The number is divisible by both 3 and 4.

9. 6,126,120

   a. Yes. The last digit is 0.

   b. Yes. The sum of the digits is 18, which is divisible by 3.

   c. Yes. The last two digits form 20, which is divisible by 4.

   d. Yes. The last digit is 0.

   e. Yes. The number is divisible by both 2 and 3.

   f. Yes. The last 3 digits form 120, which is divisible by 8.

   g. Yes. The sum of the digits is 18, which is divisible by 9.

   h. Yes. The last digit is 0.

   i. Yes. The number is divisible by both 3 and 4.

10. 5,941,221

   a. No. The last digit is 1.

   b. Yes. The sum of the digits is 24, which is divisible by 3.

   c. No. The last two digits form 21, which is not divisible by 4.

   d. No. The last digit is 1.

   e. No. The number is not divisible by both 2 and 3.

   f. No. The last 3 digits form 221, which is not divisible by 8.

   g. No. The sum of the digits is 24, which is not divisible by 9.

   h. No. The last digit is 1.

   i. No. The number is not divisible by both 3 and 4.

11. True. $5958 \div 3 = 1986$
The sum of the digits is 27, which is divisible by 3.

12. True. $8142 \div 3 = 2714$
The sum of the digits is 15, which is divisible by 3.

13. True. $10{,}612 \div 4 = 2653$
The last two digits form 12, which is divisible by 4.

14. True. $15{,}984 \div 4 = 3996$
The last two digits form 84, which is divisible by 4.

15. False

16. False

17. True. $104{,}538 \div 6 = 17{,}423$
The number is divisible by both 2 and 3.

18. True. $163{,}944 \div 6 = 27{,}324$
The number is divisible by both 2 and 3.

19. True. $20{,}104 \div 8 = 2513$
The last three digits form 104, which is divisible by 8.

20. True. $28{,}096 \div 8 = 3512$
The last three digits form 96, which is divisible by 8.

21. False

22. False

23. True. $517{,}872 \div 12 = 43{,}156$
The number is divisible by both 3 and 4.

24. True. $785{,}172 \div 12 = 65{,}431$
The number is divisible by both 3 and 4.

25.

$75 = 3 \cdot 5^2$

26.

$45 = 3^2 \cdot 5$

27.
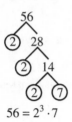
$56 = 2^3 \cdot 7$

28.
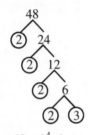
$48 = 2^4 \cdot 3$

29.

$105 = 3 \cdot 5 \cdot 7$

30.
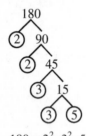
$180 = 2^2 \cdot 3^2 \cdot 5$

31.
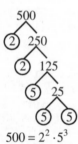
$500 = 2^2 \cdot 5^3$

32.
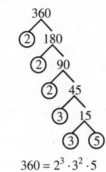
$360 = 2^3 \cdot 3^2 \cdot 5$

33.

$663 = 3 \cdot 13 \cdot 17$

34.
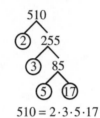
$510 = 2 \cdot 3 \cdot 5 \cdot 17$

35.

$885 = 3 \cdot 5 \cdot 59$

36.
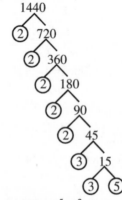
$999 = 3^3 \cdot 37$

37.
1440
$$1440 = 2^5 \cdot 3^2 \cdot 5$$

38.

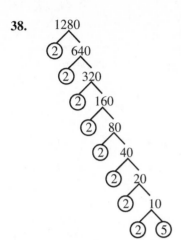

$$1280 = 2^8 \cdot 5$$

39.

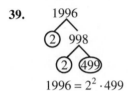

$$1996 = 2^2 \cdot 499$$

40.

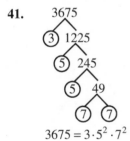

$$1575 = 3^2 \cdot 5^2 \cdot 7$$

41.

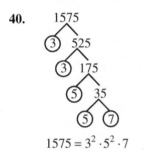

$$3675 = 3 \cdot 5^2 \cdot 7^2$$

42.

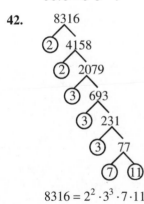

$$8316 = 2^2 \cdot 3^3 \cdot 7 \cdot 11$$

43.

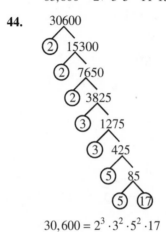

$$85,800 = 2^3 \cdot 3 \cdot 5^2 \cdot 11 \cdot 13$$

44.   30600

$$30,600 = 2^3 \cdot 3^2 \cdot 5^2 \cdot 17$$

45. $42 = 2 \cdot 3 \cdot 7$

$56 = 2^3 \cdot 7$

Greatest Common Divisor: $2 \cdot 7 = 14$

46. $25 = 5^2$

$70 = 2 \cdot 5 \cdot 7$

Greatest Common Divisor: 5

47. $16 = 2^4$

$42 = 2 \cdot 3 \cdot 7$

Greatest Common Divisor: 2

48. $66 = 2 \cdot 3 \cdot 11$

$90 = 2 \cdot 3^2 \cdot 5$

Greatest Common Divisor: $2 \cdot 3 = 6$

49. $60 = 2^2 \cdot 3 \cdot 5$

$108 = 2^2 \cdot 3^3$

Greatest Common Divisor: $2^2 \cdot 3 = 12$

50. $96 = 2^5 \cdot 3$

$212 = 2^2 \cdot 53$

Greatest Common Divisor: $2^2 = 4$

51. $72 = 2^3 \cdot 3^2$

$120 = 2^3 \cdot 3 \cdot 5$

Greatest Common Divisor: $2^3 \cdot 3 = 24$

52. $220 = 2^2 \cdot 5 \cdot 11$

$400 = 2^4 \cdot 5^2$

Greatest Common Divisor: $2^2 \cdot 5 = 20$

53. $324 = 2 \cdot 3^2 \cdot 19$

$380 = 2^2 \cdot 5 \cdot 19$

Greatest Common Divisor: $2 \cdot 19 = 38$

54. $224 = 2^5 \cdot 7$

$430 = 2 \cdot 5 \cdot 43$

Greatest Common Divisor: 2

55. $240 = 2^4 \cdot 3 \cdot 5$

$285 = 3 \cdot 5 \cdot 19$

Greatest Common Divisor: $3 \cdot 5 = 15$

56. $150 = 2 \cdot 3 \cdot 5^2$

$480 = 2^5 \cdot 3 \cdot 5$

Greatest Common Divisor: $2 \cdot 3 \cdot 5 = 30$

57. $42 = 2 \cdot 3 \cdot 7$

$56 = 2^3 \cdot 7$

Least Common Multiple: $2^3 \cdot 3 \cdot 7 = 168$

58. $25 = 5^2$

$70 = 2 \cdot 5 \cdot 7$

Least Common Multiple: $2 \cdot 5^2 \cdot 7 = 350$

59. $16 = 2^4$

$42 = 2 \cdot 3 \cdot 7$

Least Common Multiple: $2^4 \cdot 3 \cdot 7 = 336$

60. $66 = 2 \cdot 3 \cdot 11$

$90 = 2 \cdot 3^2 \cdot 5$

Least Common Multiple $= 2 \cdot 3^2 \cdot 5 \cdot 11 = 990$

61. $60 = 2^2 \cdot 3 \cdot 5$

$108 = 2^2 \cdot 3^3$

Least Common Multiple: $2^2 \cdot 3^3 \cdot 5 = 540$

62. $96 = 2^5 \cdot 3$

$212 = 2^2 \cdot 53$

Least Common Multiple $= 2^5 \cdot 3 \cdot 53 = 5088$

63. $72 = 2^3 \cdot 3^2$

$120 = 2^3 \cdot 3 \cdot 5$

Least Common Multiple: $2^3 \cdot 3^2 \cdot 5 = 360$

64. $220 = 2^2 \cdot 5 \cdot 11$

$400 = 2^4 \cdot 5^2$

Least Common Multiple $= 2^4 \cdot 5^2 \cdot 11 = 4400$

65. $342 = 2 \cdot 3^2 \cdot 19$

$380 = 2^2 \cdot 5 \cdot 19$

Least Common Multiple: $2^2 \cdot 3^2 \cdot 5 \cdot 19 = 3420$

66. $224 = 2^5 \cdot 7$

$430 = 2 \cdot 5 \cdot 43$

Least Common Multiple

$= 2^5 \cdot 5 \cdot 7 \cdot 43$

$= 48{,}160$

67. $240 = 2^4 \cdot 3 \cdot 5$

$285 = 3 \cdot 5 \cdot 19$

Least Common Multiple

$= 2^4 \cdot 3 \cdot 5 \cdot 19$

$= 4560$

68. $150 = 2 \cdot 3 \cdot 5^2$

$480 = 2^5 \cdot 3 \cdot 5$

Least Common Multiple

$= 2^5 \cdot 3 \cdot 5^2$

$= 2400$

69. $d = 8$

$9 \,|\, 12{,}348$

70. $d = 7$

$9 \,|\, 23{,}427$

71. $d = 6$

$8 \,|\, 76{,}523{,}456$

72. $d = 4$

$8 \,|\, 88{,}888{,}824$

73. $d = 2,\ 6$

$4 \,|\, 963{,}232$ and $4 \,|\, 963{,}236$

74. $d = 2, 6$

$4\lfloor 752,672$ and $4\lfloor 752,676$

75. 28 is a perfect number.

$28 = 1 + 2 + 4 + 7 + 14$

76. 6 is a perfect number.

$6 = 1 + 2 + 3$

77. 20 is not a perfect number.

$20 \neq 1 + 2 + 4 + 5 + 10$

78. 50 is not a perfect number.

$50 \neq 1 + 2 + 5 + 10 + 25$

79. 41 is not an emirp because 14 is not prime.

80. 43 is not an emirp because 34 is not prime.

81. 107 is an emirp because 701 is also prime.

82. 113 is an emirp because 311 is also prime.

83. 13 is not a Germain prime because $2(13) + 1 = 27$ is not prime.

84. 11 is a Germain prime because $2(11) + 1 = 23$ is prime.

85. 241 is not a Germain prime because $2(241) + 1 = 483$ is not prime.

86. 97 is not a Germain prime because $2(97) + 1 = 195$ is not prime.

87. The GCD of 24 and 27 is 3.
The LCM of 24 and 27 is 216.
$3 \times 216 = 648$
$24 \times 27 = 648$
The product of the greatest common divisor and least common multiple of two numbers equals the product of the two numbers.

88. The GCD of 48 and 72 is 24.
The LCM of 48 and 72 is 144.
$24 \times 144 = 3456$
$48 \times 72 = 3456$
The product of the greatest common divisor and least common multiple of two numbers equals the product of the two numbers.

89. The numbers are the prime numbers less than 100.

90. a. Multiples of 18: 18, 36, 54, 72, 90, 108, 126, 144, 162, 180, 198, 216
Multiples of 12: 12, 24, 36, 48, 60, 72, 84, 96, 108, 120, 132, 144, 156, 168, 180, 192, 204, 216
Common multiples of 12 and 18: 36, 72, 108, 144, 180, 216
Over a 216-year period, the two species will share the forest 6 times (once every 36 years).

b. The least common multiple of 17 and 13 is 221. The two species will share the forest once every 221 years.

c. By having a prime number as the length of its life cycle, the species will share the forest with other species less often.

91. $300 = 2^2 \cdot 3 \cdot 5^2$

$144 = 2^4 \cdot 3^2$

Greatest Common Divisor: $2^2 \cdot 3 = 12$
There would be 25 groups with 12 bottles of water each. There would be 12 groups with 12 cans of food each.

92. $180 = 2^2 \cdot 3^2 \cdot 5$

$144 = 2^4 \cdot 3^2$

Greatest Common Divisor: $2^2 \cdot 3^2 = 36$
There would be 5 all-male groups of 36.
There would be 4 all-female groups of 36.

93. $310 = 2 \cdot 5 \cdot 31$

$460 = 2^2 \cdot 5 \cdot 23$

Greatest Common Divisor: $2 \cdot 5 = 10$
There would be 31 groups of 10 five-dollar bills.
There would be 46 groups of 10 ten-dollar bills.

94. $360 = 2^3 \cdot 3^2 \cdot 5$

$432 = 2^4 \cdot 3^3$

Greatest Common Divisor: $2^3 \cdot 3^2 = 72$
There would be 5 groups of 72 football cards.
There would be 6 groups of 72 baseball cards.

95. $6 = 2 \cdot 3$

$10 = 2 \cdot 5$

Least Common Multiple is: $2 \cdot 3 \cdot 5 = 30$
It will be 30 more nights until both have the evening off, or July 1.

96. $40 = 2^3 \cdot 5$

$100 = 2^2 \cdot 5^2$

Least common multiple is: $2^3 \cdot 5^2 = 200$
It will be 200 minutes until each movie starts at the same time, or 3 hours and 20 minutes. The time would be 3:20 PM.

97. $15 = 3 \cdot 5$

$18 = 2 \cdot 3^2$

Least Common Multiple is: $2 \cdot 3^2 \cdot 5 = 90$
It takes 90 minutes.

98. $40 = 2^3 \cdot 5$

$45 = 3^2 \cdot 5$

Least common multiple is: $2^3 \cdot 3^2 \cdot 5 = 360$
It will take 360 seconds or 6 minutes.

110. does not make sense; Explanations will vary. Sample explanation: A prime number's only two natural number factors are 1 and itself.

111. does not make sense; Explanations will vary. Sample explanation: For the greatest common factor, select the common prime factors with the *smallest* exponent. For the least common multiple, select all prime factors with the *largest* exponent.

112. does not make sense; Explanations will vary. Sample explanation: For this you must find the greatest common factor.

113. does not make sense; Explanations will vary. Sample explanation: Not all such numbers of this form are prime.

114. Ex: 1020 is divisible by 4 but not by 8.

115. a. $GCD = 2^{14} \cdot 3^{25} \cdot 5^{30}$

  b. $LCM = 2^{17} \cdot 3^{37} \cdot 5^{31}$

116. 53
His age was prime 6 years ago at the age of 47. His age will be prime again in 6 years at the age of 59.

117. $85 + 15 = 100 = 2^2 \cdot 5^2$

$100 + 15 = 115 = 5 \cdot 23$

$LCM = 2^2 \cdot 5 \cdot 23 = 2300$
The films will begin at the same time

$2300 \text{ min} \left(= 38\frac{1}{3}\text{hr} \right)$ after noon (today), or at 2:20

A.M. on the third day.

118. 2 and 3 are the only two consecutive prime numbers whose difference is odd. Since all other primes are odd, the difference between any other two consecutive primes is even.

119. Yes, since 96 is divisible by 4, then 67,234,096 is divisible by 4.

120. No, since $1 + 2 + 5 + 4 + 1 + 7 + 5 + 0 = 25$ is not divisible by 3, then 12,541,750 is not divisible by 3.

121. Yes, since $4 + 8 + 2 + 0 + 1 + 6 + 5 + 1 = 27$ is divisible by 9, then 48,201,651 is divisible by 9.

Check Points 5.2

1.

2. a. $6 > -7$ because 6 is to the right of -2 on the number line.

  b. $-8 < -1$ because -8 is to the left of -1 on the number line.

  c. $-25 < -2$ because -25 is to the left of -2 on the number line.

  d. $-14 < 0$ because -14 is to the left of 0 on the number line.

3. a. $|-8| = 8$ because -8 is 8 units from 0.

  b. $|6| = 6$ because 6 is 6 units from 0.

  b. $-|8| = -8$ because 8 is 8 units from 0 and the negative of 8 is -8.

4. a. $30 - (-7) = 30 + 7 = 37$

  b. $-14 - (-10) = -14 + 10 = -4$

  c. $-14 - 10 = -24$

5. $\overbrace{-162}^{2007 \text{ deficit}} - \overbrace{(-455)}^{2008 \text{ deficit}} = -162 + 455 = \$293 \text{ billion}$

6. a. $(-5)^2 = (-5)(-5) = 25$

b. $-5^2 = -(5 \cdot 5) = -25$

c. $(-4)^3 = (-4)(-4)(-4) = -64$

d. $(-3)^4 = (-3)(-3)(-3)(-3) = 81$

7. $7^2 - 48 \div 4^2 \cdot 5 + 2$
$= 49 - 48 \div 16 \cdot 5 + 2$
$= 49 - 3 \cdot 5 + 2$
$= 49 - 15 + 2$
$= 34 + 2$
$= 36$

8. $(-8)^2 - (10 - 13)^2(-2)$
$= (-8)^2 - (-3)^2(-2)$
$= 64 - (9)(-2)$
$= 64 - (-18)$
$= 64 + (+18)$
$= 82$

Exercise Set 5.2

1.

2.

3.

4.

5. $-2 < 7$ because -2 is to the left of 7 on the number line.

6. $-1 < 13$ because -1 is to the left of 13 on the number line.

7. $-13 < -2$ because -13 is to the left of -2 on the number line.

8. $-1 > -13$ because -1 is to the right of -13 on the number line.

9. $8 > -50$ because 8 is to the right of -50 on the number line.

10. $7 > -9$ because 7 is to the right of -9 on the number line.

11. $-100 < 0$ because -100 is to the left of 0 on the number line.

12. $0 > -300$ because 0 is to the right of -300 on the number line.

13. $|-14| = 14$ because -14 is 14 units from 0.

14. $|-16| = 16$ because -16 is 16 units from 0.

15. $|14| = 14$ because 14 is 14 units from 0.

16. $|16| = 16$ because 16 is 16 units from 0.

17. $|-300,000| = 300,000$ because $-300,000$ is $300,000$ units from 0.

18. $|-1,000,000| = 1,000,000$ because $-1,000,000$ is $1,000,000$ units from 0.

19. $-7 + (-5) = -12$

20. $-3 + (-4) = -7$

21. $12 + (-8) = 4$

22. $13 + (-5) = 8$

23. $6 + (-9) = -3$

24. $3 + (-11) = -8$

25. $-9 + (+4) = -5$

26. $-7 + (+3) = -4$

27. $-9 + (-9) = -18$

28. $-13 + (-13) = -26$

29. $9 + (-9) = 0$

30. $13 + (-13) = 0$

31. $13 - 8 = 5$

32. $14 - 3 = 11$

33. $8 - 15 = 8 + (-15) = -7$

34. $9 - 20 = 9 + (-20) = -11$

35. $4 - (-10) = 4 + 10 = 14$

36. $3 - (-17) = 3 + 17 = 20$

37. $-6 - (-17) = -6 + 17 = 11$

38. $-4 - (-19) = -4 + 19 = 15$

39. $-12 - (-3) = -12 + 3 = -9$

40. $-19 - (-2) = -19 + 2 = -17$

41. $-11 - 17 = -11 + (-17) = -28$

42. $-19 - 21 = -19 + (-21) = -40$

43. $6(-9) = -54$

44. $5(-7) = -35$

45. $(-7)(-3) = 21$

46. $(-8)(-5) = 40$

47. $(-2)(6) = -12$

48. $(-3)(10) = -30$

49. $(-13)(-1) = 13$

50. $(-17)(-1) = 17$

51. $0(-5) = 0$

52. $0(-8) = 0$

53. $5^2 = 5 \cdot 5 = 25$

54. $6^2 = 6 \cdot 6 = 36$

55. $(-5)^2 = (-5) \cdot (-5) = 25$

56. $(-6)^2 = (-6)(-6) = 36$

57. $4^3 = 4 \cdot 4 \cdot 4 = 64$

58. $2^3 = 2 \cdot 2 \cdot 2 = 8$

59. $(-5)^3 = (-5)(-5)(-5) = 25(-5) = -125$

60. $(-4)^3 = (-4)(-4)(-4) = 16(-4) = -64$

61. $(-5)^4 = (-5)(-5)(-5)(-5) = 625$

62. $(-4)^4 = (-4)(-4)(-4)(-4) = 256$

63. $-3^4 = -[3 \cdot 3 \cdot 3 \cdot 3] = -81$

64. $-1^4 = -[1 \cdot 1 \cdot 1 \cdot 1] = -1$

65. $(-3)^4 = (-3)(-3)(-3)(-3) = 81$

66. $(-1)^4 = (-1)(-1)(-1)(-1) = 1$

67. $\dfrac{-12}{4} = -3$

68. $\dfrac{-40}{5} = -8$

69. $\dfrac{21}{-3} = -7$

70. $\dfrac{60}{-6} = -10$

71. $\dfrac{-90}{-3} = 30$

72. $\dfrac{-66}{-6} = 11$

73. $\dfrac{0}{-7} = 0$

74. $\dfrac{0}{-8} = 0$

75. $\dfrac{-7}{0}$ is undefined

76. $\dfrac{0}{0}$ is undefined.

77. $(-480) \div 24 = \dfrac{-480}{24} = -20$

78. $(-300) \div 12 = \dfrac{-300}{12} = -25$

79. $(465) \div (-15) = \dfrac{465}{-15} = -31$

80. $(-594) \div (-18) = \dfrac{-594}{-18} = 33$

81. $7 + 6 \cdot 3 = 7 + 18 = 25$

82. $-5 + (-3) \cdot 8 = -5 + (-24) = -29$

83. $(-5) - 6(-3) = -5 + 18 = 13$

84. $-8(-3) - 5(-6) = 24 - (-30) = 24 + 30 = 54$

85. $6 - 4(-3) - 5 = 6 - (-12) - 5$
$$= 6 + 12 - 5$$
$$= 18 - 5$$
$$= 13$$

86. $3 - 7(-1) - 6 = 3 - (-7) - 6$
$$= 3 + 7 - 6$$
$$= 10 - 6$$
$$= 4$$

87. $3 - 5(-4 - 2) = 3 - 5(-6)$
$$= 3 - (-30)$$
$$= 3 + 30$$
$$= 33$$

88. $3 - 9(-1 - 6) = 3 - 9(-7)$
$$= 3 - (-63)$$
$$= 3 + 63$$
$$= 66$$

89. $(2 - 6)(-3 - 5) = (-4)(-8) = 32$

90. $9 - 5(6 - 4) - 10 = 9 - 5(2) - 10$
$$= 9 - 10 - 10$$
$$= -1 - 10$$
$$= -11$$

91. $3(-2)^2 - 4(-3)^2 = 3(4) - 4(9)$
$$= 12 - 36$$
$$= -24$$

92. $5(-3)^2 - 2(-2)^3 = 5(9) - 2(-8)$
$$= 45 - (-16)$$
$$= 45 + 16$$
$$= 61$$

93. $(2 - 6)^2 - (3 - 7)^2 = (-4)^2 - (-4)^2$
$$= 16 - 16$$
$$= 0$$

94. $(4 - 6)^2 - (5 - 9)^3 = (-2)^2 - (-4)^3$
$$= 4 - (-64)$$
$$= 4 + 64$$
$$= 68$$

95. $6(3 - 5)^3 - 2(1 - 3)^3 = 6(-2)^3 - 2(-2)^3$
$$= 6(-8) - 2(-8)$$
$$= -48 + 16$$
$$= -32$$

96. $-3(-6 + 8)^3 - 5(-3 + 5)^3 = -3(2)^3 - 5(2)^3$
$$= -3(8) - 5(8)$$
$$= -24 - 40$$
$$= -64$$

97. $8^2 - 16 \div 2^2 \cdot 4 - 3 = 64 - 16 \div 4 \cdot 4 - 3$
$$= 64 - 4 \cdot 4 - 3$$
$$= 64 - 16 - 3$$
$$= 45$$

98. $10^2 - 100 \div 5^2 \cdot 2 - (-3)$
$$= 10^2 - 100 \div 25 \cdot 2 - (-3)$$
$$= 100 - 4 \cdot 2 + 3$$
$$= 100 - 8 + 3$$
$$= 92 + 3$$
$$= 95$$

99. $24 \div \left[3^2 \div (8 - 5)\right] - (-6)$
$$= 24 \div [9 \div 3] - (-6)$$
$$= 24 \div 3 + 6$$
$$= 8 + 6$$
$$= 14$$

100. $30 \div \left[5^2 \div (7 - 12)\right] - (-9)$
$$= 30 \div [25 \div (-5)] - (-9)$$
$$= 30 \div [-5] + 9$$
$$= -6 + 9$$
$$= 3$$

101. $8 - 3\left[-2(2 - 5) - 4(8 - 6)\right]$

$= 8 - 3\left[-2(-3) - 4(2)\right]$

$= 8 - 3\left[6 - 8\right]$

$= 8 - 3\left[-2\right]$

$= 8 + 6$

$= 14$

102. $8 - 3\left[-2(5 - 7) - 5(4 - 2)\right]$

$= 8 - 3\left[-2(-2) - 5(2)\right]$

$= 8 - 3\left[4 - 10\right]$

$= 8 - 3\left[-6\right]$

$= 8 + 18$

$= 26$

103. $-2^2 + 4\left[16 \div (3 - 5)\right]$

$= -4 + 4\left[16 \div (-2)\right]$

$= -4 + 4\left[-8\right]$

$= -4 - 32$

$= -36$

104. $-3^2 + 2\left[20 \div (7 - 11)\right]$

$= -9 + 2\left[20 \div (-4)\right]$

$= -9 + 2\left[-5\right]$

$= -9 - 10$

$= -19$

105. $4\left|10 - (8 - 20)\right|$

$= 4\left|10 - (-12)\right|$

$= 4\left|10 + 12\right|$

$= 4\left|22\right|$

$= 88$

106. $-5\left|7 - (20 - 8)\right|$

$= -5\left|7 - (12)\right|$

$= -5\left|-5\right|$

$= -5(5)$

$= -25$

107. $\left[-5^2 + (6 - 8)^3 - (-4)\right] - \left[\left|-2\right|^3 + 1 - 3^2\right]$

$= \left[-5^2 + (-2)^3 - (-4)\right] - \left[2^3 + 1 - 3^2\right]$

$= \left[-25 - 8 - (-4)\right] - \left[8 + 1 - 9\right]$

$= \left[-25 - 8 + 4\right] - \left[8 + 1 - 9\right]$

$= \left[-33 + 4\right] - \left[0\right]$

$= -29 - 0$

$= -29$

108. $\left[-4^2 + (7 - 10)^3 - (-27)\right] - \left[\left|-2\right|^5 + 1 - 5^2\right]$

$= \left[-4^2 + (-3)^3 - (-27)\right] - \left[2^5 + 1 - 5^2\right]$

$= \left[-16 - 27 - (-27)\right] - \left[32 + 1 - 25\right]$

$= \left[-16 - 27 + 27\right] - \left[32 + 1 - 25\right]$

$= -16 - 8$

$= -24$

109. $\dfrac{12 \div 3 \cdot 5\left|2^2 + 3^2\right|}{7 + 3 - 6^2}$

$= \dfrac{12 \div 3 \cdot 5\left|4 + 9\right|}{7 + 3 - 36}$

$= \dfrac{12 \div 3 \cdot 5\left|13\right|}{10 - 36}$

$= \dfrac{12 \div 3 \cdot 5 \cdot 13}{-26}$

$= \dfrac{4 \cdot 5 \cdot 13}{-26}$

$= \dfrac{260}{-26}$

$= -10$

110. $\dfrac{-3 \cdot 5^2 + 89}{(5 - 6)^2 - 2\left|3 - 7\right|}$

$= \dfrac{-3 \cdot 25 + 89}{(-1)^2 - 2\left|-4\right|}$

$= \dfrac{-75 + 89}{1 - 2(4)}$

$= \dfrac{14}{1 - 8}$

$= \dfrac{14}{-7}$

$= -2$

111. $-10 - (-2)^3 = -10 - (-8) = -10 + 8 = -2$

112. $-100-(-5)^3 = -100-(-125) = -100+125 = 25$

113. $[2(7-10)]^2 = [2(-3)]^2 = [-6]^2 = 36$

114. $[2(9-11)]^4 = [2(-2)]^4 = [-4]^4 = 256$

115. The difference in elevation is
$20,320-(-282)$
$= 20,320+282$
$= 20,602$ feet

116. The difference in elevation is
$19,321-(-436)$
$= 19,321+436$
$= 19,757$ feet

117. $\overbrace{-436}^{2000\text{ deficit}} - \overbrace{(-794)}^{2007\text{ deficit}} = -436+794 = \$358$ billion

118. $\overbrace{-412}^{2001\text{ deficit}} - \overbrace{(-817)}^{2006\text{ deficit}} = -412+817 = \$405$ billion

119. $\dfrac{\overbrace{-767}^{2005\text{ deficit}} + \overbrace{(-817)}^{2006\text{ deficit}}}{2} = -\$792$ billion

$\overbrace{(-794)}^{2007\text{ deficit}} - \overbrace{(-792)}^{\substack{2005/2006 \\ \text{average deficit}}} = -794+792 = -\$2$ billion

The 2007 deficit exceeded this average by $2 billion.

120. $\dfrac{\overbrace{-651}^{2004\text{ deficit}} + \overbrace{(-767)}^{2005\text{ deficit}} + \overbrace{(-817)}^{2006\text{ deficit}}}{3} = -\$745$ billion

$\overbrace{(-794)}^{2007\text{ deficit}} - \overbrace{(-745)}^{\substack{2004/2005/2006 \\ \text{average deficit}}} = -794+745 = -\$49$ billion

The 2007 deficit exceeded this average by $49 billion.

121. $1783-2158 = -375$
In 2003, the difference between the amount collected and the amount spent was –$375 billion. This represents a deficit.

122. $1880-2293 = -413$
In 2004, the difference between the amount collected and the amount spent was –$413 billion. This represents a deficit

123. 2001 surplus: $1991-1863 = 128$
2007 deficit: $2568-2730 = -162$
The difference between the 2001 surplus and the 2007 deficit was $128-(-162) = 290$ or $290 billion.

124. 2001 surplus: $1991-1863 = 128$
2006 deficit: $2407-2655 = -248$
The difference between the 2001 surplus and the 2006 deficit was $128-(-248) = 376$ or $376 billion.

125. Actual 2006 deficit: $2407-2655 = -248$
The difference between the 2006 projected surplus and the actual 2006 deficit was $505-(-248) = 753$ or $753 billion.

126. Actual 2007 deficit: $2568-2730 = -162$
The difference between the 2001 projected surplus and the actual 2007 deficit was $573-(-162) = 735$ or $735 billion.

127. $3°-(-4°) = 3°+4° = 7°$ F

128. $1°-(-12°) = 1°+12° = 13°$ F

129. $-24°-(-22°) = -24°+22° = -2°$ F

130. $-25°-(-22°) = -25°+22° = -3°$ F

140. makes sense

141. makes sense

142. does not make sense; Explanations will vary. Sample explanation: The sign rules for multiplication and division are the same.

143. makes sense

144. $8-2\cdot(3-4) = 10$

145. $(8-2)\cdot 3-4 = 14$

146. -7

147. -36

148. 150

Check Points 5.3

1. $72 = 2^3 \cdot 3^2$

$90 = 2 \cdot 5 \cdot 3^2$

Greatest Common Divisor is $2 \cdot 3^2$ or 18.

$\dfrac{72}{90} = \dfrac{72 \div 18}{90 \div 18} = \dfrac{4}{5}$

2. $2\dfrac{5}{8} = \dfrac{8 \cdot 2 + 5}{8} = \dfrac{16 + 5}{8} = \dfrac{21}{8}$

3. $\dfrac{5}{3} = 1\dfrac{2}{3}$

4. a. $\dfrac{3}{8} = 0.375$

$$
\begin{array}{r}
0.375 \\
8\overline{)3.000} \\
24 \\
\hline
60 \\
56 \\
\hline
40 \\
40 \\
\hline
0
\end{array}
$$

b. $\dfrac{5}{11} = 0.\overline{45}$

$$
\begin{array}{r}
0.4545\ldots \\
11\overline{)5.0000} \\
44 \\
\hline
60 \\
55 \\
\hline
50 \\
44 \\
\hline
60 \\
55 \\
\hline
5
\end{array}
$$

5. a. $0.9 = \dfrac{9}{10}$

b. $0.86 = \dfrac{86}{100} = \dfrac{86 \div 2}{100 \div 2} = \dfrac{43}{50}$

c. $0.053 = \dfrac{53}{1000}$

6. $n = 0.\overline{2}$

$n = 0.22222\ldots$

$10n = 2.22222\ldots$

$10n = 2.2222\ldots$

$\underline{-n = 0.2222\ldots}$

$9n = 2.0$

$n = \dfrac{2}{9}$

7. $n = 0.\overline{79}$

$n = 0.7979\ldots$

$100n = 79.7979\ldots$

$100n = 79.7979\ldots$

$\underline{-\quad n = 0.7979\ldots}$

$99n = 79$

$n = \dfrac{79}{99}$

8. a. $\dfrac{4}{11} \cdot \dfrac{2}{3} = \dfrac{8}{33}$

b. $\left(-\dfrac{3}{7}\right)\left(-\dfrac{14}{4}\right) = \dfrac{42}{28} = \dfrac{42 \div 14}{28 \div 14} = \dfrac{3}{2}$ or $1\dfrac{1}{2}$

c. $\left(3\dfrac{2}{5}\right)\left(1\dfrac{1}{2}\right) = \dfrac{17}{5} \cdot \dfrac{3}{2} = \dfrac{51}{10}$ or $5\dfrac{1}{10}$

9. a. $\dfrac{9}{11} \div \dfrac{5}{4} = \dfrac{9}{11} \cdot \dfrac{4}{5} = \dfrac{36}{55}$

b. $-\dfrac{8}{15} \div \dfrac{2}{5} = -\dfrac{8}{15} \cdot \dfrac{5}{2} = -\dfrac{40}{30} = -\dfrac{4}{3}$ or $-1\dfrac{1}{3}$

c. $3\dfrac{3}{8} \div 2\dfrac{1}{4} = \dfrac{27}{8} \div \dfrac{9}{4} = \dfrac{27}{8} \cdot \dfrac{4}{9} = \dfrac{108}{72} = \dfrac{3}{2}$ or $1\dfrac{1}{2}$

10. a. $\dfrac{5}{12} + \dfrac{3}{12} = \dfrac{5+3}{12} = \dfrac{8}{12} = \dfrac{2}{3}$

b. $\dfrac{7}{4} - \dfrac{1}{4} = \dfrac{7-1}{4} = \dfrac{6}{4} = \dfrac{3}{2}$ or $1\dfrac{1}{2}$

c. $-3\dfrac{3}{8} - \left(-1\dfrac{1}{8}\right) = -\dfrac{27}{8} - \left(-\dfrac{9}{8}\right)$

$= -\dfrac{27}{8} + \dfrac{9}{8}$

$= \dfrac{-27 + 9}{8}$

$= \dfrac{-18}{8}$

$= -\dfrac{9}{4}$

or $-2\dfrac{1}{4}$

11. $\dfrac{1}{5} + \dfrac{3}{4} = \dfrac{1}{5} \cdot \dfrac{4}{4} + \dfrac{3}{4} \cdot \dfrac{5}{5} = \dfrac{4}{20} + \dfrac{15}{20} = \dfrac{19}{20}$

12. $\dfrac{3}{10} - \dfrac{7}{12} = \dfrac{3}{10} \cdot \dfrac{6}{6} - \dfrac{7}{12} \cdot \dfrac{5}{5} = \dfrac{18}{60} - \dfrac{35}{60} = -\dfrac{17}{60}$

13. $\left(-\dfrac{1}{2}\right)^2 - \left(\dfrac{7}{10} - \dfrac{8}{15}\right)^2 (-18)$

$= \left(-\dfrac{1}{2}\right)^2 - \left(\dfrac{21}{30} - \dfrac{16}{30}\right)^2 (-18)$

$= \left(-\dfrac{1}{2}\right)^2 - \left(\dfrac{5}{30}\right)^2 (-18)$

$= \left(-\dfrac{1}{2}\right)^2 - \left(\dfrac{1}{6}\right)^2 (-18)$

$= \dfrac{1}{4} - \dfrac{1}{36}(-18)$

$= \dfrac{1}{4} + \dfrac{18}{36}$

$= \dfrac{1}{4} + \dfrac{2}{4}$

$= \dfrac{3}{4}$

14. First, find the sum:

$\dfrac{1}{3} + \dfrac{1}{2} = \dfrac{1}{3} \cdot \dfrac{2}{2} + \dfrac{1}{2} \cdot \dfrac{3}{3} = \dfrac{2}{6} + \dfrac{3}{6} = \dfrac{5}{6}$

Next, divide by 2: $\dfrac{5}{6} \div \dfrac{2}{1} = \dfrac{5}{6} \cdot \dfrac{1}{2} = \dfrac{5}{12}$

15. Amount of eggs needed

$= \dfrac{\text{desired serving size}}{\text{recipe serving size}} \times \text{eggs in recipe}$

$= \dfrac{7 \text{ dozen}}{5 \text{ dozen}} \times 2 \text{ eggs}$

$= \dfrac{14}{5} \text{ eggs}$

$= 2\dfrac{4}{5} \text{ eggs}$

$\approx 3 \text{ eggs}$

Exercise Set 5.3

1. $10 = 2 \cdot 5$

$15 = 3 \cdot 5$

Greatest Common Divisor is 5.

$\dfrac{10}{15} = \dfrac{10 \div 5}{15 \div 5} = \dfrac{2}{3}$

2. $18 = 2 \cdot 3^2$

$45 = 3^2 \cdot 5$

Greatest Common Divisor is 3^2 or 9.

$\dfrac{18}{45} = \dfrac{18 \div 9}{45 \div 9} = \dfrac{2}{5}$

3. $15 = 3 \cdot 5$

$18 = 2 \cdot 3^2$

Greatest Common Divisor is 3.

$\dfrac{15}{18} = \dfrac{15 \div 3}{18 \div 3} = \dfrac{5}{6}$

4. $16 = 2^4$

$64 = 2^6$

Greatest Common Divisor is 2^4 or 16.

$\dfrac{16}{64} = \dfrac{16 \div 16}{64 \div 16} = \dfrac{1}{4}$

5. $24 = 2^3 \cdot 3$

$42 = 2 \cdot 3 \cdot 7$

Greatest Common Divisor is $2 \cdot 3$ or 6.

$\dfrac{24}{42} = \dfrac{24 \div 6}{42 \div 6} = \dfrac{4}{7}$

6. $32 = 2^5$

$80 = 2^4 \cdot 5$

Greatest Common Divisor is 2^4 or 16.

$\dfrac{32}{80} = \dfrac{32 \div 16}{80 \div 16} = \dfrac{2}{5}$

7. $60 = 2^2 \cdot 3 \cdot 5$

$108 = 2^2 \cdot 3^3$

Greatest Common Divisor is $2^2 \cdot 3$ or 12.

$\dfrac{60}{108} = \dfrac{60 \div 12}{108 \div 12} = \dfrac{5}{9}$

8. $112 = 2^4 \cdot 7$

$128 = 2^7$

Greatest Common Divisor is 2^4 or 16.

$\dfrac{112}{128} = \dfrac{112 \div 16}{128 \div 16} = \dfrac{7}{8}$

9. $342 = 2 \cdot 3^2 \cdot 19$

$380 = 2^2 \cdot 5 \cdot 19$

Greatest Common Divisor is $2 \cdot 19$ or 38.

$\dfrac{342}{380} = \dfrac{342 \div 38}{380 \div 38} = \dfrac{9}{10}$

10. $210 = 2 \cdot 3 \cdot 5 \cdot 7$

$252 = 2^2 \cdot 3^2 \cdot 7$

Greatest Common Divisor is $2 \cdot 3 \cdot 7$ or 42.

$\dfrac{210}{252} = \dfrac{210 \div 42}{252 \div 42} = \dfrac{5}{6}$

11. $308 = 2^2 \cdot 7 \cdot 11$

$418 = 2 \cdot 11 \cdot 19$

Greatest Common Divisor is $2 \cdot 11$ or 22.

$\dfrac{308}{418} = \dfrac{308 \div 22}{418 \div 22} = \dfrac{14}{19}$

12. $144 = 2^4 \cdot 3^2$

$300 = 2^2 \cdot 3 \cdot 5^2$

Greatest Common Divisor is $2^2 \cdot 3$ or 12.

$\dfrac{144}{300} = \dfrac{144 \div 12}{300 \div 12} = \dfrac{12}{25}$

13. $2\dfrac{3}{8} = \dfrac{8 \cdot 2 + 3}{8} = \dfrac{16 + 3}{8} = \dfrac{19}{8}$

14. $2\dfrac{7}{9} = \dfrac{9 \cdot 2 + 7}{9} = \dfrac{18 + 7}{9} = \dfrac{25}{9}$

15. $-7\dfrac{3}{5} = -\dfrac{5 \cdot 7 + 3}{5} = -\dfrac{35 + 3}{5} = -\dfrac{38}{5}$

16. $-6\dfrac{2}{5} = -\dfrac{5 \cdot 6 + 2}{5} = -\dfrac{30 + 2}{5} = -\dfrac{32}{5}$

17. $12\dfrac{7}{16} = \dfrac{16 \cdot 12 + 7}{16} = \dfrac{192 + 7}{16} = \dfrac{199}{16}$

18. $11\dfrac{5}{16} = \dfrac{16 \cdot 11 + 5}{16} = \dfrac{176 + 5}{16} = \dfrac{181}{16}$

19. $\dfrac{23}{5} = 4\dfrac{3}{5}$

20. $\dfrac{47}{8} = 5\dfrac{7}{8}$

21. $-\dfrac{76}{9} = -8\dfrac{4}{9}$

22. $-\dfrac{59}{9} = -6\dfrac{5}{9}$

23. $\dfrac{711}{20} = 35\dfrac{11}{20}$

24. $\dfrac{788}{25} = 31\dfrac{13}{25}$

25. $\dfrac{3}{4} = 0.75$

$$
\begin{array}{r}
0.75 \\
4\overline{)3.00} \\
28 \\
\hline
20 \\
20 \\
\hline
0
\end{array}
$$

26. $\dfrac{3}{5} = 0.6$

$$
\begin{array}{r}
0.6 \\
5\overline{)3.0} \\
30 \\
\hline
0
\end{array}
$$

27. $\dfrac{7}{20} = 0.35$

$$\begin{array}{r} 0.35 \\ 20\overline{)7.00} \\ 60 \\ \hline 100 \\ 100 \\ \hline 0 \end{array}$$

28. $\dfrac{3}{20} = 0.15$

$$\begin{array}{r} 0.15 \\ 20\overline{)3.00} \\ 20 \\ \hline 100 \\ 100 \\ \hline 0 \end{array}$$

29. $\dfrac{7}{8} = 0.875$

$$\begin{array}{r} 0.875 \\ 8\overline{)7.000} \\ 64 \\ \hline 60 \\ 56 \\ \hline 40 \\ 40 \\ \hline 0 \end{array}$$

30. $\dfrac{5}{16} = 0.3125$

$$\begin{array}{r} 0.3125 \\ 16\overline{)5.0000} \\ 48 \\ \hline 20 \\ 16 \\ \hline 40 \\ 32 \\ \hline 80 \end{array}$$

31. $\dfrac{9}{11} = 0.\overline{81}$

$$\begin{array}{r} 0.8181\ldots \\ 11\overline{)9.0000} \\ 88 \\ \hline 20 \\ 11 \\ \hline 90 \\ 88 \\ \hline 20 \\ 11 \\ \hline 9 \end{array}$$

32. $\dfrac{3}{11} = 0.\overline{27}$

$$\begin{array}{r} 0.2727\ldots \\ 11\overline{)3.0000} \\ 22 \\ \hline 80 \\ 77 \\ \hline 30 \\ 22 \\ \hline 80 \\ 77 \\ \hline 3 \end{array}$$

33. $\dfrac{22}{7} = 3.\overline{142857}$

$$\begin{array}{r} 3.142857\ldots \\ 7\overline{)22.000000} \\ 21 \\ \hline 10 \\ 7 \\ \hline 30 \\ 28 \\ \hline 20 \\ 14 \\ \hline 60 \\ 56 \\ \hline 40 \\ 35 \\ \hline 50 \\ 49 \\ \hline 10 \end{array}$$

34. $\dfrac{20}{3} = 6.\overline{6}$

$$
\begin{array}{r}
6.66\ldots \\
3\overline{)20.00} \\
18 \\
\overline{20} \\
18 \\
\overline{20} \\
18 \\
\overline{2}
\end{array}
$$

35. $\dfrac{2}{7} = 0.\overline{285714}$

$$
\begin{array}{r}
0.2857142\ldots \\
7\overline{)2.000000} \\
14 \\
\overline{60} \\
56 \\
\overline{40} \\
35 \\
\overline{50} \\
49 \\
\overline{10} \\
7 \\
\overline{30} \\
28 \\
\overline{20} \\
14 \\
\overline{6}
\end{array}
$$

36. $\dfrac{5}{7} = 0.\overline{714285}$

$$
\begin{array}{r}
0.7142857\ldots \\
7\overline{)5.000000} \\
49 \\
\overline{10} \\
7 \\
\overline{30} \\
28 \\
\overline{20} \\
14 \\
\overline{60} \\
56 \\
\overline{40} \\
35 \\
\overline{50} \\
49 \\
\overline{1}
\end{array}
$$

37. $0.3 = \dfrac{3}{10}$

38. $0.9 = \dfrac{9}{10}$

39. $0.4 = \dfrac{4}{10} = \dfrac{4 \div 2}{10 \div 2} = \dfrac{2}{5}$

40. $0.6 = \dfrac{6}{10} = \dfrac{6 \div 2}{10 \div 2} = \dfrac{3}{5}$

41. $0.39 = \dfrac{39}{100}$

42. $0.59 = \dfrac{59}{100}$

43. $0.82 = \dfrac{82}{100} = \dfrac{82 \div 2}{100 \div 2} = \dfrac{41}{50}$

44. $0.64 = \dfrac{64}{100}$

$64 = 2^6$

$100 = 2^2 \cdot 5^2$

Greatest Common Divisor is 2^2 or 4.

$\dfrac{64}{100} = \dfrac{64 \div 4}{100 \div 4} = \dfrac{16}{25}$

45. $0.725 = \dfrac{725}{1000}$

$725 = 5^2 \cdot 29$

$1000 = 2^3 \cdot 5^3$

Greatest Common Divisor is 5^2 or 25.

$\dfrac{725}{1000} = \dfrac{725 \div 25}{1000 \div 25} = \dfrac{29}{40}$

46. $0.625 = \dfrac{625}{1000}$

$625 = 5^4$

$1000 = 2^3 \cdot 5^3$

Greatest Common Divisor is 5^3 or 125.

$\dfrac{625 \div 125}{1000 \div 125} = \dfrac{5}{8}$

47. $0.5399 = \dfrac{5399}{10,000}$

48. $0.7006 = \dfrac{7006}{10,000}$

$7006 = 2 \cdot 31 \cdot 113$

$10,000 = 2^4 \cdot 5^4$

Greatest Common Divisor is 2.

$\dfrac{7006}{10,000} = \dfrac{7006 \div 2}{10,000 \div 2} = \dfrac{3503}{5000}$

49. $n = 0.777\ldots$

$10n = 7.777\ldots$

$\begin{aligned} 10n &= 7.777\ldots \\ -n &= 0.777\ldots \\ \hline 9n &= 7 \end{aligned}$

$n = \dfrac{7}{9}$

50. $n = 0.1111\ldots$

$10n = 1.1111\ldots$

$\begin{aligned} 10n &= 1.1111\ldots \\ -n &= 0.1111\ldots \\ \hline 9n &= 1 \end{aligned}$

$n = \dfrac{1}{9}$

51. $n = 0.999\ldots$

$10n = 9.999\ldots$

$\begin{aligned} 10n &= 9.999\ldots \\ -n &= 0.999\ldots \\ \hline 9n &= 9 \end{aligned}$

$n = 1$

52. $n = 0.\overline{3}\ldots$

$10n = 3.333\ldots$

$\begin{aligned} 10n &= 3.3333\ldots \\ -n &= 0.3333\ldots \\ \hline 9n &= 3.0 \end{aligned}$

$n = \dfrac{3}{9}$ or $\dfrac{1}{3}$

53. $n = 0.3636\ldots$

$100n = 36.3636\ldots$

$\begin{aligned} 100n &= 36.3636\ldots \\ -n &= 0.3636\ldots \\ \hline 99n &= 36 \end{aligned}$

$n = \dfrac{36}{99}$ or $\dfrac{4}{11}$

54. $n = 0.8181\ldots$

$100n = 81.8181\ldots$

$\begin{aligned} 100n &= 81.8181\ldots \\ -n &= 0.8181\ldots \\ \hline 99n &= 81 \end{aligned}$

$n = \dfrac{81}{99}$ or $\dfrac{9}{11}$

55. $n = 0.257257\ldots$

$1000n = 257.257257\ldots$

$\begin{aligned} 1000n &= 257.257257\ldots \\ -n &= .257257\ldots \\ \hline 999n &= 257 \end{aligned}$

$n = \dfrac{257}{999}$

56. $n = 0.529529\ldots$

$1000n = 529.529529\ldots$

$\begin{aligned} 1000n &= 529.529529\ldots \\ -n &= 0.529529\ldots \\ \hline 999n &= 529 \end{aligned}$

$n = \dfrac{529}{999}$

57. $\dfrac{3}{8} \cdot \dfrac{7}{11} = \dfrac{3 \cdot 7}{8 \cdot 11} = \dfrac{21}{88}$

58. $\dfrac{5}{8} \cdot \dfrac{3}{11} = \dfrac{5 \cdot 3}{8 \cdot 11} = \dfrac{15}{88}$

59. $\left(-\dfrac{1}{10}\right)\left(\dfrac{7}{12}\right) = \dfrac{(-1)(7)}{10 \cdot 12} = \dfrac{-7}{120} = -\dfrac{7}{120}$

60. $\left(-\dfrac{1}{8}\right)\left(\dfrac{5}{9}\right) = \dfrac{(-1)(5)}{8 \cdot 9} = \dfrac{-5}{72} = -\dfrac{5}{72}$

61. $\left(-\dfrac{2}{3}\right)\left(-\dfrac{9}{4}\right) = \dfrac{(-2)(-9)}{3\cdot 4} = \dfrac{18}{12} = \dfrac{3}{2}$

62. $\left(-\dfrac{5}{4}\right)\left(-\dfrac{6}{7}\right) = \dfrac{(-5)(-6)}{4\cdot 7} = \dfrac{30}{28} = \dfrac{15}{14}$

63. $\left(3\dfrac{3}{4}\right)\left(1\dfrac{3}{5}\right) = \dfrac{15}{4}\cdot\dfrac{8}{5} = \dfrac{120}{20} = \dfrac{6}{1} = 6$

64. $\left(2\dfrac{4}{5}\right)\left(1\dfrac{1}{4}\right) = \dfrac{14}{5}\cdot\dfrac{5}{4} = \dfrac{70}{20} = \dfrac{7}{2}$ or $3\dfrac{1}{2}$

65. $\dfrac{5}{4}\div\dfrac{3}{8} = \dfrac{5}{4}\cdot\dfrac{8}{3} = \dfrac{5\cdot 8}{4\cdot 3} = \dfrac{40}{12} = \dfrac{10}{3}$

66. $\dfrac{5}{8}\div\dfrac{4}{3} = \dfrac{5}{8}\cdot\dfrac{3}{4} = \dfrac{5\cdot 3}{8\cdot 4} = \dfrac{15}{32}$

67. $-\dfrac{7}{8}\div\dfrac{15}{16} = -\dfrac{7}{8}\cdot\dfrac{16}{15}$

$= \dfrac{(-7)(16)}{8\cdot 15}$

$= \dfrac{-112}{120}$

$= -\dfrac{14}{15}$

68. $-\dfrac{13}{20}\div\dfrac{4}{5} = -\dfrac{13}{20}\cdot\dfrac{5}{4}$

$= \dfrac{(-13)(5)}{20\cdot 4}$

$= \dfrac{-65}{80}$

$= -\dfrac{65}{80}$

$= -\dfrac{13}{16}$

69. $6\dfrac{3}{5}\div 1\dfrac{1}{10} = \dfrac{33}{5}\div\dfrac{11}{10} = \dfrac{33}{5}\cdot\dfrac{10}{11} = \dfrac{330}{55} = \dfrac{6}{1} = 6$

70. $1\dfrac{3}{4}\div 2\dfrac{5}{8} = \dfrac{7}{4}\div\dfrac{21}{8} = \dfrac{7}{4}\cdot\dfrac{8}{21} = \dfrac{56}{84} = \dfrac{2}{3}$

71. $\dfrac{2}{11}+\dfrac{3}{11} = \dfrac{2+3}{11} = \dfrac{5}{11}$

72. $\dfrac{5}{13}+\dfrac{2}{13} = \dfrac{5+2}{13} = \dfrac{7}{13}$

73. $\dfrac{5}{6}-\dfrac{1}{6} = \dfrac{5-1}{6} = \dfrac{4}{6} = \dfrac{2}{3}$

74. $\dfrac{7}{12}-\dfrac{5}{12} = \dfrac{7-5}{12} = \dfrac{2}{12} = \dfrac{1}{6}$

75. $\dfrac{7}{12}-\left(-\dfrac{1}{12}\right) = \dfrac{7}{12}+\dfrac{1}{12} = \dfrac{7+1}{12} = \dfrac{8}{12} = \dfrac{2}{3}$

76. $\dfrac{5}{16}-\left(-\dfrac{5}{16}\right) = \dfrac{5}{16}+\dfrac{5}{16} = \dfrac{5+5}{16} = \dfrac{10}{16} = \dfrac{5}{8}$

77. $\dfrac{1}{2}+\dfrac{1}{5} = \left(\dfrac{1}{2}\right)\left(\dfrac{5}{5}\right)+\left(\dfrac{1}{5}\right)\left(\dfrac{2}{2}\right)$

$= \dfrac{5}{10}+\dfrac{2}{10}$

$= \dfrac{5+2}{10}$

$= \dfrac{7}{10}$

78. $\dfrac{1}{3}+\dfrac{1}{5} = \left(\dfrac{1}{3}\right)\left(\dfrac{5}{5}\right)+\left(\dfrac{1}{5}\right)\left(\dfrac{3}{3}\right)$

$= \dfrac{5}{15}+\dfrac{3}{15}$

$= \dfrac{5+3}{15}$

$= \dfrac{8}{15}$

79. $\dfrac{3}{4}+\dfrac{3}{20} = \left(\dfrac{3}{4}\right)\left(\dfrac{5}{5}\right)+\dfrac{3}{20}$

$= \dfrac{15}{20}+\dfrac{3}{20}$

$= \dfrac{15+3}{20}$

$= \dfrac{18}{20}$

$= \dfrac{9}{10}$

80. $\dfrac{2}{5}+\dfrac{2}{15} = \left(\dfrac{2}{5}\right)\left(\dfrac{3}{3}\right)+\dfrac{2}{15} = \dfrac{6}{15}+\dfrac{2}{15} = \dfrac{6+2}{15} = \dfrac{8}{15}$

81. $\dfrac{5}{24} + \dfrac{7}{30} = \left(\dfrac{5}{24}\right)\left(\dfrac{5}{5}\right) + \left(\dfrac{7}{30}\right)\left(\dfrac{4}{4}\right)$

$\qquad = \dfrac{25}{120} + \dfrac{28}{120}$

$\qquad = \dfrac{25 + 28}{120}$

$\qquad = \dfrac{53}{120}$

82. $\dfrac{7}{108} + \dfrac{55}{144}$

$108 = 2^2 \cdot 3^3$

$144 = 2^4 \cdot 3^2$

Least Common Multiple: $2^4 \cdot 3^3 = 432$

$\dfrac{7}{108} + \dfrac{55}{144} = \left(\dfrac{7}{108}\right)\left(\dfrac{4}{4}\right) + \left(\dfrac{55}{144}\right)\left(\dfrac{3}{3}\right)$

$\qquad = \dfrac{28}{432} + \dfrac{165}{432}$

$\qquad = \dfrac{28 + 165}{432} = \dfrac{193}{432}$

83. $\dfrac{13}{18} - \dfrac{2}{9} = \dfrac{13}{18} - \dfrac{2}{9}\left(\dfrac{2}{2}\right)$

$\qquad = \dfrac{13}{18} - \dfrac{4}{18}$

$\qquad = \dfrac{13 - 4}{18}$

$\qquad = \dfrac{9}{18}$

$\qquad = \dfrac{1}{2}$

84. $\dfrac{13}{15} - \dfrac{2}{45} = \left(\dfrac{13}{15}\right)\left(\dfrac{3}{3}\right) - \dfrac{2}{45} = \dfrac{39}{45} - \dfrac{2}{45} = \dfrac{39 - 2}{45}$

$\qquad = \dfrac{37}{45}$

85. $\dfrac{4}{3} - \dfrac{3}{4} = \dfrac{4}{3}\left(\dfrac{4}{4}\right) - \dfrac{3}{4}\left(\dfrac{3}{3}\right)$

$\qquad = \dfrac{16}{12} - \dfrac{9}{12}$

$\qquad = \dfrac{16 - 9}{12}$

$\qquad = \dfrac{7}{12}$

86. $\dfrac{3}{2} - \dfrac{2}{3} = \dfrac{3}{2}\left(\dfrac{3}{3}\right) - \dfrac{2}{3}\left(\dfrac{2}{2}\right) = \dfrac{9}{6} - \dfrac{4}{6} = \dfrac{9 - 4}{6} = \dfrac{5}{6}$

87. $\dfrac{1}{15} - \dfrac{27}{50}$

$15 = 3 \cdot 5$

$50 = 2 \cdot 5^2$

Least Common Multiple is $2 \cdot 3 \cdot 5^2 = 6 \cdot 25 = 150$

$\dfrac{1}{15}\left(\dfrac{10}{10}\right) - \dfrac{27}{50}\left(\dfrac{3}{3}\right) = \dfrac{10}{150} - \dfrac{81}{150}$

$\qquad = \dfrac{10 - 81}{150}$

$\qquad = -\dfrac{71}{150}$

88. $\dfrac{4}{15} - \dfrac{1}{6} = \dfrac{4}{15}\left(\dfrac{2}{2}\right) - \dfrac{1}{6}\left(\dfrac{5}{5}\right)$

$\qquad = \dfrac{8}{30} - \dfrac{5}{30}$

$\qquad = \dfrac{8 - 5}{30}$

$\qquad = \dfrac{3}{30}$

$\qquad = \dfrac{1}{10}$

89. $2\dfrac{2}{3} + 1\dfrac{3}{4} = 2\dfrac{8}{12} + 1\dfrac{9}{12} = \dfrac{32}{12} + \dfrac{21}{12} = \dfrac{53}{12}$ or $4\dfrac{5}{12}$

90. $2\dfrac{1}{8} + 3\dfrac{3}{4} = 2\dfrac{1}{8} + 3\dfrac{6}{8} = \dfrac{17}{8} + \dfrac{30}{8} = \dfrac{47}{8}$ or $5\dfrac{7}{8}$

91. $3\dfrac{2}{3} - 2\dfrac{1}{2} = 3\dfrac{4}{6} - 2\dfrac{3}{6} = \dfrac{22}{6} - \dfrac{15}{6} = \dfrac{7}{6}$ or $1\dfrac{1}{6}$

92. $3\dfrac{3}{4} - 2\dfrac{1}{3} = 3\dfrac{9}{12} - 2\dfrac{4}{12} = \dfrac{45}{12} - \dfrac{28}{12} = \dfrac{17}{12}$ or $1\dfrac{5}{12}$

93. $-5\dfrac{2}{3} + 3\dfrac{1}{6} = -5\dfrac{4}{6} + 3\dfrac{1}{6} = \dfrac{-34}{6} + \dfrac{19}{6} = -\dfrac{15}{6} = -\dfrac{5}{2}$

$\qquad$ or $-2\dfrac{1}{2}$

94. $-2\dfrac{1}{2} + 1\dfrac{3}{4} = -2\dfrac{2}{4} + 1\dfrac{3}{4} = \dfrac{-10}{4} + \dfrac{7}{4} = -\dfrac{3}{4}$

95. $-1\dfrac{4}{7} - \left(-2\dfrac{5}{14}\right) = -1\dfrac{8}{14} + 2\dfrac{5}{14} = \dfrac{-22}{14} + \dfrac{33}{14} = \dfrac{11}{14}$

96. $-1\dfrac{4}{9}-\left(-2\dfrac{5}{18}\right)=-1\dfrac{8}{18}+2\dfrac{5}{18}=\dfrac{-26}{18}+\dfrac{41}{18}=\dfrac{15}{18}=\dfrac{5}{6}$

97. $\left(\dfrac{1}{2}-\dfrac{1}{3}\right)\div\dfrac{5}{8}=\left[\left(\dfrac{1}{2}\right)\left(\dfrac{3}{3}\right)-\dfrac{1}{3}\left(\dfrac{2}{2}\right)\right]\div\dfrac{5}{8}$

$=\left(\dfrac{3}{6}-\dfrac{2}{6}\right)\div\dfrac{5}{8}$

$=\dfrac{1}{6}\div\dfrac{5}{8}$

$=\dfrac{1}{6}\cdot\dfrac{8}{5}$

$=\dfrac{1\cdot8}{6\cdot5}$

$=\dfrac{8}{30}$

$=\dfrac{4}{15}$

98. $\left(\dfrac{1}{2}+\dfrac{1}{4}\right)\div\left(\dfrac{1}{2}+\dfrac{1}{3}\right)=\left(\dfrac{1}{2}\cdot\dfrac{2}{2}+\dfrac{1}{4}\right)\div\left(\dfrac{1}{2}\cdot\dfrac{3}{3}+\dfrac{1}{3}\cdot\dfrac{2}{2}\right)$

$=\left(\dfrac{2}{4}+\dfrac{1}{4}\right)\div\left(\dfrac{3}{6}+\dfrac{2}{6}\right)$

$=\dfrac{3}{4}\div\dfrac{5}{6}$

$=\dfrac{3}{4}\cdot\dfrac{6}{5}$

$=\dfrac{3\cdot6}{4\cdot5}$

$=\dfrac{18}{20}$

$=\dfrac{9}{10}$

99. $-\dfrac{9}{4}\left(\dfrac{1}{2}\right)+\dfrac{3}{4}\div\dfrac{5}{6}=-\dfrac{9}{8}+\dfrac{9}{10}$

$=-\dfrac{9}{40}$

100. $\left[-\dfrac{4}{7}-\left(-\dfrac{2}{5}\right)\right]\left[-\dfrac{3}{8}+\left(-\dfrac{1}{9}\right)\right]=\left[-\dfrac{6}{35}\right]\left[-\dfrac{35}{72}\right]$

$=\dfrac{1}{12}$

101. $\dfrac{\dfrac{7}{9}-3}{\dfrac{5}{6}}\div\dfrac{3}{2}+\dfrac{3}{4}=\dfrac{-\dfrac{20}{9}}{\dfrac{5}{6}}\div\dfrac{3}{2}+\dfrac{3}{4}$

$=-\dfrac{8}{3}\times\dfrac{2}{3}+\dfrac{3}{4}$

$=-\dfrac{16}{9}+\dfrac{3}{4}$

$=-\dfrac{37}{36}$ or $-1\dfrac{1}{36}$

102. $\dfrac{\dfrac{17}{25}}{\dfrac{3}{5}-4}\div\dfrac{1}{5}+\dfrac{1}{2}=\dfrac{\dfrac{17}{25}}{-\dfrac{17}{5}}\div\dfrac{1}{5}+\dfrac{1}{2}$

$=-\dfrac{1}{5}\div\dfrac{1}{5}+\dfrac{1}{2}$

$=-1+\dfrac{1}{2}$

$=-\dfrac{1}{2}$

103. $\dfrac{1}{4}-6(2+8)\div\left(-\dfrac{1}{3}\right)\left(-\dfrac{1}{9}\right)$

$=\dfrac{1}{4}-6(10)\div3$

$=\dfrac{1}{4}-60\div3$

$=\dfrac{1}{4}-20$

$=-19\dfrac{3}{4}$

104. $\dfrac{3}{4}-4(2+7)\div\left(-\dfrac{1}{2}\right)\left(-\dfrac{1}{6}\right)$

$=\dfrac{3}{4}-4(9)\div3$

$=\dfrac{3}{4}-36\div3$

$=\dfrac{3}{4}-12$

$=-11\dfrac{1}{4}$

105. $\dfrac{1}{4}+\dfrac{1}{3}=\left(\dfrac{1}{4}\right)\left(\dfrac{3}{3}\right)+\left(\dfrac{1}{3}\right)\left(\dfrac{4}{4}\right)$

$\qquad = \dfrac{3}{12}+\dfrac{4}{12}$

$\qquad = \dfrac{3+4}{12}$

$\qquad = \dfrac{7}{12}$

$\dfrac{7}{12}\div 2 = \dfrac{7}{12}\cdot\dfrac{1}{2}=\dfrac{7}{24}$

106. $\dfrac{2}{3}+\dfrac{5}{6}=\left(\dfrac{2}{3}\right)\left(\dfrac{2}{2}\right)+\dfrac{5}{6}$

$\qquad = \dfrac{4}{6}+\dfrac{5}{6}$

$\qquad = \dfrac{4+5}{6}$

$\qquad = \dfrac{9}{6}$

$\qquad = \dfrac{3}{2}$

$\dfrac{3}{2}\div 2 = \dfrac{3}{2}\cdot\dfrac{1}{2}=\dfrac{3}{4}$

107. $\dfrac{1}{2}+\dfrac{2}{3}=\left(\dfrac{1}{2}\right)\left(\dfrac{3}{3}\right)+\left(\dfrac{2}{3}\right)\left(\dfrac{2}{2}\right)$

$\qquad = \dfrac{3}{6}+\dfrac{4}{6}$

$\qquad = \dfrac{3+4}{6}$

$\qquad = \dfrac{7}{6}$

$\dfrac{7}{6}\div 2 = \dfrac{7}{6}\cdot\dfrac{1}{2}=\dfrac{7}{12}$

108. $\dfrac{3}{5}+\dfrac{2}{3}=\left(\dfrac{3}{5}\right)\left(\dfrac{3}{3}\right)+\left(\dfrac{2}{3}\right)\left(\dfrac{5}{5}\right)$

$\qquad = \dfrac{9}{15}+\dfrac{10}{15}$

$\qquad = \dfrac{9+10}{15}$

$\qquad = \dfrac{19}{15}$

$\dfrac{19}{15}\div 2 = \dfrac{19}{15}\cdot\dfrac{1}{2}=\dfrac{19}{30}$

109. $-\dfrac{2}{3}+\left(-\dfrac{5}{6}\right)=\left(-\dfrac{2}{3}\right)\left(\dfrac{2}{2}\right)-\dfrac{5}{6}$

$\qquad = \dfrac{-4}{6}-\dfrac{5}{6}$

$\qquad = \dfrac{-4-5}{6}$

$\qquad = -\dfrac{9}{6}$

$-\dfrac{9}{6}\div 2 = -\dfrac{9}{6}\cdot\dfrac{1}{2}=-\dfrac{9}{12}=-\dfrac{3}{4}$

110. $-4+\left(-\dfrac{7}{2}\right)=(-4)\left(\dfrac{2}{2}\right)-\left(\dfrac{7}{2}\right)$

$\qquad = -\dfrac{8}{2}-\dfrac{7}{2}$

$\qquad = -\dfrac{8+7}{2}$

$\qquad = -\dfrac{15}{2}$

$-\dfrac{15}{2}\div 2 = -\dfrac{15}{2}\cdot\dfrac{1}{2}=-\dfrac{15}{4}$

111. $\dfrac{13}{4}+\dfrac{13}{9}=\dfrac{13\cdot 9}{4\cdot 9}+\dfrac{13\cdot 4}{9\cdot 4}$

$\qquad = \dfrac{117}{36}+\dfrac{52}{36}$

$\qquad = \dfrac{117+52}{36}$

$\qquad = \dfrac{169}{36}$

$\dfrac{13}{4}\times\dfrac{13}{9}=\dfrac{13\cdot 13}{4\cdot 9}$

$\qquad = \dfrac{169}{36}$

Both are equal to $\dfrac{169}{36}$

112.
$$\frac{169}{30} + \frac{13}{15} = \frac{169}{30} + \left(\frac{13}{15}\right)\left(\frac{2}{2}\right)$$
$$= \frac{169}{30} + \frac{26}{30}$$
$$= \frac{169 + 26}{30}$$
$$= \frac{195}{30}$$
$$= \frac{39}{6}$$
$$= \frac{13}{2}$$

$$\frac{169}{30} \div \frac{13}{15} = \frac{169}{30} \cdot \frac{15}{13}$$
$$= \frac{169 \cdot 15}{30 \cdot 13}$$
$$= \frac{169 \cdot \overset{1}{\cancel{15}}}{\underset{2}{\cancel{30}} \cdot 13}$$
$$= \frac{\overset{13}{\cancel{169}} \cdot 1}{2 \cdot \cancel{13}_{1}}$$
$$= \frac{13 \cdot 1}{2 \cdot 1}$$
$$= \frac{13}{2}$$

Both are equal to $\dfrac{13}{2}$

113.
$$\frac{5}{2^2 \cdot 3^2} - \frac{1}{2 \cdot 3^2} = \frac{5}{2^2 \cdot 3^2} - \frac{2}{2} \cdot \frac{1}{2 \cdot 3^2}$$
$$= \frac{5}{2^2 \cdot 3^2} - \frac{2}{2^2 \cdot 3^2}$$
$$= \frac{3}{2^2 \cdot 3^2}$$
$$= \frac{1}{2^2 \cdot 3}$$

114.
$$\frac{7}{3^2 \cdot 5^2} - \frac{1}{3 \cdot 5^3} = \frac{5}{5} \cdot \frac{7}{3^2 \cdot 5^2} - \frac{3}{3} \cdot \frac{1}{3 \cdot 5^3}$$
$$= \frac{35}{3^2 \cdot 5^3} - \frac{3}{3^2 \cdot 5^3}$$
$$= \frac{32}{3^2 \cdot 5^3}$$

115.
$$\frac{1}{2^4 \cdot 5^3 \cdot 7} + \frac{1}{2 \cdot 5^4} - \frac{1}{2^3 \cdot 5^2}$$
$$= \frac{5}{5} \cdot \frac{1}{2^4 \cdot 5^3 \cdot 7} + \frac{2^3 \cdot 7}{2^3 \cdot 7} \cdot \frac{1}{2 \cdot 5^4} - \frac{2 \cdot 5^2 \cdot 7}{2 \cdot 5^2 \cdot 7} \cdot \frac{1}{2^3 \cdot 5^2}$$
$$= \frac{5}{2^4 \cdot 5^4 \cdot 7} + \frac{56}{2^4 \cdot 5^4 \cdot 7} - \frac{350}{2^4 \cdot 5^4 \cdot 7}$$
$$= -\frac{289}{2^4 \cdot 5^4 \cdot 7}$$

116.
$$\frac{1}{2^3 \cdot 17^8} + \frac{1}{2 \cdot 17^9} - \frac{1}{2^2 \cdot 3 \cdot 17^8}$$
$$= \frac{3 \cdot 17}{3 \cdot 17} \cdot \frac{1}{2^3 \cdot 17^8} + \frac{2^2 \cdot 3}{2^2 \cdot 3} \cdot \frac{1}{2 \cdot 17^9} - \frac{2 \cdot 17}{2 \cdot 17} \cdot \frac{1}{2^2 \cdot 3 \cdot 17^8}$$
$$= \frac{51}{2^3 \cdot 3 \cdot 17^9} + \frac{12}{2^3 \cdot 3 \cdot 17^9} - \frac{34}{2^3 \cdot 3 \cdot 17^9}$$
$$= \frac{29}{2^3 \cdot 3 \cdot 17^9}$$

117. $0.\overline{54} < 0.58\overline{3}$

$$\frac{6}{11} < \frac{7}{12}$$

118. $0.80\overline{5} > 0.\overline{8}$

$$\frac{29}{36} > \frac{28}{35}$$

119. $-0.8\overline{3} > -0.\overline{8}$

$$-\frac{5}{6} > -\frac{8}{9}$$

120. $-0.008 < -0.006$

$$-\frac{1}{125} < -\frac{3}{500}$$

121. a. $\dfrac{89}{193}$

b. $\dfrac{89}{193} \approx 0.46$
Approximately 46% of countries are free.

122. a. $\dfrac{42}{193}$

b. $\dfrac{42}{193} \approx 0.22$
Approximately 22% of countries are not free.

123. For each ingredient in the recipe, multiply the original quantity by $\frac{8}{16}$ or $\frac{1}{2}$.

$\frac{2}{3} \cdot \frac{1}{2} = \frac{1}{3}$ cup butter

$5 \cdot \frac{1}{2} = \frac{5}{2} = 2\frac{1}{2}$ ounces unsweetened chocolate

$1\frac{1}{2} \cdot \frac{1}{2} = \frac{3}{2} \cdot \frac{1}{2} = \frac{3}{4}$ cup sugar

$2 \cdot \frac{1}{2} = 1$ teaspoon vanilla

$2 \cdot \frac{1}{2} = 1$ egg

$1 \cdot \frac{1}{2} = \frac{1}{2}$ cup flour

124. For each ingredient in the recipe, multiply the original quantity by $\frac{12}{16}$ or $\frac{3}{4}$.

$\frac{2}{3} \cdot \frac{3}{4} = \frac{1}{2}$ cup butter

$5 \cdot \frac{3}{4} = \frac{15}{4} = 3\frac{3}{4}$ ounces unsweetened chocolate

$1\frac{1}{2} \cdot \frac{3}{4} = \frac{3}{2} \cdot \frac{3}{4} = \frac{9}{8} = 1\frac{1}{8}$ cups sugar

$2 \cdot \frac{3}{4} = \frac{3}{2} = 1\frac{1}{2}$ teaspoons vanilla

$2 \cdot \frac{3}{4} = \frac{3}{2} = 1\frac{1}{2}$ egg

$1 \cdot \frac{3}{4} = \frac{3}{4}$ cup flour

125. For each ingredient in the recipe, multiply the original quantity by $\frac{20}{16}$ or $\frac{5}{4}$.

$\frac{2}{3} \cdot \frac{5}{4} = \frac{5}{6}$ cup butter

$5 \cdot \frac{5}{4} = \frac{25}{4} = 6\frac{1}{4}$ ounces unsweetened chocolate

$1\frac{1}{2} \cdot \frac{5}{4} = \frac{3}{2} \cdot \frac{5}{4} = \frac{15}{8} = 1\frac{7}{8}$ cups sugar

$2 \cdot \frac{5}{4} = \frac{5}{2} = 2\frac{1}{2}$ teaspoons vanilla

$2 \cdot \frac{5}{4} = \frac{5}{2} = 2\frac{1}{2}$ eggs

$1 \cdot \frac{5}{4} = \frac{5}{4} = 1\frac{1}{4}$ cups flour

126. For each ingredient in the recipe, multiply the original quantity by $\frac{24}{16}$ or $\frac{3}{2}$.

$\frac{2}{3} \cdot \frac{3}{2} = 1$ cup butter

$5 \cdot \frac{3}{2} = \frac{15}{2} = 7\frac{1}{2}$ ounces unsweetened chocolate

$1\frac{1}{2} \cdot \frac{3}{2} = \frac{3}{2} \cdot \frac{3}{2} = \frac{9}{4} = 2\frac{1}{4}$ cups sugar

$2 \cdot \frac{3}{2} = 3$ teaspoons vanilla

$2 \cdot \frac{3}{2} = 3$ eggs

$1 \cdot \frac{3}{2} = \frac{3}{2} = 1\frac{1}{2}$ cups flour

127. Begin by dividing the 1 cup of butter by the quantity of butter needed for a 16-brownie batch:

$1 \div \frac{2}{3} = 1 \times \frac{3}{2} = \frac{3}{2} = 1\frac{1}{2}$

Thus, 1 cup of butter is enough for $1\frac{1}{2}$ batches.

Since each batch makes 16 brownies, $1\frac{1}{2}$ batches will make $16 \times 1\frac{1}{2} = 24$ brownies. Thus, 1 cup of butter is enough for 24 brownies.

128. Begin by dividing the 1 cup of sugar by the quantity of sugar needed for a 16-brownie batch:

$1 \div 1\frac{1}{2} = 1 \div \frac{3}{2} = 1 \times \frac{2}{3} = \frac{2}{3}$

Thus, 1 cup of sugar is enough for $\frac{2}{3}$ batches.

Since each batch makes 16 brownies, $\frac{2}{3}$ of a batch will make $16 \times \frac{2}{3} = \frac{32}{3} = 10\frac{2}{3}$ brownies. Ignoring part of a brownie means that 1 cup of sugar is enough for 10 brownies.

129. $2\frac{2}{3} \cdot \frac{11}{8} = \frac{8}{3} \cdot \frac{11}{8} = \frac{88}{24} = \frac{11}{3}$ or $3\frac{2}{3}$ cups of water.

130. $2\frac{2}{3} \cdot \frac{6}{8} = \frac{8}{3} \cdot \frac{6}{8} = \frac{48}{24} = 2$ cups of water.

131. a. Strings D, E, G, A, and B are $\dfrac{8}{9}$ of the length of the previous string.

    b. There are black keys to the left of the keys for the notes D, E, G, A, and B.

132. a. Strings F and c are not $\dfrac{8}{9}$ of the length of the previous string.

    b. There are no black keys to the left of the keys for the notes F and c.

133. $24 - \dfrac{1}{16} - 7\dfrac{1}{2} = \dfrac{24}{1} - \dfrac{1}{16} - \dfrac{15}{2} = \dfrac{384}{16} - \dfrac{1}{16} - \dfrac{120}{16} = \dfrac{263}{16} = 16\dfrac{7}{16}$ in.

134. $36 - \dfrac{1}{16} - 7\dfrac{1}{4} = \dfrac{36}{1} - \dfrac{1}{16} - \dfrac{29}{4} = \dfrac{576}{16} - \dfrac{1}{16} - \dfrac{116}{16} = \dfrac{459}{16} = 28\dfrac{11}{16}$ in.

135. $1 - \dfrac{5}{12} - \dfrac{1}{4} = \dfrac{12}{12} - \dfrac{5}{12} - \dfrac{3}{12} = \dfrac{4}{12} = \dfrac{1}{3}$ ownership.

136. $1 - \dfrac{1}{4} - \dfrac{2}{5} - \dfrac{1}{10} = \dfrac{20}{20} - \dfrac{5}{20} - \dfrac{8}{20} - \dfrac{2}{20} = \dfrac{5}{20} = \dfrac{1}{4}$

137. The total distance is their sum: $\dfrac{3}{4} + \dfrac{2}{5} = \dfrac{15}{20} + \dfrac{8}{20} = \dfrac{23}{20}$ miles.

    The difference is the amount farther: $\dfrac{3}{4} - \dfrac{2}{5} = \dfrac{15}{20} - \dfrac{8}{20} = \dfrac{7}{20}$ mile.

138. 40 hours at \$12 rate

    6 hours at $\left(\dfrac{3}{2}\right)$\$12 rate or $\left(\dfrac{3}{2}\right)$\$12 $= \dfrac{\$36}{2} = \$18$

    $40 \cdot \$12 + 6 \cdot \$18 = \$480 + \$108 = \$588$

139. $\dfrac{3}{5}$ of the total goes to relatives, so there is $\dfrac{2}{5}$ of the estate left. $\dfrac{1}{4}$ of that $\dfrac{2}{5}$ goes for AIDS research:

    $\dfrac{1}{4} \cdot \dfrac{2}{5} = \dfrac{2}{20} = \dfrac{1}{10}$

140. $2\dfrac{3}{8} \cdot 16 = \dfrac{19}{8} \cdot \dfrac{16}{1} = \dfrac{304}{8} = 38$ miles

152. does not make sense; Explanations will vary. Sample explanation: Since the fraction is greater than 1, then the price was higher than regular price.

153. makes sense

154. does not make sense; Explanations will vary. Sample explanation: The value shown on the calculator is rounded to 7 decimal places. The exact value is $0.\overline{27}$.

155. makes sense

156. 1st measure: $\dfrac{1}{4}+\dfrac{1}{4}+\dfrac{1}{8}+\dfrac{1}{8}=\dfrac{2}{8}+\dfrac{2}{8}+\dfrac{1}{8}+\dfrac{1}{8}=\dfrac{6}{8}=\dfrac{3}{4}$

2nd measure: $\dfrac{1}{4}+\dfrac{1}{4}+\dfrac{1}{4}=\dfrac{3}{4}$

3rd measure: $\dfrac{1}{4}+\dfrac{1}{8}+\dfrac{1}{8}+\dfrac{1}{8}+\dfrac{1}{8}=\dfrac{2}{8}+\dfrac{1}{8}+\dfrac{1}{8}+\dfrac{1}{8}+\dfrac{1}{8}=\dfrac{6}{8}=\dfrac{3}{4}$

4th measure: $\dfrac{1}{4}+\dfrac{1}{4}+\dfrac{1}{8}+\dfrac{1}{8}=\dfrac{2}{8}+\dfrac{2}{8}+\dfrac{1}{8}+\dfrac{1}{8}=\dfrac{6}{8}=\dfrac{3}{4}$

say does that   Star-span-gled   Ban-ner   yet   wave O'er the

157. Conjecture: The sums of $\frac{2}{3}$, $\frac{3}{4}$, and $\frac{4}{5}$ will be followed by a sum of $\frac{5}{6}$.

Verification:
$$\dfrac{1}{1\cdot 2}+\dfrac{1}{2\cdot 3}+\dfrac{1}{3\cdot 4}+\dfrac{1}{4\cdot 5}+\dfrac{1}{5\cdot 6}=\dfrac{1}{2}+\dfrac{1}{6}+\dfrac{1}{12}+\dfrac{1}{20}+\dfrac{1}{30}$$
$$=\dfrac{30}{60}+\dfrac{10}{60}+\dfrac{5}{60}+\dfrac{3}{60}+\dfrac{2}{60}$$
$$=\dfrac{50}{60}$$
$$=\dfrac{5}{6}$$

158. a. $\dfrac{197}{800}=0.24625$

b. $\dfrac{4539}{3125}=1.45248$

c. $\dfrac{7}{6250}=0.00112$

Check Points 5.4

1. a. $\sqrt{12}=\sqrt{4\cdot 3}=\sqrt{4}\cdot\sqrt{3}=2\sqrt{3}$

b. $\sqrt{60}=\sqrt{4\cdot 15}=\sqrt{4}\cdot\sqrt{15}=2\sqrt{15}$

c. $\sqrt{55}$ cannot be simplified.

2. a. $\sqrt{3}\cdot\sqrt{10}=\sqrt{3\cdot 10}=\sqrt{30}$

b. $\sqrt{10}\cdot\sqrt{10}=\sqrt{10\cdot 10}=\sqrt{100}=10$

c. $\sqrt{6}\cdot\sqrt{2}=\sqrt{6\cdot 2}=\sqrt{12}=\sqrt{4}\cdot\sqrt{3}=2\sqrt{3}$

3. a. $\dfrac{\sqrt{80}}{\sqrt{5}} = \sqrt{\dfrac{80}{5}} = \sqrt{16} = 4$

   b. $\dfrac{\sqrt{48}}{\sqrt{6}} = \sqrt{\dfrac{48}{6}} = \sqrt{8} = \sqrt{4} \cdot \sqrt{2} = 2\sqrt{2}$

4. a. $8\sqrt{3} + 10\sqrt{3} = (8+10)\sqrt{3} = 18\sqrt{3}$

   b. $4\sqrt{13} - 9\sqrt{13} = (4-9)\sqrt{13} = -5\sqrt{13}$

   c. $7\sqrt{10} + 2\sqrt{10} - \sqrt{10} = (7+2-1)\sqrt{10} = 8\sqrt{10}$

5. a. $\sqrt{3} + \sqrt{12} = \sqrt{3} + \sqrt{4} \cdot \sqrt{3} = \sqrt{3} + 2\sqrt{3} = 3\sqrt{3}$

   b. $4\sqrt{8} - 7\sqrt{18}$

      $= 4\sqrt{4 \cdot 2} - 7\sqrt{9 \cdot 2}$

      $= 4 \cdot 2\sqrt{2} - 7 \cdot 3\sqrt{2}$

      $= 8\sqrt{2} - 21\sqrt{2}$

      $= (8-21)\sqrt{2}$

      $= -13\sqrt{2}$

6. a. $\dfrac{25}{\sqrt{10}} = \dfrac{25}{\sqrt{10}} \cdot \dfrac{\sqrt{10}}{\sqrt{10}} = \dfrac{25\sqrt{10}}{\sqrt{100}} = \dfrac{25\sqrt{10}}{10} = \dfrac{5\sqrt{10}}{2}$

   b. $\sqrt{\dfrac{2}{7}} = \dfrac{\sqrt{2}}{\sqrt{7}} = \dfrac{\sqrt{2}}{\sqrt{7}} \cdot \dfrac{\sqrt{7}}{\sqrt{7}} = \dfrac{\sqrt{14}}{\sqrt{49}} = \dfrac{\sqrt{14}}{7}$

   c. $\dfrac{5}{\sqrt{18}} = \dfrac{5}{\sqrt{18}} \cdot \dfrac{\sqrt{2}}{\sqrt{2}} = \dfrac{5\sqrt{2}}{\sqrt{36}} = \dfrac{5\sqrt{2}}{6}$

Exercise Set 5.4

1. $\sqrt{9} = 3$ because $3^2 = 9$.

2. $\sqrt{16} = 4$ because $4^2 = 16$.

3. $\sqrt{25} = 5$ because $5^2 = 25$.

4. $\sqrt{49} = 7$ because $7^2 = 49$.

5. $\sqrt{64} = 8$ because $8^2 = 64$.

6. $\sqrt{100} = 10$ because $10^2 = 100$.

7. $\sqrt{121} = 11$ because $11^2 = 121$.

8. $\sqrt{144} = 12$ because $12^2 = 144$.

9. $\sqrt{169} = 13$ because $13^2 = 169$.

10. $\sqrt{225} = 15$ because $15^2 = 225$.

11. a. $\sqrt{173} \approx 13.2$

   b. $\sqrt{173} \approx 13.15$

   c. $\sqrt{173} \approx 13.153$

12. a. $\sqrt{3176} \approx 56.4$

   b. $\sqrt{3176} \approx 56.36$

   c. $\sqrt{3176} \approx 56.356$

13. a. $\sqrt{17,761} \approx 133.3$

   b. $\sqrt{17,761} \approx 133.27$

   c. $\sqrt{17,761} \approx 133.270$

14. a. $\sqrt{779,264} \approx 882.8$

   b. $\sqrt{779,264} \approx 882.76$

   c. $\sqrt{779,264} \approx 882.759$

15. a. $\sqrt{\pi} \approx 1.8$

   b. $\sqrt{\pi} \approx 1.77$

   c. $\sqrt{\pi} \approx 1.772$

16. a. $\sqrt{2\pi} \approx 2.5$

   b. $\sqrt{2\pi} \approx 2.51$

   c. $\sqrt{2\pi} \approx 2.507$

17. $\sqrt{20} = \sqrt{4 \cdot 5} = \sqrt{4} \cdot \sqrt{5} = 2\sqrt{5}$

18. $\sqrt{50} = \sqrt{25 \cdot 2} = \sqrt{25} \cdot \sqrt{2} = 5\sqrt{2}$

19. $\sqrt{80} = \sqrt{16 \cdot 5} = \sqrt{16} \cdot \sqrt{5} = 4\sqrt{5}$

20. $\sqrt{12} = \sqrt{4 \cdot 3} = \sqrt{4} \cdot \sqrt{3} = 2\sqrt{3}$

21. $\sqrt{250} = \sqrt{25 \cdot 10} = \sqrt{25} \cdot \sqrt{10} = 5\sqrt{10}$

22. $\sqrt{192} = \sqrt{64 \cdot 3} = \sqrt{64} \cdot \sqrt{3} = 8\sqrt{3}$

23. $7\sqrt{28} = 7\sqrt{4 \cdot 7}$
$\qquad = 7\sqrt{4} \cdot \sqrt{7}$
$\qquad = 7 \cdot 2 \cdot \sqrt{7}$
$\qquad = 14\sqrt{7}$

24. $3\sqrt{52} = 3\sqrt{4 \cdot 13} = 3\sqrt{4} \cdot \sqrt{13} = 3 \cdot 2 \cdot \sqrt{13} = 6\sqrt{13}$

25. $\sqrt{7} \cdot \sqrt{6} = \sqrt{7 \cdot 6} = \sqrt{42}$

26. $\sqrt{19} \cdot \sqrt{3} = \sqrt{19 \cdot 3} = \sqrt{57}$

27. $\sqrt{6} \cdot \sqrt{6} = \sqrt{6 \cdot 6} = \sqrt{36} = 6$

28. $\sqrt{5} \cdot \sqrt{5} = \sqrt{5 \cdot 5} = \sqrt{25} = 5$

29. $\sqrt{3} \cdot \sqrt{6} = \sqrt{3 \cdot 6}$
$\qquad = \sqrt{18}$
$\qquad = \sqrt{9 \cdot 2}$
$\qquad = \sqrt{9} \cdot \sqrt{2}$
$\qquad = 3\sqrt{2}$

30. $\sqrt{12} \cdot \sqrt{2} = \sqrt{12 \cdot 2}$
$\qquad = \sqrt{24}$
$\qquad = \sqrt{4 \cdot 6}$
$\qquad = \sqrt{4} \cdot \sqrt{6}$
$\qquad = 2\sqrt{6}$

31. $\sqrt{2} \cdot \sqrt{26} = \sqrt{2 \cdot 26}$
$\qquad = \sqrt{52}$
$\qquad = \sqrt{4 \cdot 13}$
$\qquad = \sqrt{4} \cdot \sqrt{13}$
$\qquad = 2\sqrt{13}$

32. $\sqrt{5} \cdot \sqrt{50} = \sqrt{5 \cdot 50}$
$\qquad = \sqrt{250}$
$\qquad = \sqrt{25 \cdot 10}$
$\qquad = \sqrt{25} \cdot \sqrt{10}$
$\qquad = 5\sqrt{10}$

33. $\dfrac{\sqrt{54}}{\sqrt{6}} = \sqrt{\dfrac{54}{6}} = \sqrt{9} = 3$

34. $\dfrac{\sqrt{75}}{\sqrt{3}} = \sqrt{\dfrac{75}{3}} = \sqrt{25} = 5$

35. $\dfrac{\sqrt{90}}{\sqrt{2}} = \sqrt{\dfrac{90}{2}}$
$\qquad = \sqrt{45}$
$\qquad = \sqrt{9 \cdot 5}$
$\qquad = \sqrt{9} \cdot \sqrt{5}$
$\qquad = 3\sqrt{5}$

36. $\dfrac{\sqrt{60}}{\sqrt{3}} = \sqrt{\dfrac{60}{3}} = \sqrt{20} = \sqrt{4 \cdot 5} = \sqrt{4} \cdot \sqrt{5} = 2\sqrt{5}$

37. $\dfrac{-\sqrt{96}}{\sqrt{2}} = -\sqrt{\dfrac{96}{2}}$
$\qquad = -\sqrt{48}$
$\qquad = -\sqrt{16 \cdot 3}$
$\qquad = -\sqrt{16} \cdot \sqrt{3}$
$\qquad = -4\sqrt{3}$

38. $\dfrac{-\sqrt{150}}{\sqrt{3}} = -\sqrt{\dfrac{150}{3}}$
$\qquad = -\sqrt{50}$
$\qquad = -\sqrt{25 \cdot 2}$
$\qquad = -\sqrt{25} \cdot \sqrt{2}$
$\qquad = -5\sqrt{2}$

39. $7\sqrt{3} + 6\sqrt{3} = (7 + 6)\sqrt{3} = 13\sqrt{3}$

40. $8\sqrt{5} + 11\sqrt{5} = (8 + 11)\sqrt{5} = 19\sqrt{5}$

41. $4\sqrt{13} - 6\sqrt{13} = (4 - 6)\sqrt{13} = -2\sqrt{13}$

42. $6\sqrt{17} - 8\sqrt{17} = (6 - 8)\sqrt{17} = -2\sqrt{17}$

43. $\sqrt{5} + \sqrt{5} = 1\sqrt{5} + 1\sqrt{5} = (1 + 1)\sqrt{5} = 2\sqrt{5}$

44. $\sqrt{3} + \sqrt{3} = 1\sqrt{3} + 1\sqrt{3} = (1 + 1)\sqrt{3} = 2\sqrt{3}$

45. $4\sqrt{2} - 5\sqrt{2} + 8\sqrt{2} = (4 - 5 + 8)\sqrt{2} = 7\sqrt{2}$

46. $6\sqrt{3} + 8\sqrt{3} - 16\sqrt{3} = (6 + 8 - 16)\sqrt{3} = -2\sqrt{3}$

47. $\sqrt{5} + \sqrt{20} = 1\sqrt{5} + \sqrt{4} \cdot \sqrt{5}$
$= 1\sqrt{5} + 2\sqrt{5}$
$= (1 + 2)\sqrt{5}$
$= 3\sqrt{5}$

48. $\sqrt{3} + \sqrt{27} = 1\sqrt{3} + \sqrt{9} \cdot \sqrt{3}$
$= 1\sqrt{3} + 3\sqrt{3}$
$= (1 + 3)\sqrt{3}$
$= 4\sqrt{3}$

49. $\sqrt{50} - \sqrt{18} = \sqrt{25} \cdot \sqrt{2} - \sqrt{9} \cdot \sqrt{2}$
$= 5\sqrt{2} - 3\sqrt{2}$
$= (5 - 3)\sqrt{2}$
$= 2\sqrt{2}$

50. $\sqrt{63} - \sqrt{28} = \sqrt{9} \cdot \sqrt{7} - \sqrt{4} \cdot \sqrt{7}$
$= 3\sqrt{7} - 2\sqrt{7}$
$= (3 - 2)\sqrt{7}$
$= \sqrt{7}$

51. $3\sqrt{18} + 5\sqrt{50} = 3\sqrt{9} \cdot \sqrt{2} + 5\sqrt{25} \cdot \sqrt{2}$
$= 3 \cdot 3 \cdot \sqrt{2} + 5 \cdot 5\sqrt{2}$
$= 9\sqrt{2} + 25\sqrt{2}$
$= (9 + 25)\sqrt{2}$
$= 34\sqrt{2}$

52. $4\sqrt{12} + 2\sqrt{75} = 4\sqrt{4} \cdot \sqrt{3} + 2\sqrt{25} \cdot \sqrt{3}$
$= 4 \cdot 2 \cdot \sqrt{3} + 2 \cdot 5 \cdot \sqrt{3}$
$= 8\sqrt{3} + 10\sqrt{3}$
$= (8 + 10)\sqrt{3}$
$= 18\sqrt{3}$

53. $\dfrac{1}{4}\sqrt{12} - \dfrac{1}{2}\sqrt{48} = \dfrac{1}{4}\sqrt{4} \cdot \sqrt{3} - \dfrac{1}{2}\sqrt{16} \cdot \sqrt{3}$
$= \dfrac{1}{4} \cdot 2 \cdot \sqrt{3} - \dfrac{1}{2} \cdot 4 \cdot \sqrt{3}$
$= \dfrac{1}{2}\sqrt{3} - \dfrac{4}{2}\sqrt{3}$
$= \left(\dfrac{1}{2} - \dfrac{4}{2}\right)\sqrt{3}$
$= -\dfrac{3}{2}\sqrt{3}$

54. $\dfrac{1}{5}\sqrt{300} - \dfrac{2}{3}\sqrt{27} = \dfrac{1}{5} \cdot \sqrt{100} \cdot \sqrt{3} - \dfrac{2}{3} \cdot \sqrt{9} \cdot \sqrt{3}$
$= \dfrac{1}{5} \cdot 10 \cdot \sqrt{3} - \dfrac{2}{3} \cdot 3 \cdot \sqrt{3}$
$= 2\sqrt{3} - 2\sqrt{3}$
$= 0$

55. $3\sqrt{75} + 2\sqrt{12} - 2\sqrt{48}$
$= 3 \cdot \sqrt{25} \cdot \sqrt{3} + 2 \cdot \sqrt{4} \cdot \sqrt{3} - 2 \cdot \sqrt{16} \cdot \sqrt{3}$
$= 3 \cdot 5 \cdot \sqrt{3} + 2 \cdot 2 \cdot \sqrt{3} - 2 \cdot 4 \cdot \sqrt{3}$
$= 15\sqrt{3} + 4\sqrt{3} - 8\sqrt{3}$
$= (15 + 4 - 8)\sqrt{3}$
$= 11\sqrt{3}$

56. $2\sqrt{72} + 3\sqrt{50} - \sqrt{128}$
$= 2 \cdot \sqrt{36} \cdot \sqrt{2} + 3 \cdot \sqrt{25} \cdot \sqrt{2} - \sqrt{64} \cdot \sqrt{2}$
$= 2 \cdot 6 \cdot \sqrt{2} + 3 \cdot 5 \cdot \sqrt{2} - 8 \cdot \sqrt{2}$
$= 12\sqrt{2} + 15\sqrt{2} - 8\sqrt{2}$
$= (12 + 15 - 8)\sqrt{2}$
$= 19\sqrt{2}$

57. $\dfrac{5}{\sqrt{3}} = \dfrac{5}{\sqrt{3}} \cdot \dfrac{\sqrt{3}}{\sqrt{3}} = \dfrac{5\sqrt{3}}{\sqrt{9}} = \dfrac{5\sqrt{3}}{3}$

58. $\dfrac{12}{\sqrt{5}} = \dfrac{12}{\sqrt{5}} \cdot \dfrac{\sqrt{5}}{\sqrt{5}} = \dfrac{12\sqrt{5}}{\sqrt{25}} = \dfrac{12\sqrt{5}}{5}$

59. $\dfrac{21}{\sqrt{7}} = \dfrac{21}{\sqrt{7}} \cdot \dfrac{\sqrt{7}}{\sqrt{7}} = \dfrac{21\sqrt{7}}{\sqrt{49}} = \dfrac{21\sqrt{7}}{7} = 3\sqrt{7}$

60. $\dfrac{30}{\sqrt{5}} = \dfrac{30}{\sqrt{5}} \cdot \dfrac{\sqrt{5}}{\sqrt{5}} = \dfrac{30\sqrt{5}}{\sqrt{25}} = \dfrac{30\sqrt{5}}{5} = 6\sqrt{5}$

61. $\dfrac{12}{\sqrt{30}} = \dfrac{12\sqrt{30}}{\sqrt{30}\sqrt{30}}$

$= \dfrac{12\sqrt{30}}{\sqrt{900}}$

$= \dfrac{12\sqrt{30}}{30}$

$= \dfrac{2\sqrt{30}}{5}$

62. $\dfrac{15}{\sqrt{50}} = \dfrac{15}{\sqrt{50}} \cdot \dfrac{\sqrt{2}}{\sqrt{2}} = \dfrac{15\sqrt{2}}{\sqrt{100}} = \dfrac{15\sqrt{2}}{10} = \dfrac{3\sqrt{2}}{2}$

63. $\dfrac{15}{\sqrt{12}} = \dfrac{15}{\sqrt{4 \cdot 3}}$

$= \dfrac{15}{\sqrt{4}\sqrt{3}}$

$= \dfrac{15}{2\sqrt{3}}$

$= \dfrac{15\sqrt{3}}{2\sqrt{3}\sqrt{3}}$

$= \dfrac{15\sqrt{3}}{2\sqrt{9}}$

$= \dfrac{15\sqrt{3}}{2 \cdot 3}$

$= \dfrac{15\sqrt{3}}{6}$

$= \dfrac{5\sqrt{3}}{2}$

64. $\dfrac{13}{\sqrt{40}} = \dfrac{13\sqrt{10}}{\sqrt{40}\sqrt{10}} = \dfrac{13\sqrt{10}}{\sqrt{400}} = \dfrac{13\sqrt{10}}{20}$

65. $\sqrt{\dfrac{2}{5}} = \dfrac{\sqrt{2}}{\sqrt{5}} = \dfrac{\sqrt{2}}{\sqrt{5}} \cdot \dfrac{\sqrt{5}}{\sqrt{5}} = \dfrac{\sqrt{10}}{\sqrt{25}} = \dfrac{\sqrt{10}}{5}$

66. $\sqrt{\dfrac{5}{7}} = \dfrac{\sqrt{5}}{\sqrt{7}} = \dfrac{\sqrt{5}}{\sqrt{7}} \cdot \dfrac{\sqrt{7}}{\sqrt{7}} = \dfrac{\sqrt{35}}{\sqrt{49}} = \dfrac{\sqrt{35}}{7}$

67. $3\sqrt{8} - \sqrt{32} + 3\sqrt{72} - \sqrt{75}$

$= 6\sqrt{2} - 4\sqrt{2} + 18\sqrt{2} - 5\sqrt{3}$

$= 20\sqrt{2} - 5\sqrt{3}$

68. $3\sqrt{54} - 2\sqrt{24} - \sqrt{96} + 4\sqrt{63}$

$= 9\sqrt{6} - 4\sqrt{6} - 4\sqrt{6} + 12\sqrt{7}$

$= \sqrt{6} + 12\sqrt{7}$

69. $3\sqrt{7} - 5\sqrt{14} \cdot \sqrt{2} = 3\sqrt{7} - 5\sqrt{28}$

$= 3\sqrt{7} - 10\sqrt{7}$

$= -7\sqrt{7}$

70. $4\sqrt{2} - 8\sqrt{10} \cdot \sqrt{5} = 4\sqrt{2} - 8\sqrt{50}$

$= 4\sqrt{2} - 40\sqrt{2}$

$= -36\sqrt{2}$

71. $\dfrac{\sqrt{32}}{5} + \dfrac{\sqrt{18}}{7} = \dfrac{4\sqrt{2}}{5} + \dfrac{3\sqrt{2}}{7}$

$= \dfrac{28\sqrt{2}}{35} + \dfrac{15\sqrt{2}}{35}$

$= \dfrac{43\sqrt{2}}{35}$

72. $\dfrac{\sqrt{27}}{2} + \dfrac{\sqrt{75}}{7} = \dfrac{3\sqrt{3}}{2} + \dfrac{5\sqrt{3}}{7}$

$= \dfrac{21\sqrt{3}}{14} + \dfrac{10\sqrt{3}}{14}$

$= \dfrac{31\sqrt{3}}{14}$

73. $\dfrac{\sqrt{2}}{\sqrt{3}} + \dfrac{\sqrt{3}}{\sqrt{2}}$

$= \dfrac{\sqrt{2}}{\sqrt{3}} \cdot \dfrac{\sqrt{2}}{\sqrt{2}} + \dfrac{\sqrt{3}}{\sqrt{2}} \cdot \dfrac{\sqrt{3}}{\sqrt{3}}$

$= \dfrac{2}{\sqrt{6}} + \dfrac{3}{\sqrt{6}}$

$= \dfrac{5}{\sqrt{6}}$

$= \dfrac{5}{\sqrt{6}} \cdot \dfrac{\sqrt{6}}{\sqrt{6}}$

$= \dfrac{5\sqrt{6}}{6}$

74. $\dfrac{\sqrt{2}}{\sqrt{7}} + \dfrac{\sqrt{7}}{\sqrt{2}}$

$= \dfrac{\sqrt{2}}{\sqrt{7}} \cdot \dfrac{\sqrt{2}}{\sqrt{2}} + \dfrac{\sqrt{7}}{\sqrt{2}} \cdot \dfrac{\sqrt{7}}{\sqrt{7}}$

$= \dfrac{2}{\sqrt{14}} + \dfrac{7}{\sqrt{14}}$

$= \dfrac{9}{\sqrt{14}}$

$= \dfrac{9}{\sqrt{14}} \cdot \dfrac{\sqrt{14}}{\sqrt{14}}$

$= \dfrac{9\sqrt{14}}{14}$

75. $d(x) = \sqrt{\dfrac{3x}{2}}$

$d(72) = \sqrt{\dfrac{3(72)}{2}}$

$= \sqrt{3(36)}$

$= \sqrt{3} \cdot \sqrt{36}$

$= 6\sqrt{3} \approx 10.4 \text{ miles}$

A passenger on the pool deck can see roughly 10.4 miles.

76. $r(120) = \sqrt{\dfrac{3(120)}{2}} = \sqrt{180}$

$= \sqrt{36 \cdot 5} = \sqrt{36} \cdot \sqrt{5} = 6\sqrt{5} \text{ miles}$

The captain can see $6\sqrt{5} \approx 13.4 \text{ miles}$.

77. $v = \sqrt{20L}; L = 245$

$v = \sqrt{20 \cdot 245} = \sqrt{4900} = 70$

The motorist was traveling 70 miles per hour, so he was speeding.

78. $v = \sqrt{20L}; L = 45$

$v = \sqrt{20 \cdot 45} = \sqrt{900} = 30$

The motorist was traveling 30 miles per hour, so she was not speeding.

79. a. 41 in.

    b. $h = 2.9\sqrt{x} + 20.1$

$= 2.9\sqrt{50} + 20.1$

$\approx 40.6 \text{ in.}$

The estimate from part (a) describes the median height obtained from the formula quite well.

80. a. 41 in.

    b. $h = 3.1\sqrt{x} + 19$

$= 3.1\sqrt{50} + 19$

$\approx 40.9 \text{ in.}$

The estimate from part (a) describes the median height obtained from the formula quite well.

81. a. At birth we have $x = 0$.

$y = 2.9\sqrt{x} + 36$

$= 2.9\sqrt{0} + 36$

$= 2.9(0) + 36$

$= 36$

According to the model, the head circumference at birth is 36 cm.

    b. At 9 months we have $x = 9$.

$y = 2.9\sqrt{x} + 36$

$= 2.9\sqrt{9} + 36$

$= 2.9(3) + 36$

$= 44.7$

According to the model, the head circumference at 9 months is 44.7 cm.

    c. At 14 months we have $x = 14$.

$y = 2.9\sqrt{x} + 36$

$= 2.9\sqrt{14} + 36$

≈ 46.9

According to the model, the head circumference at 14 months is roughly 46.9 cm.

    d. The model describes healthy children.

82. a. At birth we have $x = 0$.

$y = 4\sqrt{x} + 35$

$= 4\sqrt{0} + 35$

$= 4(0) + 35$

$= 35$

According to the model, the head circumference at birth is 35 cm.

    b. At 9 months we have $x = 9$.

$y = 4\sqrt{x} + 35$

$= 4\sqrt{9} + 35$

$= 4(3) + 35$

$= 47$

According to the model, the head circumference at 9 months is 47 cm.

c. At 14 months we have $x = 14$.

$$y = 4\sqrt{x} + 35$$
$$= 4\sqrt{14} + 35$$
$$\approx 50$$

According to the model, the head circumference at 14 months is roughly 50 cm.

d. The model describes severe autistic children.

83. $R_f \sqrt{1 - \left(\dfrac{v}{c}\right)^2} = R_f \sqrt{1 - \left(\dfrac{0.8c}{c}\right)^2}$

$$= R_f \sqrt{1 - (0.8)^2}$$
$$= R_f \sqrt{0.36}$$
$$= 0.6 R_f$$

If 100 weeks have passed for your friend on Earth, then you were gone for $0.6(100) = 60$ weeks.

84. $R_f \sqrt{1 - \left(\dfrac{v}{c}\right)^2} = R_f \sqrt{1 - \left(\dfrac{0.9c}{c}\right)^2}$

$$= R_f \sqrt{1 - (0.9)^2}$$
$$= R_f \sqrt{0.19}$$
$$= 0.44 R_f$$

If 100 weeks have passed for your friend on Earth, then you were gone for $0.44(100) = 44$ weeks.

93. makes sense

94. does not make sense; Explanations will vary. Sample explanation: The enemy will be charged, but it will take a very long time at the rate he is counting.

95. does not make sense; Explanations will vary. Sample explanation: The denominator is rationalized correctly.

96. does not make sense; Explanations will vary. Sample explanation: The radicals can not be combined into one radical.

$$2\sqrt{20} + 4\sqrt{75} = 2\sqrt{4 \cdot 5} + 4\sqrt{25 \cdot 3}$$
$$= 4\sqrt{5} + 20\sqrt{3}$$

97. false; Changes to make the statement true will vary. A sample change is: The product of two irrational numbers can be rational or irrational.

98. false; Changes to make the statement true will vary. A sample change is: $\sqrt{9} + \sqrt{16} = 3 + 4 = 7$

99. true

100. false; Changes to make the statement true will vary.

A sample change is: $\dfrac{\sqrt{64}}{2} = \dfrac{8}{2} = 4$

101. $\sqrt{2} \approx 1.4$

$\sqrt{2} < 1.5$

102. $-\pi \approx -3.14$

$-\pi > -3.5$

103. $\dfrac{-3.14}{2} = -1.5700$

$-\dfrac{\pi}{2} \approx -1.5708$

$\dfrac{-3.14}{2} > -\dfrac{\pi}{2}$

104. The square root is multiplied by $\sqrt{2}$.

105. $-\sqrt{47} \approx -6.86$

Therefore $-\sqrt{47}$ is between -7 and -6.

106. $\sqrt{2} + \sqrt{\dfrac{1}{2}} = \sqrt{2} + \dfrac{\sqrt{1}}{\sqrt{2}} = \sqrt{2} + \dfrac{\sqrt{1}}{\sqrt{2}} \cdot \dfrac{\sqrt{2}}{\sqrt{2}}$

$$= \sqrt{2} + \dfrac{\sqrt{2}}{2} = \dfrac{2\sqrt{2}}{2} + \dfrac{\sqrt{2}}{2}$$
$$= \dfrac{2\sqrt{2} + \sqrt{2}}{2}$$
$$= \dfrac{(2+1)\sqrt{2}}{2} = \dfrac{3\sqrt{2}}{2}$$

107. Answers will vary.

Example: $\left(6 + \sqrt{2}\right) - \left(1 + \sqrt{2}\right) = 5$

Check Points 5.5

1. $\left\{-9,\ -1.3,\ 0,\ 0.\overline{3},\ \dfrac{\pi}{2},\ \sqrt{9},\ \sqrt{10}\right\}$

   a. Natural numbers: $\sqrt{9}$ because $\sqrt{9}=3$

   b. Whole numbers: $0,\ \sqrt{9}$

   c. Integers: $-9,\ 0,\ \sqrt{9}$

   d. Rational numbers: $-9,\ -1.3,\ 0,\ 0.\overline{3},\ \sqrt{9}$

   e. Irrational numbers: $\dfrac{\pi}{2},\ \sqrt{10}$

   f. Real numbers: All numbers in this set.

2. a. Associative property of multiplication

   b. Commutative property of addition

   c. Distributive property of multiplication over addition

   d. Commutative property of multiplication

   e. Identity property of addition

   f. Inverse property of multiplication

3. a. Yes, the natural numbers are closed with respect to multiplication.

   b. No, the integers are not closed with respect to division. Example: $3 \div 5 = 0.6$ which is not an integer.

Exercise Set 5.5

1. $\left\{-9,\ -\dfrac{4}{5},\ 0,\ 0.25,\ \sqrt{3},\ 9.2,\ \sqrt{100}\right\}$

   a. Natural numbers: $\sqrt{100}$ because $\sqrt{100}=10$

   b. Whole numbers: $0,\ \sqrt{100}$

   c. Integers: $-9,\ 0,\ \sqrt{100}$

   d. Rational numbers: $-9,\ -\dfrac{4}{5},\ 0,\ 0.25,\ 9.2,\ \sqrt{100}$

   e. Irrational numbers: $\sqrt{3}$

   f. Real numbers: All numbers in this set.

2. $\left\{-7,\ -0.\overline{6},\ 0,\ \sqrt{49},\ \sqrt{50}\right\}$

   a. Natural numbers: $\sqrt{49}$ because $\sqrt{49}=7$

   b. Whole numbers: $0,\ \sqrt{49}$

   c. Integers: $-7,\ 0,\ \sqrt{49}$

   d. Rational numbers: $-7,\ -0.\overline{6},\ 0,\ \sqrt{49}$

   e. Irrational numbers: $\sqrt{50}$

   f. Real numbers: All numbers in this set.

3. $\left\{-11,\ -\dfrac{5}{6},\ 0,\ 0.75,\ \sqrt{5},\ \pi,\ \sqrt{64}\right\}$

   a. Natural numbers: $\sqrt{64}$ because $\sqrt{64}=8$

   b. Whole numbers: 0 and $\sqrt{64}$

   c. Integers: $-11,\ 0,\ \sqrt{64}$

   d. Rational numbers: $-11,\ -\dfrac{5}{6},\ 0,\ 0.75,\ \sqrt{64}$

   e. Irrational numbers: $\sqrt{5},\ \pi$

   f. Real numbers: All numbers in this set.

4. $\left\{-5,\ -0.\overline{3},\ 0,\ \sqrt{2},\ \sqrt{4}\right\}$

   a. Natural numbers: $\sqrt{4}$ because $\sqrt{4}=2$

   b. Whole numbers: 0 and $\sqrt{4}$

   c. Integers: $-5,\ 0,\ \sqrt{4}$

   d. Rational numbers: $-5,\ -0.\overline{3},\ 0,\ \sqrt{4}$

   e. Irrational numbers: $\sqrt{2}$

   f. Real numbers: All numbers in this set.

5. 0 is the only whole number that is not a natural number.

6. Answers will vary. Possible answer: -1

7. Answers will vary. Possible answer: 0.5

8. Answers will vary. Possible answer: $-\dfrac{2}{5}$

9. Answers will vary. Possible answer: 7

10. Answers will vary. Possible answer: 5

11. Answers will vary. Possible answer: $\sqrt{3}$

12. Answers will vary. Possible answer: -200

13. $3 + (4 + 5) = 3 + (5 + 4)$

14. $\sqrt{5} \cdot 4 = 4 \cdot \sqrt{5}$

15. $9 \cdot (6 + 2) = 9 \cdot (2 + 6)$

16. $(3 + 7) + 9 = 3 + (7 + 9)$

17. $(4 \cdot 5) \cdot 3 = 4 \cdot (5 \cdot 3)$

18. $3 \cdot (6 + 4) = 3 \cdot 6 + 3 \cdot 4$

19. $7 \cdot (4 + 5) = 7 \cdot 4 + 7 \cdot 5$

20. $2 \cdot (7 + 3) = 2 \cdot 7 + 2 \cdot 3$

21. $5(6 + \sqrt{2}) = 5 \cdot 6 + 5 \cdot \sqrt{2} = 30 + 5\sqrt{2}$

22. $4(3 + \sqrt{5}) = 4 \cdot 3 + 4 \cdot \sqrt{5} = 12 + 4\sqrt{5}$

23. $\sqrt{7}(3 + \sqrt{2}) = \sqrt{7} \cdot 3 + \sqrt{7} \cdot \sqrt{2} = 3\sqrt{7} + \sqrt{14}$

24. $\sqrt{6}(7 + \sqrt{5}) = \sqrt{6} \cdot 7 + \sqrt{6} \cdot \sqrt{5} = 7\sqrt{6} + \sqrt{30}$

25. $\sqrt{3}(5 + \sqrt{3}) = \sqrt{3} \cdot 5 + \sqrt{3} \cdot \sqrt{3} = 5\sqrt{3} + \sqrt{9}$
    $= 5\sqrt{3} + 3$

26. $\sqrt{7}(9 + \sqrt{7}) = \sqrt{7} \cdot 9 + \sqrt{7} \cdot \sqrt{7}$
    $= 9\sqrt{7} + \sqrt{49}$
    $= 9\sqrt{7} + 7$

27. $\sqrt{6}(\sqrt{2} + \sqrt{6}) = \sqrt{6} \cdot \sqrt{2} + \sqrt{6} \cdot \sqrt{6}$
    $= \sqrt{12} + \sqrt{36}$
    $= 2\sqrt{3} + 6$

28. $\sqrt{10}(\sqrt{2} + \sqrt{10}) = \sqrt{10} \cdot \sqrt{2} + \sqrt{10} \cdot \sqrt{10}$
    $= \sqrt{20} + \sqrt{100}$
    $= 2\sqrt{5} + 10$

29. Commutative property of addition.

30. Distributive property of multiplication over addition.

31. Associative property of addition.

32. Commutative property of multiplication.

33. Commutative property of addition.

34. Commutative property of multiplication.

35. Distributive property of multiplication over addition.

36. Distributive property of multiplication over addition.

37. Associative property of multiplication

38. Commutative property of multiplication.

39. Identity property of multiplication.

40. Identity property of addition.

41. Inverse property of addition.

42. Inverse property of multiplication.

43. Inverse property of multiplication.

44. Inverse property of addition.

45. Answers will vary.
    Example: $1 - 2 = -1$

46. Answers will vary.
    Example: $\dfrac{4}{8} = \dfrac{1}{2}$

47. Answers will vary.
    Example: $\dfrac{-2}{8} = -\dfrac{1}{4}$

48. Answers will vary.
    Example: $\sqrt{3} - \sqrt{3} = 0$

49. Answers will vary.
    Example: $\sqrt{5}\sqrt{5} = \sqrt{25} = 5$

50. false

51. true

52. true

53. false

54. $7+2(x+9)$

$=7+(2x+18)$ distributive property

$=7+(18+2x)$ commutative property of addition

$=(7+18)+2x$ associative property

$=25+2x$

$=2x+25$ commutative property of addition

55. $5(x+4)+3x$

$=(5x+20)+3x$ distributive property

$=(20+5x)+3x$ commutative property of addition

$=20+(5x+3x)$ associative property

$=20+(5+3)x$ distributive property

$=20+8x$

$=8x+20$ commutative property of addition

56. vampire

57. vampire

58. not a vampire

59. vampire

60. narcissistic; $3^3+7^3+0^3=370$

61. narcissistic; $3^3+7^3+1^3=371$

62. not narcissistic; $3^3+7^3+2^3=374,\text{ not }372$

63. narcissistic; $9^4+4^4+7^4+4^4=9474$

64. Answers will vary. An example is the set of family members of a family with a 40-yr old father, 39-yr old mother, 14-yr old daughter, and 12-yr old son. The entire set has the characteristic of being allowed admittance to an R-rated movie. However, any subset that does not contain at least one of the two parents would not have this characteristic.

65. a. distributive property

b. $\dfrac{D(A+1)}{24}=\dfrac{200(12+1)}{24}$

$=\dfrac{200(13)}{24}$

$=\dfrac{2600}{24}$

≈ 108 mg

$\dfrac{DA+D}{24}=\dfrac{200\cdot12+200}{24}$

$=\dfrac{2400+200}{24}$

$=\dfrac{2600}{24}$

≈ 108 mg

74. makes sense

75. makes sense

76. does not make sense; Explanations will vary. Sample explanation: It must contain a whole number of pages.

77. makes sense

78. false; Changes to make the statement true will vary. A sample change is: Some rational numbers are not integers.

79. false; Changes to make the statement true will vary. A sample change is: All whole numbers are integers.

80. true

81. false; Changes to make the statement true will vary. A sample change is: Some irrational numbers are negative.

82. false; Changes to make the statement true will vary. A sample change is: Subtraction is not commutative.

83. false; Changes to make the statement true will vary. A sample change is: $(24\div6)\div2\neq24\div(6\div2)$

84. true

85. false; Changes to make the statement true will vary. A sample change is: $2\cdot a+5\neq5\cdot a+2$

Check Points 5.6

1. **a.** $19^0 = 1$

   b. $(3\pi)^0 = 1$

   c. $(-14)^0 = 1$

   d. $-14^0 = -1$

2. **a.** $9^{-2} = \dfrac{1}{9^2} = \dfrac{1}{81}$

   b. $6^{-3} = \dfrac{1}{6^3} = \dfrac{1}{216}$

   c. $12^{-1} = \dfrac{1}{12}$

3. **a.** $7.4 \times 10^9 = 7,400,000,000$

   b. $3.017 \times 10^{-6} = 0.000003017$

4. **a.** $7,410,000,000 = 7.41 \times 10^9$

   b. $0.000000092 = 9.2 \times 10^{-8}$

5. **a.** $306,000,000 = 3.06 \times 10^8$

   b. billion

6. $(1.3 \times 10^7) \times (4 \times 10^{-2}) = (1.3 \times 4) \times (10^7 \times 10^{-2})$
$$= 5.2 \times 10^{7+(-2)}$$
$$= 5.2 \times 10^5$$
$$= 520,000$$

7. $\dfrac{6.9 \times 10^{-8}}{3 \times 10^{-2}} = \left(\dfrac{6.9}{3}\right) \times \left(\dfrac{10^{-8}}{10^{-2}}\right)$
$$= 2.3 \times 10^{-8-(-2)}$$
$$= 2.3 \times 10^{-6}$$
$$= 0.0000023$$

8. **a.** $0.0036 \times 5,200,000$
$$= 3.6 \times 10^{-3} \times 5.2 \times 10^6$$
$$= (3.6 \times 5.2) \times (10^{-3} \times 10^6)$$
$$= 18.72 \times 10^3$$
$$= 1.872 \times 10 \times 10^3$$
$$= 1.872 \times 10^4$$

b. Based on part (a):
$0.0036 \times 5,200,000$
$$= 1.872 \times 10^4$$
$$= 18,720$$

9. $\dfrac{7.87 \times 10^{11}}{3.06 \times 10^8} = \left(\dfrac{7.87}{3.06}\right) \times \left(\dfrac{10^{11}}{10^8}\right) \approx 2.57 \times 10^3 = \$2570$

Exercise Set 5.6

1. $2^2 \cdot 2^3 = 2^{2+3} = 2^5 = 32$

2. $3^3 \cdot 3^2 = 3^{3+2} = 3^5 = 243$

3. $4 \cdot 4^2 = 4^1 \cdot 4^2 = 4^{1+2} = 4^3 = 64$

4. $5 \cdot 5^2 = 5^1 \cdot 5^2 = 5^{1+2} = 5^3 = 125$

5. $(2^2)^3 = 2^{2 \cdot 3} = 2^6 = 64$

6. $(3^3)^2 = 3^{3 \cdot 2} = 3^6 = 729$

7. $(1^4)^5 = 1^{4 \cdot 5} = 1^{20} = 1$

8. $(1^3)^7 = 1^{3 \cdot 7} = 1^{21} = 1$

9. $\dfrac{4^7}{4^5} = 4^{7-5} = 4^2 = 16$

10. $\dfrac{6^7}{6^5} = 6^{7-5} = 6^2 = 36$

11. $\dfrac{2^8}{2^4} = 2^{8-4} = 2^4 = 16$

12. $\dfrac{3^8}{3^4} = 3^{8-4} = 3^4 = 81$

13. $3^0 = 1$

14. $9^0 = 1$

15. $(-3)^0 = 1$

16. $(-9)^0 = 1$

17. $-3^0 = -1$

18. $-9^0 = -1$

19. $2^{-2} = \dfrac{1}{2^2} = \dfrac{1}{4}$

20. $3^{-2} = \dfrac{1}{3^2} = \dfrac{1}{9}$

21. $4^{-3} = \dfrac{1}{4^3} = \dfrac{1}{64}$

22. $2^{-3} = \dfrac{1}{2^3} = \dfrac{1}{8}$

23. $2^{-5} = \dfrac{1}{2^5} = \dfrac{1}{32}$

24. $2^{-6} = \dfrac{1}{2^6} = \dfrac{1}{64}$

25. $3^4 \cdot 3^{-2} = 3^{4+(-2)} = 3^2 = 9$

26. $2^5 \cdot 2^{-2} = 2^{5+(-2)} = 2^3 = 8$

27. $3^{-3} \cdot 3 = 3^{-3} \cdot 3^1 = 3^{-3+1} = 3^{-2} = \dfrac{1}{3^2} = \dfrac{1}{9}$

28. $2^{-3} \cdot 2 = 2^{-3} \cdot 2^1 = 2^{-3+1} = 2^{-2} = \dfrac{1}{2^2} = \dfrac{1}{4}$

29. $\dfrac{2^3}{2^7} = 2^{3-7} = 2^{-4} = \dfrac{1}{2^4} = \dfrac{1}{16}$

30. $\dfrac{3^4}{3^7} = 3^{4-7} = 3^{-3} = \dfrac{1}{3^3} = \dfrac{1}{27}$

31. $\left(x^5 x^3\right)^{-2} = \left(x^8\right)^{-2} = \dfrac{1}{\left(x^8\right)^2} = \dfrac{1}{x^{16}}$

32. $\left(x^2 x^4\right)^{-3} = \left(x^6\right)^{-3} = \dfrac{1}{\left(x^6\right)^3} = \dfrac{1}{x^{18}}$

33. $\dfrac{\left(x^3\right)^4}{\left(x^2\right)^7} = \dfrac{x^{12}}{x^{14}} = \dfrac{1}{x^2}$

34. $\dfrac{\left(x^2\right)^5}{\left(x^3\right)^4} = \dfrac{x^{10}}{x^{12}} = \dfrac{1}{x^2}$

35. $\left(\dfrac{x^5}{x^2}\right)^{-4} = \left(x^3\right)^{-4} = x^{-12} = \dfrac{1}{x^{12}}$

36. $\left(\dfrac{x^7}{x^2}\right)^{-3} = \left(x^5\right)^{-3} = x^{-15} = \dfrac{1}{x^{15}}$

37. $\dfrac{2x^5 \cdot 3x}{15x^6} = \dfrac{6x^6}{15x^6} = \dfrac{6}{15} = \dfrac{2}{5}$

38. $\dfrac{4x^7 \cdot 5x}{10x^8} = \dfrac{20x^8}{10x^8} = \dfrac{20}{10} = 2$

39. $\left(-2x^3 y^{-4}\right)\left(3x^{-1} y\right) = -6x^2 y^{-3} = -\dfrac{6x^2}{y^3}$

40. $\left(-5x^4 y^{-3}\right)\left(4x^{-1} y\right) = -20x^3 y^{-2} = -\dfrac{20x^3}{y^2}$

41. $\dfrac{30x^2 y^5}{-6x^8 y^{-3}} = -\dfrac{5y^8}{x^6}$

42. $\dfrac{24x^2 y^{13}}{-8x^5 y^{-2}} = -\dfrac{3y^{15}}{x^3}$

43. $2.7 \times 10^2 = 270$

44. $4.7 \times 10^3 = 4700$

45. $9.12 \times 10^5 = 912,000$

46. $8.14 \times 10^4 = 81,400$

47. $8 \times 10^7 = 8.0 \times 10^7 = 80,000,000$

48. $7 \times 10^6 = 7.0 \times 10^6 = 7,000,000$

49. $1 \times 10^5 = 1.0 \times 10^5 = 100,000$

50. $1 \times 10^8 = 1.0 \times 10^8 = 100,000,000$

51. $7.9 \times 10^{-1} = 0.79$

52. $8.6 \times 10^{-1} = 0.86$

53. $2.15 \times 10^{-2} = 0.0215$

54. $3.14 \times 10^{-2} = 0.0314$

55. $7.86 \times 10^{-4} = 0.000786$

56. $4.63 \times 10^{-5} = 0.0000463$

57. $3.18 \times 10^{-6} = 0.00000318$

58. $5.84 \times 10^{-7} = 0.000000584$

59. $370 = 3.7 \times 10^2$

60. $530 = 5.3 \times 10^2$

61. $3600 = 3.6 \times 10^3$

62. $2700 = 2.7 \times 10^3$

63. $32,000 = 3.2 \times 10^4$

64. $64,000 = 6.4 \times 10^4$

65. $220,000,000 = 2.2 \times 10^8$

66. $370,000,000,000 = 3.7 \times 10^{11}$

67. $0.027 = 2.7 \times 10^{-2}$

68. $0.014 = 1.4 \times 10^{-2}$

69. $0.0037 = 3.7 \times 10^{-3}$

70. $0.00083 = 8.3 \times 10^{-4}$

71. $0.00000293 = 2.93 \times 10^{-6}$

72. $0.000000647 = 6.47 \times 10^{-7}$

73. $820 \times 10^5 = \left(8.2 \times 10^2\right) \times 10^5 = 8.2 \times 10^7$

74. $630 \times 10^8 = \left(6.3 \times 10^2\right) \times 10^8 = 6.3 \times 10^{10}$

75. $0.41 \times 10^6 = \left(4.1 \times 10^{-1}\right) \times 10^6 = 4.1 \times 10^5$

76. $0.57 \times 10^9 = \left(5.7 \times 10^{-1}\right) \times 10^9 = 5.7 \times 10^8$

77. $2100 \times 10^{-9} = \left(2.1 \times 10^3\right) \times 10^{-9} = 2.1 \times 10^{-6}$

78. $97,000 \times 10^{-11} = \left(9.7 \times 10^4\right) \times 10^{-11} = 9.7 \times 10^{-7}$

79. $(2 \times 10^3)(3 \times 10^2) = (2 \times 3) \times (10^{3+2})$
$$= 6 \times 10^5$$
$$= 600,000$$

80. $(5 \times 10^2)(4 + 10^4) = (5 \times 4) \times (10^{2+4})$
$$= 20 \times 10^6$$
$$= 2 \times 10 \times 10^6$$
$$= 2 \times 10^7$$
$$= 20,000,000$$

81. $(2 \times 10^9)(3 \times 10^{-5}) = (2 \times 3) \times (10^{9-5})$
$$= 6 \times 10^4$$
$$= 60,000$$

82. $(4 \times 10^8)(2 \times 10^{-4}) = (4 \times 2) \times (10^{8-4})$
$$= 8 \times 10^4$$
$$= 80,000$$

83. $(4.1 \times 10^2)(3 \times 10^{-4}) = (4.1 \times 3) \times (10^{2-4})$
$$= 12.3 \times 10^{-2}$$
$$= 1.23 \times 10 \times 10^{-2}$$
$$= 1.23 \times 10^{-1}$$
$$= 0.123$$

84. $(1.2 \times 10^3)(2 \times 10^{-5}) = (1.2 \times 2) \times (10^{3-5})$
$$= 2.4 \times 10^{-2}$$
$$= 0.024$$

85. $\dfrac{12 \times 10^6}{4 \times 10^2} = \left(\dfrac{12}{4}\right) \times \left(\dfrac{10^6}{10^2}\right)$
$$= 3 \times 10^{6-2}$$
$$= 3 \times 10^4$$
$$= 30,000$$

86. $\dfrac{20 \times 10^{20}}{10 \times 10^{15}} = \left(\dfrac{20}{10}\right) \times \left(\dfrac{10^{20}}{10^{15}}\right)$
$$= 2 \times 10^{20-15}$$
$$= 2 \times 10^5$$
$$= 200,000$$

87. $\dfrac{15 \times 10^4}{5 \times 10^{-2}} = \left(\dfrac{15}{5}\right) \times \left(\dfrac{10^4}{10^{-2}}\right)$

$\qquad = 3 \times 10^{4-(-2)}$

$\qquad = 3 \times 10^6$

$\qquad = 3,000,000$

88. $\dfrac{18 \times 10^2}{9 \times 10^{-3}} = \left(\dfrac{18}{9}\right) \times \left(\dfrac{10^2}{10^{-3}}\right)$

$\qquad = 2 \times 10^{2-(-3)}$

$\qquad = 2 \times 10^5$

$\qquad = 200,000$

89. $\dfrac{6 \times 10^3}{2 \times 10^5} = \left(\dfrac{6}{2}\right) \times \left(\dfrac{10^3}{10^5}\right)$

$\qquad = 3 \times 10^{3-5}$

$\qquad = 3 \times 10^{-2}$

$\qquad = 0.03$

90. $\dfrac{8 \times 10^4}{2 \times 10^7} = \left(\dfrac{8}{2}\right) \times \left(\dfrac{10^4}{10^7}\right)$

$\qquad = 4 \times 10^{4-7}$

$\qquad = 4 \times 10^{-3}$

$\qquad = 0.004$

91. $\dfrac{6.3 \times 10^{-6}}{3 \times 10^{-3}} = \left(\dfrac{6.3}{3}\right) \times \left(\dfrac{10^{-6}}{10^{-3}}\right)$

$\qquad = 2.1 \times 10^{-6-(-3)}$

$\qquad = 2.1 \times 10^{-3}$

$\qquad = 0.0021$

92. $\dfrac{9.6 \times 10^{-7}}{3 \times 10^{-3}} = \left(\dfrac{9.6}{3}\right) \times \left(\dfrac{10^{-7}}{10^{-3}}\right)$

$\qquad = 3.2 \times 10^{-7-(-3)}$

$\qquad = 3.2 \times 10^{-4}$

$\qquad = 0.00032$

93. $(82,000,000)(3,000,000,000)$

$\qquad = (8.2 \times 10^7)(3.0 \times 10^9)$

$\qquad = (8.2 \times 3.0) \times (10^{7+9})$

$\qquad = 24.6 \times 10^{16}$

$\qquad = 2.46 \times 10 \times 10^{16}$

$\qquad = 2.46 \times 10^{17}$

94. $(94,000,000)(6,000,000,000)$

$\qquad = (9.4 \times 10^7)(6.0 \times 10^9)$

$\qquad = (9.4 \times 6.0) \times (10^{7+9})$

$\qquad = 56.4 \times 10^{16}$

$\qquad = 5.64 \times 10 \times 10^{16}$

$\qquad = 5.64 \times 10^{17}$

95. $(0.0005)(6,000,000)$

$\qquad = (5.0 \times 10^{-4})(6.0 \times 10^6)$

$\qquad = (5.0 \times 6.0)(10^{-4+6})$

$\qquad = 30 \times 10^2$

$\qquad = 3 \times 10 \times 10^2$

$\qquad = 3 \times 10^3$

96. $(0.000015)(0.004) = (1.5 \times 10^{-5})(4.0 \times 10^{-3})$

$\qquad\qquad = (1.5 \times 4.0) \times (10^{-5-3})$

$\qquad\qquad = 6 \times 10^{-8}$

97. $\dfrac{9,500,000}{500} = \dfrac{9.5 \times 10^6}{5 \times 10^2}$

$\qquad = \left(\dfrac{9.5}{5}\right) \times (10^{6-2})$

$\qquad = 1.9 \times 10^4$

98. $\dfrac{30,000}{0.0005} = \dfrac{3 \times 10^4}{5 \times 10^{-4}}$

$\qquad = \left(\dfrac{3}{5}\right) \times (10^{4-(-4)})$

$\qquad = 0.6 \times 10^8$

$\qquad = 6 \times 10^{-1} \times 10^8$

$\qquad = 6 \times 10^7$

99. $\dfrac{0.00008}{200} = \dfrac{8 \times 10^{-5}}{2 \times 10^2}$

$\qquad = \left(\dfrac{8}{2}\right) \times (10^{-5-2})$

$\qquad = 4 \times 10^{-7}$

100. $\dfrac{0.0018}{0.0000006} = \dfrac{1.8 \times 10^{-3}}{6 \times 10^{-7}}$

$= \left(\dfrac{1.8}{6}\right) \times (10^{-3-(-7)})$

$= 0.3 \times 10^4$

$= 3 \times 10^{-1} \times 10^4$

$= 3 \times 10^3$

101. $\dfrac{480,000,000,000}{0.00012} = \dfrac{4.8 \times 10^{11}}{1.2 \times 10^{-4}}$

$= \left(\dfrac{4.8}{1.2}\right) \times (10^{11-(-4)})$

$= 4 \times 10^{15}$

102. $\dfrac{0.000000096}{16,000} = \dfrac{9.6 \times 10^{-8}}{1.6 \times 10^4}$

$= \left(\dfrac{9.6}{1.6}\right) \times (10^{-8-4})$

$= 6 \times 10^{-12}$

103. $\dfrac{2^4}{2^5} + \dfrac{3^3}{3^5} = \dfrac{1}{2} + \dfrac{1}{3^2}$

$= \dfrac{1}{2} + \dfrac{1}{9}$

$= \dfrac{11}{18}$

104. $\dfrac{3^5}{3^6} + \dfrac{2^3}{2^6} = \dfrac{1}{3} + \dfrac{1}{2^3}$

$= \dfrac{1}{3} + \dfrac{1}{8}$

$= \dfrac{11}{24}$

105. $\dfrac{2^6}{2^4} - \dfrac{5^4}{5^6} = \dfrac{2^2}{1} - \dfrac{1}{5^2}$

$= 4 - \dfrac{1}{25}$

$= \dfrac{99}{25}$

$= 3\dfrac{24}{25}$

106. $\dfrac{5^6}{5^4} - \dfrac{2^4}{2^6} = \dfrac{5^2}{1} - \dfrac{1}{2^2}$

$= 25 - \dfrac{1}{4}$

$= \dfrac{99}{4}$

$= 24\dfrac{3}{4}$

107. $\dfrac{\left(5 \times 10^3\right)\left(1.2 \times 10^{-4}\right)}{\left(2.4 \times 10^2\right)} = 2.5 \times 10^{-3}$

108. $\dfrac{\left(2 \times 10^2\right)\left(2.6 \times 10^{-3}\right)}{\left(4 \times 10^3\right)} = 1.3 \times 10^{-4}$

109. $\dfrac{\left(1.6 \times 10^4\right)\left(7.2 \times 10^{-3}\right)}{\left(3.6 \times 10^8\right)\left(4 \times 10^{-3}\right)} = 0.8 \times 10^{-4} = 8 \times 10^{-5}$

110. $\dfrac{\left(1.2 \times 10^6\right)\left(8.7 \times 10^{-2}\right)}{\left(2.9 \times 10^6\right)\left(3 \times 10^{-3}\right)} = 1.2 \times 10^1$

111. a. 2.69×10^{12}

b. 3.03×10^8

c. $\dfrac{2.69 \times 10^{12}}{3.03 \times 10^8} = \dfrac{2.69}{3.03} \times \dfrac{10^{12}}{10^8}$

$= 0.888 \times 10^4$

$= 8.88 \times 10^3$

$= \$8880$

112. a. 2.52×10^{12}

b. 3×10^8

c. $\dfrac{2.52 \times 10^{12}}{3 \times 10^8} = \dfrac{2.52}{3} \times \dfrac{10^{12}}{10^8}$

$= 0.84 \times 10^4$

$= 8.4 \times 10^3$

$= \$8400$

113. $1470 \times 10^6 \cdot 6.90 = 1.47 \times 10^9 \cdot 6.9$

$= 1.47 \cdot 6.9 \times 10^9$

$= 10.143 \times 10^9$

$= 1.0143 \times 10^{10}$

Box-office receipts were $\$1.0143 \times 10^{10}$ in 2007.

114. $1400 \times 10^6 \cdot 6.40 = 1.4 \times 10^9 \cdot 6.4$
$$= 1.4 \cdot 6.4 \times 10^9$$
$$= 8.96 \times 10^9$$
Box-office receipts were $\$8.96 \times 10^9$ in 2005.

115. $5.3 \times 10^{-23} \cdot 20,000 = 5.3 \times 10^{-23} \cdot 2 \times 10^4$
$$= 5.3 \cdot 2 \times 10^{-23} \cdot 10^4$$
$$= 10.6 \times 10^{-19}$$
$$= 1.06 \times 10^1 \cdot 10^{-19}$$
$$= 1.06 \times 10^{-18}$$
The mass is 1.06×10^{-18} gram.

116. $1.67 \times 10^{-24} \cdot 80,000 = 1.67 \times 10^{-24} \cdot 8 \times 10^4$
$$= 1.67 \cdot 8 \times 10^{-24} \cdot 10^4$$
$$= 13.36 \times 10^{-20}$$
$$= 1.336 \times 10^1 \cdot 10^{-20}$$
$$= 1.336 \times 10^{-19}$$
The mass is 1.336×10^{-19} gram.

117. $3.2 \times 10^7 \cdot 127 = 3.2 \times 10^7 \cdot 1.27 \times 10^2$
$$= 3.2 \cdot 1.27 \times 10^7 \cdot 10^2$$
$$= 4.064 \times 10^9$$
Americans eat 4.064×10^9 chickens per year.

118. 365 days equals $365 \cdot 24$ or 8760 hours.
8760 hours equals $8760 \cdot 60$ or 525,600 minutes.
525,600 min. equals $525,600 \cdot 60$ or 31,536,000 seconds.
There are 3.1536×10^7 seconds in a year.

129. makes sense

130. does not make sense; Explanations will vary. Sample explanation: The expression does not contain division by 0 because $b^0 = 1$.

131. does not make sense; Explanations will vary. Sample explanation: Tax collections is the U.S. exceed $1 trillion, where as this number is only about $20 million.

132. makes sense

133. false; Changes to make the statement true will vary. A sample change is: $4^{-2} > 4^{-3}$.

134. true

135. false; Changes to make the statement true will vary. A sample change is: $(-2)^4 \neq 2^{-4}$ because $16 \neq \dfrac{1}{16}$.

136. false; Changes to make the statement true will vary. A sample change is: $5^2 \cdot 5^{-2} = 2^5 \cdot 2^{-5}$.

137. false; Changes to make the statement true will vary. A sample change is: $534.7 \neq 5347$.

138. false; Changes to make the statement true will vary. A sample change is: $\dfrac{8 \times 10^{30}}{4 \times 10^{-5}} = 2 \times 10^{30-(-5)} = 2 \times 10^{35}$.

139. false; Changes to make the statement true will vary. A sample change is: $(7 \times 10^5) + (2 \times 10^{-3}) = 700,000.002$.

140. true

141. Answers will vary. Possible answer:
$2.0 \times 10^0 = 2.0 \times 1 = 2$
There is no advantage here since $10^0 = 1$.

142. $1 - (2^{-1} + 2^{-2}) = 1 - \left(\dfrac{1}{2} + \dfrac{1}{4} \right)$
$$= \dfrac{4}{4} - \left(\dfrac{2}{4} + \dfrac{1}{4} \right)$$
$$= \dfrac{4}{4} - \dfrac{3}{4} = \dfrac{1}{4}$$

Check Points 5.7

1. $100, 100 + 20 = 120, 120 + 20 = 140, 140 + 20 = 160, 160 + 20 = 180, 180 + 20 = 200$
100, 120, 140, 160, 180, and 200

2. $8, 8 - 3 = 5, 5 - 3 = 2, 2 - 3 = -1, -1 - 3 = -4, -4 - 3 = -7$
8, 5, 2, -1, -4, and -7

3. $a_n = a_1 + (n-1)d$
$a_9 = 6 + (9-1)(-5)$
$\quad = 6 + 8(-5)$
$\quad = 6 - 40$
$\quad = -34$

4. a. $a_n = a_1 + (n-1)d$
$a_n = 36.5 + (n-1)(-0.5)$
$\quad = 36.5 - 0.5n + 0.5$
$\quad = -0.5n + 37$

b. $a_n = -0.5n + 37$
$\quad = -0.5(46) + 37$
$\quad = 14$
The percentage of full-time tenured faculty is projected to be 14% in 2020.

5. $12,\ 12\left(-\dfrac{1}{2}\right) = -6,\ -6\left(-\dfrac{1}{2}\right) = 3,\ 3\left(-\dfrac{1}{2}\right) = -\dfrac{3}{2},$

$-\dfrac{3}{2}\left(-\dfrac{1}{2}\right) = \dfrac{3}{4},\ \dfrac{3}{4}\left(-\dfrac{1}{2}\right) = -\dfrac{3}{8}$

$12,\ -6,\ 3,\ -\dfrac{3}{2},\ \dfrac{3}{4},\ -\dfrac{3}{8}$

6. $a_n = a_1 r^{n-1}$ with $a_1 = 5$, $r = -3$, and $n = 7$

$a_7 = 5(-3)^{7-1} = 5(-3)^6 = 5(729) = 3645$

7. $a_n = a_1 r^{n-1}$ with $a_1 = 3$ and $r = \dfrac{6}{3} = 2$. Thus $a_n = 3(2)^{n-1}$

$a_8 = 3(2)^{8-1} = 3(2)^7 = 3(128) = 384$

Exercise Set 5.7

1. $8,\ 8 + 2 = 10,\ 10 + 2 = 12,\ 12 + 2 = 14,\ 14 + 2 = 16,\ 16 + 2 = 18$
$8,\ 10,\ 12,\ 14,\ 16,$ and 18

2. $5,\ 5 + 3 = 8,\ 8 + 3 = 11,\ 11 + 3 = 14,\ 14 + 3 = 17,\ 17 + 3 = 20$
$5,\ 8,\ 11,\ 14,\ 17,$ and 20

3. $200,\ 200 + 20 = 220,\ 220 + 20 = 240,\ 240 + 20 = 260,\ 260 + 20 = 280,\ 280 + 20 = 300$
$200,\ 220,\ 240,\ 260,\ 280,$ and 300

4. $300,\ 300 + 50 = 350,\ 350 + 50 = 400,\ 400 + 50 = 450,\ 450 + 50 = 500,\ 500 + 50 = 550$
$300,\ 350,\ 400,\ 450,\ 500,$ and 550

5. $-7,\ -7 + 4 = -3,\ -3 + 4 = 1,\ 1 + 4 = 5,\ 5 + 4 = 9,\ 9 + 4 = 13$
$-7,\ -3,\ 1,\ 5,\ 9,$ and 13

6. $-8,\ -8 + 5 = -3,\ -3 + 5 = 2,\ 2 + 5 = 7,\ 7 + 5 = 12,\ 12 + 5 = 17$
$-8,\ -3,\ 2,\ 7,\ 12,$ and 17

7. $-400,\ -400 + 300 = -100,\ -100 + 300 = 200,\ 200 + 300 = 500,\ 500 + 300 = 800,\ 800 + 300 = 1100$
$-400,\ -100,\ 200,\ 500,\ 800,$ and 1100

8. $-500,\ -500 + 400 = -100,\ -100 + 400 = 300,\ 300 + 400 = 700,\ 700 + 400 = 1100,\ 1100 + 400 = 1500$
$-500,\ -100,\ 300,\ 700,\ 1100,$ and 1500

9. $7,\ 7 - 3 = 4,\ 4 - 3 = 1,\ 1 - 3 = -2,\ -2 - 3 = -5,\ -5 - 3 = -8$
$7,\ 4,\ 1,\ -2,\ -5,$ and -8

10. $9,\ 9 - 5 = 4,\ 4 - 5 = -1,\ -1 - 5 = -6,\ -6 - 5 = -11,\ -11 - 5 = -16$
$9,\ 4,\ -1,\ -6,\ -11,$ and -16

11. $200,\ 200 - 60 = 140,\ 140 - 60 = 80,\ 80 - 60 = 20,\ 20 - 60 = -40,\ -40 - 60 = -100$
$200,\ 140,\ 80,\ 20,\ -40,$ and -100

12. $300,\ 300 - 90 = 210,\ 210 - 90 = 120,\ 120 - 90 = 30,\ 30 - 90 = -60,\ -60 - 90 = -150$
$300,\ 210,\ 120,\ 30,\ -60,$ and -150

13. $\dfrac{5}{2}, \dfrac{5}{2}+\dfrac{1}{2}=\dfrac{6}{2}=3, \dfrac{6}{2}+\dfrac{1}{2}=\dfrac{7}{2}, \dfrac{7}{2}+\dfrac{1}{2}=\dfrac{8}{2}=4, \dfrac{8}{2}+\dfrac{1}{2}=\dfrac{9}{2}, \dfrac{9}{2}+\dfrac{1}{2}=\dfrac{10}{2}=5$

   $\dfrac{5}{2}, 3, \dfrac{7}{2}, 4, \dfrac{9}{2},$ and 5

14. $\dfrac{3}{4}, \dfrac{3}{4}+\dfrac{1}{4}=1, \dfrac{4}{4}+\dfrac{1}{4}=\dfrac{5}{4}, \dfrac{5}{4}+\dfrac{1}{4}=\dfrac{6}{4}=\dfrac{3}{2}, \dfrac{6}{4}+\dfrac{1}{4}=\dfrac{7}{4}, \dfrac{7}{4}+\dfrac{1}{4}=\dfrac{8}{4}=2$

   $\dfrac{3}{4}, 1, \dfrac{5}{4}, \dfrac{3}{2}, \dfrac{7}{4},$ and 2

15. $\dfrac{3}{2}, \dfrac{6}{4}+\dfrac{1}{4}=\dfrac{7}{4}, \dfrac{7}{4}+\dfrac{1}{4}=\dfrac{8}{4}=2, \dfrac{8}{4}+\dfrac{1}{4}=\dfrac{9}{4}, \dfrac{9}{4}+\dfrac{1}{4}=\dfrac{10}{4}=\dfrac{5}{2}, \dfrac{10}{4}+\dfrac{1}{4}=\dfrac{11}{4}$

   $\dfrac{3}{2}, \dfrac{7}{4}, 2, \dfrac{9}{4}, \dfrac{5}{2},$ and $\dfrac{11}{4}$

16. $\dfrac{3}{2}, \dfrac{6}{4}-\dfrac{1}{4}=\dfrac{5}{4}, \dfrac{5}{4}-\dfrac{1}{4}=\dfrac{4}{4}=1, \dfrac{4}{4}-\dfrac{1}{4}=\dfrac{3}{4}, \dfrac{3}{4}-\dfrac{1}{4}=\dfrac{2}{4}=\dfrac{1}{2}, \dfrac{2}{4}-\dfrac{1}{4}=\dfrac{1}{4}$

   $\dfrac{3}{2}, \dfrac{5}{4}, 1, \dfrac{3}{4}, \dfrac{1}{2},$ and $\dfrac{1}{4}$

17. $4.25, 4.25 + 0.3 = 4.55, 4.55 + 0.3 = 4.85, 4.85 + 0.3 = 5.15, 5.15 + 0.3 = 5.45, 5.45 + 0.3 = 5.75$
    $4.25, 4.55, 4.85, 5.15, 5.45,$ and 5.75

18. $6.3, 6.3 + 0.25 = 6.55, 6.55 + 0.25 = 6.8, 6.8 + 0.25 = 7.05, 7.05 + 0.25 = 7.3, 7.3 + 0.25 = 7.55$
    $6.3, 6.55, 6.8, 7.05, 7.3,$ and 7.55

19. $4.5, 4.5 - 0.75 = 3.75, 3.75 - 0.75 = 3, 3 - 0.75 = 2.25, 2.25 - 0.75 = 1.5, 1.5 - 0.75 = 0.75$
    $4.5, 3.75, 3, 2.25, 1.5,$ and 0.75

20. $3.5, 3.5 - 1.75 = 1.75, 1.75 - 1.75 = 0, 0 - 1.75 = -1.75, -1.75 - 1.75 = -3.5, -3.5 - 1.75 = -5.25$
    $3.5, 1.75, 0, -1.75, -3.5,$ and -5.25

21. $a_1 = 13, d = 4$
    $a_6 = 13 + (6-1)(4)$
    $ = 13 + 5(4)$
    $ = 13 + 20$
    $ = 33$

22. $a_1 = 9, d = 2$
    $a_{16} = 9 + (16-1)(2)$
    $\phantom{a_{16}} = 9 + 15(2)$
    $\phantom{a_{16}} = 9 + 30$
    $\phantom{a_{16}} = 39$

23. $a_1 = 7, d = 5$
    $a_{50} = 7 + (50-1)(5)$
    $\phantom{a_{50}} = 7 + 49(5)$
    $\phantom{a_{50}} = 7 + 245$
    $\phantom{a_{50}} = 252$

24. $a_1 = 8, d = 6$

$a_{60} = 8 + (60-1)(6)$

$\quad = 8 + 59(6)$

$\quad = 8 + 354$

$\quad = 362$

25. $a_1 = -5, d = 9$

$a_9 = -5 + (9-1)(9)$

$\quad = -5 + 8(9)$

$\quad = -5 + 72$

$\quad = 67$

26. $a_1 = -8, d = 10$

$a_{10} = -8 + (10-1)(10)$

$\quad = -8 + 9(10)$

$\quad = -8 + 90$

$\quad = 82$

27. $a_1 = -40, d = 5$

$a_{200} = -40 + (200-1)(5)$

$\quad = -40 + 199(5)$

$\quad = -40 + 995$

$\quad = 955$

28. $a_1 = -60, d = 5$

$a_{150} = -60 + (150-1)(5)$

$\quad = -60 + 149(5)$

$\quad = -60 + 745$

$\quad = 685$

29. $a_1 = 8, d = -10$

$a_{10} = 8 + (10-1)(-10)$

$\quad = 8 + 9(-10)$

$\quad = 8 - 90$

$\quad = -82$

30. $a_1 = 10, d = -6$

$a_{11} = 10 + (11-1)(-6)$

$\quad = 10 + 10(-6)$

$\quad = 10 + (-60)$

$\quad = -50$

31. $a_1 = 35, d = -3$

$a_{60} = 35 + (60-1)(-3)$

$\quad = 35 + 59(-3)$

$\quad = 35 + (-177)$

$\quad = -142$

32. $a_1 = -32, d = 4$

$a_{70} = -32 + (70-1)(4)$

$\quad = -32 + 69(4)$

$\quad = -32 + 276$

$\quad = 244$

33. $a_1 = 12, d = -5$

$a_{12} = 12 + (12-1)(-5)$

$\quad = 12 + 11(-5)$

$\quad = 12 + (-55)$

$\quad = -43$

34. $a_1 = -20, d = -4$

$a_{20} = -20 + (20-1)(-4)$

$\quad = -20 + 19(-4)$

$\quad = -20 + (-76)$

$\quad = -96$

35. $a_1 = -70, d = -2$

$a_{90} = -70 + (90-1)(-2)$

$\quad = -70 + 89(-2)$

$\quad = -70 + (-178)$

$\quad = -248$

36. $a_1 = 106, d = -12$

$a_{80} = 106 + (80-1)(-12)$

$\quad = 106 + 79(-12)$

$\quad = 106 + (-948)$

$\quad = -842$

37. $a_1 = 6, d = \dfrac{1}{2}$

$a_{12} = 6 + (12-1)\left(\dfrac{1}{2}\right)$

$\quad = 6 + 11\left(\dfrac{1}{2}\right)$

$\quad = \dfrac{12}{2} + \dfrac{11}{2}$

$\quad = \dfrac{23}{2}$

38. $a_1 = 8,\ d = \dfrac{1}{4}$

$$a_{14} = 8 + (14-1)\left(\dfrac{1}{4}\right)$$

$$= 8 + 13\left(\dfrac{1}{4}\right)$$

$$= \dfrac{32}{4} + \dfrac{13}{4}$$

$$= \dfrac{45}{4}$$

39. $a_1 = 14,\ d = -0.25$

$$a_{50} = 14 + (50-1)(-0.25)$$

$$= 14 + 49(-0.25)$$

$$= 14 + (-12.25)$$

$$= 1.75$$

40. $a_1 = -12,\ d = -0.5$

$$a_{110} = -12 + (110-1)(-0.5)$$

$$= -12 + 109(-0.5)$$

$$= -12 + (-54.5)$$

$$= -66.5$$

41. $a_n = a_1 + (n-1)d$ with $a_1 = 1,\ d = 4$

$$a_n = 1 + (n-1)4$$

$$= 1 + 4n - 4$$

$$= 4n - 3$$

Thus $a_{20} = 4(20) - 3 = 77$.

42. $a_n = a_1 + (n-1)d$ with $a_1 = 2,\ d = 5$

$$a_n = 2 + (n-1)5$$

$$= 2 + 5n - 5$$

$$= 5n - 3$$

Thus $a_{20} = 5(20) - 3 = 97$.

43. $a_n = a_1 + (n-1)d$ with $a_1 = 7,\ d = -4$

$$a_n = 7 + (n-1)(-4)$$

$$= 7 - 4n + 4$$

$$= -4n + 11$$

Thus $a_{20} = -4(20) + 11 = -69$.

44. $a_n = a_1 + (n-1)d$ with $a_1 = 6,\ d = -5$

$$a_n = 6 + (n-1)(-5)$$

$$= 6 - 5n + 5$$

$$= -5n + 11$$

Thus $a_{20} = -5(20) + 11 = -89$.

45. $a_n = a_1 + (n-1)d$ with $a_1 = 9$, $d = 2$

$a_n = 9 + (n-1)2$

$\quad = 9 + 2n - 2$

$\quad = 2n + 7$

Thus $a_{20} = 2(20) + 7 = 47$.

46. $a_n = a_1 + (n-1)d$ with $a_1 = 6$, $d = 3$

$a_n = 6 + (n-1)3$

$\quad = 6 + 3n - 3$

$\quad = 3n + 3$

Thus $a_{20} = 3(20) + 3 = 63$.

47. $a_n = a_1 + (n-1)d$ with $a_1 = -20$, $d = -4$

$a_n = -20 + (n-1)(-4)$

$\quad = -20 - 4n + 4$

$\quad = -4n - 16$

Thus $a_{20} = -4(20) - 16 = -96$.

48. $a_n = a_1 + (n-1)d$ with $a_1 = -70$, $d = -5$

$a_n = -70 + (n-1)(-5)$

$\quad = -70 - 5n + 5$

$\quad = -5n - 65$

Thus $a_{20} = -5(20) - 65 = -165$.

49. $a_1 = 4$, $r = 2$

4, $4 \cdot 2 = 8$, $8 \cdot 2 = 16$, $16 \cdot 2 = 32$, $32 \cdot 2 = 64$,

$64 \cdot 2 = 128$

$4, 8, 16, 32, 64, 128$

50. $a_1 = 2$, $r = 3$

2, $2 \cdot 3 = 6$, $6 \cdot 3 = 18$, $18 \cdot 3 = 54$, $54 \cdot 3 = 162$,

$162 \cdot 3 = 486$

$2, 6, 18, 54, 162, 486$

51. $a_1 = 1000$, $r = 1$

1000, $1000 \cdot 1 = 1000$, $1000 \cdot 1 = 1000, \ldots$

$1000, 1000, 1000, 1000, 1000, 1000$

52. $a_1 = 5000$, $r = 1$

5000, $5000 \cdot 1 = 5000$, $5000 \cdot 1 = 5000, \ldots$

$5000, 5000, 5000, 5000, 5000, 5000$

53. $a_1 = 3$, $r = -2$

3, $3(-2) = -6$, $-6(-2) = 12$, $12(-2) = -24$, $-24(-2) = 48$, $48(-2) = -96$

$3, -6, 12, -24, 48, -96$

54. $a_1 = 2$, $r = -3$

2, $2(-3) = -6$, $-6(-3) = 18$, $18(-3) = -54$,

$-54(-3) = 162$, $162(-3) = -486$

$2, -6, 18, -54, 162, -486$

55. $a_1 = 10$, $r = -4$

10, $10(-4) = -40$, $-40(-4) = 160$,
$160(-4) = -640$, $-640(-4) = 2560$,
$2560(-4) = -10{,}240$
10, -40, 160, -640, 2560, and $-10{,}240$

56. $a_1 = 20$, $r = -4$

20, $20(-4) = -80$, $-80(-4) = 320$,
$320(-4) = -1280$, $-1280(-4) = 5120$,
$5120(-4) = -20{,}480$
20, -80, 320, -1280, 5120, and $-20{,}480$

57. $a_1 = 2000$, $r = -1$

2000, $2000(-1) = -2000$,
$-2000(-1) = 2000$, …
2000, -2000, 2000, -2000, 2000, -2000

58. $a_1 = 3000$, $r = -1$

3000, $3000(-1) = -3000$, $-3000(-1) = 3000$, …
3000, -3000, 3000, -3000, 3000, -3000

59. $a_1 = -2$, $r = -3$

-2, $-2(-3) = 6$, $6(-3) = -18$, $-18(-3) = 54$, $54(-3) = -162$, $-162(-3) = 486$
-2, 6, -18, 54, -162, 486

60. $a_1 = -4$, $r = -2$

-4, $-4(-2) = 8$, $8(-2) = -16$, $-16(-2) = 32$,
$32(-2) = -64$, $-64(-2) = 128$
-4, 8, -16, 32, -64, 128

61. $a_1 = -6$, $r = -5$

-6, $-6(-5) = 30$, $30(-5) = -150$,
$-150(-5) = 750$, $750(-5) = -3750$,
$-3750(-5) = 18{,}750$
-6, 30, -150, 750, -3750, 18750

62. $a_1 = -8$, $r = -5$

-8, $-8(-5) = 40$, $40(-5) = -200$,
$-200(-5) = 1000$, $1000(-5) = -5000$,
$-5000(-5) = 25{,}000$
-8, 40, -200, 1000, -5000, 25000

63. $a_1 = \dfrac{1}{4}$, $r = 2$

$\dfrac{1}{4}$, $\dfrac{1}{4} \cdot 2 = \dfrac{1}{2}$, $\dfrac{1}{2} \cdot 2 = 1$, $1 \cdot 2 = 2$, $2 \cdot 2 = 4$,
$4 \cdot 2 = 8$
$\dfrac{1}{4}$, $\dfrac{1}{2}$, 1, 2, 4, 8

64. $a_1 = \dfrac{1}{2}, r = 2$

$\dfrac{1}{2}, \dfrac{1}{2} \cdot 2 = 1, 1 \cdot 2 = 2, 2 \cdot 2 = 4, 4 \cdot 2 = 8, 8 \cdot 2 = 16$

$\dfrac{1}{2}, 1, 2, 4, 8, 16$

65. $a_1 = \dfrac{1}{4}, r = \dfrac{1}{2}$

$\dfrac{1}{4}, \dfrac{1}{4} \cdot \dfrac{1}{2} = \dfrac{1}{8}, \dfrac{1}{8} \cdot \dfrac{1}{2} = \dfrac{1}{16}, \dfrac{1}{16} \cdot \dfrac{1}{2} = \dfrac{1}{32},$

$\dfrac{1}{32} \cdot \dfrac{1}{2} = \dfrac{1}{64}, \dfrac{1}{64} \cdot \dfrac{1}{2} = \dfrac{1}{128}$

$\dfrac{1}{4}, \dfrac{1}{8}, \dfrac{1}{16}, \dfrac{1}{32}, \dfrac{1}{64}, \dfrac{1}{128}$

66. $a_1 = \dfrac{1}{5}, r = \dfrac{1}{2}$

$\dfrac{1}{5}, \dfrac{1}{5} \cdot \dfrac{1}{2} = \dfrac{1}{10}, \dfrac{1}{10} \cdot \dfrac{1}{2} = \dfrac{1}{20}, \dfrac{1}{20} \cdot \dfrac{1}{2} = \dfrac{1}{40},$

$\dfrac{1}{40} \cdot \dfrac{1}{2} = \dfrac{1}{80}, \dfrac{1}{80} \cdot \dfrac{1}{2} = \dfrac{1}{160}$

$\dfrac{1}{5}, \dfrac{1}{10}, \dfrac{1}{20}, \dfrac{1}{40}, \dfrac{1}{80}, \dfrac{1}{160}$

67. $a_1 = -\dfrac{1}{16}, r = -4$

$-\dfrac{1}{16}, -\dfrac{1}{16} \cdot (-4) = \dfrac{1}{4}, \dfrac{1}{4} \cdot (-4) = -1,$
$-1(-4) = 4, 4(-4) = -16, -16(-4) = 64$

$-\dfrac{1}{16}, \dfrac{1}{4}, -1, 4, -16, 64$

68. $a_1 = -\dfrac{1}{8}, r = -2$

$-\dfrac{1}{8}, -\dfrac{1}{8}(-2) = \dfrac{1}{4}, \dfrac{1}{4}(-2) = -\dfrac{1}{2}, -\dfrac{1}{2}(-2) = 1,$
$1(-2) = -2, -2(-2) = 4$

$-\dfrac{1}{8}, \dfrac{1}{4}, -\dfrac{1}{2}, 1, -2, 4$

69. $a_1 = 2, r = 0.1$
2, 2(0.1) = 0.2, 0.2(0.1) = 0.02,
0.02(0.1) = 0.002, 0.002(0.1) = 0.0002, 0.0002(0.1) = 0.00002.
2, 0.2, 0.02, 0.002, 0.0002, 0.00002

70. $a_1 = -1000, r = 0.1$
−1000, −1000(0.1) = −100, −100(0.1) = −10, −10(0.1) = −1, −1(0.1) = −0.1, −0.1(0.1) = −0.01
−1000, −100, −10, −1, −0.1, −0.01

72. $a_1 = 4, r = 3$

$a_5 = 4(3)^{5-1}$

$\quad = 4(3)^4$

$\quad = 4(81)$

$\quad = 324$

73. $a_1 = 2, r = 3$

$a_{20} = 2(3)^{20-1}$

$\quad = 2(3)^{19}$

$\quad = 2,324,522,934$

$\quad \approx 2.32 \times 10^9$

74. $a_1 = 2, r = 2$

$a_{20} = 2(2)^{20-1}$

$\quad = 2(2)^{19}$

$\quad = 1,048,576$

75. $a_1 = 50, r = 1$

$a_{100} = 50(1)^{100-1}$

$\quad = 50(1)^{99}$

$\quad = 50$

76. $a_1 = 60, r = 1$

$a_{200} = 60(1)^{200-1}$

$\quad = 60(1)^{199}$

$\quad = 60$

77. $a_1 = 5, r = -2$

$a_7 = 5(-2)^{7-1}$

$\quad = 5(-2)^6$

$\quad = 320$

78. $a_1 = 4, r = -3$

$a_4 = 4(-3)^{4-1}$

$\quad = 4(-3)^3$

$\quad = -108$

79. $a_1 = 2, r = -1$

$a_{30} = 2(-1)^{30-1}$

$\quad = 2(-1)^{29}$

$\quad = -2$

80. $a_1 = 6, r = -1$

$a_{40} = 6(-1)^{40-1}$

$\quad = 6(-1)^{39}$

$\quad = -6$

81. $a_1 = -2, r = -3$

$a_6 = -2(-3)^{6-1}$

$\quad = -2(-3)^5$

$\quad = 486$

82. $a_1 = -5, r = -2$

$a_5 = -5(-2)^{5-1}$

$\quad = -5(-2)^4$

$\quad = -80$

83. $a_1 = 6, r = \dfrac{1}{2}$

$a_8 = 6\left(\dfrac{1}{2}\right)^{8-1}$

$\quad = 6\left(\dfrac{1}{2}\right)^7$

$\quad = \dfrac{6}{128}$

$\quad = \dfrac{3}{64}$

84. $a_1 = 12, r = \dfrac{1}{2}$

$a_8 = 12\left(\dfrac{1}{2}\right)^{8-1}$

$\quad = 12\left(\dfrac{1}{2}\right)^7$

$\quad = \dfrac{12}{128}$

$\quad = \dfrac{3}{32}$

85. $a_1 = 18,\ r = -\dfrac{1}{3}$

$$a_6 = 18\left(-\dfrac{1}{3}\right)^{6-1}$$

$$= 18\left(-\dfrac{1}{3}\right)^{5}$$

$$= -\dfrac{18}{243}$$

$$= -\dfrac{2}{27}$$

86. $a_1 = 9,\ r = -\dfrac{1}{3}$

$$a_4 = 9\left(-\dfrac{1}{3}\right)^{4-1}$$

$$= 9\left(-\dfrac{1}{3}\right)^{3}$$

$$= -\dfrac{9}{27}$$

$$= -\dfrac{1}{3}$$

87. $a_1 = 1000,\ r = -\dfrac{1}{2}$

$$a_{40} = 1000\left(-\dfrac{1}{2}\right)^{40-1}$$

$$= 1000\left(-\dfrac{1}{2}\right)^{39}$$

$$\approx -1.82 \times 10^{-9}$$

88. $a_1 = 8000,\ r = -\dfrac{1}{2}$

$$a_{30} = 8000\left(-\dfrac{1}{2}\right)^{30-1}$$

$$= 8000\left(-\dfrac{1}{2}\right)^{29}$$

$$\approx -0.000014901$$

89. $a_1 = 1,000,000,\ r = 0.1$

$$a_8 = 1,000,000(0.1)^{8-1}$$

$$= 1,000,000(0.1)^{7}$$

$$= 0.1$$

90. $a_1 = 40,000,\ r = 0.1$

$$a_8 = 40,000(0.1)^{8-1}$$

$$= 40,000(0.1)^{7}$$

$$= 0.004$$

91. $a_n = a_1 r^{n-1}$ with $a_1 = 3$ and $r = \dfrac{12}{3} = 4$.

Thus $a_n = 3(4)^{n-1}$

$$a_7 = 3(4)^{7-1} = 3(4)^6 = 3(4096) = 12,288$$

92. $a_n = a_1 r^{n-1}$ with $a_1 = 3$ and $r = \dfrac{15}{3} = 5$.

Thus $a_n = 3(5)^{n-1}$

$$a_7 = 3(5)^{7-1} = 3(5)^6 = 3(15,625) = 46,875$$

93. $a_n = a_1 r^{n-1}$ with $a_1 = 18$ and $r = \dfrac{6}{18} = \dfrac{1}{3}$.

Thus $a_n = 18\left(\dfrac{1}{3}\right)^{n-1}$

$$a_7 = 18\left(\dfrac{1}{3}\right)^{7-1} = 18\left(\dfrac{1}{3}\right)^6 = 18\left(\dfrac{1}{729}\right) = \dfrac{18}{729} = \dfrac{2}{81}$$

94. $a_n = a_1 r^{n-1}$ with $a_1 = 12$ and $r = \dfrac{6}{12} = \dfrac{1}{2}$.

Thus $a_n = 12\left(\dfrac{1}{2}\right)^{n-1}$

$$a_7 = 12\left(\dfrac{1}{2}\right)^{7-1} = 12\left(\dfrac{1}{2}\right)^6 = 12\left(\dfrac{1}{64}\right) = \dfrac{12}{64} = \dfrac{3}{16}$$

95. $a_n = a_1 r^{n-1}$ with $a_1 = 1.5$ and $r = \dfrac{-3}{1.5} = -2$.

Thus $a_n = 1.5(-2)^{n-1}$

$$a_7 = 1.5(-2)^{7-1} = 1.5(-2)^6 = 1.5(64) = 96$$

96. $a_n = a_1 r^{n-1}$ with $a_1 = 5$ and $r = \dfrac{-1}{5}$.

Thus $a_n = 5\left(-\dfrac{1}{5}\right)^{n-1}$

$a_7 = 5\left(-\dfrac{1}{5}\right)^{7-1} = 5\left(-\dfrac{1}{5}\right)^6 = 5\left(\dfrac{1}{15,625}\right) = \dfrac{5}{15,625} = \dfrac{1}{3125}$

97. $a_n = a_1 r^{n-1}$ with $a_1 = 0.0004$ and $r = \dfrac{-0.004}{0.0004} = -10$. Thus $a_n = 0.0004(-10)^{n-1}$

$a_7 = 0.0004(-10)^{7-1} = 0.0004(-10)^6 = 0.0004(1,000,000) = 400$

98. $a_n = a_1 r^{n-1}$ with $a_1 = 0.0007$ and $r = \dfrac{-0.007}{0.0007} = -10$. Thus $a_n = 0.0007(-10)^{n-1}$

$a_7 = 0.0007(-10)^{7-1} = 0.0007(-10)^6 = 0.0007(1,000,000) = 700$

99. The common difference of the arithmetic sequence is 4.
$2 + 4 = 6, 6 + 4 = 10, 10 + 4 = 14,$
$14 + 4 = 18, 18 + 4 = 22$
$2, 6, 10, 14, 18, 22, \ldots$

100. The common difference of the arithmetic sequence is 5.
$3 + 5 = 8, 8 + 5 = 13, 13 + 5 = 18, 18 + 5 = 23, 23 + 5 = 28$
$3, 8, 13, 18, 23, 28, \ldots$

101. The common ratio of the geometric sequence is 3.
$5 \cdot 3 = 15, 15 \cdot 3 = 45, 45 \cdot 3 = 135, \quad 5, 15, 45, 135, 405, 1215, \ldots$
$135 \cdot 3 = 405, 405 \cdot 3 = 1215$

102. The common ratio of the geometric sequence is 2.
$15 \cdot 2 = 30, 30 \cdot 2 = 60, 60 \cdot 2 = 120,$
$120 \cdot 2 = 240, 240 \cdot 2 = 480$
$15, 30, 60, 120, 240, 480, \ldots$

103. The common difference of the arithmetic sequence is 5.
$-7 + 5 = -2, -2 + 5 = 3, 3 + 5 = 8,$
$8 + 5 = 13, 13 + 5 = 18.$
$-7, -2, 3, 8, 13, 18, \ldots$

104. The common difference of the arithmetic sequence is 4.
$-9 + 4 = -5, -5 + 4 = -1, -1 + 4 = 3, 3 + 4 = 7,$
$7 + 4 = 11$
$-9, -5, -1, 3, 7, 11, \ldots$

105. The common ratio of the geometric sequence is $\dfrac{1}{2}$.

$3 \cdot \dfrac{1}{2} = \dfrac{3}{2}, \dfrac{3}{2} \cdot \dfrac{1}{2} = \dfrac{3}{4}, \dfrac{3}{4} \cdot \dfrac{1}{2} = \dfrac{3}{8}, \dfrac{3}{8} \cdot \dfrac{1}{2} = \dfrac{3}{16}$

$\dfrac{3}{16} \cdot \dfrac{1}{2} = \dfrac{3}{32}$

$3, \dfrac{3}{2}, \dfrac{3}{4}, \dfrac{3}{8}, \dfrac{3}{16}, \dfrac{3}{32}, \ldots$

106. The common ratio of the geometric sequence is $\dfrac{1}{2}$.

$6 \cdot \dfrac{1}{2} = 3, 3 \cdot \dfrac{1}{2} = \dfrac{3}{2}, \dfrac{3}{2} \cdot \dfrac{1}{2} = \dfrac{3}{4}, \dfrac{3}{4} \cdot \dfrac{1}{2} = \dfrac{3}{8},$

$\dfrac{3}{8} \cdot \dfrac{1}{2} = \dfrac{3}{16}$

$6, 3, \dfrac{3}{2}, \dfrac{3}{4}, \dfrac{3}{8}, \dfrac{3}{16}, \ldots$

107. The common difference of the arithmetic sequence is $\dfrac{1}{2}$.

$\dfrac{1}{2} + \dfrac{1}{2} = 1, 1 + \dfrac{1}{2} = \dfrac{3}{2}, \dfrac{3}{2} + \dfrac{1}{2} = 2, 2 + \dfrac{1}{2} = \dfrac{5}{2},$

$\dfrac{5}{2} + \dfrac{1}{2} = 3$

$\dfrac{1}{2}, 1, \dfrac{3}{2}, 2, \dfrac{5}{2}, 3, \ldots$

108. The common difference of the arithmetic sequence is $\dfrac{1}{3}$.

$\dfrac{2}{3} + \dfrac{1}{3} = 1, 1 + \dfrac{1}{3} = \dfrac{4}{3}, \dfrac{4}{3} + \dfrac{1}{3} = \dfrac{5}{3}, \dfrac{5}{3} + \dfrac{1}{3} = 2,$

$2 + \dfrac{1}{3} = \dfrac{7}{3}$

$\dfrac{2}{3}, 1, \dfrac{4}{3}, \dfrac{5}{3}, 2, \dfrac{7}{3}, \ldots$

109. The common ratio of the geometric sequence is -1.
$7(-1) = -7, -7(-1) = 7, 7(-1) = -7,$
$-7(-1) = 7, 7(-1) = -7$
$7, -7, 7, -7, 7, -7, \ldots$

110. The common ratio of the geometric sequence is -1.
$6(-1) = -6, -6(-1) = 6, 6(-1) = -6, -6(-1) = 6, 6(-1) = -6$
$6, -6, 6, -6, 6, -6, \ldots$

111. The common difference of the arithmetic sequence is -14.
$7 - 14 = -7, -7 - 14 = -21, -21 - 14 = -35, -35 - 14 = -49, -49 - 14 = -63$
$7, -7, -21, -35, -49, -63, \ldots$

112. The common difference of the arithmetic sequence
is –12.
$6 - 12 = -6, -6 - 12 = -18, -18 - 12 = -30,$
$-30 - 12 = -42, -42 - 12 = -54$
$6, -6, -18, -30, -42, -54, \ldots$

113. The common ratio of the geometric sequence is
$\sqrt{5}$.
$\sqrt{5} \cdot \sqrt{5} = 5, 5 \cdot \sqrt{5} = 5\sqrt{5}, 5\sqrt{5} \cdot \sqrt{5} = 25,$
$25 \cdot \sqrt{5} = 25\sqrt{5}, 25\sqrt{5} \cdot \sqrt{5} = 125$
$\sqrt{5}, 5, 5\sqrt{5}, 25, 25\sqrt{5}, 125, \ldots$

114. The common ratio of the geometric sequence is
$\sqrt{3}$.
$\sqrt{3} \cdot \sqrt{3} = 3, 3 \cdot \sqrt{3} = 3\sqrt{3}, 3\sqrt{3} \cdot \sqrt{3} = 9,$
$9 \cdot \sqrt{3} = 9\sqrt{3}, 9\sqrt{3} \cdot \sqrt{3} = 27$
$\sqrt{3}, 3, 3\sqrt{3}, 9, 9\sqrt{3}, 27, \ldots$

115. arithmetic; use $S_n = \dfrac{n}{2}(a_1 + a_n)$

$S_{10} = \dfrac{10}{2}(4 + 58) = 310$

116. arithmetic; use $S_n = \dfrac{n}{2}(a_1 + a_n)$

$S_{10} = \dfrac{10}{2}(7 + 115) = 610$

117. geometric; use $S_n = \dfrac{a_1(1 - r^n)}{1 - r}$

$S_{10} = \dfrac{2(1 - 3^{10})}{1 - 3} = 59,048$

118. geometric; use $S_n = \dfrac{a_1(1 - r^n)}{1 - r}$

$S_{10} = \dfrac{3(1 - 2^{10})}{1 - 2} = 3069$

119. geometric; use $S_n = \dfrac{a_1(1 - r^n)}{1 - r}$

$S_{10} = \dfrac{3\left(1 - (-2)^{10}\right)}{1 - (-2)} = -1023$

120. geometric; use $S_n = \dfrac{a_1(1 - r^n)}{1 - r}$

$S_{10} = \dfrac{4(1 - (-3)^{10})}{1 - (-3)} = -59,048$

121. arithmetic; use $S_n = \dfrac{n}{2}(a_1 + a_n)$

$S_{10} = \dfrac{10}{2}(-10 + 26) = 80$

122 arithmetic; use $S_n = \dfrac{n}{2}(a_1 + a_n)$

$S_{10} = \dfrac{10}{2}(-15 + 39) = 120$

123. $1 + 2 + 3 + 4 + \cdots + 100$

$S_{100} = \dfrac{100}{2}(1 + 100) = 5050$

124. $2 + 4 + 6 + \cdots + 200$

$S_{100} = \dfrac{100}{2}(2 + 200) = 10,100$

125. a. $a_n = a_1 + (n-1)d$
$a_n = 11.0 + (n-1)0.5$
$\quad = 11.0 + 0.5n - 0.5$
$\quad = 0.5n + 10.5$

b. $a_n = 0.5n + 10.5$
$\quad = 0.5(50) + 10.5$
$\quad = 35.5$
The percentage is projected to be 35.5% in 2019.

126 a. $a_n = a_1 + (n-1)d$
$a_n = 55.2 + (n-1)0.86$
$\quad = 55.2 + 0.86n - 0.86$
$\quad = 0.86n + 54.34$

b. $a_n = 0.86n + 54.34$
$\quad = 0.86(50) + 54.34$
$\quad = 97.34$
The percentage is projected to be 97.34% in 2019.

127. Company A: $a_{10} = 24000 + (10-1)1600 = 38,400$
Company B: $b_{10} = 28000 + (10-1)1000 = 37,000$
Company A will pay $1400 more in year 10.

128. Company A: $a_{10} = 23000 + (10-1)1200 = 33,800$
Company B: $b_{10} = 26000 + (10-1)800 = 33,200$
Company A will pay $600 more in year 10.

129. $a_1 = 1$, $r = 2$

$a_{15} = 1(2)^{15-1}$

$= 2^{14}$

$= 16,384$

On the 15th day you will put aside $16,384.

130. $a_1 = 1$, $r = 2$

$a_{30} = 1(2)^{30-1}$

$= 2^{29}$

$= 536,870,912$

On the 30th day you will put aside $536,870,912.

131. $a_7 = \$3,000,000(1.04)^{7-1}$

$\approx \$3,795,957$ salary in year 7.

132. $a_6 = \$30,000(1.05)^{6-1}$

$\approx \$38,288$ salary in year 6.

133. a. $r_{2003 \text{ to } 2004} = \dfrac{35.89}{35.48} \approx 1.01$

$r_{2004 \text{ to } 2005} = \dfrac{36.13}{35.89} \approx 1.01$

$r_{2005 \text{ to } 2006} = \dfrac{36.46}{36.13} \approx 1.01$

r is approximately 1.01 for each division.

b. $a_n = a_1 r^{n-1}$

$a_n = 35.48(1.01)^{n-1}$

c. Since year 2010 is the 8th term, find a_8.

$a_n = 35.48(1.01)^{n-1}$

$a_8 = 35.48(1.01)^{8-1} \approx 38.04$

The population of California will be approximately 38.04 million in 2010.

134. a. $r_{2003 \text{ to } 2004} = \dfrac{22.49}{22.12} \approx 1.02$

$r_{2004 \text{ to } 2005} = \dfrac{22.86}{22.49} \approx 1.02$

$r_{2005 \text{ to } 2006} = \dfrac{23.41}{22.86} \approx 1.02$

r is approximately 1.02 for each division.

b. $a_n = a_1 r^{n-1}$

$a_n = 22.12(1.02)^{n-1}$

c. Since year 2010 is the 8th term, find a_8.

$a_n = 22.12(1.02)^{n-1}$

$a_8 = 22.12(1.02)^{8-1} \approx 25.41$

The population of Texas will be approximately 25.41 million in 2010.

142. does not make sense; Explanations will vary. Sample explanation: There is not an implication that there is a negative number of sheep.

143. makes sense

144. makes sense

145. makes sense

146. false; Changes to make the statement true will vary. A sample change is: The common difference is -2.

147. false; Changes to make the statement true will vary. A sample change is: The sequence does not have a common difference and is therefore not an arithmetic sequence.

148. false; Changes to make the statement true will vary. A sample change is: The nth term is $a_1 + (n-1)d$.

149. true

150. false; Changes to make the statement true will vary. A sample change is: The sequence does not have a common ratio and is therefore not a geometric sequence.

151. false; Changes to make the statement true will vary. A sample change is: Adjacent terms of a geometric sequence have a common ratio.

152. false; Changes to make the statement true will vary. A sample change is: A sequence can be neither arithmetic nor geometric.

153. true

154. Company A:
$a_1 = 20,000,\ d = 1000$
$a_6 = 20,000 + (6-1)(1000)$
$= 20,000 + 5000$
$= 25,000$
Company B:
$a_1 = 20,000,\ r = 1.05$
$a_6 = 20,000(1.05)^{6-1}$
$= 20,000(1.05)^5$
$= 25,525.63$
Company B will pay more in the sixth year.

Chapter 5 Review Exercises

1. 238,632
   2: Yes; The last digit is 2.
   3: Yes; The sum of the digits is 24, which is divisible by 3.
   4: Yes; The last two digits form 32, which is divisible by 4.
   5: No; The last number does not end in 0 or 5.
   6: Yes; The number is divisible by both 2 and 3.
   8: Yes; The last three digits form 632, which is divisible by 8.
   9: No; The sum of the digits is 24, which is not divisible by 9.
   10: No; the last digit is not 0.
   12: Yes; The number is divisible by both 3 and 4.
   The number is divisible by 2, 3, 4, 6, 8, 12.

2. 421,153,470
   2: Yes; The last digit is 0.
   3: Yes; The sum of the digits is 27, which is divisible by 3.
   4: No; The last two digits form 70, which is not divisible by 4.
   5: Yes; The number ends in 0.
   6: Yes; The number is divisible by both 2 and 3.
   8: No; The last three digits form 470, which is not divisible by 8.
   9: Yes; The sum of the digits is 27, which is divisible by 9.
   10: Yes; The number ends in 0.
   12: No; The number is not divisible by both 3 and 4.
   The number is divisible by 2, 3, 5, 6, 9, 10.

3.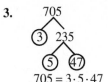
$705 = 3 \cdot 5 \cdot 47$

4.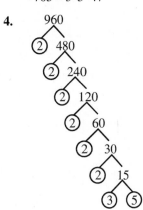
$960 = 2^6 \cdot 3 \cdot 5$

5.
6825
$6825 = 3 \cdot 5^2 \cdot 7 \cdot 13$

6. $30 = 2 \cdot 3 \cdot 5$
   $48 = 2^4 \cdot 3$
   Greatest Common Divisor $= 2 \cdot 3 = 6$
   Least Common Multiple $= 2^4 \cdot 3 \cdot 5 = 240$

7. $36 = 2^2 \cdot 3^2$
   $150 = 2 \cdot 3 \cdot 5^2$
   Greatest Common Divisor $= 2 \cdot 3 = 6$
   Least Common Multiple $= 2^2 \cdot 3^2 \cdot 5^2 = 900$

8. $216 = 2^3 \cdot 3^3$
   $254 = 2 \cdot 127$
   Greatest Common Divisor $= 2$
   Least Common Multiple $= 2^3 \cdot 3^3 \cdot 127$
   $= 27,432$

9. $24 = 2^3 \cdot 3$
   $60 = 2^2 \cdot 3 \cdot 5$
   Greatest Common Divisor $= 2^2 \cdot 3 = 12$
   There can be 12 people placed on each team.

10. $42 = 2 \cdot 3 \cdot 7$

$56 = 2^3 \cdot 7$

Least Common Multiple $= 2^3 \cdot 3 \cdot 7 = 168$

$168 \div 60 = 2.8$ or 2 hours and 48 minutes. They will begin again at 11:48 A.M.

11. $-93 < 17$ because -93 is to the left of 17 on the number line.

12. $-2 > -200$ because -2 is to the right of -200 on the number line.

13. $|-860| = 860$ because -860 is 860 units from 0 on the number line.

14. $|53| = 53$ because 53 is 53 units from 0 on the number line.

15. $|0| = 0$ because 0 is 0 units from 0 on the number line.

16. $8 + (-11) = -3$

17. $-6 + (-5) = -11$

18. $-7 - 8 = -7 + (-8) = -15$

19. $-7 - (-8) = -7 + 8 = 1$

20. $(-9)(-11) = 99$

21. $5(-3) = -15$

22. $\dfrac{-36}{-4} = 9$

23. $\dfrac{20}{-5} = -4$

24. $-40 \div 5 \cdot 2 = -8 \cdot 2 = -16$

25. $-6 + (-2) \cdot 5 = -6 + (-10) = -16$

26. $6 - 4(-3 + 2) = 6 - 4(-1) = 6 + 4 = 10$

27. $28 \div (2 - 4^2) = 28 \div (2 - 16)$
$= 28 \div (-14)$
$= -2$

28. $36 - 24 \div 4 \cdot 3 - 1 = 36 - 6 \cdot 3 - 1$
$= 36 - 18 - 1$
$= 18 - 1$
$= 17$

29. $-57 - (-715) = -57 + 715 = \$658$ billion

30. $40 = 2^3 \cdot 5$

$75 = 3 \cdot 5^2$

Greatest Common Divisor is 5.

$\dfrac{40}{75} = \dfrac{40 \div 5}{75 \div 5} = \dfrac{8}{15}$

31. $36 = 2^2 \cdot 3^2$

$150 = 2 \cdot 3 \cdot 5^2$

Greatest Common Divisor is $2 \cdot 3$ or 6.

$\dfrac{36}{150} = \dfrac{36 \div 6}{150 \div 6} = \dfrac{6}{25}$

32. $165 = 3 \cdot 5 \cdot 11$

$180 = 2^2 \cdot 3^2 \cdot 5$

Greatest Common Divisor is $3 \cdot 5$ or 15.

$\dfrac{165}{180} = \dfrac{165 \div 15}{180 \div 15} = \dfrac{11}{12}$

33. $5\dfrac{9}{11} = \dfrac{11 \cdot 5 + 9}{11} = \dfrac{64}{11}$

34. $-3\dfrac{2}{7} = -\dfrac{7 \cdot 3 + 2}{7} = -\dfrac{23}{7}$

35. $\dfrac{27}{5} = 5\dfrac{2}{5}$

36. $-\dfrac{17}{9} = -1\dfrac{8}{9}$

37. $\dfrac{4}{5} = 0.8$

$5\overline{)4.0}$ gives 0.8, $\dfrac{40}{0}$

38. $\dfrac{3}{7} = 0.\overline{428571}$

$$
\begin{array}{r}
0.4285714 \\
7\overline{)3.0000000} \\
28 \\
\overline{20} \\
14 \\
\overline{60} \\
56 \\
\overline{40} \\
35 \\
\overline{50} \\
49 \\
\overline{10} \\
7 \\
\overline{30} \\
28 \\
\overline{2}
\end{array}
$$

39. $\dfrac{5}{8} = 0.625$

$$
\begin{array}{r}
0.625 \\
8\overline{)5.000} \\
48 \\
\overline{20} \\
16 \\
\overline{40} \\
40 \\
\overline{0}
\end{array}
$$

40. $\dfrac{9}{16} = 0.5625$

$$
\begin{array}{r}
0.5625 \\
16\overline{)9.0000} \\
80 \\
\overline{100} \\
96 \\
\overline{40} \\
32 \\
\overline{80} \\
80 \\
\overline{0}
\end{array}
$$

41. $0.6 = \dfrac{6}{10} = \dfrac{6 \div 2}{10 \div 2} = \dfrac{3}{5}$

42. $0.68 = \dfrac{68}{100}$

$68 = 2^2 \cdot 17$

$100 = 2^2 \cdot 5^2$

Greatest Common Divisor is 2^2 or 4.

$\dfrac{68 \div 4}{100 \div 4} = \dfrac{17}{25}$

43. $0.588 = \dfrac{588}{1000}$

$588 = 2^2 \cdot 3 \cdot 7^2$

$1000 = 2^3 \cdot 5^3$

Greatest Common Divisor is 2^2 or 4.

$\dfrac{588 \div 4}{1000 \div 4} = \dfrac{147}{250}$

44. $0.0084 = \dfrac{84}{10,000}$

$84 = 2^2 \cdot 3 \cdot 7$

$10,000 = 2^4 \cdot 5^4$

Greatest Common Divisor is 2^2 or 4.

$\dfrac{84 \div 4}{10,000 \div 4} = \dfrac{21}{2500}$

45. $n = 0.555\ldots$
$10n = 5.555\ldots$

$$
\begin{array}{r}
10n = 5.555\ldots \\
- n = 0.555\ldots \\
\hline
9n = 5
\end{array}
$$

$n = \dfrac{5}{9}$

46. $n = 0.3434\ldots$
$100n = 34.3434\ldots$

$$
\begin{array}{r}
100n = 34.3434\ldots \\
- n = 0.3434\ldots \\
\hline
99n = 34
\end{array}
$$

$n = \dfrac{34}{99}$

47. $n = 0.113113\ldots$
$1000n = 113.113113\ldots$

$1000n = 113.113113\ldots$
$-\quad\ n = \quad 0.113113\ldots$
_____
$999n = 113$

$n = \dfrac{113}{999}$

48. $\dfrac{3}{5} \cdot \dfrac{7}{10} = \dfrac{3 \cdot 7}{5 \cdot 10} = \dfrac{21}{50}$

49. $\left(3\dfrac{1}{3}\right)\left(1\dfrac{3}{4}\right) = \dfrac{10}{3} \cdot \dfrac{7}{4} = \dfrac{70}{12} = \dfrac{35}{6}$ or $5\dfrac{5}{6}$

50. $\dfrac{4}{5} \div \dfrac{3}{10} = \dfrac{4}{5} \cdot \dfrac{10}{3} = \dfrac{4 \cdot 10}{5 \cdot 3} = \dfrac{40}{15} = \dfrac{8}{3}$

51. $-1\dfrac{2}{3} \div 6\dfrac{2}{3} = -\dfrac{5}{3} \div \dfrac{20}{3} = -\dfrac{5}{3} \cdot \dfrac{3}{20} = -\dfrac{15}{60} = -\dfrac{1}{4}$

52. $\dfrac{2}{9} + \dfrac{4}{9} = \dfrac{2+4}{9} = \dfrac{6}{9} = \dfrac{2}{3}$

53. $\dfrac{7}{9} + \dfrac{5}{12} = \dfrac{7}{9} \cdot \dfrac{4}{4} + \dfrac{5}{12} \cdot \dfrac{3}{3}$

$= \dfrac{28}{36} + \dfrac{15}{36}$

$= \dfrac{28+15}{36}$

$= \dfrac{43}{36}$

54. $\dfrac{3}{4} - \dfrac{2}{15} = \dfrac{3}{4} \cdot \dfrac{15}{15} - \dfrac{2}{15} \cdot \dfrac{4}{4}$

$= \dfrac{45}{60} - \dfrac{8}{60}$

$= \dfrac{45-8}{60}$

$= \dfrac{37}{60}$

55. $\dfrac{1}{3} + \dfrac{1}{2} \cdot \dfrac{4}{5} = \dfrac{1}{3} + \dfrac{1 \cdot 4}{2 \cdot 5}$

$= \dfrac{1}{3} + \dfrac{4}{10}$

$= \dfrac{1}{3} + \dfrac{2}{5}$

$= \dfrac{1}{3} \cdot \dfrac{5}{5} + \dfrac{2}{5} \cdot \dfrac{3}{3}$

$= \dfrac{5}{15} + \dfrac{6}{15}$

$= \dfrac{11}{15}$

56. $\dfrac{3}{8}\left(\dfrac{1}{2} + \dfrac{1}{3}\right) = \dfrac{3}{8}\left(\dfrac{1}{2} \cdot \dfrac{3}{3} + \dfrac{1}{3} \cdot \dfrac{2}{2}\right)$

$= \dfrac{3}{8}\left(\dfrac{3}{6} + \dfrac{2}{6}\right)$

$= \dfrac{3}{8}\left(\dfrac{5}{6}\right)$

$= \dfrac{15}{48}$

$= \dfrac{5}{16}$

57. $\dfrac{1}{2} - \dfrac{2}{3} \div \dfrac{5}{9} + \dfrac{3}{10} = \dfrac{1}{2} - \dfrac{2}{3} \times \dfrac{9}{5} + \dfrac{3}{10}$

$= \dfrac{1}{2} - \dfrac{6}{5} + \dfrac{3}{10}$

$= \dfrac{5}{10} - \dfrac{12}{10} + \dfrac{3}{10}$

$= -\dfrac{4}{10}$

$= -\dfrac{2}{5}$

58. $\left(\dfrac{1}{2} + \dfrac{1}{3}\right) \div \left(\dfrac{1}{4} - \dfrac{3}{8}\right) = \left(\dfrac{3}{6} + \dfrac{2}{6}\right) \div \left(\dfrac{2}{8} - \dfrac{3}{8}\right)$

$= \left(\dfrac{5}{6}\right) \div \left(\dfrac{-1}{8}\right)$

$= \dfrac{5}{6} \times \dfrac{8}{-1}$

$= -\dfrac{20}{3}$

$= -6\dfrac{2}{3}$

59. $\dfrac{1}{7}+\dfrac{1}{8}=\dfrac{1}{7}\cdot\dfrac{8}{8}+\dfrac{1}{8}\cdot\dfrac{7}{7}$

$\qquad = \dfrac{8}{56}+\dfrac{7}{56}$

$\qquad = \dfrac{15}{56}$

$\dfrac{15}{56}\div 2 = \dfrac{15}{56}\cdot\dfrac{1}{2}=\dfrac{15}{112}$

60. $\dfrac{3}{4}+\dfrac{3}{5}=\dfrac{3}{4}\cdot\dfrac{5}{5}+\dfrac{3}{5}\cdot\dfrac{4}{4}$

$\qquad = \dfrac{15}{20}+\dfrac{12}{20}$

$\qquad = \dfrac{27}{20}$

$\dfrac{27}{20}\div 2 = \dfrac{27}{20}\cdot\dfrac{1}{2}=\dfrac{27}{40}$

61. $4\dfrac{1}{2}\cdot\dfrac{15}{6}=\dfrac{9}{2}\cdot\dfrac{15}{6}=\dfrac{135}{12}=\dfrac{45}{4}$ or $11\dfrac{1}{4}$ pounds.

62. $1-\left(\dfrac{1}{4}+\dfrac{1}{3}\right)=1-\left(\dfrac{1}{4}\cdot\dfrac{3}{3}+\dfrac{1}{3}\cdot\dfrac{4}{4}\right)$

$\qquad = 1-\left(\dfrac{3}{12}+\dfrac{4}{12}\right)$

$\qquad = \dfrac{12}{12}-\dfrac{7}{12}$

$\qquad = \dfrac{5}{12}$

At the end of the second day, $\dfrac{5}{12}$ of the tank is filled with gas.

63. $\sqrt{28}=\sqrt{4\cdot 7}=\sqrt{4}\cdot\sqrt{7}=2\sqrt{7}$

64. $\sqrt{72}=\sqrt{36\cdot 2}=\sqrt{36}\cdot\sqrt{2}=6\sqrt{2}$

65. $\sqrt{150}=\sqrt{25\cdot 6}=\sqrt{25}\cdot\sqrt{6}=5\sqrt{6}$

66. $\sqrt{300}=\sqrt{100\cdot 3}=\sqrt{100}\cdot\sqrt{3}=10\sqrt{3}$

67. $\sqrt{6}\cdot\sqrt{8}=\sqrt{6\cdot 8}=\sqrt{48}=\sqrt{16}\cdot\sqrt{3}=4\sqrt{3}$

68. $\sqrt{10}\cdot\sqrt{5}=\sqrt{10\cdot 5}$

$\qquad = \sqrt{50}$

$\qquad = \sqrt{25}\cdot\sqrt{2}$

$\qquad = 5\sqrt{2}$

69. $\dfrac{\sqrt{24}}{\sqrt{2}}=\sqrt{\dfrac{24}{2}}=\sqrt{12}=\sqrt{4}\cdot\sqrt{3}=2\sqrt{3}$

70. $\dfrac{\sqrt{27}}{\sqrt{3}}=\sqrt{\dfrac{27}{3}}=\sqrt{9}=3$

71. $\sqrt{5}+4\sqrt{5}=1\sqrt{5}+4\sqrt{5}=(1+4)\sqrt{5}=5\sqrt{5}$

72. $7\sqrt{11}-13\sqrt{11}=(7-13)\sqrt{11}=-6\sqrt{11}$

73. $\sqrt{50}+\sqrt{8}=\sqrt{25}\cdot\sqrt{2}+\sqrt{4}\cdot\sqrt{2}$

$\qquad = 5\sqrt{2}+2\sqrt{2}$

$\qquad = (5+2)\sqrt{2}$

$\qquad = 7\sqrt{2}$

74. $\sqrt{3}-6\sqrt{27}=\sqrt{3}-6\sqrt{9}\cdot\sqrt{3}$

$\qquad = \sqrt{3}-6\cdot 3\sqrt{3}$

$\qquad = 1\sqrt{3}-18\sqrt{3}$

$\qquad = (1-18)\sqrt{3}$

$\qquad = -17\sqrt{3}$

75. $2\sqrt{18}+3\sqrt{8}=2\sqrt{9}\cdot\sqrt{2}+3\sqrt{4}\cdot\sqrt{2}$

$\qquad = 2\cdot 3\cdot\sqrt{2}+3\cdot 2\cdot\sqrt{2}$

$\qquad = 6\sqrt{2}+6\sqrt{2}$

$\qquad = (6+6)\sqrt{2}$

$\qquad = 12\sqrt{2}$

76. $\dfrac{30}{\sqrt{5}}=\dfrac{30}{\sqrt{5}}\cdot\dfrac{\sqrt{5}}{\sqrt{5}}=\dfrac{30\sqrt{5}}{\sqrt{25}}=\dfrac{30\sqrt{5}}{5}=6\sqrt{5}$

77. $\sqrt{\dfrac{2}{3}}=\dfrac{\sqrt{2}}{\sqrt{3}}=\dfrac{\sqrt{2}}{\sqrt{3}}\cdot\dfrac{\sqrt{3}}{\sqrt{3}}=\dfrac{\sqrt{6}}{\sqrt{9}}=\dfrac{\sqrt{6}}{3}$

78. $W=4\sqrt{2x}$

$\qquad = 4\sqrt{2\cdot 6}$

$\qquad = 4\sqrt{12}$

$\qquad = 8\sqrt{3}\approx 13.9$ feet per second

79. $\left\{-17, -\dfrac{9}{13}, 0, 0.75, \sqrt{2}, \pi, \sqrt{81}\right\}$

    a. Natural numbers:
        $\sqrt{81}$ because $\sqrt{81} = 9$

    b. Whole numbers: $0, \sqrt{81}$

    c. Integers: $-17, 0, \sqrt{81}$

    d. Rational numbers:
        $-17, -\dfrac{9}{13}, 0, 0.75, \sqrt{81}$

    e. Irrational numbers: $\sqrt{2}, \pi$

    f. Real numbers: All numbers in this set.

80. Answers will vary. Example: -3

81. Answers will vary. Example: $\dfrac{1}{2}$

82. Answers will vary: Example: $\sqrt{2}$

83. Commutative property of addition

84. Associative property of multiplication

85. Distributive property of multiplication over addition.

86. Commutative property of multiplication

87. Commutative property of multiplication

88. Commutative property of addition

89. Inverse property of multiplication

90. Identity property of multiplication

91. Answers will vary. Example: $2 \div 6 = \dfrac{1}{3}$

92. Answers will vary. Example: $4 - 5 = -1$

93. $6 \cdot 6^2 = 6^1 \cdot 6^2 = 6^{1+2} = 6^3 = 216$

94. $2^3 \cdot 2^3 = 2^{3+3} = 2^6 = 64$

95. $(2^2)^2 = 2^{2 \cdot 2} = 2^4 = 16$

96. $(3^3)^2 = 3^{3 \cdot 2} = 3^6 = 729$

97. $\dfrac{5^6}{5^4} = 5^{6-4} = 5^2 = 25$

98. $7^0 = 1$

99. $(-7)^0 = 1$

100. $6^{-3} = \dfrac{1}{6^3} = \dfrac{1}{216}$

101. $2^{-4} = \dfrac{1}{2^4} = \dfrac{1}{16}$

102. $\dfrac{7^4}{7^6} = 7^{4-6} = 7^{-2} = \dfrac{1}{7^2} = \dfrac{1}{49}$

103. $3^5 \cdot 3^{-2} = 3^{5-2} = 3^3 = 27$

104. $4.6 \times 10^2 = 460$

105. $3.74 \times 10^4 = 37,400$

106. $2.55 \times 10^{-3} = 0.00255$

107. $7.45 \times 10^{-5} = 0.0000745$

108. $7520 = 7.52 \times 10^3$

109. $3,590,000 = 3.59 \times 10^6$

110. $0.00725 = 7.25 \times 10^{-3}$

111. $0.000000409 = 4.09 \times 10^{-7}$

112. $420 \times 10^{11} = \left(4.2 \times 10^2\right) \times 10^{11} = 4.2 \times 10^{13}$

113. $0.97 \times 10^{-4} = \left(9.7 \times 10^{-1}\right) \times 10^{-4} = 9.7 \times 10^{-5}$

114. $(3 \times 10^7)(1.3 \times 10^{-5}) = (3 \times 1.3) \times 10^{7-5}$
$$= 3.9 \times 10^2$$
$$= 390$$

115. $(5 \times 10^3)(2.3 \times 10^2) = (5 \times 2.3) \times 10^{3+2}$
$$= 11.5 \times 10^5$$
$$= 1.15 \times 10 \times 10^5$$
$$= 1.15 \times 10^6$$
$$= 1,150,000$$

116. $\dfrac{6.9 \times 10^3}{3 \times 10^5} = \left(\dfrac{6.9}{3}\right) \times 10^{3-5}$

$= 2.3 \times 10^{-2}$

$= 0.023$

117. $\dfrac{2.4 \times 10^{-4}}{6 \times 10^{-6}} = \left(\dfrac{2.4}{6}\right) \times 10^{-4-(-6)}$

$= 0.4 \times 10^{-4+6}$

$= 0.4 \times 10^2$

$= 40$

118. $(60,000)(540,000) = (6.0 \times 10^4)(5.4 \times 10^5)$

$= (6.0 \times 5.4) \times 10^{4+5}$

$= 32.4 \times 10^9$

$= 3.24 \times 10 \times 10^9$

$= 3.24 \times 10^{10}$

119. $(91,000)(0.0004) = (9.1 \times 10^4)(4 \times 10^{-4})$

$= (9.1 \times 4) \times 10^{4-4}$

$= 36.4 \times 10^0$

$= 3.64 \times 10^1$

120. $\dfrac{8,400,000}{4000} = \dfrac{8.4 \times 10^6}{4 \times 10^3}$

$= \left(\dfrac{8.4}{4}\right) \times 10^{6-3}$

$= 2.1 \times 10^3$

121. $\dfrac{0.000003}{0.00000006} = \dfrac{3 \times 10^{-6}}{6 \times 10^{-8}}$

$= \left(\dfrac{3}{6}\right) \times 10^{-6-(-8)}$

$= 0.5 \times 10^2$

$= 5 \times 10^{-1} \times 10^2$

$= 5 \times 10^1$

122. $53.6 \times 10^9 = 5.36 \times 10^{10}$

123. $306 \times 10^6 = 3.06 \times 10^8$

124. $\dfrac{5.36 \times 10^{10}}{3.06 \times 10^8} = 1.75 \times 10^2 = \$175$

125. $180\left(3.2 \times 10^4\right)\left(5 \times 10^6\right) = \left(180 \times 3.2 \times 5\right) \times \left(10^4 \times 10^6\right)$

$= 2880 \times 10^{10}$

$= 2.88 \times 10^{13}$

126. $a_1 = 7,\ d = 4$

$7,\ 7 + 4 = 11,\ 11 + 4 = 15,\ 15 + 4 = 19,\ 19 + 4 = 23,$
$23 + 4 = 27$

$7,\ 11,\ 15,\ 19,\ 23,\ 27$

127. $a_1 = -4,\ d = -5$

$-4,\ -4 - 5 = -9,\ -9 - 5 = -14,\ -14 - 5 = -19,\ -19 - 5$
$= -24,\ -24 - 5 = -29$

$-4,\ -9,\ -14,\ -19,\ -24,\ -29$

128. $a_1 = \dfrac{3}{2},\ d = -\dfrac{1}{2}$

$\dfrac{3}{2},\ \dfrac{3}{2} - \dfrac{1}{2} = \dfrac{2}{2} = 1,\ \dfrac{2}{2} - \dfrac{1}{2} = \dfrac{1}{2},\ \dfrac{1}{2} - \dfrac{1}{2} = 0,$

$0 - \dfrac{1}{2} = -\dfrac{1}{2},\ -\dfrac{1}{2} - \dfrac{1}{2} = -1$

$\dfrac{3}{2},\ 1,\ \dfrac{1}{2},\ 0,\ -\dfrac{1}{2},\ -1$

129. $a_1 = 5,\ d = 3$

$a_6 = 5 + (6 - 1)(3)$

$= 5 + 5(3)$

$= 5 + 15$

$= 20$

130. $a_1 = -8,\ d = -2$

$a_{12} = -8 + (12 - 1)(-2)$

$= -8 + 11(-2)$

$= -8 + (-22)$

$= -30$

131. $a_1 = 14,\ d = -4$

$a_{14} = 14 + (14 - 1)(-4)$

$= 14 + 13(-4)$

$= 14 + (-52)$

$= -38$

132. $a_n = a_1 + (n - 1)d$ with $a_1 = -7,\ d = 4$

$a_n = -7 + (n - 1)4$

$= -7 + 4n - 4$

$= 4n - 11$

Thus $a_{20} = 4(20) - 11 = 69$.

225

133. $a_n = a_1 + (n-1)d$ with $a_1 = 200$, $d = -20$

$a_n = 200 + (n-1)(-20)$

$\quad = 200 - 20n + 20$

$\quad = -20n + 220$

Thus $a_{20} = -20(20) + 220 = -180$.

134. $a_1 = 3$, $r = 2$

$3, 3 \cdot 2 = 6, 6 \cdot 2 = 12, 12 \cdot 2 = 24,$
$24 \cdot 2 = 48, 48 \cdot 2 = 96$
$3, 6, 12, 24, 48, 96$

135. $a_1 = \dfrac{1}{2}$, $r = \dfrac{1}{2}$

$\dfrac{1}{2}, \dfrac{1}{2} \cdot \dfrac{1}{2} = \dfrac{1}{4}, \dfrac{1}{4} \cdot \dfrac{1}{2} = \dfrac{1}{8}, \dfrac{1}{8} \cdot \dfrac{1}{2} = \dfrac{1}{16},$

$\dfrac{1}{16} \cdot \dfrac{1}{2} = \dfrac{1}{32}, \dfrac{1}{32} \cdot \dfrac{1}{2} = \dfrac{1}{64}$

$\dfrac{1}{2}, \dfrac{1}{4}, \dfrac{1}{8}, \dfrac{1}{16}, \dfrac{1}{32}, \dfrac{1}{64}$

136. $a_1 = 16$, $r = -\dfrac{1}{2}$

$16, 16\left(-\dfrac{1}{2}\right) = -8, -8\left(-\dfrac{1}{2}\right) = 4, \ 4\left(-\dfrac{1}{2}\right) = -2,$

$-2\left(-\dfrac{1}{2}\right) = 1, 1\left(-\dfrac{1}{2}\right) = -\dfrac{1}{2}$

$16, -8, 4, -2, 1, -\dfrac{1}{2}$

137. $a_1 = 2$, $r = 3$

$a_4 = 2(3)^{4-1}$

$\quad = 2(3)^3$

$\quad = 2(27)$

$\quad = 54$

138. $a_1 = 16$, $r = \dfrac{1}{2}$

$a_6 = 16\left(\dfrac{1}{2}\right)^{6-1}$

$\quad = 16\left(\dfrac{1}{2}\right)^5$

$\quad = \dfrac{16}{32}$

$\quad = \dfrac{1}{2}$

139. $a_1 = -3$, $r = 2$

$a_5 = -3(2)^{5-1}$

$\quad = -3(2)^4$

$\quad = -3(16)$

$\quad = -48$

140. $a_n = a_1 r^{n-1}$ with $a_1 = 1$ and $r = \dfrac{2}{1} = 2$. Thus

$a_n = 2^{n-1}$

$a_8 = 2^{8-1} = 2^7 = 128$

141. $a_n = a_1 r^{n-1}$ with $a_1 = 100$ and $r = \dfrac{10}{100} = \dfrac{1}{10}$. Thus

$a_n = 100\left(\dfrac{1}{10}\right)^{n-1}$

$a_8 = 100\left(\dfrac{1}{10}\right)^{8-1}$

$\quad = 100\left(\dfrac{1}{10}\right)^7$

$\quad = \dfrac{100}{10,000,000}$

$\quad = \dfrac{1}{100,000}$

142. The common difference in the arithmetic sequence is 5.
$4 + 5 = 9, 9 + 5 = 14, 14 + 5 = 19,$
$19 + 5 = 24, 24 + 5 = 29$
$4, 9, 14, 19, 24, 29, \ldots$

143. The common ratio in the geometric sequence is 3.
$2 \cdot 3 = 6, 6 \cdot 3 = 18, 18 \cdot 3 = 54, 54 \cdot 3 = 162, 162 \cdot 3 = 486$
$2, 6, 18, 54, 162, 486, \ldots$

144. The common ratio in the geometric sequence is $\dfrac{1}{4}$.

$1 \cdot \dfrac{1}{4} = \dfrac{1}{4}, \dfrac{1}{4} \cdot \dfrac{1}{4} = \dfrac{1}{16}, \dfrac{1}{16} \cdot \dfrac{1}{4} = \dfrac{1}{64},$

$\dfrac{1}{64} \cdot \dfrac{1}{4} = \dfrac{1}{256}, \dfrac{1}{256} \cdot \dfrac{1}{4} = \dfrac{1}{1024}$

$1, \dfrac{1}{4}, \dfrac{1}{16}, \dfrac{1}{64}, \dfrac{1}{256}, \dfrac{1}{1024}, \ldots$

145. The common difference in the arithmetic sequence is -7.
$0 - 7 = -7, -7 - 7 = -14, -14 - 7 = -21, -21 - 7 = -28,$
$-28 - 7 = -35$
$0, -7, -14, -21, -28, -35, \ldots$

146. a. $a_n = a_1 + (n-1)d$

$a_n = 39 + (n-1)4.75$

$= 39 + 4.75n - 4.75$

$= 4.75n + 34.25$

b. $a_n = 4.75n + 34.25$

$= 4.75(13) + 34.25$

$= 96$

The percentage is predicted to be 96% in 2013.

142. a. Divide each value by the previous value:

$\dfrac{5.9}{4.2} = 1.405$

$\dfrac{8.3}{5.9} = 1.407$

$\dfrac{11.6}{8.3} = 1.398$

$\dfrac{16.2}{11.6} = 1.397$

$\dfrac{22.7}{16.2} = 1.401$

The population is increasing geometrically with $r \approx 1.4$.

b. $a_n = 4.2(1.4)^{n-1}$

c. 2080 is 9 decades after 1990 so $n = 9$.

$a_n = 4.2(1.4)^{n-1}$

$a_8 = 4.2(1.4)^{9-1} \approx 62.0$

In 2080, the model predicts the U.S. population, ages 85 and older, will be 62.0 million

Chapter 5 Test

1. 391,248

2: Yes; the last digit is 8.

3: Yes; the sum of the digits is 27, which is divisible by 3.

4: Yes; the last two digits form 48, which is divisible by 4.

5: No; the number does not end in 0 or 5.

6: Yes; the number is divisible by both 2 and 3.

8: Yes; the last three digits form 248, which is divisible by 8.

9: Yes; the sum of the digits is 27, which is divisible by 9.

10: No; the number does not end in 0.

12: Yes; the number is divisible by both 3 and 4.

391, 248 is divisible by 2, 3, 4, 6, 8, 9, 12.

2.

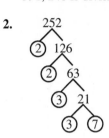

$252 = 2^2 \cdot 3^2 \cdot 7$

3. $48 = 2^4 \cdot 3$

$72 = 2^3 \cdot 3^2$

Greatest Common Divisor $= 2^3 \cdot 3 = 24$

Least Common Multiple $= 2^4 \cdot 3^2 = 144$

4. $-6 - (5 - 12) = -6 - (-7) = -6 + 7 = 1$

5. $(-3)(-4) \div (7 - 10) = (-3)(-4) \div (-3)$

$= 12 \div (-3)$

$= -4$

6. $(6-8)^2(5-7)^3 = (-2)^2(-2)^3$

$= 4(-8)$

$= -32$

7. $\dfrac{7}{12} = 0.58\overline{3}$

$$
\begin{array}{r}
0.5833\ldots \\
12\overline{)7.0000} \\
\underline{6\,0} \\
100 \\
\underline{96} \\
40 \\
\underline{36} \\
40 \\
\underline{36} \\
4
\end{array}
$$

8. $n = 0.6464...$
$100n = 64.6464...$

$100n = 64.6464...$
$\underline{-\quad n = 0.6464...}$
$99n = 64$

$n = \dfrac{64}{99}$

9. $\left(-\dfrac{3}{7}\right) \div \left(-2\dfrac{1}{7}\right) = \left(-\dfrac{3}{7}\right) \div \left(-\dfrac{15}{7}\right)$

$= \left(-\dfrac{3}{7}\right) \cdot \left(-\dfrac{7}{15}\right)$

$= \dfrac{(-3)(-7)}{7 \cdot 15}$

$= \dfrac{21}{105}$

$= \dfrac{1}{5}$

10. $\dfrac{19}{24} - \dfrac{7}{40} = \dfrac{19}{24} \cdot \dfrac{5}{5} - \dfrac{7}{40} \cdot \dfrac{3}{3}$

$= \dfrac{95}{120} - \dfrac{21}{120}$

$= \dfrac{95 - 21}{120}$

$= \dfrac{74}{120}$

$= \dfrac{37}{60}$

11. $\dfrac{1}{2} - 8\left(\dfrac{1}{4} + 1\right) = \dfrac{1}{2} - 8\left(\dfrac{5}{4}\right)$

$= \dfrac{1}{2} - 10$

$= \dfrac{1}{2} - \dfrac{20}{2}$

$= -\dfrac{19}{2}$

12. $\dfrac{1}{2} + \dfrac{2}{3} = \dfrac{1}{2} \cdot \dfrac{3}{3} + \dfrac{2}{3} \cdot \dfrac{2}{2}$

$= \dfrac{3}{6} + \dfrac{4}{6}$

$= \dfrac{7}{6}$

$\dfrac{7}{6} \div 2 = \dfrac{7}{6} \cdot \dfrac{1}{2} = \dfrac{7}{12}$

13. $\sqrt{10} \cdot \sqrt{5} = \sqrt{10 \cdot 5}$

$= \sqrt{50}$

$= \sqrt{25 \cdot 2}$

$= \sqrt{25} \cdot \sqrt{2}$

$= 5\sqrt{2}$

14. $\sqrt{50} + \sqrt{32} = \sqrt{25} \cdot \sqrt{2} + \sqrt{16} \cdot \sqrt{2}$

$= 5\sqrt{2} + 4\sqrt{2}$

$= (5 + 4)\sqrt{2}$

$= 9\sqrt{2}$

15. $\dfrac{6}{\sqrt{2}} = \dfrac{6}{\sqrt{2}} \cdot \dfrac{\sqrt{2}}{\sqrt{2}} = \dfrac{6\sqrt{2}}{\sqrt{4}} = \dfrac{6\sqrt{2}}{2} = 3\sqrt{2}$

16. The rational numbers are

$-7, \ -\dfrac{4}{5}, \ 0, \ 0.25, \ \sqrt{4}, \ \dfrac{22}{7}.$

17. Commutative property of addition

18. Distributive property of multiplication over addition

19. $3^3 \cdot 3^2 = 3^{3+2} = 3^5 = 243$

20. $\dfrac{4^6}{4^3} = 4^{6-3} = 4^3 = 64$

21. $8^{-2} = \dfrac{1}{8^2} = \dfrac{1}{64}$

22. $(3 \times 10^8)(2.5 \times 10^{-5}) = (3 \times 2.5) \times 10^{8-5}$

$= 7.5 \times 10^3$

$= 7500$

23. $\dfrac{49,000}{0.007} = \dfrac{4.9 \times 10^4}{7 \times 10^{-3}}$

$= \left(\dfrac{4.9}{7}\right) \times 10^{4-(-3)}$

$= 0.7 \times 10^7$

$= 7 \times 10^{-1} \times 10^7$

$= 7 \times 10^6$

24. a. $14.3 \times 10^{12} = (1.43 \times 10^1) \times 10^{12} = 1.43 \times 10^{13}$

b. $\dfrac{1.43 \times 10^{13}}{3.06 \times 10^8} = \left(\dfrac{1.43}{3.06}\right) \times 10^5$

$= 0.467 \times 10^5$

$= \$46,700$

25. $(\$140)(3.1 \times 10^8) = (\$140 \times 3.1) \times 10^8$

$= \$434 \times 10^8$

$= \$4.34 \times 10^{10}$

26. $a_1 = 1, d = -5$

$1, 1 - 5 = -4, -4 - 5 = -9,$

$-9 - 5 = -14, -14 - 5 = -19,$

$-19 - 5 = -24$

$1, -4, -9, -14, -19, -24$

27. $a_1 = -2, d = 3$

$a_9 = -2 + (9 - 1)(3)$

$= -2 + 8(3)$

$= -2 + 24$

$= 22$

28. $a_1 = 16, r = \dfrac{1}{2}$

$16, 16 \cdot \dfrac{1}{2} = 8, \ 8 \cdot \dfrac{1}{2} = 4, \ 4 \cdot \dfrac{1}{2} = 2, \ 2 \cdot \dfrac{1}{2} = 1, \ 1 \cdot \dfrac{1}{2} = \dfrac{1}{2}$

$16, 8, 4, 2, 1, \dfrac{1}{2}$

29. $a_1 = 5, r = 2$

$a_7 = 5(2)^{7-1}$

$= 5(2)^6$

$= 5(64)$

$= 320$

Chapter 6
Algebra: Equations and Inequalities

Check Points 6.1

1. $8 + 6(x-3)^2 = 8 + 6(13-3)^2$
$= 8 + 6(10)^2$
$= 8 + 6(100)$
$= 608$

2. If $x = -5$, then $x^2 + 4x - 7 = (-5)^2 + 4(-5) - 7$
$= 25 - 20 - 7$
$= -2$

3. If $x = 5$ and $y = -1$, then
$-3x^2 + 4xy - y^3 = -3(5)^2 + 4(5)(-1) - (-1)^3$
$= -3(25) - 20 - (-1)$
$= -75 - 20 + 1$
$= -94$

4. $M = -120x^2 + 998x + 590$
$M = -120(4)^2 + 998(4) + 590$
$= 2662$
According to the model, men between the ages of 19 and 30 with this lifestyle need 2662 calories per day. This underestimates the actual value shown in the bar graph by 38 calories.

5. $7(2x-3) - 11x = 7 \cdot 2x - 7 \cdot 3 - 11x$
$= 14x - 21 - 11x$
$= 3x - 21$

6. $7(4x^2 + 3x) + 2(5x^2 + x) = 28x^2 + 21x + 10x^2 + 2x$
$= 38x^2 + 23x$

7. $6x + 4[7 - (x-2)] = 6x + 4[7 - x + 2]$
$= 6x + 4[9 - x]$
$= 6x + 36 - 4x$
$= 2x + 36$

Exercise Set 6.1

1. $5x + 7 = 5 \cdot 4 + 7 = 20 + 7 = 27$

2. $9x + 6 = 9 \cdot 5 + 6 = 45 + 6 = 51$

3. $-7x - 5 = -7(-4) - 5 = 28 - 5 = 23$

4. $-6x - 13 = -6(-3) - 13 = 18 - 13 = 5$

5. $x^2 + 4 = 5^2 + 4 = 25 + 4 = 29$

6. $x^2 + 9 = 3^2 + 9 = 9 + 9 = 18$

7. $x^2 - 6 = (-2)^2 - 6 = 4 - 6 = -2$

8. $x^2 - 11 = (-3)^2 - 11 = 9 - 11 = -2$

9. $-x^2 + 4 = -(5)^2 + 4 = -25 + 4 = -21$

10. $-x^2 + 9 = -(3)^2 + 9 = -9 + 9 = 0$

11. $-x^2 - 6 = -(-2)^2 - 6 = -4 - 6 = -10$

12. $-x^2 - 11 = -(-3)^2 - 11 = -9 - 11 = -20$

13. $x^2 + 4x = (10)^2 + 4 \cdot 10 = 100 + 40 = 140$

14. $x^2 + 6x = 9^2 + 6 \cdot 9 = 81 + 54 = 135$

15. $8x^2 + 17 = 8(5)^2 + 17$
$= 8(25) + 17$
$= 200 + 17$
$= 217$

16. $7x^2 + 25 = 7(3)^2 + 25$
$= 7(9) + 25$
$= 63 + 25$
$= 88$

17. $x^2 - 5x = (-11)^2 - 5(-11)$
$= 121 + 55$
$= 176$

18. $x^2 - 8x = (-5)^2 - 8(-5) = 25 + 40 = 65$

19. $x^2 + 5x - 6 = 4^2 + 5 \cdot 4 - 6$
$= 16 + 20 - 6$
$= 30$

20. $x^2 + 7x - 4 = 6^2 + 7 \cdot 6 - 4 = 36 + 42 - 4 = 74$

21. $4 + 5(x-7)^3 = 4 + 5(9-7)^3$
$= 4 + 5(2)^3$
$= 4 + 5(8)$
$= 44$

22. $6 + 5(x-6)^3 = 6 + 5(8-6)^3$
$= 6 + 5(2)^3$
$= 6 + 5(8)$
$= 46$

23. $x^2 - 3(x-y) = 2^2 - 3(2-8)$
$= 4 - 3(-6)$
$= 4 + 18$
$= 22$

24. $x^2 - 4(x-y) = 3^2 - 4(3-8)$
$= 9 - 4(-5)$
$= 9 + 20$
$= 29$

25. $2x^2 - 5x - 6 = 2(-3)^2 - 5(-3) - 6$
$= 2(9) - 5(-3) - 6$
$= 18 + 15 - 6$
$= 27$

26. $3x^2 - 4x - 9 = 3(-5)^2 - 4(-5) - 9$
$= 3(25) - 4(-5) - 9$
$= 75 + 20 - 9$
$= 86$

27. $-5x^2 - 4x - 11 = -5(-1)^2 - 4(-1) - 11$
$= -5(1) - 4(-1) - 11$
$= -5 + 4 - 11$
$= -12$

28. $-6x^2 - 11x - 17 = -6(-2)^2 - 11(-2) - 17$
$= -6(4) - 11(-2) - 17$
$= -24 + 22 - 17$
$= -19$

29. $3x^2 + 2xy + 5y^2 = 3(2)^2 + 2(2)(3) + 5(3)^2$
$= 3(4) + 2(2)(3) + 5(9)$
$= 12 + 12 + 45$
$= 69$

30. $4x^2 + 3xy + 2y^2 = 4(3)^2 + 3(3)(2) + 2(2)^2$
$= 4(9) + 3(3)(2) + 2(4)$
$= 36 + 18 + 8$
$= 62$

31. $-x^2 - 4xy + 3y^3 = -(-1)^2 - 4(-1)(-2) + 3(-2)^3$
$= -(1) - 8 + 3(-8)$
$= -1 - 8 - 24$
$= -33$

32. $-x^2 - 3xy + 4y^3 = -(-3)^2 - 3(-3)(-1) + 4(-1)^3$
$= -(9) - 9 + 4(-1)$
$= -9 - 9 - 4$
$= -22$

33. If $x = -2$ and $y = 4$ then
$\dfrac{2x+3y}{x+1} = \dfrac{2(-2)+3(4)}{-2+1} = \dfrac{-4+12}{-1} = \dfrac{8}{-1} = -8$

34. $\dfrac{2x+y}{xy-2x}$; $x = -2$ and $y = 4$

$\dfrac{2(-2)+4}{(-2)(4)-2(-2)} = \dfrac{-4+4}{-8+4} = \dfrac{0}{4} = 0$

35. $C = \dfrac{5}{9}(50-32) = \dfrac{5}{9}(18) = 10$
$10°$C is equivalent to $50°$F.

36. $C = \dfrac{5}{9}(F-32) = \dfrac{5}{9}(86-32) = \dfrac{5}{9}(54) = 30$ $30°$C is
equivalent to $86°$F.

37. $h = 4 + 60t - 16t^2 = 4 + 60(2) - 16(2)^2$
$= 4 + 120 - 16(4) = 4 + 120 - 64$
$= 124 - 64 = 60$
Two seconds after it is kicked, the ball's height is 60 feet.

38. $h = 4 + 60t - 16t^2$
$= 4 + 60(3) - 16(3)^2$
$= 4 + 180 - 16(9)$
$= 4 + 180 - 144$
$= 184 - 144 = 40$
Three seconds after it is kicked, the ball's height is 40 feet.

39. $7 + 2(x+9)$
$= 7 + (2x+18)$ [distributive property]
$= 7 + (18+2x)$ [commutative property of addition]
$= (7+18) + 2x$ [associative property of addition]
$= 25 + 2x$
$= 2x + 25$ [commutative property of addition]

40. $5(x+4)+3x$

$= (5x+20)+3x$ [distributive property]

$= (20+5x)+3x$ [commutative property of addition]

$= 20+(5x+3x)$ [associative property of addition]

$= 20+(5+3)x$ [distributive property]

$= 20+8x$

$= 8x+20$ [commutative property of addition]

41. $7x+10x = 17x$

42. $5x+13x = 18x$

43. $5x^2 - 8x^2 = -3x^2$

44. $7x^2 - 10x^2 = -3x^2$

45. $3(x+5) = 3x+15$

46. $4(x+6) = 4x+24$

47. $4(2x-3) = 8x-12$

48. $3(4x-5) = 12x-15$

49. $5(3x+4)-4 = 5\cdot3x+5\cdot4-4$

$= 15x+20-4$

$= 15x+16$

50. $2(5x+4)-3 = 2\cdot5x+2\cdot4-3$

$= 10x+8-3$

$= 10x+5$

51. $5(3x-2)+12x = 5\cdot3x-5\cdot2+12x$

$= 15x-10+12x$

$= 27x-10$

52. $2(5x-1)+14x = 2\cdot5x-2\cdot1+14x$

$= 10x-2+14x$

$= 24x-2$

53. $7(3y-5)+2(4y+3)$

$= 7\cdot3y-7\cdot5+2\cdot4y+2\cdot3$

$= 21y-35+8y+6$

$= 29y-29$

54. $4(2y-6)+3(5y+10)$

$= 4\cdot2y-4\cdot6+3\cdot5y+3\cdot10$

$= 8y-24+15y+30$

$= 23y+6$

55. $5(3y-2)-(7y+2) = 15y-10-7y-2$

$= 8y-12$

56. $4(5y-3)-(6y+3) = 20y-12-6y-3$

$= 14y-15$

57. $3(-4x^2+5x)-(5x-4x^2) = -12x^2+15x-5x+4x^2$

$= -8x^2+10x$

58. $2(-5x^2+3x)-(3x-5x^2) = -10x^2+6x-3x+5x^2$

$= -5x^2+3x$

59. $7-4\left[3-(4y-5)\right] = 7-4\left[3-4y+5\right]$

$= 7-4\left[8-4y\right]$

$= 7-32+16y$

$= 16y-25$

60. $6-5[8-(2y-4)] = 6-5\left[8-2y+4\right]$

$= 6-5\left[12-2y\right]$

$= 6-60+10y$

$= 10y-54$

61. $8x-3[5-(7-6x)] = 8x-3[5-7+6x]$

$= 8x-3[-2+6x]$

$= 8x+6-18x$

$= -10x+6$

62. $7x-4[6-(8-5x)] = 7x-4[6-8+5x]$

$= 7x-4[-2+5x]$

$= 7x+8-20x$

$= -13x+8$

63. $18x^2+4-\left[6(x^2-2)+5\right]$

$= 18x^2+4-\left[6x^2-12+5\right]$

$= 18x^2+4-\left[6x^2-7\right]$

$= 18x^2+4-6x^2+7$

$= 18x^2-6x^2+4+7$

$= (18-6)x^2+11 = 12x^2+11$

64. $14x^2 + 5 - \left[7\left(x^2 - 2\right) + 4\right]$

$= 14x^2 + 5 - \left[7x^2 - 14 + 4\right]$

$= 14x^2 + 5 - \left[7x^2 - 10\right]$

$= 14x^2 + 5 - 7x^2 + 10$

$= 14x^2 - 7x^2 + 5 + 10$

$= (14 - 7)x^2 + 15$

$= 7x^2 + 15$

65. $2(3x^2 - 5) - [4(2x^2 - 1) + 3]$

$= 6x^2 - 10 - [8x^2 - 4 + 3]$

$= 6x^2 - 10 - [8x^2 - 1]$

$= 6x^2 - 10 - 8x^2 + 1$

$= -2x^2 - 9$

66. $4(6x^2 - 3) - [2(5x^2 - 1) + 1]$

$= 24x^2 - 12 - [10x^2 - 2 + 1]$

$= 24x^2 - 12 - [10x^2 - 1]$

$= 24x^2 - 12 - 10x^2 + 1$

$= 14x^2 - 11$

67. a. $H = \dfrac{7}{10}(220 - a)$

$H = \dfrac{7}{10}(220 - 20)$

$= \dfrac{7}{10}(200)$

$= 140$

The lower limit of the heart rate for a 20-year-old with this exercise goal is 140 beats per minute.

b. $H = \dfrac{4}{5}(220 - a)$

$H = \dfrac{4}{5}(220 - 20)$

$= \dfrac{4}{5}(200)$

$= 160$

The upper limit of the heart rate for a 20-year-old with this exercise goal is 160 beats per minute.

68. a. $H = \dfrac{1}{2}(220 - a)$

$H = \dfrac{1}{2}(220 - 30)$

$= \dfrac{1}{2}(190)$

$= 95$

The lower limit of the heart rate for a 30-year-old with this exercise goal is 95 beats per minute.

b. $H = \dfrac{3}{5}(220 - a)$

$H = \dfrac{3}{5}(220 - 30)$

$= \dfrac{3}{5}(190)$

$= 114$

The upper limit of the heart rate for a 30-year-old with this exercise goal is 114 beats per minute.

69. $P = -0.5x^2 + 0.1x + 26.9$

$P = -0.5(6)^2 + 0.1(6) + 26.9 = 9.5$

According to the formula, 9.5% of those in this group had contact with a police officer. That underestimates the percentage shown in the graph by 0.5.

70. $P = -0.5x^2 + 0.1x + 26.9$

$P = -0.5(2)^2 + 0.1(2) + 26.9 = 25.1$

According to the formula, 25.1% of those in this group had contact with a police officer. That underestimates the percentage shown in the graph by 1.9.

71. a. $52,000

b. $C = 1361x + 25,181$

$= 1361(20) + 25,181$

$= \$52,401$

It describes the estimate from part (a) reasonably well.

c. $C = -0.7x^2 + 1380x + 25,112$

$= -0.7(20)^2 + 1380(20) + 25,112$

$= \$52,432$

It describes the estimate from part (a) reasonably well.

72. a. $40,000

b. $C = 1361x + 25,181$

$= 1361(10) + 25,181$

$= \$38,791$

It describes the estimate from part (a) reasonably well.

c. $C = -0.7x^2 + 1380x + 25,112$

$= -0.7(10)^2 + 1380(10) + 25,112$

$= \$38,842$

It describes the estimate from part (a) reasonably well.

73. Model 1:

$C = 1361x + 25,181$

$= 1361(0) + 25,181$

$= \$25,181$

Model 2:

$C = -0.7x^2 + 1380x + 25,112$

$= -0.7(0)^2 + 1380(0) + 25,112$

$= \$25,112$

According to the graph, the cost in 1980 was $24,900. Thus, Model 2 is the better model. Model 2 overestimates the cost shown in the graph by $212.

74. Model 1:

$C = 1361x + 25,181$

$= 1361(27) + 25,181$

$= \$61,928$

Model 2:

$C = -0.7x^2 + 1380x + 25,112$

$= -0.7(27)^2 + 1380(27) + 25,112$

$= \$61861.70$

According to the graph, the cost in 2007 was $62,100. Thus, Model 1 is the better model. Model 1 underestimates the cost shown in the graph by $172.

84. makes sense

85. does not make sense; Explanations will vary. Sample explanation: Common terms must have the same variables with the same exponents.

86. makes sense

87. does not make sense; Explanations will vary. Sample explanation: The value can be estimated by letting $x = 0$.

88. false; Changes to make the statement true will vary. A sample change is: The coefficient of x is 1.

89. false; Changes to make the statement true will vary. A sample change is:
$5 + 3(x - 4) = 5 + 3x - 12 = 3x - 7$

90. false; Changes to make the statement true will vary. A sample change is: $-x - x = -x + (-x) = -2x$

91. true

92. false; Changes to make the statement true will vary. A sample change is: $3 + 7x \neq 10x$

93. false; Changes to make the statement true will vary. A sample change is: $b \cdot b = b^2$

94. true

95. false; Changes to make the statement true will vary. A sample change is: $-4y + 4 = -4(y - 1)$

96. $\dfrac{0.5x + 5000}{x}$

a. $x = 100$

$\dfrac{0.5(100) + 5000}{100} = \$50.50$

$x = 1000$

$\dfrac{0.5(1000) + 5000}{1000} = \$5.50$

$x = 10,000$

$\dfrac{0.5(10,000) + 5000}{10,000} = \$1$

b. No; the business must produce at least 10,000 clocks each week to be competitive.

Check Points 6.2

1.
$$4x + 5 = 29$$
$$4x + 5 - 5 = 29 - 5$$
$$4x = 24$$
$$\frac{4x}{4} = \frac{24}{4}$$
$$x = 6$$

Check:
$$4x + 5 = 29$$
$$4(6) + 5 = 29$$
$$24 + 5 = 29$$
$$29 = 29$$
The solution set is $\{6\}$.

2. $6(x - 3) - 10x = -10$
$$6x - 18 - 10x = -10$$
$$-4x - 18 = -10$$
$$-4x - 18 + 18 = -10 + 18$$
$$-4x = 8$$
$$\frac{-4x}{-4} = \frac{8}{-4}$$
$$x = -2$$
Check:
$$6(-2 - 3) - 10(-2) = -10$$
$$6(-5) + 20 = -10$$
$$-30 + 20 = -10$$
$$-10 = -10$$
The solution set is $\{-2\}$.

3.
$$2x + 9 = 8x - 3$$
$$2x + 9 - 8x = 8x - 3 - 8x$$
$$-6x + 9 = -3$$
$$-6x + 9 - 9 = -3 - 9$$
$$-6x = -12$$
$$\frac{-6x}{-6} = \frac{-12}{-6}$$
$$x = 2$$
The solution set is $\{2\}$.

4. $4(2x + 1) - 29 = 3(2x - 5)$
$$8x + 4 - 29 = 6x - 15$$
$$8x - 25 = 6x - 15$$
$$8x - 25 - 6x = 6x - 15 - 6x$$
$$2x - 25 = -15$$
$$2x - 25 + 25 = -15 + 25$$
$$2x = 10$$
$$\frac{2x}{2} = \frac{10}{2}$$
$$x = 5$$
The solution set is $\{5\}$.

5.
$$\frac{2x}{3} = 7 - \frac{x}{2}$$
$$6 \cdot \frac{2x}{3} = 6 \cdot \left(7 - \frac{x}{2}\right)$$
$$6 \cdot \frac{2x}{3} = 6 \cdot 7 - 6 \cdot \frac{x}{2}$$
$$2 \cdot 2x = 42 - 3x$$
$$4x = 42 - 3x$$
$$4x + 3x = 42 - 3x + 3x$$
$$7x = 42$$
$$\frac{7x}{7} = \frac{42}{7}$$
$$x = 6$$
The solution set is $\{6\}$.

6.
$$D = \frac{10}{9}x + \frac{53}{9}$$
$$10 = \frac{10}{9}x + \frac{53}{9}$$
$$9 \cdot 10 = 9 \cdot \left(\frac{10}{9}x + \frac{53}{9}\right)$$
$$90 = 10x + 53$$
$$37 = 10x$$
$$3.7 = x$$
This is shown on the graph as the point $(3.7, 10)$.

7. a.
$$\frac{10}{x} = \frac{2}{3}$$
$$10 \cdot 3 = 2x$$
$$30 = 2x$$
$$\frac{30}{2} = \frac{2x}{2}$$
$$15 = x$$
The solution set is $\{15\}$.

b.
$$\frac{22}{60-x} = \frac{2}{x}$$
$$22x = 2(60-x)$$
$$22x = 120 - 2x$$
$$22x + 2x = 120 - 2x + 2x$$
$$24x = 120$$
$$\frac{24x}{24} = \frac{120}{24}$$
$$x = 5$$
The solution set is $\{5\}$.

8. Let $x =$ the property tax on the $420,000 house.

$$\frac{\text{Tax on } \$250,000 \text{ house}}{\text{Assessed value } (\$250,000)} = \frac{\text{Tax on } \$420,000 \text{ house}}{\text{Assessed value } (\$420,000)}$$

$$\frac{\$3500}{\$250,000} = \frac{\$x}{\$420,000}$$

$$\frac{3500}{250,000} = \frac{x}{420,000}$$

$$250,000x = (3500)(420,000)$$

$$250,000x = 1,470,000,000$$

$$\frac{250,000x}{250,000} = \frac{1,470,000,000}{250,000}$$

$$x = 5880$$

The property tax is $5880.

9. Let $x =$ the number of deer in the refuge.

$$\frac{120 \text{ tagged deer}}{x} = \frac{25 \text{ tagged deer in sample}}{150 \text{ deer in sample}}$$

$$\frac{120}{x} = \frac{25}{150}$$

$$25x = (120)(150)$$

$$25x = 18,000$$

$$\frac{25x}{25} = \frac{18,000}{25}$$

$$x = 720$$

There are approximately 720 deer in the refuge.

10.
$$3x + 7 = 3(x+1)$$
$$3x + 7 = 3x + 3$$
$$3x + 7 - 3x = 3x + 3 - 3x$$
$$7 = 3$$
There is no solution, $\varnothing$.

11.
$$7x + 9 = 9(x+1) - 2x$$
$$7x + 9 = 9x + 9 - 2x$$
$$7x + 9 = 7x + 9$$
$$9 = 9$$
The solution set is $\{x \,|\, x \text{ is a real number}\}$.

Exercise Set 6.2

1.
$$x - 7 = 3$$
$$x - 7 + 7 = 3 + 7$$
$$x = 10$$
The solution set is $\{10\}$.

2.
$$x - 3 = -17$$
$$x - 3 + 3 = -17 + 3$$
$$x = -14$$
The solution set is $\{-14\}$.

3.
$$x + 5 = -12$$
$$x + 5 - 5 = -12 - 5$$
$$x = -17$$
The solution set is $\{-17\}$.

4.
$$x + 12 = -14$$
$$x + 12 - 12 = -14 - 12$$
$$x = -26$$
The solution set is $\{-26\}$.

5.
$$\frac{x}{3} = 4$$
$$3\left(\frac{x}{3}\right) = 3(4)$$
$$x = 12$$
The solution set is $\{12\}$.

6.
$$\frac{x}{5} = 3$$
$$5\left(\frac{x}{5}\right) = 5(3)$$
$$x = 15$$
The solution set is $\{15\}$.

7. $5x = 45$

$$\frac{5x}{5} = \frac{45}{5}$$

$x = 9$

The solution set is $\{9\}$.

8. $6x = 18$

$$\frac{6x}{6} = \frac{18}{6}$$

$x = 3$

The solution set is $\{3\}$.

9. $8x = -24$

$$\frac{8x}{8} = \frac{-24}{8}$$

$x = -3$

The solution set is $\{-3\}$.

10. $5x = -25$

$$\frac{5x}{5} = \frac{-25}{5}$$

$x = -5$

The solution set is $\{-5\}$.

11. $-8x = 2$

$$\frac{-8x}{-8} = \frac{2}{-8}$$

$$x = -\frac{1}{4}$$

The solution set is $\left\{-\frac{1}{4}\right\}$.

12. $-6x = 3$

$$\frac{-6x}{-6} = \frac{3}{-6}$$

$$x = -\frac{1}{2}$$

The solution set is $\left\{-\frac{1}{2}\right\}$.

13. $5x + 3 = 18$

$5x + 3 - 3 = 18 - 3$

$5x = 15$

$$\frac{5x}{5} = \frac{15}{5}$$

$x = 3$

The solution set is $\{3\}$.

14. $3x + 8 = 50$

$3x + 8 - 8 = 50 - 8$

$3x = 42$

$$\frac{3x}{3} = \frac{42}{3}$$

$x = 14$

The solution set is $\{14\}$.

15. $6x - 3 = 63$

$6x - 3 + 3 = 63 + 3$

$6x = 66$

$$\frac{6x}{6} = \frac{66}{6}$$

$x = 11$

The solution set is $\{11\}$.

16. $5x - 8 = 72$

$5x - 8 + 8 = 72 + 8$

$5x = 80$

$$\frac{5x}{5} = \frac{80}{5}$$

$x = 16$

The solution set is $\{16\}$.

17. $4x - 14 = -82$

$4x - 14 + 14 = -82 + 14$

$4x = -68$

$$\frac{4x}{4} = \frac{-68}{4}$$

$x = -17$

The solution set is $\{-17\}$.

18. $9x - 14 = -77$

$9x - 14 + 14 = -77 + 14$

$9x = -63$

$$\frac{9x}{9} = \frac{-63}{9}$$

$x = -7$

The solution set is $\{-7\}$.

19. $14 - 5x = -41$

$14 - 5x - 14 = -41 - 14$

$-5x = -55$

$$\frac{-5x}{-5} = \frac{-55}{-5}$$

$x = 11$

The solution set is $\{11\}$.

20.
$$25 - 6x = -83$$
$$25 - 6x - 25 = -83 - 25$$
$$-6x = -108$$
$$\frac{-6x}{-6} = \frac{-108}{-6}$$
$$x = 18$$
The solution set is {18}.

21.
$$9(5x - 2) = 45$$
$$45x - 18 = 45$$
$$45x - 18 + 18 = 45 + 18$$
$$45x = 63$$
$$\frac{45x}{45} = \frac{63}{45}$$
$$x = \frac{7}{5}$$
The solution set is $\left\{\frac{7}{5}\right\}$.

22.
$$10(3x + 2) = 70$$
$$30x + 20 = 70$$
$$30x + 20 - 20 = 70 - 20$$
$$30x = 50$$
$$\frac{30x}{30} = \frac{50}{30}$$
$$x = \frac{5}{3}$$
The solution set is $\left\{\frac{5}{3}\right\}$.

23.
$$5x - (2x - 10) = 35$$
$$5x - 2x + 10 = 35$$
$$3x + 10 = 35$$
$$3x + 10 - 10 = 35 - 10$$
$$3x = 25$$
$$\frac{3x}{3} = \frac{25}{3}$$
$$x = \frac{25}{3}$$
The solution set is $\left\{\frac{25}{3}\right\}$.

24.
$$11x - (6x - 5) = 40$$
$$11x - 6x + 5 = 40$$
$$5x + 5 = 40$$
$$5x + 5 - 5 = 40 - 5$$
$$5x = 35$$
$$\frac{5x}{5} = \frac{35}{5}$$
$$x = 7$$
The solution set is {7}.

25.
$$3x + 5 = 2x + 13$$
$$3x + 5 - 5 = 2x + 13 - 5$$
$$3x = 2x + 8$$
$$3x - 2x = 2x + 8 - 2x$$
$$x = 8$$
The solution set is {8}.

26.
$$2x - 7 = 6 + x$$
$$2x - 7 + 7 = 6 + x + 7$$
$$2x = x + 13$$
$$2x - x = x + 13 - x$$
$$x = 13$$
The solution set is {13}.

27.
$$8x - 2 = 7x - 5$$
$$8x - 2 + 2 = 7x - 5 + 2$$
$$8x = 7x - 3$$
$$8x - 7x = 7x - 3 - 7x$$
$$x = -3$$
The solution set is {-3}.

28.
$$13x + 14 = -5 + 12x$$
$$13x + 14 - 14 = -5 + 12x - 14$$
$$13x = 12x - 19$$
$$13x - 12x = 12x - 19 - 12x$$
$$x = -19$$
The solution set is {-19}.

29.
$$7x + 4 = x + 16$$
$$7x + 4 - 4 = x + 16 - 4$$
$$7x = x + 12$$
$$7x - x = x + 12 - x$$
$$6x = 12$$
$$\frac{6x}{6} = \frac{12}{6}$$
$$x = 2$$
The solution set is {2}.

30.
$$8x + 1 = x + 43$$
$$8x + 1 - 1 = x + 43 - 1$$
$$8x = x + 42$$
$$8x - x = x + 42 - x$$
$$7x = 42$$
$$\frac{7x}{7} = \frac{42}{7}$$
$$x = 6$$
The solution set is $\{6\}$.

31.
$$8y - 3 = 11y + 9$$
$$8y - 3 + 3 = 11y + 9 + 3$$
$$8y = 11y + 12$$
$$8y - 11y = 11y + 12 - 11y$$
$$-3y = 12$$
$$\frac{-3y}{-3} = \frac{12}{-3}$$
$$y = -4$$
The solution set is $\{-4\}$.

32.
$$5y - 2 = 9y + 2$$
$$5y - 2 + 2 = 9y + 2 + 2$$
$$5y = 9y + 4$$
$$5y - 9y = 9y + 4 - 9y$$
$$-4y = 4$$
$$\frac{-4y}{-4} = \frac{4}{-4}$$
$$y = -1$$
The solution set is $\{-1\}$.

33.
$$2(4 - 3x) = 2(2x + 5)$$
$$8 - 6x = 4x + 10$$
$$8 - 6x - 8 = 4x + 10 - 8$$
$$-6x = 4x + 2$$
$$-6x - 4x = 4x + 2 - 4x$$
$$-10x = 2$$
$$\frac{-10x}{-10} = \frac{2}{-10}$$
$$x = -\frac{1}{5}$$
The solution set is $\left\{-\frac{1}{5}\right\}$.

34.
$$3(5 - x) = 4(2x + 1)$$
$$15 - 3x = 8x + 4$$
$$15 - 3x - 15 = 8x + 4 - 15$$
$$-3x = 8x - 11$$
$$-3x - 8x = 8x - 11 - 8x$$
$$\frac{-11x}{-11} = \frac{-11}{-11}$$
$$x = 1$$
The solution set is $\{1\}$.

35.
$$8(y + 2) = 2(3y + 4)$$
$$8y + 16 = 6y + 8$$
$$8y + 16 - 16 = 6y + 8 - 16$$
$$8y = 6y - 8$$
$$8y - 6y = 6y - 8 - 6y$$
$$2y = -8$$
$$\frac{2y}{2} = \frac{-8}{2}$$
$$y = -4$$
The solution set is $\{-4\}$.

36.
$$3(3y - 1) = 4(3 + 3y)$$
$$9y - 3 = 12 + 12y$$
$$9y - 3 + 3 = 12 + 12y + 3$$
$$9y = 12y - 15$$
$$9y - 12y = 12y - 15 - 12y$$
$$-3y = 15$$
$$\frac{-3y}{-3} = \frac{15}{-3}$$
$$y = -5$$
The solution set is $\{-5\}$.

37.
$$3(x + 1) = 7(x - 2) - 3$$
$$3x + 3 = 7x - 14 - 3$$
$$3x + 3 = 7x - 17$$
$$3x + 3 - 3 = 7x - 17 - 3$$
$$3x = 7x - 20$$
$$3x - 7x = 7x - 20 - 7x$$
$$-4x = -20$$
$$\frac{-4x}{-4} = \frac{-20}{-4}$$
$$x = 5$$
The solution set is $\{5\}$.

38. $5x - 4(x+9) = 2x - 3$

$5x - 4x - 36 = 2x - 3$

$x - 36 = 2x - 3$

$x - 36 + 36 = 2x - 3 + 36$

$x = 2x + 33$

$x - 2x = 2x + 33 - 2x$

$-x = 33$

$\dfrac{-x}{-1} = \dfrac{33}{-1}$

$x = -33$

The solution set is $\{-33\}$.

39. $5(2x - 8) - 2 = 5(x - 3) + 3$

$10x - 40 - 2 = 5x - 15 + 3$

$10x - 42 = 5x - 12$

$10x - 42 + 42 = 5x - 12 + 42$

$10x = 5x + 30$

$10x - 5x = 5x + 30 - 5x$

$5x = 30$

$\dfrac{5x}{5} = \dfrac{30}{5}$

$x = 6$

The solution set is $\{6\}$.

40. $7(3x - 2) + 5 = 6(2x - 1) + 24$

$21x - 14 + 5 = 12x - 6 + 24$

$21x - 9 = 12x + 18$

$21x - 9 + 9 = 12x + 18 + 9$

$21x = 12x + 27$

$21x - 12x = 12x + 27 - 12x$

$9x = 27$

$\dfrac{9x}{9} = \dfrac{27}{9}$

$x = 3$

The solution set is $\{3\}$.

41. $6 = -4(1 - x) + 3(x + 1)$

$6 = -4 + 4x + 3x + 3$

$6 = -1 + 7x$

$6 + 1 = -1 + 7x + 1$

$7 = 7x$

$\dfrac{7}{7} = \dfrac{7x}{7}$

$1 = x$

The solution set is $\{1\}$.

42. $100 = -(x - 1) + 4(x - 6)$

$100 = -x + 1 + 4x - 24$

$100 = 3x - 23$

$123 = 3x$

$41 = x$

The solution set is $\{41\}$.

43. $10(z + 4) - 4(z - 2) = 3(z - 1) + 2(z - 3)$

$10z + 40 - 4z + 8 = 3z - 3 + 2z - 6$

$6z + 48 = 5z - 9$

$6z + 48 - 48 = 5z - 9 - 48$

$6z - 5z = 5z - 57 - 5z$

$z = -57$

The solution set is $\{-57\}$.

44. $-2(z - 4) - (3z - 2) = -2 - (6z - 2)$

$-2z + 8 - 3z + 2 = -2 - 6z + 2$

$-5z + 10 = -6z$

$z + 10 = 0$

$z = -10$

The solution set is $\{-10\}$.

45. $\dfrac{2x}{3} - 5 = 7$

To clear the equation of fractions, multiply both sides by the least common denominator (LCD), which is 3.

$3\left(\tfrac{2}{3}x - 5\right) = 3(7)$

$3 \cdot \tfrac{2}{3}x - 3 \cdot 5 = 21$

$2x - 15 = 21$

$2x - 15 + 15 = 21 + 15$

$2x = 36$

$\dfrac{2x}{2} = \dfrac{36}{2}$

$x = 18$

The solution set is $\{18\}$.

46. $\dfrac{3x}{4} - 9 = -6$

To clear the equation of fractions, multiply both sides by the least common denominator (LCD), which is 4.

$$4\left(\dfrac{3x}{4} - 9\right) = 4(-6)$$

$$4 \cdot \dfrac{3x}{4} - 4 \cdot 9 = -24$$

$$3x - 36 = -24$$

$$3x = 12$$

$$x = 4$$

The solution set is $\{4\}$.

47. $\dfrac{x}{3} + \dfrac{x}{2} = \dfrac{5}{6}$

To clear the equation of fractions, multiply both sides by the least common denominator (LCD), which is 6.

$$6\left(\dfrac{x}{3} + \dfrac{x}{2}\right) = 6\left(\dfrac{5}{6}\right)$$

$$2x + 3x = 5$$

$$5x = 5$$

$$\dfrac{5x}{5} = \dfrac{5}{5}$$

$$x = 1$$

The solution set is $\{1\}$.

48. $\dfrac{x}{4} - \dfrac{x}{5} = 1$

To clear the equation of fractions, multiply both sides by the least common denominator (LCD), which is 20.

$$20\left(\dfrac{x}{4} - \dfrac{x}{5}\right) = 20(1)$$

$$5x - 4x = 20$$

$$x = 20$$

The solution set is $\{20\}$.

49. $20 - \dfrac{z}{3} = \dfrac{z}{2}$

To clear the equation of fractions, multiply both sides by the least common denominator (LCD), which is 6.

$$6\left(20 - \dfrac{z}{3}\right) = 6\left(\dfrac{z}{2}\right)$$

$$120 - 2z = 3z$$

$$120 - 2z + 2z = 3z + 2z$$

$$120 = 5z$$

$$\dfrac{120}{5} = \dfrac{5z}{5}$$

$$24 = z$$

The solution set is $\{24\}$.

50. $\dfrac{z}{5} - \dfrac{1}{2} = \dfrac{z}{6}$

To clear the equation of fractions, multiply both sides by the least common denominator (LCD), which is 30.

$$30\left(\dfrac{z}{5} - \dfrac{1}{2}\right) = 30\left(\dfrac{z}{6}\right)$$

$$6z - 15 = 5z$$

$$z - 15 = 0$$

$$z = 15$$

The solution set is $\{15\}$.

51. $\dfrac{y}{3} + \dfrac{2}{5} = \dfrac{y}{5} - \dfrac{2}{5}$

To clear the equation of fractions, multiply both sides by the least common denominator (LCD), which is 15.

$$15\left(\dfrac{y}{3} + \dfrac{2}{5}\right) = 15\left(\dfrac{y}{5} + \dfrac{2}{5}\right)$$

$$15\left(\dfrac{y}{3}\right) + 15\left(\dfrac{2}{5}\right) = 15\left(\dfrac{y}{5}\right) + 15\left(-\dfrac{2}{5}\right)$$

$$5y + 6 = 3y - 6$$

$$5y + 6 - 3y = 3y - 6 - 3y$$

$$2y + 6 = -6$$

$$2y + 6 - 6 = -6 - 6$$

$$2y = -12$$

$$\dfrac{2y}{2} = \dfrac{-12}{2}$$

$$y = -6$$

The solution set is $\{-6\}$.

52. $\dfrac{y}{12} + \dfrac{1}{6} = \dfrac{y}{2} - \dfrac{1}{4}$

To clear the equation of fractions, multiply both sides by the least common denominator (LCD), which is 12.

$$12\left(\dfrac{y}{12} + \dfrac{1}{6}\right) = 12\left(\dfrac{y}{2} - \dfrac{1}{4}\right)$$

$$y + 2 = 6y - 3$$

$$-5y + 2 = -3$$

$$-5y = -5$$

$$y = 1$$

The solution set is $\{1\}$.

53. $\dfrac{3x}{4} - 3 = \dfrac{x}{2} + 2$

To clear the equation of fractions, multiply both sides by the least common denominator (LCD), which is 8.

$$8\left(\dfrac{3x}{4} - 3\right) = 8\left(\dfrac{x}{2} + 2\right)$$

$$8\left(\dfrac{3x}{4}\right) - 8 \cdot 3 = 8\left(\dfrac{x}{2}\right) + 8 \cdot 2$$

$$6x - 24 = 4x + 16$$

$$6x - 24 - 4x = 4x + 16 - 4x$$

$$2x - 24 = 16$$

$$2x - 24 + 24 = 16 + 24$$

$$2x = 40$$

$$\dfrac{2x}{2} = \dfrac{40}{2}$$

$$x = 20$$

The solution set is $\{20\}$.

54. $\dfrac{3x}{5} - \dfrac{2}{5} = \dfrac{x}{3} + \dfrac{2}{5}$

To clear the equation of fractions, multiply both sides by the least common denominator (LCD), which is 15.

$$15\left(\dfrac{3x}{5} - \dfrac{2}{5}\right) = 15\left(\dfrac{x}{3} + \dfrac{2}{5}\right)$$

$$9x - 6 = 5x + 6$$

$$4x - 6 = 6$$

$$4x = 12$$

$$x = 3$$

The solution set is $\{3\}$.

55. $\dfrac{3x}{5} - x = \dfrac{x}{10} - \dfrac{5}{2}$

$$10\left(\dfrac{3x}{5} - x\right) = 10\left(\dfrac{x}{10} - \dfrac{5}{2}\right)$$

$$10\left(\dfrac{3x}{5}\right) - 10(x) = 10\left(\dfrac{x}{10}\right) - 10\left(\dfrac{5}{2}\right)$$

$$6x - 10x = x - 25$$

$$-4x = x - 25$$

$$-4x - x = x - 25 - x$$

$$-5x = -25$$

$$\dfrac{-5x}{-5} = \dfrac{-25}{-5}$$

$$x = 5$$

The solution set is $\{5\}$.

56. $2x - \dfrac{2x}{7} = \dfrac{x}{2} + \dfrac{17}{2}$

$$14\left(2x - \dfrac{2x}{7}\right) = 14\left(\dfrac{x}{2} + \dfrac{17}{2}\right)$$

$$14 \cdot 2x - 14 \cdot \dfrac{2x}{7} = 14 \cdot \dfrac{x}{2} + 14 \cdot \dfrac{17}{2}$$

$$28x - 4x = 7x + 119$$

$$24x = 7x + 119$$

$$24x - 7x = 7x + 119 - 7x$$

$$17x = 119$$

$$\dfrac{17x}{17} = \dfrac{119}{17}$$

$$x = 7$$

The solution set is $\{7\}$.

57. $\dfrac{x-3}{5} - 1 = \dfrac{x-5}{4}$

To clear the equation of fractions, multiply both sides by the least common denominator (LCD), which is 20.

$$20\left(\dfrac{x-3}{5} - 1\right) = 20\left(\dfrac{x-5}{4}\right)$$

$$4(x-3) - 20 = 5(x-5)$$

$$4x - 12 - 20 = 5x - 25$$

$$4x - 5x - 32 = 5x - 5x - 25$$

$$-x - 32 = -25$$

$$-x - 32 + 32 = -25 + 32$$

$$-x = 7$$

$$-1(-x) = -1(7)$$

$$x = -7$$

The solution set is $\{-7\}$.

58. $\dfrac{x-2}{3} - 4 = \dfrac{x+1}{4}$

To clear the equation of fractions, multiply both sides by the least common denominator (LCD), which is 12.

$$12\left(\dfrac{x-2}{3}\right) - 12(4) = 12\left(\dfrac{x+1}{4}\right)$$
$$4(x-2) - 48 = 3(x+1)$$
$$4x - 8 - 48 = 3x + 3$$
$$4x - 56 = 3x + 3$$
$$x - 56 = 3$$
$$x = 59$$

The solution set is $\{59\}$.

59. $\dfrac{24}{x} = \dfrac{12}{7}$

$$12x = 24 \cdot 7$$
$$12x = 168$$
$$\dfrac{12x}{12} = \dfrac{168}{12}$$
$$x = 14$$

The solution set is $\{14\}$.

60. $\dfrac{56}{x} = \dfrac{8}{7}$

$$8x = 56 \cdot 7$$
$$8x = 392$$
$$\dfrac{8x}{8} = \dfrac{392}{8}$$
$$x = 49$$

The solution set is $\{60\}$.

61. $\dfrac{x}{6} = \dfrac{18}{4}$

$$4x = 6 \cdot 18$$
$$4x = 108$$
$$\dfrac{4x}{4} = \dfrac{108}{4}$$
$$x = 27$$

The solution set is $\{27\}$.

62. $\dfrac{x}{32} = \dfrac{3}{24}$

$$24x = 3 \cdot 32$$
$$24x = 96$$
$$\dfrac{24x}{24} = \dfrac{96}{24}$$
$$x = 4$$

The solution set is $\{4\}$.

63. $\dfrac{-3}{8} = \dfrac{x}{40}$

$$8x = -3(40)$$
$$8x = -120$$
$$\dfrac{8x}{8} = \dfrac{-120}{8}$$
$$x = -15$$

The solution set is $\{15\}$.

64. $\dfrac{-3}{8} = \dfrac{6}{x}$

$$-3x = 8 \cdot 6$$
$$-3x = 48$$
$$\dfrac{-3x}{-3} = \dfrac{48}{-3}$$
$$x = -16$$

The solution set is $\{-16\}$.

65. $\dfrac{x}{12} = -\dfrac{3}{4}$

$$4x = 12(-3)$$
$$4x = -36$$
$$x = -9$$

The solution set is $\{-9\}$.

66. $\dfrac{x}{64} = -\dfrac{9}{16}$

$$-16x = 9 \cdot 64$$
$$-16x = 576$$
$$\dfrac{-16x}{-16} = \dfrac{576}{-16}$$
$$x = -36$$

The solution set is $\{-36\}$.

67.　$\dfrac{x-2}{12} = \dfrac{8}{3}$

$3(x-2) = 12(8)$

$3x - 6 = 96$

$3x = 102$

$x = 34$

The solution set is $\{34\}$.

68.　$\dfrac{x-4}{10} = \dfrac{3}{5}$

$5(x-4) = 10 \cdot 3$

$5x - 20 = 30$

$5x = 50$

$\dfrac{5x}{5} = \dfrac{50}{5}$

$x = 10$

The solution set is $\{10\}$.

69.　$\dfrac{x}{7} = \dfrac{x+14}{5}$

$5x = 7(x+14)$

$5x = 7x + 98$

$-2x = 98$

$x = -49$

The solution set is $\{-49\}$.

70.　$\dfrac{x}{5} = \dfrac{x-3}{2}$

$2x = 5(x-3)$

$2x = 5x - 15$

$-3x = -15$

$\dfrac{-3x}{-3} = \dfrac{-15}{-3}$

$x = 5$

The solution set is $\{5\}$.

71.　$\dfrac{y+10}{10} = \dfrac{y-2}{4}$

$4(y+10) = 10(y-2)$

$4y + 40 = 10y - 20$

$4y + 40 - 40 = 10y - 20 - 40$

$4y = 10y - 60$

$4y - 10y = 10y - 60 - 10y$

$-6y = -60$

$\dfrac{-6y}{-6} = \dfrac{-60}{-6}$

$y = 10$

The solution set is $\{10\}$.

72.　$\dfrac{2}{y-5} = \dfrac{3}{y+6}$

$2(y+6) = 3(y-5)$

$2y + 12 = 3y - 15$

$2y + 12 - 2y = 3y - 15 - 2y$

$12 = y - 15$

$12 + 15 = y - 15 + 15$

$27 = y \text{ or } y = 27$

The solution set is $\{27\}$.

73.　$3x - 7 = 3(x+1)$

$3x - 7 = 3x + 3$

$3x - 7 - 3x = 3x + 3 - 3x$

$-7 = 3$

The statement is false. The solution set is { }.

74.　$2(x-5) = 2x + 10$

$2x - 10 = 2x + 10$

$2x - 10 - 2x = 2x + 10 - 2x$

$-10 = 10$

The statement is false. The solution set is { }.

75.　$2(x+4) = 4x + 5 - 2x + 3$

$2x + 8 = 2x + 8$

$2x - 8 - 2x = 2x + 8 - 2x$

$8 = 8$

The statement is true. The solution set is $\{x \mid x \text{ is a real number}\}$.

76. $3(x-1)=8x+6-5x-9$
$3x-3=3x-3$
$3x-3-3x=3x-3-3x$
$-3=-3$
The statement is true. The solution set is
$\{x|x \text{ is a real number}\}.$

77. $7+2(3x-5)=8-3(2x+1)$
$7+6x-10=8-6x-3$
$6x-3=5-6x$
$6x+6x-3=5-6x+6x$
$12x-3=5$
$12x-3+3=5+3$
$12x=8$
$\dfrac{12x}{12}=\dfrac{8}{12}$
$x=\dfrac{2}{3}$
The solution set is $\left\{\dfrac{2}{3}\right\}.$

78. $2+3(2x-7)=9-4(3x+1)$
$2+6x-21=9-12x-4$
$6x-19=-12x+5$
$18x-19=5$
$18x=24$
$x=\dfrac{24}{18}=\dfrac{4}{3}$
The solution set is $\left\{\dfrac{4}{3}\right\}.$

79. $4x+1-5x=5-(x+4)$
$-x+1=5-x-4$
$-x+1=1-x$
$-x+1+x=1-x+x$
$1=1$
The statement is true. The solution set is
$\{x|x \text{ is a real number}\}.$

80. $5x-5=3x-7+2(x+1)$
$5x-5=3x-7+2x+2$
$5x-5=5x-5$
$5x-5-5x=5x-5-5x$
$-5=-5$
The statement is true. The solution set is
$\{x|x \text{ is a real number}\}.$

81. $4(x+2)+1=7x-3(x-2)$
$4x+8+1=7x-3x+6$
$4x+9=4x+6$
$4x-4x+9=4x-4x+6$
$9=6$
The statement is false. The solution set is { }.

82. $5x-3(x+1)=2(x+3)-5$
$5x-3x-3=2x+6-5$
$2x-3=2x+1$
$2x-3-2x=2x+1-2x$
$-3=1$
The statement is false. The solution set is { }.

83. $3-x=2x+3$
$3-x+x=2x+x+3$
$3=3x+3$
$3-3=3x+3-3$
$0=3x$
$\dfrac{0}{3}=\dfrac{3x}{3}$
$0=x$
The solution set is $\{0\}.$

84. $5-x=4x+5$
$5-x-4x=4x+5-4x$
$-5x+5=5$
$-5x=0$
$\dfrac{-5x}{-5}=\dfrac{0}{-5}$
$x=0$
The solution set is $\{0\}.$

85.
$$\frac{x}{3} + 2 = \frac{x}{3}$$
$$6\left(\frac{x}{3} + 2\right) = 6\left(\frac{x}{3}\right)$$
$$2x + 12 = 2x$$
$$2x + 12 - 2x = 2x - 2x$$
$$12 = 0$$
The statement is false. The solution set is { }.

86.
$$\frac{x}{4} + 3 = \frac{x}{4}$$
$$4\left(\frac{x}{4} + 3\right) = 4\left(\frac{x}{4}\right)$$
$$x + 12 = x$$
$$x + 12 - x = x - x$$
$$12 = 0$$
The statement is false. The solution set is { }.

87.
$$\frac{x}{3} = \frac{x}{2}$$
$$3x = 2x$$
$$3x - 2x = 2x - 2x$$
$$x = 0$$
The solution set is $\{0\}$.

88.
$$\frac{x}{4} = \frac{x}{3}$$
$$4x = 3x$$
$$4x - 3x = 3x - 3x$$
$$x = 0$$
The solution set is $\{0\}$.

89.
$$\frac{x-2}{5} = \frac{3}{10}$$
$$10(x-2) = 3 \cdot 5$$
$$10x - 20 = 15$$
$$10x - 20 + 20 = 15 + 20$$
$$10x = 35$$
$$\frac{10x}{10} = \frac{35}{10}$$
$$x = \frac{7}{2}$$
The solution set is $\left\{\frac{7}{2}\right\}$.

90.
$$\frac{x+4}{8} = \frac{3}{16}$$
$$16(x+4) = 8 \cdot 3$$
$$16x + 64 = 24$$
$$16x + 64 - 64 = 24 - 64$$
$$16x = -40$$
$$\frac{16x}{16} = \frac{-40}{16}$$
$$x = -\frac{5}{2}$$
The solution set is $\left\{-\frac{5}{2}\right\}$.

91.
$$\frac{x}{2} - \frac{x}{4} + 4 = x + 4$$
$$4\left(\frac{x}{2} - \frac{x}{4} + 4\right) = 4(x + 4)$$
$$4\left(\frac{x}{2}\right) - 4\left(\frac{x}{4}\right) + 16 = 4x + 16$$
$$2x - x + 16 = 4x + 16$$
$$x + 16 = 4x + 16$$
$$x - x + 16 = 4x - x + 16$$
$$16 = 3x + 16$$
$$16 - 16 = 3x + 16 - 16$$
$$0 = 3x$$
$$\frac{0}{3} = \frac{3x}{3}$$
$$0 = x$$
The solution set is $\{0\}$.

92.
$$\frac{x}{2} + \frac{2x}{3} + 3 = x + 3$$
$$6\left(\frac{x}{2} + \frac{2x}{3} + 3\right) = 6(x + 3)$$
$$3x + 4x + 18 = 6x + 18$$
$$7x + 18 = 6x + 18$$
$$x + 18 = 18$$
$$x = 0$$
The solution set is $\{0\}$.

93. Solve: $4(x-2)+2=4x-2(2-x)$

$$4x-8+2=4x-4+2x$$
$$4x-6=6x-4$$
$$-2x-6=-4$$
$$-2x=2$$
$$x=-1$$

Now, evaluate x^2-x for $x=-1$:

$$x^2-x=(-1)^2-(-1)$$
$$=1-(-1)=1+1=2$$

94. Solve: $2(x-6)=3x+2(2x-1)$

$$2x-12=3x+4x-2$$
$$2x-12=7x-2$$
$$-5x-12=-2$$
$$-5x=10$$
$$x=-2$$

Now, evaluate x^2-x for $x=-2$:

$$x^2-x=(-2)^2-(-2)$$
$$=4-(-2)=4+2=6$$

95. Solve for x.

$$\frac{x}{5}-2=\frac{x}{3}$$
$$15\cdot\left(\frac{x}{5}-2\right)=15\cdot\frac{x}{3}$$
$$3x-30=5x$$
$$-2x=30$$
$$x=-15$$

Solve for y.

$$-2y-10=5y+18$$
$$-2y-5y=18+10$$
$$-7y=28$$
$$y=-4$$

Evaluate

$$x^2-(xy-y)=(-15)^2-[(-15)(-4)-(-4)]$$
$$=161$$

96. Solve for x.

$$\frac{3x}{2}+\frac{3x}{4}=\frac{x}{4}-4$$
$$8\left(\frac{3x}{2}+\frac{3x}{4}\right)=8\left(\frac{x}{4}-4\right)$$
$$12x+6x=2x-32$$
$$18x=2x-32$$
$$16x=-32$$
$$x=-2$$

Solve for y.

$$5-y=7(y+4)+1$$
$$5-y=7y+28+1$$
$$-8y=24$$
$$y=-3$$

Evaluate

$$x^2-(xy-y)=(-2)^2-[(-2)(-3)-(-3)]$$
$$=-5$$

97. $\left[(3+6)^2\div3\right]\cdot4=-54x$

$$\left(9^2\div3\right)\cdot4=-54x$$
$$(81\div3)\cdot4=-54x$$
$$27\cdot4=-54x$$
$$108=-54x$$
$$-2=x$$

The solution set is $\{-2\}$.

98. $2^3-\left[4(5-3)^3\right]=-8x$

$$8-\left[4(2)^3\right]=-8x$$
$$8-4\cdot8=-8x$$
$$8-32=-8x$$
$$-24=-8x$$
$$3=x$$

The solution set is $\{3\}$.

99. $5-12x=8-7x-\left[6\div3\left(2+5^3\right)+5x\right]$

$5-12x=8-7x-\left[6\div3\left(2+125\right)+5x\right]$

$5-12x=8-7x-\left[6\div3\cdot127+5x\right]$

$5-12x=8-7x-\left[2\cdot127+5x\right]$

$5-12x=8-7x-\left[254+5x\right]$

$5-12x=8-7x-254-5x$

$5-12x=-12x-246$

$5=-246$

The final statement is a contradiction, so the equation has no solution. The solution set is $\varnothing$.

100. $2\left(5x+58\right)=10x+4\left(21\div3.5-11\right)$

$10x+116=10x+4\left(6-11\right)$

$10x+116=10x+4\left(-5\right)$

$10x+116=10x-20$

$116=-20$

The final statement is a contradiction, so the equation has no solution. The solution set is $\varnothing$.

101. $0.7x+0.4(20)=0.5(x+20)$

$0.7x+8=0.5x+10$

$0.2x+8=10$

$0.2x=2$

$x=10$

The solution set is $\{10\}$.

102. $0.5(x+2)=0.1+3(0.1x+0.3)$

$0.5x+1=0.1+0.3x+0.9$

$0.5x+1=0.3x+1$

$0.2x+1=1$

$0.2x=0$

$x=0$

The solution set is $\{0\}$.

103. $4x+13-\left\{2x-\left[4(x-3)-5\right]\right\}=2(x-6)$

$4x+13-\left\{2x-\left[4x-12-5\right]\right\}=2x-12$

$4x+13-\left\{2x-\left[4x-17\right]\right\}=2x-12$

$4x+13-\left\{2x-4x+17\right\}=2x-12$

$4x+13-\left\{-2x+17\right\}=2x-12$

$4x+13+2x-17=2x-12$

$6x-4=2x-12$

$4x-4=-12$

$4x=-8$

$x=-2$

The solution set is $\{-2\}$.

104. $-2\left\{7-\left[4-2(1-x)+3\right]\right\}=10-\left[4x-2(x-3)\right]$

$-2\left\{7-\left[4-2+2x+3\right]\right\}=10-\left[4x-2x+6\right]$

$-2\left\{7-\left[2x+5\right]\right\}=10-\left[2x+6\right]$

$-2\left\{7-2x-5\right\}=10-2x-6$

$-2\left\{-2x+2\right\}=-2x+4$

$4x-4=-2x+4$

$6x-4=4$

$6x=8$

$x=\dfrac{8}{6}=\dfrac{4}{3}$

The solution set is $\left\{\dfrac{4}{3}\right\}$.

105. $\dfrac{W}{2}-3H=53$

$\dfrac{W}{2}-3(6)=53$

$\dfrac{W}{2}-18=53$

$\dfrac{W}{2}-18+18=53+18$

$\dfrac{W}{2}=71$

$2\cdot\dfrac{W}{2}=2\cdot71$

$W=142$

According to the formula, the healthy weight of a person of height 5'6" is 142 pounds. This is 13 pounds below the upper end of the range shown in the bar graph

106. $\dfrac{W}{2} - 3H = 53$

$\dfrac{W}{2} - 3(12) = 53$

$\dfrac{W}{2} - 36 = 53$

$\dfrac{W}{2} - 36 + 36 = 53 + 36$

$\dfrac{W}{2} = 89$

$2 \cdot \dfrac{W}{2} = 2 \cdot 89$

$W = 178$

According to the formula, the healthy weight of a person of height 6' is 178 pounds. This is 6 pounds below the upper end of the range shown in the bar graph.

107. $p = 15 + \dfrac{5d}{11}$

$201 = 15 + \dfrac{5d}{11}$

$201 - 15 = 15 + \dfrac{5d}{11} - 15$

$186 = \dfrac{5d}{11}$

$11(186) = 11\left(\dfrac{5d}{11}\right)$

$2046 = 5d$

$\dfrac{2046}{5} = d$

$409.2 = d$

He descended to a depth of 409.2 feet below the surface.

108. $p = 15 + \dfrac{5d}{11}$

$20 = 15 + \dfrac{5d}{11}$

$5 = \dfrac{5d}{11}$

$11(5) = 11\left(\dfrac{5d}{11}\right)$

$55 = 5d$

$11 = d$

The pressure is 20 pounds per square foot at a depth of 11 feet.

109 Let x = number of quarts.

$\dfrac{160}{5} = \dfrac{200}{x}$

$160x = 5 \cdot 200$

$160x = 1000$

$\dfrac{160x}{160} = \dfrac{1000}{160}$

$x = 6.25$

A person who weighs 200 pounds will have about 6.25 quarts of blood.

110 Let x = gallons of water.

$\dfrac{5}{30} = \dfrac{11}{x}$

$5x = 30 \cdot 11$

$5x = 330$

$\dfrac{5x}{5} = \dfrac{330}{5}$

$x = 66$

An 11 minute shower will use about 66 gallons of water.

111. Let x = the tail length.

$\dfrac{4}{3.6} = \dfrac{6}{x}$

$4x = 6 \cdot 3.6$

$4x = 21.6$

$\dfrac{4x}{4} = \dfrac{21.6}{4}$

$x = 5.4$

The tail length is 5.4 feet.

112. Let x = weight on the moon.

$\dfrac{360}{60} = \dfrac{186}{x}$

$360x = 60 \cdot 186$

$360x = 11,160$

$\dfrac{360x}{360} = \dfrac{11,160}{360}$

$x = 31$

A person who weighs 186 pounds on Earth will weigh 31 pounds on the moon.

113. Let x = the total number of fur seal pups in the rookery.

$$\frac{\text{Original \# tagged}}{\text{Total \# fur seal pups}} = \frac{\text{\# tagged in sample}}{\text{\# in sample}}$$

$$\frac{4963}{x} = \frac{218}{900}$$

$$218x = (4963)(900)$$

$$218x = 4,466,700$$

$$\frac{218x}{218} = \frac{4,466,700}{218}$$

$$x \approx 20,489$$

There were approximately 20,489 fur seal pups in the rookery.

114. Let x = the total number of bass in the lake.

$$\frac{\begin{array}{c}\text{Original number}\\\text{of tagged bass}\end{array}}{\begin{array}{c}\text{Total number}\\\text{of bass}\end{array}} = \frac{\begin{array}{c}\text{Number of tagged}\\\text{bass in sample}\end{array}}{\begin{array}{c}\text{Number of bass}\\\text{in sample}\end{array}}$$

$$\frac{50}{x} = \frac{27}{108}$$

$$27x = (50)(108)$$

$$27x = 5400$$

$$x = 200$$

There are about 200 bass in the lake.

125. makes sense

126. makes sense

127. does not make sense; Explanations will vary. Sample explanation: The solution set is all real numbers.

128. makes sense

129. Possible answers:

$$6x = 25 + x$$

$$2(x+3) = 16$$

$$-x + 9 = x - 1$$

131. Yes: Her height is slightly over 5 feet tall.

$$f = 0.432h - 10.44$$

$$16 = 0.432h - 10.44$$

$$26.44 = 0.432h$$

$$61.2 \approx h$$

Check Points 6.3

1. Let x = the average yearly salary, in thousands, of women with some college
Let $x + 3$ = the average yearly salary, in thousands, of women with an associates degree
Let $x + 23$ = the average yearly salary, in thousands, of women with a bachelor's degree or more

$$x + (x+3) + (x+23) = 134$$

$$x + x + 3 + x + 23 = 134$$

$$3x + 26 = 134$$

$$3x = 108$$

$$x = 36$$

$x = 36$, some college: \$36,000

$x + 3 = 39$, associates degree: \$39,000

$x + 23 = 59$, bachelor's degree: \$59,000

2. Let x = the number of years since 1969.

$$88 - 1.1x = 33$$

$$-1.1x = 33 - 88$$

$$-1.1x = -55$$

$$x = \frac{-55}{-1.1}$$

$$x = 50$$

33% of female freshmen will respond this way 50 years after 1969, or 2019.

3. Let x = the number of minutes at which the costs of the two plans are the same.

$$\overbrace{15 + 0.08x}^{\text{Plan A}} = \overbrace{3 + 0.12x}^{\text{Plan B}}$$

$$15 + 0.08x - 15 = 3 + 0.12x - 15$$

$$0.08x = 0.12x - 12$$

$$0.08x - 0.12x = 0.12x - 12 - 0.12x$$

$$-0.04x = -12$$

$$\frac{-0.04x}{-0.04} = \frac{-12}{-0.04}$$

$$x = 300$$

The two plans are the same at 300 minutes.

4. Let x = the computer's price before the reduction.

$$x - 0.30x = 840$$

$$0.70x = 840$$

$$x = \frac{840}{0.70}$$

$$x = 1200$$

Before the reduction the computer's price was \$1200.

5. $2l + 2w = P$

$2l + 2w - 2l = P - 2l$

$2w = P - 2l$

$\dfrac{2w}{2} = \dfrac{P - 2l}{2}$

$w = \dfrac{P - 2l}{2}$

6. $T = D + pm$

$T - D = D - D + pm$

$T - D = pm$

$\dfrac{T - D}{p} = \dfrac{pm}{p}$

$\dfrac{T - D}{p} = m$

$m = \dfrac{T - D}{p}$

Exercise Set 6.3

1. Let x = the number

$5x - 4 = 26$

$5x = 30$

$x = 6$

The number is 6.

2. Let x = the number

$2x - 3 = 11$

$2x = 14$

$x = 7$

The number is 7.

3. Let x = the number

$x - 0.20x = 20$

$0.80x = 20$

$x = 25$

The number is 25.

4. Let x = the number

$x - 0.30x = 28$

$0.70x = 28$

$x = 40$

The number is 40.

5. Let x = the number

$0.60x + x = 192$

$1.6x = 192$

$x = 120$

The number is 120.

6. Let x = the number

$0.80x + x = 252$

$1.8x = 252$

$x = 140$

The number is 140.

7. Let x = the number

$0.70x = 224$

$x = 320$

The number is 320.

8. Let x = the number

$0.70x = 252$

$x = 360$

The number is 360.

9. Let x = the number

$x + 26$ = the other number

$x + (x + 26) = 64$

$x + x + 26 = 64$

$2x + 26 = 64$

$2x = 38$

$x = 19$

If $x = 19$, then $x + 26 = 45$.

The numbers are 19 and 45.

10. Let x = the number,

Let $x + 24$ = the other number

$x + (x + 24) = 58$

$x + x + 24 = 58$

$2x + 24 = 58$

$2x = 34$

$x = 17$

If $x = 17$, then $x + 24 = 41$.

The numbers are 17 and 41.

11. $x - (x + 4) = x - x - 4 = -4$

12. $x - (8 - x) = x - 8 + x = 2x - 8$

13. $6(-5x) = -30x$

14. $10(-4x) = -40x$

15. $5x - 2x = 3x$

16. $6x - (-2x) = 6x + 2x = 8x$

17. $8x - (3x + 6) = 8x - 3x - 6 = 5x - 6$

18. $8 - 3(x + 6) = 8 - 3x - 18 = -3x - 10$

19. Let x = the median salary, in thousands, of a psychology major with less than 5 years of experience.
Let $x + 20$ = the median salary, in thousands, of a computer science major with less than 5 years of experience.

$$x + (x + 20) = 92$$
$$x + x + 20 = 92$$
$$2x + 20 = 92$$
$$2x = 72$$
$$x = 36$$
$$x + 20 = 56$$

A psychology major with less than 5 years of experience earns $36,000.
A computer science major with less than 5 years of experience earns $56,000.

20. Let x = the median salary, in thousands, of an education major with 10 to 20 years of experience.
Let $x + 20$ = the median salary, in thousands, of a computer science major with less than 5 years of experience.

$$x + (x + 4) = 108$$
$$x + x + 4 = 108$$
$$2x + 4 = 108$$
$$2x = 104$$
$$x = 52$$
$$x + 4 = 56$$

An education major with 10 to 20 years of experience earns $52,000.
A computer science major with less than 5 years of experience earns $56,000.

21. Let x = the median salary, in thousands, of a political science major with 10 to 20 years of experience.
Let $x + 18$ = the median salary, in thousands, of a computer science major with 10 to 20 years of experience.
Let $x + 21$ = the median salary, in thousands, of an economics major with 10 to 20 years of experience.

$$x + (x + 18) + (x + 21) = 273$$
$$x + x + 18 + x + 21 = 273$$
$$3x + 39 = 273$$
$$3x = 234$$
$$x = 78$$
$$x + 18 = 96$$
$$x + 21 = 99$$

A political science major with 10 to 20 years of experience earns $78,000.
A computer science major with 10 to 20 years of experience earns $96,000.
A economics major with 10 to 20 years of experience earns $99,000.

22. Let x = the median salary, in thousands, of a communications major with less than 5 years of experience.
Let $x + 1$ = the median salary, in thousands, of a biology major with less than 5 years of experience.
Let $x + 5$ = the median salary, in thousands, of a business major with less than 5 years of experience.

$$x + (x + 1) + (x + 5) = 120$$
$$x + x + 1 + x + 5 = 120$$
$$3x + 6 = 120$$
$$3x = 114$$
$$x = 38$$
$$x + 1 = 39$$
$$x + 5 = 43$$

A communications major with less than 5 years of experience earns $38,000.
A biology major with less than 5 years of experience earns $39,000.
A business major with less than 5 years of experience earns $43,000.

23. Let x = the median salary, in thousands, of a business major with less than 5 years of experience.
Let $2x - 14$ = the median salary, in thousands, of a business major with 10 to 20 years of experience.

$$x + (2x - 14) = 115$$
$$x + 2x - 14 = 115$$
$$3x - 14 = 115$$
$$3x = 129$$
$$x = 43$$
$$2x - 14 = 72$$

A business major with less than 5 years of experience earns $43,000.
A business major with 10 to 20 years of experience earns $72,000.

24. Let x = the median salary, in thousands, of an education major with less than 5 years of experience.
Let $2x-3$ = the median salary, in thousands, of a nursing major with 10 to 20 years of experience.
$$x+(2x-3)=102$$
$$x+2x-3=102$$
$$3x-3=102$$
$$3x=105$$
$$x=35$$
$$2x-3=67$$
An education major with less than 5 years of experience earns \$35,000.
A nursing major with 10 to 20 years of experience earns \$67,000.

25. a. Let x = the number of deaths, in thousands, per day.
Let $3x-92$ = the number of births, in thousands, per day.
$$(3x-92)-x=214$$
$$3x-92-x=214$$
$$2x-92=214$$
$$2x=306$$
$$x=153$$
$$3x-92=367$$
births: 367,000
deaths: 153,000

b. $214,000 \cdot 365 = 78,110,000$
$$\approx 78 \text{ million}$$

c. $\dfrac{306 \text{ million}}{78 \text{ million}} \approx 4$
It will take about 4 years.

26. a. Let x = the number of deaths, in thousands, per day.
Let $2x+61$ = the number of births, in thousands, per day.
$$(2x+61)-x=214$$
$$2x+61-x=214$$
$$x+61=214$$
$$x=153$$
$$2x+61=367$$
births: 367,000
deaths: 153,000

b. $214,000 \cdot 365 = 78,110,000$
$$\approx 78 \text{ million}$$

c. $\dfrac{306 \text{ million}}{78 \text{ million}} \approx 4$
It will take about 4 years.

27. Let x = the number of years since 1983.
$$43+1.5x=100$$
$$1.5x=100-43$$
$$1.5x=57$$
$$x=\frac{57}{1.5}$$
$$x=38$$
All American adults will approve 38 years after 1983, or 2021.

28. Let x = the number of years since 1986.
$$43+0.6x=61$$
$$0.6x=61-43$$
$$0.6x=18$$
$$x=\frac{18}{0.6}$$
$$x=30$$
61% of American adults will approve 30 years after 1986, or 2016.

29. Let x = the number of years until the car's value reaches \$9000.
$$24,000-3000x=9000$$
$$-3000x=-15,000$$
$$\frac{-3000x}{-3000}=\frac{-15,000}{-3000}$$
$$x=5$$
It will take 5 years until the car's value reaches \$9000.

29. Let x = the number of years until the car's value reaches \$10,000.
$$45,000-5000x=10,000$$
$$-5000x=-35,000$$
$$\frac{-5000x}{-5000}=\frac{-35,000}{-5000}$$
$$x=7$$
It will take 7 years until the car's value reaches \$10,000.

31. Let $x =$ the number of months.
The cost for Club A: $25x + 40$
The cost for Club B: $30x + 15$
$$25x + 40 = 30x + 15$$
$$-5x + 40 = 15$$
$$-5x = -25$$
$$x = 5$$
The total cost for the clubs will be the same at 5 months. The cost will be
$$25(5) + 40 = 30(5) + 15 = \$165$$

32. Let $g =$ the number of video games rented
$$9g = 4g + 50$$
$$5g = 50$$
$$g = 10$$
The total amount spent at each store will be the same after 10 rentals.
$$9g = 9(10) = 90$$
The total amount spent will be $90.

33. Let $x =$ the number of uses.
Cost without discount pass: $1.25x$
Cost with discount pass: $15 + 0.75x$
$$1.25x = 15 + 0.75x$$
$$0.50x = 15$$
$$x = 30$$
The bus must be used 30 times in a month for the costs to be equal.

34. Cost per crossing: $5x$
Cost with discount pass: $30 + \$3.50x$
$$5x = 30 + 3.50x$$
$$1.50x = 30$$
$$x = 20$$
The bridge must be used 20 times in a month for the costs to be equal.

35. Let $x =$ dollars of merchandise purchased.
$$\overbrace{100 + 0.80x}^{\text{Plan A}} = \overbrace{40 + 0.90x}^{\text{Plan B}}$$
$$0.80x - 0.90x = 40 - 100$$
$$-0.10x = -60$$
$$x = \$600$$
$600 of merchandise must be purchased for the costs to be equal.
The cost of each plan would be
$$100 + 0.80(600) = \$580$$

36. Let $x =$ dollars of merchandise purchased.
$$\overbrace{300 + 0.70x}^{\text{Plan A}} = \overbrace{40 + 0.90x}^{\text{Plan B}}$$
$$0.70x - 0.90x = 40 - 300$$
$$-0.20x = -260$$
$$x = \$1300$$
$1300 of merchandise must be purchased for the costs to be equal.
The cost of each plan would be
$$300 + 0.70(1300) = \$1210$$

37. Let $x =$ the number of years (after 2008).
College A's enrollment: $13,300 + 1000x$
College B's enrollment: $26,800 - 500x$
$$13,300 + 1000x = 26,800 - 500x$$
$$13,300 + 1500x = 26,800$$
$$1500x = 13,500$$
$$x = 9$$
The two colleges will have the same enrollment 9 years after 2008, or 2017.
That year the enrollments will be
$$13,300 + 1000(9)$$
$$= 26,800 - 500(9)$$
$$= 22,300 \text{ students.}$$

38. Let $x =$ the number of years after 2000
$$10,600,000 - 28,000x = 10,200,000 - 12,000x$$
$$-16,000x = -400,000$$
$$x = 25$$
The countries will have the same population 25 years after the year 2000, or the year 2025.
$$10,200,000 - 12,000x = 10,200,000 - 12,000(25)$$
$$= 10,200,000 - 300,000$$
$$= 9,900,000$$
The population in the year 2025 will be 9,900,000.

39. Let $x =$ the cost of the television set.
$$x - 0.20x = 336$$
$$0.80x = 336$$
$$x = 420$$
The television set's price is $420.

40. Let $x =$ the cost of the dictionary
$$x - 0.30x = 30.80$$
$$0.70x = 30.80$$
$$x = 44$$
The dictionary's price before the reduction was $44.

41. Let x = the nightly cost
$$x + 0.08x = 162$$
$$1.08x = 162$$
$$x = 150$$
The nightly cost is $150.

42. Let x = the nightly cost
$$x + 0.05x = 252$$
$$1.05x = 252$$
$$x = 240$$
The nightly cost is $240.

43. Let c = the dealer's cost
$$584 = c + 0.25c$$
$$584 = 1.25c$$
$$467.20 = c$$
The dealer's cost is $467.20.

44. Let c = the dealer's cost
$$15 = c + 0.25c$$
$$15 = 1.25c$$
$$12 = c$$
The dealer's cost is $12.

45. $A = LW$ for L
$$\frac{A}{W} = \frac{LW}{W}$$
$$\frac{A}{W} = L \text{ or } L = \frac{A}{W}$$

46. $D = RT$ for R
$$\frac{D}{T} = \frac{RT}{T}$$
$$\frac{D}{T} = R \text{ or } R = \frac{D}{T}$$

47. $A = \frac{1}{2}bh$ for b
$$2(A) = 2\left(\frac{1}{2}bh\right)$$
$$2A = bh$$
$$\frac{2A}{h} = \frac{bh}{h}$$
$$\frac{2A}{h} = b \text{ or } b = \frac{2A}{h}$$

48. $V = \frac{1}{3}Bh$ for B
$$3(V) = 3\left(\frac{1}{3}Bh\right)$$
$$3V = Bh$$
$$\frac{3V}{h} = \frac{Bh}{h}$$
$$\frac{3V}{h} = B \text{ or } B = \frac{3V}{h}$$

49. $I = Prt$ for P
$$\frac{I}{rt} = \frac{Prt}{rt}$$
$$\frac{I}{rt} = P \text{ or } P = \frac{I}{rt}$$

50. $C = 2\pi r$ for r
$$\frac{C}{2\pi} = \frac{2\pi r}{2\pi}$$
$$\frac{C}{2\pi} = r \text{ or } r = \frac{C}{2\pi}$$

51. $E = mc^2$ for m
$$\frac{E}{c^2} = \frac{mc^2}{c^2}$$
$$\frac{E}{c^2} = m \text{ or } m = \frac{E}{c^2}$$

52. $V = \pi r^2 h$ for h
$$\frac{V}{\pi r^2} = \frac{\pi r^2 h}{\pi r^2}$$
$$\frac{V}{\pi r^2} = h \text{ or } h = \frac{V}{\pi r^2}$$

53. $y = mx + b$ for m
$$y - b = mx + b - b$$
$$y - b = mx$$
$$\frac{y - b}{x} = \frac{mx}{x}$$
$$\frac{y - b}{x} = m \text{ or } m = \frac{y - b}{x}$$

54. $P = C + MC$ for M

$P - C = C + MC - C$

$P - C = MC$

$$\dfrac{P - C}{C} = \dfrac{MC}{C}$$

$$\dfrac{P - C}{C} = M \ \text{ or } \ M = \dfrac{P - C}{C}$$

55. $A = \dfrac{1}{2}h(a + b)$ for a

$$2 \cdot A = 2 \cdot \dfrac{1}{2}h(a + b)$$

$$2A = h(a + b)$$

$$2A = ha + hb$$

$$2A - hb = ha$$

$$\dfrac{2A - bh}{h} = \dfrac{ha}{h}$$

$$a = \dfrac{2A - bh}{h}$$

56. $A = \dfrac{1}{2}h(a + b)$ for b

$$2 \cdot A = 2 \cdot \dfrac{1}{2}h(a + b)$$

$$2A = h(a + b)$$

$$2A = ha + hb$$

$$2A - ha = hb$$

$$\dfrac{2A - ah}{h} = \dfrac{hb}{h}$$

$$b = \dfrac{2A - ah}{h}$$

57. $S = P + Prt$ for r

$S - P = P + Prt - P$

$S - P = Prt$

$$\dfrac{S - P}{Pt} = \dfrac{Prt}{Pt}$$

$$\dfrac{S - P}{Pt} = r \ \text{ or } \ r = \dfrac{S - P}{Pt}$$

58. $S = P + Prt$ for t

$S - P = P + Prt - P$

$S - P = Prt$

$$\dfrac{S - P}{Pr} = \dfrac{Prt}{Pr}$$

$$\dfrac{S - P}{Pr} = t \ \text{ or } \ t = \dfrac{S - P}{Pr}$$

59. $Ax + By = C$ for x

$Ax + By = C$

$Ax = C - By$

$$x = \dfrac{C - By}{A}$$

60. $Ax + By = C$ for y

$Ax + By = C$

$By = C - Ax$

$$y = \dfrac{C - Ax}{B}$$

61. $a_n = a_1 + (n - 1)$ for n

$$a_n = a_1 + (n - 1)d$$

$$a_n - a_1 = dn - d$$

$$a_n - a_1 + d = dn$$

$$\dfrac{a_n - a_1 + d}{d} = n$$

62. $a_n = a_1 + (n - 1)$ for d

$$a_n = a_1 + (n - 1)d$$

$$a_n - a_1 = (n - 1)d$$

$$\dfrac{a_n - a_1}{n - 1} = \dfrac{(n - 1)d}{n - 1}$$

$$\dfrac{a_n - a_1}{n - 1} = d$$

68.   does not make sense; Explanations will vary. Sample explanation: Though mathematical models can often provide excellent estimates about future attitudes, they cannot guaranty perfect precision.

69.   makes sense

70.   does not make sense; Explanations will vary. Sample explanation: Solving a formula for one of its variables does not produce a numerical value for the variable.

71.   does not make sense; Explanations will vary. Sample explanation: The correct equation is $x - 0.35x = 780$.

72.   Let $x =$ original price

$x - 0.4x = 0.6x =$ price after first reduction

$0.6x - 0.4(0.6x) =$ price after second reduction

$0.6x - 0.24x = 72$

$$0.36x = 72$$

$$x = 200$$

The original price was \$200.

73. Let x = current age of woman, then
$3x$ = current age of "uncle."
$$2(x+20) = 3x + 20$$
$$2x + 40 = 3x + 20$$
$$2x + 40 - 2x = 3x + 20 - 2x$$
$$40 = x + 20$$
$$40 - 20 = x + 20 - 20$$
$$20 = x$$
$$60 = 3x$$
The woman is 20 years and the "uncle" is 60 years.

74. Let x = number of problems solved correctly, then
$26 - x$ = number of problems done incorrectly
$$0.08x = 0.05(26 - x)$$
$$0.08x = 1.30 - 0.05x$$
$$0.08x + 0.05x = 1.30 - 0.05x + 0.05x$$
$$0.13x = 1.30$$
$$\frac{0.13x}{0.13} = \frac{1.30}{0.13}$$
$$x = 10$$
There were 10 problems solved correctly.

75. Let x = mother's amount
$2x$ = boy's amount
$\dfrac{x}{2}$ = girl's amount
$$x + 2x + \frac{x}{2} = 14,000$$
$$\frac{7}{2}x = 14,000$$
$$x = \$4,000$$
The mother received $4000, the boy received $8000, and the girl received $2000.

76. Let x = the number of plants originally stolen
After passing the first security guard, the thief has:
$$x - \left(\frac{1}{2}x + 2\right) = x - \frac{1}{2}x - 2 = \frac{1}{2}x - 2$$
After passing the second security guard, the thief
has: $\dfrac{1}{2}x - 2 - \left(\dfrac{\frac{1}{2}x - 2}{2} + 2\right) = \dfrac{1}{4}x - 3$
After passing the third security guard, the thief has:
$$\frac{1}{4}x - 3 - \left(\frac{\frac{1}{4}x - 3}{2} + 2\right) = \frac{1}{8}x - \frac{7}{2}$$

Thus, $\dfrac{1}{8}x - \dfrac{7}{2} = 1$
$$x - 28 = 8$$
$$x = 36$$
The thief stole 36 plants.

77.
$$\frac{x+a}{a} = \frac{b+c}{c}$$
$$a(b+c) = c(x+a)$$
$$ab + ac = cx + ca$$
$$ab + ac - ca = cx$$
$$ab = cx$$
$$\frac{ab}{c} = x$$

78.
$$\frac{ax-b}{b} = \frac{c-d}{d}$$
$$d(ax - b) = b(c - d)$$
$$dax - db = bc - bd$$
$$dax = bc - bd + db$$
$$dax = bc$$
$$x = \frac{bc}{ad}$$

Check Points 6.4

1. a. $x < 4$

b. $x \geq -2$

c. $-4 \leq x < 1$

2. $5x - 3 \leq 17$
$$5x - 3 + 3 \leq 17 + 3$$
$$5x \leq 20$$
$$\frac{5x}{5} \leq \frac{20}{5}$$
$$x \leq 4$$
$$\{x \mid x \leq 4\}$$

257

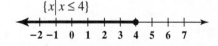

3. a. $\dfrac{1}{4}x < 2$

$4 \cdot \dfrac{1}{4}x < 4 \cdot 2$

$x < 8$

$\{x \mid x < 8\}$

b. $-6x < 18$

$\dfrac{-6x}{-6} > \dfrac{18}{-6}$

$x > -3$

$\{x \mid x > -3\}$

4. $7x - 3 > 13x + 33$

$7x - 3 + 3 > 13x + 33 + 3$

$7x > 13x + 36$

$7x - 13x > 13x + 36 - 13x$

$-6x > 36$

$\dfrac{-6x}{-6} < \dfrac{36}{-6}$

$x < -6$

$\{x \mid x < -6\}$

5. $2(x - 3) - 1 \le 3(x + 2) - 14$

$2x - 6 - 1 \le 3x + 6 - 14$

$2x - 7 \le 3x - 8$

$2x - 7 + 7 \le 3x - 8 + 7$

$2x \le 3x - 1$

$2x - 3x \le 3x - 1 - 3x$

$-x \le -1$

$\dfrac{-x}{-1} \ge \dfrac{-1}{-1}$

$x \ge 1$

$\{x \mid x \ge 1\}$

6. $1 \le 2x + 3 < 11$

$-2 \le 2x < 8$

$-1 \le x < 4$

The solution set is $\{x \mid -1 \le x < 4\}$ or $[-1, 4)$.

7. Let x = your grade on the final exam.

$\dfrac{82 + 74 + 78 + x + x}{5} \ge 80$

$\dfrac{234 + 2x}{5} \ge 80$

$5\left(\dfrac{234 + 2x}{5}\right) \ge 5(80)$

$234 + 2x \ge 400$

$234 + 2x - 234 \ge 400 - 234$

$2x \ge 166$

$\dfrac{2x}{2} \ge \dfrac{166}{2}$

$x \ge 83$

You need at least an 83% on the final to get a B in the course.

Exercise Set 6.4

1. $x > 6$

2. $x > -2$

3. $x < -4$

4. $x < 0$

5. $x \ge -3$

6. $x \ge -5$

7. $x \le 4$

8. $x \le 7$

9. $-2 < x \le 5$

10. $-3 \le x < 7$

11. $-1 < x < 4$

12. $-7 \le x \le 0$

13. $x - 3 > 2$

$x - 3 + 3 > 2 + 3$

$x > 5$

$\{x | x > 5\}$

14. $x + 1 < 5$

$x + 1 - 1 < 5 - 1$

$x < 4$

$\{x | x < 4\}$

15. $x + 4 \le 9$

$x + 4 - 4 \le 9 - 4$

$x \le 5$

$\{x | x \le 5\}$

16. $x - 5 \ge 1$

$x - 5 + 5 \ge 1 + 5$

$x \ge 6$

$\{x | x \ge 6\}$

17. $x - 3 < 0$

$x - 3 + 3 < 0 + 3$

$x < 3$

$\{x | x < 3\}$

18. $x + 4 \ge 0$

$x + 4 - 4 \ge 0 - 4$

$x \ge -4$

$\{x | x \ge -4\}$

19. $4x < 20$

$\dfrac{4x}{4} < \dfrac{20}{4}$

$x < 5$

$\{x | x < 5\}$

20. $6x \ge 18$

$\dfrac{6x}{6} \ge \dfrac{18}{6}$

$x \ge 3$

$\{x | x \ge 3\}$

21. $3x \ge -15$

$\dfrac{3x}{3} \ge \dfrac{-15}{3}$

$x \ge -5$

$\{x | x \ge -5\}$

22. $7x < -21$

$\dfrac{7x}{7} < \dfrac{-21}{7}$

$x < -3$

$\{x | x < -3\}$

23. $2x - 3 > 7$

$2x - 3 + 3 > 7 + 3$

$2x > 10$

$\dfrac{2x}{2} > \dfrac{10}{2}$

$x > 5$

$\{x | x > 5\}$

24. $3x + 2 \le 14$

$3x + 2 - 2 \le 14 - 2$

$3x \le 12$

$\dfrac{3x}{3} \le \dfrac{12}{3}$

$x \le 4$

$\{x | x \le 4\}$

25.
$$3x + 3 < 18$$
$$3x + 3 - 3 < 18 - 3$$
$$3x < 15$$
$$\frac{3x}{3} < \frac{15}{3}$$
$$x < 5$$
$$\{x \mid x < 5\}$$
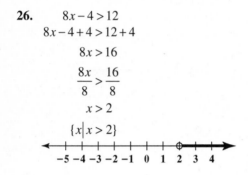

26.
$$8x - 4 > 12$$
$$8x - 4 + 4 > 12 + 4$$
$$8x > 16$$
$$\frac{8x}{8} > \frac{16}{8}$$
$$x > 2$$
$$\{x \mid x > 2\}$$
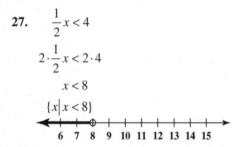

27.
$$\frac{1}{2}x < 4$$
$$2 \cdot \frac{1}{2}x < 2 \cdot 4$$
$$x < 8$$
$$\{x \mid x < 8\}$$
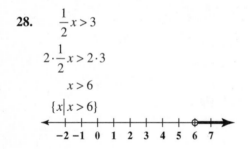

28.
$$\frac{1}{2}x > 3$$
$$2 \cdot \frac{1}{2}x > 2 \cdot 3$$
$$x > 6$$
$$\{x \mid x > 6\}$$

29.
$$\frac{x}{3} > -2$$
$$3 \cdot \frac{x}{3} > 3 \cdot (-2)$$
$$x > -6$$
$$\{x \mid x > -6\}$$

30.
$$\frac{x}{4} < -1$$
$$4 \cdot \frac{x}{4} < 4 \cdot (-1)$$
$$x < -4$$
$$\{x \mid x < -4\}$$
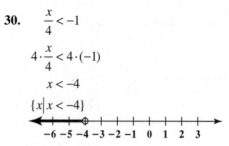

31.
$$-3x < 15$$
$$\frac{-3x}{-3} > \frac{15}{-3}$$
$$x > -5$$
$$\{x \mid x > -5\}$$
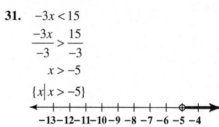

32.
$$-7x > 21$$
$$\frac{-7x}{-7} < \frac{21}{-7}$$
$$x < -3$$
$$\{x \mid x < -3\}$$
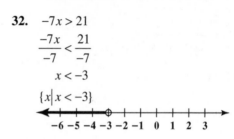

33.
$$-3x \geq -15$$
$$\frac{-3x}{-3} \leq \frac{-15}{-3}$$
$$x \leq 5$$
$$\{x \mid x \leq 5\}$$
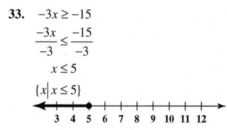

34.
$$-7x \leq -21$$
$$\frac{-7x}{-7} \geq \frac{-21}{-7}$$
$$x \geq 3$$
$$\{x \mid x \geq 3\}$$
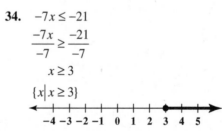

35.
$$3x + 4 \leq 2x + 7$$
$$3x + 4 - 4 \leq 2x + 7 - 4$$
$$3x \leq 2x + 3$$
$$3x - 2x \leq 2x + 3 - 2x$$
$$x \leq 3$$
$$\{x \mid x \leq 3\}$$
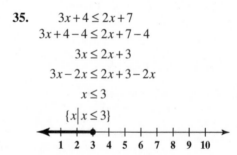

36. $2x + 9 \leq x + 2$
         $2x + 9 - 9 \leq x + 2 - 9$
              $2x \leq x - 7$
         $2x - x \leq x - 7 - x$
                $x \leq -7$
              $\{x \mid x \leq -7\}$

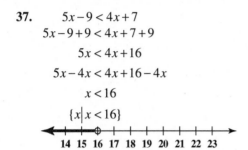

37. $5x - 9 < 4x + 7$
         $5x - 9 + 9 < 4x + 7 + 9$
              $5x < 4x + 16$
         $5x - 4x < 4x + 16 - 4x$
                $x < 16$
              $\{x \mid x < 16\}$

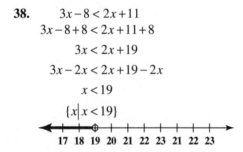

38. $3x - 8 < 2x + 11$
         $3x - 8 + 8 < 2x + 11 + 8$
              $3x < 2x + 19$
         $3x - 2x < 2x + 19 - 2x$
                $x < 19$
              $\{x \mid x < 19\}$

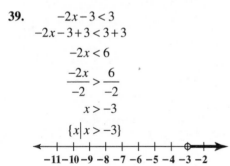

39. $-2x - 3 < 3$
         $-2x - 3 + 3 < 3 + 3$
              $-2x < 6$
              $\dfrac{-2x}{-2} > \dfrac{6}{-2}$
                $x > -3$
              $\{x \mid x > -3\}$

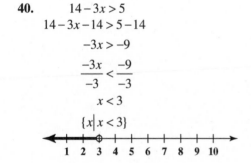

40. $14 - 3x > 5$
         $14 - 3x - 14 > 5 - 14$
              $-3x > -9$
              $\dfrac{-3x}{-3} < \dfrac{-9}{-3}$
                $x < 3$
              $\{x \mid x < 3\}$

41. $3 - 7x \leq 17$
         $3 - 7x - 3 \leq 17 - 3$
              $-7x \leq 14$
              $\dfrac{-7x}{-7} \geq \dfrac{14}{-7}$
                $x \geq -2$
              $\{x \mid x \geq -2\}$

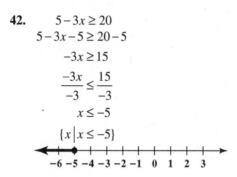

42. $5 - 3x \geq 20$
         $5 - 3x - 5 \geq 20 - 5$
              $-3x \geq 15$
              $\dfrac{-3x}{-3} \leq \dfrac{15}{-3}$
                $x \leq -5$
              $\{x \mid x \leq -5\}$

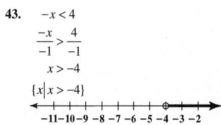

43. $-x < 4$
              $\dfrac{-x}{-1} > \dfrac{4}{-1}$
                $x > -4$
              $\{x \mid x > -4\}$

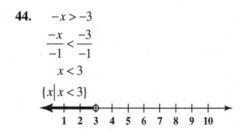

44. $-x > -3$
              $\dfrac{-x}{-1} < \dfrac{-3}{-1}$
                $x < 3$
              $\{x \mid x < 3\}$

45. $5 - x \leq 1$
         $5 - x - 5 \leq 1 - 5$
              $-x \leq -4$
              $\dfrac{-x}{-1} \geq \dfrac{-4}{-1}$
                $x \geq 4$
              $\{x \mid x \geq 4\}$

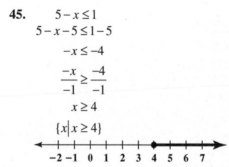

46.
$$3 - x \geq -3$$
$$3 - x - 3 \geq -3 - 3$$
$$-x \geq -6$$
$$\frac{-x}{-1} \leq \frac{-6}{-1}$$
$$x \leq 6$$
$$\{x \mid x \leq 6\}$$

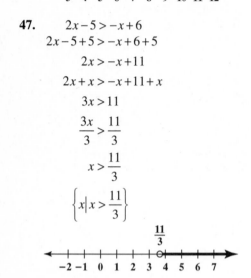

47.
$$2x - 5 > -x + 6$$
$$2x - 5 + 5 > -x + 6 + 5$$
$$2x > -x + 11$$
$$2x + x > -x + 11 + x$$
$$3x > 11$$
$$\frac{3x}{3} > \frac{11}{3}$$
$$x > \frac{11}{3}$$
$$\left\{ x \mid x > \frac{11}{3} \right\}$$

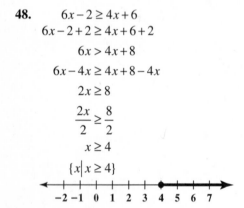

48.
$$6x - 2 \geq 4x + 6$$
$$6x - 2 + 2 \geq 4x + 6 + 2$$
$$6x > 4x + 8$$
$$6x - 4x \geq 4x + 8 - 4x$$
$$2x \geq 8$$
$$\frac{2x}{2} \geq \frac{8}{2}$$
$$x \geq 4$$
$$\{x \mid x \geq 4\}$$

49.
$$2x - 5 < 5x - 11$$
$$2x - 5 + 5 < 5x - 11 + 5$$
$$2x < 5x - 6$$
$$2x - 5x < 5x - 6 - 5x$$
$$-3x < -6$$
$$\frac{-3x}{-3} > \frac{-6}{-3}$$
$$x > 2$$
$$\{x \mid x > 2\}$$

50.
$$4x - 7 > 9x - 2$$
$$4x - 7 + 7 > 9x - 2 + 7$$
$$4x > 9x + 5$$
$$4x - 9x > 9x + 5 - 9x$$
$$-5x > 5$$
$$\frac{-5x}{-5} < \frac{5}{-5}$$
$$x < -1$$
$$\{x \mid x < -1\}$$

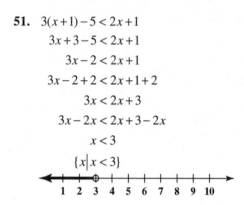

51.
$$3(x + 1) - 5 < 2x + 1$$
$$3x + 3 - 5 < 2x + 1$$
$$3x - 2 < 2x + 1$$
$$3x - 2 + 2 < 2x + 1 + 2$$
$$3x < 2x + 3$$
$$3x - 2x < 2x + 3 - 2x$$
$$x < 3$$
$$\{x \mid x < 3\}$$

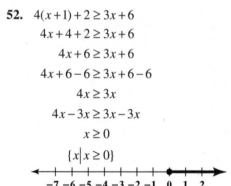

52.
$$4(x + 1) + 2 \geq 3x + 6$$
$$4x + 4 + 2 \geq 3x + 6$$
$$4x + 6 \geq 3x + 6$$
$$4x + 6 - 6 \geq 3x + 6 - 6$$
$$4x \geq 3x$$
$$4x - 3x \geq 3x - 3x$$
$$x \geq 0$$
$$\{x \mid x \geq 0\}$$

53.
$$8x + 3 > 3(2x + 1) - x + 5$$
$$8x + 3 > 6x + 3 - x + 5$$
$$8x + 3 > 5x + 8$$
$$8x + 3 - 3 > 5x + 8 - 3$$
$$8x > 5x + 5$$
$$8x - 5x > 5x + 5 - 5x$$
$$3x > 5$$
$$\frac{3x}{3} > \frac{5}{3}$$
$$x > \frac{5}{3}$$
$$\left\{ x \mid x > \frac{5}{3} \right\}$$

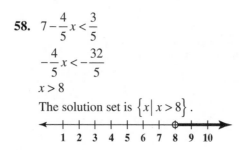

54. $7 - 2(x - 4) < 5(1 - 2x)$
$$7 - 2x + 8 < 5 - 10x$$
$$15 - 2x < 5 - 10x$$
$$15 - 2x - 15 < 5 - 10x - 15$$
$$-2x < -10 - 10x$$
$$-2x + 10x < -10 - 10x + 10x$$
$$8x < -10$$
$$\frac{8x}{8} < \frac{-10}{8}$$
$$x < -\frac{5}{4}$$
$$\left\{ x \mid x < -\frac{5}{4} \right\}$$

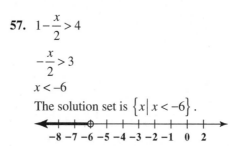

55.
$$\frac{x}{4} - \frac{3}{2} \le \frac{x}{2} + 1$$
$$\frac{4x}{4} - \frac{4 \cdot 3}{2} \le \frac{4 \cdot x}{2} + 4 \cdot 1$$
$$x - 6 \le 2x + 4$$
$$-x \le 10$$
$$x \ge -10$$
The solution set is $\left\{ x \mid x \ge -10 \right\}$.

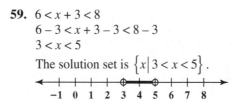

56.
$$\frac{3x}{10} + 1 \ge \frac{1}{5} - \frac{x}{10}$$
$$10 \left(\frac{3x}{10} + 1 \right) \ge 10 \left(\frac{1}{5} - \frac{x}{10} \right)$$
$$3x + 10 \ge 2 - x$$
$$4x \ge -8$$
$$x \ge -2$$
The solution set is $\left\{ x \mid x \ge -2 \right\}$.

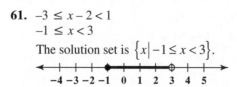

57. $1 - \frac{x}{2} > 4$
$$-\frac{x}{2} > 3$$
$$x < -6$$
The solution set is $\left\{ x \mid x < -6 \right\}$.

58. $7 - \frac{4}{5}x < \frac{3}{5}$
$$-\frac{4}{5}x < -\frac{32}{5}$$
$$x > 8$$
The solution set is $\left\{ x \mid x > 8 \right\}$.

59. $6 < x + 3 < 8$
$$6 - 3 < x + 3 - 3 < 8 - 3$$
$$3 < x < 5$$
The solution set is $\left\{ x \mid 3 < x < 5 \right\}$.

60. $7 < x + 5 < 11$
$$7 - 5 < x + 5 - 5 < 11 - 5$$
$$2 < x < 6$$
The solution set is $\left\{ x \mid 2 < x < 6 \right\}$.

61. $-3 \le x - 2 < 1$
$$-1 \le x < 3$$
The solution set is $\left\{ x \mid -1 \le x < 3 \right\}$.

62. $-6 < x - 4 \leq 1$
$-2 < x \leq 5$
The solution set is $\{x \mid -2 < x \leq 5\}$.

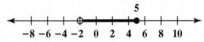

63. $-11 < 2x - 1 \leq -5$
$-10 < 2x \leq -4$
$-5 < x \leq -2$
The solution set is $\left\{x \mid -5 < x \leq -2\right\}$.

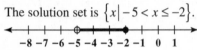

64. $3 \leq 4x - 3 < 19$
$6 \leq 4x < 22$
$\dfrac{6}{4} \leq x < \dfrac{22}{4}$
$\dfrac{3}{2} \leq x < \dfrac{11}{2}$
The solution set is $\left\{x \mid \dfrac{3}{2} \leq x < \dfrac{11}{2}\right\}$.

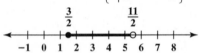

65. $-3 \leq \dfrac{2}{3}x - 5 < -1$
$2 \leq \dfrac{2}{3}x < 4$
$3 \leq x < 6$
The solution set is $\left\{x \mid 3 \leq x < 6\right\}$.

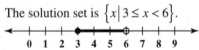

66. $-6 \leq \dfrac{1}{2}x - 4 < -3$
$-2 \leq \dfrac{1}{2}x < 1$
$-4 \leq x < 2$
The solution set is $\left\{x \mid -4 \leq x < 2\right\}$.

67. $Ax + By > C$
$Ax > C - By$
$x > \dfrac{C - By}{A}$

68. $Ax + By \leq C$
$Ax \leq C - By$
$x \leq \dfrac{C - By}{A}$

69. $Ax + By > C$
$Ax > C - By$
$x < \dfrac{C - By}{A}$

70. $Ax + By \leq C$
$Ax \leq C - By$
$x \geq \dfrac{C - By}{A}$

71. $\left\{x \mid x + 5 \geq 2x\right\}$

72. $\left\{x \mid x + 12 \geq 4x\right\}$

73. $\left\{x \mid 2(4 + x) \leq 36\right\}$

74. $\left\{x \mid 3(5 + x) \leq 48\right\}$

75. $\left\{x \mid \dfrac{3x}{5} + 4 \leq 34\right\}$

76. $\left\{x \mid \dfrac{3x}{4} - 3 \geq 9\right\}$

77. $\left\{x \mid 0 < x < 4\right\}$

78. $\left\{x \mid 0 \leq x \leq 5\right\}$

79. intimacy $\geq$ passion or
passion $\leq$ intimacy

80. commitment $\geq$ intimacy or
intimacy $\leq$ commitment

81. commitment $>$ passion or
passion $<$ commitment

82. commitment > passion or
passion < commitment

83. The maximum level of intensity for passion is 9. This occurs after 3 years.

84. After approximately $5\frac{1}{2}$ years.

85. $p = 42 - 0.5x$

$42 - 0.5x < 10$

$-0.5x < -32$

$\dfrac{-0.5x}{-0.5} > \dfrac{-32}{-0.5}$

$x > 64$

Fewer than 10% of American adults will smoke more than 64 years after 1965, or 2029.

86. $p = 42 - 0.5x$

$42 - 0.5x < 5$

$-0.5x < -37$

$\dfrac{-0.5x}{-0.5} > \dfrac{-37}{-0.5}$

$x > 74$

Fewer than 5% of American adults will smoke more than 74 years after 1965, or 2039.

87. a. $\dfrac{86 + 88 + x}{3} \geq 90$

$\dfrac{174 + x}{3} \geq 90$

$3 \cdot \dfrac{174 + x}{3} \geq 3 \cdot 90$

$174 + x \geq 270$

$174 + x - 174 \geq 270 - 174$

$x \geq 96$

You must get at least 96 on the final to earn an A in the course.

b. $\dfrac{86 + 88 + x}{3} < 80$

$\dfrac{174 + x}{3} < 80$

$3 \cdot \dfrac{174 + x}{3} < 80 \cdot 3$

$174 + x < 240$

$174 + x - 174 < 240 - 174$

$x < 66$

If you get less than a 66 on the final you will lose your B in the course.

88. a. $\dfrac{88 + 78 + 86 + 100}{4} = \dfrac{352}{4} = 88$

The average is 88. An A is not possible.

b. $\dfrac{88 + 78 + 86 + x}{4} \geq 80$

$\dfrac{252 + x}{4} \geq 80$

$4 \cdot \dfrac{252 + x}{4} \geq 80 \cdot 4$

$252 + x \geq 320$

$252 + x - 252 \geq 320 - 252$

$x \geq 68$

You must get at least 68 on the final to earn a B in the course.

89. Let x = number of miles driven.

$80 + 0.25x \leq 400$

$80 + 0.25x - 80 \leq 400 - 80$

$0.25x \leq 320$

$\dfrac{0.25x}{0.25} \leq \dfrac{320}{0.25}$

$x \leq 1280$

You can drive at most 1280 miles.

90. Let x = number of miles driven.
$$60 + 0.50x \le 600$$
$$60 + 0.50x - 60 \le 600 - 60$$
$$0.50x \le 540$$
$$\frac{0.50x}{0.50} \le \frac{540}{0.50}$$
$$x \le 1080$$
You can drive at most 1080 miles.

91. Let x = number of cement bags.
$$245 + 95x \le 3000$$
$$245 + 95x - 245 \le 3000 - 245$$
$$95x \le 2755$$
$$\frac{95x}{95} \le \frac{2755}{95}$$
$$x \le 29$$
At most 29 bags can be safely lifted.

92. Let x = number of cement bags.
$$265 + 65x \le 2800$$
$$265 + 65x - 265 \le 2800 - 265$$
$$65x \le 2535$$
$$\frac{65x}{65} \le \frac{2535}{65}$$
$$x \le 39$$
At most 39 bags can be safely lifted.

93. $28 \le 20 + 0.40(x - 60) \le 40$
$$28 \le 20 + 0.40x - 24 \le 40$$
$$28 \le 0.40x - 4 \le 40$$
$$32 \le 0.40x \le 44$$
$$80 \le x \le 110$$

Between 80 and 110 ten minutes, inclusive.

94. $\qquad 15 \le \dfrac{5}{9}(F - 32) \le 35$
$$\frac{9}{5} \cdot 15 \le \frac{9}{5} \cdot \frac{5}{9}(F - 32) \le \frac{9}{5} \cdot 35$$
$$27 \le F - 32 \le 63$$
$$27 + 32 \le F - 32 + 32 \le 63 + 32$$
$$59 \le F \le 95$$

Between $59°F$ and $95°F$, inclusive.

98. makes sense

99. makes sense

100. makes sense

101. does not make sense; Explanations will vary. Sample explanation: Because of the order of operations, you must distribute prior to doing the subtraction.

102. Let x = number of miles driven.
Basic: 260
Continental: $80 + 0.25x$
$$260 < 80 + 0.25x$$
$$260 - 80 < 80 + 0.25x - 80$$
$$180 < 0.25x$$
$$\frac{180}{0.25} < \frac{0.25x}{0.25}$$
$$720 < x \text{ or } x > 720$$
The miles driven must exceed 720 for Basic Rental to be a better deal than Continental.

103. Let x = the number of packages produced
$$5.50x > 3000 + 3.00x$$
$$5.50x - 3.00x > 3000$$
$$2.5x > 3000$$
$$2.5x > 3000$$
$$\frac{2.5x}{2.5} > \frac{3000}{2.5}$$
$$x > 1200$$
The number of packages produced must exceed 1200 for the company to generate a profit.

Check Points 6.5

1. $(x+5)(x+6) = x \cdot x + x \cdot 6 + 5 \cdot x + 5 \cdot 6$
$$= x^2 + 6x + 5x + 30$$
$$= x^2 + 11x + 30$$

2. $(7x+5)(4x-3) = 7x \cdot 4x + 7x(-3) + 5 \cdot 4x + 5(-3)$
$$= 28x^2 - 21x + 20x - 15$$
$$= 28x^2 - x - 15$$

3. $x^2 + 5x + 6 = (x+2)(x+3)$

4. $x^2 + 3x - 10 = (x+5)(x-2)$

5. $5x^2 - 14x + 8 = (5x-4)(x-2)$

6. $6y^2 + 19y - 7 = (3y-1)(2y+7)$

7. $(x+6)(x-3) = 0$
$x+6 = 0 \quad \text{or} \quad x-3 = 0$
$x = -6 \qquad\qquad x = 3$
The solution set is $\{-6, \ 3\}$.

8.
$$x^2 - 6x = 16$$
$$x^2 - 6x - 16 = 16 - 16$$
$$x^2 - 6x - 16 = 0$$
$$(x+2)(x-8) = 0$$
$x+2 = 0 \quad \text{or} \quad x-8 = 0$
$x = -2 \qquad\qquad x = 8$
The solution set is $\{-2, \ 8\}$.

9. $2x^2 + 7x - 4 = 0$
$(2x-1)(x+4) = 0$
$2x-1 = 0 \quad \text{or} \quad x+4 = 0$
$2x = 1 \qquad\qquad x = -4$
$x = \dfrac{1}{2}$
The solution set is $\left\{-4, \ \dfrac{1}{2}\right\}$.

10. $8x^2 + 2x - 1 = 0$
$$x = \frac{-b \pm \sqrt{b^2 - 4ac}}{2a}$$
$$x = \frac{-(2) \pm \sqrt{(2)^2 - 4(8)(-1)}}{2(8)}$$
$$x = \frac{-2 \pm \sqrt{4+32}}{16}$$
$$x = \frac{-2 \pm \sqrt{36}}{16}$$
$$x = \frac{-2 \pm 6}{16}$$
$x = \dfrac{-2+6}{16} \quad \text{or} \quad x = \dfrac{-2-6}{16}$
$x = \dfrac{4}{16} \qquad\qquad x = \dfrac{-8}{16}$
$x = \dfrac{1}{4} \qquad\qquad x = -\dfrac{1}{2}$
The solution set is $\left\{-\dfrac{1}{2}, \ \dfrac{1}{4}\right\}$.

11.
$$2x^2 = 6x - 1$$
$$2x^2 - 6x + 1 = 0$$
$$x = \frac{-b \pm \sqrt{b^2 - 4ac}}{2a}$$
$$x = \frac{-(-6) \pm \sqrt{(-6)^2 - 4(2)(1)}}{2(2)}$$
$$x = \frac{6 \pm \sqrt{36-8}}{4}$$
$$x = \frac{6 \pm \sqrt{28}}{4}$$
$$x = \frac{6 \pm 2\sqrt{7}}{4}$$
$$x = \frac{2(3 \pm \sqrt{7})}{4}$$
$$x = \frac{3 \pm \sqrt{7}}{2}$$
$x = \dfrac{3+\sqrt{7}}{2} \quad \text{or} \quad x = \dfrac{3-\sqrt{7}}{2}$
The solution set is $\left\{\dfrac{3+\sqrt{7}}{2}, \ \dfrac{3-\sqrt{7}}{2}\right\}$.

12.

$$P = 0.01A^2 + 0.05A + 107$$

$$115 = 0.01A^2 + 0.05A + 107$$

$$0 = 0.01A^2 + 0.05A - 8$$

$$a = 0.01, \quad b = 0.05, \quad c = -8$$

$$A = \frac{-b \pm \sqrt{b^2 - 4ac}}{2a}$$

$$A = \frac{-(0.05) \pm \sqrt{(0.05)^2 - 4(0.01)(-8)}}{2(0.01)}$$

$$A = \frac{-0.05 \pm \sqrt{0.3225}}{0.02}$$

$$A \approx \frac{-0.05 + \sqrt{0.3225}}{0.02} \qquad A \approx \frac{-0.05 - \sqrt{0.3225}}{0.02}$$

$$A \approx 26 \qquad\qquad\qquad A \approx -31$$

Age cannot be negative, reject the negative answer. Thus, a woman whose normal systolic blood pressure is 115 mm Hg is 26 years old.

Exercise Set 6.5

1. $(x+3)(x+5) = x^2 + 5x + 3x + 15$

$$= x^2 + 8x + 15$$

2. $(x+7)(x+2) = x^2 + 2x + 7x + 14$

$$= x^2 + 9x + 14$$

3. $(x-5)(x+3) = x^2 + 3x - 5x - 15$

$$= x^2 - 2x - 15$$

4. $(x-1)(x+2) = x^2 + 2x - 1x - 2$

$$= x^2 + x - 2$$

5. $(2x-1)(x+2) = 2x^2 + 4x - 1x - 2$

$$= 2x^2 + 3x - 2$$

6. $(2x-5)(x+3) = 2x^2 + 6x - 5x - 15$

$$= 2x^2 + x - 15$$

7. $(3x-7)(4x-5) = 12x^2 - 15x - 28x + 35$

$$= 12x^2 - 43x + 35$$

8. $(2x-9)(7x-4) = 14x^2 - 8x - 63x + 36$

$$= 14x^2 - 71x + 36$$

9. $x^2 + 5x + 6 = (x+2)(x+3)$

Check: $(x+2)(x+3)$

$$= x^2 + 3x + 2x + 6$$

$$= x^2 + 5x + 6$$

10. $x^2 + 8x + 15 = (x+3)(x+5)$

Check: $(x+3)(x+5)$

$$= x^2 + 5x + 3x + 15$$

$$= x^2 + 8x + 15$$

11. $x^2 - 2x - 15 = (x-5)(x+3)$

Check: $(x-5)(x+3)$

$$= x^2 + 3x - 5x - 15$$

$$= x^2 - 2x - 15$$

12. $x^2 - 4x - 5 = (x-5)(x+1)$

Check: $(x-5)(x+1)$

$$= x^2 + x - 5x - 5$$

$$= x^2 - 4x - 5$$

13. $x^2 - 8x + 15 = (x-3)(x-5)$

Check: $(x-3)(x-5)$

$$= x^2 - 5x - 3x + 15$$

$$= x^2 - 8x + 15$$

14. $x^2 - 14x + 45 = (x-9)(x-5)$

Check: $(x-9)(x-5)$

$$= x^2 - 5x - 9x + 45$$

$$= x^2 - 14x + 45$$

15. $x^2 - 9x - 36 = (x-12)(x+3)$

Check: $(x-12)(x+3)$

$$= x^2 + 3x - 12x - 36$$

$$= x^2 - 9x - 36$$

16. $x^2 - x - 90 = (x-10)(x+9)$

Check: $(x-10)(x+9)$

$$= x^2 + 9x - 10x - 90$$

$$= x^2 - x - 90$$

17. $x^2 - 8x + 32$ is prime.

18. $x^2 - 9x + 81$ is prime.

19. $x^2 + 17x + 16 = (x+16)(x+1)$

Check: $(x+16)(x+1)$
$$= x^2 + x + 16x + 16$$
$$= x^2 + 17x + 16$$

20. $x^2 - 7x - 44 = (x-11)(x+4)$

Check: $(x-11)(x+4)$
$$= x^2 + 4x - 11x - 44$$
$$= x^2 - 7x - 44$$

21. $2x^2 + 7x + 3 = (2x+1)(x+3)$

Check: $(2x+1)(x+3)$
$$= 2x^2 + 6x + x + 3$$
$$= 2x^2 + 7x + 3$$

22. $3x^2 + 7x + 2 = (3x+1)(x+2)$

Check: $(3x+1)(x+2)$
$$= 3x^2 + 6x + x + 3$$
$$= 3x^2 + 7x + 2$$

23. $2x^2 - 17x + 30 = (2x-5)(x-6)$

Check: $(2x-5)(x-6)$
$$= 2x^2 - 12x - 5x + 30$$
$$= 2x^2 - 17x + 30$$

24. $5x^2 - 13x + 6 = (5x-3)(x-2)$

Check: $(5x-3)(x-2)$
$$= 5x^2 - 10x - 3x + 6$$
$$= 5x^2 - 13x + 6$$

25. $3x^2 - x - 2 = (3x+2)(x-1)$

Check: $(3x+2)(x-1)$
$$= 3x^2 - 3x + 2x - 2$$
$$= 3x^2 - x - 2$$

26. $2x^2 + 5x - 3 = (2x-1)(x+3)$

Check: $(2x-1)(x+3)$
$$= 2x^2 + 6x - x - 3$$
$$= 2x^2 + 5x - 3$$

27. $3x^2 - 25x - 28 = (3x-28)(x+1)$

Check: $(3x-28)(x+1)$
$$= 3x^2 + 3x - 28x - 28$$
$$= 3x^2 - 25x - 28$$

28. $3x^2 - 2x - 5 = (3x-5)(x+1)$

Check: $(3x-5)(x+1)$
$$= 3x^2 + 3x - 5x - 5$$
$$= 3x^2 - 2x - 5$$

29. $6x^2 - 11x + 4 = (2x-1)(3x-4)$

Check: $(2x-1)(3x-4)$
$$= 6x^2 - 8x - 3x + 4$$
$$= 6x^2 - 11x + 4$$

30. $6x^2 - 17x + 12 = (3x-4)(2x-3)$

Check: $(3x-4)(2x-3)$
$$= 6x^2 - 9x - 8x + 12$$
$$= 6x^2 - 17x + 12$$

31. $4x^2 + 16x + 15 = (2x+5)(2x+3)$

Check: $(2x+5)(2x+3)$
$$= 4x^2 + 6x + 10x + 15$$
$$= 4x^2 + 16x + 15$$

32. $8x^2 + 33x + 4 = (8x+1)(x+4)$

Check: $(8x+1)(x+4)$
$$= 8x^2 + 32x + x + 4$$
$$= 8x^2 + 33x + 4$$

33. $(x-8)(x+3) = 0$
$$x - 8 = 0 \quad \text{or} \quad x + 3 = 0$$
$$x = 8 \qquad\qquad x = -3$$
The solution set is $\{-3, 8\}$.

34. $(x+11)(x-5) = 0$
$$x + 11 = 0 \quad \text{or} \quad x - 5 = 0$$
$$x = -11 \qquad\qquad x = 5$$
The solution set is $\{-11, 5\}$.

35. $(4x+5)(x-2) = 0$
$$4x + 5 = 0 \quad \text{or} \quad x - 2 = 0$$
$$4x = -5 \qquad\qquad x = 2$$
$$x = -\frac{5}{4}$$
The solution set is $\left\{-\frac{5}{4}, 2\right\}$.

36. $(x+9)(3x-1)=0$

$x+9=0$ or $3x-1=0$

$x=-9$ $3x=1$

$x=\dfrac{1}{3}$

The solution set is $\left\{-9,\dfrac{1}{3}\right\}$.

37. $x^2+8x+15=0$

$(x+5)(x+3)=0$

$x+5=0$ or $x+3=0$

$x=-5$ $x=-3$

The solution set is $\{-5,-3\}$.

38. $x^2+5x+6=0$

$(x+3)(x+2)=0$

$x+3=0$ or $x+2=0$

$x=-3$ $x=-2$

The solution set is $\{-3,-2\}$.

39. $x^2-2x-15=0$

$(x-5)(x+3)=0$

$x-5=0$ or $x+3=0$

$x=5$ $x=-3$

The solution set is $\{-3,5\}$.

40. $x^2+x-42=0$

$(x+7)(x-6)=0$

$x+7=0$ or $x-6=0$

$x=-7$ $x=6$

The solution set is $\{-7,6\}$.

41. $x^2-4x=21$

$x^2-4x-21=0$

$(x+3)(x-7)=0$

$x+3=0$ or $x-7=0$

$x=-3$ $x=7$

The solution set is $\{-3,7\}$.

42. $x^2+7x=18$

$x^2+7x-18=0$

$(x+9)(x-2)=0$

$x+9=0$ or $x-2=0$

$x=-9$ $x=2$

The solution set is $\{-9,2\}$.

43. $x^2+9x=-8$

$x^2+9x+8=0$

$(x+8)(x+1)=0$

$x+8=0$ or $x+1=0$

$x=-8$ $x=-1$

The solution set is $\{-8,-1\}$.

44. $x^2-11x=-10$

$x^2-11x+10=0$

$(x-1)(x-10)=0$

$x-1=0$ or $x-10=0$

$x=1$ $x=10$

The solution set is $\{1,10\}$.

45. $x^2-12x=-36$

$x^2-12x+36=0$

$(x-6)(x-6)=0$

$x-6=0$ or $x-6=0$

$x=6$ $x=6$

The solution set is $\{6\}$.

46. $x^2-14x=-49$

$x^2-14x+49=0$

$(x-7)(x-7)=0$

$x-7=0$ or $x-7=0$

$x=7$ $x=7$

The solution set is $\{7\}$.

47. $2x^2=7x+4$

$2x^2-7x-4=0$

$(2x+1)(x-4)=0$

$2x+1=0$ or $x-4=0$

$2x=-1$ $x=4$

$x=-\dfrac{1}{2}$

The solution set is $\left\{-\dfrac{1}{2},4\right\}$.

48.
$$3x^2 = x + 4$$
$$3x^2 - x - 4 = 0$$
$$(3x - 4)(x + 1) = 0$$
$$3x - 4 = 0 \quad \text{or} \quad x + 1 = 0$$
$$3x = 4 \qquad\qquad x = -1$$
$$x = \frac{4}{3}$$

The solution set is $\left\{-1, \frac{4}{3}\right\}$.

49. $5x^2 + x = 18$
$$5x^2 + x - 18 = 0$$
$$(5x - 9)(x + 2) = 0$$
$$5x - 9 = 0 \quad \text{or} \quad x + 2 = 0$$
$$5x = 9 \qquad\qquad x = -2$$
$$x = \frac{9}{5}$$

The solution set is $\left\{-2, \frac{9}{5}\right\}$.

50.
$$3x^2 - 4x = 15$$
$$3x^2 - 4x - 15 = 0$$
$$(3x + 5)(x - 3) = 0$$
$$3x + 5 = 0 \quad \text{or} \quad x - 3 = 0$$
$$3x = -5 \qquad\qquad x = 3$$
$$x = -\frac{5}{3}$$

The solution set is $\left\{-\frac{5}{3}, 3\right\}$.

51. $x(6x + 23) + 7 = 0$
$$6x^2 + 23x + 7 = 0$$
$$(2x + 7)(3x + 1) = 0$$
$$2x + 7 = 0 \quad \text{or} \quad 3x + 1 = 0$$
$$2x = -7 \qquad\qquad 3x = -1$$
$$x = -\frac{7}{2} \qquad\qquad x = -\frac{1}{3}$$

The solution set is $\left\{-\frac{7}{2}, -\frac{1}{3}\right\}$.

52. $x(6x + 13) + 6 = 0$
$$6x^2 + 13x + 6 = 0$$
$$(3x + 2)(2x + 3) = 0$$
$$3x + 2 = 0 \quad \text{or} \quad 2x + 3 = 0$$
$$3x = -2 \qquad\qquad 2x = -3$$
$$x = -\frac{2}{3} \qquad\qquad x = -\frac{3}{2}$$

The solution set is $\left\{-\frac{2}{3}, -\frac{3}{2}\right\}$.

53. $x^2 + 8x + 15 = 0$
$$x = \frac{-b \pm \sqrt{b^2 - 4ac}}{2a}$$
$$x = \frac{-8 \pm \sqrt{8^2 - 4(1)(15)}}{2(1)}$$
$$x = \frac{-8 \pm \sqrt{4}}{2}$$
$$x = \frac{-8 \pm 2}{2}$$
$$x = \frac{-8 - 2}{2} \quad \text{or} \quad x = \frac{-8 + 2}{2}$$
$$x = -5 \qquad\qquad x = -3$$

The solution set is $\{-5, -3\}$.

54. $x^2 + 8x + 12 = 0$
$$x = \frac{-b \pm \sqrt{b^2 - 4ac}}{2a}$$
$$x = \frac{-8 \pm \sqrt{8^2 - 4(1)(12)}}{2(1)}$$
$$x = \frac{-8 \pm \sqrt{16}}{2}$$
$$x = \frac{-8 \pm 4}{2}$$
$$x = \frac{-8 - 4}{2} \quad \text{or} \quad x = \frac{-8 + 4}{2}$$
$$x = -6 \qquad\qquad x = -2$$

The solution set is $\{-6, -2\}$.

55. $x^2 + 5x + 3 = 0$

$$x = \frac{-b \pm \sqrt{b^2 - 4ac}}{2a}$$

$$x = \frac{-5 \pm \sqrt{5^2 - 4(1)(3)}}{2(1)}$$

$$x = \frac{-5 \pm \sqrt{13}}{2}$$

The solution set is $\left\{ \dfrac{-5 - \sqrt{13}}{2}, \dfrac{-5 + \sqrt{13}}{2} \right\}$.

56. $x^2 + 5x + 2 = 0$

$$x = \frac{-b \pm \sqrt{b^2 - 4ac}}{2a}$$

$$x = \frac{-5 \pm \sqrt{5^2 - 4(1)(2)}}{2(1)}$$

$$x = \frac{-5 \pm \sqrt{17}}{2}$$

The solution set is $\left\{ \dfrac{-5 - \sqrt{17}}{2}, \dfrac{-5 + \sqrt{17}}{2} \right\}$.

57. $x^2 + 4x = 6$

$x^2 + 4x - 6 = 0$

$$x = \frac{-b \pm \sqrt{b^2 - 4ac}}{2a}$$

$$x = \frac{-4 \pm \sqrt{4^2 - 4(1)(-6)}}{2(1)}$$

$$x = \frac{-4 \pm \sqrt{40}}{2}$$

$$x = \frac{-4 \pm 2\sqrt{10}}{2}$$

$x = -2 \pm \sqrt{10}$

The solution set is $\left\{ -2 - \sqrt{10},\ -2 + \sqrt{10} \right\}$.

58. $x^2 + 2x = 4$

$x^2 + 2x - 4 = 0$

$$x = \frac{-b \pm \sqrt{b^2 - 4ac}}{2a}$$

$$x = \frac{-2 \pm \sqrt{2^2 - 4(1)(-4)}}{2(1)}$$

$$x = \frac{-2 \pm \sqrt{20}}{2}$$

$$x = \frac{-2 \pm 2\sqrt{5}}{2}$$

$x = -1 \pm \sqrt{5}$

The solution set is $\left\{ -1 - \sqrt{5},\ -1 + \sqrt{5} \right\}$.

59. $x^2 + 4x - 7 = 0$

$$x = \frac{-b \pm \sqrt{b^2 - 4ac}}{2a}$$

$$x = \frac{-4 \pm \sqrt{4^2 - 4(1)(-7)}}{2(1)}$$

$$x = \frac{-4 \pm \sqrt{44}}{2}$$

$$x = \frac{-4 \pm 2\sqrt{11}}{2}$$

$x = -2 \pm \sqrt{11}$

The solution set is $\left\{ -2 - \sqrt{11},\ -2 + \sqrt{11} \right\}$.

60. $x^2 + 4x + 1 = 0$

$$x = \frac{-b \pm \sqrt{b^2 - 4ac}}{2a}$$

$$x = \frac{-4 \pm \sqrt{4^2 - 4(1)(1)}}{2(1)}$$

$$x = \frac{-4 \pm \sqrt{12}}{2}$$

$$x = \frac{-4 \pm 2\sqrt{3}}{2}$$

$x = -2 \pm \sqrt{3}$

The solution set is $\left\{ -2 - \sqrt{3},\ -2 + \sqrt{3} \right\}$.

61. $x^2 - 3x = 18$

$x^2 - 3x - 18 = 0$

$x = \dfrac{-b \pm \sqrt{b^2 - 4ac}}{2a}$

$x = \dfrac{-(-3) \pm \sqrt{(-3)^2 - 4(1)(-18)}}{2(1)}$

$x = \dfrac{3 \pm \sqrt{81}}{2}$

$x = \dfrac{3 \pm 9}{2}$

$x = \dfrac{3 - 9}{2}$ or $x = \dfrac{3 + 9}{2}$

$x = -3$ $x = 6$

The solution set is $\{-3, 6\}$.

62. $x^2 - 3x = 10$

$x^2 - 3x - 10 = 0$

$x = \dfrac{-b \pm \sqrt{b^2 - 4ac}}{2a}$

$x = \dfrac{-(-3) \pm \sqrt{(-3)^2 - 4(1)(-10)}}{2(1)}$

$x = \dfrac{3 \pm \sqrt{49}}{2}$

$x = \dfrac{3 \pm 7}{2}$

$x = \dfrac{3 - 7}{2}$ or $x = \dfrac{3 + 7}{2}$

$x = -2$ $x = 5$

The solution set is $\{-2, 5\}$.

63. $6x^2 - 5x - 6 = 0$

$x = \dfrac{-b \pm \sqrt{b^2 - 4ac}}{2a}$

$x = \dfrac{-(-5) \pm \sqrt{(-5)^2 - 4(6)(-6)}}{2(6)}$

$x = \dfrac{5 \pm \sqrt{169}}{12}$

$x = \dfrac{5 \pm 13}{12}$

$x = \dfrac{5 + 13}{12}$ or $x = \dfrac{5 - 13}{12}$

$x = \dfrac{18}{12}$ $x = \dfrac{-8}{12}$

$x = \dfrac{3}{2}$ $x = -\dfrac{2}{3}$

The solution set is $\left\{ \dfrac{3}{2}, \ -\dfrac{2}{3} \right\}$.

64. $9x^2 - 12x - 5 = 0$

$x = \dfrac{-b \pm \sqrt{b^2 - 4ac}}{2a}$

$x = \dfrac{-(-12) \pm \sqrt{(-12)^2 - 4(9)(-5)}}{2(9)}$

$x = \dfrac{12 \pm \sqrt{324}}{18}$

$x = \dfrac{12 \pm 18}{18}$

$x = \dfrac{12 - 18}{18}$ or $x = \dfrac{12 + 18}{18}$

$x = -\dfrac{1}{3}$ $x = \dfrac{5}{3}$

The solution set is $\left\{ -\dfrac{1}{3}, \dfrac{5}{3} \right\}$.

65. $x^2 - 2x - 10 = 0$

$$x = \frac{-b \pm \sqrt{b^2 - 4ac}}{2a}$$

$$x = \frac{-(-2) \pm \sqrt{(-2)^2 - 4(1)(-10)}}{2(1)}$$

$$x = \frac{2 \pm \sqrt{44}}{2}$$

$$x = \frac{2 \pm 2\sqrt{11}}{2}$$

$$x = 1 \pm \sqrt{11}$$

The solution set is $\left\{1 - \sqrt{11},\ 1 + \sqrt{11}\right\}$.

66. $x^2 + 6x - 10 = 0$

$$x = \frac{-b \pm \sqrt{b^2 - 4ac}}{2a}$$

$$x = \frac{-6 \pm \sqrt{6^2 - 4(1)(-10)}}{2(1)}$$

$$x = \frac{-6 \pm \sqrt{76}}{2}$$

$$x = \frac{-6 \pm 2\sqrt{19}}{2}$$

$$x = -3 \pm \sqrt{19}$$

The solution set is $\left\{-3 - \sqrt{19},\ -3 + \sqrt{19}\right\}$.

67. $x^2 - x = 14$

$x^2 - x - 14 = 0$

$$x = \frac{-b \pm \sqrt{b^2 - 4ac}}{2a}$$

$$x = \frac{-(-1) \pm \sqrt{(-1)^2 - 4(1)(-14)}}{2(1)}$$

$$x = \frac{1 \pm \sqrt{57}}{2}$$

The solution set is $\left\{\dfrac{1 - \sqrt{57}}{2},\ \dfrac{1 + \sqrt{57}}{2}\right\}$.

68. $x^2 - 5x = 10$

$x^2 - 5x - 10 = 0$

$$x = \frac{-b \pm \sqrt{b^2 - 4ac}}{2a}$$

$$x = \frac{-(-5) \pm \sqrt{(-5)^2 - 4(1)(-10)}}{2(1)}$$

$$x = \frac{5 \pm \sqrt{65}}{2}$$

The solution set is $\left\{\dfrac{5 - \sqrt{65}}{2},\ \dfrac{5 + \sqrt{65}}{2}\right\}$.

69. $6x^2 + 6x + 1 = 0$

$$x = \frac{-b \pm \sqrt{b^2 - 4ac}}{2a}$$

$$x = \frac{-6 \pm \sqrt{6^2 - 4(6)(1)}}{2(6)}$$

$$x = \frac{-6 \pm \sqrt{12}}{12}$$

$$x = \frac{-6 \pm 2\sqrt{3}}{12}$$

$$x = \frac{-3 \pm \sqrt{3}}{6}$$

The solution set is $\left\{\dfrac{-3 - \sqrt{3}}{6},\ \dfrac{-3 + \sqrt{3}}{6}\right\}$.

70. $3x^2 = 5x - 1$

$3x^2 - 5x + 1 = 0$

$$x = \frac{-b \pm \sqrt{b^2 - 4ac}}{2a}$$

$$x = \frac{-(-5) \pm \sqrt{(-5)^2 - 4(3)(1)}}{2(3)}$$

$$x = \frac{5 \pm \sqrt{13}}{6}$$

The solution set is $\left\{\dfrac{5 - \sqrt{13}}{6},\ \dfrac{5 + \sqrt{13}}{6}\right\}$.

71.
$$4x^2 = 12x - 9$$
$$4x^2 - 12x + 9 = 0$$
$$x = \frac{-b \pm \sqrt{b^2 - 4ac}}{2a}$$
$$x = \frac{-(-12) \pm \sqrt{(-12)^2 - 4(4)(9)}}{2(4)}$$
$$x = \frac{12 \pm \sqrt{0}}{8}$$
$$x = \frac{12}{8} = \frac{3}{2}$$
The solution set is $\left\{\dfrac{3}{2}\right\}$.

72. $9x^2 + 6x + 1 = 0$
$$x = \frac{-b \pm \sqrt{b^2 - 4ac}}{2a}$$
$$x = \frac{-6 \pm \sqrt{6^2 - 4(9)(1)}}{2(9)}$$
$$x = \frac{-6 \pm \sqrt{0}}{18}$$
$$x = -\frac{6}{18} = -\frac{1}{3}$$
The solution set is $\left\{-\dfrac{1}{3}\right\}$.

73. $\dfrac{3x^2}{4} - \dfrac{5x}{2} - 2 = 0$
$$3x^2 - 10x - 8 = 0$$
$$(x - 4)(3x + 2) = 0$$
$$x - 4 = 0 \quad \text{or} \quad 3x + 2 = 0$$
$$x = 4 \qquad\qquad x = -\frac{2}{3}$$
The solution set is $\left\{-\dfrac{2}{3}, 4\right\}$.

74. $\dfrac{x^2}{3} - \dfrac{x}{2} - \dfrac{3}{2} = 0$
$$2x^2 - 3x - 9 = 0$$
$$(x - 3)(2x + 3) = 0$$
$$x - 3 = 0 \quad \text{or} \quad 2x + 3 = 0$$
$$x = 3 \qquad\qquad x = -\frac{3}{2}$$
The solution set is $\left\{-\dfrac{3}{2}, 3\right\}$.

75. $(x - 1)(3x + 2) = -7(x - 1)$
$$3x^2 - x - 2 = -7x + 7$$
$$3x^2 + 6x - 9 = 0$$
$$x^2 + 2x - 3 = 0$$
$$(x - 1)(x + 3) = 0$$
$$x - 1 = 0 \quad \text{or} \quad x + 3 = 0$$
$$x = 1 \qquad\qquad x = -3$$
The solution set is $\{-3, 1\}$.

76. $x(x + 1) = 4 - (x + 2)(x + 2)$
$$x^2 + x = 4 - x^2 - 4x - 4$$
$$x^2 + x = -x^2 - 4x$$
$$2x^2 + 5x = 0$$
$$x(2x + 5) = 0$$
$$x = 0 \quad \text{or} \quad 2x + 5 = 0$$
$$x = -\frac{5}{2}$$
The solution set is $\left\{-\dfrac{5}{2}, 0\right\}$.

77. $(2x - 6)(x + 2) = 5(x - 1) - 12$
$$(2x - 6)(x + 2) = 5x - 5 - 12$$
$$2x^2 - 2x - 12 = 5x - 17$$
$$2x^2 - 7x + 5 = 0$$
$$(x - 1)(2x - 5) = 0$$
$$x - 1 = 0 \quad \text{or} \quad 2x - 5 = 0$$
$$x = 1 \qquad\qquad x = \frac{5}{2}$$
The solution set is $\left\{1, \dfrac{5}{2}\right\}$.

78. $7x(x - 2) = 3 - 2(x + 4)$
$$7x^2 - 14x = 3 - 2x - 8$$
$$7x^2 - 14x = -2x - 5$$
$$7x^2 - 12x + 5 = 0$$
$$(x - 1)(7x - 5) = 0$$
$$x - 1 = 0 \quad \text{or} \quad 7x - 5 = 0$$
$$x = 1 \qquad\qquad x = \frac{5}{7}$$
The solution set is $\left\{\dfrac{5}{7}, 1\right\}$.

79. $2x^2 - 9x - 3 = 9 - 9x$

$$2x^2 = 12$$

$$x^2 = 6$$

$$x = \pm\sqrt{6}$$

The solution set is $\left\{\pm\sqrt{6}\right\}$.

80. $3x^2 - 6x - 3 = 12 - 6x$

$$3x^2 = 15$$

$$x^2 = 5$$

$$x = \pm\sqrt{5}$$

The solution set is $\left\{\pm\sqrt{5}\right\}$.

81. Let x = the number.

$$x^2 - (6 + 2x) = 0$$

$$x^2 - 2x - 6 = 0$$

Apply the quadratic formula.

$a = 1 \quad b = -2 \quad c = -6$

$$x = \frac{-(-2) \pm \sqrt{(-2)^2 - 4(1)(-6)}}{2(1)}$$

$$= \frac{2 \pm \sqrt{4 - (-24)}}{2}$$

$$= \frac{2 \pm \sqrt{28}}{2}$$

$$= \frac{2 \pm \sqrt{4 \cdot 7}}{2} = \frac{2 \pm 2\sqrt{7}}{2} = 1 \pm \sqrt{7}$$

We disregard $1 - \sqrt{7}$ because it is negative, and we are looking for a positive number. Thus, the number is $1 + \sqrt{7}$.

82. Let x = the number.

$$2x^2 - (1 + 2x) = 0$$

$$2x^2 - 2x - 1 = 0$$

Apply the quadratic formula.

$a = 2 \quad b = -2 \quad c = -1$

$$x = \frac{-(-2) \pm \sqrt{(-2)^2 - 4(2)(-1)}}{2(2)}$$

$$= \frac{2 \pm \sqrt{4 - (-8)}}{4}$$

$$= \frac{2 \pm \sqrt{12}}{4} = \frac{2 \pm \sqrt{4 \cdot 3}}{4} = \frac{2 \pm 2\sqrt{3}}{4} = \frac{1 \pm \sqrt{3}}{2}$$

We disregard $\frac{1 + \sqrt{3}}{2}$ because it is positive, and we are looking for a negative number. The number is $\frac{1 - \sqrt{3}}{2}$.

83. $N = \dfrac{t^2 - t}{2}$

$$36 = \frac{t^2 - t}{2}$$

$$72 = t^2 - t$$

$$0 = t^2 - t - 72$$

$$0 = (t + 8)(t - 9)$$

$t + 8 = 0 \quad$ or $\quad t - 9 = 0$

$\quad\quad t = -8 \quad\quad\quad\quad t = 9$

Thus, the league has 9 teams.

84. $N = \dfrac{t^2 - t}{2}$

$$45 = \frac{t^2 - t}{2}$$

$$90 = t^2 - t$$

$$0 = t^2 - t - 90$$

$$0 = (t + 9)(t - 10)$$

$t + 9 = 0 \quad$ or $\quad t - 10 = 0$

$\quad\quad t = -9 \quad\quad\quad\quad t = 10$

Thus, the league has 10 teams.

85. a. $p = 0.004x^2 - 0.37x + 14.1$

$p = 0.004(80)^2 - 0.37(80) + 14.1 = 10.1$

According to the model, 10.1% of the U.S. population was foreign-born in 2000. This underestimates the actual number by 0.3%.

b. $p = 0.004x^2 - 0.37x + 14.1$

$25 = 0.004x^2 - 0.37x + 14.1$

$0 = 0.004x^2 - 0.37x - 10.9$

Apply the quadratic formula.

$a = 0.004 \quad b = -0.37 \quad c = -10.9$

$$x = \frac{-(-0.37) \pm \sqrt{(-0.37)^2 - 4(0.004)(-10.9)}}{2(0.004)}$$

$x \approx -23$ or $x \approx 116$

We disregard -23 because it is prior to when the model applies.
25% of the U.S. population will be foreign-born 116 years after 1920, or 2036.

86. a. $p = 0.004x^2 - 0.37x + 14.1$

$p = 0.004(70)^2 - 0.37(70) + 14.1 = 7.8$

According to the model, 7.8% of the U.S. population was foreign-born in 1990. This underestimates the actual number by 0.2%.

b. $p = 0.004x^2 - 0.37x + 14.1$

$17 = 0.004x^2 - 0.37x + 14.1$

$0 = 0.004x^2 - 0.37x - 2.9$

Apply the quadratic formula.

$a = 0.004 \quad b = -0.37 \quad c = -2.9$

$$x = \frac{-(-0.37) \pm \sqrt{(-0.37)^2 - 4(0.004)(-2.9)}}{2(0.004)}$$

$x \approx -7$ or $x \approx 100$

We disregard -7 because it is prior to when the model applies.
17% of the U.S. population will be foreign-born 100 years after 1920, or 2020.

87. a. $\dfrac{1}{\Phi - 1}$

b.

$$\frac{\Phi}{1} = \frac{1}{\Phi - 1}$$

$$(\Phi - 1)\frac{\Phi}{1} = (\Phi - 1)\frac{1}{\Phi - 1}$$

$$\Phi^2 - \Phi = 1$$

$$\Phi^2 - \Phi - 1 = 0$$

$$\Phi = \frac{-b \pm \sqrt{b^2 - 4ac}}{2a}$$

$$\Phi = \frac{-(-1) \pm \sqrt{(-1)^2 - 4(1)(-1)}}{2(1)}$$

$$\Phi = \frac{1 \pm \sqrt{1 + 4}}{2}$$

$$\Phi = \frac{1 \pm \sqrt{5}}{2}, \text{ reject negative}$$

$$\Phi = \frac{1 + \sqrt{5}}{2}$$

c.   The golden ratio is $\dfrac{1 + \sqrt{5}}{2}$ to 1.

93.   does not make sense; Explanations will vary. Sample explanation: There are an infinite number of such pairs.

94.   does not make sense; Explanations will vary. Sample explanation: $x^2 + x + 1$ is prime.

95.   does not make sense; Explanations will vary. Sample explanation: The factoring method would be quicker.

96.   does not make sense; Explanations will vary. Sample explanation: The expression cannot be simplified because 2 is not a factor of 3.

97.   If $b^2 - 4ac$ is negative, there are no real solutions because the square root of a negative number is not real. If $b^2 - 4ac = 0$, then there is one rational solution. If $b^2 - 4ac$ is a positive perfect square, then there are two rational solutions. If $b^2 - 4ac$ is positive, but not a perfect square, then there are two irrational solutions.

98. $x^2 + bx + 15$

$(x+3)(x+5) = x^2 + 8x + 15$

$(x+1)(x+15) = x^2 + 16x + 15$

Therefore, $b = 8, 16$.

99. $x^2 + 4x + b$

$(x+3)(x+1) = x^2 + 4x + 3$

$(x+2)(x+2) = x^2 + 4x + 4$

Therefore, $b = 3, 4$.

100. $x^{2n} + 20x^n + 99 = (x^n + 9)(x^n + 11)$

101. $x^2 + 2\sqrt{3}x - 9 = 0$

$x = \dfrac{-b \pm \sqrt{b^2 - 4ac}}{2a}$

$x = \dfrac{-2\sqrt{3} \pm \sqrt{(2\sqrt{3})^2 - 4(1)(-9)}}{2(1)}$

$x = \dfrac{-2\sqrt{3} \pm \sqrt{48}}{2}$

$x = \dfrac{-2\sqrt{3} \pm 4\sqrt{3}}{2}$

$x = -\sqrt{3} \pm 2\sqrt{3}$

$x = -\sqrt{3} + 2\sqrt{3}$ or $x = -\sqrt{3} - 2\sqrt{3}$

$x = \sqrt{3}$ $x = -3\sqrt{3}$

The solution set is $\left\{-3\sqrt{3}, \sqrt{3}\right\}$

Chapter 6 Review Exercises

1. $6x + 9 = 6 \cdot 4 + 9 = 24 + 9 = 33$

2. $7x^2 + 4x - 5 = 7(-2)^2 + 4(-2) - 5$

$= 7(4) + 4(-2) - 5$

$= 28 - 8 - 5$

$= 15$

3. $6 + 2(x-8)^3 = 6 + 2(5-8)^3$

$= 6 + 2(-3)^3$

$= 6 + 2(-27)$

$= 6 - 54$

$= -48$

4. $P = -0.05x^2 + 3.6x - 15$

$P = -0.05(21)^2 + 3.6(21) - 15 = 38.55$

According to the model, 38.55% of U.S. adults who are 21 years old have been tested for HIV. This overestimates the percent displayed in the graph by 3.55.

5. $5(2x - 3) + 7x = 10x - 15 + 7x$

$= 17x - 15$

6. $3(4y - 5) - (7y - 2) = 12y - 15 - 7y + 2$

$= 5y - 13$

7. $2(x^2 + 5x) + 3(4x^2 - 3x) = 2x^2 + 10x + 12x^2 - 9x$

$= 14x^2 + x$

8. $\qquad 4x + 9 = 33$

$4x + 9 - 9 = 33 - 9$

$4x = 24$

$\dfrac{4x}{4} = \dfrac{24}{4}$

$x = 6$

The solution set is $\{6\}$.

9. $5x - 3 = x + 5$

$5x - 3 + 3 = x + 5 + 3$

$5x = x + 8$

$5x - x = x + 8 - x$

$4x = 8$

$\dfrac{4x}{4} = \dfrac{8}{4}$

$x = 2$

The solution set is $\{2\}$.

10. $\qquad 3(x+4) = 5x - 12$

$3x + 12 = 5x - 12$

$3x + 12 - 12 = 5x - 12 - 12$

$3x = 5x - 24$

$3x - 5x = 5x - 24 - 5x$

$-2x = -24$

$\dfrac{-2x}{-2} = \dfrac{-24}{-2}$

$x = 12$

The solution set is $\{12\}$.

11. $2(x-2)+3(x+5)=2x-2$

$\qquad 2x-4+3x+15=2x-2$

$\qquad\qquad\quad 5x+11=2x-2$

$\qquad 5x+11-11=2x-2-11$

$\qquad\qquad\qquad 5x=2x-13$

$\qquad\quad 5x-2x=2x-13-2x$

$\qquad\qquad\qquad 3x=-13$

$\qquad\qquad\quad \dfrac{3x}{3}=\dfrac{-13}{3}$

$\qquad\qquad\qquad x=-\dfrac{13}{3}$

The solution set is $\left\{-\dfrac{13}{3}\right\}$.

12. $\dfrac{2x}{3}=\dfrac{x}{6}+1$

$\qquad 6\left(\dfrac{2x}{3}\right)=6\left(\dfrac{x}{6}+1\right)$

$\qquad\qquad 4x=x+6$

$\qquad 4x-x=x+6-x$

$\qquad\qquad 3x=6$

$\qquad\quad \dfrac{3x}{3}=\dfrac{6}{3}$

$\qquad\qquad x=2$

The solution set is {2}.

13. $7x+5=5(x+3)+2x$

$\qquad 7x+5=5x+15+2x$

$\qquad 7x+5=7x+15$

$\qquad\quad\; 5=15$

This is a false statement. The solution set is { }.

14. $7x+13=2(2x-5)+3x+23$

$\qquad 7x+13=4x-10+3x+23$

$\qquad 7x+13=7x+13$

$\qquad\quad\;\, 13=13$

This is a true statement. The solution set is $\{x \,|\, x \text{ is a real number}\}$.

15. $\dfrac{3}{x}=\dfrac{15}{25}$

$\qquad 3\cdot 25=x\cdot 15$

$\qquad\quad 75=15x$

$\qquad\dfrac{75}{15}=\dfrac{15x}{15}$

$\qquad\quad 5=x$

The solution set is $\{5\}$.

16. $\dfrac{-7}{5}=\dfrac{91}{x}$

$\qquad -7\cdot x=5\cdot 91$

$\qquad\quad -7x=455$

$\qquad \dfrac{-7x}{-7}=\dfrac{455}{-7}$

$\qquad\qquad x=-65$

The solution set is $\{-65\}$.

17. $\dfrac{x+2}{3}=\dfrac{4}{5}$

$\qquad 5(x+2)=3\cdot 4$

$\qquad 5x+10=12$

$\qquad 5x+10-10=12-10$

$\qquad\qquad 5x=2$

$\qquad\quad \dfrac{5x}{5}=\dfrac{2}{5}$

$\qquad\qquad x=\dfrac{2}{5}$

The solution set is $\left\{\dfrac{2}{5}\right\}$.

18. $\dfrac{5}{x+7}=\dfrac{3}{x+3}$

$\qquad 5(x+3)=3(x+7)$

$\qquad 5x+15=3x+21$

$\qquad 5x+15-15=3x+21-15$

$\qquad\qquad 5x=3x+6$

$\qquad 5x-3x=3x+6-3x$

$\qquad\qquad 2x=6$

$\qquad\quad \dfrac{2x}{2}=\dfrac{6}{2}$

$\qquad\qquad x=3$

The solution set is {3}.

19. Let x = number of teachers
$$\frac{3}{50} = \frac{x}{5400}$$
$$50 \cdot x = 3 \cdot 5400$$
$$50x = 16,200$$
$$\frac{50x}{50} = \frac{16,200}{50}$$
$$x = 324$$
There should be 324 teachers for 5400 students.

20. Let x = number of trout in lake
$$\frac{32}{82} = \frac{112}{x}$$
$$32x = 82 \cdot 112$$
$$32x = 9184$$
$$\frac{32x}{32} = \frac{9184}{32}$$
$$x = 287$$
There are 287 trout in the lake.

21. a. Model 1:
$$N = 6.8x + 64$$
$$N = 6.8(0) + 64$$
$$N = 64$$

Model 2:
$$N = -0.5x^2 + 9.5x + 62$$
$$N = -0.5(0)^2 + 9.5(0) + 62$$
$$N = 62$$

Model 2 best describes the data in 2000.

b. $N = -0.5x^2 + 9.5x + 62$
$$N = -0.5(6)^2 + 9.5(6) + 62$$
$$N = 101$$
Model 2 underestimates the number of channels in 2006 by 3.

c. $N = 6.8x + 64$
$$166 = 6.8x + 64$$
$$102 = 6.8x$$
$$\frac{102}{6.8} = \frac{6.8x}{6.8}$$
$$x = 15$$
Model 1 predicts there will be 166 channels 15 years after 2000, or 2015.

22. Let x = the average hours spent studying.
Let $x + 1.8$ = the average hours spent drinking.
$$x + (x + 1.8) = 18.6$$
$$x + x + 1.8 = 18.6$$
$$2x + 1.8 = 18.6$$
$$2x = 16.8$$
$$x = 8.4$$
$$x + 1.8 = 10.2$$
studying: 8.4 hours
drinking: 10.2 hours

23. Let x = the number of years after 2000.
$$17.5 + 0.4x = 25.1$$
$$0.4x = 7.6$$
$$x = 19$$
The percentage of people in the U.S. that will speak a language other than English at home will reach 25.1% 19 years after 2000, or 2019.

24. $15 + .05x = 5 + .07x$
$$10 = .02x$$
$$500 = x$$
Both plans cost the same at 500 minutes.

25. Let x = the original price of the phone
$$48 = x - 0.20x$$
$$48 = 0.80x$$
$$60 = x$$
The original price is \$60.

26. Let x = the amount sold to earn \$800 in one week.
$$800 = 300 + 0.05x$$
$$500 = 0.05x$$
$$10,000 = x$$
Sales must be \$10,000 in one week to earn \$800.

27. $Ax - By = C$
$$Ax = By + C$$
$$\frac{Ax}{A} = \frac{By + C}{A}$$
$$x = \frac{By + C}{A}$$

28. $A = \dfrac{1}{2}bh$

     $2A = bh$

     $\dfrac{2A}{b} = \dfrac{bh}{b}$

     $\dfrac{2A}{b} = h$

       $h = \dfrac{2A}{b}$

29. $A = \dfrac{B+C}{2}$

     $2A = B+C$

     $2A - C = B$

       $B = 2A - C$

30. $vt + gt^2 = s$

     $gt^2 = s - vt$

     $\dfrac{gt^2}{t^2} = \dfrac{s - vt}{t^2}$

       $g = \dfrac{s - vt}{t^2}$

31. $2x - 5 < 3$

     $2x - 5 + 5 < 3 + 5$

       $2x < 8$

       $\dfrac{2x}{2} < \dfrac{8}{2}$

         $x < 4$

       $\{x \mid x < 4\}$

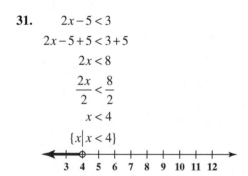

32. $\dfrac{x}{2} > -4$

   $2 \cdot \dfrac{x}{2} > 2(-4)$

      $x > -8$

   $\{x \mid x > -8\}$

33. $3 - 5x \le 18$

     $3 - 5x - 3 \le 18 - 3$

        $-5x \le 15$

        $\dfrac{-5x}{-5} \ge \dfrac{15}{-5}$

         $x \ge -3$

       $\{x \mid x \ge -3\}$

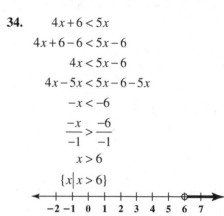

34. $4x + 6 < 5x$

     $4x + 6 - 6 < 5x - 6$

       $4x < 5x - 6$

     $4x - 5x < 5x - 6 - 5x$

        $-x < -6$

        $\dfrac{-x}{-1} > \dfrac{-6}{-1}$

         $x > 6$

       $\{x \mid x > 6\}$

35. $6x - 10 \ge 2(x + 3)$

     $6x - 10 + 10 \ge 2x + 6 + 10$

         $6x \ge 2x + 16$

     $6x - 2x \ge 2x + 16 - 2x$

         $4x \ge 16$

         $\dfrac{4x}{4} \ge \dfrac{16}{4}$

          $x \ge 4$

       $\{x \mid x \ge 4\}$

36. $4x + 3(2x - 7) \le x - 3$

     $4x + 6x - 21 \le x - 3$

       $10x - 21 \le x - 3$

   $10x - 21 + 21 \le x - 3 + 21$

         $10x \le x + 18$

     $10x - x \le x + 18 - x$

          $9x \le 18$

          $\dfrac{9x}{9} \le \dfrac{18}{9}$

           $x \le 2$

       $\{x \mid x \le 2\}$

37. $-1 < 4x + 2 \le 6$

$-1 - 2 < 4x + 2 - 2 \le 6 - 2$

$-3 < 4x \le 4$

$-\dfrac{3}{4} < x \le 1$

$\left\{ x \,\middle|\, -\dfrac{3}{4} < x \le 1 \right\}$

38. Let x = score on third test.

$\dfrac{42 + 74 + x}{3} \ge 60$

$\dfrac{116 + x}{3} \ge 60$

$3 \cdot \dfrac{116 + x}{3} \ge 3 \cdot 60$

$116 + x \ge 180$

$116 + x - 116 \ge 180 - 116$

$x \ge 64$

The score on the third test must be at least 64.

39. $(x + 9)(x - 5) = x^2 - 5x + 9x - 45$
$= x^2 + 4x - 45$

40. $(4x - 7)(3x + 2) = 12x^2 + 8x - 21x - 14$
$= 12x^2 - 13x - 14$

41. $x^2 - x - 12 = (x - 4)(x + 3)$

42. $x^2 - 8x + 15 = (x - 5)(x - 3)$

43. $x^2 + 2x + 3$ is prime.

44. $3x^2 - 17x + 10 = (3x - 2)(x - 5)$

45. $6x^2 - 11x - 10 = (3x + 2)(2x - 5)$

46. $3x^2 - 6x - 5$ is prime.

47. $x^2 + 5x - 14 = 0$

$(x + 7)(x - 2) = 0$

$x + 7 = 0 \quad \text{or} \quad x - 2 = 0$

$x = -7 \qquad\qquad x = 2$

The solution set is $\{-7, 2\}$.

48. $x^2 - 4x = 32$

$x^2 - 4x - 32 = 0$

$(x - 8)(x + 4) = 0$

$x - 8 = 0 \quad \text{or} \quad x + 4 = 0$

$x = 8 \qquad\qquad x = -4$

The solution set is $\{-4, 8\}$.

49. $2x^2 + 15x - 8 = 0$

$(2x - 1)(x + 8) = 0$

$2x - 1 = 0 \quad \text{or} \quad x + 8 = 0$

$2x = 1 \qquad\qquad x = -8$

$x = \dfrac{1}{2}$

The solution set is $\left\{ -8, \dfrac{1}{2} \right\}$.

50. $3x^2 = -21x - 30$

$3x^2 + 21x + 30 = 0$

$(3x + 6)(x + 5) = 0$

$3x + 6 = 0 \quad \text{or} \quad x + 5 = 0$

$3x = -6 \qquad\qquad x = -5$

$x = -2$

The solution set is $\{-5, -2\}$.

51. $x^2 - 4x + 3 = 0$

$x = \dfrac{-b \pm \sqrt{b^2 - 4ac}}{2a}$

$x = \dfrac{-(-4) \pm \sqrt{(-4)^2 - 4(1)(3)}}{2(1)}$

$x = \dfrac{4 \pm \sqrt{4}}{2}$

$x = \dfrac{4 \pm 2}{2}$

$x = \dfrac{4 - 2}{2} \quad \text{or} \quad x = \dfrac{4 + 2}{2}$

$x = 1 \qquad\qquad x = 3$

The solution set is $\{1, 3\}$.

52.
$$x^2 - 5x = 4$$
$$x^2 - 5x - 4 = 0$$
$$x = \frac{-b \pm \sqrt{b^2 - 4ac}}{2a}$$
$$x = \frac{-(-5) \pm \sqrt{(-5)^2 - 4(1)(-4)}}{2(1)}$$
$$x = \frac{5 \pm \sqrt{41}}{2}$$

The solution set is $\left\{ \dfrac{5 - \sqrt{41}}{2}, \ \dfrac{5 + \sqrt{41}}{2} \right\}$.

53. $2x^2 + 5x - 3 = 0$
$$x = \frac{-b \pm \sqrt{b^2 - 4ac}}{2a}$$
$$x = \frac{-5 \pm \sqrt{5^2 - 4(2)(-3)}}{2(2)}$$
$$x = \frac{-5 \pm \sqrt{49}}{4}$$
$$x = \frac{-5 \pm 7}{4}$$
$$x = \frac{-5 + 7}{4} \quad \text{or} \quad x = \frac{-5 - 7}{4}$$
$$x = \frac{1}{2} \qquad\qquad x = -3$$

The solution set is $\left\{ -3, \dfrac{1}{2} \right\}$.

54.
$$3x^2 - 6x = 5$$
$$3x^2 - 6x - 5 = 0$$
$$x = \frac{-b \pm \sqrt{b^2 - 4ac}}{2a}$$
$$x = \frac{-(-6) \pm \sqrt{(-6)^2 - 4(3)(-5)}}{2(3)}$$
$$x = \frac{6 \pm \sqrt{96}}{6}$$
$$x = \frac{6 \pm 4\sqrt{6}}{6}$$
$$x = \frac{3 \pm 2\sqrt{6}}{3}$$

The solution set is $\left\{ \dfrac{3 - 2\sqrt{6}}{3}, \ \dfrac{3 + 2\sqrt{6}}{3} \right\}$.

55. a. $M = -1.8x^2 + 21x + 15$
$$M = -1.8(4)^2 + 21(4) + 15$$
$$= 70.2$$
According to formula, 70.2% of new cellphones will play music in 2009. This overestimates the value in the graph by 0.2%.

b. $M = -1.8x^2 + 21x + 15$
$$75 = -1.8x^2 + 21x + 15$$
$$0 = -1.8x^2 + 21x - 60$$
$$0 = 1.8x^2 - 21x + 60$$
$$0 = 1.8x^2 - 21x + 60$$
$$x = \frac{-b \pm \sqrt{b^2 - 4ac}}{2a}$$
$$x = \frac{-(-21) \pm \sqrt{(-21)^2 - 4(1.8)(60)}}{2(1.8)}$$
$$x = 5 \quad x \approx 7$$
75% of new cellphones will play music 5 years after 2005, or 2010.

Chapter 6 Test

1. $x^3 - 4(x-1)^2 = (-2)^3 - 4(-2-1)^2$
$$= -8 - 4(-3)^2$$
$$= -8 - 4(9)$$
$$= -8 - 4(9)$$
$$= -44$$

2. $5(3x - 2) - (x - 6) = 15x - 10 - x + 6$
$$= 14x - 4$$

3. $T = 15{,}395 + 988x - 2x^2$
$$T = 15{,}395 + 988(10) - 2(10)^2 = 25{,}075$$
According to the formula, the average cost in 2010 will be $25,075.

4. $12x + 4 = 7x - 21$
$$5x = -25$$
$$x = -5$$
The solution set is $\{-5\}$.

5. $3(2x-4) = 9 - 3(x+1)$
$6x - 12 = 9 - 3x - 3$
$6x - 12 = 6 - 3x$
$6x - 12 + 12 = 6 - 3x + 12$
$6x = -3x + 18$
$6x + 3x = -3x + 18 + 3x$
$9x = 18$
$\dfrac{9x}{9} = \dfrac{18}{9}$
$x = 2$
The solution set is $\{2\}$.

6. $3(x-4) + x = 2(6+2x)$
$3x - 12 + x = 12 + 4x$
$4x - 12 = 4x + 12$
$-12 = 12$
This is a false statement. The solution set is $\{\ \}$.

7. $\dfrac{x}{5} - 2 = \dfrac{x}{3}$
$15\left(\dfrac{x}{5} - 2\right) = 15\left(\dfrac{x}{3}\right)$
$3x - 30 = 5x$
$-2x = 30$
$x = -15$
The solution set is $\{-15\}$.

8. $By - Ax = A$
$By = Ax + A$
$\dfrac{By}{B} = \dfrac{Ax + A}{B}$
$y = \dfrac{Ax + A}{B}$

9. $T = 383x + 3136$
$8498 = 383x + 3136$
$5362 = 383x$
$\dfrac{5362}{383} = \dfrac{383x}{383}$
$14 = x$
The model projects that the cost will be $8498 14 years after 2000, or 2014.

10. $\dfrac{5}{8} = \dfrac{x}{12}$
$8 \cdot x = 5 \cdot 12$
$8x = 60$
$\dfrac{8x}{8} = \dfrac{60}{8}$
$x = 7.5$
The solution set is $\{7.5\}$.

11. $\dfrac{x+5}{8} = \dfrac{x+2}{5}$
$5(x+5) = 8(x+2)$
$5x + 25 = 8x + 16$
$5x + 25 - 25 = 8x + 16 - 25$
$5x = 8x - 9$
$5x - 8x = 8x - 9 - 8x$
$-3x = -9$
$\dfrac{-3x}{-3} = \dfrac{-9}{-3}$
$x = 3$
The solution set is $\{3\}$.

12. Let x = number of elk in the park.
$\dfrac{5}{150} = \dfrac{200}{x}$
$5x = 150 \cdot 200$
$5x = 30,000$
$\dfrac{5x}{5} = \dfrac{30,000}{5}$
$x = 6000$
There are 6000 elk in the park.

13. Let x = the number drive-in theaters.
Let $x + 16$ = the number movie theaters.
Let $x + 64$ = the number video rental stores.
$(x) + (x+16) + (x+64) = 83$
$x + x + 16 + x + 64 = 83$
$3x + 80 = 83$
$3x = 3$
$x = 1$
$x + 16 = 17$
$x + 64 = 65$
For every one million U.S. residents, there is 1 drive-in theater, 17 movie theaters, and 65 video rental stores.

14. Let x = the number of years since the car was purchased

$$\text{Value} = 50,750 - 5500x$$
$$12,250 = 50,750 - 5500x$$
$$-38500 = -5500x$$
$$\frac{-38500}{-5500} = \frac{-5500x}{-5500}$$
$$x = 7$$

The car will have a value of $12,250 after 7 years.

15. Let x = the number of prints.

Photo Shop A: $0.11x + 1.60$
Photo Shop B: $0.13x + 1.20$
$$0.13x + 1.20 = 0.11x + 1.60$$
$$0.02x + 1.20 = 1.60$$
$$0.02x = 0.40$$
$$x = 20$$

The cost will be the same for 20 prints.
That common price is
$$0.11(20) + 1.60 = 0.13(20) + 1.20$$
$$= \$3.80$$

16. Let x = the original selling price

$$20 = x - 0.60x$$
$$20 = 0.40x$$
$$50 = x$$

The original price is $50.

17.
$$6 - 9x \geq 33$$
$$6 - 9x - 6 \geq 33 - 6$$
$$-9x \geq 27$$
$$\frac{-9x}{-9} \leq \frac{27}{-9}$$
$$x \leq -3$$
$$\{x \mid x \leq -3\}$$

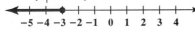

18.
$$4x - 2 > 2(x + 6)$$
$$4x - 2 > 2x + 12$$
$$4x - 2 + 2 > 2x + 12 + 2$$
$$4x > 2x + 14$$
$$4x - 2x > 2x + 14 - 2x$$
$$2x > 14$$
$$\frac{2x}{2} > \frac{14}{2}$$
$$x > 7$$
$$\{x \mid x > 7\}$$

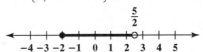

19.
$$-3 \leq 2x + 1 < 6$$
$$-3 - 1 \leq 2x + 1 - 1 < 6 - 1$$
$$-4 \leq 2x < 5$$
$$-2 \leq x < \frac{5}{2}$$
$$\left\{x \;\middle|\; -2 \leq x < \frac{5}{2}\right\}$$

20. Let x = grade on 4th examination.

$$\frac{76 + 80 + 72 + x}{4} \geq 80$$
$$\frac{228 + x}{4} \geq 80$$
$$4 \cdot \frac{228 + x}{4} \geq 80 \cdot 4$$
$$228 + x \geq 320$$
$$228 + x - 228 \geq 320 - 228$$
$$x \geq 92$$

The student must earn at least a 92 to receive a B.

21. $(2x - 5)(3x + 4) = 6x^2 + 8x - 15x - 20$
$$= 6x^2 - 7x - 20$$

22. $2x^2 - 9x + 10 = (2x - 5)(x - 2)$

23.
$$x^2 + 5x = 36$$
$$x^2 + 5x - 36 = 0$$
$$(x + 9)(x - 4) = 0$$
$$x + 9 = 0 \quad \text{or} \quad x - 4 = 0$$
$$x = -9 \qquad\qquad x = 4$$

The solution set is $\{-9, 4\}$.

24. $2x^2 + 4x = -1$

$2x^2 + 4x + 1 = 0$

$x = \dfrac{-b \pm \sqrt{b^2 - 4ac}}{2a}$

$x = \dfrac{-4 \pm \sqrt{4^2 - 4(2)(1)}}{2(2)}$

$x = \dfrac{-4 \pm \sqrt{8}}{4}$

$x = \dfrac{-4 \pm 2\sqrt{2}}{4}$

$x = \dfrac{-2 \pm \sqrt{2}}{2}$

The solution set is $\left\{ \dfrac{-2 - \sqrt{2}}{2}, \ \dfrac{-2 + \sqrt{2}}{2} \right\}$.

25. $43x + 575 = 1177$

$43x = 602$

$x = 14$

The system's income will be $1177 billion 14 years after 2004, or 2018.

26. $B = 0.07x^2 + 47.4x + 500$

$1177 = 0.07x^2 + 47.4x + 500$

$0 = 0.07x^2 + 47.4x - 677$

$0 = 0.07x^2 + 47.4x - 677$

$x = \dfrac{-b \pm \sqrt{b^2 - 4ac}}{2a}$

$x = \dfrac{-(47.4) \pm \sqrt{(47.4)^2 - 4(0.07)(-677)}}{2(0.07)}$

$x \approx 14, \quad x \approx -691 \ (\text{rejected})$

The system's income will be $1177 billion 14 years after 2004, or 2018.

27. The formulas model the data quite well.

Chapter 7
Algebra: Graphs, Functions, and Linear Systems

Check Points 7.1

1.

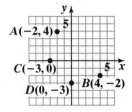

2.

x	$y = 4 - x$	(x, y)
-3	$y = 4 - (-3) = 4 + 3 = 7$	$(-3, 7)$
-2	$y = 4 - (-2) = 4 + 2 = 6$	$(-2, 6)$
-1	$y = 4 - (-1) = 4 + 1 = 5$	$(-1, 5)$
0	$y = 4 - (0) = 4 - 0 = 4$	$(0, 4)$
1	$y = 4 - (1) = 4 - 1 = 3$	$(1, 3)$
2	$y = 4 - (2) = 4 - 2 = 2$	$(2, 2)$
3	$y = 4 - (3) = 4 - 3 = 1$	$(3, 1)$

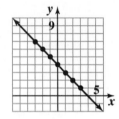

3. **a.** Without the discount pass   With the discount pass

x	$y = 2x$	(x, y)
0	$y = 2(0) = 0$	$(0, 0)$
2	$y = 2(2) = 4$	$(2, 4)$
4	$y = 2(4) = 8$	$(4, 8)$
6	$y = 2(6) = 12$	$(6, 12)$
8	$y = 2(8) = 16$	$(8, 16)$
10	$y = 2(10) = 20$	$(10, 20)$
12	$y = 2(12) = 24$	$(12, 24)$

x	$y = 10 + x$	(x, y)
0	$y = 10 + 0 = 10$	$(0, 10)$
2	$y = 10 + 2 = 12$	$(2, 12)$
4	$y = 10 + 4 = 14$	$(4, 14)$
6	$y = 10 + 6 = 16$	$(6, 16)$
8	$y = 10 + 8 = 18$	$(8, 18)$
10	$y = 10 + 10 = 20$	$(10, 20)$
12	$y = 10 + 12 = 22$	$(12, 22)$

b.

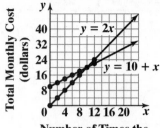

c.   The graphs intersect at $(10, 20)$. This means that if the bridge is used ten times in a month, the total monthly cost is $20 with or without the discount pass.

4. **a.** $f(x) = 4x + 5$

$f(6) = 4(6) + 5$
$= 29$

b. $g(x) = 3x^2 - 10$

$g(-5) = 3(-5)^2 - 10$
$= 65$

c. $h(r) = r^2 - 7r + 2$

$h(-4) = (-4)^2 - 7(-4) + 2$
$= 46$

5. **a.**   A car's required stopping distance at 40 miles an hour on dry pavement is about 190 feet.

b. $f(x) = 0.0875x^2 - 0.4x + 66.6$

$f(40) = 0.0875(40)^2 - 0.4(40) + 66.6 \approx 191$

6.

x	$f(x) = 2x$	(x, y) or $(x, f(x))$
-2	$f(-2) = 2(-2) = -4$	$(-2, -4)$
-1	$f(-1) = 2(-1) = -2$	$(-1, -2)$
0	$f(0) = 2(0) = 0$	$(0, 0)$
1	$f(1) = 2(1) = 2$	$(1, 2)$
2	$f(2) = 2(2) = 4$	$(2, 4)$

x	$g(x) = 2x - 3$	(x, y) or $(x, f(x))$
-2	$g(-2) = 2(-2) - 3 = -7$	$(-2, -7)$
-1	$g(-1) = 2(-1) - 3 = -5$	$(-1, -5)$
0	$g(0) = 2(0) - 3 = -3$	$(0, -3)$
1	$g(1) = 2(1) - 3 = -1$	$(1, -1)$
2	$g(2) = 2(2) - 3 = 1$	$(2, 1)$

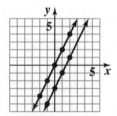

The graph of g is the graph of f shifted vertically down 3 units.

7. a. *y* is a function of *x*.

    b. *y* is a function of *x*.

    c. *y* is not a function of *x*. Two values of *y* correspond to an *x*-value.

8. a. The concentration is increasing from 0 to 3 hours.

    b. The concentration is decreasing from 3 to 13 hours.

    c. The maximum concentration of 0.05 mg per 100 ml occurs after 3 hours.

    d. None of the drug is left in the body.

    e. The graph defines *y* as a function of *x* because no vertical line intersects the graph in more than one point.

Exercise Set 7.1

1.

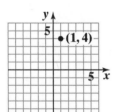

2.

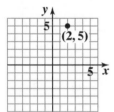

3.

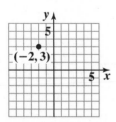

4.

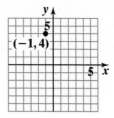

5.

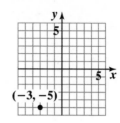

6.

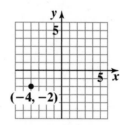

7.

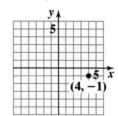

8.

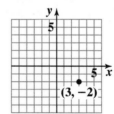

9.

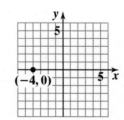

289

10.

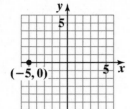

$(-5, 0)$

11.

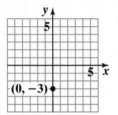

$(0, -3)$

12.

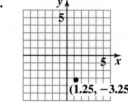

$(0, -4)$

13.

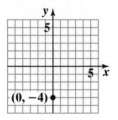

$(0, 0)$

14.

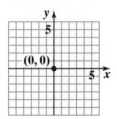

$\left(-3, -1\frac{1}{2}\right)$

15.

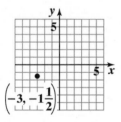

$\left(-2, -3\frac{1}{2}\right)$

16.

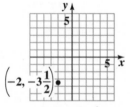

$(-5, -2.5)$

17.

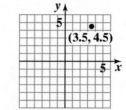

$(3.5, 4.5)$

18.

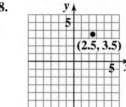

$(2.5, 3.5)$

19.

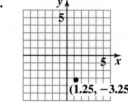

$(1.25, -3.25)$

20.

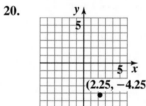

$(2.25, -4.25)$

21.

x	-3	-2	-1	0	1	2	3
$y = x^2 - 2$	7	2	-1	-2	-1	2	7

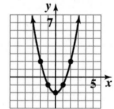

22.

x	-3	-2	-1	0	1	2	3
$y = x^2 + 2$	11	6	3	2	3	6	11

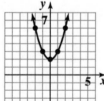

23.

x	-3	-2	-1	0	1	2	3
$y = x - 2$	-5	-4	-3	-2	-1	0	1

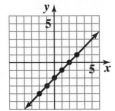

24.

x	-3	-2	-1	0	1	2	3
$y = x + 2$	-1	0	1	2	3	4	5

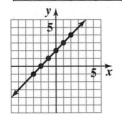

25.

x	-3	-2	-1	0	1	2	3
$y = 2x + 1$	-5	-3	-1	1	3	5	7

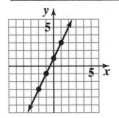

26.

x	-3	-2	-1	0	1	2	3
$y = 2x - 4$	-10	-8	-6	-4	-2	0	2

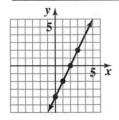

27.

x	-3	-2	-1	0	1	2	3
$y = -\frac{1}{2}x$	$\frac{3}{2}$	1	$\frac{1}{2}$	0	$-\frac{1}{2}$	-1	$-\frac{3}{2}$

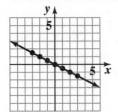

28.

x	-3	-2	-1	0	1	2	3
$y = \frac{-1}{2}x + 2$	$\frac{7}{2}$	3	$\frac{5}{2}$	2	$\frac{3}{2}$	1	$\frac{1}{2}$

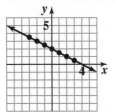

29.

x	-3	-2	-1	0	1	2	3
$y = x^3$	-27	-8	-1	0	1	8	27

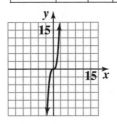

30.

x	-3	-2	-1	0	1	2	3
$y = x^3 - 1$	-28	-9	-2	-1	0	7	26

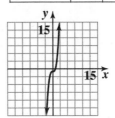

31.

x	-3	-2	-1	0	1	2	3
$y = |x| + 1$	4	3	2	1	2	3	4

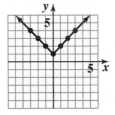

32.

x	-3	-2	-1	0	1	2	3
$y = |x| - 1$	2	1	0	-1	0	1	2

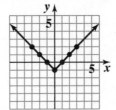

33. $f(x) = x - 4$

   a. $f(8) = 8 - 4 = 4$

   b. $f(1) = 1 - 4 = -3$

34. $f(x) = x - 6$

   a. $f(9) = 9 - 6 = 3$

   b. $f(2) = 2 - 6 = -4$

35. $f(x) = 3x - 2$

   a. $f(7) = 3(7) - 2 = 21 - 2 = 19$

   b. $f(0) = 3(0) - 2 = 0 - 2 = -2$

36. $f(x) = 4x - 3$

   a. $f(7) = 4(7) - 3 = 28 - 3 = 25$

   b. $f(0) = 4(0) - 3 = 0 - 3 = -3$

37. $g(x) = x^2 + 1$

   a. $g(2) = (2)^2 + 1 = 4 + 1 = 5$

   b. $g(-2) = (-2)^2 + 1 = 4 + 1 = 5$

38. $g(x) = x^2 + 4$

   a. $g(3) = (3)^2 + 4 = 9 + 4 = 13$

   b. $g(-3) = (-3)^2 + 4 = 9 + 4 = 13$

39. $g(x) = -x^2 + 2$

   a. $g(4) = -(4)^2 + 2 = -16 + 2 = -14$

   b. $g(-3) = -(-3)^2 + 2 = -9 + 2 = -7$

40. $g(x) = -x^2 + 1$

   a. $g(5) = -(5)^2 + 1 = -25 + 1 = -24$

   b. $g(-4) = -(-4)^2 + 1 = -16 + 1 = -15$

41. $h(r) = 3r^2 + 5$

   a. $h(4) = 3(4)^2 + 5$
$$= 3(16) + 5$$
$$= 48 + 5$$
$$= 53$$

   b. $h(-1) = 3(-1)^2 + 5 = 3 + 5 = 8$

42. $h(r) = 2r^2 - 4$

   a. $h(5) = 2(5)^2 - 4$
$$= 2(25) - 4$$
$$= 50 - 4$$
$$= 46$$

   b. $h(-1) = 2(-1)^2 - 4 = 2 - 4 = -2$

43. $f(x) = 2x^2 + 3x - 1$

   a. $f(3) = 2(3)^2 + 3(3) - 1$
$$= 2(9) + 9 - 1$$
$$= 18 + 9 - 1$$
$$= 26$$

   b. $f(-4) = 2(-4)^2 + 3(-4) - 1$
$$= 2(16) - 12 - 1$$
$$= 32 - 12 - 1$$
$$= 19$$

44. $f(x) = 3x^2 + 4x - 2$

   a. $f(2) = 3(2)^2 + 4(2) - 2$
$$= 3(4) + 8 - 2$$
$$= 12 + 8 - 2$$
$$= 18$$

   b. $f(-1) = 3(-1)^2 + 4(-1) - 2$
$$= 3 - 4 - 2$$
$$= -3$$

45. $f(x) = \dfrac{x}{|x|}$

    a. $f(6) = \dfrac{6}{|6|} = 1$

    b. $f(-6) = \dfrac{-6}{|-6|} = \dfrac{-6}{6} = -1$

46. $f(x) = \dfrac{|x|}{x}$

    a. $f(5) = \dfrac{|5|}{5} = 1$

    b. $f(-5) = \dfrac{|-5|}{-5} = \dfrac{5}{-5} = -1$

47.

x	$f(x) = x^2 - 1$
-2	3
-1	0
0	-1
1	0
2	3

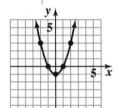

48.

x	$f(x) = x^2 + 1$
-2	5
-1	2
0	1
1	2
2	5

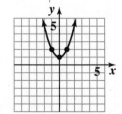

49.

x	$f(x) = x - 1$
-2	-3
-1	-2
0	-1
1	0
2	1

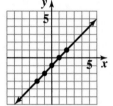

50.

x	$f(x) = x + 1$
-2	-1
-1	0
0	1
1	2
2	3

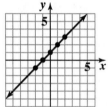

51.

x	$f(x) = (x - 2)^2$
0	4
1	1
2	0
3	1
4	4

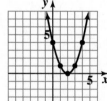

52.

x	$f(x) = (x+1)^2$
–3	4
–2	1
–1	0
0	1
1	4

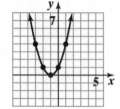

53.

x	$f(x) = x^3 + 1$
–3	–26
–2	–7
–1	0
0	1
1	2

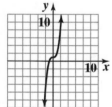

54.

x	$f(x) = (x+1)^3$
–3	–8
–2	–1
–1	0
0	1
1	8

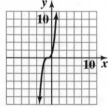

55. y is a function of x.

56. y is a function of x.

57. y is a function of x.

58. y is not a function of x. All values of y correspond to an x-value.

59. y is not a function of x. Two values of y correspond to an x-value.

60. y is not a function of x. Two values of y correspond to an x-value.

61. y is a function of x.

62. y is not a function of x. Two values of y correspond to an x-value.

63.
$$g(1) = 3(1) - 5 = 3 - 5 = -2$$
$$f(g(1)) = f(-2) = (-2)^2 - (-2) + 4$$
$$= 4 + 2 + 4 = 10$$

64.
$$g(-1) = 3(-1) - 5 = -3 - 5 = -8$$
$$f(g(-1)) = f(-8) = (-8)^2 - (-8) + 4$$
$$= 64 + 8 + 4 = 76$$

65.
$$\sqrt{3 - (-1)} - (-6)^2 + 6 \div (-6) \cdot 4$$
$$= \sqrt{3+1} - 36 + 6 \div (-6) \cdot 4$$
$$= \sqrt{4} - 36 + -1 \cdot 4$$
$$= 2 - 36 + -4$$
$$= -34 + -4$$
$$= -38$$

66.
$$\left| -4 - (-1) \right| - (-3)^2 + -3 \div 3 \cdot -6$$
$$= \left| -4 + 1 \right| - 9 + -3 \div 3 \cdot -6$$
$$= \left| -3 \right| - 9 + -1 \cdot -6$$
$$= 3 - 9 + 6 = -6 + 6 = 0$$

67.

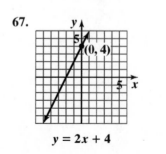

$$y = 2x + 4$$

68.

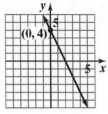

$y = 4 - 2x$

69.

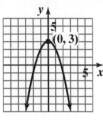

$y = 3 - x^2$

70.

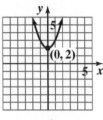

$y = x^2 + 2$

71. The coordinates of point *A* are (2,7). When the football is 2 yards from the quarterback, its height is 7 feet.

72. The coordinates of point *B* are (28,7). When the football is 28 yards from the quarterback, its height is 7 feet.

73. The coordinates of point *C* are approximately (6, 9.25).

74. The coordinates of point *D* are approximately (24, 9.5).

75. The football's maximum height is 12 feet. It reaches this height when it is 15 yards from the quarterback.

76. The football's height is 5 feet when it is caught by the receiver. The receiver is 30 yards from the quarterback when he catches the ball.

77. a. $W(20) = 13.2(20) + 443 = 707$. Approximately 707,000 bachelor's degrees were awarded to women in 2000. This is represented as (20, 707) on the graph.

   b. $W(20)$ overestimates the actual data shown by the bar graph by 2 thousand.

78. a. $M(20) = 3.5(20) + 472 = 542$. Approximately 542,000 bachelor's degrees were awarded to men in 2000. This is represented as (20, 542) on the graph.

   b. $M(20)$ overestimates the actual data shown by the bar graph by 2 thousand.

79. a. $W(10) - M(10) = [13.2(10) + 443] - [3.5(10) + 472] = 575 - 507 = 68$

Approximately 68,000 more bachelor's degrees were awarded to women than to men in 1990. The points on the graph with first coordinate 10 are 68 units apart.

b. $W(10) - M(10)$ overestimates the actual difference of 55 thousand, as shown by the data in the bar graph, by 13 thousand.

80. a. $W(5) - M(5) = [13.2(5) + 443] - [3.5(5) + 472] = 509 - 489.5 = 19.5$

Approximately 19,500 more bachelor's degrees were awarded to women than to men in 1985. The points on the graph with first coordinate 5 are 19.5 units apart.

b. $W(5) - M(5)$ underestimates the actual difference of 20 thousand, as shown by the data in the bar graph, by 0.5 thousand.

81. $f(20) = 0.4(20)^2 - 36(20) + 1000$

$= 0.4(400) - 720 + 1000$

$= 160 - 720 + 1000$

$= -560 + 1000 = 440$

Twenty-year-old drivers have 440 accidents per 50 million miles driven.
This is represented on the graph by point (20,440).

82. $f(50) = 0.4(50)^2 - 36(50) + 1000$

$= 0.4(2500) - 1800 + 1000$

$= 1000 - 1800 + 1000 = 200$

Fifty-year-old drivers have 200 accidents per 50 million miles driven.
This is represented on the graph by point (50,200).

83. The graph reaches its lowest point at $x = 45$.

$f(45) = 0.4(45)^2 - 36(45) + 1000$

$= 0.4(2025) - 1620 + 1000$

$= 810 - 1620 + 1000$

$= -810 + 1000$

$= 190$

Drivers at age 45 have 190 accidents per 50 million miles driven. This is the least number of accidents for any driver between ages 16 and 74.

84. Answers will vary.
One possible answer is age 16 and age 74.

$f(16) = 0.4(16)^2 - 36(16) + 1000$

$= 0.4(256) - 576 + 1000$

$= 102.4 - 576 + 1000 = 526.4$

$f(74) = 0.4(74)^2 - 36(74) + 1000$

$= 0.4(5476) - 2664 + 1000$

$= 2190.4 - 2664 + 1000 = 526.4$

Both 16-year-olds and 74-year-olds have approximately 526.4 accidents per 50 million miles driven.

91. makes sense

92. does not make sense; Explanations will vary. Sample explanation: The notation $f(x)$ does not mean multiplication of f by x.

93. makes sense

94. makes sense

95. $f(-1) + g(-1) = 1 + (-3) = -2$

96. $f(1) + g(1) = 3 + (-5) = -2$

97. $f(g(-1)) = f(-3) = 1$

98. $f(g(1)) = f(-5) = 3$

Check Points 7.2

1. Find the x-intercept by setting $y = 0$
$$2x + 3(0) = 6$$
$$2x = 6$$
$$x = 3; \text{ resulting point } (3, 0)$$
Find the y-intercept by setting $x = 0$
$$2(0) + 3y = 6$$
$$3y = 6$$
$$y = 2; \text{ resulting point } (0, 2)$$
Find a checkpoint by substituting any value.
$$2(1) + 3y = 6$$
$$2 + 3y = 6$$
$$3y = 4$$
$$y = \frac{4}{3}; \text{ resulting point } \left(1, \frac{4}{3}\right)$$

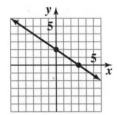

2. a. $m = \dfrac{-2 - 4}{-4 - (-3)} = \dfrac{-6}{-1} = 6$

b. $m = \dfrac{5 - (-2)}{-1 - 4} = \dfrac{7}{-5} = -\dfrac{7}{5}$

3. Step 1. Plot the y-intercept of $(0, 1)$

Step 2. Obtain a second point using the slope m.
$$m = \frac{3}{5} = \frac{\text{Rise}}{\text{Run}}$$
Starting from the y-intercept move up 3 units and move 5 units to the right. This puts the second point at $(3, 6)$.

Step 3. Draw the line through the two points.

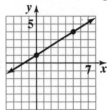

4. Solve for y.
$$3x + 4y = 0$$
$$4y = -3x + 0$$
$$\frac{4y}{4} = \frac{-3x}{4} + \frac{0}{4}$$
$$y = \frac{-3}{4}x + 0$$
$m = \dfrac{-3}{4}$ and the y-intercept is $(0, 0)$

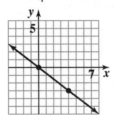

5. Draw horizontal line that intersects the y-axis at 3.

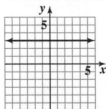

6. Draw vertical line that intersects the x-axis at -2.

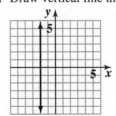

7. The two points shown on the line segment for Medicare are (2007, 446) and (2016, 909).

$$m = \frac{909 - 446}{2016 - 2007} = \frac{463}{9} \approx 51.4$$

The slope indicates that for the period from 2007 through 2016, the cost of Medicare is projected to increase by approximately \$51.4 billion per year. The rate of change is approximately \$51.4 billion per year.

8. a. Find slope by using the endpoints of the line segment.

$$m = \frac{12,680 - 5791}{9 - 0} = \frac{6889}{9} \approx 765$$

The value of b is the y-intercept, or 5791. Thus, $F(x) = mx + b$ becomes

$$F(x) = 765x + 5791.$$

b. $F(x) = 765x + 5791$

$F(12) = 765(12) + 5791 = 14,971$

The average premium for family coverage is projected to be \$14,971

Exercise Set 7.2

1. Find the x-intercept by setting $y = 0$

$x - y = 3$

$x - 0 = 3$

$x = 3$; resulting point (3, 0)

Find the y-intercept by setting $x = 0$

$0 - y = 3$

$-y = 3$

$y = -3$; resulting point (0, −3)

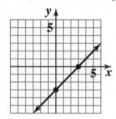

2. Find the x-intercept by setting $y = 0$

$x + y = 4$

$x + 0 = 4$

$x = 4$; resulting point (4, 0)

Find the y-intercept by setting $x = 0$

$0 + y = 4$

$y = 4$; resulting point (0, 4)

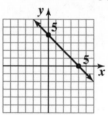

3. Find the x-intercept by setting $y = 0$

$3x - 4(0) = 12$

$3x = 12$

$x = 4$; resulting point (4, 0)

Find the y-intercept by setting $x = 0$

$3(0) - 4y = 12$

$-4y = 12$

$y = -3$; resulting point (0, −3)

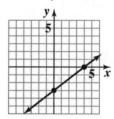

4. Find the x-intercept by setting $y = 0$

$2x - 5(0) = 10$

$2x = 10$

$x = 5$; resulting point (5, 0)

Find the y-intercept by setting $x = 0$

$2(0) - 5y = 10$

$-5y = 10$

$y = -2$; resulting point (0, −2)

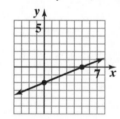

5. Find the *x*-intercept by setting $y = 0$
$$2x + 0 = 6$$
$$2x = 6$$
$$x = 3; \text{ resulting point } (3, 0)$$

Find the *y*-intercept by setting $x = 0$
$$2(0) + y = 6$$
$$y = 6; \text{ resulting point } (0, 6)$$

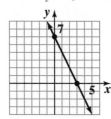

6. Find the *x*-intercept by setting $y = 0$
$$x + 3(0) = 6$$
$$x = 6; \text{ resulting point } (6, 0)$$

Find the *y*-intercept by setting $x = 0$
$$0 + 3y = 6$$
$$3y = 6$$
$$y = 2; \text{ resulting point } (0, 2)$$

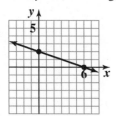

7. Find the *x*-intercept by setting $y = 0$
$$5x = 3(0) - 15$$
$$5x = -15$$
$$x = -3; \text{ resulting point } (-3, 0)$$

Find the *y*-intercept by setting $x = 0$
$$5(0) = 3y - 15$$
$$0 = 3y - 15$$
$$-3y = -15$$
$$y = 5; \text{ resulting point } (0, 5)$$

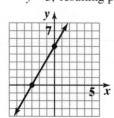

8. Find the *x*-intercept by setting $y = 0$
$$3x = 2(0) + 6$$
$$3x = 6$$
$$x = 2; \text{ resulting point } (2, 0)$$

Find the *y*-intercept by setting $x = 0$
$$3(0) = 2y + 6$$
$$0 = 2y + 6$$
$$-2y = 6$$
$$y = -3; \text{ resulting point } (0, -3)$$

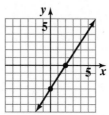

9. $m = \dfrac{5-6}{3-2} = \dfrac{-1}{1} = -1$; line falls.

10. $m = \dfrac{4-2}{3-4} = \dfrac{2}{-1} = -2$; line falls.

11. $m = \dfrac{2-1}{2-(-2)} = \dfrac{1}{4}$; line rises.

12. $m = \dfrac{4-3}{2-(-1)} = \dfrac{1}{3}$; line rises.

13. $m = \dfrac{-1-4}{-1-(-2)} = \dfrac{-5}{1} = -5$; line falls.

14. $m = \dfrac{-2-(-4)}{4-6} = \dfrac{2}{-2} = -1$; line falls.

15. $m = \dfrac{-2-3}{5-5} = \dfrac{-5}{0}$;
Slope undefined. Line is vertical.

16. $m = \dfrac{5-(-4)}{3-3} = \dfrac{9}{0}$;
Slope undefined. Line is vertical.

17. $m = \dfrac{8-0}{0-2} = \dfrac{8}{-2} = -4$; line falls.

18. $m = \dfrac{-9-0}{0-3} = \dfrac{-9}{-3} = 3$; line rises.

19. $m = \dfrac{1-1}{-2-5} = \dfrac{0}{-7} = 0$; line is horizontal.

20. $m = \dfrac{3-3}{1-(-2)} = \dfrac{0}{3} = 0$; line is horizontal.

21. $y = 2x + 3$
Slope: 2, y-intercept: 3
Plot point (0, 3) and second point using
$$m = \frac{2}{1} = \frac{\text{rise}}{\text{run}}$$

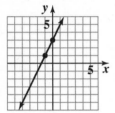

22. $y = 2x + 1$
Slope: 2, y-intercept: 1
Plot point (0, 1) and second point using
$$m = \frac{2}{1} = \frac{\text{rise}}{\text{run}}$$

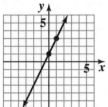

23. $y = -2x + 4$
Slope: -2, y-intercept: 4
Plot point (0, 4) and second point using
$$m = \frac{-2}{1} = \frac{\text{rise}}{\text{run}}$$

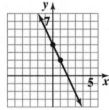

24. $y = -2x + 3$
Slope: -2, y-intercept: 3
Plot point (0, 3) and second point using
$$m = \frac{-2}{1} = \frac{\text{rise}}{\text{run}}$$

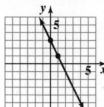

25. $y = \dfrac{1}{2}x + 3$

Slope: $\dfrac{1}{2}$, y-intercept: 3

Plot point (0, 3) and second point using
$$m = \frac{1}{2} = \frac{\text{rise}}{\text{run}}.$$

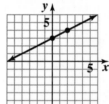

26. $y = \dfrac{1}{2}x + 2$

Slope: $\dfrac{1}{2}$, y-intercept: 2

Plot point (0, 2) and second point using
$$m = \frac{1}{2} = \frac{\text{rise}}{\text{run}}.$$

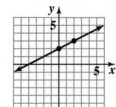

27. $f(x) = \dfrac{2}{3}x - 4$

Slope: $\dfrac{2}{3}$, y-intercept: -4

Plot point $(0, -4)$ and second point using

$m = \dfrac{2}{3} = \dfrac{\text{rise}}{\text{run}}$.

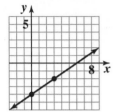

28. $f(x) = \dfrac{3}{4}x - 5$

Slope: $\dfrac{3}{4}$, y-intercept: -5

Plot point $(0, -5)$ and second point using

$m = \dfrac{3}{4} = \dfrac{\text{rise}}{\text{run}}$.

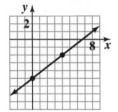

29. $y = -\dfrac{3}{4}x + 4$

Slope: $-\dfrac{3}{4}$, y-intercept: 4

Plot point $(0, 4)$ and second point using

$m = \dfrac{-3}{4} = \dfrac{\text{rise}}{\text{run}}$.

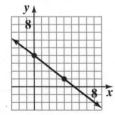

30. $y = -\dfrac{2}{3}x + 5$

Slope: $-\dfrac{2}{3}$, y-intercept: 5

Plot point $(0, 5)$ and second point using

$m = \dfrac{-2}{3} = \dfrac{\text{rise}}{\text{run}}$.

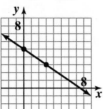

31. $f(x) = -\dfrac{5}{3}x$ or $f(x) = -\dfrac{5}{3}x + 0$

Slope: $-\dfrac{5}{3}$, y-intercept: 0

Plot point $(0, 0)$ and second point using

$m = \dfrac{-5}{3} = \dfrac{\text{rise}}{\text{run}}$.

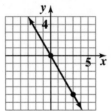

32. $f(x) = -\dfrac{4}{3}x$ or $f(x) = -\dfrac{4}{3}x + 0$

Slope: $-\dfrac{4}{3}$, y-intercept: 0

Plot point $(0, 0)$ and second point using

$m = \dfrac{-4}{3} = \dfrac{\text{rise}}{\text{run}}$.

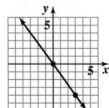

33. a. $3x + y = 0$

$y = -3x$ or $y = -3x + 0$

b. Slope $= -3$
y-intercept $= 0$

c.

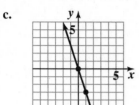

34. a. $2x + y = 0$
$y = -2x$ or $y = -2x + 0$

b. Slope $= -2$
y-intercept $= 0$

c.

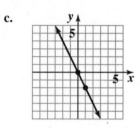

35. a. $3y = 4x$

$y = \dfrac{4}{3}x$ or $y = \dfrac{4}{3}x + 0$

b. Slope $= \dfrac{4}{3}$

y-intercept $= 0$

c.

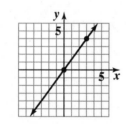

36. a. $4y = 5x$

$y = \dfrac{5}{4}x$ or $y = \dfrac{5}{4}x + 0$

b. Slope $= \dfrac{5}{4}$

y-intercept $= 0$

c.

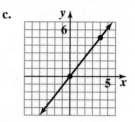

37. a. $2x + y = 3$

$y = -2x + 3$

b. Slope $= -2$
y-intercept $= 3$

c.

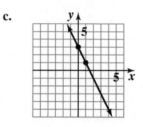

38. a. $3x + y = 4$

$y = -3x + 4$

b. Slope $= -3$
y-intercept $= 4$

c.

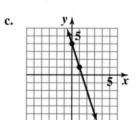

39. a. $7x + 2y = 14$

$2y = -7x + 14$

$y = -\dfrac{7}{2}x + 7$

b. Slope $= -\dfrac{7}{2}$

y-intercept $= 7$

c.

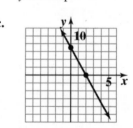

40. a. $5x + 3y = 15$

$$3y = -5x + 15$$

$$y = \frac{-5}{3}x + 5$$

b. Slope $= -\dfrac{5}{3}$

  y-intercept $= 5$

c.

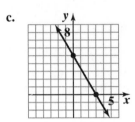

41. $y = 4$

42. $y = 2$

43. $y = -2$

44. $y = -3$

45. $x = 2$

46. $x = 4$

47. $x + 1 = 0$ or $x = -1$

48. $x + 5 = 0$ or $x = -5$

49. $m = \dfrac{0 - a}{b - 0} = \dfrac{-a}{b} = -\dfrac{a}{b}$

Since a and b are both positive, $-\dfrac{a}{b}$ is negative.
Therefore, the line falls.

50. $m = \dfrac{-b - 0}{0 - (-a)} = \dfrac{-b}{a} = -\dfrac{b}{a}$

Since a and b are both positive, $-\dfrac{b}{a}$ is negative.
Therefore, the line falls.

51. $m = \dfrac{(b + c) - b}{a - a} = \dfrac{c}{0}$

The slope is undefined.
The line is vertical.

52. $m = \dfrac{(a+c)-c}{a-(a-b)} = \dfrac{a}{b}$

Since a and b are both positive, $\dfrac{a}{b}$ is positive.

Therefore, the line rises.

53. $Ax + By = C$

$By = -Ax + C$

$y = -\dfrac{A}{B}x + \dfrac{C}{B}$

The slope is $-\dfrac{A}{B}$ and the y-intercept is $\dfrac{C}{B}$.

54. $Ax = By - C$

$Ax + C = By$

$\dfrac{A}{B}x + \dfrac{C}{B} = y$

The slope is $\dfrac{A}{B}$ and the y-intercept is $\dfrac{C}{B}$.

55. $-3 = \dfrac{4-y}{1-3}$

$-3 = \dfrac{4-y}{-2}$

$6 = 4 - y$

$2 = -y$

$-2 = y$

56. $\dfrac{1}{3} = \dfrac{-4-y}{4-(-2)}$

$\dfrac{1}{3} = \dfrac{-4-y}{4+2}$

$\dfrac{1}{3} = \dfrac{-4-y}{6}$

$6 = 3(-4-y)$

$6 = -12 - 3y$

$18 = -3y$

$-6 = y$

57. $m_1, \ m_3, \ m_2, \ m_4$

58. $b_2, \ b_1, \ b_4, \ b_3$

59. Find slope by using the endpoints of the line segment.

$m = \dfrac{10.8 - 12.9}{2007 - 2000} = \dfrac{-2.1}{7} = -0.3$

The slope indicates that for the period from 2000 through 2007, the percentage of total sales of rap-hip hop was decreasing by 0.3 per year.

60. Find slope by using the endpoints of the line segment.

$m = \dfrac{32.4 - 24.8}{2007 - 2000} = \dfrac{7.6}{7} \approx 1.1$

The slope indicates that for the period from 2000 through 2007, the percentage of total sales of rock was increasing by 1.1 per year.

61. $P(x) = -1.2x + 47$

62. $P(x) = 1.3x + 23$

63. a. Find slope by using the endpoints of the line segment.

$m = \dfrac{46 - 68}{42 - 0} \approx -0.52$

The value of b is the y-intercept, or 68.

$P(x) = mx + b$

$P(x) = -0.52x + 68$

b. $P(x) = -0.52x + 68$

$P(100) = -0.52(100) + 68$

$= 16$

In the year 2108, the percentage of whites in the U.S. will be about 16%.

64. a. Find slope by using the endpoints of the line segment.

$m = \dfrac{30 - 15}{42 - 0} \approx 0.36$

The value of b is the y-intercept, or 15.

$P(x) = mx + b$

$P(x) = 0.36x + 15$

b. $P(x) = 0.36x + 15$

$P(100) = 0.36(100) + 15$

$= 51$

In the year 2108, the percentage of whites in the U.S. will be about 51%.

74. does not make sense; Explanations will vary. Sample explanation: Either point can be considered (x_1, y_1) or (x_2, y_2).

75. does not make sense; Explanations will vary. Sample explanation: Since college cost are going up, this function has a positive slope.

76. does not make sense; Explanations will vary. Sample explanation: The slope of lines whose equations are in this form can be determined in several ways. One such way is to rewrite the equation in slope-intercept form.

77. makes sense

78. false; Changes to make the statement true will vary. A sample change is: It is possible for $m = b$.

79. false; Changes to make the statement true will vary. A sample change is: Vertical lines can not be expressed in slope-intercept form.

80. true

81. false; Changes to make the statement true will vary. A sample change is: The line $2y = 3x + 7$ is equivalent to $y = \dfrac{3}{2}x + \dfrac{7}{2}$ which has a y-intercept of $\dfrac{7}{2}$.

82. First, find the slope using the points $(0, 32)$ and $(100, 212)$.

$$m = \frac{212 - 32}{100 - 0} = \frac{180}{100} = \frac{9}{5}$$

The slope, m, is $\dfrac{9}{5}$ and the y-intercept, b, is 32.

Instead of $y = mx + b$ we will use $F = mC + b$.

$F = mC + b$

$F = \dfrac{9}{5}C + 32$

Check Points 7.3

1. Replace x with -4 and y with 3.

$$
\begin{array}{ll}
x + 2y = 2 & x - 2y = 6 \\
-4 + 2(3) = 2 & -4 - 2(3) = 6 \\
-4 + 6 = 2 & -4 - 6 = 6 \\
2 = 2 \text{ true} & -10 = 6 \text{ false}
\end{array}
$$

The pair $(-4, 3)$ does not satisfy both equations. Therefore it is not a solution of the system.

2.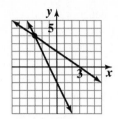

Check coordinates of intersection:

$$
\begin{array}{ll}
2x + 3y = 6 & 2x + y = -2 \\
2(-3) + 3(4) = 6 & 2(-3) + (4) = -2 \\
-6 + 12 = 6 & -6 + 2 = -2 \\
6 = 6, \text{ true} & -2 = -2, \text{ true}
\end{array}
$$

The solution set is $\{(-3, 4)\}$.

3. Step 1.   Solve one of the equations for one variable: $y = 3x - 7$

Step 2.   Substitute into the other equation:

$$5x - 2y = 8$$

$$5x - 2\overbrace{(3x - 7)}^{y} = 8$$

Step 3.   Solve: $5x - 2(3x - 7) = 8$

$$5x - 6x + 14 = 8$$
$$-x + 14 = 8$$
$$-x = -6$$
$$x = 6$$

Step 4.   Back-substitute the obtained value into the equation from step 1:

$$y = 3x - 7$$
$$y = 3(6) - 7$$
$$y = 11$$

Step 5.   Check (6, 11) in both equations:

$$
\begin{array}{ll}
y = 3x - 7 & 5x - 2y = 8 \\
11 = 3(6) - 7 & 5(6) - 2(11) = 8 \\
11 = 11, \text{ true} & 8 = 8, \text{ true}
\end{array}
$$

The solution set is $\{(6, 11)\}$.

4. Step 1. Solve one of the equations for one variable:

$x - y = 3$

$x = y + 3$

Step 2. Substitute into the other equation:

$3x + 2y = -1$

$3\overbrace{(y+3)}^{x} + 2y = -1$

Step 3. Solve: $3(y+3) + 2y = -1$

$3y + 9 + 2y = -1$

$5y + 9 = -1$

$5y = -10$

$y = -2$

Step 4. Back-substitute the obtained value into the equation from step 1:

$x = y + 3$

$x = -2 + 3$

$x = 1$

Step 5. Check $(1, -2)$ in both equations:

$x - y = 3 \qquad\qquad 3x + 2y = -1$

$1 - (-2) = 3 \qquad\quad 3(1) + 2(-2) = -1$

$3 = 3$, true $\qquad\qquad -1 = -1$, true

The solution set is $\{(1, -2)\}$.

5. Rewrite one or both equations:

$4x + 5y = 3 \xrightarrow{\text{No change}} 4x + 5y = 3$

$2x - 3y = 7 \xrightarrow{\text{Mult. by } -2} \underline{-4x + 6y = -14}$

$11y = -11$

$y = -1$

Back-substitute into either equation:

$4x + 5y = 3$

$4x + 5(-1) = 3$

$4x - 5 = 3$

$4x = 8$

$x = 2$

Checking confirms the solution set is $\{(2, -1)\}$.

6. Rewrite both equations in the form $Ax + By = C$:

$3x = 2 - 4y \quad \rightarrow \quad 3x + 4y = 2$

$5y = -1 - 2x \quad \rightarrow \quad 2x + 5y = -1$

Rewrite with opposite coefficients, then add and solve:

$3x + 4y = 2 \xrightarrow{\text{Mult. by } 2} 6x + 8y = 4$

$2x + 5y = -1 \xrightarrow{\text{Mult. by } -3} \underline{-6x - 15y = 3}$

$-7y = 7$

$y = -1$

Back-substitute into either equation:

$3x = 2 - 4y$

$3x = 2 - 4(-1)$

$3x = 6$

$x = 2$

Checking confirms the solution set is $\{(2, -1)\}$.

7. Rewrite with a pair of opposite coefficients, then add:

$x + 2y = 4 \xrightarrow{\text{Mult. by } -3} -3x - 6y = -12$

$3x + 6y = 13 \xrightarrow{\text{No change}} \underline{3x + 6y = 13}$

$0 = 1$

The statement $0 = 1$ is false which indicates that the system has no solution. The solution set is the empty set, $\varnothing$.

8. Substitute $4x - 4$ for y in the other equation:

$8x - 2\overbrace{(4x-4)}^{y} = 8$

$8x - 8x + 8 = 8$

$8 = 8$

The statement $8 = 8$ is true which indicates that the system has infinitely many solutions. The solution set is $\{(x, y) | y = 4x - 4\}$ **or** $\{(x, y) | 8x - 2y = 8\}$.

9. a. $C(x) = 300,000 + 30x$

b. $R(x) = 80x$

c. $R(x) = C(x)$

$80x = 300,000 + 30x$

$50x = 300,000$

$x = 6000$

$C(6000) = 300,000 + 30(6000) = 480,000$

Break even point $(6000, 480000)$

The company will need to make 6000 pairs of shoes and earn $480,000 to break even.

Exercise Set 7.3

1. Replace x with 2 and y with 3.

$x + 3y = 11$ $x - 5y = -13$

$2 + 3(3) = 11$ $2 - 5(3) = 13$

$2 + 9 = 11$ $2 - 15 = 13$

$11 = 11$, true $13 = 13$, true

The pair (2, 3) is a solution of the system.

2. Replace x with –3 and y with 5.

$9x + 7y = 8$ $8x - 9y = -69$

$9(-3) + 7(5) = 8$ $8(-3) - 9(5) = -69$

$-27 + 35 = 8$ $-24 - 45 = -69$

$8 = 8$, true $-69 = -69$, true

The pair (–3, 5) is a solution of the system.

3. Replace x with 2 and y with 5.

$2x + 3y = 17$

$2(2) + 3(5) = 17$

$4 + 15 = 17$

$19 = 17$, false.

The pair (2, 5) is not a solution of the system.

4. Replace x with 8 and y with 5.

$5x - 4y = 20$ $3y = 2x + 1$

$5(8) - 4(5) = 20$ $3(5) = 2(8) + 1$

$40 - 20 = 20$ $15 = 16 + 1$

$20 = 20$, true $15 = 17$, false

The pair (8, 5) is not a solution of the system.

5.

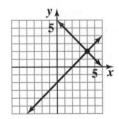

Check coordinates of intersection:

$x + y = 6$ $x - y = 2$

$4 + 2 = 6$ $4 - 2 = 2$

$6 = 6$, true $2 = 2$, true

The solution set is $\{(4, 2)\}$.

6.

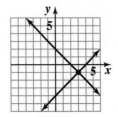

Check coordinates of intersection:

$x + y = 2$ $x - y = 4$

$3 + (-1) = 2$ $3 - (-1) = 4$

$2 = 2$, true $4 = 4$, true

The solution set is $\{(3, -1)\}$.

7.

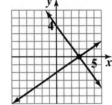

Check coordinates of intersection:

$2x - 3y = 6$ $4x + 3y = 12$

$2(3) - 3(0) = 6$ $4(3) + (0) = 12$

$6 = 6$, true $12 = 12$, true

The solution set is $\{(3, 0)\}$.

8.

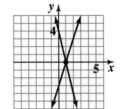

Check coordinates of intersection:

$4x + y = 4$ $3x - y = 3$

$4(1) + 0 = 4$ $3(1) - (0) = 3$

$4 = 4$, true $3 = 3$, true

The solution set is $\{(1, 0)\}$.

9.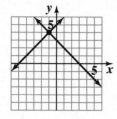

Check coordinates of intersection:

$y = x + 5$ $y = -x + 3$

$4 = -1 + 5$ $4 = -(-1) + 3$

$4 = 4$, true $4 = 4$, true

The solution set is $\{(-1, 4)\}$.

10.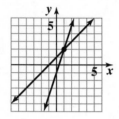

Check coordinates of intersection:

$y = x + 1$ $y = 3x - 1$

$2 = 1 + 1$ $2 = 3(1) - 1$

$2 = 2$, true $2 = 2$, true

The solution set is $\{(1, 2)\}$.

11.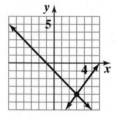

Check coordinates of intersection:

$y = -x - 1$ $4x - 3y = 24$

$-4 = -(3) - 1$ $4(3) - 3(-4) = 24$

$-4 = -4$, true $24 = 24$, true

The solution set is $\{(3, -4)\}$.

12.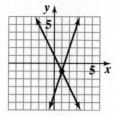

Check coordinates of intersection:

$y = 3x - 4$ $2x + y = 1$

$-1 = 3(1) - 4$ $2(1) + (-1) = 1$

$-1 = -1$, true $1 = 1$, true

The solution set is $\{(1, -1)\}$.

13. $y = 3x$ $x + y = 4$

$x + 3x = 4$

$\qquad 4x = 4$

$\qquad x = 1$

$y = 3(1) = 3$

The proposed solution is $(1, 3)$

Check: $3 = 3(1)$ $1 + 3 = 4$

$\qquad\qquad 3 = 3$, true $4 = 4$, true

The pair $(1, 3)$ satisfies both equations.

The system's solution set is $\{(1, 3)\}$.

14. $y = 2x$ $x + y = 6$

$x + 2x = 6$

$\qquad 3x = 6$

$\qquad x = 2$

$y = 2(2) = 4$

The proposed solution is $(2, 4)$.

Check: $4 = 2(2)$ $2 + 4 = 6$

$\qquad\qquad 4 = 4$, true $6 = 6$, true

The pair $(2, 4)$ satisfies both equations.

The system's solution set is $\{(2, 4)\}$.

15. $y = 2x - 9$ $x + 3y = 8$

$x + 3(2x - 9) = 8$

$\quad x + 6x - 27 = 8$

$\qquad\qquad 7x = 35$

$\qquad\qquad x = 5$

$y = 2(5) - 9 = 1$

The proposed solution is $(5, 1)$.

Check:

$1 = 2(5) - 9$ $5 + 3(1) = 8$

$1 = 10 - 9$ $5 + 3 = 8$

$1 = 1$, true $8 = 8$, true

The pair $(5, 1)$ satisfies both equations.

The system's solution set is $\{(5, 1)\}$.

16. $y = 2x + 7 \qquad 2x - 3y = -13$
$2x - 3(2x + 7) = -13$
$2x - 6x - 21 = -13$
$-4x = 8$
$x = -2$
$y = 2(-2) + 7 = -4 + 7 = 3$
The proposed solution is $(-2, 3)$.
Check:
$2(-2) - 3(3) = -13 \qquad 3 = 2(-2) + 7$
$-4 - 9 = -13 \qquad 3 = -4 + 7$
$-13 = -13$, true $\quad 3 = 3$, true
The pair $(-2, 3)$ satisfies both equations.
The system's solution set is $\{(-2, 3)\}$.

17. $x + 3y = 5$
$x = 5 - 3y \quad 4x + 5y = 13$
$4(5 - 3y) + 5y = 13$
$20 - 12y + 5y = 13$
$20 - 7y = 13$
$-7y = -7$
$y = 1$
$x = 5 - 3(1) = 2$
The proposed solution is $(2, 1)$.

Check:
$2 + 3(1) = 5 \qquad 4(2) + 5(1) = 13$
$5 = 5$, true $\qquad 8 + 5 = 13$
$13 = 13$, true
The pair $(2, 1)$ satisfies both equations.
The system's solution set is $\{(2, 1)\}$.

18. Substitute $2x + 7$ for y into $2x - y = -15$

$$2x - \overbrace{(2x + 7)}^{y} = -15$$
$2x - 2x - 7 = -15$
$-7 = -15$, false
The system's solution set is $\varnothing$.

19. $2x - y = -5$
$y = 2x + 5 \quad x + 5y = 14$
$x + 5(2x + 5) = 14$
$x + 10x + 25 = 14$
$11x = -11$
$x = -1$
$y = 2(-1) + 5 = -2 + 5 = 3$
The proposed solution is $(-1, 3)$.
Check:
$2(-1) - 3 = -5 \qquad -1 + 5(3) = 14$
$-2 - 3 = -5 \qquad -1 + 15 = 14$
$-5 = -5$, true $\qquad 14 = 14$, true
The pair $(-1, 3)$ satisfies both equations.
The system's solution set is $\{(-1, 3)\}$.

20. $x - 4y = 0$
$x = 4y \qquad 2x + 3y = 11$
$2(4y) + 3y = 11$
$8y + 3y = 11$
$11y = 11$
$y = 1$
$x = 4(1) = 4$
The proposed solution is $(4, 1)$.
Check:
$4 - 4(1) = 0 \qquad 2(4) + 3(1) = 11$
$0 = 0$, true $\qquad 8 + 3 = 11$
$11 = 11$, true
The pair $(4, 1)$ satisfies both equations.
The system's solution set is $\{(4, 1)\}$.

21. $2x - y = 3$
$y = 2x - 3 \quad 5x - 2y = 10$
$5x - 2(2x - 3) = 10$
$5x - 4x + 6 = 10$
$x = 4$
$y = 2(4) - 3 = 8 - 3 = 5$
The proposed solution is $(4, 5)$.
Check:
$2(4) - 5 = 3 \qquad 5(4) - 2(5) = 10$
$8 - 5 = 3 \qquad 20 - 10 = 10$
$3 = 3$, true $\qquad 10 = 10$, true
The pair $(4, 5)$ satisfies both equations.
The system's solution set is $\{(4, 5)\}$.

22. $-x + 3y = 10$
$x = 3y - 10$ $2x + 8y = -6$
$2(3y - 10) + 8y = -6$
$6y - 20 + 8y = -6$
$14y = 14$
$y = 1$
$x = 3(1) - 10 = -7$
The proposed solution is $(-7, 1)$.
Check:
$-(-7) + 3(1) = 10$ $2(-7) + 8(1) = -6$
$7 + 3 = 10$ $-14 + 8 = -6$
$10 = 10, \text{true}$ $-6 = -6, \text{true}$
The pair $(-7, 1)$ satisfies both equations.
The system's solution set is $\{(-7, 1)\}$.

23. $x + 8y = 6$
$x = 6 - 8y$ $2x + 4y = -3$
$2(6 - 8y) + 4y = -3$
$12 - 16y + 4y = -3$
$-12y = -15$
$\dfrac{-12y}{-12} = \dfrac{-15}{-12}$
$y = \dfrac{15}{12} = \dfrac{5}{4}$
$x = 6 - 8\left(\dfrac{5}{4}\right) = 6 - 10 = -4$

The proposed solution is $\left(-4, \dfrac{5}{4}\right)$

Check:
$-4 + 8\left(\dfrac{5}{4}\right) = 6$ $2(-4) + 4\left(\dfrac{5}{4}\right) = -3$
$-4 + 10 = 6$ $-8 + 5 = -3$
$6 = 6, \text{true}$ $-3 = -3, \text{true}$

The pair $\left(-4, \dfrac{5}{4}\right)$ satisfies both equations.

The system's solution set is $\left\{\left(-4, \dfrac{5}{4}\right)\right\}$.

24. $-4x + y = -11$
$y = -11 + 4x$ $2x - 3y = 5$
$2x - 3(-11 + 4x) = 5$
$2x + 33 - 12x = 5$
$-10x = -28$
$x = \dfrac{28}{10}$
$x = \dfrac{14}{5}$
$y = -11 + 4\left(\dfrac{14}{5}\right) = \dfrac{-55}{5} + \dfrac{56}{5} = \dfrac{1}{5}$

The proposed solution is $\left(\dfrac{14}{5}, \dfrac{1}{5}\right)$.

Check:
$-4\left(\dfrac{14}{5}\right) + \left(\dfrac{1}{5}\right) = -11$ $2\left(\dfrac{14}{5}\right) - 3\left(\dfrac{1}{5}\right) = 5$
$\dfrac{-56}{5} + \dfrac{1}{5} = -11$ $\dfrac{28}{5} - \dfrac{3}{5} = 5$
$\dfrac{-55}{5} = -11$ $\dfrac{25}{5} = 5$
$-11 = -11, \text{true}$ $5 = 5, \text{true}$

The pair $\left(\dfrac{14}{5}, \dfrac{1}{5}\right)$ satisfies both equations.

The system's solution set is $\left\{\left(\dfrac{14}{5}, \dfrac{1}{5}\right)\right\}$.

25. $x + y = 1$
$\underline{x - y = 3}$
$2x = 4$
$x = 2$
$x + y = 1$
$2 + y = 1$
$y = -1$
Check: $2 + (-1) = 1$ $2 - (-1) = 3$
$1 = 1, \text{true}$ $3 = 3, \text{true}$
The solution set is $\{(2, -1)\}$.

26. $x + y = 6$

$\underline{x - y = -2}$

$2x \quad = 4$

$x \quad = 2$

$x + y = 6$

$2 + y = 6$

$y = 4$

Check: $2 + 4 = 6 \qquad 2 - 4 = -2$

$\qquad\qquad 6 = 6$, true $\quad -2 = -2$, true

The solution set is $\{(2, 4)\}$.

27. $2x + 3y = 6$

$\underline{2x - 3y = 6}$

$4x = 12$

$x = 3$

$2x + 3y = 6$

$2 \cdot 3 + 3y = 6$

$6 + 3y = 6$

$3y = 0$

$y = 0$

Check:

$2(3) + 3(0) = 6 \qquad 2(3) - 3(0) = 6$

$\qquad 6 + 0 = 6 \qquad\qquad 6 - 0 = 6$

$\qquad\qquad 6 = 6$, true $\qquad\qquad 6 = 6$, true

The solution set is $\{(3, 0)\}$.

28. $3x + 2y = 14$

$\underline{3x - 2y = 10}$

$6x \quad = 24$

$x \quad = 4$

$3x + 2y = 14$

$3 \cdot 4 + 2y = 14$

$12 + 2y = 14$

$2y = 2$

$y = 1$

Check:

$3(4) + 2(1) = 14 \qquad 3(4) - 2(1) = 10$

$\quad 12 + 2 = 14 \qquad\qquad 12 - 2 = 10$

$\qquad\quad 14 = 14$, true $\qquad\quad 10 = 10$, true

The solution set is $\{(4, 1)\}$.

29. $x + 2y = 2$ Mult. by 3. $3x + 6y = 6$

$-4x + 3y = 25$ Mult. by -2. $\underline{8x - 6y = -50}$

$\qquad\qquad\qquad\qquad\qquad\qquad 11x = -44$

$\qquad\qquad\qquad\qquad\qquad\qquad x = -4$

$x + 2y = 2$

$-4 + 2y = 2$

$2y = 6$

$y = 3$

Check:

$-4 + 2(3) = 2 \qquad -4(-4) + 3(3) = 25$

$\quad -4 + 6 = 2 \qquad\qquad 16 + 9 = 25$

$\qquad\quad 2 = 2$, true $\qquad\qquad 25 = 25$, true

The solution set is $\{(-4, 3)\}$.

30. $2x - 7y = 2$ No change. $2x - 7y = 2$

$3x + y = -20$ Mult. by 7. $\underline{21x + 7y = -140}$

$\qquad\qquad\qquad\qquad\qquad\qquad 23x \quad = -138$

$\qquad\qquad\qquad\qquad\qquad\qquad x = -\frac{138}{23}$

$\qquad\qquad\qquad\qquad\qquad\qquad x = -6$

$3x + y = -20$

$3(-6) + y = -20$

$-18 + y = -20$

$y = -2$

Check:

$2(-6) - 7(-2) = 2 \qquad 3(-6) + (-2) = -20$

$\quad -12 + 14 = 2 \qquad\qquad -18 - 2 = -20$

$\qquad\qquad 2 = 2$, true $\qquad\quad -20 = -20$, true

The solution set is $\{(-6, -2)\}$.

31. $4x + 3y = 15$ Mult. by 5. $20x + 15y = 75$

$2x - 5y = 1$ Mult. by 3. $\underline{6x - 15y = 3}$

$\qquad\qquad\qquad\qquad\qquad\qquad 26x = 78$

$\qquad\qquad\qquad\qquad\qquad\qquad x = 3$

$4x + 3y = 15$

$4 \cdot 3 + 3y = 15$

$12 + 3y = 15$

$3y = 3$

$y = 1$

Check:

$4(3) + 3(1) = 15 \qquad 2(3) - 5(1) = 1$

$\quad 12 + 3 = 15 \qquad\qquad 6 - 5 = 1$

$\qquad 15 = 15$, true $\qquad\quad 1 = 1$, true

The solution set is $\{(3, 1)\}$.

32. $3x - 7y = 13$ Mult. by 5. $15x - 35y = 65$
   $6x + 5y = 7$ Mult. by 7. $\underline{42x + 35y = 49}$
$$57x \qquad = 114$$
$$x = \tfrac{114}{57}$$
$$x = 2$$

$6x + 5y = 7$
$6 \cdot 2 + 5y = 7$
$12 + 5y = 7$
$5y = -5$
$y = -1$

Check:
$3x - 7y = 13$ $\qquad$ $6x + 5y = 7$
$3(2) - 7(-1) = 13$ $\qquad$ $6(2) + 5(-1) = 7$
$6 + 7 = 13$ $\qquad\qquad$ $12 - 5 = 7$
$13 = 13$, true $\qquad\qquad$ $7 = 7$, true

The solution set is $\{(2, -1)\}$.

33. $3x - 4y = 11$ Mult. by 3. $9x - 12y = 33$
   $2x + 3y = -4$ Mult. by 4. $\underline{8x + 12y = -16}$
$$17x = 17$$
$$x = 1$$

$2x + 3y = -4$
$2 \cdot 1 + 3y = -4$
$2 + 3y = -4$
$3y = -6$
$y = -2$

Check:
$3(1) - 4(-2) = 11$
$3 + 8 = 11$
$11 = 11$, true
$2(1) + 3(-2) = -4$
$2 - 6 = -4$
$-4 = -4$, true

The solution set is $\{(1, -2)\}$.

34. $2x + 3y = -16$ Mult. by 10. $20x + 30y = -160$
   $5x - 10y = 30$ Mult. by 3. $\underline{15x - 30y = 90}$
$$35x \qquad = -70$$
$$x \qquad = \tfrac{-70}{35}$$
$$x \qquad = -2$$

$2x + 3y = -16$
$2(-2) + 3y = -16$
$-4 + 3y = -16$
$3y = -12$
$y = -4$

Check:
$2(-2) + 3(-4) = -16$
$-4 - 12 = -16$
$-16 = -16$, true
$5(-2) - 10(-4) = 30$
$-10 + 40 = 30$
$30 = 30$, true

The solution set is $\{(-2, -4)\}$.

35. $2x = 3y - 4$ $\begin{array}{c}\text{Rearrange and}\\ \text{Mult. by 3.}\end{array}$ $6x - 9y = -12$
   $-6x + 12y = 6$ No change. $\underline{-6x + 12y = 6}$
$$3y = -6$$
$$y = -2$$

$2x = 3y - 4$
$2x = 3(-2) - 4$
$2x = -6 - 4$
$2x = -10$
$x = -5$

Check:
$2(-5) = 3(-2) - 4$ $\qquad$ $-6(-5) + 12(-2) = 6$
$-10 = -6 - 4$ $\qquad\qquad$ $30 - 24 = 6$
$-10 = -10$, true $\qquad\qquad$ $6 = 6$, true

The solution set is $\{(-5, -2)\}$.

36.

Rearrange and

$5x = 4y - 8$ Mult. by 7. $35x - 28y = -56$

$3x + 7y = 14$ Mult. by 4. $\underline{12x + 28y = 56}$

$$47x = 0$$
$$x = 0$$

$5x = 4y - 8$

$5 \cdot 0 = 4y - 8$

$0 = 4y - 8$

$8 = 4y$

$2 = y$

Check:

$5(0) = 4(2) - 8$ $3(0) + 7(2) = 14$

$0 = 8 - 8$ $0 + 14 = 14$

$0 = 0$, true $14 = 14$, true

The solution set is $\{(0, 2)\}$.

37. $x = 9 - 2y$ $x + 2y = 13$

$(9 - 2y) + 2y = 13$

$9 = 13$ false

The system has no solution.

The solution set is the empty set, $\varnothing$.

38. $y = 2 - 3x$ $6x + 2y = 7$

$6x + 2(2 - 3x) = 7$

$6x + 4 - 6x = 7$

$4 = 7$ false

The system has no solution.

The solution set is the empty set, $\varnothing$.

39. $y = 3x - 5$ $21x - 35 = 7y$

$21x - 35 = 7(3x - 5)$

$21x - 35 = 21x - 35$

$21x - 21x = 35 - 35$

$0 = 0$, true

The system has infinitely many solutions.

The solution set is $\{(x, y) \mid y = 3x - 5\}$.

40. $y = 3x - 4$ $9x - 3y = 12$

$9x - 3(3x - 4) = 12$

$9x - 9x + 12 = 12$

$12 = 12$, true

The system has infinitely many solutions.

The solution set is $\{(x, y) \mid y = 3x - 4\}$.

41. $3x - 2y = -5$ No change. $3x - 2y = -5$

$4x + y = 8$ Mult. by 2. $\underline{8x + 2y = 16}$

$$11x = 11$$
$$x = 1$$

$4x + y = 8$

$4(1) + y = 8$

$y = 4$

Check:

$3(1) - 2(4) = -5$ $4(1) + (4) = 8$

$3 - 8 = -5$ $4 + 4 = 8$

$-5 = -5$, true $8 = 8$, true

The solution set is $\{(1, 4)\}$.

42. $2x + 5y = -4$ No change. $2x + 5y = -4$

$3x - y = 11$ Multiply by 5. $\underline{15x - 5y = 55}$

$$17x \quad\quad = 51$$
$$x = \frac{51}{17}$$
$$x = 3$$

$3x - y = 11$

$3(3) - y = 11$

$9 - y = 11$

$y = -2$

Check:

$2(3) + 5(-2) = -4$ $3(3) - (-2) = 11$

$6 - 10 = -4$ $9 + 2 = 11$

$-4 = -4$ true $11 = 11$ true

The solution set is $\{(3, -2)\}$.

43. $x + 3y = 2$

$x = 2 - 3y$ $3x + 9y = 6$

$3(2 - 3y) + 9y = 6$

$6 - 9y + 9y = 6$

$6 = 6$ true

The system has infinitely many solutions.

The solution set is $\{(x, y) \mid x + 3y = 2\}$.

44. $4x - 2y = 2$ No change. $4x - 2y = 2$

$2x - y = 1$ Mult. by -2. $\underline{-4x + 2y = -2}$

$$0 = 0 \text{ true}$$

The system has infinitely many solutions.

The solution set is $\{(x, y) \mid 4x - 2y = 2\}$.

45. The solution to a system of linear equations is the point of intersection of the graphs of the equations in the system. If $(6, 2)$ is a solution, then we need to find the lines that intersect at that point.
Looking at the graph, we see that the graphs of $x + 3y = 12$ and $x - y = 4$ intersect at the point $(6, 2)$. Therefore, the desired system of equations is

$$x + 3y = 12 \quad \text{or} \quad y = -\frac{1}{3}x + 4$$
$$x - y = 4 \qquad\qquad y = x - 4$$

46. A system whose solution set is the empty set consists of parallel lines (assuming there are only two equations in the system). Therefore, we check the graph for two parallel lines.
From the graph, the desired system is

$$x - 3y = -6 \quad \text{or} \quad y = \frac{1}{3}x + 2$$
$$x - 3y = 6 \qquad\qquad y = \frac{1}{3}x - 2$$

47. $5ax + 4y = 17$
$ax + 7y = 22$
Multiply the second equation by -5 and add the equations.

$$5ax + 4y = 17$$
$$\underline{-5ax - 35y = -110}$$
$$-31y = -93$$
$$y = 3$$

Back-substitute into one of the original equations to solve for x.

$$ax + 7y = 22$$
$$ax + 7(3) = 22$$
$$ax + 21 = 22$$
$$ax = 1$$
$$x = \frac{1}{a}$$

The solution is $\left(\frac{1}{a}, 3\right)$.

48. $4ax + by = 3$
$6ax + 5by = 8$
Multiply the first equation by -5 and add the equations.

$$-20ax - 5by = -15$$
$$\underline{6ax + 5by = 8}$$
$$-14ax = -7$$
$$x = \frac{1}{2a}$$

Back-substitute into one of the original equations to solve for y.

$$4a\left(\frac{1}{2a}\right) + by = 3$$
$$2 + by = 3$$
$$by = 1$$
$$y = \frac{1}{b}$$

The solution is $\left(\frac{1}{2a}, \frac{1}{b}\right)$.

49. $f(-2) = 11 \quad \rightarrow \quad -2m + b = 11$
$f(3) = -9 \quad \rightarrow \quad 3m + b = -9$
We need to solve the resulting system of equations:
$-2m + b = 11$
$3m + b = -9$
Subtract the two equations:

$$-2m + b = 11$$
$$\underline{3m + b = -9}$$
$$-5m = 20$$
$$m = -4$$

Back-substitute into one of the original equations to solve for b.

$$-2m + b = 11$$
$$-2(-4) + b = 11$$
$$8 + b = 11$$
$$b = 3$$

Therefore, $m = -4$ and $b = 3$.

50. $f(-3) = 23 \quad \rightarrow \quad -3m + b = 23$
$f(2) = -7 \quad \rightarrow \quad 2m + b = -7$
We need to solve the resulting system of equations:
$-3m + b = 23$
$2m + b = -7$
Subtract the two equations:

$$-3m + b = 23$$
$$\underline{2m + b = -7}$$
$$-5m = 30$$
$$m = -6$$

Back-substitute into one of the original equations to solve for b.

$$-3m + b = 23$$
$$-3(-6) + b = 23$$
$$18 + b = 23$$
$$b = 5$$

Therefore, $m = -6$ and $b = 5$.

51. At the break-even point, $R(x) = C(x)$.

$$10000 + 30x = 50x$$
$$10000 = 20x$$
$$10000 = 20x$$
$$500 = x$$

Five hundred radios must be produced and sold to break-even.

52. At the break-even point, $R(x) = C(x)$.

$$10000 + 30x = 50x$$
$$10000 = 20x$$
$$10000 = 20x$$
$$500 = x$$

Five hundred radios must be produced and sold to break-even. So more than 500 radios must be produced and sold to have a profit.

53.
$$R(x) = 50x$$
$$R(200) = 50(200) = 10000$$

$$C(x) = 10000 + 30x$$
$$C(200) = 10000 + 30(200)$$
$$= 10000 + 6000 = 16000$$

$$R(200) - C(200) = 10000 - 16000$$
$$= -6000$$

This means that if 200 radios are produced and sold the company will lose $6,000.

54.
$$R(x) = 50x$$
$$R(300) = 50(300) = 15000$$

$$C(x) = 10000 + 30x$$
$$C(300) = 10000 + 30(300)$$
$$= 10000 + 9000 = 19000$$

$$R(300) - C(300) = 15000 - 19000$$
$$= -4000$$

This means that if 300 radios are produced and sold the company will lose $4,000.

55. a.
$$P(x) = R(x) - C(x)$$
$$= 50x - (10000 + 30x)$$
$$= 50x - 10000 - 30x$$
$$= 20x - 10000$$
$$P(x) = 20x - 10000$$

b.
$$P(10000) = 20(10000) - 10000$$
$$= 200000 - 10000 = 190000$$

If 10,000 radios are produced and sold the profit will be $190,000.

56. a.
$$P(x) = R(x) - C(x)$$
$$= 50x - (10000 + 30x)$$
$$= 50x - 10000 - 30x$$
$$= 20x - 10000$$

b.
$$P(20000) = 20(20000) - 10000$$
$$= 400000 - 10000$$
$$= 390000$$

If 20,000 radios are produced and sold the profit will be $390,000.

57. a. The cost function is:
$$C(x) = 18,000 + 20x$$

b. The revenue function is:
$$R(x) = 80x$$

c. At the break-even point, $R(x) = C(x)$.

$$80x = 18000 + 20x$$
$$60x = 18000$$
$$x = 300$$

$$R(x) = 80x$$
$$R(300) = 80(300)$$
$$= 24,000$$

When approximately 300 canoes are produced the company will break-even with cost and revenue at $24,000.

58. a. The cost function is
$$C(x) = 100,000 + 100x$$

b. The revenue function is $R(x) = 300x$.

c. At the break-even point, $R(x) = C(x)$.

$$300x = 100,000 + 100x$$
$$200x = 100,000$$
$$x = 500$$

$$R(x) = 300x$$
$$R(500) = 300(500) = 150,000$$

When 500 bicycles are produced and sold, both cost and revenue are $150,000.

59. a. The cost function is:
$$C(x) = 30000 + 2500x$$

    b. The revenue function is:
$$R(x) = 3125x$$

    c. At the break-even point, $R(x) = C(x)$.
$$3125x = 30000 + 2500x$$
$$625x = 30000$$
$$x = 48$$
After 48 sold out performances, the investor will break-even. ($150,000)

60. a. The cost function is $C(x) = 30,000 + 0.02x$

    b. The revenue function is $R(x) = 0.5x$

    c. At the break-even point,
$$R(x) = C(x)$$
$$0.5x = 30,000 + 0.02x$$
$$0.48x = 30,000$$
$$x = 62,500$$

$$R(x) = 0.5x$$
$$R(62,500) = 0.5(62,500) = 31,250$$
For 62,500 cards, both cost and revenue are $31,250.

61. a. Substitute $0.375x + 3$ for p in the first equation.
$$p = -0.325x + 5.8$$

$$\overbrace{0.375x + 3}^{p} = -0.325x + 5.8$$
$$0.375x + 3 = -0.325x + 5.8$$
$$0.375x + 0.325x + 3 = -0.325x + 0.325x + 5.8$$
$$0.7x + 3 = 5.8$$
$$0.7x + 3 - 3 = 5.8 - 3$$
$$0.7x = 2.8$$
$$\frac{0.7x}{0.7} = \frac{2.8}{0.7}$$
$$x = 4$$
Back-substitute to find p.
$$p = -0.325x + 5.8$$
$$p = -0.325(4) + 5.8 = 4.5$$

The ordered pair is (4,4.5).
Equilibrium number of workers: 4 million
Equilibrium hourly wage: $4.50

    b. If workers are paid $\underline{\$4.50}$ per hour, there will be $\underline{4}$ million available workers and $\underline{4}$ million workers will be hired. In this state of market equilibrium, there is no unemployment.

    c.
$$p = -0.325x + 5.8$$
$$5.15 = -0.325x + 5.8$$
$$0.65 = -0.325x$$
$$\frac{-0.65}{-0.325} = \frac{-0.325x}{-0.325}$$
$$2 = x$$
At $5.15 per hour, 2 million workers will be hired.

    d.
$$p = 0.375x + 3$$
$$5.15 = 0.375x + 3$$
$$2.15 = 0.375x$$
$$\frac{2.15}{0.375} = \frac{0.375x}{0.375}$$
$$x \approx 5.7$$
At $5.15 per hour, there will be about 5.7 million available workers.

    e. $5.7 - 2 = 3.7$
At $5.15 per hour, there will be about 3.7 million more people looking for work than employers are willing to hire.

62. a. Demand model: $p = -50x + 2000$
Supply model: $p = 50x$
Use the substitution method.
$$p = -50x + 2000$$
$$\overbrace{50x}^{p} = -50x + 2000$$
$$50x = -50x + 2000$$
$$100x = 2000$$
$$x = 20$$
Back-substitute 20 for x and find p.
$$p = 50x$$
$$p = 50(20) = 1000$$
The solution set is $\{(20, 1000)\}$.
The equilibrium quantity is 20,000 and the equilibrium price is $1000.

    b. When rents are $\underline{\$1000}$ per month, consumers will demand $\underline{20,000}$ apartments and suppliers will offer $\underline{20,000}$ apartments for rent.

63. a. $y = 0.45x + 0.8$

b. $y = 0.15x + 2.6$

c. To find the week in the semester when both groups report the same number of symptoms, we set the two equations equal to each other and solve for x.
$$0.45x + 0.8 = 0.15x + 2.6$$
$$0.3x = 1.8$$
$$x = 6$$
The number of symptoms will be the same in week 6.
$$y = 0.15x + 2.6$$
$$y = 0.15(6) + 2.6$$
$$y = 3.5$$
The number of symptoms in week 6 will be 3.5 for both groups. This is shown in the graph by the intersection point (6, 3.5).

64. a. $D = 4.8x + 140$

b. $L = 23.6x + 46$

c. To find the year when the sales were equal, we set the two equations equal to each other and solve for x.
$$4.8x + 140 = 23.6x + 46$$
$$-18.8x = -94$$
$$x = 5$$
The sales were equal 5 years after 2004, or 2009.

To find the sales in 2009, substitute 5 into either equation.
$$D = 4.8x + 140$$
$$D = 4.8(5) + 140 = 164$$
The sales of both laptops and desktops were 164 million in 2009.

d. Graph of $D = 4.8x + 140$ and $L = 23.6x + 46$
qwertyDan-please check NewART
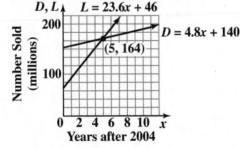

75. makes sense

76. makes sense

77. does not make sense; Explanations will vary. Sample explanation: Some linear systems have one ordered pair solution and some linear systems have no solutions.

78. does not make sense; Explanations will vary. Sample explanation: When one of equations has a variable on one side by itself, it is typically best to use the substitution method.

80. x = number of people upstairs
y = number of people downstairs
The following system results:
$$\begin{array}{ll} x - 1 = y + 1 & \\ x + 1 = 2(y - 1) \end{array} \text{ or } \begin{array}{ll} x - 1 = y + 1 \\ x + 1 = 2y - 2 \end{array}$$
Eliminate x by multiplying the first equation by -1 and adding the resulting equations.
$$-x + 1 = -y - 1$$
$$\underline{x + 1 = 2y - 2}$$
$$2 = y - 3$$

Which gives $y = 5$. Thus $x = 7$.

There are 5 people downstairs and 7 people upstairs.

81. x = first lucky number
y = second lucky number
$$3x + 6y = 12$$
$$x + 2y = 5$$
Eliminate x by multiplying the second equation by -3 and adding the resulting equations.
$$3x + 6y = 12$$
$$\underline{-3x - 6y = -15}$$
$$0 = -3$$

The false statement $0 = -3$ indicates that the system has no solution. Therefore, the twin who always lies is talking.

Check Points 7.4

1. $2x - 4y \geq 8$

    Graph the equation $2x - 4y = 8$ as a solid line.

    Choose a test point that is not on the line.

    Test $(0,0)$

    $2x - 4y \geq 8$

    $2(0) - 4(0) \geq 8$

    $\qquad 0 \geq 8, \;\; \text{false}$

    Since the statement is false, shade the other half-plane.

    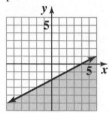

2. $y > -\dfrac{3}{4}x$

    Graph the equation $y = -\dfrac{3}{4}x$ as a dashed line.

    Choose a test point that is not on the line.

    Test $(1,1)$

    $y > -\dfrac{3}{4}x$

    $1 > -\dfrac{3}{4}(1)$

    $1 > -\dfrac{3}{4}, \;\; \text{true}$

    Since the statement is true, shade the half-plane containing the point.

    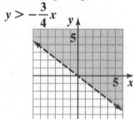

3. **a.** $y > 1$

    Graph the equation $y = 1$ as a dashed line.

    Choose a test point that is not on the line.

    Test $(0,0)$

    $y > 1$

    $0 > 1, \;\; \text{false}$

    Since the statement is false, shade the other half-plane.

    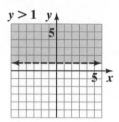

    b. Graph the equation $x = -2$ as a solid line.

    Choose a test point that is not on the line.

    Test $(0,0)$

    $x \leq -2$

    $0 \leq -2, \;\; \text{false}$

    Since the statement is false, shade the other half-plane.

    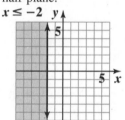

4. Point $B = (66, 130)$

    $4.9x - y \geq 165$

    $4.9(66) - 130 \geq 165$

    $\qquad 193.4 \geq 165, \;\; \text{true}$

    $3.7x - y \leq 125$

    $3.7(66) - 130 \leq 125$

    $\qquad 114.2 \leq 125, \;\; \text{true}$

    Point B is a solution of the system.

5. $x + 2y > 4$

$2x - 3y \leq -6$

Graph the equation $x + 2y = 4$ as a dashed line.
Choose a test point that is not on the line.

$\underline{\text{Test } (0,0)}$

$x + 2y > 4$

$0 + 2(0) > 4$

$0 > 4, \ \text{false}$

Since the statement is false, shade the other half-plane.

Next, graph the equation $2x - 3y = -6$ as a solid line.
Choose a test point that is not on the line.

$\underline{\text{Test } (0,0)}$

$2x - 3y \leq -6$

$2(0) - 3(0) \leq -6$

$0 \leq -6, \ \text{false}$

Since the statement is false, shade the other half-plane.

The graph is the intersection (overlapping) of the two half-planes.

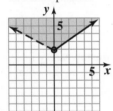

6. $x < 3$

$y \geq -1$

Graph the equation $x = 3$ as a dashed line.
Choose a test point that is not on the line.

$\underline{\text{Test } (0,0)}$

$x < 3$

$0 < 3, \ \text{true}$

Since the statement is true, shade the half-plane that contains the test point.

Next, graph the equation $y = -1$ as a solid line.

Choose a test point that is not on the line.

$\underline{\text{Test } (0,0)}$

$y \geq -1$

$0 \geq -1, \ \text{true}$

Since the statement is true, shade the half-plane that contains the test point.
The graph is the intersection (overlapping) of the two half-planes.

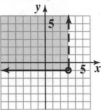

Exercise Set 7.4

1. To graph $x + y \geq 2$, begin by graphing $x + y = 2$ with a solid line because $\geq$ includes equality.

$\underline{\text{test point } (0, 0):}$

$x + y \geq 2$

$0 + 0 \geq 2$

$0 \geq 2, \text{false}$

Since the test point makes the inequality <u>false</u>, shade the half-plane <u>not containing</u> test point (0, 0).

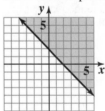

2. To graph $x - y \leq 1$, begin by graphing $x - y = 1$ with a solid line because $\leq$ includes equality.

$\underline{\text{test point } (0, 0):}$

$x - y \leq 1$

$0 - 0 \leq 1$

$0 \leq 1, \text{true}$

Since the test point makes the inequality <u>true</u>, shade the half-plane <u>containing</u> test point (0, 0).

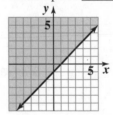

3. To graph $3x - y \geq 6$, begin by graphing $3x - y = 6$ with a solid line because $\geq$ includes equality.

test point (0, 0):

$3x - y \geq 6$

$3(0) - 0 \geq 6$

$\quad 0 \geq 6$, false

Since the test point makes the inequality _false_, shade the half-plane _not containing_ test point (0, 0).

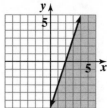

4. To graph $3x + y \leq 3$, begin by graphing $3x + y = 3$ with a solid line because $\leq$ includes equality.

test point (0, 0):

$3x + y \leq 3$

$3(0) + 0 \leq 3$

$\quad 0 \leq 3$, true

Since the test point makes the inequality _true_, shade the half-plane _containing_ test point (0, 0).

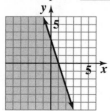

5. To graph $2x + 3y > 12$, begin by graphing $2x + 3y = 12$ with a dashed line because $>$ does not include equality.

test point (0, 0):

$2x + 3y > 12$

$2(0) + 3(0) > 12$

$\quad 0 > 12$, false

Since the test point makes the inequality _false_, shade the half-plane _not containing_ test point (0, 0).

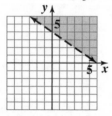

6. To graph $2x - 5y < 10$, begin by graphing $2x - 5y = 10$ with a dashed line because $<$ does not include equality.

test point (0, 0):

$2x - 5y < 10$

$2(0) - 5(0) < 10$

$\quad 0 < 10$, true

Since the test point makes the inequality _true_, shade the half-plane _containing_ test point (0, 0).

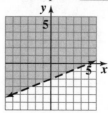

7. To graph $5x + 3y \leq -15$, begin by graphing $5x + 3y = -15$ with a solid line because $\leq$ includes equality.

test point (0, 0):

$5x + 3y \leq -15$

$5(0) + 3(0) \leq -15$

$\quad 0 \leq -15$, false

Since the test point makes the inequality _false_, shade the half-plane _not containing_ test point (0, 0).

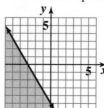

8. To graph $3x + 4y \leq -12$, begin by graphing $3x + 4y = -12$ with a solid line because $\leq$ includes equality.

test point (0, 0):

$3x + 4y \leq -12$

$3(0) + 4(0) \leq -12$

$\quad 0 \leq -12$, false

Since the test point makes the inequality _false_, shade the half-plane _not containing_ test point (0, 0).

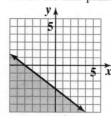

9. To graph $2y - 3x > 6$, begin by graphing $2y - 3x = 6$ with a dashed line because $>$ does not include equality.

> test point (0, 0):
> $$2y - 3x > 6$$
> $$2(0) - 3(0) > 6$$
> $$0 > 6, \text{ false}$$

Since the test point makes the inequality <u>false</u>, shade the half-plane <u>not containing</u> test point (0, 0).

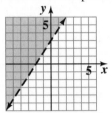

10. To graph $2y - x > 4$, begin by graphing $2y - x = 4$ with a dashed line because $>$ does not include equality.

> test point (0, 0):
> $$2y - x > 4$$
> $$2(0) - 0 > 4$$
> $$0 > 4, \text{ false}$$

Since the test point makes the inequality <u>false</u>, shade the half-plane <u>not containing</u> test point (0, 0).

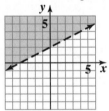

11. $y > \dfrac{1}{3}x$

Graph the equation $y = \dfrac{1}{3}$ with a dashed line.

Next, select a test point. We cannot use the origin because it lies on the line. Use $(1,1)$.

$$1 > \frac{1}{3}(1)$$

$$1 > \frac{1}{3}$$

This is a true statement, so we know the point $(1,1)$ lies in the shaded half-plane.

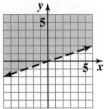

12. $y > \dfrac{1}{4}x$

Graph the equation $y = \dfrac{1}{4}$ with a dashed line.

Next, select a test point. We cannot use the origin because it lies on the line. Use $(1,1)$.

$$1 > \frac{1}{4}(1)$$

$$1 > \frac{1}{4}$$

This is a true statement, so we know the point $(1,1)$ lies in the shaded half-plane.

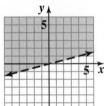

13. $y \le 3x + 2$

Graph the equation $y = 3x + 2$ with a solid line. Next, use the origin as a test point.

$$0 \le 3(0) + 2$$

$$0 \le 2$$

This is a true statement. This means that the point $(0,0)$ will fall in the shaded half-plane.

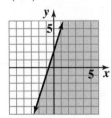

14. $y \le 2x - 1$

Graph the equation $y = 2x - 1$ with a solid line. Next, use the origin as a test point. Since that resuls in a false statement, the point $(0,0)$ will not fall in the shaded half-plane.

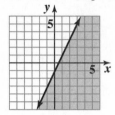

15. $y < -\dfrac{1}{4}x$

Graph the equation $y = -\dfrac{1}{4}x$ with a dashed line.

Next, select a test point. We cannot use the origin because it lies on the line. Use $(1,1)$.

$$1 < -\dfrac{1}{4}(1)$$

$$1 < -\dfrac{1}{4}$$

This is a false statement, so we know the point $(1,1)$ does not lie in the shaded half-plane.

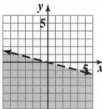

16. $y < -\dfrac{1}{3}x$

Graph the equation $y = -\dfrac{1}{3}x$ with a dashed line.

Next, select a test point. We cannot use the origin because it lies on the line. Use $(1,1)$.

$$1 < -\dfrac{1}{4}(1)$$

$$1 < -\dfrac{1}{4}$$

This is a false statement, so we know the point $(1,1)$ does not lie in the shaded half-plane.

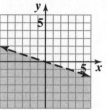

17. $x \le 2$

Graph the equation $x = 2$ with a solid line. Next, use the origin as a test point.

$$x \le 2$$

$$0 \le 2$$

This is a true statement, so we know the point $(0,0)$ lies in the shaded half-plane.

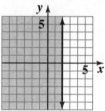

18. $x \le -4$

Graph the equation $x = -4$ with a solid line. Next, use the origin as a test point.

$$x \le -4$$

$$0 \le -4$$

This is a false statement, so we know the point $(0,0)$ does not lie in the shaded half-plane.

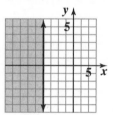

19. $y > -4$

Graph the equation $y = -4$ with a dashed line.

Next, use the origin as a test point.

$y > -4$

$0 > -4$

This is a true statement, so we know the point $(0,0)$ lies in the shaded half-plane.

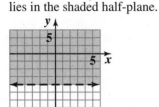

20. $y > -2$

Graph the equation $y = -2$ with a dashed line.

Next, use the origin as a test point.

$y > -2$

$0 > -2$

This is a true statement, so we know the point $(0,0)$ lies in the shaded half-plane.

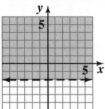

21. $y \geq 0$

Graph the equation $y = 0$ with a solid line.

Next, select a test point. We cannot use the origin because it lies on the line. Use $(1,1)$.

$y \geq 0$

$1 \geq 0$

This is a true statement, so we know the point $(1,1)$ lies in the shaded half-plane.

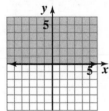

22. $x \geq 0$

Graph the equation $x = 0$ with a solid line.

Next, select a test point. We cannot use the origin because it lies on the line. Use $(1,1)$.

$x \geq 0$

$1 \geq 0$

This is a true statement, so we know the point $(1,1)$ lies in the shaded half-plane.

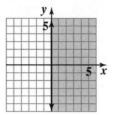

23. $3x + 6y \leq 6$

$2x + y \leq 8$

Graph the equations using the intercepts.

$3x + 6y = 6$ $\qquad$ $2x + y = 8$

$x-\text{intercept} = 2$ $\qquad$ $x-\text{intercept} = 4$

$y-\text{intercept} = 1$ $\qquad$ $y-\text{intercept} = 8$

Use the origin as a test point to determine shading.

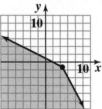

The solution set is the intersection of the shaded half-planes.

24. $x - y \geq 4$

$x + y \leq 6$

Graph the equations using solid lines.

Use the origin as a test point to determine shading.

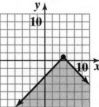

The solution set is the intersection of the shaded half-planes.

25. $2x + y < 3$
$x - y > 2$
Graph $2x + y = 3$ as a dashed line.

If $x = 0$, then $y = 3$ and if $y = 0$, then $x = \dfrac{3}{2}$.

Because $(0, 0)$ makes the inequality true, shade the half-plane containing $(0, 0)$.
Graph $x - y = 2$ as a dashed line.
If $x = 0$, then $y = -2$ and if $y = 0$, then $x = 2$.
Because $(0, 0)$ makes the inequality false, shade the half-plane not containing $(0, 0)$.

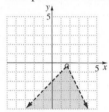

26. $x + y < 4$
$4x - 2y < 6$
Graph $x + y = 4$ as a dashed line.
If $x = 0$, then $y = 4$ and if $y = 0$, then $x = 4$.
Because $(0, 0)$ makes the inequality true, shade the half-plane containing $(0, 0)$.
Graph $4x - 2y = 6$ as a dashed line.

If $x = 0$, then $y = -3$ and if $y = 0$, then $x = \dfrac{3}{2}$.

Because $(0, 0)$ makes the inequality true, shade the half-plane containing $(0, 0)$.

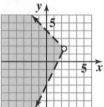

27. $2x + y < 4$
$x - y > 4$
Graph $2x + y = 4$ as a dashed line.
If $x = 0$, then $y = 4$ and if $y = 0$, then $x = 2$.
Because $(0, 0)$ makes the inequality true, shade the half-plane containing $(0, 0)$
Graph $x - y = 4$ as a dashed line.
If $x = 0$, then $y = -4$. and if $y = 0$, then $x = 4$.
Because $(0, 0)$ makes the inequality false, shade the half-plane not containing $(0, 0)$.

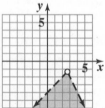

28. $2x - y < 3$
$x + y < 6$
Graph $2x - y = 3$ as a dashed line.

If $x = 0$, then $y = -3$ and if $y = 0$, then $x = \dfrac{3}{2}$.

Because $(0, 0)$ makes the inequality true, shade the half-plane containing $(0, 0)$.
Graph $x + y = 6$ as a dashed line.
If $x = 0$, then $y = 6$ and if $y = 0$, then $x = 6$.
Because $(0, 0)$ makes the inequality true, shade the half-plane containing $(0, 0)$.

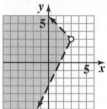

29. $x \geq 2$
$y \leq 3$

Graph $x = 2$ as a solid line.
The points in the half-plane to the right of the line satisfy $x > 2$.
Graph $y = 3$ as a solid line.
The points in the half-plane below the line satisfy $y < 3$.

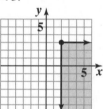

30. $x \geq 4$
$y \leq 2$

Graph $x = 4$ as a solid line.
The points in the half-plane to the right of the line satisfy $x > 4$.
Graph $y = 2$ as a solid line.
The points in the half-plane below the line satisfy $y < 2$.

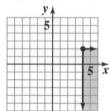

31. $x \le 5$

   $y > -3$

   Graph $x = 5$ as a solid line.
   The points in the half-plane to the left of the line
   satisfy $x < 5$.
   Graph $y = -3$ as a dashed line.
   The points in the half-plane above the line satisfy
   $y > -3$.

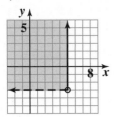

32. $x \le 3$

   $y > -1$

   Graph $x = 3$ as a solid line.
   the points in the half-plane to the left of the line
   satisfy $x < 3$.
   Graph $y = -1$ as a dashed line.
   The points in the half-plane above the line satisfy y
   > -1.

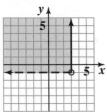

33. $x - y \le 1$

   $x \ge 2$

   Graph $x - y = 1$ as a solid line.
   If $x = 0$, then $y = -1$ and if $y = 0$, then $x = 1$.
   Because $(0, 0)$ satisfies the inequality, shade the
   half-plane containing $(0, 0)$.
   Graph $x = 2$ as a solid line.
   The points in the half-plane to the right of
   $x = 2$ satisfy the inequality $x \ge 2$.

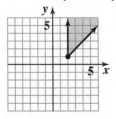

34. $4x - 5y \ge -20$

   $x \ge -3$

   Graph $4x - 5y = -20$ as a solid line.
   If $x = 0$, then $y = 4$ and if $y = 0$, then $x = -5$.
   Because $(0, 0)$ satisfies the inequality, shade the
   half-plane containing $(0, 0)$.
   Graph $x = -3$ as a solid line.
   The points in the half-plane to the right of $x = -3$
   satisfy the inequality $x > -3$.

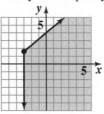

35. $y > 2x - 3$

   $y < -x + 6$

   Graph the equations using the intercepts.

   $y = 2x - 3$ $y = -x + 6$

   $x - \text{intercept} = \dfrac{3}{2}$ $x - \text{intercept} = 6$

          $y - \text{intercept} = 6$

   $y - \text{intercept} = -3$

   Use the origin as a test point to determine shading.

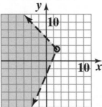

   The solution set is the intersection of the shaded
   half-planes.

36. $y < -2x + 4$

   $y < x - 4$

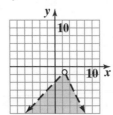

37. $x + 2y \leq 4$

$y \geq x - 3$

Graph the equations using the intercepts.

$x + 2y = 4$ $y = x - 3$

$x-\text{intercept} = 4$ $x-\text{intercept} = 3$

$y-\text{intercept} = 2$ $y-\text{intercept} = -3$

Use the origin as a test point to determine shading.

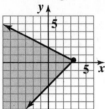

The solution set is the intersection of the shaded half-planes.

38. $x + y \leq 4$

$y \geq 2x - 4$

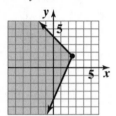

39. $y \geq -2x + 4$

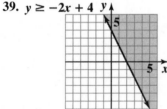

40. $y \geq -3x + 2$

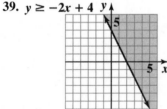

41. $x + y \leq 4$

$3x + y \leq 6$

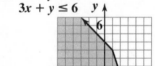

42. $x + y \leq 3$

$4x + y \leq 6$

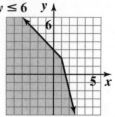

43. Find the union of solutions of

$y > \dfrac{3}{2}x - 2$ and $y < 4$.

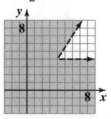

44. Find the union of solutions of

$x - y \geq -1$ and $5x - 2y \leq 10$.

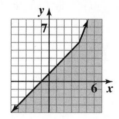

45. Point $A = (66,160)$

$5.3x - y \geq 180$

$5.3(66) - 160 \geq 180$

$189.8 \geq 180$, true

$4.1x - y \leq 14$

$4.1(66) - 160 \leq 140$

$110.6 \leq 140$, true

Point A is a solution of the system.

46. Point $B = (76,220)$

$5.3x - y \geq 180$

$5.3(76) - 220 \geq 180$

$182.8 \geq 180$, true

$4.1x - y \leq 14$

$4.1(76) - 220 \leq 140$

$91.6 \leq 140$, true

Point B is a solution of the system.

47. Point = (72,205)

$$5.3x - y \geq 180$$

$$5.3(72) - 205 \geq 180$$

$$176.6 \geq 180, \text{ false}$$

$$4.1x - y \leq 14$$

$$4.1(72) - 205 \leq 140$$

$$90.2 \leq 140, \text{ true}$$

The data does not satisfy both inequalities. The person is not within the healthy weight region.

48. Point = (68,135)

$$5.3x - y \geq 180$$

$$5.3(68) - 135 \geq 180$$

$$225.4 \geq 180, \text{ true}$$

$$4.1x - y \leq 14$$

$$4.1(68) - 135 \leq 140$$

$$143.8 \leq 140, \text{ false}$$

The data does not satisfy both inequalities. The person is not within the healthy weight region.

49. a. $50x + 150y > 2000$

   b. Graph $50x + 150y$ as a dashed line using its x-intercept, (40, 0), and its y-intercept, $\left(0, \dfrac{40}{3}\right)$.

Test (0, 0):

$$50(0) + 150(0) > 2000?$$

$$0 > 2000 \text{ false}$$

Shade the half-plane not containing (0, 0).

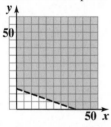

50x + 150y > 2000

   c. Ordered pairs may vary.

50. a. $165x + 110y \leq 330$

   b. Graph $165x + 110y = 330$ as a solid line by using its x-intercept, (2, 0), and its y-intercept (0, 3).

Test (0, 0):

$$165(0) + 110(0) \leq 330?$$

$$0 \leq 330 \text{ true}$$

Shade the half-plane containing (0, 0).

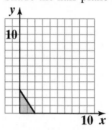

165x + 110y ≤ 330

   c. Ordered pairs may vary.

51. a. $\text{BMI} = \dfrac{703W}{H^2} = \dfrac{703(200)}{72^2} \approx 27.1$

   b. A 20 year old man with a BMI of 27.1 is classified as overweight.

52. a. $\text{BMI} = \dfrac{703W}{H^2} = \dfrac{703(105)}{66^2} \approx 16.9$

   b. A 25 year old woman with a BMI of 16.9 is classified as underweight.

58. does not make sense; Explanations will vary. Sample explanation: (0, 0) can not be used as a test point when it lies on the related equation.

59. does not make sense; Explanations will vary. Sample explanation: It is necessary to graph the linear equation with a dashed line to represent its role as a borderline.

60. makes sense

61. makes sense

62. $x \geq -2, y > -1$

63. $y > x - 3$

   $y \leq x$

64. The system $\begin{array}{l} 3x+3y<9 \\ 3x+3y>9 \end{array}$ has no solution. The number $3x+3y$ cannot both be less than 9 and greater than 9 at the same time.

65. The system $\begin{array}{l} 6x-y\le 24 \\ 6x-y>24 \end{array}$ has no solution. The number $6x-y$ cannot both be less than or equal to 24 and greater than 24 at the same time.

66. The system $\begin{array}{l} 3x+y\le 9 \\ 3x+y\ge 9 \end{array}$ has infinitely many solutions. The solutions are all points on the line $3x+y=9$.

67. The system $\begin{array}{l} 6x-y\le 24 \\ 6x-y\ge 24 \end{array}$ has infinitely many solutions. The solutions are all points on the line $6x-y=24$.

Section 7.5

Check Point Exercises

1. The total profit is 25 times the number of bookshelves, x, plus 55 times the number of desks, y. The objective function is $z=25x+55y$

2. Not more than a total of 80 bookshelves and desks can be manufactured per day. This is represented by the inequality $x+y\le 80$.

3. Objective function: $z=25x+55y$
   Constraints: $x+y\le 80$
   $\qquad\qquad 30\le x\le 80$
   $\qquad\qquad 10\le y\le 30$

4. Graph the constraints and find the corners, or vertices, of the region of intersection.

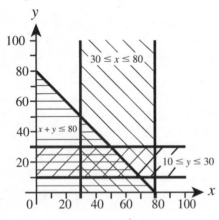
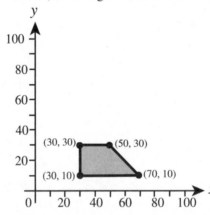

Find the value of the objective function at each corner of the graphed region.

Corner (x, y)	Objective Function $z = 25x + 55y$ z
(30, 10)	$z = 25(30) + 55(10)$ $= 750 + 550 = 1300$
(30, 30)	$z = 25(30) + 55(30)$ $= 750 + 1650 = 2400$
(50, 30)	$z = 25(50) + 55(30)$ $= 1250 + 1650 = 2900 \leftarrow$ Maximum
(70, 10)	$z = 25(70) + 55(10)$ $= 1750 + 550 = 2300$

The maximum value of z is 2900 and it occurs at the point (50, 30).
In order to maximize profit, 50 bookshelves and 30 desks must be produced each day for a profit of $2900.

Exercise Set 7.5

1. $z = 5x + 6y$
    (1, 2): $5(1) + 6(2) = 5 + 12 = 17$
    (2, 10): $5(2) + 6(10) = 10 + 60 = 70$
    (7, 5): $5(7) + 6(5) = 35 + 30 = 65$
    (8, 3): $5(8) + 6(3) = 40 + 18 = 58$
    The maximum value is $z = 70$; the minimum value is $z = 17$.

2. $z = 3x + 2y$
    (3, 2): $3(3) + 2(2) = 9 + 4 = 13$
    (4, 10): $3(4) + 2(10) = 12 + 20 = 32$
    (5, 12): $3(5) + 2(12) = 15 + 24 = 39$
    (8, 6): $3(8) + 2(6) = 24 + 12 = 36$
    (7, 4): $3(7) + 2(4) = 21 + 8 = 29$
    The maximum value is $z = 39$; the minimum value is $z = 13$.

3. $z = 40x + 50y$
    (0, 0): $40(0) + 50(0) = 0 + 0 = 0$
    (0, 8): $40(0) + 50(8) = 0 + 400 = 400$
    (4, 9): $40(4) + 50(9) = 160 + 450 = 610$
    (8, 0): $40(8) + 50(0) = 320 + 0 = 320$
    The maximum value is $z = 610$; the minimum value is $z = 0$.

4. $z = 30x + 45y$
    (0, 0): $30(0) + 45(0) = 0 + 0 = 0$
    (0, 9): $30(0) + 45(9) = 0 + 405 = 405$
    (4, 4): $30(4) + 45(4) = 120 + 180 = 300$
    (3, 0): $30(3) + 45(0) = 90 + 0 = 90$
    The maximum value is $z = 405$; the minimum value is $z = 0$.

5. a.

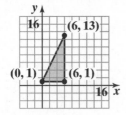

b. at $(0, 1)$ $z = 0 + 1 = 1$
    at $(6, 13)$ $z = 6 + 13 = 19$
    at $(6, 1)$ $z = 6 + 1 = 7$

c. Maximum = 19
    occurs at $x = 6$ and $y = 13$

6. a.

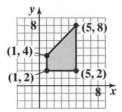

b. at $(1, 4)$ $z = 3(1) - 2(4) = -5$
    at $(5, 8)$ $z = 3(5) - 2(8) = -1$
    at $(5, 2)$ $z = 3(5) - 2(2) = 11$
    at $(1, 2)$ $z = 3(1) - 2(2) = -1$

c. Maximum = 11
    occurs at $x = 5$ and $y = 2$

7. a.

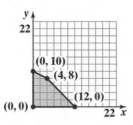

b. at $(0, 10)$ $z = 6(0) + 10(10) = 100$
    at $(4, 8)$ $z = 6(4) + 10(8) = 104$
    at $(12, 0)$ $z = 6(12) + 10(0) = 72$
    at $(0, 0)$ $z = 6(0) + 10(0)   = 0$

c. Maximum = 104
    occurs at $x = 4$ and $y = 8$

8. a.

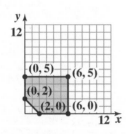

b. at $(0, 2)$ $z = 0 + 3(2) = 6$
    at $(0, 5)$ $z = 0 + 3(5) = 15$
    at $(6, 5)$ $z = 6 + 3(5) = 21$
    at $(6, 0)$ $z = 6 + 3(0) = 6$
    at $(2, 0)$ $z = 2 + 3(0) = 2$

c. Maximum = 21
    occurs at $x = 6$ and $y = 5$

9. $z = 5x - 2y$
    $0 \le x \le 5$
    $0 \le y \le 3$
    $x + y \ge 2$

a.

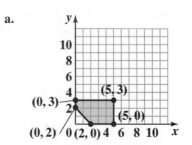

b. $(0,3): z = 5(0) - 2(3) = -6$
    $(0,2): z = 5(0) - 2(2) = -4$
    $(2,0): z = 5(2) - 2(0) = 10$
    $(5,0): z = 5(5) - 2(0) = 25$
    $(5,3): z = 5(5) - 2(3) = 19$

c. The maximum value is 25 at $x = 5$ and $y = 0$.

10. $z = 3x - 2y$
    $1 \le x \le 5$
    $y \ge 2$
    $x - y \ge -3$

a.

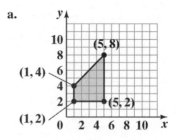

b. $(1, 2): z = 3(1) - 2(2) = -1$
    $(1, 4): z = 3(1) - 2(4) = -5$
    $(5, 8): z = 3(5) - 2(8) = -1$
    $(5, 2): z = 3(5) - 2(2) = 11$

c. Maximum value is 11 at $x = 5$ and $y = 2$.

11. $z = 10x + 12y$

    $x \geq 0, y \geq 0$

    $x + y \leq 7$

    $2x + y \leq 10$

    $2x + 3y \leq 18$

a.

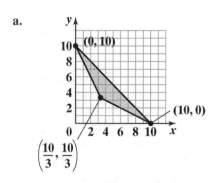

b. $(0, 6): z = 10(0) + 12(6) = 72$

    $(0, 0): z = 10(0) + 12(0) = 0$

    $(5, 0): z = 10(5) + 12(0) = 50$

    $(3, 4): z = 10(3) + 12(4)$

                   $= 30 + 48 = 78$

c.   The maximum value is 78 at $x = 3$ and $y = 4$.

12. $z = 5x + 6y$

    $x \geq 0, y \geq 0$

    $2x + y \geq 10$

    $x + 2y \geq 10$

    $x + y \leq 10$

a.

b. $(0,10): z = 5(0) + 6(10) = 60$

    $(10,0): z = 5(10) + 6(0) = 50$

    $\left(\dfrac{10}{3}, \dfrac{10}{3}\right): z = 5\left(\dfrac{10}{3}\right) + 6\left(\dfrac{10}{3}\right) = \dfrac{50}{3} + \dfrac{60}{3}$

    $= \dfrac{110}{3}$

c.   The maximum value is 60 at $x = 0$ and $y = 10$.

13. a. Let $x =$ number of hours spent tutoring and $y =$ number of hours spent as a teacher's aid. The objective is to maximize $z = 10x + 7y$.

b. The constraints are:

    $x + y \leq 20$

    $x \geq 3$

    $x \leq 8$

c.

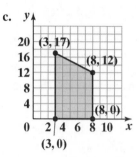

d. $(3, 0): 10(3) + 7(0) = 30 + 0 = 30$

    $(3, 17): 10(3) + 7(17) = 30 + 119 = 149$

    $(8, 12): 10(8) + 7(12) = 80 + 84 = 164$

    $(8, 0): 10(8) + 7(0) = 80 + 0 = 80$

e.   The student can earn the maximum amount per week by tutoring for 8 hours a week and working as a teacher's aid for 12 hours a week. The maximum that the student can earn each week is \$164.

14. a. $z = 125x + 200y$

b. $x \leq 450$

    $y \leq 200$

    $600x + 900y \leq 360,000$

c.   Simplify the third inequality by dividing by 300 to get $2x + 3y \leq 1200$.

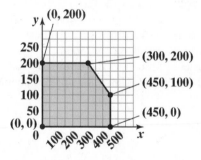

d. (0, 0): 125(0) + 200(0) = 0 + 0 = 0
  (0, 200): 125(0) + 200(200)
      = 0 + 40,000 = 40,000
  (300, 200): 125(300) + 200(200)
      = 37,500 + 40,000 = 77,500
  (450, 100): 125(450) + 200(100)
      = 56,250 + 20,000 = 76,250
  (450, 0): 125(450) + 200(0)
      = 56,250 + 0 = 56,250

e. The television manufacturer will make the greatest profit by manufacturing 300 rear-projection televisions each month and 200 plasma televisions each month. The maximum monthly profit is $77,500.

15. Let x = the number of cartons of food and y = the number of cartons of clothing.
The constraints are:
$20x + 10y \le 8,000$ or $2x + y \le 8000$
$50x + 20y \le 19,000$ or $5x + 2y \le 1900$
Graph these inequalities in the first quadrant, since x and y cannot be negative.

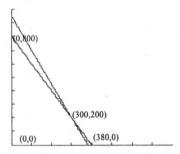

The quantity to be maximized is the number of people helped, which is $12x + 5y$.
(0, 0): 12(0) + 5(0) = 0 + 0 = 0
(0, 800): 12(0) + 5(800) = 0 + 4000 = 4000
(300, 200): 12(300) + 5(200) = 4600
(380, 0): 12(380) + 5(0) = 4500
300 cartons of food and 200 cartons of clothing should be shipped. This will help 4600 people.

16. Let x = number of computation problems,
  y = number of word problems.
Maximize: $z = 6x + 10y$
Constraints:
$2x + 4y \le 40$
$x + y \le 12$
$x \ge 0, y \ge 0$

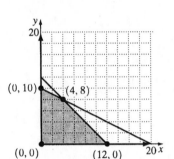

$(0,10): 6(0) + 10(10) = 100$
$(12,0): 6(12) + 10(0) = 72$
$(0,0): 6(0) + 10(0) = 0$
$(4,8): 6(4) + 10(8) = 24 + 80 = 104$
You should answer 4 computation problems and 8 word problems to get a maximum score of 104.

17. Let x = number of students attending and
  y = number of parents attending.
The constraints are
$x + y \le 150$
  $2x \ge y$
or
$x + y \le 150$
$2x - y \ge 0$
Graph these inequalities in the first quadrant, since x and y cannot be negative.

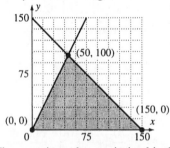

The quantity to be maximized is the amount of money raised, which is $x + 2y$.
(0, 0): 0 + 2(0) = 0 + 0 = 0
(50, 100): 50 + 2(100) = 50 + 200 = 250
(150, 0): 150 + 2(0) = 150 + 0 = 150
50 students and 100 parents should attend.

18. Let x = the number of American planes and y = the number of British planes.
The constraints are:
$$x + y \le 44$$
$$16x + 8y \le 512$$
$$9000x + 5000y \le 300{,}000$$
or
$$x + y \le 44$$
$$2x + y \le 64$$
$$9x + 5y \le 300$$
Graph these inequalities in the first quadrant, since x and y cannot be negative.

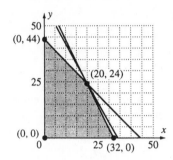

The quantity to be maximized is cargo capacity, which is $30{,}000x + 20{,}000y$.
(0, 0): $30{,}000(0) + 20{,}000(0) = 0 + 0 = 0$
(0, 44): $30{,}000(0) + 20{,}000(44) = 0 + 880{,}000$
　　　　$= 880{,}000$
(20, 24): $30{,}000(20) + 20{,}000(24)$
　　　　$= 600{,}000 + 480{,}000$
　　　　$= 1{,}080{,}000$
(32, 0): $30{,}000(32) + 20{,}000(0) = 960{,}000 + 0$
　　　　$= 960{,}000$
To maximize cargo capacity, 20 American planes and 24 British planes should be used.

24. does not make sense; Explanations will vary. Sample explanation: Solving a linear programming problem does not require graphing the objective function.

25. makes sense

26. makes sense

27. makes sense

28. Let x = amount invested in stocks and y = amount invested in bonds.
The constraints are:
$$x + y \le 10{,}000$$
$$y \ge 3000$$
$$x \ge 2000$$
$$y \ge x$$

Graph these inequalities in the first quadrant, since x and y cannot be negative.

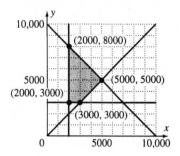

The quantity to be maximized is the return on the investment, which is $0.12x + 0.08y$.
(2000, 3000):
$0.12(2000) + 0.08(3000) = 240 + 240 = 480$
(2000, 8000):
$0.12(2000) + 0.08(8000) = 240 + 640 = 880$
(5000, 5000):
$0.12(5000) + 0.08(5000) = 600 + 400 = 1000$
(3000, 3000):
$0.12(3000) + 0.08(3000) = 360 + 240 = 600$
The greatest return occurs when \$5000 is invested in stocks and \$5000 is invested in bonds.

Section 7.6

Check Point Exercises

1.

x	$f(x) = 3^x$
-2	$\dfrac{1}{9}$
-1	$\dfrac{1}{3}$
0	1
1	3
2	9

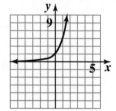

2. a. $f(x) = 0.074x + 2.287$

$f(51) = 0.074(51) + 2.287$

$f(51) \approx 6.1$

$g(x) = 2.566(1.017)^x$

$g(51) = 2.566(1.017)^{51}$

$g(51) \approx 6.1$

When rounded to one decimal place, the results from both functions model the world population for 2000 exactly.

b. $f(x) = 0.074x + 2.287$

$f(63) = 0.074(63) + 2.287$

$f(63) \approx 6.9$

$g(x) = 2.566(1.017)^x$

$g(63) = 2.566(1.017)^{63}$

$g(63) \approx 7.4$

The linear function, $f(x)$, serves as the better model for 2012.

3. $R = 6e^{12.77x}$

$= 6e^{12.77(0.01)}$

$= 6.8\%$

The risk of a car accident with a blood alcohol concentration of 0.01 is 6.8%.

4. $y = \log_3 x$ is equivalent to $x = 3^y$.

$x = 3^y$	y	(x, y)
$\dfrac{1}{9}$	-2	$\left(\dfrac{1}{9}, -2\right)$
$\dfrac{1}{3}$	-1	$\left(\dfrac{1}{3}, -1\right)$
1	0	$(1, 0)$
3	1	$(3, 1)$
9	2	$(9, 2)$

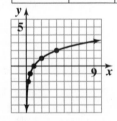

5. $f(x) = -11.6 + 13.4 \ln x$

$f(30) = -11.6 + 13.4 \ln 30$

$f(30) \approx 34°$

The function models the actual data extremely well.

6.   Step 1.   Since $a > 0$, the parabola opens upward $(a = 1)$.

Step 2.   Find the vertex given $a = 1$ and $b = 6$.

x-coordinate of vertex

$$= \frac{-b}{2a} = \frac{-6}{2(1)} = \frac{-6}{2} = -3$$

y-coordinate of vertex

$$= (-3)^2 + 6(-3) + 5 = 9 - 18 + 5 = -4$$

Thus, the vertex is the point $(-3, -4)$.

Step 3.   Replace y with 0 and solve the equation for x by factoring.

$$x^2 + 6x + 5 = 0$$

$$(x + 5)(x + 1) = 0$$

$x + 5 = 0 \quad$ or $\quad x + 1 = 0$

$x = -5 \qquad\qquad x = -1$

Thus the x-intercepts are -5 and -1, , which are located at the points $(-5, 0)$ and $(-1, 0)$.

Step 4.   Replace x with 0 and solve the equation for y.

$$y = x^2 + 6x + 5$$

$$y = (0)^2 + 6(0) + 5$$

$$y = 5$$

Thus the y-intercept is 5, which is located at the point $(0, 5)$.

Steps 5 and 6.   Plot the intercepts and the vertex. Connect these points with a smooth curve.

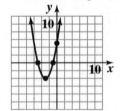

7. $f(x) = 0.004x^2 - 0.094x + 2.607$

$f(15) = 0.004(15)^2 - 0.094(15) + 2.607 \approx 2.1$

U.S. wine consumption was about 2.1 gallons per person in 1995.

This describes the value shown in the bar graph very well.

Exercise Set 7.6

1.

x	$y = 4^x$
-2	$\frac{1}{16}$
-1	$\frac{1}{4}$
0	1
1	4
2	16

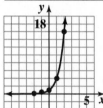

2.

x	$y = 5^x$
-2	$\frac{1}{25}$
-1	$\frac{1}{5}$
0	1
1	5
2	25

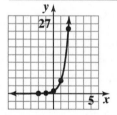

3.

x	$y = 2^{x+1}$
-2	$\frac{1}{2}$
-1	1
0	2
1	4
2	8

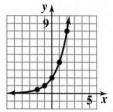

4.

x	$y = 2^{x-1}$
-2	$\frac{1}{8}$
-1	$\frac{1}{4}$
0	$\frac{1}{2}$
1	1
2	2

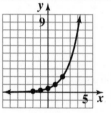

5.

x	$y = 3^{x-1}$
-2	$\frac{1}{27}$
-1	$\frac{1}{9}$
0	$\frac{1}{3}$
1	1
2	3

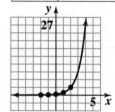

6.

x	$y = 3^{x+1}$
-2	$\dfrac{1}{3}$
-1	1
0	3
1	9
2	27

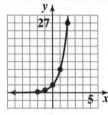

7. a. $y = \log_4 x$ is equivalent to $x = 4^y$.

b.

$x = 4^y$	y
$\dfrac{1}{16}$	-2
$\dfrac{1}{4}$	-1
1	0
4	1
16	2

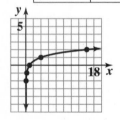

8. a. $y = \log_5 x$ is equivalent to $x = 5^y$.

b.

$x = 5^y$.	y
$\dfrac{1}{25}$	-2
$\dfrac{1}{5}$	-1
1	0
5	1
25	2

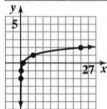

9. a. $a > 0$, thus the parabola opens upward.

b. x-coordinate: $x = \dfrac{-b}{2a} = \dfrac{-8}{2(1)} = -4$

      y-coordinate: $y = x^2 + 8x + 7$

$$= (-4)^2 + 8(-4) + 7$$
$$= -9$$

      vertex: $(-4, -9)$

c. x-intercepts: $y = x^2 + 8x + 7$

$$0 = x^2 + 8x + 7$$
$$0 = (x + 7)(x + 1)$$

      $x + 7 = 0$ or $x + 1 = 0$
        $x = -7$ $x = -1$

d. y-intercept: $y = x^2 + 8x + 7$

$$y = 0^2 + 8(0) + 7$$
$$y = 7$$

e.

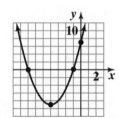

10. a. $a > 0$, thus the parabola opens upward.

b. x-coordinate: $x = \dfrac{-b}{2a} = \dfrac{-10}{2(1)} = -5$

y-coordinate: $y = x^2 + 10x + 9$
$$= (-5)^2 + 10(-5) + 9$$
$$= -16$$
vertex: $(-5, -16)$

c. x-intercepts: $y = x^2 + 10x + 9$
$$0 = x^2 + 10x + 9$$
$$0 = (x+9)(x+1)$$

$x + 9 = 0$ or $x + 1 = 0$
$\quad x = -9 \qquad\qquad x = -1$

d. y-intercept: $y = x^2 + 10x + 9$
$$y = 0^2 + 10(0) + 9$$
$$y = 9$$

e.
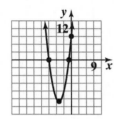

11. a. $a > 0$, thus the parabola opens upward.

b. x-coordinate: $x = \dfrac{-b}{2a} = \dfrac{-(-2)}{2(1)} = 1$

y-coordinate: $f(x) = x^2 - 2x - 8$
$$f(1) = (1)^2 - 2(1) - 8$$
$$= -9$$
vertex: $(1, -9)$

c. x-intercepts: $f(x) = x^2 - 2x - 8$
$$0 = x^2 - 2x - 8$$
$$0 = (x+2)(x-4)$$

$x + 2 = 0$ or $x - 4 = 0$
$\quad x = -2 \qquad\qquad x = 4$

d. y-intercept: $f(x) = x^2 - 2x - 8$
$$f(0) = 0^2 - 2(0) - 8$$
$$y = -8$$

e.
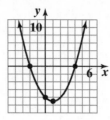

12. a. $a > 0$, thus the parabola opens upward.

b. x-coordinate: $x = \dfrac{-b}{2a} = \dfrac{-4}{2(1)} = -2$

y-coordinate: $f(x) = x^2 + 4x - 5$
$$f(-2) = (-2)^2 + 4(-2) - 5$$
$$= -9$$
vertex: $(-2, -9)$

c. x-intercepts: $f(x) = x^2 + 4x - 5$
$$0 = x^2 + 4x - 5$$
$$0 = (x+5)(x-1)$$

$x + 5 = 0$ or $x - 1 = 0$
$\quad x = -5 \qquad\qquad x = 1$

d. y-intercept: $f(x) = x^2 + 4x - 5$
$$f(0) = 0^2 + 4(0) - 5$$
$$y = -5$$

e.
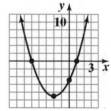

13. a. $a < 0$, thus the parabola opens downward.

b. x-coordinate: $x = \dfrac{-b}{2a} = \dfrac{-4}{2(-1)} = 2$

y-coordinate: $y = -x^2 + 4x - 3$
$$= -(2)^2 + 4(2) - 3$$
$$= 1$$
vertex: $(2, 1)$

c. x-intercepts: $y = -x^2 + 4x - 3$

$$0 = -x^2 + 4x - 3$$
$$0 = x^2 - 4x + 3$$
$$0 = (x-3)(x-1)$$

$x - 3 = 0$ or $x - 1 = 0$
$x = 3$ $x = 1$

d. y-intercept: $y = -x^2 + 4x - 3$

$$y = -0^2 + 4(0) - 3$$
$$y = -3$$

e.

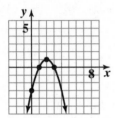

14. a. $a < 0$, thus the parabola opens downward.

b. x-coordinate: $x = \dfrac{-b}{2a} = \dfrac{-2}{2(-1)} = 1$

y-coordinate: $y = -x^2 + 2x + 3$
$$= -(1)^2 + 2(1) + 3$$
$$= 4$$

vertex: $(1, 4)$

c. x-intercepts: $y = -x^2 + 2x + 3$

$$0 = -x^2 + 2x + 3$$
$$0 = x^2 - 2x - 3$$
$$0 = (x+1)(x-3)$$

$x + 1 = 0$ or $x - 3 = 0$
$x = -1$ $x = 3$

d. y-intercept: $y = -x^2 + 2x + 3$

$$y = -0^2 + 2(0) + 3$$
$$y = 3$$

e.

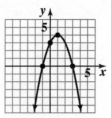

15. a.

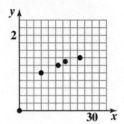

b.   logarithmic

16. a.

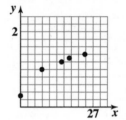

b.   logarithmic

17. a.

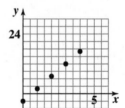

b.   linear

18. a.

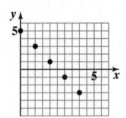

b.   linear

19. a.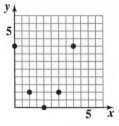

    b. quadratic

20. a.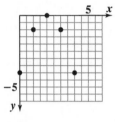

    b. quadratic

21. a.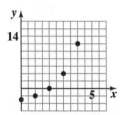

    b. exponential

22. a.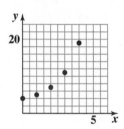

    b. exponential

23.

x	$f(x) = \left(\frac{1}{2}\right)^x$
−2	4
−1	2
0	1
1	$\frac{1}{2}$
2	$\frac{1}{4}$

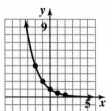

The graph is decreasing, although the rate of decrease is slowing down.

24.

x	$f(x) = \left(\frac{1}{3}\right)^x$
−2	9
−1	3
0	1
1	$\frac{1}{3}$
2	$\frac{1}{9}$

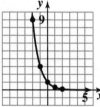

The graph is decreasing, although the rate of decrease is slowing down.

25.

$x = \left(\frac{1}{2}\right)^y$	y
4	−2
2	−1
1	0
$\frac{1}{2}$	1
$\frac{1}{4}$	2

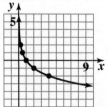

The graph is decreasing, although the rate of decrease is slowing down.

26.

$x = \left(\frac{1}{3}\right)^y$	y
9	-2
3	-1
1	0
$\frac{1}{3}$	1
$\frac{1}{9}$	2

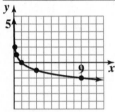

The graph is decreasing, although the rate of decrease is slowing down.

27. a. $a < 0$, thus the parabola opens downward.

b. x-coordinate: $x = \dfrac{-b}{2a} = \dfrac{-4}{2(-2)} = 1$

  y-coordinate: $f(x) = -2x^2 + 4x + 5$

  $$f(1) = -2(1)^2 + 4(1) + 5$$
  $$= 7$$

  vertex: $(1, 7)$

c. x-intercepts: $f(x) = -2x^2 + 4x + 5$

  $$0 = -2x^2 + 4x + 5$$
  $$0 = 2x^2 - 4x - 5$$

  $$x = \frac{-b \pm \sqrt{b^2 - 4ac}}{2a}$$

  $$x = \frac{-(-4) \pm \sqrt{(-4)^2 - 4(2)(-5)}}{2(2)}$$

  $$x \approx -0.9 \quad \text{or} \quad x \approx 2.9$$

d. y-intercept: $f(x) = -2x^2 + 4x + 5$

  $$f(0) = -2(0)^2 + 4(0) + 5$$
  $$f(0) = 5$$

e.

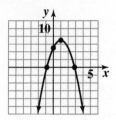

28. a. $a < 0$, thus the parabola opens downward.

b. x-coordinate: $x = \dfrac{-b}{2a} = \dfrac{-6}{2(-3)} = 1$

  y-coordinate: $f(x) = -3x^2 + 6x - 2$

  $$f(1) = -3(1)^2 + 6(1) - 2$$
  $$= 1$$

  vertex: $(1, 1)$

c. x-intercepts: $f(x) = -3x^2 + 6x - 2$

  $$0 = -3x^2 + 6x - 2$$
  $$0 = 3x^2 - 6x + 2$$

  $$x = \frac{-b \pm \sqrt{b^2 - 4ac}}{2a}$$

  $$x = \frac{-(-6) \pm \sqrt{(-6)^2 - 4(3)(2)}}{2(3)}$$

  $$x \approx 0.4 \quad \text{or} \quad x \approx 1.6$$

d. y-intercept: $f(x) = -3x^2 + 6x - 2$

  $$f(0) = -3(0)^2 + 6(0) - 2$$
  $$f(0) = -2$$

e.

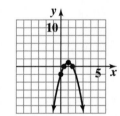

29. $y = (x-3)^2 + 2$

  $y = x^2 - 6x + 9 + 2$

  $y = x^2 - 6x + 11$

  x-coordinate: $x = \dfrac{-b}{2a} = \dfrac{-(-6)}{2(1)} = 3$

  y-coordinate: $y = x^2 - 6x + 11$

  $$y = 3^2 - 6(3) + 11$$
  $$y = 2$$

  vertex: $(3, 2)$

30. $y = (x-4)^2 + 3$

$y = x^2 - 8x + 16 + 3$

$y = x^2 - 8x + 19$

x-coordinate: $x = \dfrac{-b}{2a} = \dfrac{-(-8)}{2(1)} = 4$

y-coordinate: $y = x^2 - 8x + 19$

$\qquad\qquad\qquad y = 4^2 - 8(4) + 19$

$\qquad\qquad\qquad y = 3$

vertex: $(4, 3)$

31. a. An exponential function was used because the graph is increasing more and more rapidly.

b. $f(x) = 1.258(1.283)^x$

c. $f(28) = 1.258(1.283)^{28} \approx 1349$

The function overestimates the actual population by 106.

32. a. An exponential function was used because the graph is increasing more and more rapidly.

b. $f(x) = 1066.058(1.043)^x$

c. $f(28) = 1066.058(1.043)^{28} \approx 3465$

The function underestimates the actual population by 484.

33. a. 2005 is 50 years after 1955.

$f(x) = 0.15x + 1.44$

$f(50) = 0.15(50) + 1.44 \approx 8.9$

According to the linear model, there were about 8.9 million words in the federal tax code in 2005.

b. 2005 is 50 years after 1955.

$g(x) = 1.87e^{0.0344x}$

$g(50) = 1.87e^{0.0344(50)} \approx 10.4$

According to the exponential model, there were about 10.4 million words in the federal tax code in 2005.

c. The linear model is the better model for the data in 2005.

34. a. 1975 is 20 years after 1955.

$f(x) = 0.15x + 1.44$

$f(20) = 0.15(20) + 1.44 \approx 4.4$

According to the linear model, there were about 4.4 million words in the federal tax code in 1975.

b. 1975 is 20 years after 1955.

$g(x) = 1.87e^{0.0344x}$

$g(20) = 1.87e^{0.0344(20)} \approx 3.7$

According to the exponential model, there were about 3.7 million words in the federal tax code in 1975.

c. The exponential model is the better model for the data in 1975.

35. 2007 is 5 years after 2002.

$f(x) = 8 + 38\ln x$

$f(5) = 8 + 38\ln 5 \approx 69$

According to the function, 69% of new cellphones will have cameras in 2007. This overestimates the value shown in the graph by 1%.

36. 2006 is 4 years after 2002.

$f(x) = 8 + 38\ln x$

$f(4) = 8 + 38\ln 4 \approx 61$

According to the function, 61% of new cellphones will have cameras in 2006. This underestimates the value shown in the graph by 2%.

37. a. $f(x) = 62 + 35\log(x-4)$

$f(13) = 62 + 35\log(13-4)$

$f(13) \approx 95.3\%$

b. A logarithmic function was used because height increases rapidly at first and then more slowly.

38. a. $f(x) = 62 + 35\log(x-4)$

$f(10) = 62 + 35\log(10-4)$

$f(13) \approx 89.2\%$

b. A logarithmic function was used because height increases rapidly at first and then more slowly.

39. a. A quadratic function was used because data values decrease then increase.
The graph of the quadratic function modeling the data opens down.

b. $f(x) = -0.01x^2 + 0.07x + 1.46$

c. $f(7) = -0.01(7)^2 + 0.07(7) + 1.46 = 1.46$
According to the function, 1.46 billion movie tickets were sold in 2007.
This underestimates the number shown in the bar graph by 0.01 billion.

40. a. A quadratic function was used because data values decrease then increase.
The graph of the quadratic function modeling the data opens down.

b. $f(x) = -0.01x^2 + 0.07x + 1.46$

c. $f(3) = -0.01(3)^2 + 0.07(3) + 1.46 = 1.58$
According to the function, 1.58 billion movie tickets were sold in 2003.
This underestimates the number shown in the bar graph by 0.02 billion.

47. does not make sense; Explanations will vary.
Sample explanation: An exponential model is better than a linear model.

48. makes sense

49. does not make sense; Explanations will vary.
Sample explanation: The risk increases exponentially.

50. makes sense

51. There are two x-intercepts because the vertex is above the x-axis and the parabola opens downward $(a < 0)$.

52. There is only one x-intercept because the vertex on the x-axis. The vertex is the x-intercept.

53. There are no x-intercepts because the vertex is above the x-axis and the parabola opens upward $(a > 0)$.

Chapter 7 Review Exercises

1.

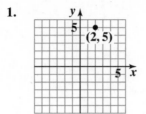

2.

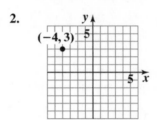

3.

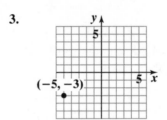

4.

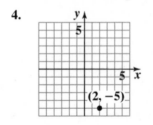

5.

x	$y = 2x - 2$
-3	-8
-2	-6
-1	-4
0	-2
1	0
2	2
3	4

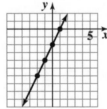

6.

x	$y = \|x\| + 2$
–3	5
–2	4
–1	3
0	2
1	3
2	4
3	5

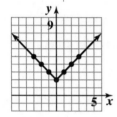

7.

x	$y = x$
–3	–3
–2	–2
–1	–1
0	0
1	1
2	2
3	3

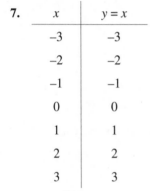

8. $f(x) = 4x + 11$

$f(-2) = 4(-2) + 11 = -8 + 11 = 3$

9. $f(x) = -7x + 5$

$f(-3) = -7(-3) + 5 = 21 + 5 = 26$

10. $f(x) = 3x^2 - 5x + 2$

$f(4) = 3(4)^2 - 5(4) + 2 = 48 - 20 + 2 = 30$

11. $f(x) = -3x^2 + 6x + 8$

$f(-4) = -3(-4)^2 + 6(-4) + 8$

$= -48 - 24 + 8 = -64$

12.

x	$f(x) = \frac{1}{2}\|x\|$
–6	3
–4	2
–2	1
0	0
2	1
4	2
6	3

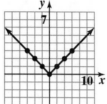

13.

x	$f(x) = x^2 - 2$
–2	2
–1	–1
0	–2
1	–1
2	2

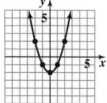

14. The graph passes the vertical line test. Thus y is a function of x.

15. The graph does not pass the vertical line test. Thus y is not a function of x.

16. a. The coordinates are (1985, 50%).

   b. The top marginal tax rate in 2005 was 35%.

   c. The highest marginal tax rate occurred in 1945 and was about 94%.

   d. The lowest marginal tax rate occurred in 1990 and was about 28%.

e. During the ten-year period from 1950 to 1960, the top marginal tax rate remained constant at about 91%.

f. During the five-year period from 1930 to 1935, the top marginal tax rate increased about 38%.

17. $2x + y = 4$
x-intercept is 2; y-intercept is 4.

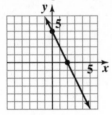

18. $2x - 3y = 6$
x-intercept is 3; y-intercept is –2.

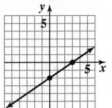

19. $5x - 3y = 15$
x-intercept is 3; y-intercept is –5.

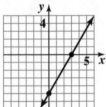

20. Slope $= \dfrac{1-2}{5-3} = -\dfrac{1}{2}$; line falls

21. Slope $= \dfrac{-4-2}{-3-(-1)} = \dfrac{-6}{-2} = 3$; line rises

22. Slope $= \dfrac{4-4}{6-(-3)} = 0$; line horizontal

23. Slope $= \dfrac{-3-3}{5-5} = \dfrac{-6}{0}$ is undefined, vertical line

24. $y = 2x - 4$; Slope: 2, y-intercept: –4
Plot point (0, –4) and second point using
$$m = \frac{2}{1} = \frac{\text{rise}}{\text{run}}.$$

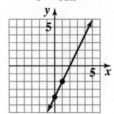

25. $y = -\dfrac{2}{3}x + 5$; Slope: $-\dfrac{2}{3}$, y-intercept: 5
Plot point (0, 5) and second point using
$$m = \frac{-2}{3} = \frac{\text{rise}}{\text{run}}.$$

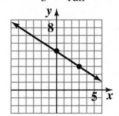

26. $y = \dfrac{3}{4}x - 2$; Slope: $\dfrac{3}{4}$, y-intercept: –2
Plot point (0, –2) and second point using
$$m = \frac{3}{4} = \frac{\text{rise}}{\text{run}}.$$

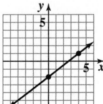

27. $y = \dfrac{1}{2}x + 0$; Slope: $\dfrac{1}{2}$, y-intercept: 0
Plot point (0, 0) and second point using
$$m = \frac{1}{2} = \frac{\text{rise}}{\text{run}}.$$

28. a. $2x + y = 0$
$y = -2x$

b. Slope $= -2$
y-intercept $= 0$

c.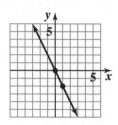

29. a. $3y = 5x$

$y = \dfrac{5}{3}x$

b. Slope $= \dfrac{5}{3}$

y-intercept $= 0$

c.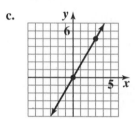

30. a. $3x + 2y = 4$
$2y = -3x + 4$

$y = -\dfrac{3}{2}x + 2$

b. Slope $= -\dfrac{3}{2}$

y-intercept $= 2$

c.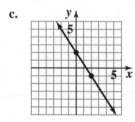

31. $x = 3$

32. $y = -4$

33. $x + 2 = 0$ or $x = -2$

34. a. The y-intercept is 254. This represents if no women in a country are literate, the mortality rate of children under five is 254 per thousand.

b. $m = \dfrac{y_2 - y_1}{x_2 - x_1} = \dfrac{110 - 254}{60 - 0} = \dfrac{-144}{60} = -2.4$

For each 1% of adult females who are literate, the mortality rate of children under five decreases by 2.4 per thousand.

c. $f(x) = -2.4x + 254$

d. $f(50) = -2.4(50) + 254 = 134$

A country where 50% of adult females are literate is predicted to have a mortality rate of children under five of 134 per thousand.

35. The intersection is (2, 3).
Check: $2 + 3 = 5$ $3(2) - 3 = 3$
$5 = 5$ true $6 - 3 = 3$
$3 = 3$ true

The solution set is $\{(2, 3)\}$.

345

36. The intersection is $(-2, -3)$.

Check: $2(-2) - (-3) = -1$ $-2 - 3 = -5$

$\qquad\qquad -4 + 3 = -1$ $-5 = -5$ true

$\qquad\qquad\qquad -1 = -1$ true

The solution set is $\{(-2, -3)\}$.

37. The intersection is $(3, 2)$.

Check: $2 = -3 + 5$ $2(3) - 2 = 4$

$\qquad\quad 2 = 2$ true $6 - 2 = 4$

$\qquad\qquad\qquad\qquad\qquad 4 = 4$ true

The solution set is $\{(3, 2)\}$.

38. $x = 3y + 10 \qquad 2x + 3y = 2$

$\quad 2(3y + 10) + 3y = 2$

$\qquad 6y + 20 + 3y = 2$

$\qquad\qquad\qquad 9y = -18$

$\qquad\qquad\qquad\ y = -2$

$x = 3(-2) + 10 = -6 + 10 = 4$

The solution set is $\{(4, -2)\}$.

39. $y = 4x + 1 \qquad\qquad 3x + 2y = 13$

$\quad 3x + 2(4x + 1) = 13$

$\qquad 3x + 8x + 2 = 13$

$\qquad\qquad\quad 11x = 11$

$\qquad\qquad\qquad\ x = 1$

$y = 4(1) + 1 = 5$

The solution set is $\{(1, 5)\}$.

40. $x + 4y = 14$

$\ x = 14 - 4y \qquad\quad 2x - y = 1$

$\ 2(14 - 4y) - y = 1$

$\quad 28 - 8y - y = 1$

$\qquad\qquad -9y = -27$

$\qquad\qquad\qquad y = 3$

$x = 14 - 4(3) = 2$

The solution set is $\{(2, 3)\}$.

41. $x + 2y = -3$ No change. $x + 2y = -3$

$\ x - y = -12$ Multiply by -1. $\underline{-x + \ y = 12}$

$\qquad\qquad\qquad\qquad\qquad\qquad\quad 3y = 9$

$\qquad\qquad\qquad\qquad\qquad\qquad\quad\ y = 3$

$x - y = -12$

$x - 3 = -12$

$\quad x = -9$

The solution set is $\{(-9, 3)\}$.

42. $2x - y = 2$ Mult. by 2. $4x - 2y = 4$

$\ x + 2y = 11$ No change $\underline{x + 2y = 11}$

$\qquad\qquad\qquad\qquad\qquad\qquad\quad 5x = 15$

$\qquad\qquad\qquad\qquad\qquad\qquad\ \ x = 3$

$x + 2y = 11$

$3 + 2y = 11$

$\quad 2y = 8$

$\quad\ y = 4$

The solution set is $\{(3, 4)\}$.

43. $5x + 3y = 1$ Mult. by 3. $15x + 9y = 3$

$\ 3x + 4y = -6$ Mult. by -5. $\underline{-15x - 20y = 30}$

$\qquad\qquad\qquad\qquad\qquad\qquad\qquad\quad -11y = 33$

$\qquad\qquad\qquad\qquad\qquad\qquad\qquad\qquad\ y = -3$

$\quad 5x + 3y = 1$

$\quad 5x + 3(-3) = 1$

$\qquad\quad 5x = 10$

$\qquad\qquad x = 2$

The solution set is $\{(2, -3)\}$.

44. $y = -x + 4 \qquad\qquad 3x + 3y = -6$

$\ 3x + 3(-x + 4) = -6$

$\quad 3x - 3x + 12 = -6$

$\qquad\qquad\qquad 12 = -6$, false

There is no solution or $\{\ \}$.

45. $3x + y = 8$

$\quad y = 8 - 3x \qquad\qquad 2x - 5y = 11$

$\ 2x - 5(8 - 3x) = 11$

$\ 2x - 40 + 15x = 11$

$\qquad\qquad\quad 17x = 51$

$\qquad\qquad\qquad\ x = 3$

$y = 8 - 3(3) = -1$

The solution set is $\{(3, -1)\}$.

46. $3x - 2y = 6$ Mult. by -2. $-6x + 4y = -12$

$\ 6x - 4y = 12$ No change. $\underline{6x - 4y = 12}$

$\qquad\qquad\qquad\qquad\qquad\qquad\qquad\quad 0 = 0$

The system has infinitely many solutions.

The solution set is $\left\{(x, y) \big| 3x - 2y = 6\right\}$.

47. a. $C(x) = 60,000 + 200x$

b. $R(x) = 450x$

c. $450x = 60000 + 200x$

$250x = 60000$
$x = 240$
$450(240) = 108,000$
The company must make 240 desks at a cost of $108,000 to break even.

48. a. Answers will vary. Approximate point is $(2004,180)$. This means that in 2004 the number of cellphones and land-lines were both 180 million.

b. $y = 19.8x + 98$

c. Using substitution,
$$4.3x + y = 198$$

$$4.3x + \overbrace{(19.8x + 98)}^{y} = 198$$
$$4.3x + 19.8x + 98 = 198$$
$$24.1x + 98 = 198$$
$$24.1x = 100$$
$$x \approx 4$$

The number of cellphone and land-line customers will be they same 4 years after 2000, or 2004.
$$y = 19.8x + 98$$
$$y = 19.8(4) + 98$$
$$y = 177.2$$
$$y \approx 180$$
The number of customers that each will have in 2004 is about 180 million.

d. The models describe the point of intersection quite well.

49. To graph $x - 3y \leq 6$, begin by graphing $x - 3y = 6$ with a solid line because $\leq$ includes equality.
test point $(0, 0)$:

$x - 3y \leq 6$
$0 - 3(0) \leq 6$
$\quad\quad 0 \leq 6$, true

Since the test point makes the inequality <u>true</u>, shade the half-plane <u>containing</u> test point $(0, 0)$.

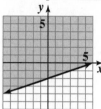

50. To graph $2x + 3y \geq 12$, begin by graphing $2x + 3y = 12$ with a solid line because $\geq$ includes equality.
test point $(0, 0)$:

$2x + 3y \geq 12$
$2(0) + 3(0) \geq 12$
$\quad\quad 0 \geq 12$, false

Since the test point makes the inequality <u>false</u>, shade the half-plane <u>not containing</u> test point $(0, 0)$.

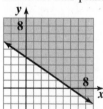

51. To graph $2x - 7y > 14$, begin by graphing $2x - 7y = 14$ with a dashed line because $>$ does not include equality.
test point $(0, 0)$:

$2x - 7y > 14$
$2(0) - 7(0) > 14$
$\quad\quad 0 > 14$, false

Since the test point makes the inequality <u>false</u>, shade the half-plane <u>not containing</u> test point $(0, 0)$.

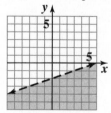

52. To graph $y > \frac{3}{5}x$, begin by graphing $y = \frac{3}{5}x$ as a dashed line passing through the origin with a slope of $\frac{3}{5}$, then shade above the line.

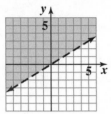

53. To graph $y \leq -\frac{1}{2}x + 2$, begin by graphing $y = -\frac{1}{2}x + 2$ as a solid line passing through $(0, 2)$ with a slope of $\frac{-1}{2}$, then shade below the line.

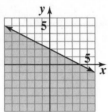

54. To graph $x \leq 2$, begin by graphing $x = 2$ as a solid vertical line passing through $x = 2$, then shade to the left of the line.

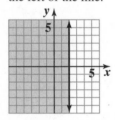

55. To graph $y > -3$, begin by graphing $y = -3$ as a dashed horizontal line passing through $y = -3$, then shade above the line.

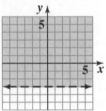

56. $3x - y \leq 6$
$x + y \geq 2$
Graph $3x - y = 6$ as a solid line.
Because $(0, 0)$ makes the inequality true, shade the half-plane containing $(0,0)$.
Graph $x + y = 2$ as a solid line.
Because $(0, 0)$ makes the inequality false, shade the half-plane not containing $(0, 0)$.

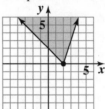

57. $x + y < 4$
$x - y < 4$
Graph $x + y = 4$ as a dashed line.
Because $(0, 0)$ makes the inequality true, shade the half-plane containing $(0, 0)$.
Graph $x - y = 4$ as a dashed line.
Because $(0, 0)$ makes the inequality true, shade the half-plane containing $(0, 0)$.

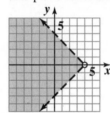

58. $x \leq 3$
$y > -2$
Graph $x = 3$ as a solid line.
The points in the half-plane to the left of the line satisfy $x < 3$.
Graph $y = -2$ as a dashed line.
The points in the half-plane above the line satisfy $y > -2$.

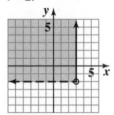

59. $4x + 6y = 24$

   $y > 2$

Graph $4x + 6y = 24$ as a solid line.

Because (0, 0) makes the inequality true, shade the half-plane containing (0, 0).

Graph $y = 2$ as a dashed line.

The points in the half-plane above the line satisfy $y > 2$.

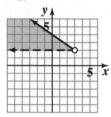

60. $x + y \leq 6$

   $y \geq 2x - 3$

Graph $x + y = 6$ as a solid line.

Because (0, 0) makes the inequality true, shade the half-plane containing (0, 0).

Graph $y = 2x - 3$ as a solid line.

Because (0, 0) makes the inequality true, shade the half-plane containing (0, 0).

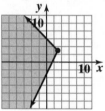

61. $y < -x + 4$

   $y > x - 4$

Graph $y < -x + 4$ as a dashed line.

Because (0, 0) makes the inequality true, shade the half-plane containing (0, 0).

Graph $y = x - 4$ as a dashed line.

Because (0, 0) makes the inequality true, shade the half-plane containing (0, 0).

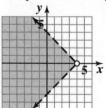

62. $z = 2x + 3y$

   at (1, 0) $z = 2(1) + 3(0) = 2$

   at $\left(\dfrac{1}{2}, \dfrac{1}{2}\right)$ $z = 2\left(\dfrac{1}{2}\right) + 3\left(\dfrac{1}{2}\right) = \dfrac{5}{2}$

   at (2, 2) $z = 2(2) + 3(2) = 10$

   at (4, 0) $z = 2(4) + 3(0) = 8$

Maximum value of the objective function is 10.
Minimum value of the objective function is 2.

63. $z = 2x + 3y$

   Constraints: $x \leq 6$

   $y \leq 5$

   $x + y \geq 2$

   $x \geq 0$

   $y \geq 0$

   a.

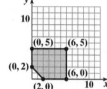

   b.   at (0, 2) $z = 2(0) + 3(2) = 6$

   at (0, 5) $z = 2(0) + 3(5) = 15$

   at (6, 5) $z = 2(6) + 3(5) = 27$

   at (6, 0) $z = 2(6) + 3(0) = 12$

   at (2, 0) $z = 2(2) + 3(0) = 4$

   c.   The maximum value of the objective function is 27. It occurs at $x = 6$ and $y = 5$.
   The minimum value of the objective function is 4. It occurs at $x = 2$ and $y = 0$.

64. a. $z = 500x + 350y$

   b. $x + y \leq 200$
   $x \geq 10$
   $y \geq 80$

   c.

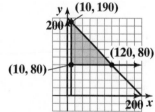

   $x + y \leq 200$
   $x \geq 10, y \geq 80$

d.   Vertex   Objective Function

$$z = 500x + 350y$$

(10, 80) $z = 500(10) + 350(80)$
             $= 33,000$

(10, 190) $z = 500(10) + 350(190)$
             $= 71,500$

(120, 80) $z = 500(120) + 350(80)$
             $= 88,000$

e. The company will make the greatest profit by producing 120 units of writing paper and 80 units of newsprint each day. The maximum daily profit is $88,000.

65.

x	$y = 2^x$
-2	$\frac{1}{4}$
-1	$\frac{1}{2}$
0	1
1	2
2	4

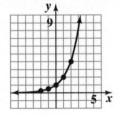

66.

x	$y = 2^{x+1}$
-2	$\frac{1}{2}$
-1	1
0	2
1	4
2	8

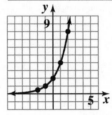

67. $y = \log_2 x$ is equivalent to $x = 2^y$.

$x = 2^y$	y
$\frac{1}{4}$	-2
$\frac{1}{2}$	-1
1	0
2	1
4	2

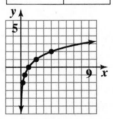

68. a. $a > 0$, thus the parabola opens upward.

b. x-coordinate: $x = \frac{-b}{2a} = \frac{-(-6)}{2(1)} = 3$

y-coordinate: $f(x) = x^2 - 6x - 7$

$f(3) = (3)^2 - 6(3) - 7$
$= -16$

vertex: $(3, -16)$

c. x-intercepts: $f(x) = x^2 - 6x - 7$

$$0 = x^2 - 6x - 7$$
$$0 = (x+1)(x-7)$$

$x + 1 = 0$ or $x - 7 = 0$
$\quad x = -1 \qquad\qquad x = 7$

d. y-intercept: $f(x) = x^2 - 6x - 7$

$$f(0) = 0^2 - 6(0) - 7$$
$$y = -7$$

e.

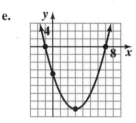

69. a. $a < 0$, thus the parabola opens downward.

b. x-coordinate: $x = \dfrac{-b}{2a} = \dfrac{-(-2)}{2(-1)} = -1$

y-coordinate: $f(x) = -x^2 - 2x + 3$

$$f(-1) = -(-1)^2 - 2(-1) + 3$$
$$= 4$$

vertex: $(-1, 4)$

c. x-intercepts: $f(x) = -x^2 - 2x + 3$

$$0 = -x^2 - 2x + 3$$
$$0 = x^2 + 2x - 3$$
$$0 = (x+3)(x-1)$$

$x + 3 = 0$ or $x - 1 = 0$
$\quad x = -3 \qquad\qquad x = 1$

d. y-intercept: $f(x) = -x^2 - 2x + 3$

$$f(0) = -0^2 - 2(0) + 3$$
$$y = 3$$

e.

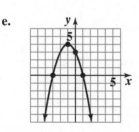

70. a.   QwertyDan please check NewArt

Age of U.S. Drivers and Fatal Crashes

b.   quadratic

71. a.

b.   exponential

72. a.

b.   logarithmic

73. a.   The slope is 47. For each additional hour spent at a shopping mall, the average amount spent increases by $47. The rate of change is $47 per hour.

b. $f(x) = 47x + 22$

$$f(3.5) = 47(3.5) + 22 = 186.5$$

$g(x) = 42.2(1.56)^x$

$$g(3.5) = 42.2(1.56)^{3.5} = 200.1$$

The exponential function is the better model.

74. $f(x) = -0.4x + 25.4$

$f(60) = -0.4(60) + 25.4 = 1.4$

$g(x) = 54.8 - 12.3 \ln x$

$g(60) = 54.8 - 12.3 \ln(60) \approx 4.4$

The logarithmic function is the better model.

Chapter 7 Test

1.

x	$y = |x| - 2$
-3	1
-2	0
-1	-1
0	-2
1	-1
2	0
3	1

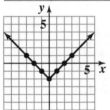

2. $f(-2) = 3(-2)^2 - 7(-2) - 5 = 12 + 14 - 5 = 21$

3. The graph does not pass the vertical line test. Thus y is not a function of x.

4. The graph passes the vertical line test. Thus y is a function of x.

5. a. Yes, it is a function. The graph passes the vertical line test.

   b. $f(15) = 0$ means that the eagle was on the ground after 15 seconds.

   c. The maximum height was 45 meters.

   d. The eagle was descending between second 3 and second 12.

6.

Set $y = 0$	Set $x = 0$
$4x - 2 \cdot 0 = -8$	$4 \cdot 0 - 2y = -8$
$4x = -8$	$-2y = -8$
$x = -2$	$y = 4$
x-intercept is -2.	y-intercept is 4.

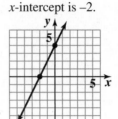

7. $\text{Slope} = \dfrac{-2 - 4}{-5 - (-3)} = \dfrac{-6}{-2} = 3$

8. $y = \dfrac{2}{3}x - 1$

Slope: $\dfrac{2}{3}$, y-intercept: -1

Plot the point $(0, -1)$ and a second point using

$m = \dfrac{2}{3} = \dfrac{\text{rise}}{\text{run}}$.

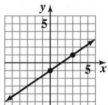

9. $f(x) = -2x + 3$

Slope: -2, y-intercept: 3
Plot the point $(0, 3)$ and a second point using

$m = \dfrac{-2}{1} = \dfrac{\text{rise}}{\text{run}}$.

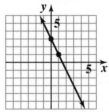

10. a. The y-intercept is 449. In 2002, approximately 449,000 students were enrolled exclusively in online education.

   b. $m = \dfrac{1489 - 449}{4 - 0} = 260$

   Each year the number of students enrolled exclusively in online education increases by 260 thousand. The rate of change is 260 thousand students per year.

c. $y = mx + b$

$L(x) = 260x + 449$

d. $L(x) = 260x + 449$

$L(10) = 260(10) + 449 = 3049$

The function predicts that there will be 3049 thousand, or 3,049,000 students enrolled exclusively in online education in 2012.

11. The intersection is (2, 4)

Check: $2 + 4 = 6$ $4(2) - 4 = 4$

$6 = 6$ true $8 - 4 = 4$

$4 = 4$ true

The solution set is $\{(2, 4)\}$.

12. $x = y + 4$ $3x + 7y = -18$

$3(y + 4) + 7y = -18$

$3y + 12 + 7y = -18$

$10y = -30$

$y = -3$

$x = -3 + 4 = 1$

The solution set is $\{(1, -3)\}$.

13. $5x + 4y = 10$ $\xrightarrow{\text{Mult. by 3}}$ $15x + 12y = 30$

$3x + 5y = -7$ $\xrightarrow{\text{Mult. by } -5}$ $\underline{-15x - 25y = 35}$

$-13y = 65$

$y = -5$

$5x + 4y = 10$

$5x + 4(-5) = 10$

$5x = 30$

$x = 6$

The solution set is $\{(6, -5)\}$.

14. a. $C(x) = 360,000 + 850x$

b. $R(x) = 1150x$

c. $1150x = 360,000 + 850x$

$300x = 360,000$

$x = 1200$

Substitute 1200 into either equation to find the amount of cost and revenue at $x = 1200$.

$R(1200) = 1150(1200) = \$1,380,000$

The company will break even if it produces and sells 1200 computers.

15. $3x - 2y < 6$

Graph $3x - 2y = 6$ as a dashed line.

x-intercept:

$3x - 2 \cdot 0 = 6$

$3x = 6$

$x = 2$

y-intercept:

$3 \cdot 0 - 2y = 6$

$-2y = 6$

$y = -3$

Test point: (0, 0).

Is $3 \cdot 0 - 2 \cdot 0 < 6$?

$0 < 6$, true

Shade the half-plane containing (0, 0).

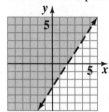

16. Graph $y = \frac{1}{2}x - 1$ as a solid line.

Use y-intercept of –1 and slope of $\frac{1}{2}$

Shade below this line.

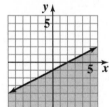

17. $y > -1$

Graph $y = -1$ as a dashed line.

Test point: (0, 0).

Is $0 > -1$?

$0 > -1$, true

Shade the half-plane containing (0, 0).

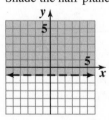

18. $2x - y \leq 4$

$2x - y > -1$

Graph $2x - y = 4$ as a solid line.
Because (0, 0) makes the inequality true, shade the half-plane containing (0, 0).
Graph $2x - y = -1$ as a dashed line.
Because (0, 0) makes the inequality true, shade the half-plane containing (0, 0).

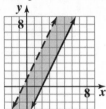

19. $z = 3x + 2y$

at (2, 0) $z = 3(2) + 2(0) = 6$

at (2, 6) $z = 3(2) + 2(6) = 18$

at (6, 3) $z = 3(6) + 2(3) = 24$

at (8, 0) $z = 3(8) + 2(0) = 24$

The maximum value of the objective function is 24.
The minimum value of the objective function is 6.

20.

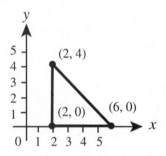

Objective function: $z = 3x + 5y$

at (2, 0) $z = 3(2) + 5(0) = 6$

at (6, 0) $z = 3(6) + 5(0) = 18$

at (2, 4) $z = 3(2) + 5(4) = 26$

The maximum value of the objective function is 26.

21.

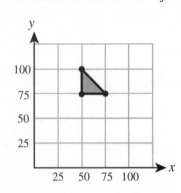

Objective function: $z = 200x + 250y$

Constraints: $x \geq 50$; $y \geq 75$; $x + y \leq 150$

Substitute vertices into objective function:

at (50, 100) $z = 200(50) + 250(100) = 35,000$

at (75, 75) $z = 200(75) + 250(75) = 33,750$

at (50, 75) $z = 200(50) + 250(75) = 28,750$

The company will make the greatest profit by producing 50 regular jet skis and 100 deluxe jet skis each week. The maximum weekly profit is $35,000.

22.

x	$f(x) = 3^x$
–2	$\frac{1}{9}$
–1	$\frac{1}{3}$
0	1
1	3
2	9

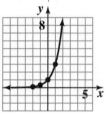

23. $y = \log_2 x$ is equivalent to $x = 3^y$.

$x = 3^y$	y
$\frac{1}{9}$	–2
$\frac{1}{3}$	–1
1	0
3	1
9	2

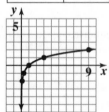

24. *x*-coordinate: $x = \dfrac{-b}{2a} = \dfrac{-(-2)}{2(1)} = 1$

y-coordinate: $f(x) = x^2 - 2x - 8$

$\qquad\qquad f(1) = 1^2 - 2(1) - 8$

$\qquad\qquad y = -9$

vertex: $(1, -9)$

x-intercepts: $f(x) = x^2 - 2x - 8$

$\qquad\qquad 0 = x^2 - 2x - 8$

$\qquad\qquad 0 = (x + 2)(x - 4)$

$\qquad x + 2 = 0 \quad$ or $\quad x - 4 = 0$

$\qquad x = -2 \qquad\qquad x = 4$

y-intercept: $f(x) = x^2 - 2x - 8$

$\qquad\qquad f(0) = 0^2 - 2(0) - 8$

$\qquad\qquad y = -8$

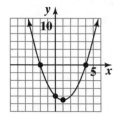

25. Plot the ordered pairs.

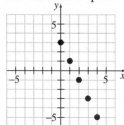

The values appear to belong to a linear function.

26. Plot the ordered pairs.

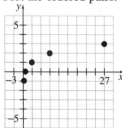

The values appear to belong to a logarithmic function.

27. Plot the ordered pairs.

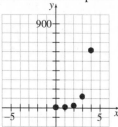

The values appear to belong to an exponential function.

28. Plot the ordered pairs.

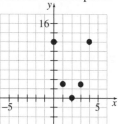

The values appear to belong to a quadratic function.

30. a. $m = 5.3$, which means each year the number of monthly text messages increases by 5.3 billion.

b. An exponential function appears to be the better model because the number of monthly text messages increases more and more rapidly.

c. linear function: $f(x) = 5.3x - 14.7$

$\qquad\qquad f(7) = 5.3(7) - 14.7 = 22.4$

exponential function:

$\qquad g(x) = 0.14(2.14)^x$

$\qquad g(7) = 0.14(2.14)^7 \approx 28.8$

The exponential function serves better for 2007. This is consistent with the answer for part b.

Chapter 8
Consumer Mathematics and Financial Management

Check Points 8.1

1. Step 1: $\dfrac{1}{8} = 1 \div 8 = 0.125$

   Step 2: $0.125 \cdot 100 = 12.5$
   Step 3: 12.5%

2. $0.023 = 2.3\%$

3. **a.** $67\% = 0.67$

   b. $250\% = 2.50 = 2.5$

4. **a.** 6% of $\$1260 = 0.06 \times \$1260 = \$75.60$
   The tax paid is $\$75.60$

   b. $\$1260.00 + \$75.60 = \$1335.60$
   The total cost is $\$1335.60$

5. **a.** 35% of $\$380 = 0.35 \times \$380 = \$133$
   The discount is $\$133$

   b. $\$380 - \$133 = \$247$
   The sale price is $\$247$

6. Step 1. Determine the adjusted gross income.
   Adj. gross income = Gross income – Adjustments
   Adj. gross income = $\$40,000 - \$1000$
   $\qquad\qquad = \$39,000$

   Step 2. Determine the taxable income.
   Since the total deduction of $\$4800$ is less than the standard deduction of $\$5450$, use $\$5450$.
   Taxable inc. = Adj. gross inc – (Exempt.+Deduct.)
   Taxable inc. = $\$39,000 - (\$3500 + \$5450)$
   $\qquad\qquad = \$30,050$

   Step 3. Determine the income tax.
   Tax Computation
   $= 0.10(8025) + 0.15(30,050 - 8025)$
   $= \$4106.25$
   Income tax = Tax Computation – Tax credits
   Income tax = $\$4106.25 - \$0$
   $\qquad\qquad = \$4106.25$

7. **a.** Percent of increase $= \dfrac{\text{amount of increase}}{\text{original amount}}$

   $= \dfrac{4}{6} = 0.66\frac{2}{3} = 66\frac{2}{3}\%$

   b. Percent of decrease $= \dfrac{\text{amount of decrease}}{\text{original amount}}$

   $= \dfrac{4}{10} = 0.4 = 40\%$

8. Amount of decrease: $\$940 - \$611 = \$329$
   $\dfrac{\text{amount of decrease}}{\text{original amount}} = \dfrac{\$329}{\$940} = 0.35 = 35\%$
   There was a 35% decrease from 1998 to 1999.

9. Amount of increase: $12\% - 10\% = 2\%$
   $\dfrac{\text{amount of increase}}{\text{original amount}} = \dfrac{2\%}{10\%} = 0.2 = 20\%$
   There was a 20% increase for this episode.

10. **a.** 20% of $\$1200 = 0.20 \times \$1200 = \$240$
    Taxes for year 1 are $\$1200 - \$240 = \$960$
    20% of $\$960 = 0.20 \times \$960 = \$192$
    Taxes for year 2 are $\$960 + \$192 = \$1152$

    b. $\dfrac{\$1200 - \$1152}{\$1200} = \dfrac{\$48}{\$1200} = 0.04 = 4\%$
    Taxes for year 2 are 4% less than the original amount.

Exercise Set 8.1

1. $\dfrac{2}{5} = 2 \div 5 = 0.4 = 40\%$

2. $\dfrac{3}{5} = 3 \div 5 = 0.6 = 60\%$

3. $\dfrac{1}{4} = 1 \div 4 = 0.25 = 25\%$

4. $\dfrac{3}{4} = 3 \div 4 = 0.75 = 75\%$

5. $\dfrac{3}{8} = 3 \div 8 = 0.375 = 37.5\%$

6. $\dfrac{7}{8} = 7 \div 8 = 0.875 = 87.5\%$

7. $\dfrac{1}{40} = 1 \div 40 = 0.025 = 2.5\%$

8. $\dfrac{3}{40} = 3 \div 40 = 0.075 = 7.5\%$

9. $\dfrac{9}{80} = 9 \div 80 = 0.1125 = 11.25\%$

10. $\dfrac{13}{80} = 13 \div 80 = 0.1625 = 16.25\%$

11. $0.59 = 59\%$

12. $0.96 = 96\%$

13. $0.3844 = 38.44\%$

14. $0.003 = 0.3\%$

15. $2.87 = 287\%$

16. $9.83 = 983\%$

17. $14.87 = 1487\%$

18. $19.63 = 1963\%$

19. $100 = 10{,}000\%$

20. $95 = 9500\%$

21. $72\% = 0.72$

22. $38\% = 0.38$

23. $43.6\% = 0.436$

24. $6.25\% = 0.0625$

25. $130\% = 1.3$

26. $260\% = 2.6$

27. $2\% = 0.02$

28. $6\% = 0.06$

29. $\dfrac{1}{2}\% = 0.5\% = 0.005$

30. $\dfrac{3}{4}\% = 0.75\% = 0.0075$

31. $\dfrac{5}{8}\% = 0.625\% = 0.00625$

32. $\dfrac{1}{8}\% = 0.125\% = 0.00125$

33. $62\dfrac{1}{2}\% = 62.5\% = 0.625$

34. $87\dfrac{1}{2}\% = 87.5\% = 0.875$

35. $A = PB$
$A = 0.03 \cdot 200$
$A = 6$

36. $A = PB$
$A = 0.08 \cdot 300$
$A = 24$

37. $A = PB$
$A = 0.18 \cdot 40$
$A = 7.2$

38. $A = PB$
$A = 0.16 \cdot 90$
$A = 14.4$

39. $A = PB$
$3 = 0.60 \cdot B$
$\dfrac{3}{0.60} = \dfrac{0.60B}{0.60}$
$5 = B$

40. $A = PB$
$8 = 0.40 \cdot B$
$\dfrac{8}{0.40} = \dfrac{0.40B}{0.40}$
$20 = B$

41. $A = PB$
$40.8 = 0.24 \cdot B$
$\dfrac{40.8}{0.24} = \dfrac{0.24B}{0.24}$
$170 = B$

42. $A = PB$
$51.2 = 0.32 \cdot B$
$\dfrac{51.2}{0.32} = \dfrac{0.32B}{0.32}$
$160 = B$

43. $A = PB$
$$3 = P \cdot 15$$
$$\frac{3}{15} = \frac{P \cdot 15}{15}$$
$$0.2 = P$$
$$P = 20\%$$

44. $A = PB$
$$18 = P \cdot 90$$
$$\frac{18}{90} = \frac{P \cdot 90}{90}$$
$$0.2 = P$$
$$P = 20\%$$

45. $A = PB$
$$0.3 = P \cdot 2.5$$
$$\frac{0.3}{2.5} = \frac{P \cdot 2.5}{2.5}$$
$$0.12 = P$$
$$P = 12\%$$

46. $A = PB$
$$0.6 = P \cdot 7.5$$
$$\frac{0.6}{7.5} = \frac{P \cdot 7.5}{7.5}$$
$$0.08 = P$$
$$P = 8\%$$

47. a. $(0.06)(32,800) = \$1968$

   b. $32,800 + 1968 = \$34,768$

48. a. $(0.07)(96) = \$6.72$

   b. $96 + 6.72 = \$102.72$

49. a. $(0.12)(860) = \$103.20$

   b. $860 - 103.20 = \$756.80$

50. a. $(0.40)(16.50) = \$6.60$

   b. $16.50 - 6.60 = \$9.90$

51. Step 1. Determine the adjusted gross income.
Adj. gross income = Gross income – Adjustments
Adj. gross income = $75,000 - $4000
$$= \$71,000$$

Step 2. Determine the taxable income.
Since the total deduction of $35,200 is greater than
the standard deduction of $5450, use $35,200.

Taxable inc. = Adj. gross inc– (Exempt.+Deduct.)
Taxable inc. = $71,000 - ($3500 + $35,200)$
$$= \$32,300$$

Step 3. Determine the income tax.
Tax Computation
$$= 0.10(8025) + 0.15(32,300 - 8025)$$
$$= \$4443.75$$
Income tax = Tax Computation – Tax credits
Income tax = $4443.75 - $0
$$= \$4443.75$$

52. Step 1. Determine the adjusted gross income.
Adj. gross income = Gross income – Adjustments
Adj. gross income = $70,000 - $2000
$$= \$68,000$$

Step 2. Determine the taxable income.
Since the total deduction of $13,700 is greater than
the standard deduction of $5450, use $13,700.
Taxable inc. = Adj. gross inc– (Exempt.+Deduct.)
Taxable inc. = $68,000 - ($3500 + $13,700)$
$$= \$50,800$$

Step 3. Determine the income tax.
Tax Computation
$$= 0.10(8025) + 0.15(32,550 - 8025)$$
$$+ 0.25(50,800 - 32,550)$$
$$= \$9043.75$$
Income tax = Tax Computation – Tax credits
Income tax = $9043.75 - $0
$$= \$9043.75$$

53. Step 1. Determine the adjusted gross income.
Adj. gross income = Gross income – Adjustments
Adj. gross income = $50,000 - $0
$$= \$50,000$$

Step 2. Determine the taxable income.
Since the total deduction of $6500 is less than the
standard deduction of $8000, use $8000.
Taxable inc. = Adj. gross inc– (Exempt.+Deduct.)
Taxable inc. = $50,000 - ($3500 \cdot 3 + $8000)$
$$= \$31,500$$

Step 3. Determine the income tax.
Tax Computation
$$= 0.10(11,450) + 0.15(31,500 - 11,450)$$
$$= \$4152.50$$
Income tax = Tax Computation – Tax credits
Income tax = $4152.50 - $2000
$$= \$2152.50$$

54. Step 1. Determine the adjusted gross income.
Adj. gross income = Gross income – Adjustments
Adj. gross income = $40,000 − $1500
$$= \$38,500$$

Step 2. Determine the taxable income.
Since the total deduction of $4400 is less than the standard deduction of $8000, use $8000.
Taxable inc. = Adj. gross inc– (Exempt.+Deduct.)
Taxable inc. = $38,500 − ($3500 · 2 + $8000)
$$= \$23,500$$

Step 3. Determine the income tax.
Tax Computation
$$= 0.10(11,450) + 0.15(23,500 - 11,450)$$
$$= \$2952.50$$
Income tax = Tax Computation – Tax credits
Income tax = $2952.50 − $2500
$$= \$452.50$$

55. FICA tax
$$= 0.0765(102,000) + 0.0145(120,000 - 102,000)$$
$$= \$8064$$

56. FICA tax
$$= 0.0765(102,000) + 0.0145(140,000 - 102,000)$$
$$= \$8354$$

57. FICA tax
$$= 0.0765(102,000) + 0.0145(150,000 - 102,000)$$
$$= \$8499$$
Since, this person is self-employed the FICA rate is doubled: $8499 × 2 = $16,998

58. FICA tax
$$= 0.0765(102,000) + 0.0145(160,000 - 102,000)$$
$$= \$8644$$
Since, this person is self-employed the FICA rate is doubled: $8644 × 2 = $17,288

59. a. FICA tax = 0.0765(20,000)
$$= \$1530$$

b. Step 1. Determine the adjusted gross income.
Adj. gross income = Gross income – Adjustments
Adj. gross income = $20,000 − $0 = $20,000

Step 2. Determine the taxable income.
The standard deduction is $5450.
Taxable inc. = Adj. gross inc– (Exempt.+Deduct.)
Taxable inc. = $20,000 − ($3500 + $5450)
$$= \$11,050$$

Step 3. Determine the income tax.
Tax Computation
$$= 0.10(8025) + 0.15(11,050 - 8025)$$
$$= \$1256.25$$
Income tax = Tax Computation – Tax credits
Income tax = $1256.25 − $0
$$= \$1256.25$$

c. $$\frac{1530 + 1256.25}{20,000} \approx 0.139 = 13.9\%$$

60. a. FICA tax = 0.0765(18,000)
$$= \$1377$$

b. Step 1. Determine the adjusted gross income.
Adj. gross income = Gross income – Adjustments
Adj. gross income = $18,000 − $0 = $18,000

Step 2. Determine the taxable income.
The standard deduction is $5450.
Taxable inc. = Adj. gross inc– (Exempt.+Deduct.)
Taxable inc. = $18,000 − ($3500 + $5450)
$$= \$9050$$

Step 3. Determine the income tax.
Tax Computation
$$= 0.10(8025) + 0.15(9050 - 8025)$$
$$= \$956.25$$
Income tax = Tax Computation – Tax credits
Income tax = $956.25 − $0
$$= \$956.25$$

c. $$\frac{1377 + 956.25}{18,000} \approx 0.130 = 13.0\%$$

61. $\dfrac{974-624}{624} \approx 0.561 = 56.1\%$

62. $\dfrac{589-387}{387} \approx 0.522 = 52.2\%$

63. $\dfrac{93-62}{62} = 0.5 = 50.0\%$

64. $\dfrac{682-460}{460} \approx 0.483 = 48.3\%$

65. $\dfrac{840-714}{840} = 0.15 = 15\%$

66. $\dfrac{380-266}{380} = 0.30 = 30\%$

67. Amount after first year
$= 10,000 - (0.3)(10,000)$
$= \$7000$
Amount after second year
$= 7000 + (0.4)(7000)$
$= \$9800$
Your adviser is not using percentages properly.
Actual change:
$\dfrac{10,000-9800}{10,000} = 0.02 = 2\%$ decrease.

68. The salesman is misusing percentages.
$100\% - 30\% = 70\%$
20% of $70\% = 0.70(0.20) = 0.14 = 14\%$
Percent reduction $= 30\% + 14\% = 44\%$

76. does not make sense; Explanations will vary.
Sample explanation: 20% of $80 is $16. This will make the total $96.

77. does not make sense; Explanations will vary.
Sample explanation: A price can not drop more than 100%.

78. does not make sense; Explanations will vary.
Sample explanation: Since $1.01 \times 1.01 = 1.0201$ the percent of increase is 2.01%.

79. does not make sense; Explanations will vary.
Sample explanation: The increase is
$\dfrac{30\%-20\%}{20\%} = \dfrac{10\%}{20\%} = \dfrac{1}{2} = 0.5 = 50\%$.

80. Tax owed $= \dfrac{\$3.40}{\$100} \cdot \dfrac{\$78,500}{1} = \$2669$
Discount $= (0.03)(2669) = \$80.07$
Tax paid $= 2669 - 80.07 = \$2588.93$

81. January sales $= 60 \cdot \$500 = \$30,000$
Number of customers in February
$= 60 - (0.10)(60) = 60 - 6 = 54$
Price of washing machine in February
$= 500 + (0.20)(500) = 500 + 100 = \$600$
February sales $= 54 \cdot \$600 = \$32,400$
$\$32,400 - \$30,000 = \$2400$ increase.

Check Points 8.2

1. $I = Prt = (\$3000)(0.05)(1) = \$150$

2. $I = Prt = (\$2400)(0.07)(2) = \$336$

3. $A = P(1+rt) = 2040\left[1 + (0.075)\left(\dfrac{4}{12}\right)\right] = \$2091$

4. $\quad A = P(1+rt)$
$6800 = 5000\left[1 + r(2)\right]$
$6800 = 5000 + 10,000r$
$1800 = 10,000r$
$\dfrac{1800}{10,000} = \dfrac{10,000r}{10,000}$
$0.18 = r$
$r = 18\%$

5. $\quad A = P(1+rt)$
$4000 = P\left[1 + (0.08)\left(\tfrac{6}{12}\right)\right]$
$4000 = P(1.04)$
$\dfrac{4000}{1.04} = \dfrac{P(1.04)}{1.04}$
$3846.153 \approx P$
$P \approx \$3846.16$

6. a. $I = Prt = (5000)(0.12)(2) = 1200$
The loan's discount is $1200.

b. Amount received: $\$5000 - \$1200 = \$3800$

c. $\quad I = Prt$

$1200 = (3800)(r)(2)$

$1200 = 7600r$

$\dfrac{1200}{7600} = \dfrac{7600r}{7600}$

$0.158 = r$

$r = 15.8\%$

Exercise Set 8.2

1. $I = (\$4000)(0.06)(1) = \$240$

2. $I = (\$7000)(0.05)(1) = \$350$

3. $I = (\$180)(0.03)(2) = \$10.80$

4. $I = (\$260)(0.04)(3) = \$31.20$

5. $I = (\$5000)(0.085)\left(\dfrac{9}{12}\right) = \$318.75$

6. $I = (\$18,000)(0.075)\left(\dfrac{18}{12}\right) = \$2025$

7. $I = (\$15,500)(0.11)\left(\dfrac{90}{360}\right) = \$426.25$

8. $I = (\$12,600)(0.09)\left(\dfrac{60}{360}\right) = \$189$

9. $A = P(1+rt) = 3000\left[1+(0.07)(2)\right] = \$3420$

10. $A = P(1+rt) = 2000\left[1+(0.06)(3)\right] = \$2360$

11. $A = P(1+rt) = 26,000\left[1+(0.095)(5)\right] = \$38,350$

12. $A = P(1+rt) = 24,000\left[1+(0.085)(6)\right] = \$36,240$

13. $A = P(1+rt) = 9000\left[1+(0.065)\left(\tfrac{8}{12}\right)\right] = \$9390$

14. $A = P(1+rt) = 6000\left[1+(0.045)\left(\tfrac{9}{12}\right)\right] = \$6202.50$

15. $\quad A = P(1+rt)$

$2150 = 2000\left[1+r(1)\right]$

$2150 = 2000 + 2000r$

$150 = 2000r$

$\dfrac{150}{2000} = \dfrac{2000r}{2000}$

$0.075 = r$

$r = 7.5\%$

16. $\quad A = P(1+rt)$

$3180 = 3000\left[1+r(1)\right]$

$3180 = 3000 + 3000r$

$180 = 3000r$

$\dfrac{180}{3000} = \dfrac{3000r}{3000}$

$0.06 = r$

$r = 6\%$

17. $\quad A = P(1+rt)$

$5900 = 5000\left[1+r(2)\right]$

$900 = 5000 + 10,000r$

$900 = 10,000r$

$\dfrac{900}{10,000} = \dfrac{10,000r}{10,000}$

$0.09 = r$

$r = 9\%$

18. $\quad A = P(1+rt)$

$14,060 = 10,000\left[1+r(2)\right]$

$14,060 = 10,000 + 20,000r$

$4060 = 20,000r$

$\dfrac{4060}{20,000} = \dfrac{20,000r}{20,000}$

$0.203 = r$

$r = 20.3\%$

19. $\quad A = P(1+rt)$

$2840 = 2300\left[1+r\left(\tfrac{9}{12}\right)\right]$

$2840 = 2300 + 1725r$

$540 = 1725r$

$\dfrac{540}{1725} = \dfrac{1725r}{1725}$

$0.313 = r$

$r = 31.3\%$

20.
$$A = P(1+rt)$$
$$1820 = 1700\left[1 + r\left(\tfrac{6}{12}\right)\right]$$
$$1820 = 1700 + 850r$$
$$120 = 850r$$
$$\frac{120}{850} = \frac{850r}{850}$$
$$0.141 = r$$
$$r = 14.1\%$$

21.
$$A = P(1+rt)$$
$$6000 = P\left[1 + (0.08)(2)\right]$$
$$6000 = P(1.16)$$
$$\frac{6000}{1.16} = \frac{P(1.16)}{1.16}$$
$$5172.414 \approx P$$
$$P \approx \$5172.42$$

22.
$$A = P(1+rt)$$
$$8500 = P\left[1 + (0.07)(3)\right]$$
$$8500 = P(1.21)$$
$$\frac{8500}{1.21} = \frac{P(1.21)}{1.21}$$
$$7024.793 \approx P$$
$$P \approx \$7024.80$$

23.
$$A = P(1+rt)$$
$$14{,}000 = P\left[1 + (0.095)(6)\right]$$
$$14{,}000 = P(1.57)$$
$$\frac{14{,}000}{1.57} = \frac{P(1.57)}{1.57}$$
$$8917.197 \approx P$$
$$P \approx \$8917.20$$

24.
$$A = P(1+rt)$$
$$16{,}000 = P\left[1 + (0.115)(5)\right]$$
$$16{,}000 = P(1.575)$$
$$\frac{16{,}000}{1.575} = \frac{P(1.575)}{1.575}$$
$$10158.7302 \approx P$$
$$P \approx \$10{,}158.74$$

25.
$$A = P(1+rt)$$
$$5000 = P\left[1 + (0.145)\left(\tfrac{9}{12}\right)\right]$$
$$5000 = P(1.10875)$$
$$\frac{5000}{1.10875} = \frac{P(1.10875)}{1.10875}$$
$$4509.583 \approx P$$
$$P \approx \$4509.59$$

26.
$$A = P(1+rt)$$
$$2000 = P\left[1 + (0.126)\left(\tfrac{8}{12}\right)\right]$$
$$2000 = P(1.084)$$
$$\frac{2000}{1.084} = \frac{P(1.084)}{1.084}$$
$$1845.018 \approx P$$
$$P \approx \$1845.02$$

27. a. $I = Prt = (2000)(0.07)\left(\tfrac{8}{12}\right) = \$93.33$

b. Amount received: $\$2000 - \$93.33 = \$1906.67$

c.
$$I = Prt$$
$$93.33 = (1906.67)(r)\left(\tfrac{8}{12}\right)$$
$$93.33 = 1271.113r$$
$$\frac{93.33}{1271.113} = \frac{1271.113r}{1271.113}$$
$$0.073 = r$$
$$r = 7.3\%$$

28. a. $I = Prt = (3000)(0.08)\left(\tfrac{9}{12}\right) = \$180$

b. Amount received: $\$3000 - \$180 = \$2820$

c.
$$I = Prt$$
$$180 = (2820)(r)\left(\tfrac{9}{12}\right)$$
$$180 = 2115r$$
$$\frac{180}{2115} = \frac{2115r}{2115}$$
$$0.085 = r$$
$$r = 8.5\%$$

29. a. $I = Prt = (12,000)(0.065)(2) = \$1560$

b. Amount received: $\$12,000 - \$1560 = \$10,440$

c.
$$I = Prt$$
$$1560 = (10,440)(r)(2)$$
$$1560 = 20,880r$$
$$\frac{1560}{20,880} = \frac{20,880r}{20,880}$$
$$0.075 = r$$
$$r = 7.5\%$$

30. a. $I = Prt = (20,000)(0.085)(3) = \$5100$

b. Amount received: $\$20,000 - \$5100 = \$14,900$

c.
$$I = Prt$$
$$5100 = (14,900)(r)(2)$$
$$5100 = 44,700r$$
$$\frac{5100}{44,700} = \frac{44,700r}{44,700}$$
$$0.114 = r$$
$$r = 11.4\%$$

31.
$$A = P(1 + rt)$$
$$A = P + Prt$$
$$A - P = Prt$$
$$\frac{A - P}{Pt} = \frac{Prt}{Pt}$$
$$\frac{A - P}{Pt} = r$$
$$r = \frac{A - P}{Pt}$$

32.
$$A = P(1 + rt)$$
$$A = P + Prt$$
$$A - P = Prt$$
$$\frac{A - P}{Pr} = \frac{Prt}{Pr}$$
$$\frac{A - P}{Pr} = t$$
$$t = \frac{A - P}{Pr}$$

33.
$$A = P(1 + rt)$$
$$\frac{A}{1 + rt} = \frac{P(1 + rt)}{1 + rt}$$
$$\frac{A}{1 + rt} = P$$
$$P = \frac{A}{1 + rt}$$

34.
$$A = P\left(1 + \frac{r}{n}\right)^{nt}$$
$$\frac{A}{\left(1 + \frac{r}{n}\right)^{nt}} = \frac{P\left(1 + \frac{r}{n}\right)^{nt}}{\left(1 + \frac{r}{n}\right)^{nt}}$$
$$\frac{A}{\left(1 + \frac{r}{n}\right)^{nt}} = P$$
$$P = \frac{A}{\left(1 + \frac{r}{n}\right)^{nt}}$$

35. a.
$$I = Prt$$
$$= (\$4000)(0.0825)\left(\frac{9}{12}\right)$$
$$= \$247.50$$

b. $\$4000 + \$247.50 = \$4247.50$

36. a.
$$I = Prt$$
$$= (\$20,000)(0.12)\left(\frac{7}{12}\right)$$
$$= \$1400$$

b. $\$20,000 + \$1400 = \$21,400$

37.
$$A = P(1 + rt)$$
$$2000 = 1400\left[1 + r(2)\right]$$
$$2000 = 1400 + 2800r$$
$$600 = 2800r$$
$$\frac{600}{2800} = \frac{2800r}{2800}$$
$$0.214 = r$$
$$r = 21.4\%$$

38.
$$A = P(1+rt)$$
$$1000 = 981.60\left[1+r(2)\right]$$
$$1000 = 981.6 + 1963.2r$$
$$18.4 = 1963.2r$$
$$\frac{18.4}{1963.2} = \frac{1963.2r}{1963.2}$$
$$0.075 = r$$
$$r = 7.5\%$$

39.
$$A = P(1+rt)$$
$$1472 = 960\left[1+r\left(\frac{1}{12}\right)\right]$$
$$1472 = 960 + 80r$$
$$512 = 80r$$
$$\frac{512}{80} = \frac{80r}{80}$$
$$6.4 = r$$
$$r = 640\%$$

40.
$$A = P(1+rt)$$
$$851 = 552\left[1+r\left(\frac{1}{12}\right)\right]$$
$$851 = 552 + 46r$$
$$299 = 46r$$
$$\frac{299}{46} = \frac{46r}{46}$$
$$6.5 = r$$
$$r = 650\%$$

41.
$$A = P(1+rt)$$
$$3000 = P\left[1+(0.065)(2)\right]$$
$$3000 = P(1.13)$$
$$\frac{3000}{1.13} = \frac{P(1.13)}{1.13}$$
$$2654.867 \approx P$$
$$P \approx \$2654.87$$

42.
$$A = P(1+rt)$$
$$8000 = P\left[1+(0.055)(2)\right]$$
$$8000 = P(1.11)$$
$$\frac{8000}{1.11} = \frac{P(1.11)}{1.11}$$
$$7207.207 \approx P$$
$$P \approx \$7207.21$$

43. a. $I = Prt = (\$8000)(0.08)(3) = \$1920$

b. $\$8000 - \$1920 = \$6080$

c.
$$I = Prt$$
$$1920 = (6080)r(3)$$
$$1920 = 18,240r$$
$$r = \frac{1920}{18,240} \approx 0.105 = 10.5\%$$

44. a. $I = Prt = (\$20,000)(0.06)(4) = \$4800$

b. $\$20,000 - \$4800 = \$15,200$

c.
$$I = Prt$$
$$4800 = (15,200)r(4)$$
$$4800 = 60,800r$$
$$r = \frac{4800}{60,800} \approx 0.079 = 7.9\%$$

48. does not make sense; Explanations will vary. Sample explanation: This would be the amount of interest after one year.

49. does not make sense; Explanations will vary. Sample explanation: The Banker's rule produces a greater amount of interest.

50. does not make sense; Explanations will vary. Sample explanation: The principal should be rounded up to $3846.16 to make sure there is enough money.

51. makes sense

52.
$$A = P(1+rt)$$
$$2P = P(1+rt)$$
$$\frac{2P}{P} = \frac{P(1+rt)}{P}$$
$$2 = 1 + rt$$
$$1 = rt$$
$$\frac{1}{r} = \frac{rt}{r}$$
$$\frac{1}{r} = t$$
$$t = \frac{1}{r}$$

53. a. $A = P(1+rt)$

$A = 5000[1+(0.055)t]$

$A = 5000 + 275t$

b. The slope is 275. This means the *rate of change* for the account is $275 per year.

Check Points 8.3

1. a. $A = \$1000(1+0.04)^5 \approx \$1216.65$

b. $\$1216.65 - \$1000 = \$216.65$

2. a. $A = \$4200\left(1+\dfrac{0.04}{4}\right)^{4\cdot 10} \approx \$6253.23$

b. $\$6253.23 - \$4200 = \$2053.23$

3. a. $A = P\left(1+\dfrac{r}{n}\right)^{nt}$

$A = 10,000\left(1+\dfrac{0.08}{4}\right)^{4(5)}$

$= \$14,859.47$

b. $A = Pe^{rt}$

$A = 10,000e^{0.08(5)}$

$= \$14,918.25$

4. $P = \dfrac{A}{\left(1+\dfrac{r}{n}\right)^{nt}}$

$A = \$10,000,\ r = 0.07,\ n = 52,\ t = 8$

$P = \dfrac{10,000}{\left(1+\dfrac{0.07}{52}\right)^{52\cdot 8}} \approx \dfrac{10,000}{1.750013343} \approx \$5714.25$

5. a. $A = \$6000\left(1+\dfrac{0.10}{12}\right)^{12\cdot 1} \approx \$6628.28$

b. $A = P(1+rt)$

$6628.28 = 6000[1+(r)(1)]$

$6628.28 = 6000 + 6000r$

$628.28 = 6000r$

$\dfrac{628.28}{6000} = \dfrac{6000r}{6000}$

$0.105 \approx r$

$r \approx 10.5\%$

6. $Y = \left(1+\dfrac{r}{n}\right)^{n} - 1$

$Y = \left(1+\dfrac{0.08}{4}\right)^{4} - 1 \approx 0.0824 = 8.24\%$

Exercise Set 8.3

1. a. $A = \$10,000(1+0.04)^2 = \$10,816$

b. $\$10,816 - \$10,000 = \$816$

2. a. $A = \$8000(1+0.06)^3 = \$9528.13$

b. $\$9528.13 - \$8000 = \$1528.13$

3. a. $A = \$3000\left(1+\dfrac{0.05}{2}\right)^{2\cdot 4}$

$= \$3000(1.025)^8$

$= \$3655.21$

b. $\$3655.21 - \$3000 = \$655.21$

4. a. $A = \$4000\left(1+\dfrac{0.04}{2}\right)^{2\cdot 5}$

$= \$4000(1.02)^{10}$

$= \$4875.98$

b. $\$4875.98 - \$4000 = \$875.98$

5. a. $A = \$9500\left(1+\dfrac{0.06}{4}\right)^{4\cdot 5}$

$= \$9500(1.015)^{20}$

$= \$12,795.12$

b. $\$12,795.12 - \$9500 = \$3295.12$

6. a. $A = \$2500\left(1+\dfrac{0.08}{4}\right)^{4\cdot 6}$

$= \$2500(1.02)^{24}$

$= \$4021.09$

b. $\$4021.09 - \$2500 = \$1521.09$

7. a. $A = \$4500\left(1+\dfrac{0.045}{12}\right)^{12\cdot 3}$

$= \$4500(1.0038)^{36}$

$= \$5149.12$

b. $\$5149.12 - \$4500 = \$649.12$

8. a. $A = \$2500\left(1+\dfrac{0.065}{12}\right)^{12\cdot4}$

$= \$2500(1.0054)^{48}$

$= \$3240.05$

b. $\$3240.05 - \$2500 = \$740.05$

9. a. $A = \$1500\left(1+\dfrac{0.085}{360}\right)^{360\cdot2.5}$

$= \$1500(1.000236)^{900}$

$= \$1855.10$

b. $\$1855.10 - \$1500 = \$355.10$

10. a. $A = \$1200\left(1+\dfrac{0.085}{360}\right)^{360\cdot3.5}$

$= \$1200(1.000236)^{1260}$

$= \$1615.73$

b. $\$1615.73 - \$1200 = \$415.73$

11. a. $A = \$20,000\left(1+\dfrac{0.045}{360}\right)^{360\cdot20}$

$= \$20,000(1.000125)^{7200}$

$= \$49,189.30$

b. $\$49,189.30 - \$20,000 = \$29,189.30$

12. a. $A = \$25,000\left(1+\dfrac{0.055}{360}\right)^{360\cdot20}$

$= \$25,000(1.000153)^{7200}$

$= \$75,097.84$

b. $\$75,097.84 - \$25,000 = \$50,097.84$

13. a. $A = 10,000\left(1+\dfrac{0.055}{2}\right)^{2(5)}$

$\approx \$13,116.51$

b. $A = 10,000\left(1+\dfrac{0.055}{4}\right)^{4(5)}$

$\approx \$13,140.67$

c. $A = 10,000\left(1+\dfrac{0.055}{12}\right)^{12(5)}$

$\approx \$13,157.04$

d. $A = 10,000e^{0.055(5)}$

$\approx \$13,165.31$

14. a. $A = 5000\left(1+\dfrac{0.065}{2}\right)^{2(10)} \approx \$9479.19$

b. $A = 5000\left(1+\dfrac{0.065}{4}\right)^{4\cdot10} \approx \$9527.79$

c. $A = 5000\left(1+\dfrac{0.065}{12}\right)^{12(10)} \approx = \$9560.92$

d. $A = 5000(e)^{0.065(10)} \approx 9577.70$

15. $A = 12,000\left(1+\dfrac{0.07}{12}\right)^{12(3)}$

$\approx 14,795.11$ (7% yield)

$A = 12,000e^{0.0685(3)}$

$\approx 14,737.67$ (6.85% yield)

Investing \$12,000 for 3 years at 7% compounded monthly yields the greater return.

16. $A = 6000\left(1+\dfrac{0.0825}{4}\right)^{4(4)}$

$\approx \$8317.84$ (8.25% yield)

$A = 6000\left(1+\dfrac{0.083}{2}\right)^{2(4)}$

$\approx \$8306.64$ (8.3% yield)

Investing \$6000 for 4 years at 8.25% compounded quarterly yields the greater return.

17. $A = \$10,000, r = 0.06, n = 2, t = 3$

$P = \dfrac{10,000}{\left(1+\frac{0.06}{2}\right)^{2\cdot3}} = \dfrac{10,000}{(1.03)^6} = \$8374.85$

18. $A = \$12,000, r = 0.07, n = 2, t = 4$

$P = \dfrac{12,000}{\left(1+\frac{0.07}{2}\right)^{2\cdot4}} = \dfrac{12,000}{(1.035)^8} = \$9112.94$

19. $A = \$10,000, r = 0.095, n = 12, t = 3$

$P = \dfrac{10,000}{\left(1+\frac{0.095}{12}\right)^{12\cdot3}} = \dfrac{10,000}{(1.00791667)^{36}} = \$7528.59$

20. $A = \$22,000, r = 0.105, n = 12, t = 4$

$P = \dfrac{22,000}{\left(1+\frac{0.105}{12}\right)^{12\cdot4}} = \dfrac{22,000}{(1.00875)^{48}} = \$14,481.47$

21. a.
$$A = \$10,000\left(1+\frac{0.045}{4}\right)^{4 \cdot 1}$$
$$= \$10,000(1.01125)^4$$
$$= \$10,457.65$$

b.
$$A = P(1+rt)$$
$$10,457.65 = 10,000\left[1+r(1)\right]$$
$$10,457.65 = 10,000 + 10,000r$$
$$457.65 = 10,000r$$
$$\frac{457.65}{10,000} = \frac{10,000r}{10,000}$$
$$0.046 \approx r$$
$$r \approx 4.6\%$$

22. a.
$$A = \$12,000\left(1+\frac{0.065}{4}\right)^{4 \cdot 1}$$
$$= \$12,000(1.01625)^4$$
$$= \$12,799.22$$

b.
$$A = P(1+rt)$$
$$12,799.22 = 12,000\left[1+r(1)\right]$$
$$12,799.22 = 12,000 + 12,000r$$
$$799.22 = 12,000r$$
$$\frac{799.22}{12,000} = \frac{12,000r}{12,000}$$
$$0.067 \approx r$$
$$r \approx 6.7\%$$

23. $Y = \left(1+\frac{0.06}{2}\right)^2 - 1 = 0.061 = 6.1\%$

24. $Y = \left(1+\frac{0.06}{4}\right)^4 - 1 \approx 0.061 = 6.1\%$

25. $Y = \left(1+\frac{0.06}{12}\right)^{12} - 1 \approx 0.062 = 6.2\%$

26. $Y = \left(1+\frac{0.06}{360}\right)^{360} - 1 \approx 0.062 = 6.2\%$

27. $Y = \left(1+\frac{0.06}{1000}\right)^{1000} - 1 \approx 0.062 = 6.2\%$

28. $Y = \left(1+\frac{0.06}{100,000}\right)^{1000} - 1 \approx 0.062 = 6.2\%$

29.
$$Y = \left(1+\frac{0.08}{12}\right)^{12} - 1 \approx 0.0830 = 8.3\%$$
$$Y = \left(1+\frac{0.0825}{1}\right)^{1} - 1 \approx 0.0825 = 8.25\%$$
8% compounded monthly is better..

30.
$$Y = \left(1+\frac{0.05}{12}\right)^{12} - 1 \approx 0.0512 = 5.1\%$$
$$Y = \left(1+\frac{0.0525}{4}\right)^{4} - 1 \approx 0.0535 = 5.4\%$$
5.25% compounded quarterly is better.

31.
$$Y = \left(1+\frac{0.055}{2}\right)^{2} - 1 \approx 0.0558 = 5.6\%$$
$$Y = \left(1+\frac{0.054}{360}\right)^{360} - 1 \approx 0.05548 = 5.5\%$$
5.5% compounded semiannually is better.

32.
$$Y = \left(1+\frac{0.07}{1}\right)^{1} - 1 = 0.07 = 7\%$$
$$Y = \left(1+\frac{0.0685}{360}\right)^{360} - 1 \approx 0.07089 = 7.1\%$$
6.85% compounded daily is better.

33.
$$A = P(1+r)^t$$
$$3P = P(1+0.05)^t$$
$$3 = (1.05)^t$$
$$t \approx 22.5 \text{ years}$$

34.
$$A = P(1+r)^t$$
$$3P = P(1+0.10)^t$$
$$3 = (1.10)^t$$
$$t \approx 11.5 \text{ years}$$

35.
$$A = P(1+r)^t$$
$$1.5P = P(1+0.10)^t$$
$$1.5 = (1.10)^t$$
$$t \approx 4.3 \text{ years}$$

36. $A = P(1+r)^t$

$1.5P = P(1+0.05)^t$

$1.5 = (1.05)^t$

$t \approx 8.3$ years

37. $A = P(1+r)^t$

$1.9P = P(1+0.08)^t$

$1.9 = (1.08)^t$

$t \approx 8.3$ years

38. $A = P(1+r)^t$

$1.9P = P(1+0.12)^t$

$1.9 = (1.12)^t$

$t \approx 5.7$ years

39. $A = P\left(1+\dfrac{r}{n}\right)^{nt} = 12{,}000\left(1+\dfrac{0.06}{2}\right)^{2 \cdot 21} \approx \$41{,}528$

40. $A = P\left(1+\dfrac{r}{n}\right)^{nt} = 10{,}000\left(1+\dfrac{0.05}{2}\right)^{2 \cdot 21} \approx \$28{,}210$

41. a. $A = P\left(1+\dfrac{r}{n}\right)^{nt} = 2600\left(1+\dfrac{0.04}{1}\right)^{1 \cdot 1} \approx \$2704$

$A = P\left(1+\dfrac{r}{n}\right)^{nt} = 2200\left(1+\dfrac{0.05}{12}\right)^{12 \cdot 1} \approx \$2312.56$

You will have $\$2704 - \$2312.56 = \$391.44$ or approximately $\$391$ more.

b. $A = P\left(1+\dfrac{r}{n}\right)^{nt} = 2600\left(1+\dfrac{0.04}{1}\right)^{1 \cdot 5} \approx \$3163.30$

$A = P\left(1+\dfrac{r}{n}\right)^{nt} = 2200\left(1+\dfrac{0.05}{12}\right)^{12 \cdot 5} \approx \$2823.39$

You will have $\$3163.30 - \$2823.39 = \$339.91$ or approximately $\$340$ more.

c. $A = P\left(1+\dfrac{r}{n}\right)^{nt} = 2600\left(1+\dfrac{0.04}{1}\right)^{1 \cdot 20} \approx \$5696.92$

$A = P\left(1+\dfrac{r}{n}\right)^{nt} = 2200\left(1+\dfrac{0.05}{12}\right)^{12 \cdot 20} \approx \$5967.81$

Your friend will have $\$5967.81 - \$5696.92 = \$270.89$ or approximately $\$271$ more.

42. a. $A = P\left(1+\dfrac{r}{n}\right)^{nt} = 3000\left(1+\dfrac{0.035}{1}\right)^{1\cdot1} \approx \$3105$

$A = P\left(1+\dfrac{r}{n}\right)^{nt} = 2500\left(1+\dfrac{0.048}{12}\right)^{12\cdot1} \approx \$2622.68$

You will have $\$3105 - \$2622.68 = \$482.32$ or approximately $482 more.

b. $A = P\left(1+\dfrac{r}{n}\right)^{nt} = 3000\left(1+\dfrac{0.035}{1}\right)^{1\cdot5} \approx \$3563.06$

$A = P\left(1+\dfrac{r}{n}\right)^{nt} = 2500\left(1+\dfrac{0.048}{12}\right)^{12\cdot5} \approx \$3176.60$

You will have $\$3563.06 - \$3176.60 = \$386.46$ or approximately $386 more.

c. $A = P\left(1+\dfrac{r}{n}\right)^{nt} = 3000\left(1+\dfrac{0.035}{1}\right)^{1\cdot20} \approx \$5969.37$

$A = P\left(1+\dfrac{r}{n}\right)^{nt} = 2500\left(1+\dfrac{0.048}{12}\right)^{12\cdot20} \approx \$6516.75$

Your friend will have $\$6516.75 - \$5969.37 = \$547.38$ or approximately $547 more.

43. $A = P\left(1+\dfrac{r}{n}\right)^{nt} = 3000\left(1+\dfrac{0.07}{2}\right)^{2\cdot10} \approx \$5969.37$

$A = P\left(1+\dfrac{r}{n}\right)^{nt} = 5969.37\left(1+\dfrac{0.0725}{4}\right)^{4\cdot6} \approx \$9186.60$

The value of the account will be approximately $9187.

44. $A = P\left(1+\dfrac{r}{n}\right)^{nt} = 6000\left(1+\dfrac{0.0525}{2}\right)^{2\cdot10} \approx \$10,074.29$

$A = P\left(1+\dfrac{r}{n}\right)^{nt} = 10,074.29\left(1+\dfrac{0.054}{4}\right)^{4\cdot8} \approx \$15,473.01$

The value of the account will be approximately $15,473.

45. a. $A = 24\left(1+\dfrac{0.05}{12}\right)^{12\cdot384} \approx \$5,027,400,000$

b. $A = 24\left(1+\dfrac{0.05}{360}\right)^{360\cdot384} \approx \$5,225,000,000$

46. $A = P\left(1+\dfrac{r}{n}\right)^{nt}$

$A = \$450,000\left(1+\dfrac{0.06}{360}\right)^{360\cdot212}$

$= \$450,000(1.00016667)^{76,320}$

$\approx \$150,306,600,000$

47. $I = Prt = 2000(0.06)(1) = \$120$

$A = P\left(1 + \dfrac{r}{n}\right)^{nt} = 2000\left(1 + \dfrac{0.059}{360}\right)^{360 \cdot 1} \approx \$2122$

$I = \$2122 - 2000 = \$122$

The account that pays 5.9% compounded daily earns $\$122 - \$120 = \$2$ more interest.

48. $I = Prt = 1000(0.07)(1) = \$70$

$A = P\left(1 + \dfrac{r}{n}\right)^{nt} = 1000\left(1 + \dfrac{0.069}{360}\right)^{360 \cdot 1} \approx \$1071$

$I = \$1071 - 1000 = \$71$

The account that pays 6.9% compounded daily earns $\$71 - \$70 = \$1$ more interest.

49. For compound interest once per year, use the formula $A = 5000(1 + 0.055)^t$.

For compound interest continuously, use the formula $A = 5000e^{0.055t}$.

Years	Once a Year Amount	Once a Year Interest	Continous Amount	Continous Interest
1	$5275	$275	$5283	$283
5	$6535	$1535	$6583	$1583
10	$8541	$3541	$8666	$3666
20	$14,589	$9589	$15,021	$10,021

50. For compound interest once per year, use the formula $A = 10,000(1 + 0.065)^t$.

For compound interest continuously, use the formula $A = 10,000e^{0.065t}$.

Years	Once a Year Amount	Once a Year Interest	Continous Amount	Continous Interest
1	$10,650	$650	$10,672	$672
5	$13,701	$3701	$13,840	$3840
10	$18,771	$8771	$19,155	$9155
20	$35,236	$25,236	$36,693	$26,693

51. $P = \dfrac{A}{\left(1 + \dfrac{r}{n}\right)^{nt}}$

$A = \$80,000, r = 0.06, n = 2, t = 13$

$P = \dfrac{80,000}{\left(1 + \dfrac{0.06}{2}\right)^{2 \cdot 13}} = \dfrac{80,000}{(1.03)^{26}} = \$37,096$

52. $P = \dfrac{A}{\left(1 + \dfrac{r}{n}\right)^{nt}}$

$A = \$500,000, \; r = 0.07, \; n = 12, \; t = 65 - 30 = 35$

$P = \dfrac{500,000}{\left(1 + \dfrac{0.07}{12}\right)^{12 \cdot 35}} \approx \$43,456$

53. $P = \dfrac{A}{\left(1 + \dfrac{r}{n}\right)^{nt}} = \dfrac{75,000}{\left(1 + \dfrac{0.045}{1}\right)^{1 \cdot 15}} \approx \$38,755$

$P = \dfrac{A}{\left(1 + \dfrac{r}{n}\right)^{nt}} = \dfrac{75,000}{\left(1 + \dfrac{0.04}{360}\right)^{360 \cdot 15}} \approx \$41,163$

54. $P = \dfrac{A}{\left(1 + \dfrac{r}{n}\right)^{nt}} = \dfrac{150,000}{\left(1 + \dfrac{0.055}{1}\right)^{1 \cdot 20}} \approx \$51,410$

$P = \dfrac{A}{\left(1 + \dfrac{r}{n}\right)^{nt}} = \dfrac{150,000}{\left(1 + \dfrac{0.05}{360}\right)^{360 \cdot 20}} \approx \$55,186$

55. $Y = \left(1 + \dfrac{r}{n}\right)^{n} - 1 = \left(1 + \dfrac{0.054}{360}\right)^{360} - 1 \approx 0.0555 = 5.55\%$

56. $Y = \left(1 + \dfrac{r}{n}\right)^{n} - 1 = \left(1 + \dfrac{0.0375}{360}\right)^{360} - 1 \approx 0.0382 = 3.82\%$

57. $Y = \left(1 + \dfrac{r}{n}\right)^{n} - 1 = \left(1 + \dfrac{0.042}{4}\right)^{4} - 1 \approx 0.043 = 4.3\%$

$Y = \left(1 + \dfrac{r}{n}\right)^{n} - 1 = \left(1 + \dfrac{0.042}{12}\right)^{12} - 1 \approx 0.043 = 4.3\%$

$Y = \left(1 + \dfrac{r}{n}\right)^{n} - 1 = \left(1 + \dfrac{0.042}{360}\right)^{360} - 1 \approx 0.043 = 4.3\%$

As the number of compounding periods increases, the effective annual yield increases slightly. However, with the rates rounded to the nearest tenth of a percent, this increase is not evident.

58. $Y = \left(1 + \dfrac{r}{n}\right)^n - 1 = \left(1 + \dfrac{0.046}{4}\right)^4 - 1 \approx 0.047 = 4.7\%$

$Y = \left(1 + \dfrac{r}{n}\right)^n - 1 = \left(1 + \dfrac{0.046}{12}\right)^{12} - 1 \approx 0.047 = 4.7\%$

$Y = \left(1 + \dfrac{r}{n}\right)^n - 1 = \left(1 + \dfrac{0.046}{360}\right)^{360} - 1 \approx 0.047 = 4.7\%$

As the number of compounding periods increases, the effective annual yield increases slightly. However, with the rates rounded to the nearest tenth of a percent, this increase is not evident.

59. $Y = \left(1 + \dfrac{r}{n}\right)^n - 1 = \left(1 + \dfrac{0.045}{2}\right)^2 - 1 \approx 0.0455 = 4.55\%$

$Y = \left(1 + \dfrac{r}{n}\right)^n - 1 = \left(1 + \dfrac{0.044}{360}\right)^{360} - 1 \approx 0.0450 = 4.50\%$

The account paying 4.5% compounded semiannually is the better investment.

60. $Y = \left(1 + \dfrac{r}{n}\right)^n - 1 = \left(1 + \dfrac{0.049}{2}\right)^2 - 1 \approx 0.0496 = 4.96\%$

$Y = \left(1 + \dfrac{r}{n}\right)^n - 1 = \left(1 + \dfrac{0.048}{360}\right)^{360} - 1 \approx 0.0492 = 4.92\%$

The account paying 4.9% compounded semiannually is the better investment.

65. does not make sense; Explanations will vary. Sample explanation: At the same rate, any compounding period will be a better deal than simple interest.

66. does not make sense; Explanations will vary. Sample explanation: The best deal can not be determined without knowing the compounding period as well.

67. does not make sense; Explanations will vary. Sample explanation: Compounding continuously does not result in an infinite amount of money.

68. makes sense

69. $A = P\left(1 + \dfrac{r}{n}\right)^{nt}$

Have \$6000 in the account for 6 years:

$A = \$6000\left(1 + \dfrac{0.05}{2}\right)^{2 \cdot 6} = \$8069.33$

Have \$4000 in the account for 4 years:

$A = \$4000\left(1 + \dfrac{0.05}{2}\right)^{2 \cdot 4} = \$4873.61$

Balance after 6 years $= \$8069.33 + \$4873.61$
$= \$12,942.94$

70. $A = P\left(1+\dfrac{r}{n}\right)^{nt}$

Start with $5000 in account for 2 years: $A = \$5000\left(1+\dfrac{0.08}{12}\right)^{12\cdot 2} = \$5864.44$

Then withdraw $1500, which leaves $5864.44 − $1500 = $4364.44

Leave $4364.44 in the account for 1 year: $A = \$4364.44\left(1+\dfrac{0.08}{12}\right)^{12\cdot 1} = \$4726.69$

Then add $2000, so now have $4726.69 + $2000 = $6726.69

Have $6726.69 in account for 3 years: $A = 6726.69\left(1+\dfrac{0.08}{12}\right)^{12\cdot 3} = \$8544.49$

71. Substitute Y for r in $A = P(1+rt)$

Thus, $A = P(1+Yt)$

Substitute $P(1+Yt)$ for A in $A = P\left(1+\dfrac{r}{n}\right)^{nt}$ and substitute 1 for t.

$$P(1+Yt) = P\left(1+\dfrac{r}{n}\right)^{nt}$$

$$\frac{P\left[1+Y(1)\right]}{P} = \frac{P\left(1+\dfrac{r}{n}\right)^{n(1)}}{P}$$

$$1+Y = \left(1+\dfrac{r}{n}\right)^{n}$$

$$Y = \left(1+\dfrac{r}{n}\right)^{n} - 1$$

Check Points 8.4

1. a. Value at end of year 1
$2000
Value at end of year 2
$2000(1+0.10) + \$2000 = \$4200$
Value at end of year 3
$4200(1+0.10) + \$2000 = \$6620$

b. $\$6620 - \$2000 \cdot 3 = \$620$

2. a. $A = \dfrac{P\left[(1+r)^{t} - 1\right]}{r}$

$A = \dfrac{3000\left[(1+0.08)^{40} - 1\right]}{0.08}$

$\approx \$777{,}170$

b. $\$777{,}170 - 40 \times \$3000 = \$657{,}170$

3.　**a.**　$A = \dfrac{P\left[\left(1+\frac{r}{n}\right)^{nt} - 1\right]}{\frac{r}{n}}$

$A = \dfrac{100\left[\left(1+\frac{0.095}{12}\right)^{12\times 35} - 1\right]}{\frac{0.095}{12}}$

$\approx \$333,946$

b.　$\$333,946 - \$100\cdot 12\cdot 35 = \$291,946$

4.　**a.**　$P = \dfrac{A\left(\frac{r}{n}\right)}{\left[\left(1+\frac{r}{n}\right)^{nt} - 1\right]}$

$P = \dfrac{100,000\left(\frac{0.09}{12}\right)}{\left[\left(1+\frac{0.09}{12}\right)^{12\times 18} - 1\right]}$

$\approx \$187$

b.　Deposits: $\$187\times 18\times 12 = \$40,392$
Interest: $\$100,000 - \$40,392 = \$59,608$

5.　**a.**　High price = \$63.38,
Low price = \$42.37

b.　Dividend $= \$0.72\cdot 3000 = \$2160$

c.　Annual return for dividends alone = 1.5%
1.5% is much lower than the 3.5% bank rate.

d.　Shares traded =
$72,032\cdot 100 = 7,203,200$ shares

e.　High price = \$49.94,
Low price = \$48.33

f.　Price at close = \$49.50

g.　The price went up \$0.03 per share.

h.　Annual earnings per share $= \dfrac{\$49.50}{37} \approx \$1.34$

Exercise Set 8.4

1.　**a.**　$A = \dfrac{P\left[(1+r)^{t} - 1\right]}{r}$

$A = \dfrac{2000\left[(1+0.05)^{20} - 1\right]}{0.05}$

$\approx \$66,132$

b.　$\$66,132 - 20\times \$2000 = \$26,132$

2.　**a.**　$A = \dfrac{P\left[(1+r)^{t} - 1\right]}{r}$

$A = \dfrac{3000\left[(1+0.04)^{20} - 1\right]}{0.04}$

$\approx \$89,334$

b.　$\$89,334 - 20\times \$3000 = \$29,334$

3.　**a.**　$A = \dfrac{P\left[(1+r)^{t} - 1\right]}{r}$

$A = \dfrac{4000\left[(1+0.065)^{40} - 1\right]}{0.065}$

$\approx \$702,528$

b.　$\$702,528 - 40\times \$4000 = \$542,528$

4.　**a.**　$A = \dfrac{P\left[(1+r)^{t} - 1\right]}{r}$

$A = \dfrac{4000\left[(1+0.055)^{40} - 1\right]}{0.055}$

$\approx \$546,422$

b.　$\$546,422 - 40\times \$4000 = \$386,422$

5.　**a.**　$A = \dfrac{P\left[\left(1+\frac{r}{n}\right)^{nt} - 1\right]}{\frac{r}{n}}$

$A = \dfrac{50\left[\left(1+\frac{0.06}{12}\right)^{12\times 30} - 1\right]}{\frac{0.06}{12}}$

$\approx \$50,226$

b.　$\$50,226 - \$50\cdot 12\cdot 30 = \$32,226$

6. a. $A = \dfrac{P\left[\left(1+\frac{r}{n}\right)^{nt}-1\right]}{\frac{r}{n}}$

$A = \dfrac{60\left[\left(1+\frac{0.05}{12}\right)^{12\times30}-1\right]}{\frac{0.05}{12}}$

$\approx \$49,936$

b. $\$49,936 - \$60\cdot12\cdot30 = \$28,336$

7. a. $A = \dfrac{P\left[\left(1+\frac{r}{n}\right)^{nt}-1\right]}{\frac{r}{n}}$

$A = \dfrac{100\left[\left(1+\frac{0.045}{2}\right)^{2\times25}-1\right]}{\frac{0.045}{2}}$

$\approx \$9076$

b. $\$9076 - \$100\cdot2\cdot25 = \$4076$

8. a. $A = \dfrac{P\left[\left(1+\frac{r}{n}\right)^{nt}-1\right]}{\frac{r}{n}}$

$A = \dfrac{150\left[\left(1+\frac{0.065}{2}\right)^{2\times25}-1\right]}{\frac{0.065}{2}}$

$\approx \$18,225$

b. $\$18,225 - \$150\cdot2\cdot25 = \$10,725$

9. a. $A = \dfrac{P\left[\left(1+\frac{r}{n}\right)^{nt}-1\right]}{\frac{r}{n}}$

$A = \dfrac{1000\left[\left(1+\frac{0.0625}{4}\right)^{4\times6}-1\right]}{\frac{0.0625}{4}}$

$\approx \$28,850$

b. $\$28,850 - \$1000\cdot4\cdot6 = \$4850$

10. a. $A = \dfrac{P\left[\left(1+\frac{r}{n}\right)^{nt}-1\right]}{\frac{r}{n}}$

$A = \dfrac{1200\left[\left(1+\frac{0.0325}{4}\right)^{4\times6}-1\right]}{\frac{0.0325}{4}}$

$\approx \$31,658$

b. $\$31,658 - \$1200\cdot4\cdot6 = \$2858$

11. a. $P = \dfrac{A\left(\frac{r}{n}\right)}{\left[\left(1+\frac{r}{n}\right)^{nt}-1\right]}$

$P = \dfrac{140,000\left(\frac{0.06}{1}\right)}{\left[\left(1+\frac{0.06}{1}\right)^{1\times18}-1\right]}$

$\approx \$4530$

b. Deposits: $\$4530\times1\times18 = \$81,540$
Interest: $\$140,000 - \$81,540 = \$58,460$

12. a. $P = \dfrac{A\left(\frac{r}{n}\right)}{\left[\left(1+\frac{r}{n}\right)^{nt}-1\right]}$

$P = \dfrac{150,000\left(\frac{0.05}{1}\right)}{\left[\left(1+\frac{0.05}{1}\right)^{1\times18}-1\right]}$

$\approx \$5332$

b. Deposits: $\$5332\times1\times18 = \$95,976$
Interest: $\$150,000 - \$95,976 = \$54,024$

13. a. $P = \dfrac{A\left(\frac{r}{n}\right)}{\left[\left(1+\frac{r}{n}\right)^{nt}-1\right]}$

$P = \dfrac{200,000\left(\frac{0.045}{12}\right)}{\left[\left(1+\frac{0.045}{12}\right)^{12\times10}-1\right]}$

$\approx \$1323$

b. Deposits: $\$1323\times12\times10 = \$158,760$
Interest: $\$200,000 - \$158,760 = \$41,240$

14. a. $P = \dfrac{A\left(\frac{r}{n}\right)}{\left[\left(1+\frac{r}{n}\right)^{nt}-1\right]}$

$P = \dfrac{250,000\left(\frac{0.075}{12}\right)}{\left[\left(1+\frac{0.075}{12}\right)^{12\times10}-1\right]}$

$\approx \$1406$

b. Deposits: $\$1406\times12\times10 = \$168,720$
Interest: $\$250,000 - \$168,720 = \$81,280$

15. a. $P = \dfrac{A\left(\frac{r}{n}\right)}{\left[\left(1+\frac{r}{n}\right)^{nt}-1\right]}$

$P = \dfrac{1,000,000\left(\frac{0.0725}{12}\right)}{\left[\left(1+\frac{0.0725}{12}\right)^{12\times40}-1\right]}$

$\approx \$356$

b. Deposits: $\$356\times12\times40 = \$170,880$

Interest: $\$1,000,000 - \$170,880 = \$829,120$

16. a. $P = \dfrac{A\left(\frac{r}{n}\right)}{\left[\left(1+\frac{r}{n}\right)^{nt}-1\right]}$

$P = \dfrac{1,500,000\left(\frac{0.0825}{12}\right)}{\left[\left(1+\frac{0.0825}{12}\right)^{12\times40}-1\right]}$

$\approx \$400$

b. Deposits: $\$400\times12\times40 = \$192,000$

Interest: $\$1,500,000 - \$192,000 = \$1,308,000$

17. a. $P = \dfrac{A\left(\frac{r}{n}\right)}{\left[\left(1+\frac{r}{n}\right)^{nt}-1\right]}$

$P = \dfrac{20,000\left(\frac{0.035}{4}\right)}{\left[\left(1+\frac{0.035}{4}\right)^{4\times5}-1\right]}$

$\approx \$920$

b. Deposits: $\$920\times4\times5 = \$18,400$

Interest: $\$20,000 - \$18,400 = \$1600$

18. a. $P = \dfrac{A\left(\frac{r}{n}\right)}{\left[\left(1+\frac{r}{n}\right)^{nt}-1\right]}$

$P = \dfrac{25,000\left(\frac{0.045}{4}\right)}{\left[\left(1+\frac{0.045}{4}\right)^{4\times5}-1\right]}$

$\approx \$1122$

b. Deposits: $\$1122\times4\times5 = \$22,440$

Interest: $\$25,000 - \$22,440 = \$2560$

19. a. High price = $\$73.25$,
Low price = $\$45.44$

b. Dividend $= \$1.20\cdot700 = \$840$

c. Annual return for dividends alone = 2.2%
2.2% is lower than a 3% bank rate.

d. Shares traded $= 5915\cdot100 = 591,500$ shares

e. High price = $\$56.38$,
Low price = $\$54.38$

f. Price at close = $\$55.50$

g. The price went up $1.25 per share.

h. Annual earnings per share $= \dfrac{\$55.50}{17}$

$\approx \$3.26$

20. a. High price = $\$78.34$, Low price = $\$35.38$

b. Dividend $= \$2.18\cdot700 = \$1526$

c. Annual return for dividends alone = 4.7%
4.7% is higher than a 3% bank rate.

d. Shares traded $= 7473\cdot100 = 747,300$ shares

e. High price = $\$48.19$, Low price = $\$46.63$

f. Price at close $= \$46.88$

g. The price went down $1.31 per share

h. Annual earnings per share

$= \dfrac{\$46.88}{22} \approx \$2.13$

21. a. Lump-Sum Deposit:

$A = P(1+r)^t$

$A = 30,000(1+0.05)^{20}$

$\approx \$79,599$

Periodic Deposit:

$A = \dfrac{P\left[(1+r)^t-1\right]}{r}$

$A = \dfrac{1500\left[(1+0.05)^{20}-1\right]}{0.05}$

$\approx \$49,599$

The lump-sum investment will have
$\$79,599 - \$49,599 = \$30,000$ more.

b. Lump-Sum Interest:
$\$79,599 - \$30,000 = \$49,599$
Periodic Deposit Interest:
$\$49,599 - \$30,000 = \$19,599$
The lump-sum investment will have
$\$49,599 - \$19,599 = \$30,000$ more.

22. a. Lump-Sum Deposit:

$A = P(1+r)^t$

$A = 40,000(1+0.065)^{25}$

$\approx \$193,108$

Periodic Deposit:

$A = \dfrac{P\left[(1+r)^t - 1\right]}{r}$

$A = \dfrac{1600\left[(1+0.065)^{25} - 1\right]}{0.065}$

$\approx \$94,220$

The lump-sum investment will have $\$193,108 - \$94,220 = \$98,888$ more.

b. Lump-Sum Interest:

$\$193,108 - \$40,000 = \$153,108$

Periodic Deposit Interest:

$\$94,220 - \$40,000 = \$54,220$

The lump-sum investment will have $\$153,108 - \$54,220 = \$98,888$ more.

23. a. $P = \dfrac{A\left(\frac{r}{n}\right)}{\left[\left(1+\frac{r}{n}\right)^{nt} - 1\right]}$

$P = \dfrac{1,000,000\left(\frac{0.08}{12}\right)}{\left[\left(1+\frac{0.08}{12}\right)^{12\times40} - 1\right]}$

$\approx \$287$

b. Adjusted gross income *with* IRA:

Adj. gross income $= \$50,000 - \$287 \cdot 12$

$= \$46,556$

Taxable income *with* IRA:

Taxable inc $= \$46,556 - (\$3200 + \$5000)$

$= \$38,356$

Income tax *with* IRA:

$= 0.10(7300) + 0.15(29,700 - 7300)$

$\quad + 0.25(38,356 - 29,700)$

$= \$6254$

Adjusted gross income *without* IRA:

Adj. gross income $= \$50,000 - \$0$

$= \$50,000$

Taxable income *without* IRA:

Taxable inc $= \$50,000 - (\$3200 + \$5000)$

$= \$41,800$

Income tax *without* IRA:

$= 0.10(7300) + 0.15(29,700 - 7300)$

$\quad + 0.25(41,800 - 29,700)$

$= \$7115$

c. Percent of gross income *with* IRA:

$\dfrac{6254}{50,000} \approx 12.5\%$

Percent of gross income *without* IRA:

$\dfrac{7115}{50,000} \approx 14.2\%$

24. a. $P = \dfrac{A\left(\frac{r}{n}\right)}{\left[\left(1+\frac{r}{n}\right)^{nt} - 1\right]}$

$P = \dfrac{650,000\left(\frac{0.07}{12}\right)}{\left[\left(1+\frac{0.07}{12}\right)^{12\times40} - 1\right]}$

$\approx \$248$

b. Adjusted gross income *with* IRA:

Adj. gross income $= \$50,000 - \$248 \cdot 12$

$= \$47,024$

Taxable income *with* IRA:

Taxable inc $= \$47,024 - (\$3200 + \$5000)$

$= \$38,824$

Income tax *with* IRA:

$= 0.10(7300) + 0.15(29,700 - 7300)$

$\quad + 0.25(38,824 - 29,700)$

$= \$6371$

Adjusted gross income *without* IRA:

Adj. gross income $= \$50,000 - \$0$

$= \$50,000$

Taxable income *without* IRA:

Taxable inc $= \$50,000 - (\$3200 + \$5000)$

$= \$41,800$

Income tax *without* IRA:

$= 0.10(7300) + 0.15(29,700 - 7300)$

$\quad + 0.25(41,800 - 29,700)$

$= \$7115$

c. Percent of gross income *with* IRA:

$\dfrac{6371}{50,000} \approx 12.7\%$

Percent of gross income *without* IRA:

$\dfrac{7115}{50,000} \approx 14.2\%$

25.
$$A = \frac{P\left[(1+r)^t - 1\right]}{r}$$

$$Ar = P\left[(1+r)^t - 1\right]$$

$$\frac{Ar}{\left[(1+r)^t - 1\right]} = \frac{P\left[(1+r)^t - 1\right]}{\left[(1+r)^t - 1\right]}$$

$$\frac{Ar}{(1+r)^t - 1} = P$$

$$P = \frac{Ar}{(1+r)^t - 1}$$

This formula describes the deposit necessary at the end of each year that yields A dollars after t years with interest rate r compounded annually.

26.
$$A = \frac{P\left[\left(1+\frac{r}{n}\right)^{nt} - 1\right]}{\frac{r}{n}}$$

$$A\left(\frac{r}{n}\right) = P\left[\left(1+\frac{r}{n}\right)^{nt} - 1\right]$$

$$\frac{A\left(\frac{r}{n}\right)}{\left[\left(1+\frac{r}{n}\right)^{nt} - 1\right]} = \frac{P\left[\left(1+\frac{r}{n}\right)^{nt} - 1\right]}{\left[\left(1+\frac{r}{n}\right)^{nt} - 1\right]}$$

$$\frac{A\left(\frac{r}{n}\right)}{\left(1+\frac{r}{n}\right)^{nt} - 1} = P$$

$$P = \frac{A\left(\frac{r}{n}\right)}{\left(1+\frac{r}{n}\right)^{nt} - 1}$$

This formula describes the deposit necessary at the end of each compounding period that yields A dollars after t years with interest rate r and n compounding periods per year.

27. a.
$$A = \frac{P\left[(1+r)^t - 1\right]}{r}$$

$$A = \frac{2000\left[(1+0.075)^5 - 1\right]}{0.075}$$

$$\approx \$11,617$$

b. $\$11,617 - 5 \times \$2000 = \$1617$

28. a.
$$A = \frac{P\left[(1+r)^t - 1\right]}{r}$$

$$A = \frac{2500\left[(1+0.0625)^5 - 1\right]}{0.0625}$$

$$\approx \$14,163$$

b. $\$14,163 - 5 \times \$2500 = \$1663$

29. a.
$$A = \frac{P\left[\left(1+\frac{r}{n}\right)^{nt} - 1\right]}{\frac{r}{n}}$$

$$A = \frac{50\left[\left(1+\frac{0.055}{12}\right)^{12\times40} - 1\right]}{\frac{0.055}{12}}$$

$$\approx \$87,052$$

b. $\$87,052 - \$50 \cdot 12 \cdot 40 = \$63,052$

30. a.
$$A = \frac{P\left[\left(1+\frac{r}{n}\right)^{nt} - 1\right]}{\frac{r}{n}}$$

$$A = \frac{75\left[\left(1+\frac{0.065}{12}\right)^{12\times40} - 1\right]}{\frac{0.065}{12}}$$

$$\approx \$171,271$$

b. $\$171,271 - \$75 \cdot 12 \cdot 40 = \$135,271$

31. a.
$$A = \frac{P\left[\left(1+\frac{r}{n}\right)^{nt} - 1\right]}{\frac{r}{n}}$$

$$A = \frac{10,000\left[\left(1+\frac{0.105}{4}\right)^{4\times10} - 1\right]}{\frac{0.105}{4}}$$

$$\approx \$693,031$$

b. $\$693,031 - \$10,000 \cdot 4 \cdot 10 = \$293,031$

32. a.
$$A = \frac{P\left[\left(1+\frac{r}{n}\right)^{nt} - 1\right]}{\frac{r}{n}}$$

$$A = \frac{15,000\left[\left(1+\frac{0.09}{4}\right)^{4\times10} - 1\right]}{\frac{0.09}{4}}$$

$$\approx \$956,793$$

b. $\$956,793 - \$15,000 \cdot 4 \cdot 10 = \$356,793$

33. a. $P = \dfrac{A\left(\frac{r}{n}\right)}{\left[\left(1+\frac{r}{n}\right)^{nt}-1\right]}$

$P = \dfrac{3500\left(\frac{0.05}{2}\right)}{\left[\left(1+\frac{0.05}{2}\right)^{2\times4}-1\right]}$

$\approx \$401$

b. Deposits: $\$401 \times 2 \times 4 = \$3208$
Interest: $\$3500 - \$3208 = \$292$

34. a. $P = \dfrac{A\left(\frac{r}{n}\right)}{\left[\left(1+\frac{r}{n}\right)^{t}-1\right]}$

$P = \dfrac{4000\left(\frac{0.07}{2}\right)}{\left[\left(1+\frac{0.07}{2}\right)^{2\times4}-1\right]}$

$\approx \$442$

b. Deposits: $\$442 \times 2 \times 4 = \$3536$
Interest: $\$4000 - \$3536 = \$464$

35. $P = \dfrac{A\left(\frac{r}{n}\right)}{\left[\left(1+\frac{r}{n}\right)^{nt}-1\right]}$

$P = \dfrac{2{,}000{,}000\left(\frac{0.065}{12}\right)}{\left[\left(1+\frac{0.065}{12}\right)^{12\times45}-1\right]}$

$\approx \$620$
You must invest $620 per month.

Amount from interest:
$\$2{,}000{,}000 - \$620 \cdot 12 \cdot 45 = \$1{,}665{,}200$

36. $P = \dfrac{A\left(\frac{r}{n}\right)}{\left[\left(1+\frac{r}{n}\right)^{nt}-1\right]}$

$P = \dfrac{4{,}000{,}000\left(\frac{0.085}{12}\right)}{\left[\left(1+\frac{0.085}{12}\right)^{12\times45}-1\right]}$

$\approx \$641$
You must invest $641 per month.

Amount from interest:
$\$4{,}000{,}000 - \$641 \cdot 12 \cdot 45 = \$3{,}653{,}860$

50. does not make sense; Explanations will vary. Sample explanation: An annuity is the same as a lump-sum deposit.

51. does not make sense; Explanations will vary. Sample explanation: At the end of 30 years you will only have:

$$A = \frac{P\left[\left(1+\frac{r}{n}\right)^{nt}-1\right]}{\frac{r}{n}} = \frac{20\left[\left(1+\frac{0.035}{12}\right)^{12\times30}-1\right]}{\frac{0.035}{12}} \approx \$12,708.25.$$

52. makes sense

53. does not make sense; Explanations will vary. Sample explanation: With stocks it is possible to lose part or all of your investment.

54. Use the simple interest formula to find the principal necessary to earn $60,000 per year.

$$I = Prt$$

$$60,000 = P(0.08)(1)$$

$$\frac{60,000}{0.08} = P$$

$$750,000 = P$$

Next, find the necessary monthly deposit that will result a principal of $750,000 after 30 years.

$$P = \frac{A\left(\frac{r}{n}\right)}{\left[\left(1+\frac{r}{n}\right)^{nt}-1\right]}$$

$$P = \frac{750,000\left(\frac{0.08}{12}\right)}{\left[\left(1+\frac{0.08}{12}\right)^{12\times30}-1\right]}$$

$$\approx \$504$$

Check Points 8.5

1. a. $PMT = \dfrac{P\left(\frac{r}{n}\right)}{1-\left(1+\frac{r}{n}\right)^{-nt}} = \dfrac{175,500\left(\frac{0.075}{12}\right)}{1-\left(1+\frac{0.075}{12}\right)^{-12\cdot15}} \approx \$1627$

b. $\$1627 \cdot 12 \cdot 15 - \$175,500 = \$117,360$

c. $\$266,220 - \$117,360 = \$148,860$

2. Interest for first month = $Prt = \$200,000 \times 0.07 \times \dfrac{1}{12} \approx \$1166.67$

Principle payment = $\$1550.00 - \$1166.67 = \$383.33$
Balance of loan = $\$200,000 - \$383.33 = \$199,616.67$

Interest for second month = $Prt = \$199,616.67 \times 0.07 \times \dfrac{1}{12} \approx \$1164.43$

Principle payment = $\$1550.00 - \$1164.43 = \$385.57$
Balance of loan = $\$199,616.67 - \$385.57 = \$199,231.10$

Payment Number	Interest Payment	Principal Payment	Balance of Loan
1	$1166.67	$383.33	$199,616.67
2	$1164.43	$385.57	$199,231.10

3. a. $PMT = \dfrac{P\left(\frac{r}{n}\right)}{1-\left(1+\frac{r}{n}\right)^{-nt}} = \dfrac{15{,}000\left(\frac{0.08}{12}\right)}{1-\left(1+\frac{0.08}{12}\right)^{-12(4)}} \approx \$366$

Total interest for loan A: $\$367 \cdot 12 \cdot 4 - \$15{,}000 = \$2616$

b. $PMT = \dfrac{P\left(\frac{r}{n}\right)}{1-\left(1+\frac{r}{n}\right)^{-nt}} = \dfrac{15{,}000\left(\frac{0.10}{12}\right)}{1-\left(1+\frac{0.10}{12}\right)^{-12(6)}} \approx \$278$

Total interest for loan A: $\$278 \cdot 12 \cdot 6 - \$15{,}000 = \$5016$

c. Monthly payments are less with the longer-term loan, but there is more interest with the longer-term loan.

4. a. Make a table that shows the unpaid balance for each transaction date, the number of days at each unpaid balance, and then multiply each unpaid balance by the number of days that the balance was outstanding.

Date	Unpaid Balance	Number of Days at Each Unpaid Balance	$\left(\begin{array}{c}\text{Unpaid}\\\text{Balance}\end{array}\right)\cdot\left(\begin{array}{c}\text{Number}\\\text{of Days}\end{array}\right)$
May 1	$8240.00	6	$49,440.00
May 7	$8240.00 - $350.00 = $7890.00	8	$63,120.00
May 15	$7890.00 + $1405.00 = $9295.00	2	$18,590.00
May 17	$9295.00 + $45.20 = $9340.20	13	$121,422.60
May 30	$9340.20 + $180.72 = $9520.92	2	$19,041.84
		Total days: 31	Total: $271,614.44

Average daily balance $= \dfrac{\text{Sum of unpaid balances}}{\text{Number of days in the billing period}}$

$= \dfrac{\$271{,}614.44}{31}$

$\approx \$8{,}761.76$

b. $I = Prt$

$= (\$8761.76)(0.016)(1)$

$\approx \$140.19$

c. Balance due $= \$9520.92 + \$140.19 = \$9661.11$

d. Because the balance exceeds $360, the minimum payment is $\dfrac{1}{36}$ of the balance due.

Minimum Payment $= \dfrac{\$9661.11}{36} \approx \$269$

Exercise Set 8.5

1. a. $\$220,000(0.20) = \$44,000$

   b. $\$220,000 - \$44,000 = \$176,000$

   c. $\$176,000(0.03) = \$5280$

   d. $PMT = \dfrac{P\left(\frac{r}{n}\right)}{1-\left(1+\frac{r}{n}\right)^{-nt}} = \dfrac{176,000\left(\frac{0.07}{12}\right)}{1-\left(1+\frac{0.07}{12}\right)^{-12(30)}} \approx \$1171$

   e. $\$1171(12)(30) - \$176,000 = \$245,560$

2. a. $\$180,000(0.05) = \$9000$

   b. $\$180,000 - \$9,000 = \$171,000$

   c. $\$171,000(0.01) = \$1710$

   d. $PMT = \dfrac{P\left(\frac{r}{n}\right)}{1-\left(1+\frac{r}{n}\right)^{-nt}} = \dfrac{171,000\left(\frac{0.08}{12}\right)}{1-\left(1+\frac{0.08}{12}\right)^{-12(30)}} \approx \$1255$

   e. $\$1255(12)(30) - \$171,000 = \$280,800$

3. Mortgage amount: $\$100,000 - \$100,000(0.05) = \$95,000$

Payment for 20-year loan: $PMT = \dfrac{P\left(\frac{r}{n}\right)}{1-\left(1+\frac{r}{n}\right)^{-nt}} = \dfrac{95,000\left(\frac{0.08}{12}\right)}{1-\left(1+\frac{0.08}{12}\right)^{-12(20)}} \approx \$795$

Interest for 20-year loan: $\$795(12)(20) - \$100,000 = \$90,800$

Payment for 30-year loan: $PMT = \dfrac{P\left(\frac{r}{n}\right)}{1-\left(1+\frac{r}{n}\right)^{-nt}} = \dfrac{95,000\left(\frac{0.08}{12}\right)}{1-\left(1+\frac{0.08}{12}\right)^{-12(30)}} \approx \$697$

Interest for 30-year loan: $\$697(12)(30) - \$100,000 = \$150,920$
The buyer saves $\$150,920 - \$90,800 = \$60,120$

4. Mortgage amount: $\$160,000 - \$160,000(0.15) = \$136,000$

Payment for 15-year loan: $PMT = \dfrac{P\left(\frac{r}{n}\right)}{1-\left(1+\frac{r}{n}\right)^{-nt}} = \dfrac{136,000\left(\frac{0.08}{12}\right)}{1-\left(1+\frac{0.08}{12}\right)^{-12(15)}} \approx \$1300$

Interest for 15-year loan: $\$1300(12)(15) - \$160,000 = \$74,000$

Payment for 30-year loan: $PMT = \dfrac{P\left(\frac{r}{n}\right)}{1-\left(1+\frac{r}{n}\right)^{-nt}} = \dfrac{136,000\left(\frac{0.08}{12}\right)}{1-\left(1+\frac{0.08}{12}\right)^{-12(30)}} \approx \$998$

Interest for 30-year loan: $\$998(12)(30) - \$160,000 = \$199,280$
The buyer saves $\$199,280 - \$74,000 = \$125,280$

5. Payment for 30-year 8% loan: $PMT = \dfrac{P\left(\frac{r}{n}\right)}{1-\left(1+\frac{r}{n}\right)^{-nt}} = \dfrac{150{,}000\left(\frac{0.08}{12}\right)}{1-\left(1+\frac{0.08}{12}\right)^{-12(30)}} \approx \$1101$

Interest for 30-year loan: $\$1101(12)(30) - \$150{,}000 = \$246{,}360$

Payment for 20-year 7.5% loan: $PMT = \dfrac{P\left(\frac{r}{n}\right)}{1-\left(1+\frac{r}{n}\right)^{-nt}} = \dfrac{150{,}000\left(\frac{0.075}{12}\right)}{1-\left(1+\frac{0.075}{12}\right)^{-12(20)}} \approx \$1208$

Interest for 20-year loan: $\$1208(12)(20) - \$150{,}000 = \$139{,}920$

The 20-year 7.5% loan is more economical. The buyer saves $\$246{,}360 - 139{,}920 = \$106{,}440$

6. Payment for 30-year 8% loan: $PMT = \dfrac{P\left(\frac{r}{n}\right)}{1-\left(1+\frac{r}{n}\right)^{-nt}} = \dfrac{90{,}000\left(\frac{0.08}{12}\right)}{1-\left(1+\frac{0.08}{12}\right)^{-12(30)}} \approx \$660$

Interest for 30-year loan: $\$660(12)(30) - \$90{,}000 = \$147{,}600$

Payment for 15-year 7.5% loan: $PMT = \dfrac{P\left(\frac{r}{n}\right)}{1-\left(1+\frac{r}{n}\right)^{-nt}} = \dfrac{90{,}000\left(\frac{0.075}{12}\right)}{1-\left(1+\frac{0.075}{12}\right)^{-12(15)}} \approx \$834$

Interest for 15-year loan: $\$834(12)(15) - \$90{,}000 = \$60{,}120$

The 15-year 7.5% loan is more economical. The buyer saves $\$147{,}600 - \$60{,}120 = \$87{,}480$

7. Payment for Mortgage A: $PMT = \dfrac{P\left(\frac{r}{n}\right)}{1-\left(1+\frac{r}{n}\right)^{-nt}} = \dfrac{120{,}000\left(\frac{0.07}{12}\right)}{1-\left(1+\frac{0.07}{12}\right)^{-12(30)}} \approx \$798$

Interest for Mortgage A: $\$798(12)(30) - \$120{,}000 = \$167{,}280$

Points for Mortgage A: $\$120{,}000(0.01) = \$1200$

Cost for Mortgage A: $\$2000 + \$1200 + \$167{,}280 = \$170{,}480$

Payment for Mortgage B: $PMT = \dfrac{P\left(\frac{r}{n}\right)}{1-\left(1+\frac{r}{n}\right)^{-nt}} = \dfrac{120{,}000\left(\frac{0.065}{12}\right)}{1-\left(1+\frac{0.065}{12}\right)^{-12(30)}} \approx \$758$

Interest for Mortgage B: $\$758(12)(30) - \$120{,}000 = \$152{,}880$

Points for Mortgage B: $\$120{,}000(0.04) = \$4800$

Cost for Mortgage B: $\$1500 + \$4800 + \$152{,}880 = \$159{,}180$

Mortgage A has the greater cost by $\$170{,}480 - \$159{,}180 = \$11{,}300$

8. Payment for Mortgage A: $PMT = \dfrac{P\left(\frac{r}{n}\right)}{1-\left(1+\frac{r}{n}\right)^{-nt}} = \dfrac{250{,}000\left(\frac{0.0725}{12}\right)}{1-\left(1+\frac{0.0725}{12}\right)^{-12(30)}} \approx \$1705$

Interest for Mortgage A: $\$1705(12)(30) - \$250{,}000 = \$363{,}800$

Points for Mortgage A: $\$250{,}000(0.01) = \$2500$

Cost for Mortgage A: $\$2000 + \$2500 + \$363{,}800 = \$368{,}300$

Payment for Mortgage B: $PMT = \dfrac{P\left(\frac{r}{n}\right)}{1-\left(1+\frac{r}{n}\right)^{-nt}} = \dfrac{250{,}000\left(\frac{0.0625}{12}\right)}{1-\left(1+\frac{0.0625}{12}\right)^{-12(30)}} \approx \$1539$

Interest for Mortgage B: $\$1539(12)(30) - \$250{,}000 = \$304{,}040$

Points for Mortgage B: $\$250{,}000(0.04) = \$10{,}000$

Cost for Mortgage B: $\$350 + \$10{,}000 + \$304{,}040 = \$314{,}390$

Mortgage A has the greater cost by $\$368{,}300 - \$314{,}390 = \$53{,}910.$

9. a. $PMT = \dfrac{P\left(\frac{r}{n}\right)}{1-\left(1+\frac{r}{n}\right)^{-nt}} = \dfrac{4200\left(\frac{0.18}{12}\right)}{1-\left(1+\frac{0.18}{12}\right)^{-12(2)}} \approx \$210$

b. $\$210(12)(2) - \$4200 = \$840$

10. a. $PMT = \dfrac{P\left(\frac{r}{n}\right)}{1-\left(1+\frac{r}{n}\right)^{-nt}} = \dfrac{3600\left(\frac{0.165}{12}\right)}{1-\left(1+\frac{0.165}{12}\right)^{-12(2)}} \approx \$178$

b. $\$178(12)(2) - \$3600 = \$672$

11. a. $PMT = \dfrac{P\left(\frac{r}{n}\right)}{1-\left(1+\frac{r}{n}\right)^{-nt}} = \dfrac{4200\left(\frac{0.105}{12}\right)}{1-\left(1+\frac{0.105}{12}\right)^{-12(3)}} \approx \$137;$ This payment is lower.

b. $\$137(12)(3) - \$4200 = \$732;$ This loan has less interest.

12. a. $PMT = \dfrac{P\left(\frac{r}{n}\right)}{1-\left(1+\frac{r}{n}\right)^{-nt}} = \dfrac{3600\left(\frac{0.095}{12}\right)}{1-\left(1+\frac{0.095}{12}\right)^{-12(3)}} \approx \$116;$ This payment is lower.

b. $\$116(12)(3) - \$3600 = \$576;$ This loan has less interest.

13. $PMT = \dfrac{P\left(\frac{r}{n}\right)}{1-\left(1+\frac{r}{n}\right)^{-nt}} = \dfrac{4200\left(\frac{0.18}{12}\right)}{1-\left(1+\frac{0.18}{12}\right)^{-12(1)}} \approx \$386$

Total interest: $\$386(12)(1) - \$4200 = \$432$

Additional each month: $\$386 - \$210 = \$176$

Less total interest: $\$840 - \$432 = \$408$

14. $PMT = \dfrac{P\left(\frac{r}{n}\right)}{1-\left(1+\frac{r}{n}\right)^{-nt}} = \dfrac{3600\left(\frac{0.165}{12}\right)}{1-\left(1+\frac{0.165}{12}\right)^{-12(1)}} \approx \$328$

Total interest: $\$328(12)(1) - \$3600 = \$336$

Additional each month: $\$328 - \$178 = \$150$

Less total interest: $\$672 - \$336 = \$336$

15. a. $PMT = \dfrac{P\left(\frac{r}{n}\right)}{1-\left(1+\frac{r}{n}\right)^{-nt}} = \dfrac{10,000\left(\frac{0.08}{12}\right)}{1-\left(1+\frac{0.08}{12}\right)^{-12(4)}} \approx \$244.13$

Total interest: $\$244.13(12)(4) - \$10,000 = \$1718.24$

b.

Payment Number	Interest	Principal	Loan Balance
1	$10,000(0.08)\left(\frac{1}{12}\right)$ $= \$66.67$	$244.13 - 66.67$ $= \$177.46$	$10,000 - 177.46$ $= \$9822.54$
2	$9822.54(0.08)\left(\frac{1}{12}\right)$ $= \$65.48$	$244.13 - 65.48$ $= \$178.65$	$9822.54 - 178.65$ $= \$9643.89$
3	$9643.89(0.08)\left(\frac{1}{12}\right)$ $= \$64.29$	$244.13 - 64.29$ $= \$179.84$	$9643.89 - 179.84$ $= \$9464.05$

16. a. $PMT = \dfrac{P\left(\frac{r}{n}\right)}{1-\left(1+\frac{r}{n}\right)^{-nt}} = \dfrac{30{,}000\left(\frac{0.08}{12}\right)}{1-\left(1+\frac{0.08}{12}\right)^{-12(4)}} \approx \$732.39$

Total interest: $\$732.39(12)(4) - \$30{,}000 = \$5154.72$

b.

Payment Number	Interest	Principal	Loan Balance
1	$30{,}000(0.08)\left(\frac{1}{12}\right)$ $= \$200.00$	$732.39 - 200.00$ $= \$532.39$	$30{,}000 - 532.39$ $= \$29{,}467.61$
2	$29{,}467.61(0.08)\left(\frac{1}{12}\right)$ $= \$196.45$	$732.39 - 196.45$ $= \$535.94$	$29{,}467.61 - 535.94$ $= \$28{,}931.67$
3	$28{,}931.67(0.08)\left(\frac{1}{12}\right)$ $= \$192.88$	$732.39 - 192.88$ $= \$539.51$	$28{,}931.67 - 539.51$ $= \$28{,}392.16$

17. a. $PMT = \dfrac{P\left(\frac{r}{n}\right)}{1-\left(1+\frac{r}{n}\right)^{-nt}} = \dfrac{40{,}000\left(\frac{0.085}{12}\right)}{1-\left(1+\frac{0.085}{12}\right)^{-12(20)}} \approx \$347.13$

Total interest: $\$347.13(12)(20) - \$40{,}000 = \$43{,}311.20$

b.

Payment Number	Interest	Principal	Loan Balance
1	$40{,}000(0.085)\left(\frac{1}{12}\right)$ $= \$283.33$	$347.13 - 283.33$ $= \$63.80$	$40{,}000 - 63.80$ $= \$39{,}936.20$
2	$39{,}936.20(0.085)\left(\frac{1}{12}\right)$ $= \$282.88$	$347.13 - 282.88$ $= \$64.25$	$39{,}936.20 - 64.25$ $= \$39{,}871.95$
3	$39{,}871.95(0.085)\left(\frac{1}{12}\right)$ $= \$282.43$	$347.13 - 282.43$ $= \$64.70$	$39{,}871.95 - 64.70$ $= \$39{,}807.25$

c. $PMT = \dfrac{P\left(\frac{r}{n}\right)}{1-\left(1+\frac{r}{n}\right)^{-nt}} = \dfrac{40{,}000\left(\frac{0.085}{12}\right)}{1-\left(1+\frac{0.085}{12}\right)^{-12(10)}} \approx \$495.94$

Amount by which the monthly payment for the 10-year loan is greater: $\$495.94 - \$347.13 = \$148.81$

Total interest for 10-year loan: $\$495.94(12)(10) - \$40{,}000 = \$19{,}512.80$

Savings from 10-year loan: $\$43{,}311.20 - \$19{,}512.80 = \$23{,}798.40$

18. a. $PMT = \dfrac{P\left(\frac{r}{n}\right)}{1-\left(1+\frac{r}{n}\right)^{-nt}} = \dfrac{50,000\left(\frac{0.075}{12}\right)}{1-\left(1+\frac{0.075}{12}\right)^{-12(20)}} \approx \$402.80$

Total interest: $\$402.80(12)(20) - \$50,000 = \$46,672$

b.

Payment Number	Interest	Principal	Loan Balance
1	$50,000(0.075)\left(\frac{1}{12}\right)$ $= \$312.50$	$402.80 - 312.50$ $= \$90.30$	$50,000 - 90.30$ $= \$49,909.70$
2	$49,909.70(0.075)\left(\frac{1}{12}\right)$ $= \$311.94$	$402.80 - 311.94$ $= \$90.86$	$49,909.70 - 90.86$ $= \$49,818.84$
3	$49,818.84(0.075)\left(\frac{1}{12}\right)$ $= \$311.37$	$402.80 - 311.37$ $= \$91.43$	$49,818.84 - 91.43$ $= \$49,727.41$

c. $PMT = \dfrac{P\left(\frac{r}{n}\right)}{1-\left(1+\frac{r}{n}\right)^{-nt}} = \dfrac{50,000\left(\frac{0.075}{12}\right)}{1-\left(1+\frac{0.075}{12}\right)^{-12(10)}} \approx \$593.51$

Amount by which the monthly payment for the 10-year loan is greater: $\$593.51 - \$402.80 = \$190.71$

Total interest for 10-year loan: $\$593.51(12)(10) - \$50,000 = \$21,221.20$

Savings from 10-year loan: $\$46,672 - \$21,221.20 = \$25,450.80$

19. a.   Make a table that shows the unpaid balance for each transaction date, the number of days at each unpaid balance, and then multiply each unpaid balance by the number of days that the balance was outstanding.

Date	Unpaid Balance	Number of Days at Each Unpaid Balance	$\left(\begin{array}{c}\text{Unpaid}\\\text{Balance}\end{array}\right) \cdot \left(\begin{array}{c}\text{Number}\\\text{of Days}\end{array}\right)$
March 1	$6240.00	4	$24,960.00
March 5	$6240.00 - $300.00 = $5940.00	2	$11,880.00
March 7	$5940.00 + $40.00 = $5980.00	5	$29,900.00
March 12	$5980.00 + $90.00 = $6070.00	9	$54,630.00
March 21	$6070.00 + $230.00 = $6300.00	11	$69,300.00
		Total days: 31	Total: $190,670.00

$\text{Average daily balance} = \dfrac{\text{Sum of unpaid balances}}{\text{Number of days in the billing period}}$

$= \dfrac{\$190,670.00}{31}$

$\approx \$6150.65$

b. $I = Prt$

$= (\$6150.65)(0.015)(1)$

$\approx \$92.26$

c.   Balance due $= \$6300.00 + \$92.26 = \$6392.26$

d.   Because the balance exceeds $360, the minimum payment is $\dfrac{1}{36}$ of the balance due.

$\text{Minimum Payment} = \dfrac{\$6392.26}{36} \approx \$178$

20. a. Make a table that shows the unpaid balance for each transaction date, the number of days at each unpaid balance, and then multiply each unpaid balance by the number of days that the balance was outstanding.

Date	Unpaid Balance	Number of Days at Each Unpaid Balance	$\left(\begin{matrix}\text{Unpaid}\\\text{Balance}\end{matrix}\right) \cdot \left(\begin{matrix}\text{Number}\\\text{of Days}\end{matrix}\right)$
March 1	$7150.00	3	$21,450.00
March 5	$7150.00 − $400.00 = $6750.00	2	$13,500.00
March 7	$6750.00 + $1200.00 = $7950.00	9	$71,550.00
March 12	$7950.00 + $40.00 = $7990.00	15	$119,850.00
March 21	$7990.00 + $50.00 = $8040.00	2	$16,080.00
		Total days: 31	Total: $242,430.00

$$\text{Average daily balance} = \frac{\text{Sum of unpaid balances}}{\text{Number of days in the billing period}}$$

$$= \frac{\$242,430.00}{31}$$

$$\approx \$7820.32$$

b. $I = Prt$

$$= (\$7820.32)(0.015)(1)$$

$$\approx \$117.30$$

c. Balance due = $8040.00 + $117.30 = $8157.30

d. Because the balance exceeds $360, the minimum payment is $\frac{1}{36}$ of the balance due.

$$\text{Minimum Payment} = \frac{\$8157.30}{36} \approx \$227$$

21. a. Make a table that shows the unpaid balance for each transaction date, the number of days at each unpaid balance, and then multiply each unpaid balance by the number of days that the balance was outstanding.

Date	Unpaid Balance	Number of Days at Each Unpaid Balance	$\left(\begin{matrix}\text{Unpaid}\\\text{Balance}\end{matrix}\right) \cdot \left(\begin{matrix}\text{Number}\\\text{of Days}\end{matrix}\right)$
June 1	$2653.48	5	$13,267.40
June 6	$2653.48 − $1000.00 = $1653.48	2	$3306.96
June 8	$1653.48 + $36.25 = $1689.73	1	$1689.73
June 9	$1689.73 + $138.43 = $1828.16	8	$14,625.28
June 17	$1828.16 + $42.36 + $127.19 = $1997.71	10	$19,977.10
June 27	$1997.71 + $214.83 = $2212.54	4	$8850.16
		Total days: 30	Total: $61,716.63

$$\text{Average daily balance} = \frac{\text{Sum of unpaid balances}}{\text{Number of days in the billing period}}$$

$$= \frac{\$61,716.63}{30}$$

$$\approx \$2057.22$$

b. $I = \mathrm{Pr}\,t$

$= (\$2057.22)(0.012)(1)$

$\approx \$24.69$

c. Balance due $= \$2212.54 + \$24.69 = \$2237.23$

d. Because the balance exceeds \$400, the minimum payment is $\dfrac{1}{25}$ of the balance due.

Minimum Payment $= \dfrac{\$2237.24}{25} \approx \$90$

22. a. Make a table that shows the unpaid balance for each transaction date, the number of days at each unpaid balance, and then multiply each unpaid balance by the number of days that the balance was outstanding.

Date	Unpaid Balance	Number of Days at Each Unpaid Balance	$\left(\begin{array}{c}\text{Unpaid}\\\text{Balance}\end{array}\right) \cdot \left(\begin{array}{c}\text{Number}\\\text{of Days}\end{array}\right)$
June 1	\$4037.93	4	\$16,151.72
June 5	\$4037.93 − \$350.00 = \$3687.93	5	\$18,439.65
June 10	\$3687.93 + \$31.17 = \$3719.10	5	\$18,595.50
June 15	\$3719.10 + \$42.50 = \$3761.60	7	\$26,331.20
June 22	\$3761.60 + \$43.86 + \$112.91 = \$3918.37	7	\$27,428.59
June 29	\$3918.37 + \$96.73 = \$4015.10	2	\$8030.20
		Total days: 30	Total: \$114,976.86

Average daily balance $= \dfrac{\text{Sum of unpaid balances}}{\text{Number of days in the billing period}}$

$= \dfrac{\$114,976.86}{30}$

$\approx \$3832.56$

b. $I = \mathrm{Pr}\,t$

$= (\$3832.56)(0.012)(1)$

$\approx \$45.99$

c. Balance due $= \$4015.10 + \$45.99 = \$4061.09$

d. Because the balance exceeds \$400, the minimum payment is $\dfrac{1}{25}$ of the balance due.

Minimum Payment $= \dfrac{\$4061.09}{25} \approx \$163$

33. does not make sense; Explanations will vary. Sample explanation: The 3.5% rate will not eliminate paying more on interest than on the principal.

34. does not make sense; Explanations will vary. Sample explanation: The payments could still be larger with the 3-year loan.

35. does not make sense; Explanations will vary. Sample explanation: Paying the minimum payment will cost more money in interest over the long run.

36. does not make sense; Explanations will vary. Sample explanation: The given formula is for fixed installment loans not credit card payments.

37.
$$P\left(1+\tfrac{r}{n}\right)^{nt} = \frac{PMT\left[\left(1+\tfrac{r}{n}\right)^{nt}-1\right]}{\tfrac{r}{n}}$$

$$P\left(\tfrac{r}{n}\right)\left(1+\tfrac{r}{n}\right)^{nt} = PMT\left[\left(1+\tfrac{r}{n}\right)^{nt}-1\right]$$

$$\frac{P\left(\tfrac{r}{n}\right)\left(1+\tfrac{r}{n}\right)^{nt}}{\left(1+\tfrac{r}{n}\right)^{nt}-1} = \frac{PMT\left[\left(1+\tfrac{r}{n}\right)^{nt}-1\right]}{\left(1+\tfrac{r}{n}\right)^{nt}-1}$$

$$\frac{P\left(\tfrac{r}{n}\right)\left(1+\tfrac{r}{n}\right)^{nt}}{\left(1+\tfrac{r}{n}\right)^{nt}-1} = PMT$$

$$\frac{\dfrac{P\left(\tfrac{r}{n}\right)\left(1+\tfrac{r}{n}\right)^{nt}}{\left(1+\tfrac{r}{n}\right)^{nt}}}{\dfrac{\left(1+\tfrac{r}{n}\right)^{nt}-1}{\left(1+\tfrac{r}{n}\right)^{nt}}} = PMT$$

$$\frac{P\left(\tfrac{r}{n}\right)}{\dfrac{\left(1+\tfrac{r}{n}\right)^{nt}}{\left(1+\tfrac{r}{n}\right)^{nt}}-\dfrac{1}{\left(1+\tfrac{r}{n}\right)^{nt}}} = PMT$$

$$\frac{P\left(\tfrac{r}{n}\right)}{1-\left(1+\tfrac{r}{n}\right)^{-nt}} = PMT$$

38. a. Begin with $PMT = PV\dfrac{\tfrac{r}{n}}{1-\left(1+\tfrac{r}{n}\right)^{-nt}}$

Next multiply both sides by $\dfrac{1-\left(1+\tfrac{r}{n}\right)^{-nt}}{\tfrac{r}{n}}$

which gives: $PMT\dfrac{1-\left(1+\tfrac{r}{n}\right)^{-nt}}{\tfrac{r}{n}} = PV\dfrac{\tfrac{r}{n}}{1-\left(1+\tfrac{r}{n}\right)^{-nt}}\cdot\dfrac{1-\left(1+\tfrac{r}{n}\right)^{-nt}}{\tfrac{r}{n}}$

Canceling produces: $PMT\dfrac{1-\left(1+\tfrac{r}{n}\right)^{-nt}}{\tfrac{r}{n}} = PV$

Finally, interchange the sides: $PV = PMT\dfrac{1-\left(1+\tfrac{r}{n}\right)^{-nt}}{\tfrac{r}{n}}$

b. $PV = PMT\dfrac{1-\left(1+\tfrac{r}{n}\right)^{-nt}}{\tfrac{r}{n}} = 1002.74\,\dfrac{1-\left(1+\tfrac{0.063}{12}\right)^{-12\cdot20}}{\tfrac{0.063}{12}} \approx \$136,641.85$

Chapter 8 Review Exercises

1. $\dfrac{4}{5} = 4 \div 5 = 0.80 = 80\%$

2. $\dfrac{1}{8} = 1 \div 8 = 0.125 = 12.5\%$

3. $\dfrac{3}{4} = 3 \div 4 = 0.75 = 75\%$

4. $0.72 = 72\%$

5. $0.0035 = 0.35\%$

6. $4.756 = 475.6\%$

7. $65\% = 0.65$

8. $99.7\% = 0.997$

9. $150\% = 1.50$

10. $3\% = 0.03$

11. $0.65\% = 0.0065$

12. $\frac{1}{4}\% = 0.25\% = 0.0025$

13. $A = PB$
    $A = 0.08 \cdot 120$
    $A = 9.6$

14. **a.** Tax $= 0.06(\$24) = \$1.44$

    b. Total cost $= \$24 + \$1.44 = \$25.44$

15. **a.** Amount of discount $= 0.35(\$850)$
    $= \$297.50$

    b. Sale price $= \$850 - \$297.50 = \$552.50$

16. Step 1. Determine the adjusted gross income.
    Adj. gross income = Gross income – Adjustments
    Adj. gross income $= \$40,000 - \$2500$
    $= \$37,500$

    Step 2. Determine the taxable income.
    Since the total deduction of $8300 is greater than
    the standard deduction of $5450, use $8300.
    Taxable inc. = Adj. gross inc– (Exempt.+Deduct.)
    Taxable inc. $= \$37,500 - (\$3500 + \$8300)$
    $= \$25,700$

    Step 3. Determine the income tax.
    Tax Computation
    $= 0.10(8025) + 0.15(25,700 - 8025)$
    $= \$3453.75$
    Income tax = Tax Computation – Tax credits
    Income tax $= \$3453.75 - \$0$
    $= \$3453.75$

17. $\dfrac{45 - 40}{40} = 0.125 = 12.5\%$ increase.

18. $\dfrac{\$56.00 - \$36.40}{\$56.00} = 0.35 = 35\%$ decrease.

19. The statement is not true.
    The 10% loss is $1000.
    $\left[0.10 \times 10,000 = 1000 \right]$
    This leaves $9000.
    The 10% rise is $900.
    $\left[0.10 \times 9,000 = 900 \right]$
    Thus there is $9900 in the portfolio.
    Find the percent of decrease:
    $\dfrac{\text{amount of decrease}}{\text{original amount}} = \dfrac{100}{10,000} = 0.01 = 1\%$
    The net loss of $100 is a 1% decrease from the
    original.

20. $I = Prt = (\$6000)(0.03)(1) = \$180$

21. $I = Prt = (\$8400)(0.05)(6) = \$2520$

22. $I = Prt = (\$20,000)(0.08)\left(\dfrac{9}{12} \right) = \$1200$

23. $I = Prt = (\$36,000)(0.15)\left(\dfrac{60}{360} \right) = \$900$

24. **a.** $I = Prt = (\$3500)(0.105)\left(\dfrac{4}{12}\right)$

$= \$122.50$

b. Maturity value $= \$3500 + \$122.50$

$= \$3622.50$

25. $A = P(1 + rt)$

$A = 12{,}000(1 + 0.082 \times \frac{9}{12})$

$A = \$12{,}738$

26. $A = P(1 + rt)$

$5750 = 5000\big(1 + r(2)\big)$

$5750 = 5000 + 10{,}000r$

$750 = 10{,}000r$

$0.075 = r$

$r = 7.5\%$

27. $A = P(1 + rt)$

$16{,}000 = P\big(1 + (0.065)(3)\big)$

$16{,}000 = 1.195P$

$13{,}389.12 = P$

$P = \$13{,}389.12$

28. $A = P(1 + rt)$

$12{,}000 = P\big(1 + (0.073)(4)\big)$

$12{,}000 = 1.292P$

$9287.93 = P$

$P = \$9287.93$

29. $A = P(1 + rt)$

$1800 = 1500\big(1 + r\left(\frac{1}{2}\right)\big)$

$1800 = 1500 + 750r$

$300 = 750r$

$0.4 = r$

$r = 40\%$

30. **a.** $I = Prt = (1800)(0.07)\left(\frac{9}{12}\right) = \$94.50$

b. Amount received: $\$1800 - \$94.50 = \$1705.50$

c. $I = Prt$

$94.50 = (1705.50)(r)\left(\frac{9}{12}\right)$

$94.50 = 1279.125r$

$0.0739 = r$

$r = 7.4\%$

31. **a.** $A = \$7000(1 + 0.03)^5$

$= \$7000(1.03)^5$

$\approx \$8114.92$

b. Interest $= \$8114.92 - \$7000$

$= \$1114.92$

32. **a.** $A = \$30{,}000\left(1 + \dfrac{0.025}{4}\right)^{4 \cdot 10}$

$= \$30{,}000(1.00625)^{40}$

$\approx \$38{,}490.80$

b. Interest $= \$38{,}490.80 - \$30{,}000$

$= \$8490.80$

33. **a.** $A = \$2500\left(1 + \dfrac{0.04}{12}\right)^{12 \cdot 20}$

$= \$2500(1.003333)^{240}$

$\approx \$5556.46$

b. Interest $= \$5556.46 - \$2500$

$= \$3056.46$

34. $A = P\left(1 + \frac{r}{n}\right)^{nt}$

$A = 14{,}000\left(1 + \frac{0.07}{12}\right)^{12(10)}$

$\approx \$28{,}135$

$A = Pe^{rt}$

$A = 14{,}000e^{0.0685(10)}$

$\approx \$27{,}773$

The 7% compounded monthly is the better investment by $\$28{,}135 - \$27{,}773 = \$362$.

35. $P = \dfrac{100{,}000}{\left(1 + \dfrac{0.07}{12}\right)^{12 \cdot 18}} \approx \$28{,}469.44$

36. $P = \dfrac{75{,}000}{\left(1 + \dfrac{0.05}{4}\right)^{4 \cdot 35}} \approx \$13{,}175.19$

37. a. $A = \$2000\left(1 + \dfrac{0.06}{4}\right)^{4 \cdot 1}$

$= \$2000(1.015)^4$

$= \$2122.73$

b. $A = P(1 + rt)$

$2122.73 = 2000\left[1 + r(1)\right]$

$2122.73 = 2000 + 2000r$

$122.73 = 2000r$

$0.061365 \approx r$

$r \approx 6.1\%$

38. $Y = \left(1 + \dfrac{0.055}{4}\right)^4 - 1 \approx 0.0561 = 5.6\%$

5.5% compounded quarterly is equivalent to 5.6% compounded annually.

39. 6.25% compounded monthly:

$Y = \left(1 + \dfrac{0.0625}{12}\right)^{12} - 1 \approx 0.0643 = 6.4\%$

6.3% compounded annually:

$Y = \left(1 + \dfrac{0.063}{1}\right)^1 - 1 \approx 0.063 = 6.3\%$

6.25% compounded monthly is better than 6.3% compounded annually.

40. a. $A = \dfrac{P\left[(1 + r)^t - 1\right]}{r}$

$A = \dfrac{520\left[(1 + 0.06)^{20} - 1\right]}{0.06}$

$\approx \$19{,}129$

b. $\$19{,}129 - 20 \times \$520 = \$8729$

41. a. $A = \dfrac{P\left[\left(1 + \frac{r}{n}\right)^{nt} - 1\right]}{\frac{r}{n}}$

$A = \dfrac{100\left[\left(1 + \frac{0.055}{12}\right)^{12(30)} - 1\right]}{\frac{0.055}{12}}$

$\approx \$91{,}361$

b. $\$91{,}361 - 30 \times 12 \times \$100 = \$55{,}361$

42. a. $P = \dfrac{A\left(\frac{r}{n}\right)}{\left[\left(1 + \frac{r}{n}\right)^{nt} - 1\right]}$

$P = \dfrac{25{,}000\left(\frac{0.0725}{4}\right)}{\left[\left(1 + \frac{0.0725}{4}\right)^{4(5)} - 1\right]}$

$\approx \$1049$

b. Deposits: $5 \times 4 \times \$1049 = \$20{,}980$

Interest: $\$25{,}000 - \$20{,}980 = \$4020$

43. High = $64.06, Low = $26.13

44. Dividend = $0.16(900) = \$144$

45. Annual return for dividends alone = 0.3%

46. Shares traded yesterday = $5458 \cdot 100$

$= 545{,}800$ shares

47. High = $61.25, Low = $59.25

48. Price at close = $61

49. Change in price = $1.75 increase

50. Annual earnings per share $\dfrac{\$61}{41} \approx \$1.49$

52. a. $\$240{,}000(0.20) = \$48{,}000$

b. $\$240{,}000 - \$48{,}000 = \$192{,}000$

c. $\$192{,}000(0.02) = \$3840$

d. $PMT = \dfrac{P\left(\frac{r}{n}\right)}{1 - \left(1 + \frac{r}{n}\right)^{-nt}}$

$= \dfrac{192{,}000\left(\frac{0.07}{12}\right)}{1 - \left(1 + \frac{0.07}{12}\right)^{-12(30)}}$

$\approx \$1277$

e. $\$1277(12)(30) - \$192{,}000 = \$267{,}720$

53. Payment for 30-year mortgage:

$$PMT = \frac{P\left(\frac{r}{n}\right)}{1-\left(1+\frac{r}{n}\right)^{-nt}} = \frac{70,000\left(\frac{0.085}{12}\right)}{1-\left(1+\frac{0.085}{12}\right)^{-12(30)}} \approx \$538$$

Interest for 30-year mortgage:
$\$538(12)(30)-\$70,000 = \$123,680$

Payment for 20-year mortgage:

$$PMT = \frac{P\left(\frac{r}{n}\right)}{1-\left(1+\frac{r}{n}\right)^{-nt}} = \frac{70,000\left(\frac{0.08}{12}\right)}{1-\left(1+\frac{0.08}{12}\right)^{-12(20)}} \approx \$586$$

Interest for 20-year mortgage: $\$586(12)(20)-\$70,000 = \$70,640$

The 20-year mortgage saves $\$123,680-\$70,640 = \$53,040$.

An advantage of the 30-year loan is the lower monthly payment. A disadvantage of the 30-year loan is the greater total interest.

An advantage of the 20-year loan is the lower total interest. A disadvantage of the 20-year loan is the higher monthly payment.

54. a. Payment for Mortgage A:

$$PMT = \frac{P\left(\frac{r}{n}\right)}{1-\left(1+\frac{r}{n}\right)^{-nt}} = \frac{100,000\left(\frac{0.085}{12}\right)}{1-\left(1+\frac{0.085}{12}\right)^{-12(30)}} \approx \$769$$

Payment for Mortgage B:

$$PMT = \frac{P\left(\frac{r}{n}\right)}{1-\left(1+\frac{r}{n}\right)^{-nt}} = \frac{100,000\left(\frac{0.075}{12}\right)}{1-\left(1+\frac{0.075}{12}\right)^{-12(30)}} \approx \$699$$

b. Interest for Mortgage A:
$\$769(12)(30)-\$100,000 = \$176,840$

Cost for Mortgage A:
$\$0+\$0+\$176,840 = \$176,840$

Interest for Mortgage B:
$\$699(12)(30)-\$100,000 = \$151,640$

Points for Mortgage B:
$\$100,000(0.03) = \$3000$

Cost for Mortgage B:
$\$1300+\$3000+\$151,640 = \$155,940$

Mortgage A has the greater cost by $\$176,840-\$155,940 = \$20,900$.

55. a. Payment for Loan A:

$$PMT = \frac{P\left(\frac{r}{n}\right)}{1-\left(1+\frac{r}{n}\right)^{-nt}} = \frac{100,000\left(\frac{0.072}{12}\right)}{1-\left(1+\frac{0.072}{12}\right)^{-12(3)}} \approx \$465$$

Interest for Loan A:
$\$465(12)(3)-\$15,000 = \$1740$

b. Payment for Loan B:

$$PMT = \frac{P\left(\frac{r}{n}\right)}{1-\left(1+\frac{r}{n}\right)^{-nt}} = \frac{100,000\left(\frac{0.081}{12}\right)}{1-\left(1+\frac{0.081}{12}\right)^{-12(5)}} \approx \$305$$

Interest for Loan B:
$305(12)(5) - $15,000 = $3300

c. The longer term has a lower monthly payment but greater total interest.

56. a. $$PMT = \frac{P\left(\frac{r}{n}\right)}{1-\left(1+\frac{r}{n}\right)^{-nt}} = \frac{11,211\left(\frac{0.18}{12}\right)}{1-\left(1+\frac{0.18}{12}\right)^{-12(2)}} \approx \$559.70$$

b. Total interest: $559.70(12)(2) - $11,211 = $2221.80

c.

Payment Number	Interest	Principal	Loan Balance
1	$11,211(0.18)\left(\frac{1}{12}\right)$ $= \$168.17$	$559.70 - 168.17$ $= \$391.53$	$11,211 - 391.53$ $= \$10,819.47$
2	$10,819.47(0.18)\left(\frac{1}{12}\right)$ $= \$162.29$	$559.70 - 162.29$ $= \$397.41$	$10,819.47 - 397.41$ $= \$10,422.06$
3	$10,422.06(0.18)\left(\frac{1}{12}\right)$ $= \$156.33$	$559.70 - 156.33$ $= \$403.37$	$10,422.06 - 403.37$ $= \$10,018.69$

57. a. Make a table that shows the unpaid balance for each transaction date, the number of days at each unpaid balance, and then multiply each unpaid balance by the number of days that the balance was outstanding.

Date	Unpaid Balance	Number of Days at Each Unpaid Balance	$\left(\begin{array}{c}\text{Unpaid}\\\text{Balance}\end{array}\right)\cdot\left(\begin{array}{c}\text{Number}\\\text{of Days}\end{array}\right)$
November 1	$4620.80	6	$27,724.80
November 7	$4620.80 - $650.00 = $3970.80	4	$15,883.20
November 11	$3970.80 + $350.25 = $4,321.05	14	$60,494.70
November 25	$4321.05 + $125.70 = $4446.75	3	$13,340.25
November 28	$4446.75 + $38.25 = $4485.00	3	$13,455.00
		Total days: 30	Total: $130,897.95

$$\text{Average daily balance} = \frac{\text{Sum of unpaid balances}}{\text{Number of days in the billing period}}$$

$$= \frac{\$130,897.95}{30}$$

$$\approx \$4363.27$$

b. $I = Prt$

$= (\$4363.27)(0.011)(1)$

$\approx \$48.00$

c. Balance due $= \$4485.00 + \$48.00 = \$4533.00$

d. Because the balance exceeds $360, the minimum payment is $\frac{1}{36}$ of the balance due.

$$\text{Minimum Payment} = \frac{\$4533.00}{36} \approx \$126$$

Chapter 8 Test

1. **a.** Discount = 0.15($120) = $18

   b. Sale price = $120 − $18 = $102

2. Step 1. Determine the adjusted gross income.
   Adj. gross income = Gross income − Adjustments
   Adj. gross income = $36,500 − $2000
   $$= \$34,500$$

   Step 2. Determine the taxable income.
   Since the total deduction of $6000 is greater than the standard deduction of $5000, use $6000.
   Taxable inc. = Adj. gross inc− (Exempt.+Deduct.)
   Taxable inc. = $34,500 − ($3500 + $6000)
   $$= \$25,000$$

   Step 3. Determine the income tax.
   Tax Computation = 0.10(8025) + 0.15(25,000 − 8025)
   $$= \$3348.75$$
   Income tax = Tax Computation − Tax credits
   Income tax = $3348.75 − $0
   $$= \$3348.75$$

3. $\dfrac{3500 - 2000}{2000} = 0.75 = 75\%$ increase

4. $A = P(1 + rt)$

   $A = 2400\left(1 + (0.12)\left(\frac{3}{12}\right)\right)$

   $A = \$2472$
   The future value is $2472.
   The interest earned is $72.

5. $\quad A = P(1 + rt)$

   $3000 = 2000\left(1 + r(2)\right)$

   $3000 = 2000 + 4000r$

   $1000 = 4000r$

   $0.25 = r$

   $\quad r = 25\%$

6. $\quad\quad A = P(1 + rt)$

   $7000 = P\left(1 + (0.09)\left(\frac{6}{12}\right)\right)$

   $7000 = 1.045P$

   $6698.57 = P$

   $\quad\quad P = \$6698.57$

7. $Y = \left(1 + \dfrac{0.045}{4}\right)^4 - 1 \approx 0.0458 = 4.58\%$

4.5% compounded quarterly is equivalent to 4.58% compounded annually.

8. **a.** $A = P\left(1 + \frac{r}{n}\right)^{nt}$

$A = 6000\left(1 + \frac{0.065}{12}\right)^{12(5)}$

$\approx \$8297$

b. $\$8297 - \$6000 = \$2297$

9. **a.** $A = \dfrac{P\left[\left(1 + \frac{r}{n}\right)^{nt} - 1\right]}{\frac{r}{n}}$

$A = \dfrac{100\left[\left(1 + \frac{0.065}{12}\right)^{12(5)} - 1\right]}{\frac{0.065}{12}}$

$\approx \$7067$

b. $\$7067 - \$6000 = \$1067$

c.   answers will vary

10. $P = \dfrac{A}{\left(1 + \frac{r}{n}\right)^{nt}}$

$P = \dfrac{3000}{\left(1 + \frac{0.095}{2}\right)^{2(4)}}$

$\approx \$2070$

11. $P = \dfrac{A\left(\frac{r}{n}\right)}{\left[\left(1 + \frac{r}{n}\right)^{nt} - 1\right]}$

$P = \dfrac{1,500,000\left(\frac{0.0625}{12}\right)}{\left[\left(1 + \frac{0.0625}{12}\right)^{12(40)} - 1\right]}$

$\approx \$704$

Interest $= \$1,500,000 - \$704(12)(40)$

$= \$1,162,080$

12.   High $= \$25.75$, Low $= \$25.50$

13.   Dividend $= \$2.03 \cdot 1000 = \$2030$

14.   Total price paid $= 600(\$25.75) = \$15,450$

Broker's commission $= 0.025(\$15,450) = \$386.25$

15.   Down payment $= 0.10(\$120,000) = \$12,000$

16.   Amount of mortgage $= \$120,000 - \$12,000$

$= \$108,000$

17. Two points $= 0.02(\$108,000) = \$2160$

18. $PMT = \dfrac{P\left(\frac{r}{n}\right)}{1-\left(1+\frac{r}{n}\right)^{-nt}} = \dfrac{108,000\left(\frac{0.085}{12}\right)}{1-\left(1+\frac{0.085}{12}\right)^{-12(30)}} \approx \$830$

19. Total cost of interest
$= 360(\$830) - \$108,000$
$= \$190,800$

20. a. $PMT = \dfrac{P\left(\frac{r}{n}\right)}{1-\left(1+\frac{r}{n}\right)^{-nt}} = \dfrac{20,000\left(\frac{0.068}{12}\right)}{1-\left(1+\frac{0.068}{12}\right)^{-12(10)}} \approx \$230$

Total interest: $\$230(12)(10) - \$20,000 = \$7600$

b.

Payment Number	Interest	Principal	Loan Balance
1	$20,000(0.068)\left(\frac{1}{12}\right)$ $= \$113.33$	$230-113.33$ $= \$116.67$	$20,000-116.67$ $= \$19,883.33$
2	$19,883.33(0.068)\left(\frac{1}{12}\right)$ $= \$112.67$	$230-112.67$ $= \$117.33$	$19,883.33-117.33$ $= \$19,766.00$

21. a. Make a table that shows the unpaid balance for each transaction date, the number of days at each unpaid balance, and then multiply each unpaid balance by the number of days that the balance was outstanding.

Date	Unpaid Balance	Number of Days at Each Unpaid Balance	$\left(\begin{array}{c}\text{Unpaid}\\\text{Balance}\end{array}\right)\cdot\left(\begin{array}{c}\text{Number}\\\text{of Days}\end{array}\right)$
September 1	$3800.00	4	$15,200.00
September 5	$3800.00 - \$800.00 = \$3000.00$	4	$12,000.00
September 9	$3000.00 + \$40.00 = \$3040.00$	10	$30,400.00
September 19	$3040.00 + \$160.00 = \$3200.00$	8	$25,600.00
September 27	$3200.00 + \$200.00 = \$3400.00$	4	$13,600.00
		Total days: 30	Total: $96,800.00

Average daily balance $= \dfrac{\text{Sum of unpaid balances}}{\text{Number of days in the billing period}}$

$= \dfrac{\$96,800.00}{30}$

$\approx \$3226.67$

b. $I = \Pr t$

$= (\$3226.67)(0.02)(1)$

$\approx \$64.53$

c. Balance due $= \$3400.00 + \$64.53 = \$3464.53$

d. Because the balance exceeds $360, the minimum payment is $\dfrac{1}{36}$ of the balance due.

Minimum Payment $= \dfrac{\$3464.53}{36} \approx \$97$

Chapter 9
Measurement

Check Points 9.1

1. a. $78 \text{ in.} = \dfrac{78 \text{ in.}}{1} \cdot \dfrac{1 \text{ ft}}{12 \text{ in.}} = 6.5 \text{ ft}$

b. $17{,}160 \text{ ft} = \dfrac{17{,}160 \text{ ft}}{1} \cdot \dfrac{1 \text{ mi}}{5280 \text{ ft}} = 3.25 \text{ mi}$

c. $3 \text{ in.} = \dfrac{3 \text{ in.}}{1} \cdot \dfrac{1 \text{ yd}}{36 \text{ in.}} = \dfrac{1}{12} \text{ yd}$

2. a. $8000 \text{ m} = 8 \text{ km}$

b. $53 \text{ m} = 53{,}000 \text{ mm}$

c. $604 \text{ cm} = 0.0604 \text{ hm}$

d. $6.72 \text{ dam} = 6720 \text{ cm}$

3. a. $8 \text{ ft} = \dfrac{8 \text{ ft}}{1} \cdot \dfrac{30.48 \text{ cm}}{1 \text{ ft}} = 243.84 \text{ cm}$

b. $20 \text{ m} = \dfrac{20 \text{ m}}{1} \cdot \dfrac{1 \text{ yd}}{0.9 \text{ m}} \approx 22.22 \text{ yd}$

c. $30 \text{ m} = 3000 \text{ cm}$

$= \dfrac{3000 \text{ cm}}{1} \cdot \dfrac{1 \text{ in.}}{2.54 \text{ cm}}$

$\approx 1181.1 \text{ in.}$

4. $\dfrac{60 \text{ km}}{\text{hr}} = \dfrac{60 \text{ km}}{\text{hr}} \cdot \dfrac{1 \text{ mi}}{1.6 \text{ km}} = 37.5 \text{ mi/hr}$

Exercise Set 9.1

1. $30 \text{ in.} = \dfrac{30 \text{ in.}}{1} \cdot \dfrac{1 \text{ ft}}{12 \text{ in.}} = 2.5 \text{ ft}$

2. $100 \text{ in.} = \dfrac{100 \text{ in.}}{1} \cdot \dfrac{1 \text{ ft}}{12 \text{ in.}} \approx 8.33 \text{ ft}$

3. $30 \text{ ft} = \dfrac{30 \text{ ft}}{1} \cdot \dfrac{12 \text{ in.}}{1 \text{ ft}} = 360 \text{ in.}$

4. $100 \text{ ft} = \dfrac{100 \text{ ft}}{1} \cdot \dfrac{12 \text{ in.}}{1 \text{ ft}} = 1200 \text{ in.}$

5. $6 \text{ in.} = \dfrac{6 \text{ in.}}{1} \cdot \dfrac{1 \text{ yd}}{36 \text{ in.}} \approx 0.17 \text{ yd}$

6. $21 \text{ in.} = \dfrac{21 \text{ in.}}{1} \cdot \dfrac{1 \text{ yd}}{36 \text{ in.}} \approx 0.58 \text{ yd}$

7. $6 \text{ yd} = \dfrac{6 \text{ yd}}{1} \cdot \dfrac{36 \text{ in.}}{1 \text{ yd}} = 216 \text{ in.}$

8. $21 \text{ yd} = \dfrac{21 \text{ yd}}{1} \cdot \dfrac{36 \text{ in.}}{1 \text{ yd}} = 756 \text{ in.}$

9. $6 \text{ yd} = \dfrac{6 \text{ yd}}{1} \cdot \dfrac{3 \text{ ft}}{1 \text{ yd}} = 18 \text{ ft}$

10. $12 \text{ yd} = \dfrac{12 \text{ yd}}{1} \cdot \dfrac{3 \text{ ft}}{1 \text{ yd}} = 36 \text{ ft}$

11. $6 \text{ ft} = \dfrac{6 \text{ ft}}{1} \cdot \dfrac{1 \text{ yd}}{3 \text{ ft}} = 2 \text{ yd}$

12. $12 \text{ ft} = \dfrac{12 \text{ ft}}{1} \cdot \dfrac{1 \text{ yd}}{3 \text{ ft}} = 4 \text{ yd}$

13. $23{,}760 \text{ ft} = \dfrac{23{,}760 \text{ ft}}{1} \cdot \dfrac{1 \text{ mi}}{5280 \text{ ft}} = 4.5 \text{ mi}$

14. $19{,}800 \text{ ft} = \dfrac{19{,}800 \text{ ft}}{1} \cdot \dfrac{1 \text{ mi}}{5280 \text{ ft}} = 3.75 \text{ mi}$

15. $0.75 \text{ mi} = \dfrac{0.75 \text{ mi}}{1} \cdot \dfrac{5280 \text{ ft}}{1 \text{ mi}} = 3960 \text{ ft}$

16. $0.25 \text{ mi} = \dfrac{0.25 \text{ mi}}{1} \cdot \dfrac{5280 \text{ ft}}{1 \text{ mi}} = 1320 \text{ ft}$

17. $5 \text{ m} = 500 \text{ cm}$

18. $8 \text{ dam} = 80 \text{ m}$

19. $16.3 \text{ hm} = 1630 \text{ m}$

20. $0.37 \text{ hm} = 37 \text{ m}$

21. $317.8 \text{ cm} = 0.03178 \text{ hm}$

22. $8.64 \text{ hm} = 86{,}400 \text{ cm}$

23. $0.023 \text{ mm} = 0.000023 \text{ m}$

24. $0.00037 \text{ km} = 37 \text{ cm}$

25. $2196 \text{ mm} = 21.96 \text{ dm}$

26. $71 \text{ dm} = 0.0071 \text{ km}$

27. $14 \text{ in.} = \dfrac{14 \text{ in.}}{1} \cdot \dfrac{2.54 \text{ cm}}{1 \text{ in.}} \approx 35.56 \text{ cm}$

28. $26 \text{ in.} = \dfrac{26 \text{ in.}}{1} \cdot \dfrac{2.54 \text{ cm}}{1 \text{ in.}} \approx 66.04 \text{ cm}$

29. $14 \text{ cm} = \dfrac{14 \text{ cm}}{1} \cdot \dfrac{1 \text{ in.}}{2.54 \text{ cm}} \approx 5.51 \text{ in.}$

30. $26 \text{ cm} = \dfrac{26 \text{ cm}}{1} \cdot \dfrac{1 \text{ in.}}{2.54 \text{ cm}} \approx 10.24 \text{ in.}$

31. $265 \text{ mi} = \dfrac{265 \text{ mi}}{1} \cdot \dfrac{1.6 \text{ km}}{1 \text{ mi}} \approx 424 \text{ km}$

32. $776 \text{ mi} = \dfrac{776 \text{ mi}}{1} \cdot \dfrac{1.6 \text{ km}}{1 \text{ mi}} \approx 1241.6 \text{ km}$

33. $265 \text{ km} = \dfrac{265 \text{ km}}{1} \cdot \dfrac{1 \text{ mi}}{1.6 \text{ km}} \approx 165.625 \text{ mi}$

34. $776 \text{ km} = \dfrac{776 \text{ km}}{1} \cdot \dfrac{1 \text{ mi}}{1.6 \text{ km}} \approx 485 \text{ mi}$

35. $12 \text{ m} = \dfrac{12 \text{ m}}{1} \cdot \dfrac{1 \text{ yd}}{0.9 \text{ m}} \approx 13.33 \text{ yd}$

36. $20 \text{ m} = \dfrac{20 \text{ m}}{1} \cdot \dfrac{1 \text{ yd}}{0.9 \text{ m}} \approx 22.22 \text{ yd}$

37. $14 \text{ dm} = 140 \text{ cm} = \dfrac{140 \text{ cm}}{1} \cdot \dfrac{1 \text{ in.}}{2.54 \text{ cm}} \approx 55.12 \text{ in.}$

38. $1.2 \text{ dam} = 1200 \text{ cm}$

$\phantom{1.2 \text{ dam}} = \dfrac{1200 \text{ cm}}{1} \cdot \dfrac{1 \text{ in.}}{2.54 \text{ cm}}$

$\phantom{1.2 \text{ dam}} \approx 472.44 \text{ in.}$

39. $160 \text{ in.} = \dfrac{160 \text{ in.}}{1} \cdot \dfrac{2.54 \text{ cm}}{1 \text{ in.}}$

$\phantom{160 \text{ in.}} \approx 406.4 \text{ cm}$

$\phantom{160 \text{ in.}} = 0.4064 \text{ dam}$

40. $180 \text{ in.} = \dfrac{180 \text{ in.}}{1} \cdot \dfrac{2.54 \text{ cm}}{1 \text{ in.}}$

$\phantom{180 \text{ in.}} \approx 457.2 \text{ cm}$

$\phantom{180 \text{ in.}} = 0.04572 \text{ hm}$

41. $5 \text{ ft} = \dfrac{5 \text{ ft}}{1} \cdot \dfrac{30.48 \text{ cm}}{1 \text{ ft}} \approx 152.4 \text{ cm} \approx 1.524 \text{ m}$

42. $8 \text{ ft} = \dfrac{8 \text{ ft}}{1} \cdot \dfrac{30.48 \text{ cm}}{1 \text{ ft}} \approx 243.84 \text{ cm} \approx 2.4384 \text{ m}$

43. $5 \text{ m} = 500 \text{ cm} = \dfrac{500 \text{ cm}}{1} \cdot \dfrac{1 \text{ ft}}{30.48 \text{ cm}} \approx 16.40 \text{ ft}$

44. $8 \text{ m} = 800 \text{ cm} = \dfrac{800 \text{ cm}}{1} \cdot \dfrac{1 \text{ ft}}{30.48 \text{ cm}} \approx 26.25 \text{ ft}$

45. $\dfrac{96 \text{ km}}{\text{hr}} = \dfrac{96 \text{ km}}{\text{hr}} \cdot \dfrac{1 \text{ mi}}{1.6 \text{ km}} \approx 60 \text{ mi/hr}$

46. $\dfrac{104 \text{ km}}{\text{hr}} = \dfrac{104 \text{ km}}{\text{hr}} \cdot \dfrac{1 \text{ mi}}{1.6 \text{ km}} \approx 65 \text{ mi/hr}$

47. $\dfrac{45 \text{ mi}}{\text{hr}} = \dfrac{45 \text{ mi}}{\text{hr}} \cdot \dfrac{1.6 \text{ km}}{1 \text{ mi}} \approx 72 \text{ km/hr}$

48. $\dfrac{50 \text{ mi}}{\text{hr}} = \dfrac{50 \text{ mi}}{\text{hr}} \cdot \dfrac{1.6 \text{ km}}{1 \text{ mi}} \approx 80 \text{ km/hr}$

49. $5 \text{ yd} = \dfrac{5 \text{ yd}}{1} \cdot \dfrac{36 \text{ in.}}{1 \text{ yd}} \cdot \dfrac{2.54 \text{ cm}}{1 \text{ in.}} \approx 457.2 \text{ cm}$

50. $8 \text{ yd} = \dfrac{8 \text{ yd}}{1} \cdot \dfrac{36 \text{ in.}}{1 \text{ yd}} \cdot \dfrac{2.54 \text{ cm}}{1 \text{ in.}} \approx 731.52 \text{ cm}$

51. $762 \text{ cm} = \dfrac{762 \text{ cm}}{1} \cdot \dfrac{1 \text{ in.}}{2.54 \text{ cm}} \cdot \dfrac{1 \text{ yd}}{36 \text{ in.}} \approx 8\dfrac{1}{3} \text{ yd}$

52. $1016 \text{ cm} = \dfrac{1016 \text{ cm}}{1} \cdot \dfrac{1 \text{ in.}}{2.54 \text{ cm}} \cdot \dfrac{1 \text{ yd}}{36 \text{ in.}} \approx 11\dfrac{1}{9} \text{ yd}$

53. $30 \text{ mi} = \dfrac{30 \text{ mi}}{1} \cdot \dfrac{5280 \text{ ft}}{1 \text{ mi}} \cdot \dfrac{12 \text{ in.}}{1 \text{ ft}} \cdot \dfrac{2.54 \text{ cm}}{1 \text{ in.}} \cdot \dfrac{1 \text{ m}}{100 \text{ cm}} \cdot \dfrac{1 \text{ km}}{1000 \text{ m}} \approx 48.28032 \text{ km}$

54. $50 \text{ mi} = \dfrac{50 \text{ mi}}{1} \cdot \dfrac{5280 \text{ ft}}{1 \text{ mi}} \cdot \dfrac{12 \text{ in.}}{1 \text{ ft}} \cdot \dfrac{2.54 \text{ cm}}{1 \text{ in.}} \cdot \dfrac{1 \text{ m}}{100 \text{ cm}} \cdot \dfrac{1 \text{ km}}{1000 \text{ m}} \approx 80.4672 \text{ km}$

55. $\dfrac{120 \text{ mi}}{\text{hr}} = \dfrac{120 \text{ mi}}{\text{hr}} \cdot \dfrac{5280 \text{ ft}}{1 \text{ mi}} \cdot \dfrac{1 \text{ hr}}{60 \text{ min.}} \cdot \dfrac{1 \text{ min.}}{60 \text{ sec}} = \dfrac{176 \text{ ft}}{1 \text{ sec}} = 176 \text{ ft/sec}$

56. $\dfrac{100 \text{ mi}}{\text{hr}} = \dfrac{100 \text{ mi}}{\text{hr}} \cdot \dfrac{5280 \text{ ft}}{1 \text{ mi}} \cdot \dfrac{1 \text{ hr}}{60 \text{ min.}} \cdot \dfrac{1 \text{ min.}}{60 \text{ sec}} = \dfrac{146\frac{2}{3} \text{ ft}}{1 \text{ sec}} = 146\dfrac{2}{3} \text{ ft/sec}$

57. meter

58. meter

59. millimeter

60. kilometer

61. meter

62. meter

63. millimeter

64. kilometer

65. millimeter

66. millimeter

67. b.

68. c.

69. a.

70. b.

71. c.

72. c.

73. a.

74. b.

75. $2 \cdot 4 \cdot 27 \text{ m} = 216 \text{ m} = 0.216 \text{ km}$

76. $6 \cdot 700 \text{ m} = 4200 \text{ m} = 4.2 \text{ km}$

77. $93 \text{ million miles} = \dfrac{93,000,000 \text{ mi}}{1} \cdot \dfrac{1.6 \text{ km}}{1 \text{ mi}}$

$= 148.8 \text{ million kilometers}$

78. $4690 \text{ km} = \dfrac{4690 \text{ km}}{1} \cdot \dfrac{1 \text{ mi}}{1.6 \text{ km}} = 2931.25 \text{ mi}$

79. Amazon: 6400 km

Nile: $4130 \text{ miles} = \dfrac{4130 \text{ mi}}{1} \cdot \dfrac{1.6 \text{ km}}{1 \text{ mi}} = 6608 \text{ km}$

Difference: $6608 - 6400 = 208$
The Nile is 208 km longer.

80. Mississippi: 6275 km

Yangtze: $3940 \text{ miles} = \dfrac{3940 \text{ mi}}{1} \cdot \dfrac{1.6 \text{ km}}{1 \text{ mi}} = 6304 \text{ km}$

Difference: $6304 - 6275 = 29$
The Yangtze is 29 km longer.

81. K2: 8611 meters

Everest: $29,035 \text{ feet} = \dfrac{29,035 \text{ ft}}{1} \cdot \dfrac{30.48 \text{ cm}}{1 \text{ ft}} \approx 884986.8 \text{ cm} = 8849.868 \text{ m} \approx 8850 \text{ m}$

Difference: $8850 - 8611 = 239$
Everest is 239 meters higher.

82. Lhotse: 8516 meters

Kangchenjunga: $28,170 \text{ feet} = \dfrac{28,170 \text{ ft}}{1} \cdot \dfrac{30.48 \text{ cm}}{1 \text{ ft}} \approx 858621.6 \text{ cm} = 8586.216 \text{ m} \approx 8586 \text{ m}$

Difference: $8586 - 8516 = 70$
Kangchenjunga is 70 meters higher.

83. Waialeale: 451 inches

Debundscha: $10,280 \text{ mm} = 1028 \text{ cm} = \dfrac{1028 \text{ cm}}{1} \cdot \dfrac{1 \text{ in.}}{2.54 \text{ cm}} \approx 405 \text{ in.}$

Difference: $451 - 405 = 46$
Waialeale has 46 inches greater average rainfall.

84. Cherrapunji: 498 inches

Mawsynram: $11,870 \text{ mm} = 1187 \text{ cm} = \dfrac{1187 \text{ cm}}{1} \cdot \dfrac{1 \text{ in.}}{2.54 \text{ cm}} \approx 467 \text{ in.}$

Difference: $498 - 467 = 31$
Cherrapunji has 31 inches greater average rainfall.

92. makes sense

93. makes sense

94. does not make sense; Explanations will vary. Sample explanation: Dimensional analysis is not necessary when changing units within the metric system.

95. does not make sense; Explanations will vary. Sample explanation: To introduce a unit of measure when using dimensional analysis, that unit of measure should be placed in the numerator.

96. 6000 cm = 6 dam

97. 900 m = 9 hm

98. 7000 dm = 7 hm

99. 11,000 mm = 11 m

100. 0.0002 km = 2 dm

Check Points 9.2

1. The area is 8 square units.

2. $\dfrac{36,457,549 \text{ people}}{158,633 \text{ square miles}} \approx 229.8$ people per sq. mile

3. a. $1.8 \text{ acres} = \dfrac{1.8 \text{ acres}}{1} \cdot \dfrac{0.4 \text{ ha}}{1 \text{ acre}} = 0.72 \text{ ha}$

b. $\dfrac{\$415,000}{0.72 \text{ ha}} = \$576,389$ per hectare

4. The volume is 9 cubic units.

5. $10,000 \text{ ft}^3 = \dfrac{10,000 \text{ ft}^3}{1} \cdot \dfrac{7.48 \text{ gal}}{1 \text{ ft}^3} = 74,800 \text{ gal}$

6. $220,000 \text{ cm}^3 = \dfrac{220,000 \text{ cm}^3}{1} \cdot \dfrac{1 \text{ L}}{1000 \text{ cm}^3} = 220 \text{ L}$

Exercise Set 9.2

1. $4 \cdot 4 = 16$ square units

2. $5 \cdot 3 = 15$ square units

3. 8 square units

4. 16 square units

5. $14 \text{ cm}^2 = \dfrac{14 \text{ cm}^2}{1} \cdot \dfrac{1 \text{ in.}^2}{6.5 \text{ cm}^2} \approx 2.15 \text{ in.}^2$

6. $20 \text{ m}^2 = \dfrac{20 \text{ m}^2}{1} \cdot \dfrac{1 \text{ ft}^2}{0.09 \text{ m}^2} \approx 222.22 \text{ ft}^2$

7. $30 \text{ m}^2 = \dfrac{30 \text{ m}^2}{1} \cdot \dfrac{1 \text{ yd}^2}{0.8 \text{ m}^2} = 37.5 \text{ yd}^2$

8. $14 \text{ mi}^2 = \dfrac{14 \text{ mi}^2}{1} \cdot \dfrac{2.6 \text{ km}^2}{1 \text{ mi}^2} = 36.4 \text{ km}^2$

9. $10.2 \text{ ha} = \dfrac{10.2 \text{ ha}}{1} \cdot \dfrac{1 \text{ acre}}{0.4 \text{ ha}} = 25.5 \text{ acres}$

10. $20.6 \text{ ha} = \dfrac{20.6 \text{ ha}}{1} \cdot \dfrac{1 \text{ acre}}{0.4 \text{ ha}} = 51.5 \text{ acres}$

11. $14 \text{ in.}^2 = \dfrac{14 \text{ in.}^2}{1} \cdot \dfrac{6.5 \text{ cm}^2}{1 \text{ in.}^2} = 91 \text{ cm}^2$

12. $20 \text{ in.}^2 = \dfrac{20 \text{ in.}^2}{1} \cdot \dfrac{6.5 \text{ cm}^2}{1 \text{ in.}^2} = 130 \text{ cm}^2$

13. $2 \cdot 4 \cdot 3 = 24$ cubic units

14. $4 \cdot 3 \cdot 5 = 60$ cubic units

15. $10,000 \text{ ft}^3 = \dfrac{10,000 \text{ ft}^3}{1} \cdot \dfrac{7.48 \text{ gal}}{1 \text{ ft}^3}$
$= 74,800 \text{ gal}$

16. $25,000 \text{ ft}^3 = \dfrac{25,000 \text{ ft}^3}{1} \cdot \dfrac{7.48 \text{ gal}}{1 \text{ ft}^3}$
$= 187,000 \text{ gal}$

17. $8 \text{ yd}^3 = \dfrac{8 \text{ yd}^3}{1} \cdot \dfrac{200 \text{ gal}}{1 \text{ yd}^3} = 1600 \text{ gal}$

18. $35 \text{ yd}^3 = \dfrac{35 \text{ yd}^3}{1} \cdot \dfrac{200 \text{ gal}}{1 \text{ yd}^3} = 7000 \text{ gal}$

19. $2079 \text{ in.}^3 = \dfrac{2079 \text{ in.}^3}{1} \cdot \dfrac{1 \text{ gal}}{231 \text{ in.}^3} = 9 \text{ gal}$

20. $6237 \text{ in.}^3 = \dfrac{6237 \text{ in.}^3}{1} \cdot \dfrac{1 \text{ gal}}{231 \text{ in.}^3} = 27 \text{ gal}$

21. $2700 \text{ gal} = \dfrac{2700 \text{ gal}}{1} \cdot \dfrac{1 \text{ yd}^3}{200 \text{ gal}} = 13.5 \text{ yd}^3$

22. $1496 \text{ gal} = \dfrac{1496 \text{ gal}}{1} \cdot \dfrac{1 \text{ ft}^3}{7.48 \text{ gal}} = 200 \text{ ft}^3$

23. $45,000 \text{ cm}^3 = \dfrac{45,000 \text{ cm}^3}{1} \cdot \dfrac{1 \text{ L}}{1000 \text{ cm}^3} = 45 \text{ L}$

24. $75,000 \text{ cm}^3 = \dfrac{75,000 \text{ cm}^3}{1} \cdot \dfrac{1 \text{ L}}{1000 \text{ cm}^3} = 75 \text{ L}$

25. $17 \text{ cm}^3 = \dfrac{17 \text{ cm}^3}{1} \cdot \dfrac{1 \text{ L}}{1000 \text{ cm}^3} \cdot \dfrac{1 \text{ mL}}{0.001 \text{ L}} = 17 \text{ mL}$

26. $19 \text{ cm}^3 = \dfrac{19 \text{ cm}^3}{1} \cdot \dfrac{1 \text{ L}}{1000 \text{ cm}^3} \cdot \dfrac{1 \text{ mL}}{0.001 \text{ L}} = 19 \text{ mL}$

27. $1.5 \text{ L} = \dfrac{1.5 \text{ L}}{1} \cdot \dfrac{1000 \text{ cm}^3}{1 \text{ L}} = 1500 \text{ cm}^3$

28. $4.5 \text{ L} = \dfrac{4.5 \text{ L}}{1} \cdot \dfrac{1000 \text{ cm}^3}{1 \text{ L}} = 4500 \text{ cm}^3$

29. $150 \text{ mL} = \dfrac{150 \text{ mL}}{1} \cdot \dfrac{0.001 \text{ L}}{\text{mL}} \cdot \dfrac{1000 \text{ cm}^3}{1 \text{ L}}$
$= 150 \text{ cm}^3$

30. $250 \text{ mL} = \dfrac{250 \text{ mL}}{1} \cdot \dfrac{0.001 \text{ L}}{\text{mL}} \cdot \dfrac{1000 \text{ cm}^3}{1 \text{ L}}$
$= 250 \text{ cm}^3$

31. $12 \text{ kL} = \dfrac{12 \text{ kL}}{1} \cdot \dfrac{1000 \text{ L}}{1 \text{ kL}} \cdot \dfrac{1 \text{ dm}^3}{1 \text{ L}}$
$= 12,000 \text{ dm}^3$

32. $16 \text{ kL} = \dfrac{12 \text{ kL}}{1} \cdot \dfrac{1000 \text{ L}}{1 \text{ kL}} \cdot \dfrac{1 \text{ dm}^3}{1 \text{ L}}$
$= 16,000 \text{ dm}^3$

33. a. Population density in 1900:
$\dfrac{75,994,575 \text{ people}}{2,969,834 \text{ square miles}}$
≈ 25.6 people per square mile

Population density in 2000:
$\dfrac{281,421,906 \text{ people}}{3,537,441 \text{ square miles}}$
≈ 79.6 people per square mile

b. $\dfrac{79.6 - 25.6}{25.6} \approx 2.109 = 210.9\%$ increase

34. a. Population density in 1800:
$\dfrac{5,308,483 \text{ people}}{864,746 \text{ square miles}}$
≈ 6.1 people per square mile

Population density in 2000:
$\dfrac{281,421,906 \text{ people}}{3,537,441 \text{ square miles}}$
≈ 79.6 people per square mile

b. $\dfrac{79.6 - 6.1}{6.1} \approx 12.049 = 1204.9\%$ increase

35. $\dfrac{131,669,275 \text{ people}}{2,977,128 \text{ square miles}}$
$= \dfrac{131,669,275 \text{ people}}{2,977,128 \text{ mi}^2} \cdot \dfrac{1 \text{ mi}^2}{2.6 \text{ km}^2}$
≈ 17.0 people per square kilometer

36. $\dfrac{226,545,805 \text{ people}}{3,539,289 \text{ square miles}}$
$= \dfrac{226,545,805 \text{ people}}{3,539,289 \text{ mi}^2} \cdot \dfrac{1 \text{ mi}^2}{2.6 \text{ km}^2}$
≈ 24.6 people per square kilometer

37. a. $8 \text{ ha} = \dfrac{8 \text{ ha}}{1} \cdot \dfrac{1 \text{ acre}}{0.4 \text{ ha}} = 20 \text{ acres}$

b. $\dfrac{\$250,000}{20 \text{ acres}} = \$12,500 \text{ per acre}$

38. a. $100 \text{ ha} = \dfrac{100 \text{ ha}}{1} \cdot \dfrac{1 \text{ acre}}{0.4 \text{ ha}} = 250 \text{ acres}$

b. $\dfrac{\$350,000}{250 \text{ acres}} = \$1400 \text{ per acre}$

39. square centimeters or square meters

40. square centimeters

41. square kilometers

42. square meters

43. b

44. b

45. b

46. b

47. $45,000 \text{ ft}^3 = \dfrac{45,000 \text{ ft}^3}{1} \cdot \dfrac{7.48 \text{ gal}}{1 \text{ ft}^3}$

$\qquad\qquad = 336,600 \text{ gal}$

48. $66,000 \text{ ft}^3 = \dfrac{66,000 \text{ ft}^3}{1} \cdot \dfrac{7.48 \text{ gal}}{1 \text{ ft}^3}$

$\qquad\qquad = 493,680 \text{ gal}$

49. $4000 \text{ cm}^3 = \dfrac{4000 \text{ cm}^3}{1} \cdot \dfrac{1 \text{ L}}{1000 \text{ cm}^3} = 4 \text{ L}$

50. $17,500 \text{ cm}^3 = \dfrac{17,500 \text{ cm}^3}{1} \cdot \dfrac{1 \text{ L}}{1000 \text{ cm}^3} = 17.5 \text{ L}$

51. Philippines: $300,000 \text{ km}^2$
Japan:

$145,900 \text{ mi}^2 = \dfrac{145,900 \text{ mi}^2}{1} \cdot \dfrac{2.6 \text{ km}^2}{1 \text{ mi}^2} \approx 379,000 \text{ km}^2$

Difference: $379,000 - 300,000 = 79,000$

Japan's area is approximately $79,000 \text{ km}^2$ greater.

52. Iceland: $103,000 \text{ km}^2$
Cuba:

$42,800 \text{ mi}^2 = \dfrac{42,800 \text{ mi}^2}{1} \cdot \dfrac{2.6 \text{ km}^2}{1 \text{ mi}^2} \approx 111,000 \text{ km}^2$

Difference: $111,000 - 103,000 = 8000$

Cuba's area is approximately 8000 km^2 greater.

53. Baffin Island: $194,574 \text{ mi}^2$
Sumatra:

$443,070 \text{ km}^2 = \dfrac{443,070 \text{ km}^2}{1} \cdot \dfrac{1 \text{ mi}^2}{2.6 \text{ km}^2} \approx 170,412 \text{ mi}^2$

Difference: $194,574 - 170,412 = 24,162$

Sumatra's area is approximately $24,162 \text{ mi}^2$ greater.

54. Honshu: $87,805 \text{ mi}^2$
Victoria Island:

$217,300 \text{ km}^2 = \dfrac{217,300 \text{ km}^2}{1} \cdot \dfrac{1 \text{ mi}^2}{2.6 \text{ km}^2} \approx 83,577 \text{ mi}^2$

Difference: $87,805 - 83,577 = 4228$

Honshu's area is approximately 4228 mi^2 greater.

61. does not make sense; Explanations will vary. Sample explanation: The capacity unit must be a measure of volume. Meters measure length.

62. does not make sense; Explanations will vary. Sample explanation: Population density can be measured as people per *square mile*, but not as people per *mile*.

63. makes sense

64. makes sense

65. $\dfrac{46,690 \text{ people}}{1000 \text{ ha}}$

$\approx \dfrac{46,690 \text{ people}}{1000 \text{ ha}} \cdot \dfrac{0.4 \text{ ha}}{1 \text{ acre}} \cdot \dfrac{640 \text{ acre}}{1 \text{ square mile}}$

$\approx 11952.64 \text{ people per square mile}$

66. $\dfrac{1,768,331 \text{ people}}{x} = 22.9 \text{ people per square mile}$

$\qquad x = \dfrac{1,768,331 \text{ people}}{22.9 \text{ people per square mile}}$

$\qquad x \approx 77,200 \text{ square miles}$

67. Answers will vary.

68. You must consider how the population is distributed throughout the state. "Elbow room" can vary from region to region.

69. Approximately 6.5 liters. 6.5 mL is only a little more than a teaspoon and 6.5 kL is thousands of gallons.

70. Approximately 1 cm^3. 1 mm^3 is about the size of a pencil tip and 1 dm^3 is bigger than a baseball.

Check Points 9.3

1. a. $4.2 \text{ dg} = 420 \text{ mg}$

   b. $620 \text{ cg} = 6.2 \text{ g}$

2. $0.145 \text{ m}^3 = \dfrac{0.145 \text{ m}^3}{1} \cdot \dfrac{1000 \text{ kg}}{1 \text{ m}^3} = 145 \text{ kg}$

The water weighs 145 kg.

3. a. $186 \text{ lb} = \dfrac{186 \text{ lb}}{1} \cdot \dfrac{0.45 \text{ kg}}{1 \text{ lb}} = 83.7 \text{ kg}$

   b. $83.7 \times 1.2 \text{ mg} = 100.44 \text{ mg}$ dose

4. $F = \dfrac{9}{5} \cdot 50 + 32 = 122$

$50°C = 122°F$

5. $C = \dfrac{5}{9}(59 - 32) = 15$

$59°F = 15°C$

Exercise Set 9.3

1. 7.4 dg = 740 mg

2. 6.9 dg = 690 mg

3. 870 mg = 0.87 g

4. 640 mg = 0.64 g

5. 8 g = 800 cg

6. 7 g = 700 cg

7. 18.6 kg = 18,600 g

8. 0.37 kg = 370 g

9. 0.018 mg = 0.000018 g

10. 0.029 mg = 0.000029 g

11. $0.05 \text{ m}^3 = \dfrac{0.05 \text{ m}^3}{1} \cdot \dfrac{1000 \text{ kg}}{1 \text{ m}^3} = 50 \text{ kg}$

12. $0.02 \text{ m}^3 = \dfrac{0.02 \text{ m}^3}{1} \cdot \dfrac{1000 \text{ kg}}{1 \text{ m}^3} = 20 \text{ kg}$

13. $4.2 \text{ kg} = \dfrac{4.2 \text{ kg}}{1} \cdot \dfrac{1000 \text{ cm}^3}{1 \text{ kg}} = 4200 \text{ cm}^3$

14. $5.8 \text{ kg} = \dfrac{5.8 \text{ kg}}{1} \cdot \dfrac{1000 \text{ cm}^3}{1 \text{ kg}} = 5800 \text{ cm}^3$

15. $1100 \text{ m}^3 = 1100 \text{ t}$

16. $1500 \text{ t} = 1500 \text{ m}^3$

17. $0.04 \text{ kL} = \dfrac{0.04 \text{ kL}}{1} \cdot \dfrac{1000 \text{ kg}}{1 \text{ kL}} \cdot \dfrac{1000 \text{ g}}{1 \text{ kg}} = 40,000 \text{ g}$

18. $0.03 \text{ kL} = \dfrac{0.03 \text{ kL}}{1} \cdot \dfrac{1000 \text{ kg}}{1 \text{ kL}} \cdot \dfrac{1000 \text{ g}}{1 \text{ kg}} = 30,000 \text{ g}$

19. $36 \text{ oz} = \dfrac{36 \text{ oz}}{1} \cdot \dfrac{1 \text{ lb}}{16 \text{ oz}} = 2.25 \text{ lb}$

20. $26 \text{ oz} = \dfrac{26 \text{ oz}}{1} \cdot \dfrac{1 \text{ lb}}{16 \text{ oz}} \approx 1.625 \text{ lb}$

21. $36 \text{ oz} = \dfrac{36 \text{ oz}}{1} \cdot \dfrac{28 \text{ g}}{1 \text{ oz}} = 1008 \text{ g}$

22. $26 \text{ oz} = \dfrac{26 \text{ oz}}{1} \cdot \dfrac{28 \text{ g}}{1 \text{ oz}} = 728 \text{ g}$

23. $540 \text{ lb} = \dfrac{540 \text{ lb}}{1} \cdot \dfrac{0.45 \text{ kg}}{1 \text{ lb}} = 243 \text{ kg}$

24. $220 \text{ lb} = \dfrac{220 \text{ lb}}{1} \cdot \dfrac{0.45 \text{ kg}}{1 \text{ lb}} = 99 \text{ kg}$

25. $80 \text{ lb} = \dfrac{80 \text{ lb}}{1} \cdot \dfrac{0.45 \text{ kg}}{1 \text{ lb}} \cdot \dfrac{1000 \text{ g}}{1 \text{ kg}} = 36,000 \text{ g}$

or $80 \text{ lb} = \dfrac{80 \text{ lb}}{1} \cdot \dfrac{16 \text{ oz}}{1 \text{ lb}} \cdot \dfrac{28 \text{ g}}{1 \text{ oz}} = 35,840 \text{ g}$

26. $150 \text{ lb} = \dfrac{150 \text{ lb}}{1} \cdot \dfrac{0.45 \text{ kg}}{1 \text{ lb}} \cdot \dfrac{1000 \text{ g}}{1 \text{ kg}} = 67,500 \text{ g}$

or $150 \text{ lb} = \dfrac{150 \text{ lb}}{1} \cdot \dfrac{16 \text{ oz}}{1 \text{ lb}} \cdot \dfrac{28 \text{ g}}{1 \text{ oz}} = 67,200 \text{ g}$

27. $540 \text{ kg} = \dfrac{540 \text{ kg}}{1} \cdot \dfrac{1 \text{ lb}}{0.45 \text{ kg}} = 1200 \text{ lb}$

28. $220 \text{ kg} = \dfrac{220 \text{ kg}}{1} \cdot \dfrac{1 \text{ lb}}{0.45 \text{ kg}} \approx 488.89 \text{ lb}$

29. $200 \text{ t} = \dfrac{200 \text{ t}}{1} \cdot \dfrac{1 \text{ T}}{0.9 \text{ t}} \approx 222.22 \text{ T}$

30. $100 \text{ t} = \dfrac{100 \text{ t}}{1} \cdot \dfrac{1 \text{ T}}{0.9 \text{ t}} \approx 111.11 \text{ T}$

31. $10°$ C

$$F = \frac{9}{5} \cdot 10 + 32$$

$10°$ C $= 50°$ F

32. $20°$C

$$F = \frac{9}{5} \cdot 20 + 32$$

$20°$ C$= 68°$F

33. $35°$ C

$$F = \frac{9}{5} \cdot 35 + 32$$

$35°$C $= 95°$F

34. $45°$C

$$F = \frac{9}{5} \cdot 45 + 32$$

$45°$ C $= 113°$F

35. $57°$ C

$$F = \frac{9}{5} \cdot 57 + 32$$

$57°$ C $= 134.6°$F

36. $98°$C

$$F = \frac{9}{5} \cdot 98 + 32$$

$98°$ C $= 208.4°$F

37. $-5°$ C

$$F = \frac{9}{5}(-5) + 32$$

$-5°$C $= 23°$F

38. $-10°$C

$$F = \frac{9}{5}(-10) + 32$$

$-10°$ C $= 14°$F

39. $68°$ F

$$C = \frac{5}{9}(68 - 32)$$

$68°$F $= 20°$C

40. $86°$F

$$C = \frac{5}{9}(86 - 32)$$

$86°$ F $= 30°$C

41. $41°$ F

$$C = \frac{5}{9}(41 - 32)$$

$41°$F $= 5°$C

42. $50°$ F

$$C = \frac{5}{9}(50 - 32)$$

$50°$ F $= 10°$C

43. $72°$ F

$$C = \frac{5}{9}(72 - 32)$$

$72°$F $\approx 22.2°$C

44. $90°$ F

$$C = \frac{5}{9}(90 - 32)$$

$90°$ F $\approx 32.2°$C

45. $23°$ F

$$C = \frac{5}{9}(23 - 32)$$

$23°$F $= -5°$C

46. $14°$ F

$$C = \frac{5}{9}(14 - 32)$$

$14°$ F $= -10°$C

47. $350°$ F

$$C = \frac{5}{9}(350 - 32)$$

$350°$F $\approx 176.7°$C

48. $475°$ F

$$C = \frac{5}{9}(475 - 32)$$

$475°$ F $\approx 246.1°$C

49. $-22°$ F

$$C = \frac{5}{9}(-22 - 32)$$

$-22°$F $= -30°$C

50. $-31°$ F

$$C = \frac{5}{9}(-31 - 32)$$

$-31°$ F $= -35°$C

51. a. $m = \dfrac{68-32}{20-0} = \dfrac{36}{20} = \dfrac{9}{5}$

This means that the Fahrenheit temperature increases by $\dfrac{9^{\circ}}{5}$ for each 1° change in Celsius temperature.

b. $y = mx + b$

$F = mC + b$

$F = \dfrac{9}{5}C + 32$

52. $F = \dfrac{9}{5}C + 32$

$F - 32 = \dfrac{9}{5}C$

$\dfrac{5}{9}(F-32) = \dfrac{5}{9} \cdot \dfrac{9}{5}C$

$\dfrac{5}{9}(F-32) = C$

$C = \dfrac{5}{9}(F-32)$

53. milligram

54. kilogram

55. gram

56. tonne

57. kilogram

58. gram

59. kilogram

60. d

61. b

62. a

63. a

64. b

65. c

66. b

67. $720\ g = 0.720\ kg$
$14 - 0.720 = 13.28\ kg$

77. a

68. $5\ g = 0.005\ kg$

$\dfrac{4\ kg}{0.005\ kg\ per\ nickel} = 800\ nickels$

69. $86\ g = \dfrac{86\ \cancel{g}}{1} \cdot \dfrac{1\ oz}{28\ \cancel{g}} \approx 3.07\ oz$

The cost will be for 4 ounces.
Cost: $44\cancel{c} + 3(24\cancel{c}) = 116\cancel{c} = \$1.16$

70. Answers will vary.

71. $\dfrac{\$3.15}{3\ kg} = \$1.05$ per kg for economy size

$720\ g = 0.72\ kg$

$\dfrac{\$.60}{0.72\ kg} = \$.83$ per kg for regular size

It is more economical to purchase the regular size.

72. $200\ lb = \dfrac{200\ \cancel{lb}}{1} \cdot \dfrac{0.45\ kg}{1\ \cancel{lb}} = 90\ kg$

$90 \times 20\ mg = 1800\ mg$ dose

73. $80\ lb = \dfrac{80\ \cancel{lb}}{1} \cdot \dfrac{0.45\ kg}{1\ \cancel{lb}} = 36\ kg$

$36 \times 2.5\ mg = 90\ mg$ dose

74. a. $\dfrac{1.87\ g}{tsp} = \dfrac{1.87\ g}{\cancel{tsp}} \cdot \dfrac{2\ \cancel{tsp}}{1\ dose} = 3.74\ g/dose$

b. $\dfrac{1.87\ g}{tsp}$

$= \dfrac{1.87\ g}{\cancel{tsp}} \cdot \dfrac{\cancel{tsp}}{5\ \cancel{ml}} \cdot \dfrac{30\ \cancel{ml}}{1\ \cancel{oz}} \cdot \dfrac{4\ \cancel{oz}}{1\ bottle}$

$= 44.88\ g/bottle$

75. a. $\dfrac{21.5\ mg}{tsp} = \dfrac{21.5\ mg}{\cancel{tsp}} \cdot \dfrac{2\ \cancel{tsp}}{1\ dose} = 43\ mg/dose$

b. $\dfrac{21.5\ mg}{tsp}$

$= \dfrac{21.5\ mg}{\cancel{tsp}} \cdot \dfrac{\cancel{tsp}}{5\ \cancel{ml}} \cdot \dfrac{30\ \cancel{ml}}{1\ \cancel{oz}} \cdot \dfrac{4\ \cancel{oz}}{1\ bottle}$

$= 516\ mg/bottle$

76. c

78. a

79. c

80. Assab: 86.8°F

Dalol: $F = \dfrac{9}{5}C + 32$

$\qquad = \dfrac{9}{5}(34.6) + 32$

$\qquad \approx 94.3°F$

Difference: $94.3 - 86.8 = 7.5$

Dalol's average temperature is 7.5°F hotter.

81. Berbera: 86.8°F

Néma: $F = \dfrac{9}{5}C + 32$

$\qquad = \dfrac{9}{5}(30.3) + 32$

$\qquad \approx 86.5°F$

Difference: $86.8 - 86.5 = 0.3$

Néma's average temperature is 0.3°F hotter.

82. Plateau: −56.7°C

Amundsen-Scott: $C = \dfrac{5}{9}(F - 32)$

$\qquad = \dfrac{5}{9}(-56.2 - 32)$

$\qquad = -49.0°F$

Difference: $-49.0 - (-56.7) = 7.7$

Plateau's average temperature is 7.7°C colder.

83. Eismitte: −29.2°C

Resolute: $C = \dfrac{5}{9}(F - 32)$

$\qquad = \dfrac{5}{9}(-11.6 - 32)$

$\qquad \approx -24.2°F$

Difference: $-24.2 - (-29.2) = 5$

Eismitte's average temperature is 5°C colder.

90. does not make sense; Explanations will vary. Sample explanation: 250 km is equivalent to about 550 pounds.

91. does not make sense; Explanations will vary. Sample explanation: 500 mg is 0.5 g.

92. does not make sense; Explanations will vary. Sample explanation: The English system does not easily show these relationships.

93. makes sense

94. false; $2000 \text{ g} = 2 \text{ kg} = \dfrac{2 \text{ kg}}{1} \cdot \dfrac{1 \text{ lb}}{0.45 \text{ kg}} \approx 4.4 \text{ lb}$

95. false; $100 \text{ mg} = 0.1 \text{ g} = \dfrac{0.1 \text{ g}}{1} \cdot \dfrac{1 \text{ oz}}{28 \text{ g}} \approx 0.0036 \text{ oz}$

96. false; $50 \text{ g} = \dfrac{50 \text{ g}}{1} \cdot \dfrac{1 \text{ oz}}{28 \text{ g}} \approx 1.8 \text{ oz}$

97. true, $4 \text{ kg} = \dfrac{4 \text{ kg}}{1} \cdot \dfrac{1 \text{ lb}}{0.45 \text{ kg}} \approx 8.9 \text{ lb}$

98. false; $\dfrac{3¢}{1 \text{ g}} \cdot \dfrac{1000 \text{ g}}{1 \text{ kg}} \cdot \dfrac{0.45 \text{ kg}}{1 \text{ lb}} = 1350¢ \text{ per pound}$

99. true

100. false; $2 \text{ kg} = \dfrac{2 \text{ kg}}{1} \cdot \dfrac{1 \text{ lb}}{0.45 \text{ kg}} \approx 4.4 \text{ lb}$

101. false; $350 \text{ kg} = \dfrac{350 \text{ kg}}{1} \cdot \dfrac{1 \text{ lb}}{0.45 \text{ kg}} \approx 778 \text{ lb}$

Chapter 9 Review Exercises

1. $69 \text{ in.} = \dfrac{69 \text{ in.}}{1} \cdot \dfrac{1 \text{ ft}}{12 \text{ in.}} = 5.75 \text{ ft}$

2. $9 \text{ in.} = \dfrac{9 \text{ in.}}{1} \cdot \dfrac{1 \text{ yd}}{36 \text{ in.}} = 0.25 \text{ yd}$

3. $21 \text{ ft} = \dfrac{21 \text{ ft}}{1} \cdot \dfrac{1 \text{ yd}}{3 \text{ ft}} = 7 \text{ yd}$

4. $13{,}200 \text{ ft} = \dfrac{13{,}200 \text{ ft}}{1} \cdot \dfrac{1 \text{ mi}}{5280 \text{ ft}} = 2.5 \text{ mi}$

5. $22.8 \text{ m} = 2280 \text{ cm}$

6. $7 \text{ dam} = 70 \text{ m}$

7. $19.2 \text{ hm} = 1920 \text{ m}$

8. $144 \text{ cm} = 0.0144 \text{ hm}$

9. $0.5 \text{ mm} = 0.0005 \text{ m}$

10. 18 cm = 180 mm

11. 23 in. = $\dfrac{23\,\text{in.}}{1} \cdot \dfrac{2.54\,\text{cm}}{1\,\text{in.}} = 58.42$ cm

12. 19 cm = $\dfrac{19\,\text{cm}}{1} \cdot \dfrac{1\,\text{in.}}{2.54\,\text{cm}} \approx 7.48$ in.

13. 330 mi = $\dfrac{330\,\text{mi}}{1} \cdot \dfrac{1.6\,\text{km}}{1\,\text{mi}} = 528$ km

14. 600 km = $\dfrac{600\,\text{km}}{1} \cdot \dfrac{1\,\text{mi}}{1.6\,\text{km}} = 375$ mi

15. 14 m = $\dfrac{14\,\text{m}}{1} \cdot \dfrac{1\,\text{yd}}{0.9\,\text{m}} \approx 15.56$ yd

16. 12 m = $\dfrac{12\,\text{m}}{1} \cdot \dfrac{100\,\text{cm}}{1\,\text{m}} \cdot \dfrac{1\,\text{in.}}{2.54\,\text{cm}} \cdot \dfrac{1\,\text{ft}}{12\,\text{in.}} = 39.37$ ft

17. 45 km per hour = $\dfrac{45\,\text{km}}{1\,\text{hr}} \cdot \dfrac{1\,\text{mi}}{1.6\,\text{km}}$
≈ 28.13 miles/hour

18. 60 mi per hour = $\dfrac{60\,\text{mi}}{1\,\text{hr}} \cdot \dfrac{1.6\,\text{km}}{1\,\text{mi}}$
$= 96$ km/hr

19. 0.024 km; 24,000 cm; 2400 m

20. $6 \cdot 800$ m = 4800 m = 4.8 km

21. $3 \cdot 8 = 24$ square units

22. $\dfrac{298,923,319\ \text{people}}{3,537,441\ \text{square miles}}$
≈ 84.5 people per square mile
In April 2006 the U.S. had a population density of 84.5 people per square mile.

23. 7.2 ha = $\dfrac{7.2\,\text{ha}}{1} \cdot \dfrac{1\,\text{acre}}{0.4\,\text{ha}} = 18$ acres

24. 30 m^2 = $\dfrac{30\,\text{m}^2}{1} \cdot \dfrac{1\,\text{ft}^2}{0.09\,\text{m}^2} \approx 333.33$ ft^2

25. 12 mi^2 = $\dfrac{12\,\text{mi}^2}{1} \cdot \dfrac{2.6\,\text{km}^2}{1\,\text{mi}^2} = 31.2$ km^2

26. a

27. $2 \cdot 4 \cdot 3 = 24$ cubic units

28. 33,600 cubic feet = $\dfrac{33,600\,\text{ft}^3}{1} \cdot \dfrac{7.48\,\text{gal}}{1\,\text{ft}^3}$
$= 251,328$ gal

29. 76,000 cm^3 = $\dfrac{76,000\,\text{cm}^3}{1} \cdot \dfrac{1\,\text{L}}{1000\,\text{cm}^3} = 76$ L

30. c

31. There are $3 \times 3 = 9$ square feet in a square yard.

32. "Cubic miles" is a unit of volume, not area.

33. 12.4 dg = 1240 mg

34. 12 g = 1200 cg

35. 0.012 mg = 0.000012 g

36. 450 mg = 0.00045 kg

37. 50 kg = $\dfrac{50\,\text{kg}}{1} \cdot \dfrac{1000\,\text{cm}^3}{1\,\text{kg}} = 50,000$ cm^3

38. 4 kL = $\dfrac{4\,\text{kL}}{1} \cdot \dfrac{1000\,\text{kg}}{1\,\text{kL}} \cdot \dfrac{1\,\text{dm}^3}{1\,\text{kg}} = 4000$ dm^3
4000 dm^3 = $\dfrac{4000\,\text{dm}^3}{1} \cdot \dfrac{1000\,\text{g}}{1\,\text{dm}^3} = 4,000,000$ g

39. 210 lb $\approx \dfrac{210\,\text{lb}}{1} \cdot \dfrac{0.45\,\text{kg}}{1\,\text{lb}} \approx 94.5$ kg

40. 392 g $\approx \dfrac{392\,\text{g}}{1} \cdot \dfrac{1\,\text{oz}}{28\,\text{g}} \approx 14$ oz

41. Kilograms; Answers will vary.

42. 36 oz = $\dfrac{36\,\text{oz}}{1} \cdot \dfrac{1\,\text{lb}}{16\,\text{oz}} = 2.25$ lb

43. a

44. c

45. $F = \dfrac{9}{5} \cdot 15 + 32 = 59° \text{ F}$

46. $F = \dfrac{9}{5} \cdot 100 + 32 = 212° \text{ F}$

47. $F = \dfrac{9}{5} \cdot 5 + 32 = 41°\text{F}$

48. $F = \dfrac{9}{5} \cdot 0 + 32 = 32° \text{ F}$

49. $-F = \dfrac{9}{5}(-25) + 32 = -13° \text{ F}$

50. $C = \dfrac{5}{9}(59 - 32) = 15° \text{ C}$

51. $C = \dfrac{5}{9}(41 - 32) = 5°\text{C}$

52. $C = \dfrac{5}{9}(212 - 32) = 100° \text{ C}$

53. $C = \dfrac{5}{9}(98.6 - 32) = 37° \text{ C}$

54. $C = \dfrac{5}{9}(0 - 32) \approx -17.8°\text{C}$

55. $C = \dfrac{5}{9}(14 - 32) = -10° \text{ C}$

56. A decrease of $15°C$ is more than a decrease of $15°F$; Explanations will vary.

Chapter 9 Test

1. 807 mm = 0.00807 hm

2. $635 \text{ cm} = \dfrac{635 \text{ cm}}{1} \cdot \dfrac{1 \text{ in.}}{2.54 \text{ cm}} = 250 \text{ in.}$

3. $8 \cdot 600 \text{ m} = 4800 \text{ m} = 4.8 \text{ km}$

4. mm

5. cm

6. km

7. $80 \text{ miles per hour} = \dfrac{80 \text{ mi}}{1 \text{ hr}} \cdot \dfrac{1.6 \text{ km}}{1 \text{ mi}}$
$= 128 \text{ km/hr}$

8. $1 \text{ yd}^2 = (3 \text{ ft})(3 \text{ ft}) = 9 \text{ ft}^2$
A square yard is 9 times greater than a square foot.

9. $\dfrac{40,491,051 \text{ people}}{194,896 \text{ square miles}}$
$\approx 207.8 \text{ people per square mile}$
In Spain, there is an average of 207.8 people for each square mile.

10. $18 \text{ ha} = \dfrac{18 \text{ ha}}{1} \cdot \dfrac{1 \text{ acre}}{0.4 \text{ ha}} = 45 \text{ acres}$

11. b

12. Answers will vary.
$1 \text{ m}^3 = (10 \text{ dm})(10 \text{ dm})(10 \text{ dm}) = 1000 \text{ dm}^3$
A cubic meter is 1000 times greater than a cubic decimeter.

13. $10,000 \text{ ft}^3 = \dfrac{10,000 \text{ ft}^3}{1} \cdot \dfrac{7.48 \text{ gal}}{1 \text{ ft}^3}$
$= 74,800 \text{ gal}$

14. b

15. 137 g = 0.137 kg

16. $90 \text{ lb} = \dfrac{90 \text{ lb}}{1} \cdot \dfrac{0.45 \text{ kg}}{1 \text{ lb}} = 40.5 \text{ kg}$

17. kg

18. mg

19. $F = \dfrac{9}{5} \cdot 30 + 32 = 86° \text{ F}$

20. $C = \dfrac{5}{9}(176 - 32) = 80°\text{C}$

21. d

Check Points 10.1

1. Hand moves $\dfrac{1}{12}$ of a rotation

   $\dfrac{1}{12} \cdot 360° = 30°$

2. $90° - 19° = 71°$

3. $m\angle DBC + m\angle ABD = 180°$

   $x + (x + 88°) = 180°$

   $2x + 88° = 180°$

   $2x = 92°$

   $x = 46°$

   Thus, $m\angle DBC = 46°$ and $m\angle ABD = 134°$

4. $m\angle 1 = 57°$

   $m\angle 2 = 180° - 57° = 123°$

   $m\angle 3 = m\angle 2 = 123°$

5. $m\angle 1 = m\angle 8 = 29°$

   $m\angle 5 = m\angle 8 = 29°$

   $m\angle 2 = m\angle 8 = 29°$

   $m\angle 6 = 180° - m\angle 8 = 180° - 29° = 151°$

   $m\angle 7 = m\angle 6 = 151°$

   $m\angle 3 = m\angle 7 = 151°$

   $m\angle 4 = m\angle 3 = 151°$

Exercise Set 10.1

1. Hand moves $\dfrac{5}{12}$ of a rotation

   $\dfrac{5}{12} \cdot 360° = 150°$

2. Hand moves $r = \dfrac{1}{2} \cdot 6$ yd $= 3$ yd   of a rotation

   $V = \dfrac{1}{3}\pi(3 \text{ yd})^2 \cdot 5 \text{ yd}$

   $\approx 47 \text{ yd}^3$

   $\dfrac{1}{3} \cdot 360° = 120°$

3. Hand moves $\dfrac{4-1}{12} = \dfrac{3}{12} = \dfrac{1}{4}$ of a rotation

   $\dfrac{1}{4} \cdot 360° = 90°$

4. Hand moves $\dfrac{7-1}{12} = \dfrac{6}{12} = \dfrac{1}{2}$ of a rotation

   $\dfrac{1}{2} \cdot 360° = 180°$

5. $20°$ is acute.

6. $130°$ is obtuse.

7. $160°$ is obtuse.

8. $50°$ is acute.

9. $180°$ is straight.

10. $90°$ is right.

11. $90° - 25° = 65°$

12. $90° - 32° = 58°$

13. $180° - 34° = 146°$

14. $180° - 13° = 167°$

15. Complement:
    $90° - 48° = 42°$
    Supplement:
    $180° - 48° = 132°$

16. Complement:
    $90° - 52° = 38°$
    Supplement:
    $180° - 52° = 128°$

17. Complement:
    $90° - 89° = 1°$
    Supplement:
    $180° - 89° = 91°$

18. Complement:
    $90° - 1° = 89°$
    Supplement:
    $180° - 1° = 179°$

19. Complement:
$90° - 37.4° = 52.6°$
Supplement:
$180° - 37.4° = 142.6°$

20. Complement:
$90° - 15\dfrac{1}{3}° = 74\dfrac{2}{3}°$
Supplement:
$180° - 15\dfrac{1}{3}° = 164\dfrac{2}{3}°$

21. Let x = the measure of the angle's complement.
Then $x + 12°$ represents the angle.
$$x + (x + 12°) = 90°$$
$$2x + 12° = 90°$$
$$2x = 78°$$
$$x = 39°$$
$$x + 12° = 51°$$
The complements are $39°$ and $51°$.

22. Let x = the measure of the angle's complement.
Then $x + 56°$ represents the angle.
$$x + (x + 56°) = 90°$$
$$2x + 56° = 90°$$
$$2x = 34°$$
$$x = 17°$$
$$x + 56° = 73°$$
The complements are $17°$ and $73°$.

23. Let x = the measure of the angle's supplement.
Then $3x$ represents the angle.
$$x + 3x = 180°$$
$$4x = 180°$$
$$x = 45°$$
$$3x = 135°$$
The supplements are $45°$ and $135°$.

24. Let x = the measure of the angle's supplement.
Then $2x + 81°$ represents the angle.
$$x + (2x + 81°) = 180°$$
$$3x + 81° = 180°$$
$$3x = 99°$$
$$x = 33°$$
$$2x + 81° = 147°$$
The supplements are $33°$ and $147°$

25. $m\angle 1 = 180° - 72° = 108°$
$m\angle 2 = 72°$
$m\angle 3 = m\angle 1 = 108°$

26. $m\angle 1 = 180° - 133° = 47°$
$m\angle 2 = 133°$
$m\angle 3 = m\angle 1 = 47°$

27. $m\angle 1 = 90° - 40° = 50°$
$m\angle 2 = 90°$
$m\angle 3 = m\angle 1 = 50°$

28. $m\angle 1 = 90° - 30° = 60°$
$m\angle 2 = 90°$
$m\angle 3 = m\angle 1 = 60°$

29. $m\angle 1 = 180° - 112° = 68°$
$m\angle 2 = m\angle 1 = 68°$
$m\angle 3 = 112°$
$m\angle 4 = 112°$
$m\angle 5 = m\angle 1 = 68°$
$m\angle 6 = m\angle 2 = 68°$
$m\angle 7 = m\angle 3 = 112°$

30. $m\angle 1 = 180° - 54° = 126°$
$m\angle 2 = 54°$
$m\angle 3 = m\angle 1 = 126°$
$m\angle 4 = m\angle 1 = 126°$
$m\angle 5 = 54°$
$m\angle 6 = m\angle 2 = 54°$
$m\angle 7 = m\angle 3 = 126°$

31. $m\angle 1 = 38°$
$m\angle 2 = 90° - 38° = 52°$
$m\angle 3 = 180° - 38° = 142°$

32. $m\angle 2 = 90° - 40° = 50°$
$m\angle 1 = 180° - 40° - 50° = 90°$
$m\angle 3 = m\angle 1 + 40° = 90° + 40° = 130°$

33. $m\angle 1 = 65°$
$m\angle 2 = 180° - m\angle 1 - 59°$
$\qquad = 180° - 65° - 59°$
$\qquad = 56°$
$m\angle 3 = m\angle 1 + 59°$
$\qquad = 65° + 59°$
$\qquad = 124°$

34. $m\angle 1 = 63°$
$m\angle 1 + m\angle 2 + 60° = 180°$
$63° + m\angle 2 + 60° = 180°$
$\qquad m\angle 2 + 123° = 180°$
$\qquad\qquad m\angle 2 = 57°$
$m\angle 3 = m\angle 1 + m\angle 2$
$m\angle 3 = 63° + 57°$
$m\angle 3 = 120°$

35. false; Changes to make the statement true will vary. A sample change is: $m\angle 2 = 53°$

36. false; Changes to make the statement true will vary. A sample change is: $m\angle 1 \neq m\angle 2$

37. true

38. false; Changes to make the statement true will vary. A sample change is: $m\angle 3 \neq m\angle 4$

39. false; Changes to make the statement true will vary. A sample change is: $m\angle 1 = 108°$

40. true

41. false; Changes to make the statement true will vary. A sample change is: $m\angle 2 = 108°$

42. false; Changes to make the statement true will vary. A sample change is: $m\angle 3 = 52°$

43. The two angles are complementary.
$$\left(2x+50°\right)+\left(4x+10°\right)=90°$$
$$6x+60° = 90°$$
$$6x = 30°$$
$$x = 5°$$
Angle 1: $2x+50° = 2(5°)+50° = 60°$
Angle 2: $4x+10° = 4(5°)+10° = 30°$

44. The two angles are supplementary.
$$\left(3x+134°\right)+\left(6x+10°\right)=180°$$
$$9x+144° = 180°$$
$$9x = 36°$$
$$x = 4°$$
Angle 1: $3x+134° = 3(4°)+134° = 146°$
Angle 2: $6x+10° = 6(4°)+10° = 34°$

45. The two angles are equal.
$$11x-20° = 7x+28°$$
$$4x = 48°$$
$$x = 12°$$
Angle 1: $11x-20° = 11(12°)-20° = 112°$
Angle 2: $7x+28° = 7(12°)+28° = 112°$

46. The two angles are equal.
$$12x-3° = 10x+15°$$
$$2x = 18°$$
$$x = 9°$$
Angle 1: $12x-3° = 12(9°)-3° = 105°$
Angle 2: $10x+15° = 10(9°)+15° = 105°$

47. $\overline{AC} \cap \overline{BD} = \overline{BC}$

48. $\overline{AB} \cap \overline{BC} = B$

49. $\overline{AC} \cup \overline{BD} = \overline{AD}$

50. $\overline{AB} \cup \overline{BC} = \overline{AC}$

51. $\overrightarrow{BA} \cup \overrightarrow{BC} = \overleftrightarrow{AD}$

52. $\overrightarrow{CB} \cup \overrightarrow{CD} = \overleftrightarrow{AD}$

53. $\overleftrightarrow{AD} \cap \overleftrightarrow{BD} = \overleftrightarrow{AD}$

54. $\overrightarrow{AC} \cap \overrightarrow{CB} = \overline{AC}$

55. $\dfrac{360°}{8} = 45°$

56. Parallel lines appear to meet at a far away distance. The joke in this cartoon is that the lines did meet.

57. When two parallel lines are intersected by a transversal, corresponding angles have the same measure.

58. E, F, H, N, and Z contain parallel line segments.

59. E, F, H, and T contain perpendicular line segments.

69. does not make sense; Explanations will vary. Sample explanation: Two distinct lines cannot intersect twice.

70. does not make sense; Explanations will vary. Sample explanation: The length of the sides of an angle to not determine the angle's measure.

71. does not make sense; Explanations will vary. Sample explanation: Two angles can be neither complementary nor supplementary.

72. makes sense

73. d, since $m\angle 1 = m\angle 4$ and $m\angle 4 + m\angle 5 = 90°$, then $m\angle 1 + m\angle 5 = 90°$

74. $m\angle BGD = m\angle BGC + m\angle CGD$
We know
$m\angle AGB + m\angle BGC + m\angle CGD + m\angle DGE = 180°$.
Since $m\angle AGB = m\angle BGC$ and
$m\angle CGD = m\angle DGE$, this becomes
$m\angle BGC + m\angle BGC + m\angle CGD + m\angle CGD = 180°$
or $2(m\angle BGC) + 2(m\angle CGD) = 180°$
or $m\angle BGC + m\angle CGD = 90°$
Therefore, $m\angle BGD = 90°$.

Check Points 10.2

1. $m\angle A + 116° + 15° = 180°$
$m\angle A + 131° = 180°$
$m\angle A = 180° - 131°$
$m\angle A = 49°$

2. $m\angle 1 = 180° - 90° = 90°$
$m\angle 2 = 180° - 36° - m\angle 1$
$= 180° - 36° - 90°$
$= 54°$
$m\angle 3 = m\angle 2 = 54°$
$m\angle 4 = 180° - 58° - m\angle 3$
$= 180° - 58° - 54°$
$= 68°$
$m\angle 5 = 180° - m\angle 4$
$= 180° - 68°$
$= 112°$

3. Two angles of the small triangle are equal in measure to two angles of the large triangle. One angle pair is given to have the same measure (right angles). Another angle pair consists of vertical angles with the same measure.
Corresponding sides are proportional.
$\dfrac{8}{12} = \dfrac{10}{x}$
$8 \cdot x = 10 \cdot 12$
$8x = 120$
$\dfrac{8x}{8} = \dfrac{120}{8}$
$x = 15$ cm

4. $\dfrac{h}{2} = \dfrac{56}{3.5}$
$3.5 \cdot h = 2 \cdot 56$
$3.5h = 112$
$\dfrac{3.5h}{3.5} = \dfrac{112}{3.5}$
$h = 32$ yd

5. $c^2 = a^2 + b^2$
$c^2 = 7^2 + 24^2$
$c^2 = 49 + 576$
$c^2 = 625$
$c = \sqrt{625}$
$c = 25$ ft

6. $a^2 + b^2 = c^2$
$a^2 + (50)^2 = (130)^2$
$a^2 + 2500 = 16{,}900$
$a^2 = 14{,}400$
$a = \pm 120$
-120 must be rejected.
The tower is 120 yards tall.

Exercise Set 10.2

1. $m\angle A = 180° - 46° - 67° = 67°$

2. $m\angle A = 180° - 48° - 59° = 73°$

3. $m\angle A = 180° - 58° - 90° = 32°$

4. $m\angle A = 180° - 55° - 90° = 35°$

5. $= 50$ yd $\cdot 30$ yd $\cdot 14$ yd $= 21{,}000$ yd^3
$m\angle 2 = 180° - m\angle 1 = 180° - 50° = 130°$
$m\angle 3 = m\angle 1 = 50°$
$m\angle 4 = m\angle 2 = 130°$
$m\angle 5 = 180° - 80° - m\angle 3$
$= 180° - 80° - 50°$
$= 50°$

6. $m\angle 1 = 180° - 50° - 90° = 40°$
$m\angle 2 = 180° - m\angle 1 = 180° - 40° = 140°$
$m\angle 3 = m\angle 1 = 40°$
$m\angle 4 = m\angle 2 = 140°$
$m\angle 5 = 180° - 105° - m\angle 3$
$= 180° - 105° - 40°$
$= 35°$

7. $m\angle 1 = 180° - 130° = 50°$
$m\angle 2 = m\angle 1 = 50°$
$m\angle 3 = 180° - m\angle 1 - m\angle 2$
$= 180° - 50° - 50°$
$= 80°$
$m\angle 4 = 180° - m\angle 2 = 180° - 50° = 130°$
$m\angle 5 = m\angle 4 = 130°$

8. $m\angle 1 = 180° - 115° = 65°$
   $m\angle 2 = m\angle 1 = 65°$
   $m\angle 3 = 180° - m\angle 1 - m\angle 2$
   $\qquad = 180° - 65° - 65°$
   $\qquad = 50°$
   $m\angle 4 = 180° - m\angle 2 = 180° - 65° = 115°$
   $m\angle 5 = m\angle 2 = 65°$

9. $m\angle 1 = 55°$
   $m\angle 1 + m\angle 2 = 120°$
   $55° + m\angle 2 = 120°$
   $\qquad m\angle 2 = 65°$
   $m\angle 1 + m\angle 2 + m\angle 3 = 180°$
   $55° + 65° + m\angle 3 = 180°$
   $\qquad\qquad m\angle 3 = 60°$
   $m\angle 4 = m\angle 2 = 65°$
   $m\angle 5 = m\angle 3 = 60°$
   $m\angle 6 = 120°$
   $m\angle 7 = m\angle 3 = 60°$
   $m\angle 8 = m\angle 7 = 60°$
   $m\angle 9 = m\angle 1 = 55°$
   $m\angle 10 = m\angle 9 = 55°$

10. $m\angle 1 = 65°$
    $m\angle 1 + m\angle 2 = 135°$
    $65° + m\angle 2 = 135°$
    $\qquad m\angle 2 = 70°$
    $m\angle 1 + m\angle 2 + m\angle 3 = 180°$
    $65° + 70° + m\angle 3 = 180°$
    $\qquad\qquad m\angle 3 = 45°$
    $m\angle 4 = m\angle 3 = 45°$
    $m\angle 5 = m\angle 2 = 70°$
    $m\angle 6 = m\angle 3 = 45°$
    $m\angle 7 = m\angle 6 = 45°$
    $m\angle 8 = 135°$
    $m\angle 9 = m\angle 1 = 65°$
    $m\angle 10 = m\angle 9 = 65°$

11. The three angles of the large triangle are given to have the same measures as the three angles of the small triangle.
    $$\frac{18}{9} = \frac{10}{x}$$
    $18 \cdot x = 9 \cdot 10$
    $18x = 90$
    $$\frac{18x}{18} = \frac{90}{18}$$
    $x = 5$ in.

12. The three angles of the large triangle are given to have the same measures as the three angles of the small triangle.
    $$\frac{15}{10} = \frac{12}{x}$$
    $15 \cdot x = 10 \cdot 12$
    $15x = 120$
    $$\frac{15x}{15} = \frac{120}{15}$$
    $x = 8$ in.

13. Two angles of the large triangle are given to have the same measures as two angles of the small triangle.
    $$\frac{30}{10} = \frac{18}{x}$$
    $30 \cdot x = 10 \cdot 18$
    $30x = 180$
    $$\frac{30x}{30} = \frac{180}{30}$$
    $x = 6$ m

14. One angle pair is given to have the same measure (right angles). The triangles also share a common angle.
    $$\frac{5}{4} = \frac{x+5}{5}$$
    $4(x+5) = 5 \cdot 5$
    $4x + 20 = 25$
    $4x = 5$
    $$\frac{4x}{4} = \frac{5}{4}$$
    $x = \dfrac{5}{4}$ in.
    $x = 1.25$ in.

15. One angle pair is given to have the same measure (right angles). Another angle pair consists of vertical angles with the same measure.
    $$\frac{20}{15} = \frac{x}{12}$$
    $15x = 20 \cdot 12$
    $15x = 240$
    $$\frac{15x}{15} = \frac{240}{15}$$
    $x = 16$ in.

16. One angle pair is given to have the same measure. Another angle pair consists of vertical angles with the same measure.

$$\frac{5}{7.5} = \frac{4}{x}$$
$$5 \cdot x = 4 \cdot 7.5$$
$$5x = 30$$
$$\frac{5x}{5} = \frac{30}{5}$$
$$x = 6 \text{ ft}$$

17. Let $x = \overline{CA}$
$$\frac{CA}{EA} = \frac{BC}{DE}$$
$$\frac{x}{15} = \frac{3}{9}$$
$$9x = 3 \cdot 15$$
$$9x = 45$$
$$x = 5$$
$$\overline{CA} = 5$$

18. Let $x = \overline{DB}$
Then $x + 3 = \overline{DA}$
$$\frac{DA}{BA} = \frac{DE}{BC}$$
$$\frac{x+3}{3} = \frac{9}{3}$$
$$x + 3 = 9$$
$$x = 6$$
$$\overline{DB} = 6$$

19. Let $x = \overline{DA}$
$$\frac{DA}{BA} = \frac{DE}{BC}$$
$$\frac{x}{3} = \frac{9}{3}$$
$$x = 9$$
$$\overline{DA} = 9$$

20. Since the lines are parallel, $m\angle EDA = m\angle CBA$ and $m\angle DEA = m\angle BCA$. Clearly $m\angle A = m\angle A$, thus all corresponding angles have equal measure.

21. $c^2 = 8^2 + 15^2$
$$c^2 = 64 + 225$$
$$c^2 = 289$$
$$c = 17 \text{ m}$$

22. $c^2 = 7^2 + 24^2$
$$c^2 = 49 + 576$$
$$c^2 = 625$$
$$c = 25 \text{ m}$$

23. $c^2 = 15^2 + 36^2$
$$c^2 = 225 + 1296$$
$$c^2 = 1521$$
$$c = 39 \text{ m}$$

24. $c^2 = 5^2 + 11^2$
$$c^2 = 25 + 121$$
$$c^2 = 146$$
$$c \approx 12.1 \text{ in.}$$

25. $a^2 + 16^2 = 20^2$
$$a^2 + 256 = 400$$
$$a^2 = 144$$
$$a = 12 \text{ cm}$$

26. $a^2 + 5^2 = 13^2$
$$a^2 + 25 = 169$$
$$a^2 = 144$$
$$a = 12 \text{ ft}$$

27. The sum of the measures of the three angles of any triangle is $180°$, so $x + x + (x + 30) = 180$.
Solve for x.
$$3x + 30 = 180$$
$$3x = 150$$
$$x = 50$$
If $x = 50$, $x + 30 = 80$, so the three angle measures are $50°, 50°,$ and $80°$. This solution checks because $50° + 50° + 80° = 180°$.

28. The sum of the measures of the three angles of a triangle is $180°$, so $x + 3x + (x + 40) = 180$.
Solve this equation.
$$5x + 40 = 180$$
$$5x = 140$$
$$x = 28$$
If $x = 28$, then $3x = 3(28) = 84$, and $x + 40 = 68$, so the three angle measures are $28°$, $84°$, and $68°$. This solution checks because $28° + 84° + 68° = 180°$.

29. Let x = the measure of the smallest angle.
Let $2x$ = the measure of the second angle.
Let $x + 20$ = the measure of the third angle.
$$x + 2x + (x + 20) = 180$$
$$4x + 20 = 180$$
$$4x = 160$$
$$x = 40$$
Measure of smallest angle is $40°$.
Measure of second angle is $2x = 80°$.
Measure of third angle is $x + 20 = 60°$.

30. Let x = the measure of the smallest angle.
Then $3x$ = the measure of the second angle.
$x + 30$ = the measure of the third angle.
$$x + 3x + (x + 30) = 180$$
$$5x + 30 = 180$$
$$5x = 150$$
$$x = 30$$
Measure of the smallest angle = x = $30°$
Measure of the second angle = $3x = 90$
Measure of the third angle = $x + 30 = 60°$

31. If $a^2 + b^2 = c^2$, then the triangle is a right triangle.

32. $a^2 + b^2 = c^2$
$10^2 + 24^2 = 26^2$
$100 + 576 = 676$
$676 = 676$ true
This is a right triangle.

33. $a^2 + b^2 = c^2$
$4^2 + 8^2 = 9^2$
$16 + 64 = 81$
$80 = 81$ false
This is not a right triangle.

34. $a^2 + b^2 = c^2$
$\sqrt{2}^2 + \sqrt{7}^2 = 3^2$
$2 + 7 = 9$
$9 = 9$ true
This is a right triangle.

35. Let x = height of tree.
$$\frac{x}{5} = \frac{86}{6}$$
$$6 \cdot x = 5 \cdot 86$$
$$6x = 430$$
$$x \approx 71.7 \text{ ft}$$

36. Let x = height of tree.
$$\frac{x}{8} = \frac{12}{6}$$
$$6 \cdot x = 12 \cdot 8$$
$$6x = 96$$
$$x = 16 \text{ ft}$$

37. Let x = distance from home to second base.
$$x^2 = 90^2 + 90^2$$
$$x^2 = 8100 + 8100$$
$$x^2 = 16,200$$
$$x \approx 127.3 \text{ ft}$$

38. Let x = the length of the ladder.
$$x^2 + 15^2 = 20^2$$
$$x^2 + 225 = 400$$
$$x^2 = 175$$
$$x \approx 13.2 \text{ ft}$$

39. Let x = the length of each cable.
Let $3x$ = the total length of the 3 cables.
$$x^2 = 9^2 + (16 - 4)^2$$
$$x^2 = 81 + 144$$
$$x^2 = 225$$
$$x = 15 \text{ yd}$$
$$3x = 45 \text{ yd}$$

40. Let x = the length of each cable.
Let $3x$ = the total length of the 3 cables.
$$x^2 = 8^2 + (10 - 4)^2$$
$$x^2 = 64 + 36$$
$$x^2 = 100$$
$$x = 10 \text{ yd}$$
$$3x = 30 \text{ yd}$$

41. Let x = the length of the diagonal.
$$x^2 = 5^2 + 12^2$$
$$x^2 = 25 + 144$$
$$x^2 = 169$$
$$x = 13 \text{ ft}$$

42. Let x = the distance from the launch site to one tracking station.
Let $2x$ = the distance between the tracking stations.

$$x^2 + 4^2 = 5^2$$

$$x^2 + 16 = 25$$

$$x^2 = 9$$

$$x = 3 \text{ km}$$

$$2x = 6 \text{ km}$$

43. Let c = the length of the new road.

$$c^2 = 3000^2 + 4000^2$$

$$c^2 = 9,000,000 + 16,000,000$$

$$c^2 = 25,000,000$$

$$c = 5000 \text{ m}$$

$$c = 5 \text{ km}$$

Thus, the cost is $5 \times \$150,000 = \$750,000$

44. a.
$$a^2 + c^2 = b^2$$

$$a^2 + 5^2 = 6^2$$

$$a^2 + 25 = 36$$

$$a^2 = 11$$

$$a = \sqrt{11}$$

$$a \approx 3.3 \text{ m}$$

Convert meters to feet:

$$3.3 \text{ m} = 330 \text{ cm} = \frac{330 \text{ cm}}{1} \cdot \frac{1 \text{ ft}}{30.48 \text{ cm}} \approx 10.8 \text{ ft}$$

This is too high to be a realistic jump.

b. $a = \sqrt{11}$ which rounds to $a \approx 3.32$ m.
This is 2 cm more than the tests answer.
Convert centimeters to inches:

$$2 \text{ cm} = \frac{2 \text{ cm}}{1} \cdot \frac{1 \text{ in.}}{2.54 \text{ cm}} \approx 1 \text{ in.}$$

It is unlikely a carpenter would make this error.

c. $6 \text{ m} = 600 \text{ cm} = \frac{600 \text{ cm}}{1} \cdot \frac{1 \text{ ft}}{30.48 \text{ cm}} \approx 19.7 \text{ ft}$

Hardware stores do not typically carry boards of this size.

54. does not make sense; Explanations will vary. Sample explanation: A triangle cannot have two right angles.

55. makes sense

56. does not make sense; Explanations will vary. Sample explanation: Two right triangles are not necessarily similar. The two acute angles of one triangle may or may not have the same measure as the two acute angles of the other triangle.

57. does not make sense; Explanations will vary. Sample explanation: The Pythagorean Theorem can only apply to right triangles.

58. $m\angle PQT = 180° - 70° - 60° = 50°$

$$m\angle SQR = 180° - m\angle PQT - 50°$$
$$= 180° - 50° - 50°$$
$$= 80°$$

$$m\angle R = 180° - m\angle SQR - 30°$$
$$= 180° - 80° - 30°$$
$$= 70°$$

59. Let x = the left portion of $\overline{AB}$
Let y = the right portion of $\overline{AB}$

$$x^2 + 12^2 = 13^2$$

$$x^2 + 144 = 169$$

$$x^2 = 25$$

$$x = 5 \text{ ft}$$

$$y^2 + 12^2 = 20^2$$

$$y^2 + 144 = 400$$

$$y^2 = 256$$

$$y = 16 \text{ ft}$$

$$\overline{AB} = x + y = 5 + 16 = 21 \text{ ft}$$

60.

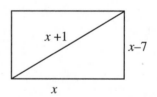

$$x^2 + (x-7)^2 = (x+1)^2$$

$$x^2 + x^2 - 14x + 49 = x^2 + 2x + 1$$

$$x^2 - 16x + 48 = 0$$

$$(x-12)(x-4) = 0$$

$x = 4$ must be rejected

$$x = 12$$

$$x - 7 = 5$$

The caret's dimensions are 5 ft by 12 ft.

Check Points 10.3

1. Note: 50 yds equals 150 ft and 30 yds equals 90 ft
   $P = 2l + 2w$
   $P = 2 \cdot 150 \text{ ft} + 2 \cdot 90 \text{ ft} = 480 \text{ ft}$

   $\text{Cost} = \dfrac{480 \cancel{\text{ feet}}}{1} \cdot \dfrac{\$6.50}{\cancel{\text{ foot}}} = \$3120$

2. **a.** $\text{Sum} = (n - 2)180°$
   $= (12 - 2)\, 180°$
   $= 10 \cdot 180°$
   $= 1800°$

   b. $m\angle A = \dfrac{1800°}{12} = 150°$

3. Each angle is $\dfrac{(n - 2)\, 180°}{n} = \dfrac{(8 - 2)\, 180°}{8} = 135°$
   Regular octagons can not be used to create a tessellation because $360°$ is not a multiple of $135°$.

Exercise Set 10.3

1. Quadrilateral (4 sides)

2. Octagon (8 sides)

3. Pentagon (5 sides)

4. Heptagon (7 sides)

5. a (square), b (rhombus), d (rectangle), and e (parallelogram) all have two pairs of parallel sides.

6. a (square), b (rhombus)

7. a (square), d (rectangle)

8. c (trapezoid), d (rectangle), e (parallelogram)

9. c (trapezoid)

10. a (square)

11. $P = 2 \cdot 3 \text{ cm} + 2 \cdot 12 \text{ cm}$
    $= 6 \text{ cm} + 24 \text{ cm}$
    $= 30 \text{ cm}$

12. $P = 2 \cdot 9 \text{ cm} + 2 \cdot 14 \text{ cm}$
    $= 18 \text{ cm} + 28 \text{ cm}$
    $= 46 \text{ cm}$

13. $P = 2 \cdot 6 \text{ yd} + 2 \cdot 8 \text{ yd}$
    $= 12 \text{ yd} + 16 \text{ yd}$
    $= 28 \text{ yd}$

14. $P = 2 \cdot 7 \text{ in.} + 2 \cdot 18 \text{ in.} = 14 \text{ in.} + 36 \text{ in.} = 50 \text{ in.}$

15. $P = 4 \cdot 250 \text{ in.} = 1000 \text{ in.}$

16. $P = 4 \cdot 3.5 \text{ m} = 14 \text{ m}$

17. $P = 9 \text{ ft} + 7 \text{ ft} + 11 \text{ ft} = 27 \text{ ft}$

18. $P = 10 \text{ yd} + 16 \text{ yd} + 8.5 \text{ yd} = 34.5 \text{ yd}$

19. $P = 3 \cdot 6 \text{ yd} = 18 \text{ yd}$

20. $P = 6 \cdot 4 \text{ mm} = 24 \text{ mm}$

21. $P = 12 \text{ yd} + 12 \text{ yd} + 9 \text{ yd} + 9 \text{ yd} + 21 \text{ yd} + 21 \text{ yd}$
    $= 84 \text{ yd}$

22. $P = 4 \text{ in.} + 9 \text{ in.} + 13 \text{ in} + 5 \text{ in.} + 17 \text{ in.} + 14 \text{ in.}$
    $= 62 \text{ in.}$

23. First determine lengths of unknown sides.

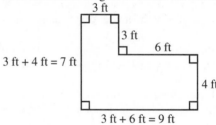

$P = 3 \text{ ft} + 3 \text{ ft} + 6 \text{ ft} + 4 \text{ ft} + 9 \text{ ft} + 7 \text{ ft} = 32 \text{ ft}$

24. First determine lengths of unknown sides.

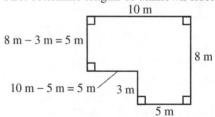

$P = 10 \text{ m} + 8 \text{ m} + 5 \text{ m} + 3 \text{ m} + 5 \text{ m} + 5 \text{ m} = 36 \text{ m}$

25. $\text{Sum} = (n - 2)180°$
    $= (5 - 2)\, 180°$
    $= 3 \cdot 180°$
    $= 540°$

26. $\text{Sum} = (n - 2)\, 180°$
    $= (6 - 2)\, 180°$
    $= 4 \cdot 180°$
    $= 720°$

27. Sum $= (n-2)180°$
$$= (4-2)180°$$
$$= 2 \cdot 180°$$
$$= 360°$$

28. Sum $= (n-2)\,180°$
$$= (7-2)\,180°$$
$$= 5 \cdot 180°$$
$$= 900°$$

29. From Exercise 25, we know the sum of the measures of the angles of a pentagon is 540°. Since all 5 angles have the same degree measure, $m\angle A = \dfrac{540°}{5} = 108°$.
$$m\angle B = 180° - 108° = 72°$$

30. From Exercise 26. we know the sum of the measures of the angles of a hexagon is 720°. Since all 6 angles have the same degree measure, $m\angle A = \dfrac{720°}{6} = 120°$. $m\angle B = 180° - 120° = 60°$

31. a. From Exercise 25, we know the sum of the measures of the angles of a pentagon is 540°.

b. $m\angle A = 540° - 70° - 150° - 90° - 90° = 140°$ and $m\angle B = 180° - 140° = 40°$

32. a. From Exercise 27, we know the sum of the measures of the angles of a quadrilateral is 360°.

b. $m\angle A = 360° - 90° - 90° - 42° = 138°$ and $m\angle B = 180° - 138° = 42°$

33. a. squares, hexagons, dodecagons

b. The 3 angles that come together are 90°, 120°, and 150°.

c. The tessellation is possible because $90° + 120° + 150° = 360°$.

34. a. triangles, squares, hexagons

b. The 4 angles that come together are 60°, 90°, 90°, and 120°.

c. The tessellation is possible because $60° + 90° + 90° + 120° = 360°$.

35. a. triangles, hexagons

b. The 4 angles that come together are 60°, 60°, 120°, and 120°.

c. The tessellation is possible because $60° + 60° + 120° + 120° = 360°$.

36. a. triangles, dodecagons

b. The 3 angles that come together are 60°, 150°, and 150°.

c. The tessellation is possible because $60° + 150° + 150° = 360°$.

37. Each angle is $\dfrac{(n-2)\,180°}{n} = \dfrac{(9-2)\,180°}{9} = 140°$ Regular nine-sided polygons can not be used to create a tessellation because 360° is not a multiple of 140°.

38. Each angle is $\dfrac{(n-2)\,180°}{n} = \dfrac{(10-2)\,180°}{10} = 144°$ Regular ten-sided polygons can not be used to create a tessellation because 360° is not a multiple of 144°.

39. Let w = the width of the field (in yards). Let $4w$ = the length. The perimeter of a rectangle is twice the width plus twice the length, so $2w + 2(4w) = 500$
$$2w + 8w = 500$$
$$10w = 500$$
$$w = 50$$
The width is 50 yards and the length is 4(50) = 200 yards. This checks because 2(50) + 2(200) = 500.

40. Let w = the width of the field (in yards). Then $5w$ = the length of the field. The perimeter of a rectangle is twice the length plus twice the width, so $2w + 2(5w) = 288$
$$2w + 10w = 288$$
$$12w = 288$$
$$w = 24$$
The width is 24 yards and the length is 5(24) = 120 yards. This checks because 2(24) + 2(120) = 48 + 240 = 288.

41. Let w = the width of a football field (in feet).
Let $w + 200$ = the length.
$$2w + 2(w + 200) = 1040$$
$$2w + 2w + 400 = 1040$$
$$4w + 400 = 1040$$
$$4w = 640$$
$$w = 160$$

The width 160 feet and the length is $160 + 200 =$ 360 feet. This checks because $2(160) + 2(200) =$ 720.

42. Let w = the width of a basketball court (in meters).
Then $w + 13$ = the length of the court.
$$2w + 2(w + 13) = 86$$
$$2w + 2w + 26 = 86$$
$$4w + 26 = 86$$
$$4w = 60$$
$$w = 15$$

The width is 15 meters and the length is $15 + 13 =$ 28 meters. This checks because $2(15) + 2(28) = 30 + 56 = 86$.

43. $x + x + (x + 5°) + (x + 5°) + 120° + 130° = (6 - 2)180°$
$$4x + 260° = 720°$$
$$4x = 460°$$
$$x = 115°$$
$$x + 5° = 120°$$

The angles are 115°, 115°, 120°, and 120°.

44. $(3x + 48°) + (4x + 28°) +$
$$(5x + 8°) + (6x - 12°) + 108° = (5 - 2)180°$$
$$18x + 180° = 540°$$
$$18x = 360°$$
$$x = 20°$$
$$3x + 48° = 108°$$
$$4x + 28° = 108°$$
$$5x + 8° = 108°$$
$$6x - 12° = 108°$$

The angles are all 108°.

45. $\dfrac{(8 - 2)180°}{8} + \dfrac{(6 - 2)180°}{6} + \dfrac{(5 - 2)180°}{5} = 363°$

If the polygons were all regular polygons, the sum would be 363°. The tessellation is fake because the sum is not 360°.

46. $\dfrac{(7 - 2)180°}{7} + \dfrac{(7 - 2)180°}{7} + \dfrac{(5 - 2)180°}{5} = 365\frac{1}{7}°$

If the polygons were all regular polygons, the sum would be $365\frac{1}{7}°$. The tessellation is fake because the sum is not 360°.

47. $P = 2 \cdot 400 \text{ ft} + 2 \cdot 200 \text{ ft}$
$= 800 \text{ ft} + 400 \text{ ft}$
$= 1200 \text{ ft}$

$\text{Cost} = \dfrac{1200 \text{ ft}}{1} \cdot \dfrac{1 \text{ yd}}{3 \text{ ft}} \cdot \dfrac{\$14}{1 \text{ yd}} = \$5600$

48. $P = 2l + 2w$
$P = 2 \cdot 70 \text{ ft} + 2 \cdot 30 \text{ ft} = 200 \text{ ft}$

$\text{Cost} = \dfrac{200 \text{ feet}}{1} \cdot \dfrac{1 \text{ yd}}{3 \text{ feet}} \cdot \dfrac{\$8}{1 \text{ yd}} \approx \$533.33$

49. Since the side of the square is 8 ft, its perimeter is 32 ft.
32 ft. is equivalent to 384 inches.
Thus, the total number of

$\text{flowers} = \dfrac{384}{8} = 48 \text{ flowers}$.

50. First determine lengths of unknown sides.

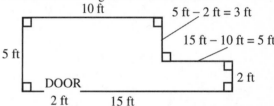

$P = 5 \text{ ft} + 10 \text{ ft} + 3 \text{ ft} + 5 \text{ ft} + 2 \text{ ft} + 15 \text{ ft} - 2 \text{ ft}$
$= 38 \text{ ft}$

$\text{Cost} = \dfrac{38 \text{ ft}}{1} \cdot \dfrac{\$0.25}{1 \text{ ft}} = \$9.50$

58. does not make sense; Explanations will vary. Sample explanation: The sides of a polygon must connect at their endpoints.

59. makes sense

60. makes sense

61. does not make sense; Explanations will vary. Sample explanation: A tessellation cannot be created using only regular pentagons.

62. First determine lengths of unknown sides.

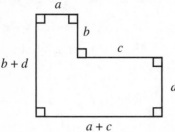

$P = a + b + c + d + (a + c) + (b + d)$
$\quad = 2a + 2b + 2c + 2d$
$\quad = 2(a + b + c + d)$

63. All sides have length a, therefore $P = 6a$.

64. First, find the measures of the two unknown angles:
$180° - 63° = 117°$ and
$180° - 97° = 83°$
Sum of measures of angles $= (n-2)180°$
$\qquad\qquad\qquad\qquad\quad = (5-2)180°$
$\qquad\qquad\qquad\qquad\quad = 540°$
$m\angle 1 = 540° - 117° - 140° - 83° - 135°$
$\qquad\quad = 65°$

Check Points 10.4

1. Area of large rectangle:
$A_{\text{large}} = lw$
$\qquad\quad = (13 \text{ ft} + 3 \text{ ft}) \times (3 \text{ ft} + 6 \text{ ft})$
$\qquad\quad = 16 \text{ ft} \cdot 9 \text{ ft}$
$\qquad\quad = 144 \text{ ft}^2$
Area of small rectangle:
$A_{\text{small}} = lw$
$\qquad\quad = 13 \text{ ft} \cdot 6 \text{ ft}$
$\qquad\quad = 78 \text{ ft}^2$
Area of path $= 144 \text{ ft}^2 - 78 \text{ ft}^2 = 66 \text{ ft}^2$

2. First convert the linear measures in feet to linear yards.

$18 \text{ ft} = \dfrac{18 \text{ ft}}{1} \cdot \dfrac{1 \text{ yd}}{3 \text{ ft}} = 6 \text{ yd}$

$21 \text{ ft} = \dfrac{21 \text{ ft}}{1} \cdot \dfrac{1 \text{ yd}}{3 \text{ ft}} = 7 \text{ yd}$

Area of floor $= 6 \text{ yd} \cdot 7 \text{ yd} = 42 \text{ yd}^2$

Cost of carpet $= \dfrac{42 \text{ yd}^2}{1} \cdot \dfrac{\$16}{1 \text{ yd}^2} = \$672$

3. $A = bh$
$A = 10 \text{ in.} \cdot 6 \text{ in.} = 60 \text{ in.}^2$

4. $A = \dfrac{1}{2}bh$
$A = \dfrac{1}{2} \cdot 12 \text{ ft} \cdot 5 \text{ ft} = 30 \text{ ft}^2$

5. $A = \dfrac{1}{2}h(a+b)$
$\quad = \dfrac{1}{2} \cdot 7 \text{ ft} \cdot (20 \text{ ft} + 10 \text{ ft})$
$\quad = \dfrac{1}{2} \cdot 7 \text{ ft} \cdot 30 \text{ ft}$
$\quad = 105 \text{ ft}^2$

6. $C = \pi d$
$\quad = \pi(10 \text{ in.})$
$\quad = 10\pi \text{ in.}$
$\quad \approx 31.4 \text{ in.}$

7. Find the circumference of the semicircle:
$C_{\text{semicircle}} = \dfrac{1}{2}\pi d$
$\qquad\qquad \approx \dfrac{1}{2}\pi(10 \text{ ft})$
$\qquad\qquad \approx 15.7 \text{ ft}$
Length of trim $= 10 \text{ ft} + 12 \text{ ft} + 12 \text{ ft} + 15.7 \text{ ft}$
$\qquad\qquad\qquad = 49.7 \text{ ft}$

8. First, find the area of pizzas.

Large:	Medium:
$A = \pi r^2$	$A = \pi r^2$
$\quad = \pi(9 \text{ in.})^2$	$\quad = \pi(7 \text{ in.})^2$
$\quad = 81\pi \text{ in.}^2$	$\quad = 49\pi \text{ in.}^2$
$\quad \approx 254 \text{ in.}^2$	$\quad \approx 154 \text{ in.}^2$

Next, find the price per square inch.

Large:	Medium:
$\dfrac{\$20.00}{81\pi \text{ in.}^2}$	$\dfrac{\$14.00}{49\pi \text{ in.}^2}$
$\approx \dfrac{\$20.00}{254 \text{ in.}^2}$	$\approx \dfrac{\$14.00}{154 \text{ in.}^2}$
$\approx \dfrac{\$0.08}{\text{in.}^2}$	$\approx \dfrac{\$0.09}{\text{in.}^2}$

The large pizza is a better buy.

Exercise Set 10.4

1. $A = 6 \text{ m} \cdot 3 \text{ m} =$

$120 \text{ ft} = \dfrac{120 \text{ ft}}{1} \cdot \dfrac{1 \text{ yd}}{3 \text{ ft}} = 40 \text{ yd}$

$980 \text{ ft} = \dfrac{980 \text{ ft}}{1} = \dfrac{1 \text{ yd}}{3 \text{ ft}} \approx 326.667 \text{ yd}$

$B = (40 \text{ yd})^2 = 1600 \text{ yd}^2$

$V = \dfrac{1}{3} \cdot 1600 \text{ yd}^2 \cdot 327 \text{ yd} = 174{,}222 \text{ yd}^3$

2. $A = 3 \text{ ft} \cdot 4 \text{ ft} = 12 \text{ ft}^2$

3. $A = (4 \text{ in.})^2 = 16 \text{ in.}^2$

4. $A = (3 \text{ cm})^2 = 9 \text{ cm}^2$

5. $A = 50 \text{ cm} \cdot 42 \text{ cm} = 2100 \text{ cm}^2$

6. $A = 58 \text{ ft} \cdot 43 \text{ ft} = 2494 \text{ ft}^2$

7. $A = \dfrac{1}{2} \cdot 14 \text{ in.} \cdot 8 \text{ in.} = 56 \text{ in.}^2$

8. $A = \dfrac{1}{2} \cdot 30 \text{ m} \cdot 33 \text{ m} = 495 \text{ m}^2$

9. $A = \dfrac{1}{2} \cdot 9.8 \text{ yd} \cdot 4.2 \text{ yd} = 20.58 \text{ yd}^2$

10. $A = \dfrac{1}{2} \cdot 8 \text{ yd} \cdot 3.5 \text{ yd} = 14 \text{ yd}^2$

11. $a^2 + b^2 = c^2$

$h^2 + 12^2 = 13^2$

$h^2 + 144 = 169$

$h^2 = 25$

$h = 5$

$A = \dfrac{1}{2} \cdot 12 \text{ in.} \cdot 5 \text{ in.} = 30 \text{ in.}^2$

12. $a^2 + b^2 = c^2$

$h^2 + 8^2 = 10^2$

$h^2 + 64 = 100$

$h^2 = 36$

$h = 6$

$A = \dfrac{1}{2} \cdot 8 \text{ m} \cdot 6 \text{ m} = 24 \text{ m}^2$

13. $A = \dfrac{1}{2} \cdot 18 \text{ m} \cdot (37 \text{ m} + 26 \text{ m})$

$= 9 \text{ m}(63 \text{ m})$

$= 567 \text{ m}^2$

14. $A = \dfrac{1}{2} \cdot 7 \text{ m} \cdot (20.8 \text{ m} + 10 \text{ m})$

$= \dfrac{7}{2} \text{ m} \cdot (30.8 \text{ m})$

$= 107.8 \text{ m}^2$

15. $C = 2\pi \cdot 4 \text{ cm} = 8\pi \text{ cm} \approx 25.1 \text{ cm}$

$A = \pi(4 \text{ cm})^2 = 16\pi \text{ cm}^2 \approx 50.3 \text{ cm}^2$

16. $C = 2\pi \cdot 9 \text{ m} = 18\pi \text{ m} \approx 56.5 \text{ m}$

$A = \pi(9 \text{ m})^2 = 81\pi \text{ m}^2 \approx 254.5 \text{ m}^2$

17. $C = \pi \cdot 12 \text{ yd} = 12\pi \text{ yd} \approx 37.7 \text{ yd}$

$r = \dfrac{d}{2} = \dfrac{12 \text{ yd}}{2} = 6 \text{ yd}$

$A = \pi(6 \text{ yd})^2 = 36\pi \text{ yd}^2 \approx 113.1 \text{ yd}^2$

18. $C = \pi \cdot 40 \text{ ft} = 40\pi \text{ ft} \approx 125.7 \text{ ft}$

$r = \dfrac{d}{2} = \dfrac{40 \text{ ft}}{2} = 20 \text{ ft}$

$A = \pi(20 \text{ ft})^2 = 400\pi \text{ ft}^2 \approx 1256.6 \text{ ft}^2$

19. The figure breaks into a lower rectangle and an upper rectangle.

Area of lower rectangle:

$A = lw$

$A = (12 \text{ m})(3 \text{ m})$

$A = 36 \text{ m}^2$

Area of upper rectangle:

$A = lw$

$A = (9 \text{ m})(4 \text{ m})$

$A = 36 \text{ m}^2$

Total area $= 36 \text{ m}^2 + 36 \text{ m}^2 = 72 \text{ m}^2$

20. The figure breaks into a lower rectangle and an upper rectangle.

Area of lower rectangle:

$A = lw$

$A = (9 \text{ ft})(2 \text{ ft})$

$A = 18 \text{ ft}^2$

Area of upper rectangle:

$A = lw$

$A = (7 \text{ ft})(3 \text{ ft})$

$A = 21 \text{ ft}^2$

Total area $= 18 \text{ ft}^2 + 21 \text{ ft}^2 = 39 \text{ ft}^2$

21. The figure breaks into a lower rectangle and an upper triangle.

Area of rectangle:

$A = lw$

$A = (24 \text{ m})(10 \text{ m})$

$A = 240 \text{ m}^2$

Area of triangle:

$A = \frac{1}{2}bh$

$A = \frac{1}{2}(24 \text{ m})(5 \text{ m})$

$A = 60 \text{ m}^2$

Total area $= 240 \text{ m}^2 + 60 \text{ m}^2 = 300 \text{ m}^2$

22. The figure breaks into a left rectangle and a triangle on the right.

Area of rectangle:

$A = lw$

$A = (6 \text{ cm})(10 \text{ cm})$

$A = 60 \text{ cm}^2$

Area of triangle:

$A = \frac{1}{2}bh$

$A = \frac{1}{2}(3 \text{ cm})(7 \text{ cm})$

$A = 10.5 \text{ cm}^2$

Total area $= 60 \text{ cm}^2 + 10.5 \text{ cm}^2 = 70.5 \text{ cm}^2$

23. The figure's area can be obtained by adding the area of a square of side 10 cm, to twice the area of a circle of radius 5 cm.

Area of square:

$A = s^2$

$A = (10 \text{ cm})^2$

$A = 100 \text{ cm}^2$

Area of circles:

$A = \pi r^2$

$A = \pi(5 \text{ cm})^2$

$A = 25\pi \text{ cm}^2$

Total area $= 100 \text{ cm}^2 + 25\pi \text{ cm}^2 + 25\pi \text{ cm}^2$

$= (100 + 50\pi) \text{ cm}^2$

$\approx 257.1 \text{ cm}^2$

24. $a^2 + b^2 = c^2$

$h^2 + 9^2 = 15^2$

$h^2 + 81 = 225$

$h^2 = 144$

$h = 12$

The figure's area can be obtained by adding the area of the triangle to half the area of a circle of radius 6 in.

Area of triangle:

$A = \frac{1}{2}bh$

$A = \frac{1}{2} \cdot 9 \text{ in.} \cdot 12 \text{ in.}$

$A = 54 \text{ in.}^2$

Area of circle:

$A = \pi r^2$

$A = \pi(6 \text{ in.})^2$

$A = 36\pi \text{ in.}^2$

Total area $= 54 \text{ in.}^2 + \frac{1}{2} \cdot 36\pi \text{ in.}^2$

$= (54 + 18\pi) \text{ in.}^2$

$\approx 110.5 \text{ in.}^2$

25. $A = ab + \frac{1}{2}(c-a)b$

$= b\left(a + \frac{1}{2}(c-a)\right)$

$= b\left(a + \frac{1}{2}c - \frac{1}{2}a\right)$

$= b\left(\frac{1}{2}a + \frac{1}{2}c\right)$

$= \frac{1}{2}b(a+c)$

26. $A = ab + \frac{1}{2}b^2$

$= b\left(a + \frac{1}{2}b\right)$

$= b\left(\frac{1}{2}a + \frac{1}{2}a + \frac{1}{2}b\right)$

$= \frac{1}{2}b(a + a + b)$

$= \frac{1}{2}b(2a + b)$

27. $A = a^2 + \frac{1}{2}b(a+a) + a^2$

$= 2a^2 + \frac{1}{2}b(2a)$

$= 2a^2 + ab$

28. $A = (4a)a + \pi a^2$

$= 4a^2 + \pi a^2$

$= (4 + \pi)a^2$

29. Area of larger triangle:

$A = \frac{1}{2}bh$

$A = \frac{1}{2} \cdot (8 \text{ cm} + 8 \text{ cm} + 8 \text{ cm}) \cdot (12 \text{ cm} + 6 \text{ cm})$

$A = \frac{1}{2} \cdot 24 \text{ cm} \cdot 18 \text{ cm}$

$A = 216 \text{ cm}^2$

Area of smaller triangle:

$A = \frac{1}{2}bh$

$A = \frac{1}{2} \cdot 8 \text{ cm} \cdot 6 \text{ cm}$

$A = 24 \text{ cm}^2$

Shaded area $= 216 \text{ cm}^2 - 24 \text{ cm}^2 = 192 \text{ cm}^2$

30. Area of larger triangle:

$A = \frac{1}{2}bh$

$A = \frac{1}{2} \cdot 16$ in. $\cdot (9$ in. $+ 6$ in.)

$A = \frac{1}{2} \cdot 16$ in. $\cdot 15$ in.

$A = 120$ in.^{2}

Area of smaller triangle:

$A = \frac{1}{2}bh$

$A = \frac{1}{2} \cdot 16$ in. $\cdot 6$ in.

$A = 48$ in.^{2}

Shaded area $= 120$ in.$^2 - 48$ in.$^2 = 72$ in.^{2}

31. $A = $ (area of large circle) $- 2$(area of small circle)

$A = \pi(4 \text{ cm})^2 - 2\left[\pi(2 \text{ cm})^2\right]$

$A = 16\pi \text{ cm}^2 - 8\pi \text{ cm}^2$

$A = 8\pi \text{ cm}^2$

32. $A = $ (area of large circle) $-$ (area of small circle)

$A = \pi(4 \text{ cm})^2 - \pi(2 \text{ cm})^2$

$A = 16\pi \text{ cm}^2 - 4\pi \text{ cm}^2$

$A = 12\pi \text{ cm}^2$

33. Use the Pythagorean theorem to find the radius, r.

$c^2 = a^2 + b^2$

$(2r)^2 = (6)^2 + (8)^2$

$4r^2 = 36 + 64$

$4r^2 = 100$

$r^2 = 25$

$r = 5$

$A = $ (area of semicircle) $-$ (area of triangle)

$A = \frac{1}{2}\pi(5 \text{ in.})^2 - \frac{1}{2}(6 \text{ in.})(8 \text{ in.})$

$A = 12.5\pi$ in.$^2 - 24$ in.^{2}

$A = (12.5\pi - 24)$ in.^{2}

34. $A = $ (area of square) $- 4$(area of small circle)

$A = (6 \text{ in.})^2 - 4\pi(1.5 \text{ in.})^2$

$A = 36$ in.$^2 - 4\pi(2.25$ in.$^2)$

$A = 36$ in.$^2 - 9\pi$ in.^{2}

$A = (36 - 9\pi)$ in.^{2}

35. Perimeter:

$2\sqrt{8^2 + 15^2} + 2\sqrt{6^2 + 8^2} = 2\sqrt{289} + 2\sqrt{100}$

$= 2 \cdot 17 + 2 \cdot 10$

$= 54$ ft

Area:

$\frac{1}{2}(15)(8) + \frac{1}{2}(15)(8) + \frac{1}{2}(6)(8) + \frac{1}{2}(6)(8) = 168$ ft^2

36. Perimeter:

$2\pi 20 + 2 \cdot 80 = 160 + 40\pi$

≈ 285.7 m

Area:

$\pi(20)^2 + 80 \cdot 40 = 3200 + 400\pi$

≈ 4456.6 m^2

37. First convert the linear measures in feet to linear yards.

$9 \text{ ft} = \frac{9 \text{ ft}}{1} \cdot \frac{1 \text{ yd}}{3 \text{ ft}} = 3 \text{ yd}$

$21 \text{ ft} = \frac{21 \text{ ft}}{1} \cdot \frac{1 \text{ yd}}{3 \text{ ft}} = 7 \text{ yd}$

Area of floor $= 3$ yd $\cdot 7$ yd $= 21$ yd^2

Cost of carpet $= \frac{21 \text{ yd}^2}{1} \cdot \frac{\$26.50}{1 \text{ yd}^2} = \$556.50$

38. First convert the linear measures in feet to linear yards.

$60 \text{ ft} = \frac{60 \text{ ft}}{1} \cdot \frac{1 \text{ yd}}{3 \text{ ft}} = 20 \text{ yd}$

$9 \text{ ft} = \frac{9 \text{ ft}}{1} \cdot \frac{1 \text{ yd}}{3 \text{ ft}} = 3 \text{ yd}$

Area of wall $= 20$ yd $\cdot 3$ yd $= 60$ yd^2

Cost of plastering $= \frac{60 \text{ yd}^2}{1} \cdot \frac{\$18}{1 \text{ yd}^2} = \$1080$

39. Area of tile $= $ (Area of floor) $-$ (Area of store) $-$ (Area of refrigerator)

$= (12 \text{ ft} \cdot 15 \text{ ft}) - (3 \text{ ft} \cdot 4 \text{ ft}) - (4 \text{ ft} \cdot 5 \text{ ft})$

$= 180$ ft$^2 - 12$ ft$^2 - 20$ ft$^2 = 148$ ft^2

40. Area of room $= 12\text{ ft}\cdot 15\text{ ft} = 180\text{ ft}^2$

Convert linear measures of tiles in inches to linear feet.

$3\text{ in.} = \dfrac{3\text{ in.}}{1}\cdot\dfrac{1\text{ ft}}{12\text{ in.}} = \dfrac{1}{4}\text{ ft}$, and $2\text{ in.} = \dfrac{2\text{ in.}}{1}\cdot\dfrac{1\text{ ft}}{12\text{ in.}} = \dfrac{1}{6}\text{ ft}$. Therefore, the area of one tile $= \dfrac{1}{4}\text{ ft}\cdot\dfrac{1}{6}\text{ ft} = \dfrac{1}{24}\text{ ft}^2$

Number of tiles needed $= \dfrac{\text{Area of room}}{\text{Area of one tile}} = \dfrac{180\text{ ft}^2}{\frac{1}{24}\text{ ft}^2} = 4320$ tiles

Cost of tiles $= \dfrac{4320\text{ tiles}}{1}\cdot\dfrac{\$0.30}{10\text{ tiles}} = \$129.60$

41. a. Area of lawn = (Area of lot) − (Area of house) − (Area of shed) − (Area of driveway)

$= 200\text{ ft}\cdot 500\text{ ft} - 60\text{ ft}\cdot 100\text{ ft} - (20\text{ ft})^2 - 100\text{ ft}\cdot 20\text{ ft}$

$= 100{,}000\text{ ft}^2 - 6000\text{ ft}^2 - 400\text{ ft}^2 - 2000\text{ ft}^2$

$= 91{,}600\text{ ft}^2$

Maximum number of bags of fertilizer $= \dfrac{1\text{ bag}}{4000\text{ ft}^2}\cdot\dfrac{91{,}600\text{ ft}^2}{1} = 22.9$ bags $\to 23$ bags

b. Total cost of fertilizer $= \dfrac{\$25.00}{1\text{ bag}}\cdot\dfrac{23\text{ bags}}{2} = \$575$

42. Area of office $= 20\text{ ft}\cdot 16\text{ ft} = 320\text{ ft}^2$

Amount of electrical bills that are deductible $= \dfrac{320\text{ ft}^2}{2200\text{ ft}^2}\cdot\$4800 \approx \$698.18$

43. a. Area of a front wall $= \left[20\text{ ft}\cdot 40\text{ ft}\right] + \left[\frac{1}{2}\cdot 40\text{ ft}\cdot 10\text{ ft}\right] = 1000\text{ ft}^2$

Area of a side wall $= 50\text{ ft}\cdot 20\text{ ft} = 1000\text{ ft}^2$

Area of windows $= 4\left[8\text{ ft}\cdot 5\text{ ft}\right] + 2\left[30\text{ ft}\cdot 2\text{ ft}\right] = 280\text{ ft}^2$

Area of doors $= 2\left[80\text{ in.}\cdot 36\text{ in.}\right] = 2\left[6\frac{2}{3}\text{ ft}\cdot 3\text{ ft}\right] = 40\text{ ft}^2$

Area of paint = 2(Area of front wall) + 2(Area of side wall) − (Area of windows and doors)

$= 2\left(1000\text{ ft}^2\right) + 2\left(1000\text{ ft}^2\right) - \left(280\text{ ft}^2 + 40\text{ ft}^2\right)$

$= 2000\text{ ft}^2 + 2000\text{ ft}^2 - 320\text{ ft}^2$

$= 3680\text{ ft}^2$

b. Two coats will require enough paint for $2\cdot 3680\text{ ft}^2 = 7360\text{ ft}^2$.

$7360\text{ ft}^2 = \dfrac{7360\text{ ft}^2}{1}\cdot\dfrac{1\text{ gallon}}{500\text{ ft}^2} = 14.72$ gallons ≈ 15 gallons.

c. $\$26.95\times 15 = \$404.25$ is the cost to buy the paint.

44. Square footage (area) of home $= 54\text{ ft}\cdot 30\text{ ft} = 1620\text{ ft}^2$

Cost of building home $\$95\cdot 1620 = \$153{,}900$

45. Area of Master Bedroom $= 14 \text{ ft} \cdot 14 \text{ ft} = 196 \text{ ft}^2$

Area of Bedroom #2 $= 11 \text{ ft} \cdot 12 \text{ ft} = 132 \text{ ft}^2$

Area of Bedroom #3 $= 12 \text{ ft} \cdot 11 \text{ ft} = 132 \text{ ft}^2$

Total area $= 196 \text{ ft}^2 + 132 \text{ ft}^2 + 132 \text{ ft}^2 = 460 \text{ ft}^2$

Since there are 9 square feet in a square yard, $460 \text{ ft}^2 \approx 51.1 \text{ yd}^2$.

52 yd^2 at \$17.95 per square yard costs \$933.40.

46. Area of kitchen $= 12 \text{ ft} \cdot 14 \text{ ft} = 168 \text{ ft}^2$

Area of dining room $= 10 \text{ ft} \cdot 14 \text{ ft} = 140 \text{ ft}^2$

Total area $= 168 \text{ ft}^2 + 140 \text{ ft}^2 = 308 \text{ ft}^2$

Since there are 9 square feet in a square yard, $308 \text{ ft}^2 \approx 34.2 \text{ yd}^2$.

35 yd^2 at \$26.95 per square yard costs \$943.25.

47. Amount of fencing $= C = 2\pi \cdot 20 \text{ m} = 40\pi \text{ m} \approx 125.7 \text{ m}$

48. Feet of fringe $= C = \pi d = \pi \cdot 6 \text{ ft} = 6\pi \text{ ft} \approx 18.8 \text{ ft}$

49. $C = 2\pi \cdot 30 \text{ ft} \approx 188.5 \text{ ft}$

$188.5 \text{ ft} = \dfrac{188.5 \text{ ft}}{1} \cdot \dfrac{12 \text{ in.}}{1 \text{ ft}} = 2262 \text{ in.}$

Number of plants $= \dfrac{1 \text{ plant}}{6 \text{ in.}} \cdot \dfrac{2262 \text{ in.}}{1} = 377$ plants

50. Perimeter of rectangle $= 3 \text{ ft} + 6 \text{ ft} + 6 \text{ ft} = 15 \text{ ft}$

Perimeter of semicircle $= \dfrac{1}{2}C = \dfrac{1}{2}\pi \cdot 3 \text{ ft} \approx 4.7 \text{ ft}$

Approximately $15 \text{ ft} + 4.7 \text{ ft} = 19.7 \text{ ft}$ of stripping will be needed.

51. First, find the area of the pizzas.

Large: Medium:

$A = \pi r^2$ $A = \pi r^2$

$\quad = \pi (7 \text{ in.})^2$ $= \pi (3.5 \text{ in.})^2$

$\quad = 49\pi \text{ in.}^2$ $= 12.25\pi \text{ in.}^2$

$\quad \approx 153.9 \text{ in.}^2$ $\approx 38.5 \text{ in.}^2$

Next, find the price per square inch.

Large: Medium:

$\dfrac{\$12.00}{49\pi \text{ in.}^2}$ $\dfrac{\$5.00}{12.25\pi \text{ in.}^2}$

$\approx \dfrac{\$12.00}{153.9 \text{ in.}^2}$ $\approx \dfrac{\$5.00}{38.5 \text{ in.}^2}$

$\approx \dfrac{\$0.08}{\text{in.}^2}$ $\approx \dfrac{\$0.13}{\text{in.}^2}$

The large pizza is a better buy.

52. First, find the area of pizzas.

      Large: Small:

$$A = \pi r^2 \qquad\qquad A = \pi r^2$$

$$ = \pi (8 \text{ in.})^2 \qquad\quad = \pi (5 \text{ in.})^2$$

$$ = 64\pi \text{ in.}^2 \qquad\quad = 25\pi \text{ in.}^2$$

$$ \approx 201.1 \text{ in.}^2 \qquad\quad \approx 78.5 \text{ in.}^2$$

                            2 small pizzas:

$$\approx 2 \cdot 78.5 \text{ in.}^2$$

$$\approx 157 \text{ in.}^2$$

The large pizza is a better buy because it has a larger area for the same price.

58. does not make sense; Explanations will vary. Sample explanation: Mansions are much larger than 1500 square feet.

59. makes sense

60. does not make sense; Explanations will vary. Sample explanation: To determine fencing, you should use the circumference formula.

61. does not make sense; Explanations will vary. Sample explanation: A pizza with twice the radius would be four times as large as the smaller pizza.

62. A square of side 50 ft will enclose the most area.

63. Original Area $= 8 \text{ ft} \cdot 10 \text{ ft} = 80 \text{ ft}^2$

New area $= 12 \text{ ft} \cdot 15 \text{ ft} = 180 \text{ ft}^2$

$$\text{Ratio} = \frac{180 \text{ ft}^2}{80 \text{ ft}^2} = \frac{9}{4}$$

The cost will increase by a factor of $\dfrac{9}{4}$, or 2.25.

64. First, find the area of the large rectangle that includes the path and the pool.
The length of the large rectangle is 30 ft + 3 ft + 3 ft = 36 ft.
The width of the large rectangle is 14 ft + 3 ft + 3 ft = 20 ft.
Area of large rectangular $= 36 \text{ ft} \cdot 20 \text{ ft} = 720 \text{ ft}^2$
Next, find the area of the pool.
Area of pool $= 30 \text{ ft} \cdot 14 \text{ ft} = 420 \text{ ft}^2$
Area of path = (Area of large Rectangle) – (Area of Pool)
$= 720 \text{ ft}^2 - 420 \text{ ft}^2 = 300 \text{ ft}^2$

$$\text{Cost of resurfacing} = \frac{300 \text{ ft}^2}{1} \cdot \frac{\$2}{\text{ft}^2} = \$600$$

65. Length of pipeline $= \dfrac{16.8 \text{ mi}}{1} \cdot \dfrac{5280 \text{ ft}}{1 \text{ mi}} = 88,704$ ft

Area of land$=88,704$ ft $\cdot 200$ ft $=17,740,800 \text{ ft}^2$

Area of land in acres $= \dfrac{17,740,800 \text{ ft}^2}{1} \cdot \dfrac{1 \text{ acre}}{43,560 \text{ ft}^2} \approx 407.2727$ acres

Total cost $= \dfrac{\$32}{1 \text{ acre}} \cdot \dfrac{407.2727 \text{ acres}}{1} = \$13,032.73$

Check Points 10.5

1. $V = 5 \text{ ft} \cdot 3 \text{ ft} \cdot 7 \text{ ft} = 105 \text{ ft}^3$

2. $= \dfrac{6 \text{ ft}}{1} \cdot \dfrac{1 \text{ yd}}{3 \text{ ft}} = 2 \text{ yd}$

$V = (2 \text{ yd})^3 = 8 \text{ yd}^3$

3. $B = (6 \text{ ft})^2 = 36 \text{ ft}^2$

$V = \dfrac{1}{3} \cdot 36 \text{ ft}^2 \cdot 4 \text{ ft}$

$= 48 \text{ ft}^3$

4. $r = \dfrac{1}{2}(8 \text{ cm}) = 4 \text{ cm}$

$V = \pi(4 \text{ in.})^2 \cdot 6 \text{ in.} \approx 302 \text{ in.}^3$

5. $V = \dfrac{1}{3}\pi(4 \text{ in.})^2 \cdot 6 \text{ in.} \approx 101 \text{ in.}^3$

6. No, it is not enough air.

$V = \dfrac{4}{3}\pi(4.5 \text{ in.})^3 \approx 382 \text{ in.}^3$

7. New dimensions: $l = 16 \text{ yd}, \ w = 10 \text{ yd}, \ h = 6 \text{ yd}$

$SA = 2lw + 2lh + 2wh$

$= 2 \cdot 16 \text{ yd} \cdot 10 \text{ yd} + 2 \cdot 16 \text{ yd} \cdot 6 \text{ yd} + 2 \cdot 10 \text{ yd} \cdot 6 \text{ yd}$

$= 320 \text{ yd}^2 + 192 \text{ yd}^2 + 120 \text{ yd}^2$

$= 632 \text{ yd}^2$

Exercise Set 10.5

1. $V = 3 \text{ in.} \cdot 3 \text{ in.} \cdot 4 \text{ in.} = 36 \text{ in.}^3$

2. $V = 3 \text{ cm} \cdot 5 \text{ cm} \cdot 3 \text{ cm} = 45 \text{ cm}^3$

3. $V = (4 \text{ cm})^3 = 64 \text{ cm}^3$

4. $V = (5 \text{ in.})^3 = 125 \text{ in.}^3$

5. $B = 7 \text{ yd} \cdot 5 \text{ yd} = 35 \text{ yd}^2$

    $V = \dfrac{1}{3} \cdot 35 \text{ yd}^2 \cdot 15 \text{ yd}$

    $\quad = 175 \text{ yd}^3$

6. $B = 8 \text{ yd} \cdot 15 \text{ yd} = 120 \text{ yd}^2$

    $V = \dfrac{1}{3} \cdot 120 \text{ yd}^2 \cdot 20 \text{ yd}$

    $\quad = 800 \text{ yd}^3$

7. $B = 4 \text{ in.} \cdot 7 \text{ in.} = 28 \text{ in.}^2$

    $V = \dfrac{1}{3} \cdot 28 \text{ in.}^2 \cdot 6 \text{ in.}$

    $\quad = 56 \text{ in.}^3$

8. $B = (10 \text{ m})^2 = 100 \text{ m}^2$

    $V = \dfrac{1}{3} \cdot 100 \text{ m}^2 \cdot 12 \text{ m}$

    $\quad = 400 \text{ m}^3$

9. $V = \pi (5 \text{ cm})^2 \cdot 6 \text{ cm} = 150\pi \text{ cm}^3 \approx 471 \text{ cm}^3$

10. $V = \pi (6 \text{ cm})^2 \cdot 8 \text{ cm} = 288\pi \text{ cm}^3 \approx 905 \text{ cm}^3$

11. $r = \dfrac{1}{2}(24 \text{ in.}) = 12 \text{ in.}$

    $V = \pi (12 \text{ in.})^2 \cdot 21 \text{ in.} = 3024\pi \text{ in.}^3 \approx 9500 \text{ in.}^3$

12. $r = \dfrac{1}{2}(14 \text{ cm}) = 7 \text{ cm}$

    $V = \pi (7 \text{ cm})^2 \cdot 12 \text{ cm} = 588\pi \text{ cm}^3 \approx 1847 \text{ cm}^3$

13. $V = \dfrac{1}{3}\pi (4 \text{ m})^2 \cdot 9 \text{ m} = 48\pi \text{ m}^3 \approx 151 \text{ m}^3$

14. $V = \dfrac{1}{3}\pi (5 \text{ m})^2 \cdot 16 \text{ m} = 133\frac{1}{3}\pi \text{ m}^3 \approx 419 \text{ m}^3$

15. $r = \dfrac{1}{2} \cdot 6 \text{ yd} = 3 \text{ yd}$

    $V = \dfrac{1}{3}\pi (3 \text{ yd})^2 \cdot 5 \text{ yd} = 15\pi \text{ yd}^3 \approx 47 \text{ yd}^3$

16. $r = \dfrac{1}{2} \cdot 6 \text{ yd} = 3 \text{ yd}$

    $V = \dfrac{1}{3}\pi (3 \text{ yd})^2 \cdot 7 \text{ yd} = 21\pi \text{ yd}^3 \approx 66 \text{ yd}^3$

17. $V = \dfrac{4}{3}\pi(6\,\text{m})^3 = 288\pi\,\text{m}^3 \approx 905\,\text{m}^3$

18. $V = \dfrac{4}{3}\pi(15\ \text{m})^3 = 4500\pi\ \text{m}^3 \approx 14{,}137\ \text{m}^3$

19. $r = \dfrac{1}{2}\cdot 18\ \text{cm} = 9\ \text{cm}$

$V = \dfrac{4}{3}\pi(9\ \text{cm})^3 = 972\pi\ \text{cm}^3 \approx 3054\ \text{cm}^3$

20. $r = \dfrac{1}{2}\cdot 24\ \text{in.} = 12\ \text{in.}$

$V = \dfrac{4}{3}\pi(12\ \text{in.})^3 = 2304\pi\ \text{in.}^3 \approx 7238\ \text{in.}^3$

21. Surface Area $= 2(5\ \text{m}\cdot 3\ \text{m}) + 2(2\ \text{m}\cdot 3\ \text{m}) + 2(5\ \text{m}\cdot 2\ \text{m})$

$\qquad\qquad = 2\cdot 15\ \text{m}^2 + 2\cdot 6\ \text{m}^2 + 2\cdot 10\ \text{m}^2$

$\qquad\qquad = 30\ \text{m}^2 + 12\ \text{m}^2 + 20\ \text{m}^2$

$\qquad\qquad = 62\ \text{m}^2$

22. Surface area $= 2(6\ \text{m}\cdot 3\ \text{m}) + 2(4\ \text{m}\cdot 3\ \text{m}) + 2(6\ \text{m}\cdot 4\ \text{m})$

$\qquad\qquad = 2(18\ \text{m}^2) + 2(12\ \text{m}^2) + 2(24\ \text{m}^2)$

$\qquad\qquad = 36\ \text{m}^2 + 24\ \text{m}^2 + 48\ \text{m}^2$

$\qquad\qquad = 108\ \text{m}^2$

23. Surface Area $= 6(4\,\text{ft})^2 = 96\,\text{ft}^2$

24. Surface Area $= 6(6\ \text{ft})^2 = 216\ \text{ft}^2$

25. Volume = (volume of cone) + (volume of hemisphere)

$V = \dfrac{1}{3}\pi(6\ \text{cm})^2\cdot 15\ \text{cm} + \dfrac{1}{2}\left[\dfrac{4}{3}\pi(6\ \text{cm})^3\right] = 324\pi\ \text{cm}^3 \approx 1018\ \text{cm}^3$

26. Volume = (volume of cone) + (volume of hemisphere)

$V = \dfrac{1}{3}\pi(5\ \text{cm})^2\cdot 8\ \text{cm} + \dfrac{1}{2}\left[\dfrac{4}{3}\pi(5\ \text{cm})^3\right] = 150\pi\ \text{cm}^3 \approx 471\ \text{cm}^3$

27. Volume = (volume of right circular cylinder) + (volume of cone)

$V = \pi(6\ \text{in.})^2\cdot 11\ \text{in.} + \dfrac{1}{3}\pi(6\ \text{in.})^2(14\ \text{in.} - 11\ \text{in.}) = 432\pi\ \text{in.}^3 \approx 1357\ \text{in.}^3$

28. Volume = (volume of right circular cylinder) + (volume of cone)

$V = \pi(3\ \text{m})^2\cdot 12\ \text{m} + \dfrac{1}{3}\pi(3\ \text{m})^2(17\ \text{m} - 12\ \text{m}) = 123\pi\ \text{m}^3 \approx 386\ \text{m}^3$

29. Volume = (volume of right circular cylinder) + (volume hemisphere)

$V = \pi(7\ \text{m})^2\cdot 18\ \text{m} + \dfrac{1}{2}\left[\dfrac{4}{3}\pi(7\ \text{m})^3\right] = \dfrac{3332}{3}\pi\ \text{m}^3 \approx 3489\ \text{m}^3$

30. Volume = (volume of right circular cylinder) + (volume hemisphere)

$$V = \pi(10 \text{ m})^2 \cdot 50 \text{ m} + \frac{1}{2}\left[\frac{4}{3}\pi(10 \text{ m})^3\right] = \frac{17{,}000}{3}\pi \text{ m}^3 \approx 17{,}802 \text{ m}^3$$

31. Surface area:

$$\overbrace{2[(5)(5)+(4)(3)]}^{\text{front and back}} + \overbrace{[(5)(4)+(3)(4)+(2)(4)]}^{\text{left and right sides}} + \overbrace{[(5)(4)+(4)(4)+(9)(4)]}^{\text{top(s) and bottom}} = 186 \text{ yd}^2$$

Volume:

$$\overbrace{(5)(5)(4)}^{\text{left part of block}} + \overbrace{(4)(4)(3)}^{\text{right part of block}} = 100 + 48 = 148 \text{ yd}^3$$

32. Surface area:

$$\overbrace{2(16)(8)}^{\text{front and back}} + \overbrace{2(8)(8)}^{\text{left and right}} + \overbrace{2[2(16)(1)+4(6)(1)]}^{\text{top and bottom}} + \overbrace{[6(6)(8)+6(4)(8)]}^{\text{three inside hollows}} = \overbrace{256}^{\text{front and back}} + \overbrace{128}^{\text{left and right}} + \overbrace{2[56]}^{\text{top and bottom}} + \overbrace{[288+192]}^{\text{three inside hollows}} = 976 \text{ in.}^2$$

Volume:

$$\overbrace{(8)(8)(16)}^{\text{block if solid}} - \overbrace{3(4)(6)(8)}^{\text{3 hollows}} = 1024 - 576 = 448 \text{ in.}^3$$

33. Surface area:

$$\overbrace{2[(10)(5)+\tfrac{1}{2}(4)(10+4)]}^{\text{front and back}} + \overbrace{4(15)(5)}^{\text{left, right, and 2 upper slants}} + \overbrace{(15)(4)}^{\text{top}} + \overbrace{(15)(10)}^{\text{bottom}} = \overbrace{2[50+28]}^{\text{front and back}} + \overbrace{300}^{\text{left, right, and 2 upper slants}} + \overbrace{60}^{\text{top}} + \overbrace{150}^{\text{bottom}} = 666 \text{ yd}^2$$

34. Volume $= lwh = \overbrace{(12-2-2)}^{l}\overbrace{(12-2-2)}^{w}\overbrace{(2)}^{h} = (2)(8)(8) = 128 \text{ in.}^3$

35. $\dfrac{\frac{4}{3}\pi 3^3}{\frac{4}{3}\pi 6^3} = \dfrac{\frac{4}{\cancel{3}}\cancel{\pi}\, 3^3}{\frac{4}{\cancel{3}}\cancel{\pi}\, 6^3} = \left(\dfrac{3}{6}\right)^3 = \left(\dfrac{1}{2}\right)^3 = \dfrac{1}{8}$

36. $\dfrac{\frac{4}{3}\pi 3^3}{\frac{4}{3}\pi 9^3} = \dfrac{\frac{4}{\cancel{3}}\cancel{\pi}\, 3^3}{\frac{4}{\cancel{3}}\cancel{\pi}\, 9^3} = \left(\dfrac{3}{9}\right)^3 = \left(\dfrac{1}{3}\right)^3 = \dfrac{1}{27}$

37. Smaller cylinder: $r = 3$ in, $h = 4$ in.

$V = \pi r^2 h = \pi(3)^2 \cdot 4 = 36\pi$

The volume of the smaller cylinder is $36\pi \, in^3$.

Larger cylinder: r = 3(3 in) = 9 in, h = 4 in.

$V = \pi r^2 h = \pi(9)^2 \cdot 4 = 324\pi$

The volume of the larger cylinder is 324π. The ratio of the volumes of the two cylinders is $\dfrac{V_{\text{larger}}}{V_{\text{smaller}}} = \dfrac{324\pi}{36\pi} = \dfrac{9}{1}$.

So, the volume of the larger cylinder is 9 times the volume of the smaller cylinder.

38. Smaller cylinder; $r = 2$ in., $h = 3$ in.

$$V = \pi r^2 h$$
$$V = \pi (2)^2 \cdot 3$$
$$V = 12\pi$$

The volume of the smaller cylinder is 12π in^3.
Large cylinder: $r = 4(2 \text{ in.}) = 8$ in.,
$h = 3$ in.

$$V = \pi r^2 h$$
$$V = \pi (8)^2 \cdot 3$$
$$V = 192\pi$$

The volume of the larger cylinder is 192π.

The ratio of the volumes of the two cylinders is $\dfrac{V_{\text{Larger}}}{V_{\text{Smaller}}} = \dfrac{192\pi}{12\pi} = \dfrac{16}{1}$,

so the volume of the larger cylinder is 16 times the volume of the smaller cylinder.

39. First convert all linear measures in feet to linear yards.

$$12 \text{ ft} = \frac{12 \cancel{\text{ft}}}{1} \cdot \frac{1 \text{ yd}}{3 \cancel{\text{ft}}} = 4 \text{ yd}$$

$$9 \text{ ft} = \frac{9 \cancel{\text{ft}}}{1} \cdot \frac{1 \text{ yd}}{3 \cancel{\text{ft}}} = 3 \text{ yd}$$

$$6 \text{ ft} = \frac{6 \cancel{\text{ft}}}{1} \cdot \frac{1 \text{ yd}}{3 \cancel{\text{ft}}} = 2 \text{ yd}$$

Total dirt $= 4 \text{ yd} \cdot 3 \text{ yd} \cdot 2 \text{ yd} = 24 \text{ yd}^3$

$$\text{Total cost} = \frac{24 \cancel{\text{yd}^3}}{1} \cdot \frac{1 \cancel{\text{truck}}}{6 \cancel{\text{yd}^3}} \cdot \frac{\$10}{1 \cancel{\text{truck}}} = \$40$$

40. First convert all linear measures in feet to linear yards.

$$15 \text{ ft} = \frac{15 \cancel{\text{ft}}}{1} \cdot \frac{1 \text{ yd}}{3 \cancel{\text{ft}}} = 5 \text{ yd}$$

$$8 \text{ ft} = \frac{8 \cancel{\text{ft}}}{1} \cdot \frac{1 \text{ yd}}{3 \cancel{\text{ft}}} = \frac{8}{3} \text{ yd}$$

$$9 \text{ in.} = \frac{9 \cancel{\text{in.}}}{1} \cdot \frac{1 \cancel{\text{ft}}}{12 \cancel{\text{in.}}} \cdot \frac{1 \text{ yd}}{3 \cancel{\text{ft}}} = \frac{1}{4} \text{ yd}$$

Volume of walkway $= 5 \text{ yd} \cdot \dfrac{8}{3} \text{ yd} \cdot \dfrac{1}{4} \text{ yd} = \dfrac{10}{3} \text{ yd}^3$

$$\text{Cost} = \frac{\$30}{1 \cancel{\text{yd}^3}} \cdot \frac{\frac{10}{3} \cancel{\text{yd}^3}}{1} = \$100$$

41. Volume of house $= 1400 \text{ ft}^2 \cdot 9 \text{ ft} = 12{,}600 \text{ ft}^3$
No. This furnace will not be adequate.

42. Change in height $= 20 \text{ yd} - 6 \text{ yd} = 14 \text{ yd}$
Water used $= 50 \text{ yd} \cdot 30 \text{ yd} \cdot 14 \text{ yd} = 21{,}000 \text{ yd}^3$

43. a. First convert linear measures in feet to linear yards.

$$756 \text{ ft} = \frac{756 \, \cancel{\text{ft}}}{1} \cdot \frac{1 \text{ yd}}{3 \, \cancel{\text{ft}}} = 252 \text{ yd}$$

$$480 \text{ ft} = \frac{480 \, \cancel{\text{ft}}}{1} \cdot \frac{1 \text{ yd}}{3 \, \cancel{\text{ft}}} = 160 \text{ yd}$$

$$B = (252 \text{ yd})^2 = 63,504 \text{ yd}^2$$

$$V = \frac{1}{3} \cdot 63,504 \text{ yd}^2 \cdot 160 \text{ yd}$$

$$= 3,386,880 \text{ yd}^3$$

b. $\dfrac{1 \text{ block}}{1.5 \, \cancel{\text{yd}^3}} \cdot \dfrac{3,386,880 \, \cancel{\text{yd}^3}}{1} = 2,257,920 \text{ blocks}$

44. First convert all linear measures in feet to linear yards.

$$120 \text{ ft} = \frac{120 \, \cancel{\text{ft}}}{1} \cdot \frac{1 \text{ yd}}{3 \, \cancel{\text{ft}}} = 40 \text{ yd}$$

$$980 \text{ ft} = \frac{980 \, \cancel{\text{ft}}}{1} = \frac{1 \text{ yd}}{3 \, \cancel{\text{ft}}} \approx 326.667 \text{ yd}$$

$$B = (40 \text{ yd})^2 = 1600 \text{ yd}^2$$

$$V \approx \frac{1}{3} \cdot 1600 \text{ yd}^2 \cdot 327 \text{ yd} \approx 174,222 \text{ yd}^3$$

45. Volume of tank $= \pi (3 \text{ ft})^2 \cdot \dfrac{7}{3} \text{ ft} \approx 66 \text{ ft}^3$

Yes. The volume of the tank is less than 67 cubic feet.

46. Volume of can 1 $= \pi (3 \text{ in.})^2 \cdot 5 \text{ in.} \approx 141 \text{ in.}^3$

Volume of can 2 $= \pi \left(\dfrac{5}{2} \text{ in.} \right)^2 \cdot 6 \text{ in.} \approx 118 \text{ in.}^3$

The can with a diameter of 6 inches and a height of 5 inches contains more soup.

47. Volume of pool (in cubic feet) $= \pi (12 \text{ ft})^2 \cdot 4 \text{ ft} = 576\pi \text{ ft}^3 \approx 1809.6 \text{ ft}^3$

Volume of pool (in gallons) $= 1809.6 \text{ ft}^3 = \dfrac{1809.6 \, \cancel{\text{ft}^3}}{1} \cdot \dfrac{7.48 \text{ gallons}}{1 \, \cancel{\text{ft}^3}} \approx 13,536 \text{ gallons}$

Cost to fill the pool $= \$2 \cdot 13.535 \approx \$27$

48. $V = 3 \cdot \dfrac{1}{2} \cdot \pi (4 \text{ m})^2 \cdot 50,000 \text{ m} = 1,200,000\pi \text{ m}^3 \approx 3,769,911 \text{ m}^3$

51. does not make sense; Explanations will vary. Sample explanation: Basketballs are spheres.

52. does not make sense; Explanations will vary. Sample explanation: The taller (yet more narrow) can holds less soup.

Volume of 4-inch-high cylinder $= \pi (1.5 \text{ in.})^2 \cdot 4 \text{ in.} = 9\pi \text{ in.}^3$

Volume of 3-inch-high cylinder $= \pi (2 \text{ in.})^2 \cdot 3 \text{ in.} = 12\pi \text{ in.}^3$

53. does not make sense; Explanations will vary. Sample explanation: You must divide by 12^3, or 1728.

54. does not make sense; Explanations will vary. Sample explanation: Surface area is measured in square units.

55. New volume $= \frac{4}{3}\pi(2r)^3 = \frac{4}{3}\pi \cdot 8r^3 = 8\left(\frac{4}{3}\pi r^3\right)$

The volume is multiplied by 8.

56. $10 \cdot 10 \cdot 10 = 1000$ times

57. Volume of darkly shaded region = (Volume of rectangular solid) – (Volume of pyramid)

$$= 6 \text{ cm} \cdot 6 \text{ cm} \cdot 7 \text{ cm} - \frac{1}{3}(6 \text{ cm})^2 \cdot 7 \text{ cm}$$

$$= 168 \text{ cm}^3$$

58. Volume of darkly shaded region = (volume of outer cylinder) – (volume of inner cylinder)

$$= \pi(3 \text{ in.})^2 \cdot 10 \text{ in.} - \pi(1 \text{ in.})^2 \cdot 10 \text{ in.}$$

$$\approx 251 \text{ in.}^3$$

59. Surface area = (Areas of 3 rectangles) + (Area of 2 triangles)

$$= (5 \text{ cm} \cdot 6 \text{ cm} + 4 \text{ cm} \cdot 6 \text{ cm} + 3 \text{ cm} \cdot 6 \text{ cm}) + 2\left(\frac{1}{2} \cdot 3 \text{ cm} \cdot 4 \text{ cm}\right)$$

$$= 72 \text{ cm}^2 + 12 \text{ cm}^2$$

$$= 84 \text{ cm}^2$$

Check Points 10.6

1. Begin by finding the measure of the hypotenuse c using the Pythagorean Theorem.

$c^2 = a^2 + b^2 = 3^2 + 4^2 = 25$

$c = \sqrt{25} = 5$

$\sin A = \frac{3}{5}$

$\cos A = \frac{4}{5}$

$\tan A = \frac{3}{4}$

2. $\tan A = \frac{a}{b}$

$\tan 62° = \frac{a}{140}$

$a = 140 \tan 62° \approx 263 \text{ cm}$

3. $\cos A = \dfrac{b}{c}$

$\cos 62° = \dfrac{140}{c}$

$c \cos 62° = 140$

$c = \dfrac{140}{\cos 62°}$

$c \approx 298 \text{ cm}$

4. Let a = the height of the tower.

$\tan 85.4° = \dfrac{a}{80}$

$a = 80 \tan 85.4° \approx 994 \text{ ft}$

5. $\tan A = \dfrac{14}{10}$

$A = \tan^{-1}\left(\dfrac{14}{10}\right) \approx 54°$

Exercise Set 10.6

1. $\sin A = \dfrac{3}{5}$

$\cos A = \dfrac{4}{5}$

$\tan A = \dfrac{3}{4}$

2. $\sin A = \dfrac{6}{10} = \dfrac{3}{5}$

$\cos A = \dfrac{8}{10} = \dfrac{4}{5}$

$\tan A = \dfrac{6}{8} = \dfrac{3}{4}$

3. First find the length of missing side.

$a^2 = 29^2 - 21^2 = 400$

$a = 20$

$\sin A = \dfrac{20}{29}$

$\cos A = \dfrac{21}{29}$

$\tan A = \dfrac{20}{21}$

4. First find the length of missing side.

$a^2 = 17^2 - 15^2 = 64$

$a = 8$

$\sin A = \dfrac{8}{17}$

$\cos A = \dfrac{15}{17}$

$\tan A = \dfrac{8}{15}$

5. First find the length of missing side.

$b^2 = 26^2 - 10^2 = 576$

$b = 24$

$\sin A = \dfrac{10}{26} = \dfrac{5}{13}$

$\cos A = \dfrac{24}{26} = \dfrac{12}{13}$

$\tan A = \dfrac{10}{24} = \dfrac{5}{12}$

6. First find the length of missing side.

$a^2 = 41^2 - 40^2 = 81$

$a = 9$

$\sin A = \dfrac{9}{41}$

$\cos A = \dfrac{40}{41}$

$\tan A = \dfrac{9}{40}$

7. First find the length of missing side.

$a^2 = 35^2 - 21^2 = 784$

$a = 28$

$\sin A = \dfrac{28}{35} = \dfrac{4}{5}$

$\cos A = \dfrac{21}{35} = \dfrac{3}{5}$

$\tan A = \dfrac{28}{21} = \dfrac{4}{3}$

8. First find the length of missing side.

$b^2 = 25^2 - 24^2 = 49$

$b = 7$

$\sin A = \dfrac{24}{25}$

$\cos A = \dfrac{7}{25}$

$\tan A = \dfrac{24}{7}$

9. $\tan A = \dfrac{a}{b}$

$\tan 37° = \dfrac{a}{250}$

$a = 250 \tan 37° \approx 188$ cm

10. $\tan A = \dfrac{a}{b}$

$\tan 61° = \dfrac{a}{10}$

$a = 10 \tan 61° \approx 18$ cm

11. $\cos 34° = \dfrac{b}{220}$

$b = 220 \cos 34° \approx 182$ in.

12. $\cos 72° = \dfrac{b}{15}$

$b = 15 \cos 72° \approx 5$ cm

13. $\sin 34° = \dfrac{a}{13}$

$a = 13 \sin 34° \approx 7$ m

14. $\sin 49° = \dfrac{a}{18}$

$a = 18 \sin 49° \approx 14$ m

15. $\tan 33° = \dfrac{14}{b}$

$b = \dfrac{14}{\tan 33°} \approx 22$ yd

16. $\tan 44° = \dfrac{23}{b}$

$b = \dfrac{23}{\tan 44°} \approx 24$ yd

17. $\sin 30° = \dfrac{20}{c}$

$c = \dfrac{20}{\sin 30°} = 40$ m

18. $\sin 23° = \dfrac{16}{c}$

$c = \dfrac{16}{\sin 23°} \approx 41$ m

19. $m\angle B = 90° - 40° = 50°$

Side a: $\tan 40° = \dfrac{a}{22}$

$a = 22 \tan 40° \approx 18$ yd

Side c: $\cos 40° = \dfrac{22}{c}$

$c = \dfrac{22}{\cos 40°} \approx 29$ yd

$m\angle B = 50°$, $a \approx 18$ yd, $c \approx 28$ yd

20. $m\angle B = 90° - 57° = 33°$

Side a: $\tan 57° = \dfrac{a}{48}$

$a = 48 \tan 57° \approx 74$ yd

Side c: $\cos 57° = \dfrac{48}{c}$

$c = \dfrac{48}{\cos 57°} \approx 88$ yd

$m\angle B = 33°$, $a \approx 74$ yd, $c \approx 88$ yd

21. $m\angle B = 90° - 52° = 38°$

Side a: $\sin 52° = \dfrac{a}{54}$

$a = 54 \sin 52° \approx 43$ cm

Side b: $\cos 52° = \dfrac{b}{54}$

$b = 54 \cos 52° \approx 33$ cm

$m\angle B = 38°$, $a \approx 43$ cm, $b \approx 33$ cm

22. $m\angle B = 90° - 39° = 51°$

Side a: $\sin 39° = \dfrac{a}{86}$

$a = 86 \sin 39° \approx 54$ cm

Side b: $\cos 39° = \dfrac{b}{86}$

$b = 86 \cos 39° \approx 67$ cm

$m\angle B = 51°$, $a \approx 54$ cm, $b \approx 67$ cm

23. $\sin A = \dfrac{30}{50}$

$A = \sin^{-1}\left(\dfrac{30}{50}\right) \approx 37°$

24. $\tan A = \dfrac{10}{24}$

$A = \tan^{-1}\left(\dfrac{10}{24}\right) \approx 23°$

25. $\cos A = \dfrac{15}{17}$

$A = \cos^{-1}\left(\dfrac{15}{17}\right) \approx 28°$

26. $\sin A = \dfrac{11}{65}$

$A = \sin^{-1}\left(\dfrac{11}{65}\right) \approx 10°$

27. $x = 500\tan 40° + 500\tan 25°$

$x \approx 653$

28. $x = 100\tan 20° + 100\tan 8°$

$x \approx 50$

29. $x = 600\tan 28° - 600\tan 25°$

$x \approx 39$

30. $x = 400\tan 40° - 400\tan 28°$

$x \approx 123$

31. $x = \dfrac{300}{\tan 34°} - \dfrac{300}{\tan 64°}$

$x \approx 298$

32. $x = \dfrac{500}{\tan 20°} - \dfrac{500}{\tan 48°}$

$x \approx 924$

33. $x = \dfrac{400\tan 40° \tan 20°}{\tan 40° - \tan 20°}$

$x \approx 257$

34. $x = \dfrac{100\tan 43° \tan 38°}{\tan 43° - \tan 38°}$

$x \approx 482$

35. $\tan 40° = \dfrac{a}{630}$

$a = 630\tan 40° \approx 529$ yd

36. $\tan 40° = \dfrac{h}{35}$

$h = 35\tan 40° \approx 29$ ft

37. $\sin 10° = \dfrac{500}{c}$

$c = \dfrac{500}{\sin 10°} \approx 2879$ ft

38. $\sin 5° = \dfrac{a}{5000}$

$a = 5000\sin 5° \approx 436$ ft

39. Let h = the height of the tower.

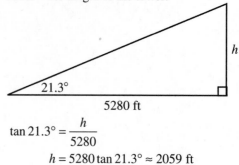

$\tan 21.3° = \dfrac{h}{5280}$

$h = 5280\tan 21.3° \approx 2059$ ft

40. Let h = the height of the building.

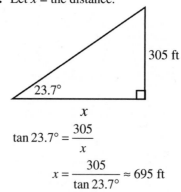

$\tan 38.7° = \dfrac{h}{30}$

$h = 30\tan 38.7° \approx 24$ yd ≈ 72 ft

41. Let x = the distance.

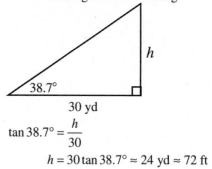

$\tan 23.7° = \dfrac{305}{x}$

$x = \dfrac{305}{\tan 23.7°} \approx 695$ ft

42. Let x = the distance.

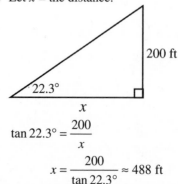

$\tan 22.3° = \dfrac{200}{x}$

$x = \dfrac{200}{\tan 22.3°} \approx 488$ ft

43. $\tan x = \dfrac{125}{172}$

$x = \tan^{-1}\left(\dfrac{125}{172}\right) \approx 36°$

44. $\tan x = \dfrac{555}{1320}$

$x = \tan^{-1}\left(\dfrac{555}{1320}\right) \approx 23°$

45. $m\angle P = 36°$

$\tan 36° = \dfrac{1000}{d}$

$d = \dfrac{1000}{\tan 36°} \approx 1376 \text{ ft}$

46. The angle of elevation from the car to the helicopter is also 72°.

$\tan 72° = \dfrac{800}{d}$

$d = \dfrac{800}{\tan 72°} \approx 260 \text{ ft}$

47. Let A = the angle of elevation.

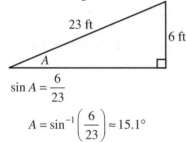

$\sin A = \dfrac{6}{23}$

$A = \sin^{-1}\left(\dfrac{6}{23}\right) \approx 15.1°$

48. Let A = the angle of elevation.

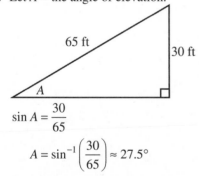

$\sin A = \dfrac{30}{65}$

$A = \sin^{-1}\left(\dfrac{30}{65}\right) \approx 27.5°$

57. does not make sense; Explanations will vary. Sample explanation: The sine is the ratio of two sides of the triangle. As the size of the triangle increases, this ratio does not change.

58. does not make sense; Explanations will vary. Sample explanation: The "adjacent" refers to the *leg* that is adjacent to the acute angle.

59. makes sense

60. makes sense

61. The sine and cosine of an acute angle cannot be greater than or equal to 1 because they are each the ratio of a leg of a right triangle to the hypotenuse. The hypotenuse of a right triangle is always the longest side; this results in a value less than 1.

62. As the angle gets close to 90°, the tangent gets very large. The tangent at 90° is undefined.

63.

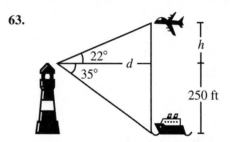

a. $\tan 35° = \dfrac{250}{d}$

$d = \dfrac{250}{\tan 35°} \approx 357 \text{ ft}$

b. $\tan 22° = \dfrac{h}{d} = \dfrac{h}{357}$

$h = 357 \tan 22° \approx 144 \text{ ft}$

Height of plane = 250 ft + 144 ft = 394 ft.

64.

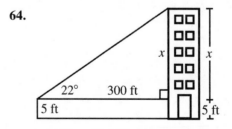

$\tan 22° = \dfrac{x}{300}$

$x = 300 \tan 22° \approx 121 \text{ ft}$

Height of building = 121 ft + 5 ft = 126 ft

Check Points 10.7

1. Answers will vary. Possible answer: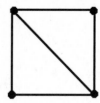

   The upper left and lower right vertices are odd.
   The lower left and upper right vertices are even.
   One possible tracing:
   Start at the upper left, trace around the square, then trace down the diagonal.

Exercise Set 10.7

1. **a.** *A* and *C* are even vertices.
   B and *D* are odd vertices.
   Because this graph has two odd vertices, by Euler's second rule, it is traversable.

   b. Sample path: *D, A, B, D, C, B*

2. **a.** *A, B, C* are even vertices. *D* and *E* are odd vertices. Because this graph has two odd vertices, by Euler's second rule, it is traversable.

   b. Sample path: *D, A, B, E, C, D, E*

3. **a.** *C, D, E* are even vertices.
   A and *B* are odd vertices.
   Because this graph has two odd vertices, by Euler's second rule, it is traversable.

   b. Sample path: *A, D, C, B, D, E, A, B*

4. **a.** *A, B, C* are even vertices. *D* and *E* are odd vertices. Because this graph has two odd vertices, by Euler's second rule, it is traversable.

   b. Sample path: *D, A, C, D, E, B, A, B, C, E*

5. *A, B, D, E* are odd vertices.
   Because this graph has more than two odd vertices, by Euler's third rule, it is not traversable.

6. **a.** *A, D, E, F* are even vertices. *B* and *C* are odd vertices. Because this graph has two odd vertices, by Euler's second rule, it is traversable.

   b. Sample path: *B, E, D, B, E, F, D, C, F, C, A, B, C*

7.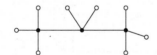

8. Each vertex for a carbon atom is even, with degree 4.
   Each vertex for a hydrogen atom is odd with degree 1.

9. No, the graph is not traversable because there are more than 2 odd vertices.

10. 2 doors connect room *A* to the outside. This is shown in the graph by connecting 2 edges from *A* to *E*.

11. 2 doors connect room *C* to the outside. This is shown in the graph by connecting 2 edges from *C* to *E*.

12. Yes. B and D are the only two odd vertices. It is traversable by Euler's second rule.

13. Sample path: *B, E, A, B, D, C, A, E, C, E, D*

14. 3

15. 2

16. 2

17. 4

18. Pitcher and wrench

19. Answers will vary.

20. The sum of the angles in such a triangle is greater than 180°.

21. The sum of the angles of such a quadrilateral is greater than 360°.

22. Yes

23. Yes

24. No

42. does not make sense; Explanations will vary. Sample explanation: The best way to determine if a graph is traversable is to check the degree of every vertex.

43. makes sense

44. does not make sense; Explanations will vary. Sample explanation: In non-Euclidean geometries, the sum of the angles is not necessarily 180˚.

45. does not make sense; Explanations will vary. Sample explanation: Euclidean geometry is limited in this regard.

Chapter 10 Review Exercises

1. $\angle 3$

2. $\angle 5$

3. $\angle 4$ and $\angle 6$

4. $\angle 1$ and $\angle 6$

5. $\angle 1$ and $\angle 4$

6. $\angle 2$

7. $\angle 5$

8. $180° - 115° = 65°$

9. $90° - 41° = 49°$

10. Measure of complement $= 90° - 73° = 17°$

11. Measure of supplement $= 180° - 46° = 134°$

12. $m\angle 1 = 180° - 70° = 110°$
$m\angle 2 = 70°$
$m\angle 3 = m\angle 1 = 110°$

13. $m\angle 1 = 180° - 42° = 138°$
$m\angle 2 = 42°$
$m\angle 3 = m\angle 1 = 138°$
$m\angle 4 = m\angle 1 = 138°$
$m\angle 5 = m\angle 2 = 42°$
$m\angle 6 = 42°$
$m\angle 7 = m\angle 3 = 138°$

14. $m\angle A = 180° - 60° - 48° = 72°$

15. $m\angle A = 90° - 39° = 51°$

16. $m\angle 1 = 180° - 50° - 40° = 90°$
$m\angle 2 = 180° - 90° = 90°$
$m\angle 3 = 180° - 40° = 140°$
$m\angle 4 = 40°$
$m\angle 5 = m\angle 3 = 140°$

17. $m\angle 2 = 180° - 115° = 65°$
$\angle 1$ is in a triangle with angles of $65°$ and $35°$.
Thus, $m\angle 1 = 180° - 65° - 35° = 80°$
$m\angle 3 = 115°$
$m\angle 4 = m\angle 1 = 80°$
$m\angle 5 = 180° - 80° = 100°$
$m\angle 6 = m\angle 1 = 80°$

18. $\dfrac{8}{4} = \dfrac{10}{x}$
$8x = 40$
$x = 5 \text{ ft}$

19. $\dfrac{9}{x} = \dfrac{7+5}{5}$
$\dfrac{9}{x} = \dfrac{12}{5}$
$12x = 45$
$x = \dfrac{45}{12} = 3.75 \text{ ft}$

20. $c^2 = 8^2 + 6^2$
$c^2 = 64 + 36$
$c^2 = 100$
$c = 10 \text{ ft}$

21. $c^2 = 6^2 + 4^2$
$c^2 = 36 + 16$
$c^2 = 52$
$c \approx 7.2 \text{ in.}$

22. $b^2 = 15^2 - 11^2$
$b^2 = 225 - 121$
$b^2 = 104$
$b \approx 10.2 \text{ cm}$

23. $\dfrac{x}{5} = \dfrac{9+6}{6}$
$\dfrac{x}{5} = \dfrac{15}{6}$
$6x = 75$
$x = 12.5 \text{ ft}$

24. $a^2 = 25^2 - 20^2$
$a^2 = 625 - 400$
$a^2 = 225$
$a = 15 \text{ ft}$

25. $b^2 = 13^2 + 5^2$
$b^2 = 169 - 25$
$b^2 = 144$
$b = 12 \text{ yd}$

26. Rectangle, square

27. Rhombus, square

28. Parallelogram, rhombus, trapezoid

29. $P = 2\,(6 \text{ cm}) + 2(9 \text{ cm})$
$= 12 \text{ cm} + 18 \text{ cm}$
$= 30 \text{ cm}$

30. $P = 2 \cdot 1000 \text{ yd} + 2 \cdot 1240 \text{ yd}$
$= 2000 \text{ yd} + 2480 \text{ yd}$
$= 4480 \text{ yd}$

31. First find the lengths of missing sides.

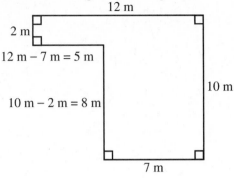

$P = 12\ \text{m} + 10\ \text{m} + 7\ \text{m} + 8\ \text{m} + 5\ \text{m} + 2\ \text{m}$
$\quad = 44\ \text{m}$

32. $\begin{aligned} \text{Sum} &= (n-2)\ 180° \\ &= (12-2)\ 180° \\ &= 10 \cdot 180° \\ &= 1800° \end{aligned}$

33. $\begin{aligned} \text{Sum} &= (n-2)\ 180° \\ &= (8-2)\ 180° \\ &= 6 \cdot 180° \\ &= 1080° \end{aligned}$

34. $\begin{aligned} \text{Sum of measures of angles} &= (n-2)180° \\ &= (8-2)180° \\ &= 6 \cdot 180° \\ &= 1080° \end{aligned}$

$m\angle 1 = \dfrac{1080°}{8} = 135°$
$m\angle 2 = 180° - 135° = 45°$

35. Amount of baseboard
$= \text{Perimeter of room} - \text{Lengths of doorways}$
$= 2 \cdot 35\ \text{ft} + 2 \cdot 15\ \text{ft} - 4 \cdot 3\ \text{ft}$
$= 70\ \text{ft} + 30\ \text{ft} - 12\ \text{ft}$
$= 88\ \text{ft}$

$\text{Cost} = \dfrac{\$1.50}{1\ \text{ft}} \cdot \dfrac{88\ \text{ft}}{1} = \$132$

36. a. triangles, hexagons

   b. The 5 angles that come together are
   $60°$, $60°$, $60°$, $60°$, and $120°$.

   c. The tessellation is possible because
   $60° + 60° + 60° + 60° + 120° = 360°$.

37. Each angle is $\dfrac{(n-2)\ 180°}{n} = \dfrac{(6-2)\ 180°}{6} = 120°$
Regular hexagons can be used to create a
tessellation because $360°$ is a multiple of $120°$.

38. $A = 5\ \text{ft} \cdot 6.5\ \text{ft} = 32.5\,\text{ft}^2$

39. $A = 5\ \text{m} \cdot 4\ \text{m} = 20\ \text{m}^2$

40. $A = \dfrac{1}{2} \cdot 20\ \text{cm} \cdot 5\ \text{cm} = 50\,\text{cm}^2$

41. $A = \dfrac{1}{2} \cdot 10\ \text{yd} \cdot (22\ \text{yd} + 5\ \text{yd})$
$\quad = \dfrac{1}{2} \cdot 10\ \text{yd} \cdot (27\ \text{yd})$
$\quad = 135\ \text{yd}^2$

42. $C = \pi \cdot 20\ \text{m} = 20\pi\ \text{m} \approx 62.8\ \text{m}$
$r = \dfrac{1}{2}d = \dfrac{1}{2} \cdot 20\ \text{m} = 10\ \text{m}$
$A = \pi r^2 = \pi(10\,\text{m})^2 = 100\pi\,\text{m}^2 \approx 314.2\ \text{m}^2$

43. $\begin{aligned} \text{Area} &= (\text{Area of square}) + (\text{Area of triangle}) \\ &= (12\ \text{in.})^2 + \dfrac{1}{2} \cdot 12\ \text{in.} \cdot 8\ \text{in.} \\ &= 144\ \text{in.}^2 + 48\ \text{in.}^2 \\ &= 192\ \text{in.}^2 \end{aligned}$

44. $\begin{aligned} \text{Area} &= (\text{Area of top rectangle}) \\ &\quad + (\text{Area of bottom rectangle}) \\ &= 8\ \text{m} \cdot 2\ \text{m} + 6\ \text{m} \cdot 2\ \text{m} \\ &= 16\ \text{m}^2 + 12\ \text{m}^2 \\ &= 28\ \text{m}^2 \end{aligned}$

45. $A = (\text{area of rectange}) - (\text{area of triangle})$
$A = (13\ \text{ft})(24\ \text{ft}) - \tfrac{1}{2}(5\ \text{ft})(13\ \text{ft})$
$A = 312\ \text{ft}^2 - 32.5\ \text{ft}^2$
$A = 279.5\ \text{ft}^2$

46. $A = (\text{area of rectange}) - 2(\text{area of small circle})$
$A = (8\ \text{in.})(16\ \text{in.}) - 2\left[\pi(4\ \text{in.})^2\right]$
$A = 128\ \text{in.}^2 - 32\pi\ \text{in.}^2$
$A = (128 - 32\pi)\ \text{in.}^2$
$A \approx 27.5\ \text{in.}^2$

47. First convert linear measurements in feet to linear yards.

$$15 \text{ ft} = \frac{15 \text{ ft}}{1} \cdot \frac{1 \text{ yd}}{3 \text{ ft}} = 5 \text{ yd}$$

$$21 \text{ ft} = \frac{21 \text{ ft}}{1} \cdot \frac{1 \text{ yd}}{3 \text{ ft}} = 7 \text{ yd}$$

$$\text{Area} = 5 \text{ yd} \cdot 7 \text{ yd} = 35 \text{ yd}^2$$

$$\text{Cost} = \frac{\$22.50}{1 \text{ yd}^2} \cdot \frac{35 \text{ yd}^2}{1} = \$787.50$$

48. Area of floor $= 40 \text{ ft} \cdot 50 \text{ ft} = 2000 \text{ ft}^2$

Area of each tile $= (2 \text{ ft})^2 = 4 \text{ ft}^2$

$$\text{Number of tiles} = \frac{2000 \text{ ft}^2}{4 \text{ ft}^2} = 500 \text{ tiles}$$

$$\text{Cost} = \frac{\$13}{10 \text{ tiles}} \cdot \frac{500 \text{ tiles}}{1} = \$650$$

49. $C = \pi d = \pi \cdot 10 \text{ yd} = 10\pi \text{ yd} \approx 31 \text{ yd}$

50. $V = 5 \text{ cm} \cdot 3 \text{ cm} \cdot 4 \text{ cm} = 60 \text{ cm}^3$

51. $V = $ (Volume of rectangular solid)
$\qquad\qquad + $ (Volume of Pyramid)

$$= 8 \text{ m} \cdot 9 \text{ m} \cdot 10 \text{ m} + \frac{1}{3}(8 \text{ m} \cdot 9 \text{ m}) \, 10 \text{ m}$$

$$\approx 720 \text{ m}^3 + 240 \text{ m}^3 = 960 \text{ m}^3$$

52. $V = \pi (4 \text{ yd})^2 \cdot 8 \text{ yd} = 128\pi \text{ yd}^3 \approx 402 \text{ yd}^3$

53. $V = \frac{1}{3}\pi (40 \text{ in.})^2 \cdot 28 \text{ in.}$

$\qquad = \frac{44,800}{3}\pi \text{ in.}^3 \approx 46,914 \text{ in.}^3$

54. $V = \frac{4}{3}\pi (6 \text{ m})^3 = 288\pi \text{ m}^3 \approx 905 \text{ m}^3$

55. Surface area
$= 2(5 \text{ m})(3 \text{ m}) + 2(3 \text{ m})(6 \text{ m}) + 2(5 \text{ m})(6 \text{ m})$
$= 30 \text{ m}^2 + 36 \text{ m}^2 + 60 \text{ m}^2$
$= 126 \text{ m}^2$

56. Volume of one box $= 8 \text{ m} \cdot 4 \text{ m} \cdot 3 \text{ m} = 96 \text{ m}^3$

Volume of 50 boxes $= 50 \cdot 96 \text{ m}^3 = 4800 \text{ m}^3$

57. $V = \frac{1}{3}(145 \text{ m})^2 \cdot 93 \text{ m} = 651,775 \text{ m}^3$

58. First convert linear measures in feet to linear yards.

$$27 \text{ ft} = \frac{27 \text{ ft}}{1} \cdot \frac{1 \text{ yd}}{3 \text{ ft}} = 9 \text{ yd}$$

$$4 \text{ ft} = \frac{4 \text{ ft}}{1} \cdot \frac{1 \text{ yd}}{3 \text{ ft}} = \frac{4}{3} \text{ yd}$$

$$6 \text{ in.} = \frac{6 \text{ in.}}{1} \cdot \frac{1 \text{ yd}}{36 \text{ in.}} = \frac{1}{6} \text{ yd}$$

$$\text{Volume} = 9 \text{ yd} \cdot \frac{4}{3} \text{ yd} \cdot \frac{1}{6} \text{ yd} = 2 \text{ yd}^3$$

$$\text{Cost} = \frac{\$40}{1 \text{ yd}^3} \cdot \frac{2 \text{ yd}^3}{1} = \$80$$

59. First compute length of hypotenuse
$c^2 = 12^2 + 9^2 = 144 + 81 = 225$
$c = 15$

$$\sin A = \frac{9}{15} = \frac{3}{5}$$

$$\cos A = \frac{12}{15} = \frac{4}{5}$$

$$\tan A = \frac{9}{12} = \frac{3}{4}$$

60. $\tan 23° = \dfrac{a}{100}$

$\qquad\quad a = 100 \tan 23° \approx 42 \text{ mm}$

61. $\sin 61° = \dfrac{20}{c}$

$\qquad\quad c = \dfrac{20}{\sin 61°} \approx 23 \text{ cm}$

62. $\sin 48° = \dfrac{a}{50}$

$\qquad\quad a = 50 \sin 48° \approx 37 \text{ in.}$

63. $\sin A = \dfrac{17}{20}$

$\qquad\quad A = \sin^{-1}\left(\dfrac{17}{20}\right) \approx 58°$

64. $\dfrac{1}{2} \text{ mi} = \dfrac{0.5 \text{ mi}}{1} \cdot \dfrac{5280 \text{ ft}}{1 \text{ mi}} = 2640 \text{ ft}$

$\qquad \sin 17° = \dfrac{h}{2640}$

$\qquad\qquad h = 2640 \sin 17° \approx 772 \text{ ft}$

65. $\tan 32° = \dfrac{d}{50}$

$d = 50 \tan 32° \approx 31$ m

66.

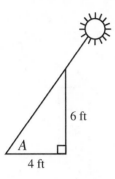

$\tan A = \dfrac{6}{4}$

$A = \tan^{-1}\left(\dfrac{6}{4}\right) \approx 56°$

67. The graph is not traversable because there are more than two odd vertices.

68. All vertices have even degrees, so the graph is traversable. Possible path: *A, B, C, D, A, B, C, D, A*

69. 0

70. 2

71. 1

72. 2

Chapter 10 Test

1. Measure of complement = $90° - 54° = 36°$
Measure of supplement = $180° - 54° = 126°$

2. $m\angle 1 = 133°$ because alternate exterior angles are equal.

3. $m\angle 1 = 180° - 40° - 70° = 70°$

4. First find measures of other angles of triangle.

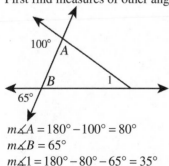

$m\angle A = 180° - 100° = 80°$
$m\angle B = 65°$
$m\angle 1 = 180° - 80° - 65° = 35°$

5. $\dfrac{x}{8} = \dfrac{4}{10}$

$10x = 4 \cdot 8$

$10x = 32$

$x = \dfrac{32}{10} = 3.2$ in.

6. $b^2 = 26^2 - 24^2$

$b^2 = 676 - 576$

$b^2 = 100$

$b = 10$ ft

7. Sum $= (n - 2)\,180°$
$= (10 - 2)\,180°$
$= 8 \cdot 180°$
$= 1440°$

8. First find lengths of missing sides.

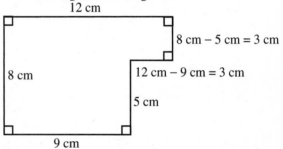

$P = 12$ cm $+ 3$ cm $+ 3$ cm $+ 5$ cm $+ 9$ cm $+ 8$ cm
$= 40$ cm

9. d

10. a. triangles, squares

b. The 5 angles that come together are $60°, 60°, 60°, 90°,$ and $90°$.

c. The tessellation is possible because $60° + 60° + 60° + 90° + 90° = 360°$.

11. $A = \dfrac{1}{2}bh$

$A = \dfrac{1}{2} \cdot 47\,\text{m} \cdot 22\,\text{m} = 517\,\text{m}^2$

12. $A = \dfrac{1}{2} \cdot 15\,\text{in.}(40\,\text{in.} + 30\,\text{in.})$

$= \dfrac{1}{2} \cdot 15\,\text{in.}(70\,\text{in.})$

$= 525\,\text{in.}^2$

13. a.
$$a^2 + b^2 = c^2$$
$$a^2 + 5^2 = 13^2$$
$$a^2 + 25 = 169$$
$$a^2 = 144$$
$$a = 12 \text{ cm}$$

b. $P = 5 \text{ cm} + 12 \text{ cm} + 13 \text{ cm} = 30 \text{ cm}$

c. $A = \frac{1}{2}bh = \frac{1}{2} \cdot 12 \text{ cm} \cdot 5 \text{ cm} = 30 \text{ cm}^2$

14. $C = \pi d = \pi \cdot 40 \text{ m} = 40\pi \text{ m} \approx 125.7 \text{ m}$
$A = \pi r^2 = \pi (20 \text{ m})^2 = 400\pi \text{ m}^2 \approx 1256.6 \text{ m}^2$

15. Area of floor $8 \text{ ft} \cdot 6 \text{ ft} = 48 \text{ ft}^2$
Convert inches to feet:
$$8 \text{ in.} = \frac{8 \text{ in.}}{1} \cdot \frac{1 \text{ ft}}{12 \text{ in.}} = \frac{2}{3} \text{ ft}$$
Area of one tile
$$= \left(\frac{2}{3} \text{ ft}\right)^2 = \frac{4}{9} \text{ ft}^2$$
Number of tiles
$$= \frac{48 \text{ ft}^2}{\frac{4}{9} \text{ ft}^2} = 108 \text{ tiles}$$

16. $V = 3 \text{ ft} \cdot 2 \text{ ft} \cdot 3 \text{ ft} = 18 \text{ ft}^3$

17. $V = \frac{1}{3}(4 \text{ m} \cdot 3 \text{ m}) 4 \text{ m} = 16 \text{ m}^3$

18. $V = \pi (5 \text{ cm})^2 \cdot 7 \text{ cm} = 175\pi \text{ cm}^3 \approx 550 \text{ cm}^3$

19. $\sin 28° = \dfrac{40}{c}$
$$c = \frac{40}{\sin 28°} \approx 85 \text{ cm}$$

20.

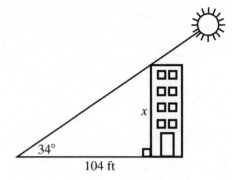

$$\tan 34° = \frac{h}{104}$$
$$h = 104 \tan 34° \approx 70 \text{ ft}$$

21. The graph is traversable because there are two odd vertices (*B* and *E*). Sample path: *BCAECDE*

Chapter 11
Counting Methods and Probability Theory

Check Points 11.1

1. Multiply the number of choices for each of the two courses of the meal:

    <u>Appetizers :</u> <u>Main Courses:</u>

    10 × 15 = 150

2. Multiply the number of choices for each of the two courses:

    <u>Psychology :</u> <u>Social Science:</u>

    10 × 4 = 40

3. Multiply the number of choices for each of the three decisions:

    <u>Size :</u> <u>Crust :</u> <u>Topping:</u>

    2 × 3 × 5 = 30

4. Multiply the number of choices for each of the five options:

    <u>Color:</u> <u>A/C:</u> <u>Electric/Gas:</u> <u>Onboard Computer:</u> <u>Global Positioning System:</u>

    10 × 2 × 2 × 2 × 2 = 160

5. Multiply the number of choices for each of the six questions:

    <u>Question #1:</u> <u>Question #2:</u> <u>Question #3:</u> <u>Question #4:</u> <u>Question #5:</u> <u>Question #6:</u>

    3 × 3 × 3 × 3 × 3 × 3 = 3^6 = 729

6. Multiply the number of choices for each of the five digits:

    $\overbrace{\text{Digit 1:}}^{1-9}$ $\overbrace{\text{Digit 2:}}^{0-9}$ $\overbrace{\text{Digit 3:}}^{0-9}$ $\overbrace{\text{Digit 4:}}^{0-9}$ $\overbrace{\text{Digit 5:}}^{0-9}$

    9 × 10 × 10 × 10 × 10 = 90,000

Exercise Set 11.1

1. $8 \cdot 10 = 80$

2. $9 \cdot 3 = 27$

3. $3 \cdot 4 = 12$

4. $5 \cdot 6 = 30$

5. $3 \cdot 2 = 6$

6. $26 \cdot 9 = 234$

7. Multiply the number of choices for each of the three decisions:

    <u>Drink:</u> <u>Size:</u> <u>Flavor:</u>

    2 × 4 × 5 = 40

8. Multiply the number of choices for each of the three decisions:

    <u>Size :</u> <u>Crust :</u> <u>Topping :</u>

    3 × 4 × 6 = 72

9. Multiply the number of choices for each of the four menu categories:

Main Course:		Vegetables:		Beverages:		Desserts:		
4	×	3	×	4	×	3	=	144

   This includes, for example, an order of ham and peas with tea and cake.
   This also includes an order of beef and peas with milk and pie.

10. Multiply the number of choices for each of the four apartment options:

Option A:		Option B:		Option C:		Option D:		
3	×	2	×	2	×	3	=	36

    This includes, for example, a first floor, golf course view apartment with one bedroom and one bathroom.
    This also includes a first floor, lake view apartment with two bedrooms and one bathroom.

11. Multiply the number of choices for each of the three categories:

Gender:		Age:		Payment method:		
2	×	2	×	2	=	8

12. Multiply the number of choices for each of the three groups of highways.

A to B:		B to C:		C to D:		
3	×	2	×	4	=	24

13. Multiply the number of choices for each of the five options:

Color:		A/C:		Transmission:		Windows:		CD Player:		
6	×	2	×	2	×	2	×	2	=	96

14. Multiply the number of choices for each of the five options:

Color:		A/C:		Sun Roof:		Transmission:		Brakes:		
9	×	2	×	2	×	2	×	2	=	144

15. Multiply the number of choices for each of the five questions:

Question 1:		Question 2:		Question 3:		Question 4:		Question 5:		
3	×	3	×	3	×	3	×	3	=	243

16. This situation involves making choices with eight groups of items. Each question is considered a group and each group has 3 choices. Multiply choices: $3 \times 3 \times 3 \times 3 \times 3 \times 3 \times 3 \times 3 = 3^8 = 6561$

17. Multiply the number of choices for each of the three digits:

Digit 1:		Digit 2:		Digit 3:		
8	×	2	×	9	=	144

18. Multiply the number of choices for each of the four digits:

Digit 4:		Digit 5:		Digit 6:		Digit 7:		
10	×	10	×	10	×	10	=	10,000

19. Multiply the number of choices for each of the letters and digits:

Letter 1:		Letter 2:		Digit 1:		Digit 2:		Digit 3:		
26	×	26	×	10	×	10	×	10	=	676,000

20. Multiply the number of choices for each of the four letters:

Letter 1:		Letter 2:		Letter 3:		Letter 4:		
2	×	26	×	26	×	26	=	35,152

21. This situation involves making choices with seven groups of items. Each stock is a group, and each group has three choices. Multiply choices: $3 \times 3 \times 3 \times 3 \times 3 \times 3 \times 3 = 3^7 = 2187$

22. This situation involves making choices with nine groups of items. Each digit is a group, and each group has ten choices. Multiply choices: $10 \times 10 \times 10 \times 10 \times 10 \times 10 \times 10 \times 10 \times 10 = 10^9 = 1,000,000,000$

26. makes sense

27. makes sense

28. does not make sense; Explanations will vary. Sample explanation: There are 26! or 403,291,461,126,605,635,584,000,000 ways to arrange these letters.

29. makes sense

30. Multiply the number of choices for each of the four digits:

	1–9		0–9		0–9		1, 3, 5, 7, 9		
	Digit 1:		Digit 2:		Digit 3:		Digit 4:		
	9	×	10	×	10	×	5	=	4500

31. Multiply the number of choices for each of the four groups of items:

Bun:		Sauce:		Lettuce:		Tomatoes:		
12	×	30	×	4	×	3	=	4320

Total time $= 10 \times 4320 = 43,200$ minutes, which is $43,200 \div 60 = 720$ hours.

Check Points 11.2

1. There are 5 men to choose from for the first joke. This leaves 5 choices for the second joke. The number of choices then decreases by 1 each time a joke is selected.

1st joke :		2nd joke:		3rd joke:		4th joke:		5th joke:		6th joke:	
5	×	5	×	4	×	3	×	2	×	1	= 600

2. The number of choices decreases by 1 each time a book is selected.

1st Book:		2nd Book:		3rd Book:		4th Book:		5th Book:	
5	×	4	×	3	×	2	×	1	= 120

3. a. $\dfrac{9!}{6!} = \dfrac{9 \cdot 8 \cdot 7 \cdot 6!}{6!} = \dfrac{9 \cdot 8 \cdot 7 \cdot \cancel{6!}}{\cancel{6!}} = 9 \cdot 8 \cdot 7 = 504$

b. $\dfrac{16!}{11!} = \dfrac{16 \cdot 15 \cdot 14 \cdot 13 \cdot 12 \cdot 11!}{11!} = \dfrac{16 \cdot 15 \cdot 14 \cdot 13 \cdot 12 \cdot \cancel{11!}}{\cancel{11!}} = 16 \cdot 15 \cdot 14 \cdot 13 \cdot 12 = 524,160$

c. $\dfrac{100!}{99!} = \dfrac{100 \cdot 99!}{99!} = \dfrac{100 \cdot \cancel{99!}}{\cancel{99!}} = 100$

4. $_7P_4 = \dfrac{7!}{(7-4)!} = \dfrac{7!}{3!} = \dfrac{7 \cdot 6 \cdot 5 \cdot 4 \cdot 3!}{3!} = \dfrac{7 \cdot 6 \cdot 5 \cdot 4 \cdot \cancel{3!}}{\cancel{3!}} = 7 \cdot 6 \cdot 5 \cdot 4 = 840$

5. $_9P_5 = \dfrac{9!}{(9-5)!} = \dfrac{9!}{4!} = \dfrac{9 \cdot 8 \cdot 7 \cdot 6 \cdot 5 \cdot 4!}{4!} = \dfrac{9 \cdot 8 \cdot 7 \cdot 6 \cdot 5 \cdot \cancel{4!}}{\cancel{4!}} = 9 \cdot 8 \cdot 7 \cdot 6 \cdot 5 = 15{,}120$

6. There a 7 letters with 2 O's and 3 S's. Thus, $\dfrac{n!}{p!q!} = \dfrac{7!}{2!3!} = \dfrac{7 \cdot 6 \cdot 5 \cdot 4 \cdot \cancel{3!}}{2 \cdot 1 \cdot \cancel{3!}} = 420$

Exercise Set 11.2

1. The number of choices decreases by 1 each time a performer is selected.

1st Performer :	2nd Performer:	3rd Performer:	4th Performer:	5th Performer:	6th Performer:	
6 ×	5 ×	4 ×	3 ×	2 ×	1	= 720

2. The number of choices decreases by 1 each time a singer is selected.

1st Singer:	2nd Singer:	3rd Singer:	4th Singer:	5th Singer:	
5 ×	4 ×	3 ×	2 ×	1	= 120

3. The number of choices decreases by 1 each time a sentence is selected.

1st Sentence:	2nd Sentence:	3rd Sentence:	4th Sentence:	5th Sentence:	
5 ×	4 ×	3 ×	2 ×	1	= 120

4. The number of choices decreases by 1 each time a suspect is selected.

1st Person :	2nd:	3rd Person:	4th:	5th Person:	6th:	7th Person:	8th:	
8 ×	7 ×	6 ×	5 ×	4 ×	3 ×	2 ×	1	= 40,320

5. There is only one choice for the 6th performer. The number of choices decreases by 1 each time a performer is selected.

1st Performer :	2nd Performer:	3rd Performer:	4th Performer:	5th Performer:	6th Performer:	
5 ×	4 ×	3 ×	2 ×	1 ×	1	= 120

6. There is only one choice for the 5th singer. The number of choices decreases by 1 each time a singer is selected.

1st Singer:	2nd Singer:	3rd Singer:	4th Singer:	5th Singer:	
4 ×	3 ×	2 ×	1 ×	1	= 24

7. The number of choices decreases by 1 each time a book is selected.

1st Book:	2nd:	3rd Book:	4th:	5th Book:	6th:	7th Book:	8th:	9th Book:	
9 ×	8 ×	7 ×	6 ×	5 ×	4 ×	3 ×	2 ×	1	= 362,880

8. The number of choices decreases by 1 each time a book is selected.

1st Photo:	2nd:	3rd Photo:	4th:	5th Photo:	6th:	7th Photo:	8th:	9th Photo:	10th:	
10 ×	9 ×	8 ×	7 ×	6 ×	5 ×	4 ×	3 ×	2 ×	1	= 3,628,800

9. There is only one choice each for the first and last sentences. For the other values, the number of choices decreases by 1 each time a sentence is selected.

1st Sentence:	2nd Sentence:	3rd Sentence:	4th Sentence:	5th Sentence:	
1 ×	3 ×	2 ×	1 ×	1	= 6

10. There is only one choice each for the first and second sentences. For the other values, the number of choices decreases by 1 each time a sentence is selected.

1st Sentence:	2nd Sentence:	3rd Sentence:	4th Sentence:	5th Sentence:	
1	× 1	× 3	× 2	× 1	= 6

11. There are two choices for the first movie and one for the second. There is only one choice for the last movie. This leaves two choices for the third movie and one for the fourth.

    $\overbrace{\hspace{3cm}}^{\text{G rated}}$ $\overbrace{\hspace{4cm}}^{\text{Other two movies}}$ $\overbrace{\hspace{2cm}}^{\text{NC-17 Rated}}$

1st Movie:	2nd Movie:	3rd Movie:	4th Movie:	5th Movie:	
2	× 1	× 2	× 1	× 1	= 4

12. There is only one choice each for the fourth and fifth seats. For the other values, the number of choices decreases by 1 each time a seat is selected.

    $\overbrace{\hspace{2cm}}^{\text{counselor}}$ $\overbrace{\hspace{2cm}}^{\text{food fighter}}$

1st Seat:	2nd Seat:	3rd Seat:	4th Seat:	5th Seat:	6th Seat:	7th Seat:	
5	× 4	× 3	× 1	× 1	× 2	× 1	= 120

13. $\dfrac{9!}{6!} = \dfrac{9 \cdot 8 \cdot 7 \cdot 6!}{6!} = 9 \cdot 8 \cdot 7 = 504$

14. $\dfrac{12!}{10!} = \dfrac{12 \cdot 11 \cdot 10!}{10!} = 12 \cdot 11 = 132$

15. $\dfrac{29!}{25!} = \dfrac{29 \cdot 28 \cdot 27 \cdot 26 \cdot 25!}{25!}$
    $= 29 \cdot 28 \cdot 27 \cdot 26$
    $= 570,024$

16. $\dfrac{31!}{28!} = \dfrac{31 \cdot 30 \cdot 29 \cdot 28!}{28!} = 31 \cdot 30 \cdot 29 = 26,970$

17. $\dfrac{19!}{11!} = \dfrac{19 \cdot 18 \cdot 17 \cdot 16 \cdot 15 \cdot 14 \cdot 13 \cdot 12 \cdot 11!}{11!}$
    $= 19 \cdot 18 \cdot 17 \cdot 16 \cdot 15 \cdot 14 \cdot 13 \cdot 12$
    $= 3,047,466,240$

18. $\dfrac{17!}{9!} = \dfrac{17 \cdot 16 \cdot 15 \cdot 14 \cdot 13 \cdot 12 \cdot 11 \cdot 10 \cdot 9!}{9!}$
    $= 17 \cdot 16 \cdot 15 \cdot 14 \cdot 13 \cdot 12 \cdot 11 \cdot 10$
    $= 980,179,200$

19. $\dfrac{600!}{599!} = \dfrac{600 \cdot 599!}{599!} = 600$

20. $\dfrac{700!}{699!} = \dfrac{700 \cdot 699!}{699!} = 700$

21. $\dfrac{104!}{102!} = \dfrac{104 \cdot 103 \cdot 102!}{102!} = 104 \cdot 103 = 10,712$

22. $\dfrac{106!}{104!} = \dfrac{106 \cdot 105 \cdot 104!}{104!} = 106 \cdot 105 = 11{,}130$

23. $7! - 3! = 5040 - 6 = 5034$

24. $6! - 3! = 720 - 6 = 714$

25. $(7-3)! = 4! = 4 \cdot 3 \cdot 2 \cdot 1 = 24$

26. $(6-3)! = 3! = 3 \cdot 2 \cdot 1 = 6$

27. $\left(\dfrac{12}{4}\right)! = 3! = 3 \cdot 2 \cdot 1 = 6$

28. $\left(\dfrac{45}{9}\right)! = 5! = 5 \cdot 4 \cdot 3 \cdot 2 \cdot 1 = 120$

29. $\dfrac{7!}{(7-2)!} = \dfrac{7!}{5!} = \dfrac{7 \cdot 6 \cdot 5!}{5!} = 7 \cdot 6 = 42$

30. $\dfrac{8!}{(8-5)!} = \dfrac{8!}{3!}$

$= \dfrac{8 \cdot 7 \cdot 6 \cdot 5 \cdot 4 \cdot 3!}{3!}$

$= 8 \cdot 7 \cdot 6 \cdot 5 \cdot 4$

$= 6720$

31. $\dfrac{13!}{(13-3)!} = \dfrac{13!}{10!}$

$= \dfrac{13 \cdot 12 \cdot 11 \cdot 10!}{10!}$

$= 13 \cdot 12 \cdot 11$

$= 1716$

32. $\dfrac{17!}{(17-3)!} = \dfrac{17!}{14!}$

$= \dfrac{17 \cdot 16 \cdot 15 \cdot 14!}{14!}$

$= 17 \cdot 16 \cdot 15$

$= 4080$

33. $_9P_4 = \dfrac{9!}{(9-4)!}$

$= \dfrac{9!}{5!}$

$= \dfrac{9 \cdot 8 \cdot 7 \cdot 6 \cdot 5!}{5!}$

$= 9 \cdot 8 \cdot 7 \cdot 6$

$= 3024$

34. $_7P_3 = \dfrac{7!}{(7-3)!}$

$= \dfrac{7!}{4!}$

$= \dfrac{7 \cdot 6 \cdot 5 \cdot 4!}{4!}$

$= 7 \cdot 6 \cdot 5$

$= 210$

35. $_8P_5 = \dfrac{8!}{(8-5)!}$

$= \dfrac{8!}{3!}$

$= \dfrac{8 \cdot 7 \cdot 6 \cdot 5 \cdot 4 \cdot 3!}{3!}$

$= 8 \cdot 7 \cdot 6 \cdot 5 \cdot 4$

$= 6720$

36. $_{10}P_4 = \dfrac{10!}{(10-4)!}$

$= \dfrac{10!}{6!}$

$= \dfrac{10 \cdot 9 \cdot 8 \cdot 7 \cdot 6!}{6!}$

$= 10 \cdot 9 \cdot 8 \cdot 7$

$= 5040$

37. $_6P_6 = \dfrac{6!}{(6-6)!} = \dfrac{6!}{0!} = \dfrac{6 \cdot 5 \cdot 4 \cdot 3 \cdot 2 \cdot 1}{1} = 720$

38. $_9P_9 = \dfrac{9!}{(9-9)!}$

$= \dfrac{9!}{0!}$

$= \dfrac{9 \cdot 8 \cdot 7 \cdot 6 \cdot 5 \cdot 4 \cdot 3 \cdot 2 \cdot 1}{1}$

$= 362{,}880$

39. $_8P_0 = \dfrac{8!}{(8-0)!} = \dfrac{8!}{8!} = 1$

40. $_6P_0 = \dfrac{6!}{(6-0)!} = \dfrac{6!}{6!} = 1$

41. $_{10}P_3 = \dfrac{10!}{(10-3)!}$

$= \dfrac{10!}{7!}$

$= \dfrac{10 \cdot 9 \cdot 8 \cdot 7!}{7!}$

$= 10 \cdot 9 \cdot 8$

$= 720$

42. $_7P_4 = \dfrac{7!}{(7-4)!}$

$= \dfrac{7!}{3!}$

$= \dfrac{7 \cdot 6 \cdot 5 \cdot 4 \cdot 3!}{3!}$

$= 7 \cdot 6 \cdot 5 \cdot 4$

$= 840$

43. $_{13}P_7 = \dfrac{13!}{(13-7)!}$

$= \dfrac{13!}{6!}$

$= \dfrac{13 \cdot 12 \cdot 11 \cdot 10 \cdot 9 \cdot 8 \cdot 7 \cdot 6!}{6!}$

$= 13 \cdot 12 \cdot 11 \cdot 10 \cdot 9 \cdot 8 \cdot 7$

$= 8,648,640$

44. $_{20}P_3 = \dfrac{20!}{(20-3)!}$

$= \dfrac{20!}{17!}$

$= \dfrac{20 \cdot 19 \cdot 18 \cdot 17!}{17!}$

$= 20 \cdot 19 \cdot 18$

$= 6840$

45. $_6P_3 = \dfrac{6!}{(6-3)!}$

$= \dfrac{6!}{3!}$

$= \dfrac{6 \cdot 5 \cdot 4 \cdot 3!}{3!}$

$= 6 \cdot 5 \cdot 4$

$= 120$

46. $_8P_3 = \dfrac{8!}{(8-3)!}$

$= \dfrac{8!}{5!}$

$= \dfrac{8 \cdot 7 \cdot 6 \cdot 5!}{5!}$

$= 8 \cdot 7 \cdot 6$

$= 336$

47. $_9P_5 = \dfrac{9!}{(9-5)!}$

$= \dfrac{9!}{4!}$

$= \dfrac{9 \cdot 8 \cdot 7 \cdot 6 \cdot 5 \cdot 4!}{4!}$

$= 9 \cdot 8 \cdot 7 \cdot 6 \cdot 5$

$= 15,120$

48. $_7P_4 = \dfrac{7!}{(7-4)!}$

$= \dfrac{7!}{3!}$

$= \dfrac{7 \cdot 6 \cdot 5 \cdot 4 \cdot 3!}{3!}$

$= 7 \cdot 6 \cdot 5 \cdot 4$

$= 840$

49. $\dfrac{n!}{p!q!} = \dfrac{6!}{2!2!} = \dfrac{6 \cdot 5 \cdot 4 \cdot 3 \cdot 2 \cdot 1}{2 \cdot 1 \cdot 2 \cdot 1} = 180$

50. $\dfrac{n!}{p!q!} = \dfrac{7!}{2!2!} = \dfrac{7 \cdot 6 \cdot 5 \cdot 4 \cdot 3 \cdot 2 \cdot 1}{2 \cdot 1 \cdot 2 \cdot 1} = 1260$

51. $\dfrac{n!}{p!q!r!s!} = \dfrac{11!}{3!2!2!2!}$

$= \dfrac{11 \cdot 10 \cdot 9 \cdot 8 \cdot 7 \cdot 6 \cdot 5 \cdot 4 \cdot \cancel{3!}}{\cancel{3!} \cdot 2 \cdot 1 \cdot 2 \cdot 1 \cdot 2 \cdot 1}$

$= 831,600$

52. $\dfrac{n!}{p!q!r!} = \dfrac{9!}{4!2!2!} = \dfrac{9 \cdot 8 \cdot 7 \cdot 6 \cdot 5 \cdot \cancel{4!}}{\cancel{4!} \cdot 2 \cdot 1 \cdot 2 \cdot 1} = 3780$

53. $\dfrac{n!}{p!q!} = \dfrac{7!}{4!2!} = \dfrac{7 \cdot 6 \cdot 5 \cdot \cancel{4!}}{\cancel{4!} \cdot 2 \cdot 1} = 105$

54. $\dfrac{n!}{p!q!r!} = \dfrac{7!}{2!2!2!} = \dfrac{7 \cdot 6 \cdot 5 \cdot 4 \cdot 3 \cdot 2 \cdot 1}{2 \cdot 1 \cdot 2 \cdot 1 \cdot 2 \cdot 1} = 630$

55. $\dfrac{n!}{p!q!} = \dfrac{8!}{4!3!} = \dfrac{8 \cdot 7 \cdot 6 \cdot 5 \cdot \cancel{4!}}{\cancel{4!} \cdot 3 \cdot 2 \cdot 1} = 280$

56. $\dfrac{n!}{p!q!} = \dfrac{9!}{5!3!} = \dfrac{9 \cdot 8 \cdot 7 \cdot 6 \cdot \cancel{5!}}{\cancel{5!} \cdot 3 \cdot 2 \cdot 1} = 504$

63. Because the letter B is repeated in the word BABE, the number of permutations is given by $\dfrac{n!}{p!} = \dfrac{4!}{2!} = \dfrac{4 \cdot 3 \cdot 2 \cdot 1}{2 \cdot 1} = 12$

64. makes sense

65. makes sense

66. does not make sense; Explanations will vary. Sample explanation: Since the order does not matter, this situation calls for the combination formula.

67. does not make sense; Explanations will vary. Sample explanation: This situation calls for the formula for permutations of duplicate items.

68. $_{12}P_{10} = \dfrac{12!}{(12-10)!}$

$\qquad = \dfrac{12!}{2!}$

$\qquad = \dfrac{12 \cdot 11 \cdot 10 \cdot 9 \cdot 8 \cdot 7 \cdot 6 \cdot 5 \cdot 4 \cdot 3 \cdot 2!}{2!}$

$\qquad = 12 \cdot 11 \cdot 10 \cdot 9 \cdot 8 \cdot 7 \cdot 6 \cdot 5 \cdot 4 \cdot 3$

$\qquad = 239,500,800$

69. Multiply the number of ways to select the two first place horses by the number of orders in which the remaining four horses can finish.
$_6C_2 \times _4P_4 = 15 \times 24 = 360$

70. First select 3 out of the 8 jazz groups.

There are $_8P_3 = \dfrac{8!}{(8-3)!} = \dfrac{8!}{5!} = 336$ ways to arrange the 1st, 3rd, and 8th performers.

This leaves 13 groups (5 remaining jazz groups and 8 rock groups) to be arranged.

There are $_{13}P_{13} = \dfrac{13!}{(13-13)!} = \dfrac{13!}{0!} = 13! = 6,227,020,800$ ways to arrange the remaining performers.

The total number of arrangements is found by multiplying these values: $336 \times 6,227,020,800 = 2.09 \times 10^{12}$

71. There are 5! ways to arrange the women, and 5! ways to arrange the men. The total number of arrangements is found by multiplying these values: $(5!)(5!) = 120 \cdot 120 = 14,400$

72. Multiply the number of choices for each of the four digits:

2, 4	2, 4, 6, 7, 8, 9	2, 4, 6, 7, 8, 9	7, 9		
Digit 1:	Digit 2:	Digit 3:	Digit 4:		
2 ×	6 ×	6 ×	2	=	144

73. $_nP_{n-2} = \dfrac{n!}{(n-(n-2))!} = \dfrac{n!}{(n-n+2)!} = \dfrac{n!}{2!} = \dfrac{n(n-1)(n-2) \times \cdots \times 3 \times 2 \times 1}{2} = n(n-1)(n-2) \times \cdots \times 3$

Check Points 11.3

1. **a.** The order in which you select the DVDs does not matter. This problem involves combinations.

   b. Order matters. This problem involves permutations.

2. $_7C_3 = \dfrac{7!}{(7-3)!3!} = \dfrac{7!}{4!3!} = \dfrac{7 \cdot 6 \cdot 5 \cdot 4!}{4! \cdot 3 \cdot 2 \cdot 1} = \dfrac{7 \cdot 6 \cdot 5 \cdot \cancel{4!}}{\cancel{4!} \cdot 3 \cdot 2 \cdot 1} = \dfrac{7 \cdot 6 \cdot 5}{3 \cdot 2 \cdot 1} = 35$

   35 such combinations are possible.

3. $_{16}C_4 = \dfrac{16!}{(16-4)!4!} = \dfrac{16!}{12!4!} = \dfrac{16 \cdot 15 \cdot 14 \cdot 13 \cdot 12!}{12! \cdot 4 \cdot 3 \cdot 2 \cdot 1} = \dfrac{16 \cdot 15 \cdot 14 \cdot 13 \cdot \cancel{12!}}{\cancel{12!} \cdot 4 \cdot 3 \cdot 2 \cdot 1} = \dfrac{16 \cdot 15 \cdot 14 \cdot 13}{4 \cdot 3 \cdot 2 \cdot 1} = 1820$

   1820 such hands can be dealt.

4. Choose the male bears: $_6C_2 = \dfrac{6!}{(6-2)!2!} = \dfrac{6!}{4!2!} = \dfrac{6 \cdot 5 \cdot 4!}{4! \cdot 2 \cdot 1} = \dfrac{6 \cdot 5 \cdot \cancel{4!}}{\cancel{4!} \cdot 2 \cdot 1} = \dfrac{30}{2} = 15$

   Choose the female bears: $_7C_3 = \dfrac{7!}{(7-3)!3!} = \dfrac{7!}{4!3!} = \dfrac{7 \cdot 6 \cdot 5 \cdot 4!}{4! \cdot 3 \cdot 2 \cdot 1} = \dfrac{7 \cdot 6 \cdot 5 \cdot \cancel{4!}}{\cancel{4!} \cdot 3 \cdot 2 \cdot 1} = \dfrac{210}{6} = 35$

   Multiply the choices: $15 \times 35 = 525$
   There are 525 five-bear collections possible.

Exercise Set 11.3

1. Order does not matter. This problem involves combinations.

2. Order matters. This problem involves permutations.

3. Order matters. This problem involves permutations.

4. Order does not matter. This problem involves combinations.

5. $_6C_5 = \dfrac{6!}{(6-5)!5!} = \dfrac{6!}{1!5!} = \dfrac{6 \cdot 5!}{1 \cdot 5!} = 6$

6. $_8C_7 = \dfrac{8!}{(8-7)!7!} = \dfrac{8!}{1!7!} = \dfrac{8 \cdot 7!}{1 \cdot 7!} = 8$

7. $_9C_5 = \dfrac{9!}{(9-5)!5!} = \dfrac{9!}{4!5!} = \dfrac{9 \cdot 8 \cdot 7 \cdot 6 \cdot 5!}{4 \cdot 3 \cdot 2 \cdot 1 \cdot 5!} = 126$

8. $_{10}C_6 = \dfrac{10!}{(10-6)!6!} = \dfrac{10!}{4!6!} = \dfrac{10 \cdot 9 \cdot 8 \cdot 7 \cdot 6!}{4 \cdot 3 \cdot 2 \cdot 1 \cdot 6!} = 210$

9. $_{11}C_4 = \dfrac{11!}{(11-4)!4!} = \dfrac{11!}{7!4!} = \dfrac{11 \cdot 10 \cdot 9 \cdot 8 \cdot 7!}{7! \cdot 4 \cdot 3 \cdot 2 \cdot 1} = 330$

10. $_{12}C_5 = \dfrac{12!}{(12-5)!5!} = \dfrac{12!}{7!5!} = \dfrac{12 \cdot 11 \cdot 10 \cdot 9 \cdot 8 \cdot 7!}{7! \cdot 5 \cdot 4 \cdot 3 \cdot 2 \cdot 1} = 792$

11. $_8C_1 = \dfrac{8!}{(8-1)!1!} = \dfrac{8!}{7!1!} = \dfrac{8\cdot 7!}{7!1} = 8$

12. $_7C_1 = \dfrac{7!}{(7-1)!1!} = \dfrac{7!}{6!1!} = \dfrac{7\cdot 6!}{6!1} = 7$

13. $_7C_7 = \dfrac{7!}{(7-7)!7!} = \dfrac{7!}{0!7!} = 1$

14. $_4C_4 = \dfrac{4!}{(4-4)!4!} = \dfrac{4!}{0!4!} = 1$

15. $_{30}C_3 = \dfrac{30!}{(30-3)!3!} = \dfrac{30!}{27!3!} = \dfrac{30\cdot 29\cdot 28\cdot 27!}{27!\cdot 3\cdot 2\cdot 1} = 4060$

16. $_{25}C_4 = \dfrac{25!}{(25-4)!4!} = \dfrac{25!}{21!4!} = \dfrac{25\cdot 24\cdot 23\cdot 22\cdot 21!}{21!\cdot 4\cdot 3\cdot 2\cdot 1} = 12{,}650$

17. $_5C_0 = \dfrac{5!}{(5-0)!0!} = \dfrac{5!}{5!0!} = 1$

18. $_6C_0 = \dfrac{6!}{(6-0)!0!} = \dfrac{6!}{6!0!} = 1$

19. $\dfrac{_7C_3}{_5C_4} = \dfrac{\frac{7!}{(7-3)!3!}}{\frac{5!}{(5-4)!4!}} = \dfrac{\frac{7!}{4!3!}}{\frac{5!}{1!4!}} = \dfrac{\frac{7\cdot 6\cdot 5\cdot 4!}{4!\cdot 3\cdot 2\cdot 1}}{\frac{5\cdot 4!}{1\cdot 4!}} = \dfrac{35}{5} = 7$

20. $\dfrac{_{10}C_3}{_6C_4} = \dfrac{\frac{10!}{(10-3)!3!}}{\frac{6!}{(6-4)!4!}} = \dfrac{\frac{10!}{7!3!}}{\frac{6!}{2!4!}} = \dfrac{\frac{10\cdot 9\cdot 8\cdot 7!}{7!\cdot 3\cdot 2\cdot 1}}{\frac{6\cdot 5\cdot 4!}{2\cdot 1\cdot 4!}} = \dfrac{120}{15} = 8$

21. $\dfrac{_7P_3}{3!} - {_7C_3} = \dfrac{\frac{7!}{(7-3)!}}{3!} - \dfrac{7!}{(7-3)!3!} = \dfrac{\frac{7!}{4!}}{3!} - \dfrac{7!}{4!3!} = \dfrac{7!}{4!3!} - \dfrac{7!}{4!3!} = 0$

22. $\dfrac{_{20}P_2}{2!} - {_{20}C_2} = \dfrac{\frac{20!}{(20-2)!}}{2!} - \dfrac{20!}{(20-2)!2!} = \dfrac{20!}{(20-2)!2!} - \dfrac{20!}{(20-2)!2!} = 0$

23. $1 - \dfrac{_3P_2}{_4P_3} = 1 - \dfrac{\frac{3!}{(3-2)!}}{\frac{4!}{(4-3)!}} = 1 - \dfrac{\frac{3!}{1!}}{\frac{4!}{1!}} = 1 - \dfrac{3!}{4!} = 1 - \dfrac{3!}{4\cdot 3!} = 1 - \dfrac{1}{4} = \dfrac{3}{4}$

24. $1 - \dfrac{_5P_3}{_{10}P_4} = 1 - \dfrac{\frac{5!}{(5-3)!}}{\frac{10!}{(10-4)!}} = 1 - \dfrac{\frac{5!}{2!}}{\frac{10!}{6!}} = 1 - \dfrac{5!}{2!}\cdot\dfrac{6!}{10!} = 1 - \dfrac{5\cdot 4\cdot 3\cdot \cancel{2!}\cdot \cancel{6!}}{\cancel{2!}\cdot 10\cdot 9\cdot 8\cdot 7\cdot \cancel{6!}} = 1 - \dfrac{60}{5040} = \dfrac{83}{84}$

25. $\dfrac{_7C_3}{_5C_4} - \dfrac{98!}{96!} = \dfrac{\dfrac{7!}{(7-3)!3!}}{\dfrac{5!}{(5-4)!4!}} - \dfrac{98\cdot97\cdot96!}{96!} = \dfrac{\dfrac{7!}{4!3!}}{\dfrac{5!}{1!4!}} - 95067 = \dfrac{\dfrac{7\cdot6\cdot5\cdot4!}{4!3\cdot2\cdot1}}{\dfrac{5\cdot4!}{1!4!}} - 9506 = \dfrac{35}{5} - 9506 = 7 - 9506 = -9499$

26. $\dfrac{_{10}C_3}{_6C_4} - \dfrac{46!}{44!} = \dfrac{\dfrac{10!}{(10-3)!3!}}{\dfrac{6!}{(6-4)!4!}} - \dfrac{46\cdot45\cdot44!}{44!} = \dfrac{\dfrac{10!}{7!3!}}{\dfrac{6!}{2!4!}} - 46\cdot45 = \dfrac{\dfrac{10\cdot9\cdot8\cdot7!}{7!3!}}{\dfrac{6!}{2!4!}} - 2070 = \dfrac{\dfrac{10\cdot9\cdot8}{3\cdot2\cdot1}}{\dfrac{6\cdot5}{2\cdot1}} - 2070$

$= \dfrac{10\cdot9\cdot8}{3\cdot6\cdot5} - 2070 = 8 - 2070 = -2062$

27. $\dfrac{_4C_2\cdot_6C_1}{_{18}C_3} = \dfrac{\dfrac{4!}{(4-2)!2!}\cdot\dfrac{6!}{(6-1)!1!}}{\dfrac{18!}{(18-3)!3!}} = \dfrac{\dfrac{4!}{2!2!}\cdot\dfrac{6!}{5!1!}}{\dfrac{18!}{15!3!}} = \dfrac{\dfrac{4\cdot3\cdot2!}{2!2\cdot1}\cdot\dfrac{6\cdot5!}{5!1!}}{\dfrac{18\cdot17\cdot16\cdot15!}{15!3\cdot2\cdot1}} = \dfrac{36}{816} = \dfrac{3}{68}$

28. $\dfrac{_5C_1\cdot_7C_2}{_{12}C_3} = \dfrac{\dfrac{5!}{(5-1)!1!}\cdot\dfrac{7!}{(7-2)!2!}}{\dfrac{12!}{(12-3)!3!}} = \dfrac{\dfrac{5!}{4!1!}\cdot\dfrac{7!}{5!2!}}{\dfrac{12!}{9!3!}} = \dfrac{\dfrac{5\cdot4!}{4!\cdot1}\cdot\dfrac{7\cdot6\cdot5!}{5!\cdot2\cdot1}}{\dfrac{12\cdot11\cdot10\cdot9!}{9!\cdot3\cdot2\cdot1}} = \dfrac{1260}{2640} = \dfrac{21}{44}$

29. $_6C_3 = \dfrac{6!}{(6-3)!3!} = \dfrac{6!}{3!3!} = \dfrac{6\cdot5\cdot4\cdot3!}{3!3\cdot2\cdot1} = 20$

30. $_{11}C_4 = \dfrac{11!}{(11-4)!4!} = \dfrac{11!}{7!4!} = \dfrac{11\cdot10\cdot9\cdot8\cdot7!}{7!4\cdot3\cdot2\cdot1} = 330$

31. $_{12}C_4 = \dfrac{12!}{(12-4)!4!} = \dfrac{12!}{8!4!} = \dfrac{12\cdot11\cdot10\cdot9\cdot8!}{8!4\cdot3\cdot2\cdot1} = 495$

32. $_{14}C_6 = \dfrac{14!}{(14-6)!6!} = \dfrac{14!}{8!6!} = \dfrac{14\cdot13\cdot12\cdot11\cdot10\cdot9\cdot8!}{8!6\cdot5\cdot4\cdot3\cdot2\cdot1} = 3003$

33. $_{17}C_8 = \dfrac{17!}{(17-8)!8!} = \dfrac{17!}{9!8!} = \dfrac{17\cdot16\cdot15\cdot14\cdot13\cdot12\cdot11\cdot10\cdot9!}{9!8\cdot7\cdot6\cdot5\cdot4\cdot3\cdot2\cdot1} = 24,310$

34. $_{100}C_{18} = \dfrac{100!}{(100-18)!18!} = \dfrac{100!}{82!18!}$

$= \dfrac{100\cdot99\cdot98\cdot97\cdot96\cdot95\cdot94\cdot93\cdot92\cdot91\cdot90\cdot89\cdot88\cdot87\cdot86\cdot85\cdot84\cdot83\cdot82!}{82!18\cdot17\cdot16\cdot15\cdot14\cdot13\cdot12\cdot11\cdot10\cdot9\cdot8\cdot7\cdot6\cdot5\cdot4\cdot3\cdot2\cdot1} \approx 3.07\times10^{19}$

35. $_{53}C_6 = \dfrac{53!}{(53-6)!6!} = \dfrac{53!}{47!6!} = \dfrac{53\cdot52\cdot51\cdot50\cdot49\cdot48\cdot47!}{47!6\cdot5\cdot4\cdot3\cdot2\cdot1} = 22,957,480$

36. $_{59}C_6 = \dfrac{59!}{(59-6)!6!} = \dfrac{59!}{53!6!} = \dfrac{59\cdot58\cdot57\cdot56\cdot55\cdot54\cdot53!}{53!6\cdot5\cdot4\cdot3\cdot2\cdot1} = 45,057,474$

37. Choose the men: $_7C_4 = \dfrac{7!}{(7-4)!4!} = \dfrac{7!}{3!4!} = \dfrac{7\cdot 6\cdot 5\cdot 4!}{3\cdot 2\cdot 1\cdot 4!} = 35$

Choose the women: $_7C_5 = \dfrac{7!}{(7-5)!5!} = \dfrac{7!}{2!5!} = \dfrac{7\cdot 6\cdot 5!}{2\cdot 1\cdot 5!} = 21$

Multiply the choices: $35 \cdot 21 = 735$

38. Choose the professors: $_5C_2 = \dfrac{5!}{(5-2)!2!} = \dfrac{5!}{3!2!} = \dfrac{5\cdot 4\cdot 3!}{3!2\cdot 1} = 10$

Choose the students: $_{15}C_{10} = \dfrac{15!}{(15-10)!10!} = \dfrac{15!}{5!10!} = \dfrac{15\cdot 14\cdot 13\cdot 12\cdot 11\cdot 10!}{5\cdot 4\cdot 3\cdot 2\cdot 1\cdot 10!} = 3003$

Multiply the choices: $10 \times 3003 = 30{,}030$

39. Choose the Republicans: $_{55}C_4 = \dfrac{55!}{(55-4)!4!} = \dfrac{55!}{51!4!} = \dfrac{55\cdot 54\cdot 53\cdot 52\cdot 51!}{51!\cdot 4\cdot 3\cdot 2\cdot 1} = 341{,}055$

Choose the Democrats: $_{44}C_3 = \dfrac{44!}{(44-3)!3!} = \dfrac{44!}{41!3!} = \dfrac{44\cdot 43\cdot 42\cdot 41!}{3\cdot 2\cdot 1\cdot 41!} = 13{,}244$

Multiply the choices: $341{,}055 \times 13{,}244 = 4{,}516{,}932{,}420$

40. Choose the multiple-choice questions: $_{10}C_8 = \dfrac{10!}{(10-8)!8!} = \dfrac{10!}{2!8!} = \dfrac{10\cdot 9\cdot 8!}{2\cdot 1\cdot 8!} = 45$

Choose the open-ended problems: $_5C_3 = \dfrac{5!}{(5-3)!3!} = \dfrac{5!}{2!3!} = \dfrac{5\cdot 4\cdot 3!}{2\cdot 1\cdot 3!} = 10$

Multiply the choices: $45 \cdot 10 = 450$

41. $_6P_4 = \dfrac{6!}{2!} = 6\cdot 5\cdot 4\cdot 3 = 360$ ways

42. $_{40}C_8 = \dfrac{40!}{32!8!} = 76{,}904{,}685$ selections

43. $_{13}C_6 = \dfrac{13!}{7!6!} = \dfrac{13\cdot 12\cdot 11\cdot 10\cdot 9\cdot 8}{6\cdot 5\cdot 4\cdot 3\cdot 2\cdot 1}$

$\qquad = 1716$ ways

44. $_{50}P_3 = \dfrac{50!}{47!} = 50\cdot 49\cdot 48 = 177{,}600$ ways

45. $_{20}C_3 = \dfrac{20!}{17!3!} = \dfrac{20\cdot 19\cdot 18}{3\cdot 2\cdot 1} = 1140$ ways

46. $_{50}C_3 = \dfrac{50!}{47!3!} = \dfrac{50\cdot 49\cdot 48}{3\cdot 2\cdot 1} = 19{,}600$ ways

47. $_7P_4 = \dfrac{7!}{3!} = 840$ passwords

48. $_9P_5 = \dfrac{9!}{4!} = 9\cdot 8\cdot 7\cdot 6\cdot 5 = 15{,}120$ ways

49. $_{15}P_3 = \dfrac{15!}{12!} = 15\cdot 14\cdot 13 = 2730$ cones

50. $_{31}C_3 = \dfrac{31!}{28!3!} = \dfrac{31 \cdot 30 \cdot 29}{3 \cdot 2 \cdot 1} = 4495$ bowls

51. $_5C_2 = \dfrac{5!}{3!2!} = \dfrac{5 \cdot 4}{2 \cdot 1} = 10$ outcomes

52. $_6C_3 = \dfrac{6!}{3!3!} = \dfrac{6 \cdot 5 \cdot 4}{3 \cdot 2 \cdot 1} = 20$ groups

53. $3 \times 2 \times 2 = 12$ outcomes

54. $_4C_2 = \dfrac{4!}{2!2!} = \dfrac{4 \cdot 3}{2 \cdot 1} = 6$ outcomes

55. $_5C_3 = \dfrac{5!}{2!3!} = \dfrac{5 \cdot 4}{2 \cdot 1} = 20$ outcomes

56. $_4C_3 = \dfrac{4!}{1!3!} = \dfrac{4}{1} = 4$ ways

57. Choose the Democrats: $_4C_2 = \dfrac{4!}{2!2!} = \dfrac{4 \cdot 3}{2 \cdot 1} = 6$

Choose the Republicans: $_5C_2 = \dfrac{5!}{3!2!} = \dfrac{5 \cdot 4}{2 \cdot 1} = 10$

Multiply the choices: $6 \cdot 10 = 60$

58. $_6C_2 = \dfrac{6!}{4!2!} = \dfrac{6 \cdot 5}{2 \cdot 1} = 15$ ways

59. $_{12}P_5 = \dfrac{12!}{(12-5)!} = 12 \cdot 11 \cdot 10 \cdot 9 \cdot 8 = 95{,}040$ ways

60. $_7P_2 = \dfrac{7!}{(7-2)!} = 7 \cdot 6 = 42$ outcomes

61. $_6P_6 = \dfrac{6!}{(6-6)!} = 6 \cdot 5 \cdot 4 \cdot 3 \cdot 2 \cdot 1 = 720$ ways

62. $_5P_5 = \dfrac{5!}{(5-5)!} = 5 \cdot 4 \cdot 3 \cdot 2 \cdot 1 = 120$ ways

63. $_6C_3 = \dfrac{6!}{(6-3)!3!} = \dfrac{6!}{3!3!} = \dfrac{6 \cdot 5 \cdot 4 \cdot 3!}{3 \cdot 2 \cdot 1 \cdot 3!} = 20$ ways

64. $_6C_2 = \dfrac{6!}{(6-2)!2!} = \dfrac{6!}{4!2!} = \dfrac{6 \cdot 5 \cdot 4!}{2 \cdot 1 \cdot 4!} = 15$ ways

65. $_4P_4 = \dfrac{4!}{(4-4)!} = 4 \cdot 3 \cdot 2 \cdot 1 = 24$ ways

66. $2 \cdot {}_5P_5 = \dfrac{5!}{(5-5)!} = 2 \cdot 5 \cdot 4 \cdot 3 \cdot 2 \cdot 1 = 240$ ways

67. $2 \cdot {_4}C_2 = 2 \cdot \dfrac{4!}{(4-2)!2!} = 2 \cdot \dfrac{4!}{2!2!} = 2 \cdot \dfrac{4 \cdot 3 \cdot 2!}{2 \cdot 1 \cdot 2!} = 12$ ways

68. $2 \cdot {_4}C_3 = 2 \cdot \dfrac{4!}{(4-3)!3!} = 2 \cdot \dfrac{4!}{1!3!} = 2 \cdot \dfrac{4 \cdot 3!}{1 \cdot 3!} = 8$ ways

72. does not make sense; Explanations will vary. Sample explanation: Since order matters, the permutation formula is necessary.

73. does not make sense; Explanations will vary. Sample explanation: Since order matters, the permutation formula is necessary.

74. makes sense

75. makes sense

77. Selections for 6/53 lottery: ${_{53}}C_6 = \dfrac{53!}{(53-6)!6!} = \dfrac{53!}{47!6!} = \dfrac{53 \cdot 52 \cdot 51 \cdot 50 \cdot 49 \cdot 48 \cdot 47!}{47!6 \cdot 5 \cdot 4 \cdot 3 \cdot 2 \cdot 1} = 22{,}957{,}480$

Selections for 5/36 lottery: ${_{36}}C_5 = \dfrac{36!}{(36-5)!5!} = \dfrac{36!}{31!5!} = \dfrac{36 \cdot 35 \cdot 34 \cdot 33 \cdot 32 \cdot 31!}{31!5 \cdot 4 \cdot 3 \cdot 2 \cdot 1} = 376{,}992$

The 5/36 lottery is easier to win because there are fewer possible selections.

78.
$${_n}P_r = 6 \cdot {_n}C_r$$

$\dfrac{n!}{(n-r)!} = 6 \cdot \dfrac{n!}{(n-r)!r!}$ [apply the cross products principle]

$n!(n-r)!r! = 6 \cdot n!(n-r)!$ [divide both sides by $n!(n-r)!$]

$\dfrac{n!(n-r)!r!}{n!(n-r)!} = \dfrac{6 \cdot n!(n-r)!}{n!(n-r)!}$

$r! = 6$

$r! = 3 \cdot 2 \cdot 1$

$r = 3$

No, there is not enough information to determine the value of n. The number of permutations will be six times the number of combinations for all values of n when $r = 3$.

79. For a group of 20 people:

${_{20}}C_2 = \dfrac{20!}{(20-2)!2!} = \dfrac{20!}{18!2!} = \dfrac{20 \cdot 19 \cdot 18!}{18!2 \cdot 1} = 190$ handshakes

Time $= 3 \times 190 = 570$ seconds, which gives $570 \div 60 = 9.5$ minutes.

For a group of 40 people:

${_{40}}C_2 = \dfrac{40!}{(40-2)!2!} = \dfrac{40!}{38!2!} = \dfrac{40 \cdot 39 \cdot 38!}{38!2 \cdot 1} = 780$ handshakes

Time $= 3 \times 780 = 2340$ seconds, which gives $2340 \div 60 = 39$ minutes.

80. Since there are 5 defective phones, we must select 4 out of the 15 good phones.

${_{15}}C_4 = \dfrac{15!}{(15-4)!4!} = \dfrac{15!}{11!4!} = \dfrac{15 \cdot 14 \cdot 13 \cdot 12 \cdot 11!}{11!4 \cdot 3 \cdot 2 \cdot 1} = 1365$

Check Points 11.4

1. **a.** The event of getting a 2 can occur in one way.

   $$P(2) = \frac{\text{number of ways a 2 can occur}}{\text{total number of possible outcomes}} = \frac{1}{6}$$

   b. The event of getting a number less than 4 can occur in three ways: 1, 2, 3.

   $$P(\text{less than 4}) = \frac{\text{number of ways a number less than 4 can occur}}{\text{total number of possible outcomes}} = \frac{3}{6} = \frac{1}{2}$$

   c. The event of getting a number greater than 7 cannot occur.

   $$P(\text{greater than 7}) = \frac{\text{number of ways a number greater than 7 can occur}}{\text{total number of possible outcomes}} = \frac{0}{6} = 0$$

   The probability of an event that cannot occur is 0.

   d. The event of getting a number less than 7 can occur in six ways: 1, 2, 3, 4, 5, 6.

   $$P(\text{less than 7}) = \frac{\text{number of ways a number less than 7 can occur}}{\text{total number of possible outcomes}} = \frac{6}{6} = 1$$

   The probability of any certain event is 1.

2. **a.** $P(\text{ace}) = \dfrac{\text{number of ways a ace can occur}}{\text{total number of possibilities}} = \dfrac{4}{52} = \dfrac{1}{13}$

   b. $P(\text{red card}) = \dfrac{\text{number of ways a red card can occur}}{\text{total number of possible outcomes}} = \dfrac{26}{52} = \dfrac{1}{2}$

   c. $P(\text{red king}) = \dfrac{\text{number of ways a red king can occur}}{\text{total number of possible outcomes}} = \dfrac{2}{52} = \dfrac{1}{26}$

3. The table shows the four equally likely outcomes. The Cc and cC children will be carriers who are not actually sick.

   $$P(\text{carrier, not sick}) = P(Cc) = \frac{\text{number of ways } Cc \text{ or } cC \text{ can occur}}{\text{total number of possible outcomes}} = \frac{2}{4} = \frac{1}{2}$$

4. **a.** $P(\text{never married}) = \dfrac{\text{number of persons never married}}{\text{total number of U.S. adults}} = \dfrac{69.2}{235.8} \approx 0.29$

   b. $P(\text{male}) = \dfrac{\text{number of males}}{\text{total number of U.S. adults}} = \dfrac{114.5}{235.8} \approx 0.49$

Exercise Set 11.4

1. $P(4) = \dfrac{\text{number of ways a 4 can occur}}{\text{total number of possible outcomes}} = \dfrac{1}{6}$

2. $P(5) = \dfrac{\text{number of ways a five can occur}}{\text{total number of possible outcomes}} = \dfrac{1}{6}$

3. $P(\text{odd number}) = \dfrac{\text{number of ways an odd number can occur}}{\text{total number of possible outcomes}} = \dfrac{3}{6} = \dfrac{1}{2}$

4. $P(\text{greater than 3}) = \dfrac{\text{number of ways a number of greater than 3 can occur}}{\text{total number of possible outcomes}} = \dfrac{3}{6} = \dfrac{1}{2}$

5. $P(\text{less than 3}) = \dfrac{\text{number of ways a number less than 3 can occur}}{\text{total number of possible outcomes}} = \dfrac{2}{6} = \dfrac{1}{3}$

6. $P(\text{greater than 4}) = \dfrac{\text{number of ways a number greater than 4 can occur}}{\text{total number of possible outcomes}} = \dfrac{2}{6} = \dfrac{1}{3}$

7. $P(\text{less than 20}) = \dfrac{\text{number of ways a number less than 20 can occur}}{\text{total number of possible outcomes}} = \dfrac{6}{6} = 1$

8. $P(\text{less than 8}) = \dfrac{\text{number of ways a number less than 8 can occur}}{\text{total number of possible outcomes}} = \dfrac{6}{6} = 1$

9. $P(\text{greater than 20}) = \dfrac{\text{number of ways a number greater than 20 can occur}}{\text{total number of possible outcomes}} = \dfrac{0}{6} = 0$

10. $P(\text{greater than 8}) = \dfrac{\text{number of ways a number greater than 8 can occur}}{\text{total number of possible outcomes}} = \dfrac{0}{6} = 0$

11. $P(\text{queen}) = \dfrac{\text{number of ways a queen can occur}}{\text{total number of possibilities}} = \dfrac{4}{52} = \dfrac{1}{13}$

12. $P(\text{jack}) = \dfrac{\text{number of ways a jack can occur}}{\text{total number of possibilities}} = \dfrac{4}{52} = \dfrac{1}{13}$

13. $P(\text{club}) = \dfrac{\text{number of ways a club can occur}}{\text{total number of possibilities}} = \dfrac{13}{52} = \dfrac{1}{4}$

14. $P(\text{diamond}) = \dfrac{\text{number of ways a diamond can occur}}{\text{total number of possibilities}} = \dfrac{13}{52} = \dfrac{1}{4}$

15. $P(\text{picture card}) = \dfrac{\text{number of ways a picture card can occur}}{\text{total number of possibilities}} = \dfrac{12}{52} = \dfrac{3}{13}$

16. $P(\text{greater than 3 and less than 7}) = \dfrac{\text{number of ways a card greater than 3 and less than 7 can occur}}{\text{total number of possibilities}} = \dfrac{12}{52} = \dfrac{3}{13}$

17. $P(\text{queen of spades}) = \dfrac{\text{number of ways a queen of spades can occur}}{\text{total number of possibilities}} = \dfrac{1}{52}$

18. $P(\text{ace of clubs}) = \dfrac{\text{number of ways an ace of clubs can occur}}{\text{total number of possibilities}} = \dfrac{1}{52}$

19. $P(\text{diamond and spade}) = \dfrac{\text{number of ways a diamond and a spade can occur}}{\text{total number of possibilities}} = \dfrac{0}{52} = 0$

20. $P(\text{green heart}) = \dfrac{\text{number of ways a card with a green heart can occur}}{\text{total number of possibilities}} = \dfrac{0}{52} = 0$

21. $P(\text{two heads}) = \dfrac{\text{number of ways two heads can occur}}{\text{total number of possibilities}} = \dfrac{1}{4}$

22. $P(\text{two tails}) = \dfrac{\text{number of ways two tails can occur}}{\text{total number of possibilities}} = \dfrac{1}{4}$

23. $P(\text{same on each toss}) = \dfrac{\text{number of ways the same outcome on each toss can occur}}{\text{total number of possibilities}} = \dfrac{2}{4} = \dfrac{1}{2}$

24. $P(\text{different on each toss}) = \dfrac{\text{number of ways different outcomes on each toss can occur}}{\text{total number of possibilities}} = \dfrac{2}{4} = \dfrac{1}{2}$

25. $P(\text{head on second toss}) = \dfrac{\text{number of ways a head on the second toss can occur}}{\text{total number of possibilities}} = \dfrac{2}{4} = \dfrac{1}{2}$

26. $P(\text{at least one head}) = \dfrac{\text{number of ways at least one head can occur (HH, HT, TH)}}{\text{total number of possibilities}} = \dfrac{3}{4}$

27. $P(\text{exactly one female child}) = \dfrac{\text{number of ways exactly one female child can occur}}{\text{total number of possibilities}} = \dfrac{3}{8}$

28. $P(\text{exactly one male child}) = \dfrac{\text{number of ways exactly one male child can occur}}{\text{total number of possibilities}} = \dfrac{3}{8}$

29. $P(\text{exactly two male children}) = \dfrac{\text{number of ways exactly two male children can occur}}{\text{total number of possibilities}} = \dfrac{3}{8}$

30. $P(\text{exactly two female children}) = \dfrac{\text{number of ways exactly two female children can occur}}{\text{total number of possibilities}} = \dfrac{3}{8}$

31. $P(\text{at least one male child}) = \dfrac{\text{number of ways at least one male child can occur}}{\text{total number of possiblities}} = \dfrac{7}{8}$

32. $P(\text{at least two female children}) = \dfrac{\text{number of ways at least two female children can occur}}{\text{total number of possibilities}} = \dfrac{4}{8} = \dfrac{1}{2}$

33. $P(\text{four male children}) = \dfrac{\text{number of ways four male children can occur}}{\text{total number of possibilities}} = \dfrac{0}{8} = 0$

34. $P(\text{fewer than four female children}) = \dfrac{\text{number of ways fewer than four female children can occur}}{\text{total number of possibilities}} = \dfrac{8}{8} = 1$

35. $P(\text{two even numbers}) = \dfrac{\text{number of ways two even numbers can occur}}{\text{total number of possibilities}} = \dfrac{9}{36} = \dfrac{1}{4}$

36. $P(\text{two odd numbers}) = \dfrac{\text{number of ways two odd numbers can occur}}{\text{total number of possibilities}} = \dfrac{9}{36} = \dfrac{1}{4}$

37. $P(\text{two numbers whose sum is 5}) = \dfrac{\text{number of ways two numbers whose sum is 5 can occur}}{\text{total number of possibilities}} = \dfrac{4}{36} = \dfrac{1}{9}$

38. $P(\text{two numbers of whose sum is 6}) = \dfrac{\text{number of ways two numbers whose sum is 6 can occur}}{\text{total number of possibilities}} = \dfrac{5}{36}$

39. $P(\text{two numbers whose sum exceeds 12})$

$= \dfrac{\text{number of ways two numbers whose sum exceeds 12 can occur}}{\text{total number of possibilities}} = \dfrac{0}{36} = 0$

40. $P(\text{two numbers whose sum is less than 13})$

$= \dfrac{\text{number of ways two numbers whose sum is less than 13 can occur}}{\text{total number of possibilities}} = \dfrac{36}{36} = 1$

41. $P(\text{red region}) = \dfrac{\text{number of ways a red region can occur}}{\text{total number of possibilities}} = \dfrac{3}{10}$

42. $P(\text{yellow region}) = \dfrac{\text{number of ways a yellow region can occur}}{\text{total number of possibilities}} = \dfrac{2}{10} = \dfrac{1}{5}$

43. $P(\text{blue region}) = \dfrac{\text{number of ways a blue region can occur}}{\text{total number of possibilities}} = \dfrac{2}{10} = \dfrac{1}{5}$

44. $P(\text{brown region}) = \dfrac{\text{number of ways a brown region can occur}}{\text{total number of possibilities}} = \dfrac{3}{10}$

45. $P(\text{region that is red or blue}) = \dfrac{\text{number of ways a region that is red or blue can occur}}{\text{total number of possibilities}} = \dfrac{5}{10} = \dfrac{1}{2}$

46. $P(\text{region that is yellow or brown}) = \dfrac{\text{number of ways a region that is yellow or brown can occur}}{\text{total number of possibilities}} = \dfrac{5}{10} = \dfrac{1}{2}$

47. $P(\text{region that is red and blue}) = \dfrac{\text{number of ways a region that is red and blue can occur}}{\text{total number of possibilities}} = \dfrac{0}{10} = 0$

48. $P(\text{region that is yellow and brown}) = \dfrac{\text{number of ways a region that is yellow and brown can occur}}{\text{total number of possibilities}} = \dfrac{0}{10} = 0$

49. $P(\text{sickle cell anemia}) = \dfrac{\text{number of ways sickle cell anemia can occur}}{\text{total number of possibilities}} = \dfrac{1}{4}$

50. $P(\text{sickle cell trait}) = \dfrac{\text{number of ways sickle cell trait can occur}}{\text{total number of possibilities}} = \dfrac{2}{4} = \dfrac{1}{2}$

51. $P(\text{healthy}) = \dfrac{\text{number of ways a healthy child can occur}}{\text{total number of possibilities}} = \dfrac{1}{4}$

52. $P(\text{sickle cell anemia}) = \dfrac{\text{number of ways sickle cell anemia can occur}}{\text{total number of possibilities}} = \dfrac{0}{4} = 0$

53. $P(\text{sickle cell trait}) = \dfrac{\text{number of ways sickle cell trait can occur}}{\text{total number of possibilities}} = \dfrac{2}{4} = \dfrac{1}{2}$

54. $P(\text{healthy}) = \dfrac{\text{number of ways a healthy child can occur}}{\text{total number of possibilities}} = \dfrac{2}{4} = \dfrac{1}{2}$

55. $P(\text{male}) = \dfrac{\text{number of males}}{\text{total number of Americans living alone}} = \dfrac{12.5}{29.3} \approx 0.43$

56. $P(\text{female}) = \dfrac{\text{number of females}}{\text{total number of Americans living alone}} = \dfrac{16.8}{29.3} \approx 0.57$

57. $P(25 - 34 \text{ age range}) = \dfrac{\text{number in } 25 - 34 \text{ age range}}{\text{total number of Americans living alone}} = \dfrac{3.8}{29.3} \approx 0.13$

58. $P(35 - 44 \text{ age range}) = \dfrac{\text{number in } 35 - 44 \text{ age range}}{\text{total number of Americans living alone}} = \dfrac{4.2}{29.3} \approx 0.14$

59. $P(\text{woman in } 15 - 24 \text{ age range}) = \dfrac{\text{number of women in } 15 - 24 \text{ age range}}{\text{total number of Americans living alone}} = \dfrac{0.8}{29.3} \approx 0.03$

60. $P(\text{man in } 45 - 64 \text{ age range}) = \dfrac{\text{number of men in } 45 - 64 \text{ age range}}{\text{total number of Americans living alone}} = \dfrac{4.3}{29.3} \approx 0.15$

Table For #61–66	Moved to Same State	Moved to Different State	Moved to Different Country	Total
Owner	11.7	2.8	0.3	14.8
Renter	18.7	4.5	1.0	24.2
Total	30.4	7.3	1.3	39.0

61. $P(\text{owner}) = \dfrac{\text{number of owners}}{\text{total number of Americans who moved in 2004}} = \dfrac{14.8}{39.0} \approx 0.38$

62. $P(\text{renter}) = \dfrac{\text{number of renters}}{\text{total number of Americans who moved in 2004}} = \dfrac{24.2}{39.0} \approx 0.62$

63. $P(\text{moved within state}) = \dfrac{\text{number that moved within state}}{\text{total number of Americans who moved in 2004}} = \dfrac{30.4}{39.0} \approx 0.78$

64. $P(\text{moved to different country}) = \dfrac{\text{number that moved to different country}}{\text{total number of Americans who moved in 2004}} = \dfrac{1.3}{39.0} \approx 0.03$

65. $P(\text{renter who moved to different state}) = \dfrac{\text{number of renters who moved to a different state}}{\text{total number of Americans who moved in 2004}} = \dfrac{4.5}{39.0} \approx 0.12$

66. $P(\text{owner who moved to different state}) = \dfrac{\text{number of owners who moved to a different state}}{\text{total number of Americans who moved in 2004}} = \dfrac{2.8}{39.0} \approx 0.07$

Table For #67–70	Less Than 4 Years High School	4 Years High School Only	Some College (Less than 4 years)	4 Years College (or More)	Total
Male	3.6	5.0	2.6	3.9	15.1
Female	5.2	8.0	4.1	3.0	20.3
Total	8.8	13.0	6.7	6.9	35.4

67. $P(\text{had less than 4 years of high school}) = \dfrac{\text{number with less than 4 years of high school}}{\text{total number of Americans aged 65 and older}} = \dfrac{8.8}{35.4} \approx 0.25$

68. $P(\text{had 4 years of high school only}) = \dfrac{\text{number with 4 years of high school only}}{\text{total number of Americans aged 65 and older}} = \dfrac{13.0}{35.4} \approx 0.37$

69. $P(\text{a woman with 4 years of college or more}) = \dfrac{\text{number of women with 4 years of college or more}}{\text{total number of Americans aged 65 and older}} = \dfrac{3.0}{35.4} \approx 0.08$

70. $P(\text{a man with 4 years of college or more}) = \dfrac{\text{number of men with 4 years of college or more}}{\text{total number of Americans aged 65 and older}} = \dfrac{3.9}{35.4} \approx 0.11$

79. does not make sense; Explanations will vary. Sample explanation: Even if there are only two choices, it does not necessarily follow that they are equally likely to be selected.

80. does not make sense; Explanations will vary. Sample explanation: The probability can not be greater than 1 (100%).

81. makes sense

82. makes sense

83. The area of the target is $(12 \text{ in.})^2 = 144 \text{ in.}^2$

The area of the yellow region is $(9 \text{ in.})^2 - (6 \text{ in.})^2 + (3 \text{ in.})^2 = 54 \text{ in.}^2$

The probability that the dart hits a yellow region is $\dfrac{54 \text{ in.}^2}{144 \text{ in.}^2} = 0.375$

84. First count the number of three-digit numbers that read the same forward and backward:

$$\overbrace{\text{Digit 1:}}^{1-9} \quad \overbrace{\text{Digit 2:}}^{0-9} \quad \overbrace{\text{Digit 3:}}^{\text{Same as 1st digit}}$$

$$9 \quad \times \quad 10 \quad \times \quad 1 \quad = \quad 90$$

$P(\text{three-digit number reads the same forward and backward})$

$= \dfrac{\text{number of three-digit numbers that read the same forward and backward}}{\text{total number of three-digit numbers}} = \dfrac{90}{900} = \dfrac{1}{10}$

Check Points 11.5

1. total number of permutations $= 6! = 6 \cdot 5 \cdot 4 \cdot 3 \cdot 2 \cdot 1 = 720$
   For the given outcome there are 3 choices (first names beginning with G) for the first joke, which would leave 4 choices for the last joke (the 4 remaining men). The remaining jokes have 4, 3, 2, and 1 choice respectively.

First name begins with G		4 jokes other than first and last				man (other than first joke)	
1st:		2nd:	3rd:	4th:	5th:	6th:	
3	×	4 ×	3 ×	2 ×	1 ×	4	= 288

   $P(\text{first joke is by a man whose name begins with G and the last is by a man}) = \dfrac{288}{720} = \dfrac{2}{5}$

2. Number of LOTTO selections: $_{49}C_6 = \dfrac{49!}{(49-6)!6!} = \dfrac{49!}{43!6!} = \dfrac{49 \cdot 48 \cdot 47 \cdot 46 \cdot 45 \cdot 44 \cdot 43!}{43! 6 \cdot 5 \cdot 4 \cdot 3 \cdot 2 \cdot 1} = 13,983,816$

   $P(\text{winning}) = \dfrac{\text{one LOTTO ticket}}{\text{total number of LOTTO combinations}} = \dfrac{1}{13,983,816} \approx 0.0000000715$

3. total number of combinations: $_{10}C_3 = \dfrac{10!}{(10-3)!3!} = \dfrac{10!}{7!3!} = \dfrac{10 \cdot 9 \cdot 8 \cdot 7!}{7!3 \cdot 2 \cdot 1} = 120$

   a. total number of combinations of 3 men: $_6C_3 = \dfrac{6!}{(6-3)!3!} = \dfrac{6!}{3!3!} = \dfrac{6 \cdot 5 \cdot 4 \cdot 3!}{3 \cdot 2 \cdot 1 \cdot 3!} = 20$

   $P(3 \text{ men}) = \dfrac{\text{number of combinations with 3 men}}{\text{total number of combinations}} = \dfrac{20}{120} = \dfrac{1}{6}$

   b. Select 2 out of 6 men: $_6C_2 = \dfrac{6!}{(6-2)!2!} = \dfrac{6!}{4!2!} = \dfrac{6 \cdot 5 \cdot 4!}{4!2 \cdot 1} = 15$

   Select 1 out of 4 women: $_4C_1 = \dfrac{4!}{(4-1)!1!} = \dfrac{4!}{3!1!} = \dfrac{4 \cdot 3!}{3!} = \dfrac{4 \cdot 3!}{3!} = 4$

   total number of combinations of 2 men and 1 woman: $15 \times 4 = 60$

   $P(2 \text{ men, 1 woman}) = \dfrac{\text{number of combinations with 2 men, 1 woman}}{\text{total number of combinations}} = \dfrac{60}{120} = \dfrac{1}{2}$

Exercise Set 11.5

1. a. $5! = 5 \cdot 4 \cdot 3 \cdot 2 \cdot 1 = 120$

   b.
Martha	Lee, Nancy, Paul			Armando
1st:	2nd:	3rd:	4th:	5th:
1 ×	3 ×	2 ×	1 ×	1 = 6

   c. $P(\text{Martha first and Armando last}) = \dfrac{6}{120} = \dfrac{1}{20}$

2. a. $6! = 6 \cdot 5 \cdot 4 \cdot 3 \cdot 2 \cdot 1 = 720$

   b.
1st woman:	1st man:	2nd woman:	2nd man:	3rd woman:	3rd man:
3 ×	3 ×	2 ×	2 ×	1 ×	1 = 36

   c. $P(\text{first person is a woman and line alternates by gender}) = \dfrac{36}{720} = \dfrac{1}{20}$

3. a. total number of permutations $= 6! = 6 \cdot 5 \cdot 4 \cdot 3 \cdot 2 \cdot 1 = 720$
number of permutations with E first $= 1 \cdot 5 \cdot 4 \cdot 3 \cdot 2 \cdot 1 = 120$

$$P(\text{E first}) = \frac{\text{number of permutations with E first}}{\text{total number of permutations}} = \frac{120}{720} = \frac{1}{6}$$

b. number of permutations with C fifth and B last $= 4 \cdot 3 \cdot 2 \cdot 1 \cdot 1 \cdot 1 = 24$

$$P(\text{C fifth and B last}) = \frac{\text{number of permutations with C fifth and B last}}{\text{total number of permutations}} = \frac{24}{720} = \frac{1}{30}$$

c. $P(\text{D, E, C, A, B, F}) = \dfrac{\text{number of permutations with order D, E, C, A, B, F}}{\text{total number of permutations}} = \dfrac{1}{720}$

d. number of permutations with A or B first $= 2 \cdot 5 \cdot 4 \cdot 3 \cdot 2 \cdot 1 = 240$

$$P(\text{A or B first}) = \frac{\text{number of permutations with A or B first}}{\text{total number of permutations}} = \frac{240}{720} = \frac{1}{3}$$

4. a. total number of permutations $= 7 \cdot 6 \cdot 5 \cdot 4 \cdot 3 \cdot 2 \cdot 1 = 5040$
number of permutations with D first $= 1 \cdot 6 \cdot 5 \cdot 4 \cdot 3 \cdot 2 \cdot 1 = 720$

$$P(\text{D first}) = \frac{\text{number of permutations with D first}}{\text{total number of permutations}} = \frac{720}{5040} = \frac{1}{7}$$

b. number of permutations with E sixth and B last $= 5 \cdot 4 \cdot 3 \cdot 2 \cdot 1 \cdot 1 \cdot 1 = 120$

$$P(\text{E sixth and B last}) = \frac{\text{number of permutations with E sixth and B last}}{\text{total number of permutations}} = \frac{120}{5040} = \frac{1}{42}$$

c. $P(\text{C, D, B, A, G, F, E}) = \dfrac{\text{number of permutations with order C, D, B, A, G, F, E}}{\text{total number of permutations}} = \dfrac{1}{5040}$

d. number of permutations with F or G first $= 2 \cdot 6 \cdot 5 \cdot 4 \cdot 3 \cdot 2 \cdot 1 = 1440$

$$P(\text{F or G first}) = \frac{\text{number of permutations with F or G first}}{\text{total number of permutations}} = \frac{1440}{5040} = \frac{2}{7}$$

5. a. $\displaystyle {}_9C_3 = \frac{9!}{(9-3)!3!} = \frac{9!}{6!3!} = \frac{9 \cdot 8 \cdot 7 \cdot 6!}{6!3 \cdot 2 \cdot 1} = 84$

b. $\displaystyle {}_5C_3 = \frac{5!}{(5-3)!3!} = \frac{5!}{2!3!} = \frac{5 \cdot 4 \cdot 3!}{2 \cdot 1 \cdot 3!} = 10$

c. $P(\text{all women}) = \dfrac{\text{number of ways to select 3 women}}{\text{total number of possible combinations}} = \dfrac{10}{84} = \dfrac{5}{42}$

6. a. $\displaystyle {}_{11}C_4 = \frac{11!}{(11-4)!4!} = \frac{11!}{7!4!} = \frac{11 \cdot 10 \cdot 9 \cdot 8 \cdot 7!}{7!4 \cdot 3 \cdot 2 \cdot 1} = 330$

b. $\displaystyle {}_6C_4 = \frac{6!}{(6-4)!4!} = \frac{6!}{2!4!} = \frac{6 \cdot 5 \cdot 4!}{2 \cdot 1 \cdot 4!} = 15$

c. $P(\text{all Republicans}) = \dfrac{\text{number of ways to select 4 Republicans}}{\text{total number of possible combinations}} = \dfrac{15}{330} = \dfrac{1}{22}$

7. $_{51}C_6 = \dfrac{51!}{(51-6)!6!} = \dfrac{51!}{45!6!} = \dfrac{51 \cdot 50 \cdot 49 \cdot 48 \cdot 47 \cdot 46 \cdot 45!}{45!6 \cdot 5 \cdot 4 \cdot 3 \cdot 2 \cdot 1} = 18{,}009{,}460$

$P(\text{winning}) = \dfrac{\text{number of ways of winning}}{\text{total number of possible combinations}} = \dfrac{1}{18{,}009{,}460} \approx 0.0000000555$

If 100 different tickets are purchased, $P(\text{winning}) = \dfrac{100}{18{,}009{,}460} \approx 0.00000555$

8. $_{30}C_5 = \dfrac{30!}{(30-5)!5!} = \dfrac{30!}{25!5!} = \dfrac{30 \cdot 29 \cdot 28 \cdot 27 \cdot 26 \cdot 25!}{25!5 \cdot 4 \cdot 3 \cdot 2 \cdot 1} = 142{,}506$

$P(\text{winning}) = \dfrac{\text{number of ways of winning}}{\text{total number of possible combinations}} = \dfrac{1}{142{,}506} \approx 0.00000702$

If 100 different tickets are purchased, $P(\text{winning}) = \dfrac{100}{142{,}506} \approx 0.000702$.

9. a. $_{25}C_6 = \dfrac{25!}{(25-6)!6!} = \dfrac{25!}{19!6!} = \dfrac{25 \cdot 24 \cdot 23 \cdot 22 \cdot 21 \cdot 20 \cdot 19!}{19!6 \cdot 5 \cdot 4 \cdot 3 \cdot 2 \cdot 1} = 177{,}100$

$P(\text{all are defective}) = \dfrac{\text{number of ways to choose 6 defective transistors}}{\text{total number of possible combinations}} = \dfrac{1}{177{,}100} \approx 0.00000565$

b. $_{19}C_6 = \dfrac{19!}{(19-6)!6!} = \dfrac{19!}{13!6!} = \dfrac{19 \cdot 18 \cdot 17 \cdot 16 \cdot 15 \cdot 14 \cdot 13!}{13!6 \cdot 5 \cdot 4 \cdot 3 \cdot 2 \cdot 1} = 27{,}132$

$P(\text{none are defective}) = \dfrac{\text{number of ways to choose 6 good transistors}}{\text{total number of possible permutations}} = \dfrac{27{,}132}{177{,}100} = \dfrac{969}{6325} \approx 0.153$

10. a. $_{13}C_5 = \dfrac{13!}{(13-5)!5!} = \dfrac{13!}{8!5!} = \dfrac{13 \cdot 12 \cdot 11 \cdot 10 \cdot 9 \cdot 8!}{8!5 \cdot 4 \cdot 3 \cdot 2 \cdot 1} = 1287$

$_6C_5 = \dfrac{6!}{(6-5)!5!} = \dfrac{6!}{1!5!} = \dfrac{6 \cdot 5!}{1 \cdot 5!} = 6$

$P(\text{all lawyers}) = \dfrac{\text{number of ways to select 5 lawyers}}{\text{total number of possible combinations}} = \dfrac{6}{1287} = \dfrac{2}{429} \approx 0.00466$

b. $_7C_5 = \dfrac{7!}{(7-5)!5!} = \dfrac{7!}{2!5!} = \dfrac{7 \cdot 6 \cdot 5!}{2 \cdot 1 \cdot 5!} = 21$

$P(\text{none are lawyers}) = \dfrac{\text{number of ways to select 5 teachers}}{\text{total number of possible combinations}} = \dfrac{21}{1287} = \dfrac{7}{429} \approx 0.0163$

11. total number of possible combinations: $_{10}C_3 = \dfrac{10!}{(10-3)!3!} = \dfrac{10!}{7!3!} = \dfrac{10 \cdot 9 \cdot 8 \cdot 7!}{7!3 \cdot 2 \cdot 1} = 120$

number of ways to select one Democrat: $_6C_1 = \dfrac{6!}{(6-1)!1!} = \dfrac{6!}{5!1!} = \dfrac{6 \cdot 5!}{5!1} = 6$

number of ways to select two Republicans: $_4C_2 = \dfrac{4!}{(4-2)!2!} = \dfrac{4!}{2!2!} = \dfrac{4 \cdot 3 \cdot 2!}{2!2 \cdot 1} = 6$

number of ways to select one Democrat and two Republicans: $_6C_1 \cdot {}_4C_2 = 6 \cdot 6 = 36$

$P(\text{one Democrat and two Republicans}) = \dfrac{36}{120} = \dfrac{3}{10} = 0.3$

12. total number of possible combinations: $_{20}C_4 = \dfrac{20!}{(20-4)!4!} = \dfrac{20!}{16!4!} = \dfrac{20 \cdot 19 \cdot 18 \cdot 17 \cdot 16!}{16!4 \cdot 3 \cdot 2 \cdot 1} = 4845$

number of ways to select two parents: $_{15}C_2 = \dfrac{15!}{(15-2)!2!} = \dfrac{15!}{13!2!} = \dfrac{15 \cdot 14 \cdot 13!}{13!2 \cdot 1} = 105$

number of ways to select two teachers: $_5C_2 = \dfrac{5!}{(5-2)!2!} = \dfrac{5!}{3!2!} = \dfrac{5 \cdot 4 \cdot 3!}{3!2 \cdot 1} = 10$

number of ways to select two parents and two teachers: $_{15}C_2 \cdot {_5C_2} = 105 \cdot 10 = 1050$

$P(\text{two parents and two teachers}) = \dfrac{1050}{4845} = \dfrac{70}{323} \approx 0.217$

13. a. $_{52}C_5 = \dfrac{52!}{(52-5)!5!} = \dfrac{52!}{47!5!} = \dfrac{52 \cdot 51 \cdot 50 \cdot 49 \cdot 48 \cdot 47!}{47!5 \cdot 4 \cdot 3 \cdot 2 \cdot 1} = 2,598,960$

b. $_{13}C_5 = \dfrac{13!}{(13-5)!5!} = \dfrac{13!}{8!5!} = \dfrac{13 \cdot 12 \cdot 11 \cdot 10 \cdot 9 \cdot 8!}{8!5 \cdot 4 \cdot 3 \cdot 2 \cdot 1} = 1287$

c. $P(\text{diamond flush}) = \dfrac{\text{number of possible 5-card diamond flushes}}{\text{total number of possible combinations}} = \dfrac{1287}{2,598,960} \approx 0.000495$

14. a. $_{52}C_5 = \dfrac{52!}{(52-5)!5!} = \dfrac{52!}{47!5!} = \dfrac{52 \cdot 51 \cdot 50 \cdot 49 \cdot 48 \cdot 47!}{47!5 \cdot 4 \cdot 3 \cdot 2 \cdot 1} = 2,598,960$

b. $_4C_4 = \dfrac{4!}{(4-4)!4!} = \dfrac{4!}{0!4!} = 1$

c. $_4C_1 = \dfrac{4!}{(4-1)!1!} = \dfrac{4!}{3!1!} = \dfrac{4 \cdot 3!}{3!1} = 4$

d. $_4C_4 \cdot {_4C_1} = 1 \cdot 4 = 4$

e. $P(\text{4 aces and 1 king}) = \dfrac{\text{number of hands with 4 aces and 1 king}}{\text{total number of possible combinations}} = \dfrac{4}{2,598,960} \approx 0.00000154$

15. total number of possible combinations: $_{52}C_3 = \dfrac{52!}{(52-3)!3!} = \dfrac{52!}{49!3!} = \dfrac{52 \cdot 51 \cdot 50 \cdot 49!}{49!3 \cdot 2 \cdot 1} = 22,100$

number of ways to select 3 picture cards: $_{12}C_3 = \dfrac{12!}{(12-3)!3!} = \dfrac{12!}{9!3!} = \dfrac{12 \cdot 11 \cdot 10 \cdot 9!}{9!3 \cdot 2 \cdot 1} = 220$

$P(\text{3 picture cards}) = \dfrac{220}{22,100} = \dfrac{11}{1105} \approx 0.00995$

16. total number of possible combinations: $_{52}C_4 = \dfrac{52!}{(52-4)!4!} = \dfrac{52!}{48!4!} = \dfrac{52 \cdot 51 \cdot 50 \cdot 49 \cdot 48!}{48!4 \cdot 3 \cdot 2 \cdot 1} = 270,725$

number of ways to select 4 hearts: $_{13}C_4 = \dfrac{13!}{(13-4)!4!} = \dfrac{13!}{9!4!} = \dfrac{13 \cdot 12 \cdot 11 \cdot 10 \cdot 9!}{9!4 \cdot 3 \cdot 2 \cdot 1} = 715$

$P(\text{all 4 are hearts}) = \dfrac{715}{270,725} = \dfrac{11}{4165} \approx 0.00264$

17. total number of possible combinations: $_{52}C_4 = \dfrac{52!}{(52-4)!4!} = \dfrac{52!}{48!4!} = \dfrac{52 \cdot 51 \cdot 50 \cdot 49 \cdot 48!}{48!4 \cdot 3 \cdot 2 \cdot 1} = 270,725$

number of ways to select 2 queens: $_4C_2 = \dfrac{4!}{(4-2)!2!} = \dfrac{4!}{2!2!} = \dfrac{4 \cdot 3 \cdot 2!}{2!2 \cdot 1} = 6$

number of ways to select 2 kings: $_4C_2 = 6$

number of ways to select 2 queens and 2 kings: $_4C_2 \cdot {_4C_2} = 6 \cdot 6 = 36$

$P(\text{2 queens and 2 kings}) = \dfrac{36}{270,725} \approx 0.000133$

18. total number of possible combinations: $_{52}C_4 = \dfrac{52!}{(52-4)!4!} = \dfrac{52!}{48!4!} = \dfrac{52 \cdot 51 \cdot 50 \cdot 49 \cdot 48!}{48!4 \cdot 3 \cdot 2 \cdot 1} = 270,725$

number of ways to select 3 jacks: $_4C_3 = \dfrac{4!}{(4-3)!3!} = \dfrac{4!}{1!3!} = \dfrac{4 \cdot 3!}{1 \cdot 3!} = 4$

number of ways to select 1 queen: $_4C_1 = \dfrac{4!}{(4-1)!1!} = \dfrac{4!}{3!1!} = \dfrac{4 \cdot 3!}{3!1} = 4$

number of ways to select 3 jacks and 1 queen: $_4C_3 \cdot {_4C_1} = 4 \cdot 4 = 16$

$P(\text{3 jacks and 1 queen}) = \dfrac{16}{270,725} \approx 0.0000591$

22. makes sense

23. does not make sense; Explanations will vary. Sample explanation: Each possible combination is equally likely.

24. makes sense

25. makes sense

26. total number of possible combinations: $3 \cdot 2 \cdot 2 \cdot 3 = 36$
number of combinations the person wants: $1 \cdot 1 \cdot 1 \cdot 2 = 2$

$P(\text{what the person wants is available}) = \dfrac{\text{number of combinations the person wants}}{\text{total number of possible combinations}} = \dfrac{2}{36} = \dfrac{1}{18}$

27. Refer to solution 7: $_{51}C_6 = 18,009,460$

$P(\text{winning}) = \dfrac{\text{number of ways of winning } (x)}{\text{total number of possible combinations}} = \dfrac{x}{18,009,460} = \dfrac{1}{2}$, therefore $x = 9,004,730$.

At \$1 per ticket, a person must spend \$9,004,730 to have a probability of winning of $\dfrac{1}{2}$.

28. Other players could also purchase the winning combination and share the prize money, possibly making this person's share of the prize less than what this person paid for the tickets.

29. total number of possible combinations:

Digit 1:		Digit 2:		Digit 3:		
5	×	4	×	3	=	60

number of even numbers greater than 500:

5	1, 3, and 2 or 4	2 or 4				
Digit 1:		Digit 2:		Digit 3:		
1	×	3	×	2	=	6

$P(\text{even and greater than 500}) = \dfrac{\text{number of even numbers greater than 500}}{\text{total number of possible combinations}} = \dfrac{6}{60} = \dfrac{1}{10}$

30. total number of possible combinations: $_{52}C_5 = \dfrac{52!}{(52-5)!5!} = \dfrac{52!}{47!5!} = \dfrac{52 \cdot 51 \cdot 50 \cdot 49 \cdot 48 \cdot 47!}{47!5 \cdot 4 \cdot 3 \cdot 2 \cdot 1} = 2{,}598{,}960$

number of ways to select one ace: $_4C_1 = \dfrac{4!}{(4-1)!1!} = \dfrac{4!}{3!1!} = \dfrac{4 \cdot 3!}{3!1} = 4$

Note: one card is an ace, so the other four must not be aces.
number of ways to select 4 cards with no face cards and no aces:

$_{36}C_4 = \dfrac{36!}{(36-4)!4!} = \dfrac{36!}{32!4!} = \dfrac{36 \cdot 35 \cdot 34 \cdot 33 \cdot 32!}{32!4 \cdot 3 \cdot 2 \cdot 1} = 58{,}905$

number of hands with one ace and no face cards: $_4C_1 \cdot {_{36}C_4} = 4 \cdot 58{,}905 = 235{,}620$

$P(\text{one ace and no face cards}) = \dfrac{\text{number of hands with one ace and no face cards}}{\text{total number of possible combinations}} = \dfrac{235{,}620}{2{,}598{,}960} \approx 0.0907$

Check Points 11.6

1. $P(\text{not a diamond}) = 1 - P(\text{diamond}) = 1 - \dfrac{13}{52} = \dfrac{39}{52} = \dfrac{3}{4}$

2. **a.** $P(\text{not } 50-59) = 1 - P(50-59) = 1 - \dfrac{31}{191} = \dfrac{160}{191}$

   b. $P(\text{at least 20 years old}) = 1 - P(\text{less than 20 years}) = 1 - \dfrac{9}{191} = \dfrac{182}{191}$

3. $P(4 \text{ or } 5) = P(4) + P(5) = \dfrac{1}{6} + \dfrac{1}{6} = \dfrac{2}{6} = \dfrac{1}{3}$

4. $P(\text{math or psychology}) = P(\text{math}) + P(\text{psychology}) - P(\text{math and psychology}) = \dfrac{23}{50} + \dfrac{11}{50} - \dfrac{7}{50} = \dfrac{27}{50}$

5. $P(\text{odd or less than 5}) = P(\text{odd}) + P(\text{less than 5}) - P(\text{odd and less than 5}) = \dfrac{4}{8} + \dfrac{4}{8} - \dfrac{2}{8} = \dfrac{6}{8} = \dfrac{3}{4}$

6. **a.** These events are not mutually exclusive.
   $P(\text{at least } \$100{,}000 \text{ or was not audited})$
   $= P(\text{at least } \$100{,}000) + P(\text{was not audited}) - P(\text{at least } \$100{,}000 \text{ and was not audited})$
   $= \dfrac{12{,}893{,}802}{122{,}158{,}336} + \dfrac{121{,}174{,}907}{122{,}158{,}336} - \dfrac{12{,}726{,}963}{122{,}158{,}336} = \dfrac{121{,}341{,}746}{122{,}158{,}336} \approx 0.99$

   b. These events are mutually exclusive.
   $P(\text{less than } \$25{,}000 \text{ or between } \$50{,}000 \text{ and } \$99{,}999, \text{ inclusive})$
   $= P(\text{less than } \$25{,}000) + P(\text{between } \$50{,}000 \text{ and } \$99{,}999, \text{ inclusive})$
   $= \dfrac{51{,}971{,}629}{122{,}158{,}336} + \dfrac{26{,}463{,}973}{122{,}158{,}336} = \dfrac{78{,}435{,}602}{122{,}158{,}336} \approx 0.64$

7. There are 2 red queens. Number of favorable outcomes = 2, Number of unfavorable outcomes = 50

   a. Odds in favor of getting a red queen are 2 to 50 or 2:50 which reduces to 1:25.

   b. Odds against getting a red queen are 50 to 2 or 50:2 which reduces to 25:1.

8. number of unfavorable outcomes = 995, number of favorable outcomes = 5
   Odds against winning the scholarship are 995 to 5 or 995:5 which reduces to 199:1.

9. number of unfavorable outcomes = 15, number of favorable outcomes = 1
   Odds in favor of the horse winning the race are 1 to 15

   $P(\text{the horse wins race}) = \dfrac{1}{1+15} = \dfrac{1}{16} = 0.0625$ or 6.3%.

Exercise Set 11.6

1. $P(\text{not an ace}) = 1 - P(\text{ace}) = 1 - \dfrac{4}{52} = \dfrac{48}{52} = \dfrac{12}{13}$

2. $P(\text{not a 3}) = 1 - P(3) = 1 - \dfrac{4}{52} = 1 - \dfrac{1}{13} = \dfrac{12}{13}$

3. $P(\text{not a heart}) = 1 - P(\text{heart}) = 1 - \dfrac{13}{52} = \dfrac{39}{52} = \dfrac{3}{4}$

4. $P(\text{not a club}) = 1 - P(\text{club}) = 1 - \dfrac{13}{52} = \dfrac{39}{52} = \dfrac{3}{4}$

5. $P(\text{not a picture card}) = 1 - P(\text{picture card}) = 1 - \dfrac{12}{52} = \dfrac{40}{52} = \dfrac{10}{13}$

6. $P(\text{not a red picture card}) = 1 - P(\text{red picture card}) = 1 - \dfrac{6}{52} = \dfrac{46}{52} = \dfrac{23}{26}$

7. $P(\text{not a straight flush}) = 1 - P(\text{straight flush}) = 1 - \dfrac{36}{2,598,960} = \dfrac{2,598,924}{2,598,960} \approx 0.999986$

8. $P(\text{not four of a kind}) = 1 - P(\text{four of a kind}) = 1 - \dfrac{624}{2,598,960} = \dfrac{2,598,336}{2,598,960} \approx 0.999760$

9. $P(\text{not a full house}) = 1 - P(\text{full house}) = 1 - \dfrac{3744}{2,598,960} = \dfrac{2,595,216}{2,598,960} \approx 0.998559$

10. $P(\text{not a flush}) = 1 - P(\text{flush}) = 1 - \dfrac{5108}{2,598,960} = \dfrac{2,593,852}{2,598,960} \approx 0.998035$

11. **a.** 0.10 (read from graph)

    b. $1.00 - 0.10 = 0.90$

12. **a.** 0.78 (read from graph)

    b. $1.00 - 0.78 = 0.22$

13. $P(\text{not } \$50,000 - \$74,999) = 1 - P(\$50,000 - \$74,999) = 1 - \dfrac{21}{118} = \dfrac{97}{118}$

14. $P(\text{not } \$15,000 - \$24,999) = 1 - P(\$15,000 - \$24,999) = 1 - \dfrac{14}{118} = \dfrac{104}{118} = \dfrac{52}{59}$

15. $P(\text{less than } \$100,000) = 1 - P(\$100,000 \text{ or more}) = 1 - \dfrac{24}{118} = \dfrac{94}{118} = \dfrac{47}{59}$

16. $P(\text{at least } \$10,000) = 1 - P(\text{less than } \$10,000) = 1 - \dfrac{8}{118} = \dfrac{110}{118} = \dfrac{55}{59}$

17. $P(2 \text{ or } 3) = P(2) + P(3) = \dfrac{4}{52} + \dfrac{4}{52} = \dfrac{8}{52} = \dfrac{2}{13}$

18. $P(7 \text{ or } 8) = P(7) + P(8) = \dfrac{4}{52} + \dfrac{4}{52} = \dfrac{8}{52} = \dfrac{2}{13}$

19. $P(\text{red 2 or black 3}) = P(\text{red 2}) + P(\text{black 3}) = \dfrac{2}{52} + \dfrac{2}{52} = \dfrac{4}{52} = \dfrac{1}{13}$

20. $P(\text{red 7 or black 8}) = P(\text{red 7}) + P(\text{black 8}) = \dfrac{2}{52} + \dfrac{2}{52} = \dfrac{4}{52} = \dfrac{1}{13}$

21. $P(2 \text{ of hearts or 3 of spades}) = P(2 \text{ of hearts}) + P(3 \text{ of spades}) = \dfrac{1}{52} + \dfrac{1}{52} = \dfrac{2}{52} = \dfrac{1}{26}$

22. $P(7 \text{ or hearts or 8 of spades}) = P(7 \text{ of hearts}) + P(8 \text{ of spades}) = \dfrac{1}{52} + \dfrac{1}{52} = \dfrac{2}{52} = \dfrac{1}{26}$

23. $P(\text{professor or instructor}) = P(\text{professor}) + P(\text{instructor}) = \dfrac{8}{44} + \dfrac{10}{44} = \dfrac{18}{44} = \dfrac{9}{22}$

24. $P(\text{Independent or Green}) = P(\text{Independent}) + P(\text{Green}) = \dfrac{8}{67} + \dfrac{4}{67} = \dfrac{12}{67}$

25. $P(\text{even or less than 5}) = P(\text{even}) + P(\text{less than 5}) - P(\text{even and less than 5}) = \dfrac{3}{6} + \dfrac{4}{6} - \dfrac{2}{6} = \dfrac{5}{6}$

26. $P(\text{odd or less than 4}) = P(\text{odd}) + P(\text{less than 4}) - P(\text{odd and less than 4}) = \dfrac{3}{6} + \dfrac{3}{6} - \dfrac{2}{6} = \dfrac{4}{6} = \dfrac{2}{3}$

27. $P(7 \text{ or red}) = P(7) + P(\text{red}) - P(\text{red 7}) = \dfrac{4}{52} + \dfrac{26}{52} - \dfrac{2}{52} = \dfrac{28}{52} = \dfrac{7}{13}$

28. $P(5 \text{ or black}) = P(5) + P(\text{black}) - P(\text{black 5}) = \dfrac{4}{52} + \dfrac{26}{52} - \dfrac{2}{52} = \dfrac{28}{52} = \dfrac{7}{13}$

29. $P(\text{heart or picture card}) = P(\text{heart}) + P(\text{picture card}) - P(\text{heart and picture card}) = \dfrac{13}{52} + \dfrac{12}{52} - \dfrac{3}{52} = \dfrac{22}{52} = \dfrac{11}{26}$

30. P(greater than 2 and less than 7, or diamond)

    $= P$(greater than 2 and less than 7) $+ P$(diamond) $- P$(diamond greater than 2 and less than 7)

    $= \dfrac{16}{52} + \dfrac{13}{52} - \dfrac{4}{52} = \dfrac{25}{52}$

31. P(odd or less than 6) $= P$(odd) $+ P$(less than 6) $- P$(odd and less than 6) $= \dfrac{4}{8} + \dfrac{5}{8} - \dfrac{3}{8} = \dfrac{6}{8} = \dfrac{3}{4}$

32. P(odd or greater than 3) $= P$(odd)$+P$(greater than 3) $- P$(odd and greater than 3) $= \dfrac{4}{8} + \dfrac{5}{8} - \dfrac{2}{8} = \dfrac{7}{8}$

33. P(even or greater than 5) $= P$(even) $+ P$(greater than 5) $- P$(even and greater than 5) $= \dfrac{4}{8} + \dfrac{3}{8} - \dfrac{2}{8} = \dfrac{5}{8}$

34. P(even or less than 4) $= P$(even) $+ P$(less than 4) $- P$(even and less than 4) $= \dfrac{4}{8} + \dfrac{3}{8} - \dfrac{1}{8} = \dfrac{6}{8} = \dfrac{3}{4}$

35. P(professor or male) $= P$(professor) $+ P$(male) $- P$(male professor) $= \dfrac{19}{40} + \dfrac{22}{40} - \dfrac{8}{40} = \dfrac{33}{40}$

36. P(professor or female) $= P$(professor) $+ P$(female) $- P$(female professor) $= \dfrac{19}{40} + \dfrac{18}{40} - \dfrac{11}{40} = \dfrac{26}{40} = \dfrac{13}{20}$

37. P(teach. assist. or female) $= P$(teach. assist.) $+ P$(female) $- P$(female teach. assist.) $= \dfrac{21}{40} + \dfrac{18}{40} - \dfrac{7}{40} = \dfrac{32}{40} = \dfrac{4}{5}$

38. P(teaching assistant or male) $= P$(teach. assist.) $+ P$(male) $- P$(male teach. assist.) $= \dfrac{21}{40} + \dfrac{22}{40} - \dfrac{14}{40} = \dfrac{29}{40}$

39. P(Democrat or business major) $= P$(Democrat) $+ P$(business major) $- P$(Democrat and business major)

    $= \dfrac{29}{50} + \dfrac{11}{50} - \dfrac{5}{50} = \dfrac{35}{50} = \dfrac{7}{10}$

40. P(math or english) $= P$(math) $+ P$(english) $- P$(math and english) $= \dfrac{135}{200} + \dfrac{85}{200} - \dfrac{65}{200} = \dfrac{155}{200} = \dfrac{31}{40}$

41. P(not completed 4 years or more) $= 1 - P$(completed 4 years or more) $= 1 - \dfrac{45}{174} = \dfrac{129}{174} = \dfrac{43}{58}$

42. P(not completed 4 years of high school) $= \dfrac{29}{174} = \dfrac{1}{6}$

43. P(completed 4 years of high school only or less than four years of college)

    $= P$(completed 4 years of high school only) $+ P$(less than four years of college)

    $= \dfrac{56}{174} + \dfrac{44}{174} = \dfrac{100}{174} = \dfrac{50}{87}$

44. P(completed less than 4 years of high school or 4 years of high school only)

$= P$(completed less than 4 years of high school) $+ P$(4 years of high school only)

$= \dfrac{29}{174} + \dfrac{56}{174} = \dfrac{85}{174}$

45. P(completed 4 years of high school only or is a man)

$= P$(completed 4 years of high school only) $+ P$(male) $- P$(completed 4 years of high school only and is a man)

$= \dfrac{56}{174} + \dfrac{82}{174} - \dfrac{25}{174} = \dfrac{113}{174}$

46. P(completed 4 years of high school only or is a woman)

$= P$(completed 4 years of high school only) $+ P$(female) $- P$(completed 4 years of high school only and is a woman)

$= \dfrac{56}{174} + \dfrac{92}{174} - \dfrac{31}{174} = \dfrac{117}{174} = \dfrac{39}{58}$

47. The number that meets the characteristic is 45. The number that does not meet the characteristic is $174 - 45 = 129$.
Odds in favor: 45 to 129 which reduces to 15 to 43
Odds against: 129 to 45 which reduces to 43 to 5

48. The number that meets the characteristic is 29. The number that does not meet the characteristic is $174 - 29 = 145$.
Odds in favor: 29 to 145 which reduces to 1 to 5
Odds against: 145 to 29 which reduces to 5 to 1

49. P(not in the Army) $= 1 - P$(in the Army) $= 1 - \dfrac{450 + 70}{1380} = 1 - \dfrac{520}{1380} = \dfrac{43}{69}$

50. P(not in the Marines) $= 1 - P$(in the Marines) $= 1 - \dfrac{170 + 10}{1380} = 1 - \dfrac{180}{1380} = \dfrac{20}{23}$

51. P(in the Navy or a man) $= P$(in the Navy) $+ P$(a man) $- P$(in the Navy and a man)

$= \dfrac{290 + 50}{1380} + \dfrac{280 + 450 + 170 + 290}{1380} - \dfrac{290}{1380}$

$= \dfrac{340}{1380} + \dfrac{1190}{1380} - \dfrac{290}{1380}$

$= \dfrac{1240}{1380}$

$= \dfrac{62}{69}$

52. P(in the Army or a woman) $= P$(in the Army) $+ P$(a woman) $- P$(in the Army and a woman)

$= \dfrac{450 + 70}{1380} + \dfrac{60 + 70 + 10 + 50}{1380} - \dfrac{70}{1380}$

$= \dfrac{520}{1380} + \dfrac{190}{1380} - \dfrac{70}{1380}$

$= \dfrac{32}{69}$

53. P(in the Air Force or the Marines) $= P$(in the Air Force) $+ P$(in the Marines) $= \dfrac{280 + 60}{1380} + \dfrac{170 + 10}{1380} = \dfrac{26}{69}$

54. P(in the Army or the Navy) $= P$(in the Army) $+ P$(in the Navy) $= \dfrac{450+70}{1380} + \dfrac{290+50}{1380} = \dfrac{860}{1380} = \dfrac{43}{69}$

55. The number that meets the characteristic is $290 + 50 = 340$.
    The number that does not meet the characteristic is $1380 - 340 = 1040$.
    Odds in favor: 340 to 1040 which reduce 17 to 52
    Odds against: 1040 to 340 which reduce 52 to 17

56. The number that meets the characteristic is $450 + 70 = 520$.
    The number that does not meet the characteristic is $1380 - 520 = 860$.
    Odds in favor: 520 to 860 which reduce 26 to 43
    Odds against: 860 to 520 which reduce 43 to 26

57. The number that meets the characteristic is 10. The number that does not meet the characteristic is $1380 - 10 = 1370$.
    Odds in favor: 10 to 1370 which reduce 1 to 137
    Odds against: 1370 to 10 which reduce 137 to 1

58. The number that meets the characteristic is 60. The number that does not meet the characteristic is $1380 - 60 = 1320$.
    Odds in favor: 60 to 1320 which reduce 1 to 22
    Odds against: 1320 to 60 which reduce 22 to 1

59. The number that meets the characteristic is $280 + 450 + 170 + 290 = 1190$.
    The number that does not meet the characteristic is $1380 - 1190 = 190$.
    Odds in favor: 1190 to 190 which reduce 119 to 19
    Odds against: 190 to 1190 which reduce 19 to 119

60. The number that meets the characteristic is $60 + 70 + 10 + 50 = 190$.
    The number that does not meet the characteristic is $1380 - 190 = 1190$.
    Odds favor: 190 to 1190 which reduce 19 to 119
    Odds in against: 1190 to 190 which reduce 119 to 19

61. number of favorable outcomes = 4, number of unfavorable outcomes = 2
    Odds in favor of getting a number greater than 2 are 4:2, or 2:1.

62. number of favorable outcomes = 4, number of unfavorable outcomes = 2
    Odds in favor of getting a number less than 5 are 4:2, or 2:1.

63. number of unfavorable outcomes = 2, number of favorable outcomes = 4
    Odds against getting a number greater than 2 or 2:4, or 1:2.

64. number of unfavorable outcomes = 2, number of favorable outcomes = 4
    Odds against getting a number less than 5 are 2:4, or 1:2.

65. number of favorable outcomes = 9, number of unfavorable outcomes $= 100 - 9 = 91$

    a. Odds in favor of a child in a one-parent household having a parent who is a college graduate are 9:91.

    b. Odds against a child in a one-parent household having a parent who is a college graduate are 91:9.

66. number of favorable outcomes = 29, number of unfavorable outcomes $= 100 - 29 = 71$

    a. Odds in favor of a child in a two-parent household having parents who are college graduates are 29:71.

    b. Odds against a child in a two-parent household having parents who are college graduates are 71:29.

67. number of favorable outcomes = 13, number of unfavorable outcomes = 39
    Odds in favor of a heart are 13:39, or 1:3.

68. number of favorable outcomes = 12, number of unfavorable outcomes = 40
Odds in favor of a picture card are 12:40, or 3:10.

69. number of favorable outcomes = 26, number of unfavorable outcomes = 26
Odds in favor of a red card are 26:26, or 1:1.

70. number of favorable outcomes = 26, number of unfavorable outcomes = 26
Odds in favor of a black card are 26:26, or 1:1.

71. number of unfavorable outcomes = 48, number of favorable outcomes = 4
Odds against a 9 are 48:4, or 12:1.

72. number of unfavorable outcomes = 48, number of favorable outcomes = 4
Odds against a 5 are 48:4, or 12:1.

73. number of unfavorable outcomes = 50, number of favorable outcomes = 2
Odds against a black king are 50:2, or 25:1.

74. number of unfavorable outcomes = 50, number of favorable outcomes = 2
Odds against a red jack are 50:2, or 25:1.

75. number of unfavorable outcomes = 47, number of favorable outcomes = 5
Odds against a spade greater than 3 and less than 9 are 47:5.

76. number of unfavorable outcomes = 47, number of favorable outcomes = 5
Odds against a club greater than 4 and less than 9 are 47:5.

77. number of unfavorable outcomes = 980, number of favorable outcomes = 20
Odds against winning are 980:20, or 49:1.

78. number of unfavorable outcomes = 4970, number of favorable outcomes = 30
Odds against winning are 4970:30, or 497:3.

79. The number that meets the characteristic is 18. The number that does not meet the characteristic is $38 - 18 = 20$.
Odds in favor: 18 to 20 which reduce 9 to 10

80. The number that meets the characteristic is 10. The number that does not meet the characteristic is $38 - 10 = 28$.
Odds in favor: 10 to 28 which reduce 5 to 14

81. The number that meets the characteristic is 10. The number that does not meet the characteristic is $38 - 10 = 28$.
Odds against: 28 to 10 which reduce 14 to 5

82. The number that meets the characteristic is 18. The number that does not meet the characteristic is $38 - 18 = 20$.
Odds against: 20 to 18 which reduce 10 to 9

83. The number that meets the characteristic is $18 + 10 = 28$.
The number that does not meet the characteristic is $38 - 28 = 10$.
Odds in favor: 28 to 10 which reduce 14 to 5

84. The number that meets the characteristic is $10 + 10 = 20$.
The number that does not meet the characteristic is $38 - 20 = 18$.
Odds in favor: 20 to 18 which reduce 10 to 9

85. The number that meets the characteristic is $10 + 10 = 20$.
The number that does not meet the characteristic is $38 - 20 = 18$.
Odds against: 18 to 20 which reduce 9 to 10

86. The number that meets the characteristic is $18 + 10 = 28$.
    The number that does not meet the characteristic is $38 - 28 = 10$.
    Odds against: 10 to 28 which reduce 5 to 14

87. $P(\text{winning}) = \dfrac{3}{3+4} = \dfrac{3}{7}$

88. $P(\text{winning}) = \dfrac{3}{3+7} = \dfrac{3}{10}$

89. $P(\text{miss free throw}) = \dfrac{4}{21+4} = \dfrac{4}{25} = 0.16 = 16\%$
    In 100 free throws, on average he missed 16, so he made $100 - 16 = 84$.

90. $P(\text{still alive at age 70}) = \dfrac{193}{193+270} = \dfrac{193}{463} \approx 41.7\%$

91. $P(\text{contracting an airborn illness}) = \dfrac{1}{1+999} = \dfrac{1}{1000}$

92. $P(\text{deep-vein thrombosis}) = \dfrac{1}{1+28} = \dfrac{1}{29}$

100. does not make sense; Explanations will vary. Sample explanation: The two probabilities must add to 1.

101. does not make sense; Explanations will vary. Sample explanation: Since 1 card is a heart *and* a king, the probability is
    $\dfrac{4}{52} + \dfrac{13}{52} - \dfrac{1}{52} = \dfrac{16}{52} = \dfrac{4}{13}$.

102. does not make sense; Explanations will vary. Sample explanation: The probability of selecting a king or a heart is
    $\dfrac{4}{52} + \dfrac{13}{52} - \dfrac{1}{52} = \dfrac{16}{52} = \dfrac{4}{13}$. The probability of selecting the king of hearts is $\dfrac{1}{52}$.

103. does not make sense; Explanations will vary. Sample explanation: The odds are more likely 1:9.

104. **a.** $P(\text{Democrat who is not a business major})$
    $= 1 - P(\text{not a Democrat or Democrat and business major})$
    $= 1 - [P(\text{not a Democrat}) + P(\text{Democrat and business major})]$
    $= 1 - \left(\dfrac{21}{50} + \dfrac{5}{50}\right)$
    $= 1 - \dfrac{26}{50}$
    $= \dfrac{24}{50}$
    $= \dfrac{12}{25}$

b. P(neither Democrat nor business major)

$= 1 - P$(Democrat or business major)

$= 1 - [P(\text{Democrat}) + P(\text{business major}) - P(\text{Democrat and business major})]$

$= 1 - \left(\dfrac{29}{50} + \dfrac{11}{50} - \dfrac{5}{50}\right)$

$= 1 - \dfrac{35}{50}$

$= \dfrac{15}{50}$

$= \dfrac{3}{10}$

105. P(driving intoxicated or driving accident)

$= P(\text{driving intoxicated}) + P(\text{driving accident}) - P(\text{driving accident while intoxicated})$

Substitute the three given probabilities and solve for the unknown probability:

$$0.35 = 0.32 + 0.09 - P(\text{driving accident while intoxicated})$$

$P(\text{driving accident while intoxicated}) = 0.32 + 0.09 - 0.35$

$P(\text{driving accident while intoxicated}) = 0.06$

106.
$$\dfrac{P(E)}{1 - P(E)} = \dfrac{a}{b}$$

$$\dfrac{P(E)}{1 - P(E)} \cdot \dfrac{b(1 - P(E))}{1} = \dfrac{a}{b} \cdot \dfrac{b(1 - P(E))}{1}$$

$$bP(E) = a(1 - P(E))$$

$$bP(E) = a - aP(E)$$

$$aP(E) + bP(E) = a$$

$$P(E)(a + b) = a$$

$$\dfrac{P(E)(a + b)}{a + b} = \dfrac{a}{a + b}$$

$$P(E) = \dfrac{a}{a + b}$$

Check Points 11.7

1. $P(\text{green and green}) = P(\text{green}) \cdot P(\text{green}) = \dfrac{2}{38} \cdot \dfrac{2}{38} = \dfrac{1}{19} \cdot \dfrac{1}{19} = \dfrac{1}{361} \approx 0.00277$

2. $P(\text{4 boys in a row}) = P(\text{boy and boy and boy and boy}) = P(\text{boy}) \cdot P(\text{boy}) \cdot P(\text{boy}) \cdot P(\text{boy}) = \dfrac{1}{2} \cdot \dfrac{1}{2} \cdot \dfrac{1}{2} \cdot \dfrac{1}{2} = \dfrac{1}{16}$

3. a. $P(\text{hit four years in a row}) = P(\text{hit}) \cdot P(\text{hit}) \cdot P(\text{hit}) \cdot P(\text{hit}) = \dfrac{5}{19} \cdot \dfrac{5}{19} \cdot \dfrac{5}{19} \cdot \dfrac{5}{19} = \dfrac{625}{130{,}321} \approx 0.005$

b.   Note: $P(\text{not hit in any single year}) = 1 - P(\text{hit in any single year}) = 1 - \dfrac{5}{19} = \dfrac{14}{19}$,. Therefore,

$P(\text{not hit in next four years})$

$= P(\text{not hit}) \cdot P(\text{not hit}) \cdot P(\text{not hit}) \cdot P(\text{not hit}) = \dfrac{14}{19} \cdot \dfrac{14}{19} \cdot \dfrac{14}{19} \cdot \dfrac{14}{19} = \dfrac{38,416}{130,321} \approx 0.295$

c. $P(\text{hit at least once in next four years}) = 1 - P(\text{not hit in next four years}) = 1 - \frac{38,416}{130,321} = \frac{91,905}{130,321} \approx 0.705$

4. $P(2 \text{ kings}) = P(\text{king}) \cdot P(\text{king given the first card was a king}) = \dfrac{4}{52} \cdot \dfrac{3}{51} = \dfrac{1}{13} \cdot \dfrac{1}{17} = \dfrac{1}{221} \approx 0.00452$

5. $P(3 \text{ hearts}) = P(\text{heart}) \cdot P(\text{heart given the first card was a heart}) \cdot P(\text{heart given the first two cards were hearts})$

$= \dfrac{13}{52} \cdot \dfrac{12}{51} \cdot \dfrac{11}{50} = \dfrac{1}{4} \cdot \dfrac{4}{17} \cdot \dfrac{11}{50} = \dfrac{1}{1} \cdot \dfrac{1}{17} \cdot \dfrac{11}{50} = \dfrac{11}{850} \approx 0.0129$

6.   The sample space is given by $S = \{a,e,i,o,u\}$.
     Of these 5 elements, only a and e precede h.
     Thus the probability is $P\left(\text{letter precedes } h \mid \text{vowel}\right) = \dfrac{2}{5}$.

7.   a.   The sample space is the set of 13 spades.
          Of these 13 elements, all 13 cards are black.
          Thus the probability is $P\left(\text{black card} \mid \text{spade}\right) = \dfrac{13}{13} = 1$.

     b.   The sample space is the set of 26 black cards.
          Of these 26 elements, 13 cards are spades.
          Thus the probability is $P\left(\text{spade} \mid \text{black card}\right) = \dfrac{13}{26} = \dfrac{1}{2}$.

Exercise Set 11.7

1. $P(\text{green and then red}) = P(\text{green}) \cdot P(\text{red}) = \dfrac{2}{6} \cdot \dfrac{3}{6} = \dfrac{1}{3} \cdot \dfrac{1}{2} = \dfrac{1}{6}$

2. $P(\text{yellow and then green}) = P(\text{yellow}) \cdot P(\text{green}) = \dfrac{1}{6} \cdot \dfrac{2}{6} = \dfrac{1}{6} \cdot \dfrac{1}{3} = \dfrac{1}{18}$

3. $P(\text{yellow and then yellow}) = P(\text{yellow}) \cdot P(\text{yellow}) = \dfrac{1}{6} \cdot \dfrac{1}{6} = \dfrac{1}{36}$

4. $P(\text{red and then red}) = P(\text{red}) \cdot P(\text{red}) = \dfrac{3}{6} \cdot \dfrac{3}{6} = \dfrac{1}{2} \cdot \dfrac{1}{2} = \dfrac{1}{4}$

5. $P(\text{color other than red each time}) = P(\text{not red}) \cdot P(\text{not red}) = \dfrac{3}{6} \cdot \dfrac{3}{6} = \dfrac{1}{2} \cdot \dfrac{1}{2} = \dfrac{1}{4}$

6. $P(\text{color other than green each time}) = P(\text{not green}) \cdot P(\text{not green}) = \dfrac{4}{6} \cdot \dfrac{4}{6} = \dfrac{2}{3} \cdot \dfrac{2}{3} = \dfrac{4}{9}$

7. $P(\text{green and then red and then yellow}) = P(\text{green}) \cdot P(\text{red}) \cdot P(\text{yellow}) = \dfrac{2}{6} \cdot \dfrac{3}{6} \cdot \dfrac{1}{6} = \dfrac{1}{3} \cdot \dfrac{1}{2} \cdot \dfrac{1}{6} = \dfrac{1}{36}$

8. $P(\text{red and then red and then green}) = P(\text{red}) \cdot P(\text{red}) \cdot P(\text{green}) = \dfrac{3}{6} \cdot \dfrac{3}{6} \cdot \dfrac{2}{6} = \dfrac{1}{2} \cdot \dfrac{1}{2} \cdot \dfrac{1}{3} = \dfrac{1}{12}$

9. $P(\text{red every time}) = P(\text{red}) \cdot P(\text{red}) \cdot P(\text{red}) = \dfrac{3}{6} \cdot \dfrac{3}{6} \cdot \dfrac{3}{6} = \dfrac{1}{2} \cdot \dfrac{1}{2} \cdot \dfrac{1}{2} = \dfrac{1}{8}$

10. $P(\text{green every time}) = P(\text{green}) \cdot P(\text{green}) \cdot P(\text{green}) = \dfrac{2}{6} \cdot \dfrac{2}{6} \cdot \dfrac{2}{6} = \dfrac{1}{3} \cdot \dfrac{1}{3} \cdot \dfrac{1}{3} = \dfrac{1}{27}$

11. $P(2 \text{ and then } 3) = P(2) \cdot P(3) = \dfrac{1}{6} \cdot \dfrac{1}{6} = \dfrac{1}{36}$

12. $P(5 \text{ and then } 1) = P(5) \cdot P(1) = \dfrac{1}{6} \cdot \dfrac{1}{6} = \dfrac{1}{36}$

13. $P(\text{even and then greater than } 2) = P(\text{even}) \cdot P(\text{greater than } 2) = \dfrac{3}{6} \cdot \dfrac{4}{6} = \dfrac{1}{2} \cdot \dfrac{2}{3} = \dfrac{1}{3}$

14. $P(\text{odd and then less than } 3) = P(\text{odd}) \cdot P(\text{less than } 3) = \dfrac{3}{6} \cdot \dfrac{2}{6} = \dfrac{1}{2} \cdot \dfrac{1}{3} = \dfrac{1}{6}$

15. $P(\text{picture card and then heart}) = P(\text{picture card}) \cdot P(\text{heart}) = \dfrac{12}{52} \cdot \dfrac{13}{52} = \dfrac{3}{13} \cdot \dfrac{1}{4} = \dfrac{3}{52}$

16. $P(\text{jack and then club}) = P(\text{jack}) \cdot P(\text{club}) = \dfrac{4}{52} \cdot \dfrac{13}{52} = \dfrac{1}{13} \cdot \dfrac{1}{4} = \dfrac{1}{52}$

17. $P(2 \text{ kings}) = P(\text{king}) \cdot P(\text{king}) = \dfrac{4}{52} \cdot \dfrac{4}{52} = \dfrac{1}{13} \cdot \dfrac{1}{13} = \dfrac{1}{169}$

18. $P(3 \text{ each time}) = P(3) \cdot P(3) = \dfrac{4}{52} \cdot \dfrac{4}{52} = \dfrac{1}{13} \cdot \dfrac{1}{13} = \dfrac{1}{169}$

19. $P(\text{red each time}) = P(\text{red}) \cdot P(\text{red}) = \dfrac{26}{52} \cdot \dfrac{26}{52} = \dfrac{1}{2} \cdot \dfrac{1}{2} = \dfrac{1}{4}$

20. $P(\text{black each time}) = P(\text{black}) \cdot P(\text{black}) = \dfrac{26}{52} \cdot \dfrac{26}{52} = \dfrac{1}{2} \cdot \dfrac{1}{2} = \dfrac{1}{4}$

21. $P(\text{all heads}) = P(\text{heads}) \cdot P(\text{heads}) \cdot P(\text{heads}) \cdot P(\text{heads}) \cdot P(\text{heads}) \cdot P(\text{heads}) = \dfrac{1}{2} \cdot \dfrac{1}{2} \cdot \dfrac{1}{2} \cdot \dfrac{1}{2} \cdot \dfrac{1}{2} \cdot \dfrac{1}{2} = \dfrac{1}{64}$

22. $P(\text{all tails}) = P(\text{tails}) \cdot P(\text{tails}) \cdot P(\text{tails}) \cdot P(\text{tails}) \cdot P(\text{tails}) \cdot P(\text{tails}) \cdot P(\text{tails}) = \dfrac{1}{2} \cdot \dfrac{1}{2} \cdot \dfrac{1}{2} \cdot \dfrac{1}{2} \cdot \dfrac{1}{2} \cdot \dfrac{1}{2} \cdot \dfrac{1}{2} = \dfrac{1}{128}$

23. $P(\text{head and number greater than } 4) = P(\text{head}) \cdot P(\text{number greater than } 4) = \dfrac{1}{2} \cdot \dfrac{2}{6} = \dfrac{1}{6}$

24. $P(\text{tail and number less than 5}) = P(\text{tail}) \cdot P(\text{number less than 5}) = \dfrac{1}{2} \cdot \dfrac{4}{6} = \dfrac{1}{2} \cdot \dfrac{2}{3} = \dfrac{1}{3}$

25. a. $P(\text{hit two years in a row}) = P(\text{hit}) \cdot P(\text{hit}) = \dfrac{1}{16} \cdot \dfrac{1}{16} = \dfrac{1}{256} \approx 0.00391$

    b. $P(\text{Hit three consecutive years}) = P(\text{hit}) \cdot P(\text{hit}) \cdot P(\text{hit}) = \dfrac{1}{16} \cdot \dfrac{1}{16} \cdot \dfrac{1}{16} = \dfrac{1}{4096} \approx 0.000244$

    c. $P(\text{not hit in next ten years}) = [P(\text{not hit})]^{10} = \left(1 - \dfrac{1}{16}\right)^{10} = \left(\dfrac{15}{16}\right)^{10} \approx 0.524$

    d. $P(\text{hit at least once in next ten years}) = 1 - P(\text{not hit in next ten years}) \approx 1 - 0.524 \approx 0.476$

26. a. $P(\text{flood two years in a row}) = P(\text{flood}) \cdot P(\text{flood}) = \dfrac{1}{10} \cdot \dfrac{1}{10} = \dfrac{1}{100}$

    b. $P(\text{flood three consecutive years}) = P(\text{flood}) \cdot P(\text{flood}) \cdot P(\text{flood}) = \dfrac{1}{10} \cdot \dfrac{1}{10} \cdot \dfrac{1}{10} = \dfrac{1}{1000}$

    c. $P(\text{no flooding in ten years}) = [P(\text{no flood})]^{10} = [1 - P(\text{flood})]^{10} = \left(1 - \dfrac{1}{10}\right)^{10} = \left(\dfrac{9}{10}\right)^{10} \approx 0.349$

    d. $P(\text{flooding at least once in ten years}) = 1 - P(\text{no flooding in ten years}) \approx 1 - 0.349 \approx 0.651$

27. $P(\text{both suffer from depression - from general population}) = P(\text{depression}) \cdot P(\text{depression}) = 0.12 \cdot 0.12 = 0.0144$

28. $P(\text{both suffer from depression - from population of smokers}) = P(\text{depression}) \cdot P(\text{depression}) = 0.28 \cdot 0.28 = 0.0784$

29. $P(\text{all three suffer from frequent hangovers - from population of smokers})$
    $= P(\text{frequent hangovers}) \cdot P(\text{frequent hangovers}) \cdot P(\text{frequent hangovers}) = 0.20 \cdot 0.20 \cdot 0.20 = 0.008$

30. $P(\text{all three suffer from frequent hangovers - from general population})$
    $= P(\text{frequent hangovers}) \cdot P(\text{frequent hangovers}) \cdot P(\text{frequent hangovers}) = 0.10 \cdot 0.10 \cdot 0.10 = 0.001$

31. $P(\text{at least one of three suffers from anxiety/panic disorder - from population of smokers})$
    $= 1 - \big[1 - P(\text{anxiety/panic disorder})\big] \cdot \big[1 - P(\text{anxiety/panic disorder})\big] \cdot \big[1 - P(\text{anxiety/panic disorder})\big]$
    $= 1 - [1 - 0.19] \cdot [1 - 0.19] \cdot [1 - 0.19]$
    $= 1 - [0.81] \cdot [0.81] \cdot [0.81]$
    $\approx 1 - 0.5314$
    $= 0.4686$

32. $P(\text{at least one of three suffers from severe pain - from population of smokers})$
    $= 1 - \big[1 - P(\text{severe pain})\big] \cdot \big[1 - P(\text{severe pain})\big] \cdot \big[1 - P(\text{severe pain})\big]$
    $= 1 - [1 - 0.14] \cdot [1 - 0.14] \cdot [1 - 0.14]$
    $= 1 - [0.86] \cdot [0.86] \cdot [0.86]$
    $\approx 1 - 0.6361$
    $= 0.3639$

33. $P(\text{solid and solid}) = P(\text{solid}) \cdot P(\text{solid given first was solid}) = \dfrac{15}{30} \cdot \dfrac{14}{29} = \dfrac{1}{2} \cdot \dfrac{14}{29} = \dfrac{7}{29}$

34. $P(\text{two caramel}) = P(\text{caramel}) \cdot P(\text{caramel given first was caramel}) = \dfrac{10}{30} \cdot \dfrac{9}{29} = \dfrac{1}{3} \cdot \dfrac{9}{29} = \dfrac{3}{29}$

35. $P(\text{coconut then caramel}) = P(\text{coconut}) \cdot P(\text{caramel given first was coconut}) = \dfrac{5}{30} \cdot \dfrac{10}{29} = \dfrac{1}{6} \cdot \dfrac{10}{29} = \dfrac{5}{87}$

36. $P(\text{coconut then solid}) = P(\text{coconut}) \cdot P(\text{solid given first was coconut}) = \dfrac{5}{30} \cdot \dfrac{15}{29} = \dfrac{1}{6} \cdot \dfrac{15}{29} = \dfrac{5}{58}$

37. $P(\text{two Democrats}) = P(\text{Democrat}) \cdot P(\text{Democrat given first was Democrat}) = \dfrac{5}{15} \cdot \dfrac{4}{14} = \dfrac{1}{3} \cdot \dfrac{2}{7} = \dfrac{2}{21}$

38. $P(\text{two Republicans}) = P(\text{Republican}) \cdot P(\text{Republican given first was Republican})$

    $= \dfrac{6}{15} \cdot \dfrac{5}{14} = \dfrac{2}{5} \cdot \dfrac{5}{14} = \dfrac{1}{7}$

39. $P(\text{Independent then Republican}) = P(\text{Independent}) \cdot P(\text{Republican given first was Independent})$

    $= \dfrac{4}{15} \cdot \dfrac{6}{14} = \dfrac{4}{15} \cdot \dfrac{3}{7} = \dfrac{4}{35}$

40. $P(\text{Independent then Democrat}) = P(\text{Independent}) \cdot P(\text{Democrat given first was Independent})$

    $= \dfrac{4}{15} \cdot \dfrac{5}{14} = \dfrac{2}{21}$

41. $P(\text{no Independents}) = P(\text{not Independent}) \cdot P(\text{not Independent given first was not Independent})$

    $= \dfrac{11}{15} \cdot \dfrac{10}{14} = \dfrac{11}{15} \cdot \dfrac{5}{7} = \dfrac{11}{21}$

42. $P(\text{no Democrats}) = P(\text{not Democrat}) \cdot P(\text{not Democrat given first was not Democrat}) = \dfrac{10}{15} \cdot \dfrac{9}{14} = \dfrac{2}{3} \cdot \dfrac{9}{14} = \dfrac{3}{7}$

43. $P(\text{three cans of apple juice})$

    $= P(\text{apple juice}) \cdot P\left(\begin{array}{c}\text{apple juice given} \\ \text{first was apple juice}\end{array}\right) \cdot P\left(\begin{array}{c}\text{apple juice given first} \\ \text{two were apple juice}\end{array}\right) = \dfrac{6}{20} \cdot \dfrac{5}{19} \cdot \dfrac{4}{18} = \dfrac{1}{57}$

44. $P(\text{three cans of grape juice})$

    $= P(\text{grape juice}) \cdot P\left(\begin{array}{c}\text{grape juice given} \\ \text{first was grape juice}\end{array}\right) \cdot P\left(\begin{array}{c}\text{grape juice given first} \\ \text{two were grape juice}\end{array}\right) = \dfrac{8}{20} \cdot \dfrac{7}{19} \cdot \dfrac{6}{18} = \dfrac{14}{285}$

45. $P(\text{grape juice then orange juice then mango juice})$

    $= P(\text{grape juice}) \cdot P\left(\begin{array}{c}\text{orange juice given} \\ \text{first was grape juice}\end{array}\right) \cdot P\left(\begin{array}{c}\text{mango juice given first was grape juice} \\ \text{and second was orange juice}\end{array}\right) = \dfrac{8}{20} \cdot \dfrac{4}{19} \cdot \dfrac{2}{18} = \dfrac{8}{855}$

46. $P(\text{apple juice then grape juice then orange juice})$

    $= P(\text{apple juice}) \cdot P\left(\begin{array}{c}\text{grape juice given} \\ \text{first was apple juice}\end{array}\right) \cdot P\left(\begin{array}{c}\text{orange juice given first was apple juice} \\ \text{and second was grape juice}\end{array}\right) = \dfrac{6}{20} \cdot \dfrac{8}{19} \cdot \dfrac{4}{18} = \dfrac{8}{285}$

47. P(no grape juice)

$$= P(\text{not grape juice}) \cdot P\left(\begin{array}{c}\text{not grape juice given} \\ \text{first was not grape juice}\end{array}\right) \cdot P\left(\begin{array}{c}\text{not grape juice given first} \\ \text{two were not grape juice}\end{array}\right) = \frac{12}{20} \cdot \frac{11}{19} \cdot \frac{10}{18} = \frac{11}{57}$$

48. P(no apple juice)

$$= P(\text{not apple juice}) \cdot P\left(\begin{array}{c}\text{not apple juice given} \\ \text{first was not apple juice}\end{array}\right) \cdot P\left(\begin{array}{c}\text{not apple juice given first} \\ \text{two were not apple juice}\end{array}\right) = \frac{14}{20} \cdot \frac{13}{19} \cdot \frac{12}{18} = \frac{91}{285}$$

49. $P(3|\text{red}) = \dfrac{1}{5}$

50. $P(7|\text{yellow}) = \dfrac{1}{3}$

51. $P(\text{even}|\text{yellow}) = \dfrac{2}{3}$

52. $P(\text{odd}|\text{red}) = \dfrac{3}{5}$

53. $P(\text{red}|\text{odd}) = \dfrac{3}{4}$

54. $P(\text{yellow}|\text{odd}) = \dfrac{1}{4}$

55. $P(\text{red}|\text{at least }5) = \dfrac{3}{4}$

56. $P(\text{yellow}|\text{at most }3) = \dfrac{1}{3}$

57. $P(\text{surviving}|\text{wore seat belt}) = \dfrac{412,368}{412,878} = \dfrac{68,728}{68,813} \approx 0.999$

58. $P(\text{not surviving}|\text{did not wear seat belt}) = \dfrac{1601}{164,128} \approx 0.010$

59. $P(\text{wore seat belt}|\text{driver survived}) = \dfrac{412,368}{574,895} \approx 0.717$

60. $P(\text{did not wear seat belt}|\text{not surviving}) = \dfrac{1601}{2111} \approx 0.758$

61. $P(\text{not divorced}) = 1 - P(\text{divorced}) = 1 - \dfrac{22.8}{235.8} \approx 0.903$

62. $P(\text{not widowed}) = 1 - P(\text{widowed}) = 1 - \dfrac{13.9}{235.8} \approx 0.941$

63. $P(\text{widowed or divorced}) = P(\text{widowed}) + P(\text{divorced}) = \dfrac{13.9}{235.8} + \dfrac{22.8}{235.8} = \dfrac{36.7}{235.8} \approx 0.156$

64. $P(\text{never married or is divorced}) = P(\text{never married}) + P(\text{divorced}) = \dfrac{69.2}{235.8} + \dfrac{22.8}{235.8} = \dfrac{92.0}{235.8} \approx 0.390$

65. $P(\text{male or is divorced}) = P(\text{male}) + P(\text{divorced}) - P(\text{male and is divorced}) = \dfrac{114.5}{235.8} + \dfrac{22.8}{235.8} - \dfrac{9.6}{235.8} = \dfrac{127.7}{235.8} \approx 0.542$

66. $P(\text{female or is divorced}) = P(\text{female}) + P(\text{divorced}) - P(\text{female and is divorced})$

$$= \dfrac{121.3}{235.8} + \dfrac{22.8}{235.8} - \dfrac{13.2}{235.8} = \dfrac{130.9}{235.8} \approx 0.555$$

67. $P\big(\text{male}\,\big|\,\text{divorced}\big) = \dfrac{9.6}{22.8} \approx 0.421$

68. $P\big(\text{female}\,\big|\,\text{divorced}\big) = \dfrac{13.2}{22.8} \approx 0.579$

69. $P\big(\text{widowed}\,\big|\,\text{woman}\big) = \dfrac{11.2}{121.3} \approx 0.092$

70. $P\big(\text{divorced}\,\big|\,\text{man}\big) = \dfrac{9.6}{114.5} \approx 0.084$

71. $P\big(\text{never married or married}\,\big|\,\text{man}\big) = \dfrac{37.5}{114.5} + \dfrac{64.7}{114.5} = \dfrac{102.2}{114.5} \approx 0.893$

72. $P\big(\text{never married or married}\,\big|\,\text{woman}\big) = \dfrac{31.7}{121.3} + \dfrac{65.2}{121.3} = \dfrac{96.9}{121.3} \approx 0.799$

81. does not make sense; Explanations will vary. Sample explanation: The previous three children do not affect the odds of the fourth child. The odds are 1:1.

82. does not make sense; Explanations will vary. Sample explanation: The probability of the second selection being a man, given that the first was a man is $\dfrac{4}{9}$.

83. makes sense

84. does not make sense; Explanations will vary. Sample explanation: $P(A|B)$ does not necessarily equal $P(B|A)$.

85. $P(\text{no one hospitalized}) = [P(\text{not hospitalized})]^5 = (0.9)(0.9)(0.9)(0.9)(0.9) = (0.9)^5 \approx 0.59049 \approx 59.0\%$

86. $P(\text{2 on 1st, 3rd, and 4th rolls only}) = P(2) \cdot P(\text{not 2}) \cdot P(2) \cdot P(2) \cdot P(\text{not 2}) = \dfrac{1}{6} \cdot \dfrac{5}{6} \cdot \dfrac{1}{6} \cdot \dfrac{1}{6} \cdot \dfrac{5}{6} = \dfrac{25}{7776} \approx 0.00322$

87. a. The first person can have any of 365 birthdays. To not match, the second person can then have any of the remaining 364 birthdays.

b. $P(\text{three different birthdays}) = \dfrac{365}{365} \cdot \dfrac{364}{365} \cdot \dfrac{363}{365} \approx 0.992$

c. $P(\text{at least two have same birthday}) = 1 - P(\text{three different birthdays}) = 1 - 0.992 = 0.008$

d. $P(20 \text{ different birthdays})$

$= \dfrac{365 \cdot 364 \cdot 363 \cdot 362 \cdot 361 \cdot 360 \cdot 359 \cdot 358 \cdot 357 \cdot 356 \cdot 355 \cdot 354 \cdot 353 \cdot 352 \cdot 351 \cdot 350 \cdot 349 \cdot 348 \cdot 347 \cdot 346}{365 \cdot 365 \cdot 365 \cdot 365 \cdot 365 \cdot 365 \cdot 365 \cdot 365 \cdot 365 \cdot 365 \cdot 365 \cdot 365 \cdot 365 \cdot 365 \cdot 365 \cdot 365 \cdot 365 \cdot 365 \cdot 365 \cdot 365} \approx 0.589$

$P(\text{at least two have same birthday}) = 1 - P(20 \text{ different birthdays}) = 1 - 0.589 = 0.411$

e. 23 people (determine by trial-and-error using method shown in part d)

88. There are 5 odd numbered cards and therefore there are $_5C_2 = 10$ ways to get two odd cards.

There are 4 even numbered cards and therefore there are $_4C_2 = 6$ ways to get two even cards.

Note that the sum of two odds is an even number and that the sum of two evens is also an even number. Since selecting one even card and one odd card would result in an odd sum, we only need to consider the 16 possible outcomes calculated above.

$P\left(\text{both odd}\,\middle|\,\text{sum even}\right) = \dfrac{\text{number of outcomes with both odd and even sum}}{\text{number of outcomes where the sum is even}} = \dfrac{10}{16} = \dfrac{5}{8}$

89. The sample space has 36 elements. Of these elements, the following 11 fit the given condition: 1&5, 1&6, 3&5, 3&6, 5&1, 5&3, 5&5, 5&6, 6&1, 6&3, 6&5. Thus the probability is $\dfrac{11}{36}$.

Check Points 11.8

1. $E = 1 \cdot \dfrac{1}{4} + 2 \cdot \dfrac{1}{4} + 3 \cdot \dfrac{1}{4} + 4 \cdot \dfrac{1}{4} = \dfrac{1 + 2 + 3 + 4}{4} = \dfrac{10}{4} = 2.5$

2. $E = 0 \cdot \dfrac{1}{16} + 1 \cdot \dfrac{4}{16} + 2 \cdot \dfrac{6}{16} + 3 \cdot \dfrac{4}{16} + 4 \cdot \dfrac{1}{16} = \dfrac{0 + 4 + 12 + 12 + 4}{16} = \dfrac{32}{16} = 2$

3. a. $E = \$0(0.01) + \$2000(0.15) + \$4000(0.08) + \$6000(0.05) + \$8000(0.01) + \$10{,}000(0.70) = \$8000$
This means that in the long run, the average cost of a claim is expected to be $8000.

b. An average premium charge of $8000 would cause the company to neither lose nor gain money.

4. $E = (1)\left(\dfrac{1}{5}\right) + \left(-\dfrac{1}{4}\right)\left(\dfrac{4}{5}\right) = \dfrac{1}{5} + \left(-\dfrac{1}{5}\right) = 0$

Since the expected value is 0, there is nothing to gain or lose on average by guessing.

5. Values of gain or loss:
Grand Prize: $\$1000 - \$2 = \$998$, Consolation Prize: $\$50 - \$2 = \$48$, Nothing: $\$0 - \$2 = -\$2$

$E = (-\$2)\left(\dfrac{997}{1000}\right) + (\$48)\left(\dfrac{2}{1000}\right) + (\$998)\left(\dfrac{1}{1000}\right) = \dfrac{-\$1994 + \$96 + \$998}{1000} = -\dfrac{\$900}{1000} = -\$0.90$

The expected value for one ticket is $-\$0.90$. This means that in the long run a player can expect to lose $0.90 for each ticket bought. Buying five tickets will make your likelihood of winning five times greater, however there is no advantage to this strategy because the *cost* of five tickets is also five times greater than one ticket.

6. $E = (\$2.20)\left(\dfrac{20}{80}\right) + (-\$1.00)\left(\dfrac{60}{80}\right) = \dfrac{\$44 - \$60}{80} = \dfrac{-\$16}{80} = -\$0.20$

   This means that in the long run a player can expect to lose an average of $0.20 for each $1 bet.

Exercise Set 11.8

1. $E = 1 \cdot \dfrac{1}{2} + 2 \cdot \dfrac{1}{4} + 3 \cdot \dfrac{1}{4} = 1.75$

2. $E = 1 \cdot \dfrac{1}{8} + 2 \cdot \dfrac{1}{8} + 3 \cdot \dfrac{1}{2} + 4 \cdot \dfrac{1}{4} = 2.875$

3. **a.** $E = \$0(0.65) + \$50,000(0.20) + \$100,000(0.10) + \$150,000(0.03) + \$200,000(0.01) + \$250,000(0.01) = \$29,000$
   This means that in the long run the average cost of a claim is $29,000.

   b. $29,000

   c. $29,050

4. **a.** $E = \$0(0.70) + \$20,000(0.20) + \$40,000(0.06) + \$60,000(0.02) + \$80,000(0.01) + \$100,000(0.01) = \$9400$
   This means that in the long run the average cost of a claim is $9400.

   b. $9400

   c. $9450

5. $E = -\$10,000(0.9) + \$90,000(0.1) = \$0$. This means on the average there will be no gain or loss.

6. $E = -\$1500\left(\dfrac{4}{5}\right) + \$38,500\left(\dfrac{1}{5}\right) = \$6500$. This means an expected gain on the average.

7. $E = -\$99,999\left(\dfrac{27}{10,000,000}\right) + \$1\left(\dfrac{9,999,973}{10,000,000}\right) = \$0.73$

8. $E = -\$9,900(0.002) + \$100(0.998) = \$80$

9. Probabilities after eliminating one possible answer: Guess Correctly: $\dfrac{1}{4}$, Guess Incorrectly: $\dfrac{3}{4}$

   $E = (1)\left(\dfrac{1}{4}\right) + \left(-\dfrac{1}{4}\right)\left(\dfrac{3}{4}\right) = \dfrac{1}{4} + \left(-\dfrac{3}{16}\right) = \dfrac{1}{16}$ expected points on a guess if one answer is eliminated.

   Yes, it is advantageous to guess after eliminating one possible answer.

10. Probabilities after eliminating two possible answers: Guess Correctly: $\dfrac{1}{3}$, Guess Incorrectly: $\dfrac{2}{3}$

    $E = (1)\left(\dfrac{1}{3}\right) + \left(-\dfrac{1}{4}\right)\left(\dfrac{2}{3}\right) = \dfrac{1}{3} + \left(-\dfrac{1}{6}\right) = \dfrac{1}{6}$ expected points on a guess if two answers are eliminated.

    Yes, it is advantageous to guess after eliminating two possible answers.

11. First mall: $E = \$300,000\left(\dfrac{1}{2}\right) - \$100,000\left(\dfrac{1}{2}\right) = \$100,000$

Second mall: $E = \$200,000\left(\dfrac{3}{4}\right) - \$60,000\left(\dfrac{1}{4}\right) = \$135,000$

Choose the second mall.

12. Site A: $E = \$80(0.2) - \$10(0.8) = \$8$ million
Site B: $E = \$120(0.1) - \$18(0.9) = -\$4.2$ million
Site A has the larger expected profit.
$\$8$ million $- (-\$4.2$ million$) = \$12.2$ million
Site A's profit exceeds Site B's by $\$12.2$ million.

13. a. $E = \$700,000(0.2) + \$0(0.8) = \$140,000$

 b. No

14. $E = \$80\left(\dfrac{99}{100}\right) - \$270\left(\dfrac{1}{100}\right) = \$76.50$

15. $E = \$4\left(\dfrac{1}{6}\right) - \$1\left(\dfrac{5}{6}\right) = -\$\dfrac{1}{6} \approx -\$0.17$. This means an expected loss of approximately \$0.17 per game.

16. $E = -\$.25\left(\dfrac{1}{6}\right) + \$.75\left(\dfrac{1}{6}\right) + \$1.75\left(\dfrac{1}{6}\right) - \$1.25\left(\dfrac{3}{6}\right) = -\$0.25$. This means an expected loss of \$0.25 per game.

17. $E = \$1\left(\dfrac{18}{38}\right) - \$1\left(\dfrac{20}{38}\right) \approx -\$0.053$. This means an expected loss of approximately \$0.053 per \$1.00 bet.

18. $E = \$4\left(\dfrac{3}{10}\right) + \$2\left(\dfrac{1}{10}\right) - \$2\left(\dfrac{4}{10}\right) - \$3\left(\dfrac{2}{10}\right) = \$0$. A player should expect to break even.

19. $E = \$499\left(\dfrac{1}{1000}\right) - \$1\left(\dfrac{999}{1000}\right) = -\$0.50$. This means an expected loss of \$0.50 per \$1.00 bet.

26. does not make sense; Explanations will vary. Sample explanation: The expectation does not need to be a whole number.

27. makes sense

28. does not make sense; Explanations will vary. Sample explanation: The likely outcome of playing longer is more losses.

29. does not make sense; Explanations will vary. Sample explanation: The expected value of a lottery game is less than the cost of the ticket.

30. First determine the probabilities.

Total number of possible combinations $= {}_{35}C_5 = \dfrac{35!}{30!5!} = 324,632$

Number of ways to select all 5 $= {}_5C_5 = 1$

Number of ways to select 4 of the 5 winning numbers and 1 of the 30 losing numbers $= {}_5C_4 \times {}_{30}C_1 = 5 \times 30 = 150$

Number of ways to select 3 of the 5 winning numbers and 2 of the 30 losing numbers $= {}_5C_3 \times {}_{30}C_2 = 10 \times 435 = 4350$

$P(\text{all }5) = \dfrac{1}{324,632}$; $P(4 \text{ of } 5) = \dfrac{150}{324,632}$; $P(3 \text{ of } 5) = \dfrac{4350}{324,632}$; $P(\text{losing}) = \dfrac{324,632 - 1 - 150 - 4350}{324,632} = \dfrac{320,131}{324,632}$

$E = \$49,999\left(\dfrac{1}{324,632}\right) + \$499\left(\dfrac{150}{324,632}\right) + \$4\left(\dfrac{4350}{324,632}\right) - \$1\left(\dfrac{320,131}{324,632}\right) \approx -\$0.55$

This means an expected loss of $0.55 per $1.00 ticket.

31. Let x = the charge for the policy. Note, the expected value, $E = \$60$.

$\$60 = (x - \$200,000)(0.0005) + (x)(0.9995)$

$\$60 = 0.0005x - \$100 + 0.9995x$

$\$160 = x$

The insurance company should charge $160 for the policy.

Chapter 11 Review Exercises

1. Use the Fundamental Counting Principle with two groups of items. $20 \cdot 40 = 800$

2. Use the Fundamental Counting Principle with two groups of items. $4 \cdot 5 = 20$

3. Use the Fundamental Counting Principle with two groups of items. $100 \cdot 99 = 9900$

4. Use the Fundamental Counting Principle with three groups of items. $5 \cdot 5 \cdot 5 = 125$

5. Use the Fundamental Counting Principle with five groups of items. $3 \cdot 3 \cdot 3 \cdot 3 \cdot 3 = 243$

6. Use the Fundamental Counting Principle with four groups of items. $5 \cdot 2 \cdot 2 \cdot 3 = 60$

7. $\dfrac{16!}{14!} = \dfrac{16 \cdot 15 \cdot 14!}{14!} = 240$

8. $\dfrac{800!}{799!} = \dfrac{800 \cdot 799!}{799!} = 800$

9. $5! - 3! = 5 \cdot 4 \cdot 3 \cdot 2 \cdot 1 - 3 \cdot 2 \cdot 1 = 120 - 6 = 114$

10. $\dfrac{11!}{(11-3)!} = \dfrac{11!}{8!} = \dfrac{11 \cdot 10 \cdot 9 \cdot 8!}{8!} = 990$

11. ${}_{10}P_6 = \dfrac{10!}{(10-6)!} = \dfrac{10!}{4!} = \dfrac{10 \cdot 9 \cdot 8 \cdot 7 \cdot 6 \cdot 5 \cdot 4!}{4!} = 151,200$

12. ${}_{100}P_2 = \dfrac{100!}{(100-2)!} = \dfrac{100!}{98!} = \dfrac{100 \cdot 99 \cdot 98!}{98!} = 9900$

13. ${}_{11}C_7 = \dfrac{11!}{(11-7)!7!} = \dfrac{11!}{4!7!} = \dfrac{11 \cdot 10 \cdot 9 \cdot 8 \cdot 7!}{4 \cdot 3 \cdot 2 \cdot 1 \cdot 7!} = 330$

14. $_{14}C_5 = \dfrac{14!}{(14-5)!5!} = \dfrac{14!}{9!5!} = \dfrac{14 \cdot 13 \cdot 12 \cdot 11 \cdot 10 \cdot 9!}{9! \cdot 5 \cdot 4 \cdot 3 \cdot 2 \cdot 1} = 2002$

15. Order does not matter. This problem involves combinations.

16. Order matters. This problem involves permutations.

17. Order does not matter. This problem involves combinations.

18. Use the Fundamental Counting Principle with six groups of items. $6 \cdot 5 \cdot 4 \cdot 3 \cdot 2 \cdot 1 = 720$

19. $_{15}P_4 = \dfrac{15!}{(15-4)!} = \dfrac{15!}{11!} = \dfrac{15 \cdot 14 \cdot 13 \cdot 12 \cdot 11!}{11!} = 32,760$

20. $_{10}C_4 = \dfrac{10!}{(10-4)!4!} = \dfrac{10!}{6!4!} = \dfrac{10 \cdot 9 \cdot 8 \cdot 7 \cdot 6!}{6!4 \cdot 3 \cdot 2 \cdot 1} = 210$

21. $\dfrac{n!}{p!q!} = \dfrac{7!}{3!2!} = \dfrac{7 \cdot 6 \cdot 5 \cdot 4 \cdot \cancel{3!}}{\cancel{3!} \cdot 2 \cdot 1} = 420$

22. $_{20}C_3 = \dfrac{20!}{(20-3)!3!} = \dfrac{20!}{17!3!} = \dfrac{20 \cdot 19 \cdot 18 \cdot 17!}{17!3 \cdot 2 \cdot 1} = 1140$

23. Use the Fundamental Counting Principle with seven groups of items. $1 \cdot 5 \cdot 4 \cdot 3 \cdot 2 \cdot 1 \cdot 1 = 120$

24. $_{20}P_5 = \dfrac{20!}{(20-5)!} = \dfrac{20!}{15!} = \dfrac{20 \cdot 19 \cdot 18 \cdot 17 \cdot 16 \cdot 15!}{15!} = 1,860,480$

25. Use the Fundamental Counting Principle with five groups of items. $5 \cdot 4 \cdot 3 \cdot 2 \cdot 1 = 120$

26. $_{13}C_5 = \dfrac{13!}{(13-5)!5!} = \dfrac{13!}{8!5!} = \dfrac{13 \cdot 12 \cdot 11 \cdot 10 \cdot 9 \cdot 8!}{8!5 \cdot 4 \cdot 3 \cdot 2 \cdot 1} = 1287$

27. Choose the Republicans: $_{12}C_5 = \dfrac{12!}{(12-5)!5!} = \dfrac{12!}{7!5!} = \dfrac{12 \cdot 11 \cdot 10 \cdot 9 \cdot 8 \cdot 7!}{7!5 \cdot 4 \cdot 3 \cdot 2 \cdot 1} = 792$

Choose the Democrats: $_8C_4 = \dfrac{8!}{(8-4)!4!} = \dfrac{8!}{4!4!} = \dfrac{8 \cdot 7 \cdot 6 \cdot 5 \cdot 4!}{4!4 \cdot 3 \cdot 2 \cdot 1} = 70$

Multiply the choices: $792 \cdot 70 = 55,440$

28. $\dfrac{n!}{p!q!} = \dfrac{6!}{3!2!} = \dfrac{6 \cdot 5 \cdot 4 \cdot \cancel{3!}}{\cancel{3!} \cdot 2 \cdot 1} = 60$

29. $P(6) = \dfrac{\text{number of ways a 6 can occur}}{\text{total number of possible outcomes}} = \dfrac{1}{6}$

30. $P(\text{less than } 5) = \dfrac{\text{number of ways a number less than 5 can occur}}{\text{total number of possible outcomes}} = \dfrac{4}{6} = \dfrac{2}{3}$

31. $P(\text{less than } 7) = \dfrac{\text{number of ways a number less than 7 can occur}}{\text{total number of possible outcomes}} = \dfrac{6}{6} = 1$

32. $P(\text{greater than 6}) = \dfrac{\text{number of ways a number greater than 6 can occur}}{\text{total number of possible outcomes}} = \dfrac{0}{6} = 0$

33. $P(5) = \dfrac{\text{number of ways a 5 can occur}}{\text{total number of possible outcomes}} = \dfrac{4}{52} = \dfrac{1}{13}$

34. $P(\text{picture card}) = \dfrac{\text{number of ways a picture card can occur}}{\text{total number of possible outcomes}} = \dfrac{12}{52} = \dfrac{3}{13}$

35. $P(\text{greater than 4 and less than 8}) = \dfrac{\text{number of ways a card greater than 4 and less than 8 can occur}}{\text{total number of possible outcomes}} = \dfrac{12}{52} = \dfrac{3}{13}$

36. $P(\text{4 of diamonds}) = \dfrac{\text{number of ways a 4 of diamonds can occur}}{\text{total number of possible outcomes}} = \dfrac{1}{52}$

37. $P(\text{red ace}) = \dfrac{\text{number of ways a red ace can occur}}{\text{total number of possible outcomes}} = \dfrac{2}{52} = \dfrac{1}{26}$

38. $P(\text{chocolate}) = \dfrac{\text{number of ways a chocolate can occur}}{\text{total number of possible outcomes}} = \dfrac{15}{30} = \dfrac{1}{2}$

39. $P(\text{caramel}) = \dfrac{\text{number of ways a caramel can occur}}{\text{total number of possible outcomes}} = \dfrac{10}{30} = \dfrac{1}{3}$

40. $P(\text{peppermint}) = \dfrac{\text{number of ways a peppermint can occur}}{\text{total number of possible outcomes}} = \dfrac{5}{30} = \dfrac{1}{6}$

41. **a.** $P(\text{carrier without the disease}) = \dfrac{\text{number of ways to be a carrier without the disease}}{\text{total number of possible outcomes}} = \dfrac{2}{4} = \dfrac{1}{2}$

   b. $P(\text{disease}) = \dfrac{\text{number of ways to have the disease}}{\text{total number of possible outcomes}} = \dfrac{0}{4} = 0$

42. $P(\text{employed}) = \dfrac{139.2}{223.4} \approx 0.623$

43. $P(\text{female}) = \dfrac{115.7}{223.4} \approx 0.518$

44. $P(\text{unemployed male}) = \dfrac{33.2}{223.4} \approx 0.149$

45.   number of ways to visit in order D, B, A, C = 1
      total number of possible permutations = $4 \cdot 3 \cdot 2 \cdot 1 = 24$

      $P(\text{D, B, A, C}) = \dfrac{1}{24}$

46.   number of permutations with C last = $5 \cdot 4 \cdot 3 \cdot 2 \cdot 1 \cdot 1 = 120$
      total number of possible permutations = $6 \cdot 5 \cdot 4 \cdot 3 \cdot 2 \cdot 1 = 720$

      $P(\text{C last}) = \dfrac{120}{720} = \dfrac{1}{6}$

47. number of permutations with B first and A last $= 1 \cdot 4 \cdot 3 \cdot 2 \cdot 1 \cdot 1 = 24$
total number of possible permutations $= 6 \cdot 5 \cdot 4 \cdot 3 \cdot 2 \cdot 1 = 720$

$$P(\text{B first and A last}) = \frac{24}{720} = \frac{1}{30}$$

48. number of permutations in order F, E, A, D, C, B $= 1$
total number of possible permutations $= 6 \cdot 5 \cdot 4 \cdot 3 \cdot 2 \cdot 1 = 720$

$$P(\text{F, E, A, D, C, B}) = \frac{1}{720}$$

49. number of permutations with A or C first $= 2 \cdot 5 \cdot 4 \cdot 3 \cdot 2 \cdot 1 = 240$
total number of possible permutations $= 6 \cdot 5 \cdot 4 \cdot 3 \cdot 2 \cdot 1 = 720$

$$P(\text{A or C first}) = \frac{240}{720} = \frac{1}{3}$$

50. a. number of ways to win $= 1$
total number of possible combinations:

$$_{20}C_5 = \frac{20!}{(20-5)!5!} = \frac{20!}{15!5!} = \frac{20 \cdot 19 \cdot 18 \cdot 17 \cdot 16 \cdot 15!}{15!5 \cdot 4 \cdot 3 \cdot 2 \cdot 1} = 15{,}504$$

$$P(\text{winning with one ticket}) = \frac{1}{15{,}504} \approx 0.0000645$$

b. number of ways to win $= 100$

$$P(\text{winning with 100 different tickets}) = \frac{100}{15{,}504} \approx 0.00645$$

51. a. number of ways to select 4 Democrats: $_6C_4 = \dfrac{6!}{(6-4)!4!} = \dfrac{6!}{2!4!} = \dfrac{6 \cdot 5 \cdot 4!}{2 \cdot 1 \cdot 4!} = 15$

total number of possible combinations: $_{10}C_4 = \dfrac{10!}{(10-4)!4!} = \dfrac{10!}{6!4!} = \dfrac{10 \cdot 9 \cdot 8 \cdot 7 \cdot 6!}{6!4 \cdot 3 \cdot 2 \cdot 1} = 210$

$$P(\text{all Democrats}) = \frac{15}{210} = \frac{1}{14}$$

b. number of ways to select 2 Democrats: $_6C_2 = \dfrac{6!}{(6-2)!2!} = \dfrac{6!}{4!2!} = \dfrac{6 \cdot 5 \cdot 4!}{4!2 \cdot 1} = 15$

number of ways to select 2 Republicans: $_4C_2 = \dfrac{4!}{(4-2)!2!} = \dfrac{4!}{2!2!} = \dfrac{4 \cdot 3 \cdot 2!}{2!2 \cdot 1} = 6$

number of ways to select 2 Democrats and 2 Republicans $= 15 \cdot 6 = 90$

$$P(\text{2 Democrats and 2 Republicans}) = \frac{90}{210} = \frac{3}{7}$$

52. number of ways to get 2 picture cards: $_6C_2 = \dfrac{6!}{(6-2)!2!} = \dfrac{6!}{4!2!} = \dfrac{6 \cdot 5 \cdot 4!}{4!2 \cdot 1} = 15$

number of ways to get one non-picture card $= 20$
number of ways to get 2 picture cards and one non-picture card $= 15 \cdot 20 = 300$

total number of possible combinations: $_{26}C_3 = \dfrac{26!}{(26-3)!3!} = \dfrac{26!}{23!3!} = \dfrac{26 \cdot 25 \cdot 24 \cdot 23!}{23!3 \cdot 2 \cdot 1} = 2600$

$$P(\text{2 picture cards}) = \frac{300}{2600} = \frac{3}{26}$$

53. $P(\text{not a } 5) = 1 - P(5) = 1 - \dfrac{1}{6} = \dfrac{5}{6}$

54. $P(\text{not less than } 4) = 1 - P(\text{less than } 4) = 1 - \dfrac{3}{6} = 1 - \dfrac{1}{2} = \dfrac{1}{2}$

55. $P(3 \text{ or } 5) = P(3) + P(5) = \dfrac{1}{6} + \dfrac{1}{6} = \dfrac{2}{6} = \dfrac{1}{3}$

56. $P(\text{less than 3 or greater than 4}) = P(\text{less than } 3) + P(\text{greater than } 4) = \dfrac{2}{6} + \dfrac{2}{6} = \dfrac{1}{3} + \dfrac{1}{3} = \dfrac{2}{3}$

57. $P(\text{less than 5 or greater than 2}) = P(\text{less than } 5) + P(\text{greater than } 2) - P(\text{less than 5 and greater than 2})$

$$= \dfrac{4}{6} + \dfrac{4}{6} - \dfrac{2}{6} = 1$$

58. $P(\text{not a picture card}) = 1 - P(\text{picture card}) = 1 - \dfrac{12}{52} = 1 - \dfrac{3}{13} = \dfrac{10}{13}$

59. $P(\text{not a diamond}) = 1 - P(\text{diamond}) = 1 - \dfrac{13}{52} = 1 - \dfrac{1}{4} = \dfrac{3}{4}$

60. $P(\text{ace or king}) = P(\text{ace}) + P(\text{king}) = \dfrac{4}{52} + \dfrac{4}{52} = \dfrac{1}{13} + \dfrac{1}{13} = \dfrac{2}{13}$

61. $P(\text{black 6 or red 7}) = P(\text{black } 6) + P(\text{red } 7) = \dfrac{2}{52} + \dfrac{2}{52} = \dfrac{1}{26} + \dfrac{1}{26} = \dfrac{2}{26} = \dfrac{1}{13}$

62. $P(\text{queen or red card}) = P(\text{queen}) + P(\text{red card}) - P(\text{red queen}) = \dfrac{4}{52} + \dfrac{26}{52} - \dfrac{2}{52} = \dfrac{28}{52} = \dfrac{7}{13}$

63. $P(\text{club or picture card}) = P(\text{club}) + P(\text{picture card}) - P(\text{club and picture card}) = \dfrac{13}{52} + \dfrac{12}{52} - \dfrac{3}{52} = \dfrac{22}{52} = \dfrac{11}{26}$

64. $P(\text{not } 4) = 1 - P(4) = 1 - \dfrac{1}{6} = \dfrac{5}{6}$

65. $P(\text{not yellow}) = 1 - P(\text{yellow}) = 1 - \dfrac{1}{6} = \dfrac{5}{6}$

66. $P(\text{not red}) = 1 - P(\text{red}) = 1 - \dfrac{3}{6} = 1 - \dfrac{1}{2} = \dfrac{1}{2}$

67. $P(\text{red or yellow}) = P(\text{red}) + P(\text{yellow}) = \dfrac{3}{6} + \dfrac{1}{6} = \dfrac{4}{6} = \dfrac{2}{3}$

68. $P(\text{red or even}) = P(\text{red}) + P(\text{even}) - P(\text{red and even}) = \dfrac{3}{6} + \dfrac{3}{6} - \dfrac{0}{6} = 1$

69. $P(\text{red or greater than 3}) = P(\text{red}) + P(\text{greater than 3}) - P(\text{red and greater than 3}) = \dfrac{3}{6} + \dfrac{3}{6} - \dfrac{1}{6} = \dfrac{5}{6}$

70. $P(\text{African American or male}) = P(\text{African American}) + P(\text{male}) - P(\text{African American male})$

$$= \frac{50+20}{200} + \frac{50+90}{200} - \frac{50}{200} = \frac{160}{200} = \frac{4}{5}$$

71. $P(\text{female or white}) = P(\text{female}) + P(\text{white}) - P(\text{white female}) = \frac{20+40}{200} + \frac{90+40}{200} - \frac{40}{200} = \frac{150}{200} = \frac{3}{4}$

72. $P(\text{public college}) = \frac{252}{350} = \frac{18}{25}$

73. $P(\text{not from high-income family}) = 1 - P(\text{from high-income family}) = 1 - \frac{50}{350} = \frac{350}{350} - \frac{50}{350} = \frac{300}{350} = \frac{6}{7}$

74. $P(\text{from middle-income family or high-income family}) = \frac{160+50}{350} = \frac{210}{350} = \frac{3}{5}$

75. $P(\text{attended private college or is from a high income family})$

$= P(\text{private college}) + P(\text{high income family}) - P(\text{attended private college and is from a high income family})$

$= \frac{98}{350} + \frac{50}{350} - \frac{28}{350} = \frac{120}{350} = \frac{12}{35}$

76. number of favorable outcomes = 4, number of unfavorable outcomes = 48
Odds in favor of getting a queen are 4:48, or 1:12. Odds against getting a queen are 12:1.

77. number of favorable outcomes = 20, number of unfavorable outcomes = 1980
Odds against winning are 1980: 20, or 99:1.

78. $P(\text{win}) = \frac{3}{3+1} = \frac{3}{4}$

79. $P(\text{yellow then red}) = P(\text{yellow}) \cdot P(\text{red}) = \frac{2}{6} \cdot \frac{4}{6} = \frac{1}{3} \cdot \frac{2}{3} = \frac{2}{9}$

80. $P(1 \text{ then } 3) = P(1) \cdot P(3) = \frac{1}{6} \cdot \frac{1}{6} = \frac{1}{36}$

81. $P(\text{yellow both times}) = P(\text{yellow}) \cdot P(\text{yellow}) = \frac{2}{6} \cdot \frac{2}{6} = \frac{1}{3} \cdot \frac{1}{3} = \frac{1}{9}$

82. $P(\text{yellow then 4 then odd}) = P(\text{yellow}) \cdot P(4) \cdot P(\text{odd}) = \frac{2}{6} \cdot \frac{1}{6} \cdot \frac{3}{6} = \frac{1}{3} \cdot \frac{1}{6} \cdot \frac{1}{2} = \frac{1}{36}$

83. $P(\text{red every time}) = P(\text{red}) \cdot P(\text{red}) \cdot P(\text{red}) = \frac{4}{6} \cdot \frac{4}{6} \cdot \frac{4}{6} = \frac{2}{3} \cdot \frac{2}{3} \cdot \frac{2}{3} = \frac{8}{27}$

84. $P(\text{five boys in a row}) = P(\text{boy}) \cdot P(\text{boy}) \cdot P(\text{boy}) \cdot P(\text{boy}) \cdot P(\text{boy}) = \frac{1}{2} \cdot \frac{1}{2} \cdot \frac{1}{2} \cdot \frac{1}{2} \cdot \frac{1}{2} = \frac{1}{2^5} = \frac{1}{32}$

85. a. $P(\text{flood two years in a row}) = P(\text{flood}) \cdot P(\text{flood}) = (0.2)(0.2) = 0.04$

   b. $P(\text{flood for three consecutive years}) = P(\text{flood}) \cdot P(\text{flood}) \cdot P(\text{flood}) = (0.2)(0.2)(0.2) = 0.008$

   c. $P(\text{no flooding for four consecutive years}) = [1 - P(\text{flood})]^4 = (1 - 0.2)^4 = (0.8)^4 = 0.4096$

   d. $P(\text{flood at least once in next four years}) = 1 - P(\text{no flooding for four consecutive years})$
   $$= 1 - 0.4096 = 0.5904$$

86. $P(\text{music major then psychology major}) = P(\text{music major}) \cdot P\left(\begin{array}{c}\text{psychology major given}\\\text{first was music major}\end{array}\right) = \frac{2}{9} \cdot \frac{4}{8} = \frac{2}{9} \cdot \frac{1}{2} = \frac{1}{9}$

87. $P(\text{two business majors}) = P(\text{bus. major}) \cdot P(\text{bus. major given first was bus. major}) = \frac{3}{9} \cdot \frac{2}{8} = \frac{1}{3} \cdot \frac{1}{4} = \frac{1}{12}$

88. $P(\text{solid then two cherry})$
   $= P(\text{solid}) \cdot P\left(\begin{array}{c}\text{cherry given}\\\text{first was solid}\end{array}\right) \cdot P\left(\begin{array}{c}\text{cherry given first was solid}\\\text{and second was cherry}\end{array}\right) = \frac{30}{50} \cdot \frac{5}{49} \cdot \frac{4}{48} = \frac{3}{5} \cdot \frac{5}{49} \cdot \frac{1}{12} = \frac{1}{196}$

89. $P(5|\text{odd}) = \dfrac{1}{3}$

90. $P(\text{vowel}|\text{precedes the letter k}) = \dfrac{3}{10}$

91. a. $P(\text{odd}|\text{red}) = \dfrac{2}{4} = \dfrac{1}{2}$

   b. $P(\text{yellow}|\text{at least 3}) = \dfrac{2}{7}$

92. $P(\text{does not have TB}) = \dfrac{11 + 124}{9 + 1 + 11 + 124} = \dfrac{135}{145} = \dfrac{27}{29}$

93. $P(\text{tests positive}) = \dfrac{9 + 11}{9 + 1 + 11 + 124} = \dfrac{20}{145} = \dfrac{4}{29}$

94. $P(\text{does not have TB or tests positive})$
   $= P(\text{does not have TB}) + P(\text{tests positive}) - P(\text{does not have TB and tests positive})$
   $= \dfrac{11 + 124}{145} + \dfrac{9 + 11}{145} - \dfrac{11}{145}$
   $= \dfrac{144}{145}$

95. $P(\text{does not have TB}|\text{positive test}) = \dfrac{11}{9 + 11} = \dfrac{11}{20}$

96. $P(\text{tests positive}|\text{does not have TB}) = \dfrac{11}{11 + 124} = \dfrac{11}{135}$

97. $P(\text{has TB}|\text{negative Test}) = \dfrac{1}{1+124} = \dfrac{1}{125}$

98. $P(\text{two people with TB}) = P(\text{TB}) \cdot P(\text{TB}|\text{first person selected has TB}) = \dfrac{10}{145} \cdot \dfrac{9}{144} = \dfrac{1}{232}$

99. $P(\text{two people with positive tests}) = P(\text{positive test}) \cdot P(\text{positive test}|\text{first person has positive test}) = \dfrac{20}{145} \cdot \dfrac{19}{144} = \dfrac{19}{1044}$

100. $P(\text{male}) = \dfrac{25,546}{29,625} \approx 0.862$

101. $P(\text{age } 25-44) = \dfrac{11,044}{29,625} = \dfrac{5793}{15,121} \approx 0.373$

102. $P(\text{less than } 75) = 1 - P(\text{greater than or equal to } 75) = 1 - \dfrac{2334}{29,625} = \dfrac{27,291}{29,625} = \dfrac{9097}{9875} \approx 0.921$

103. $P(\text{age } 20-24 \text{ or } 25-44) = P(\text{age } 20-24) + P(\text{age } 25-44) = \dfrac{4053}{29,625} + \dfrac{11,044}{29,625} = \dfrac{15,097}{29,625} \approx 0.510$

104. $P(\text{female or younger than } 5) = P(\text{female}) + P(\text{younger than } 5) - P(\text{female and younger than } 5)$

$$= \dfrac{4079}{29,625} + \dfrac{58}{29,625} - \dfrac{27}{29,625} = \dfrac{4110}{29,625} = \dfrac{274}{1975} \approx 0.139$$

105. $P(\text{age } 20-24|\text{male}) = \dfrac{3700}{25,546} = \dfrac{1850}{12,773} \approx 0.145$

106. $P(\text{male}|\text{at least } 75) = \dfrac{2123}{2334} \approx 0.910$

107. $E = 1 \cdot \dfrac{1}{4} + 2 \cdot \dfrac{1}{8} + 3 \cdot \dfrac{1}{8} + 4 \cdot \dfrac{1}{4} + 5 \cdot \dfrac{1}{4} = 3.125$

108. **a.** $E = \$0(0.9999995) + (-\$1,000,000)(0.0000005) = -\$.50$
The insurance company spends an average of $0.50 per person insured.

   b. charge $9.50 - (-\$0.50) = \$10.00$

109. $E = \$27,000\left(\dfrac{1}{4}\right) + (-\$3000)\left(\dfrac{3}{4}\right) = \$4500.$ The expected gain is $4500 per bid.

110. $E = \$1\left(\dfrac{2}{4}\right) + \$1\left(\dfrac{1}{4}\right) + (-\$4)\left(\dfrac{1}{4}\right) = -\$0.25.$ The expected loss is $0.25 per game.

Chapter 11 Test

1. Use the Fundamental Counting Principle with five groups of items. $10 \cdot 2 \cdot 2 \cdot 2 \cdot 3 = 240$

2. Use the Fundamental Counting Principle with four groups of items. $4 \cdot 3 \cdot 2 \cdot 1 = 24$

3. Use the Fundamental Counting Principle with seven groups of items. $1 \cdot 6 \cdot 5 \cdot 4 \cdot 3 \cdot 2 \cdot 1 = 720$

4. $_{11}P_3 = \dfrac{11!}{(11-3)!} = \dfrac{11!}{8!} = \dfrac{11 \cdot 10 \cdot 9 \cdot 8!}{8!} = 990$

5. $_{10}C_4 = \dfrac{10!}{(10-4)!4!} = \dfrac{10!}{6!4!} = \dfrac{10 \cdot 9 \cdot 8 \cdot 7 \cdot 6!}{6!4 \cdot 3 \cdot 2 \cdot 1} = 210$

6. $\dfrac{n!}{p!q!} = \dfrac{7!}{3!2!} = \dfrac{7 \cdot 6 \cdot 5 \cdot 4 \cdot 3!}{3! \cdot 2 \cdot 1} = 420$

7. $P(\text{freshman}) = \dfrac{12}{50} = \dfrac{6}{25}$

8. $P(\text{not a sophomore}) = 1 - P(\text{sophomore}) = 1 - \dfrac{16}{50} = 1 - \dfrac{8}{25} = \dfrac{17}{25}$

9. $P(\text{junior or senior}) = P(\text{junior}) + P(\text{senior}) = \dfrac{20}{50} + \dfrac{2}{50} = \dfrac{22}{50} = \dfrac{11}{25}$

10. $P(\text{greater than 4 and less than 10}) = \dfrac{20}{52} = \dfrac{5}{13}$

11. $P(C \text{ first}, A \text{ next-to-last}, E \text{ last})$
$= P(C) \cdot P(A \text{ given } C \text{ was first}) \cdot P(E \text{ given } C \text{ was first and } A \text{ was next-to-last}) = \dfrac{1}{7} \cdot \dfrac{1}{6} \cdot \dfrac{1}{5} = \dfrac{1}{210}$

12. total number of possible combinations: $_{15}C_6 = \dfrac{15!}{(15-6)!6!} = \dfrac{15!}{9!6!} = \dfrac{15 \cdot 14 \cdot 13 \cdot 12 \cdot 11 \cdot 10 \cdot 9!}{9!6 \cdot 5 \cdot 4 \cdot 3 \cdot 2 \cdot 1} = 5005$

$P(\text{winning with 50 tickets}) = \dfrac{50}{5005} = \dfrac{10}{1001} \approx 0.00999$

13. $P(\text{red or blue}) = P(\text{red}) + P(\text{blue}) = \dfrac{2}{8} + \dfrac{2}{8} = \dfrac{4}{8} = \dfrac{1}{2}$

14. $P(\text{red then blue}) = P(\text{red}) \cdot P(\text{blue}) = \dfrac{2}{8} \cdot \dfrac{2}{8} = \dfrac{1}{4} \cdot \dfrac{1}{4} = \dfrac{1}{16}$

15. $P(\text{flooding for three consecutive years}) = P(\text{flood}) \cdot P(\text{flood}) \cdot P(\text{flood}) = \dfrac{1}{20} \cdot \dfrac{1}{20} \cdot \dfrac{1}{20} = \dfrac{1}{8000}$

16. $P(\text{black or picture card}) = P(\text{black}) + P(\text{picture card}) - P(\text{black picture card}) = \dfrac{26}{52} + \dfrac{12}{52} - \dfrac{6}{52} = \dfrac{32}{52} = \dfrac{8}{13}$

17. $P(\text{freshman or female}) = P(\text{freshman}) + P(\text{female}) - P(\text{female freshman}) = \dfrac{10+15}{50} + \dfrac{15+5}{50} - \dfrac{15}{50} = \dfrac{30}{50} = \dfrac{3}{5}$

18. $P(\text{both red}) = P(\text{red}) \cdot P(\text{red given first ball was red}) = \dfrac{5}{20} \cdot \dfrac{4}{19} = \dfrac{1}{4} \cdot \dfrac{4}{19} = \dfrac{1}{19}$

19. $P(\text{all correct}) = P(\text{correct}) \cdot P(\text{correct}) \cdot P(\text{correct}) \cdot P(\text{correct}) = \dfrac{1}{4} \cdot \dfrac{1}{4} \cdot \dfrac{1}{4} \cdot \dfrac{1}{4} = \left(\dfrac{1}{4}\right)^4 = \dfrac{1}{256}$

20. number of favorable outcomes = 20, number of unfavorable outcomes = 15
Odds against being a man are 15:20, or 3:4.

21. a. Odds in favor are 4:1.   **b.** $P(\text{win}) = \dfrac{4}{1+4} = \dfrac{4}{5}$

22. $P(\text{not brown eyes}) = \dfrac{18+10+20+12}{22+18+10+18+20+12} = \dfrac{60}{100} = \dfrac{3}{5}$

23. $P(\text{brown eyes or blue eyes}) = \dfrac{22+18+18+20}{22+18+10+18+20+12} = \dfrac{78}{100} = \dfrac{39}{50}$

24. $P(\text{female or green eyes}) = P(\text{female}) + P(\text{green eyes}) - P(\text{female and green eyes})$

$$= \dfrac{18+20+12}{100} + \dfrac{10+12}{100} - \dfrac{12}{100}$$

$$= \dfrac{50}{100} + \dfrac{22}{100} - \dfrac{12}{100}$$

$$= \dfrac{60}{100}$$

$$= \dfrac{3}{5}$$

25. $P(\text{male}|\text{blue eyes}) = \dfrac{18}{18+20} = \dfrac{18}{38} = \dfrac{9}{19}$

26. $P(\text{two people with green eyes}) = P(\text{green eyes}) \cdot P(\text{green eyes}|\text{first person has green eyes}) = \dfrac{22}{100} \cdot \dfrac{21}{99} = \dfrac{7}{150}$

27. $E = \$65{,}000(0.2) + (-\$15{,}000)(0.8) = \$1000$. This means the expected gain is $1000 for this bid.

28. $E = (-\$19) \cdot \dfrac{10}{20} + (-\$18) \cdot \dfrac{5}{20} + (-\$15) \cdot \dfrac{3}{20} + (-\$10) \cdot \dfrac{1}{20} + (\$80) \cdot \dfrac{1}{20}$

$= \dfrac{-\$190 - \$90 - \$45 - \$10 + \$80}{20} = \dfrac{-\$255}{20} = -\$12.75$

This expected value of $-\$12.75$ means that a player will lose an average of $12.75 per play in the long run.

Chapter 12
Statistics

Check Points 12.1

1. a. The population is the set containing all the of the city's homeless people.

    b. This is not a good idea. This sample of people currently in a shelter is more likely to hold opinions that favor required residence in city shelters than the population of all the city's homeless.

2. The sampling technique described in Check Point 1b does not produce a random sample because homeless people who do not go to shelters have no chance of being selected for the survey. In this instance, an appropriate method would be to randomly select neighborhoods of the city and then randomly survey homeless people within the selected neighborhood.

3.

Grade	Number of students
A	3
B	5
C	9
D	2
F	1
	20

4.

Exam Scores (class)	Tally	Number of students (frequency)
40 – 49	|	1
50 – 59	||||	5
60 – 69	||||	4
70 – 79	|||| |||| ||||	15
80 – 89	||||	5
90 – 99	|||| ||	7
		37

5.

Stems	Leaves
4	1
5	8 2 8 0 7
6	8 2 9 9
7	3 5 9 9 7 5 5 3 3 6 7 1 7 1 5
8	7 3 9 9 1
9	4 6 9 7 5 8 0

Exercise Set 12.1

1. c

2. c

3. A stress rating of 7 was reported by 31 students.

4. A stress rating of 1 was reported by 1 student.

5. Totaling the frequency column shows that 151 students were involved in the study.

6. $26 + 15 + 14 = 55$. Thus, 55 students reported a stress level of 8 or more.

7.

Time Spent on Homework (in hours)	Number of students
15	4
16	5
17	6
18	5
19	4
20	2
21	2
22	0
23	0
24	2
	30

8.

Height (in inches)	Number of students
66	1
67	3
68	2
69	1
70	3
71	7
72	5
73	5
74	1
75	2
	30

9. The lower class limits are 0, 5, 10, 15, 20, 25, 30, 35, 40, and 45.

10. The upper class limits are 4, 9, 14, 19, 24, 29, 34, 39, 44, and 49.

11. The class width is 5, the difference between successive lower limits.

12. Totaling the frequency column shows that 94 students were involved in the study.

13. $4 + 3 + 3 + 3 = 13$. Thus, 13 students had at least 30 social interactions.

14. $12 + 16 + 16 = 44$. Thus, 44 students had at most 14 social interactions.

15. The $5 - 9$ class.

16. The $35 - 39$ class.

17.

Age	Frequency
41–45	2
46–50	8
51–55	15
56–60	9
61–65	7
66–70	2
	43

18.

IQ Score	Number of students
85–89	2
90–94	5
95–99	12
100–104	14
105–109	15
110–114	11
115–119	8
120–124	3
	70

19. Histogram for Stress Rating:

Frequency Polygon for Stress Rating:

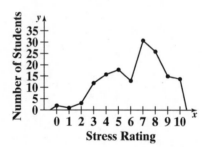

20. Histogram for Time Spent on Homework:

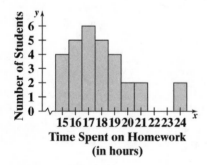

Frequency Polygon for Time Spent on Homework:

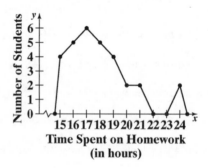

21. Histogram for Height: Frequency Polygon for Height:

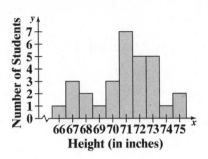   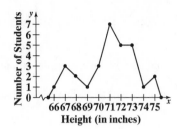

22. false

23. false

24. true

25. false

26. false

27. true

28. false

29. false

30.

Stems	Leaves
4	2 3 6 6 7 8 9 9
5	0 0 1 1 1 1 2 2 4 4 4 4 4 5 5 5 5 6 6 6 7 7 7 7 8
6	0 1 1 1 2 4 4 5 8 9

31.

Stems	Leaves
2	8 8 9 5
3	8 7 0 1 2 7 6 4 0 5
4	8 2 2 1 4 5 4 6 2 0 8 2 7 9
5	9 4 1 9 1 0
6	3 2 3 6 6 3

The greatest number of college professors are in their 40s.

32. a.   31

  b. $80 - 21 = 59$

  c.   56

  d.   Actresses tend to win Oscars at younger ages than actors. Explanations will vary.

33. The bars on the horizontal axis are evenly spaced, yet the time intervals that they represent vary greatly. This may give the misleading impression of linear growth.

34. The sizes of the books are not scaled proportionally in terms of the data they represent.

35. The sectors representing these six countries use up 100% of the pie graph, yet the percentages for these six countries total only 57%. This may give the misleading impression that the U.S. has about 50% of the world's computer use.

36. The sizes of the TV screens are not scaled proportionally in terms of the data they represent.

37. Each film's star extends above the bar giving a misimpression of the data represented.

48. does not make sense; Explanations will vary. Sample explanation: The number of people hospitalized could be very small.

49. does not make sense; Explanations will vary. Sample explanation: The rise has not been rapid.

50. does not make sense; Explanations will vary. Sample explanation: They should select a random sample of all their contributors.

51. makes sense

52. Answers will vary. Sample answer:

River length	Frequency (number of rivers)
501–1000	12
1001–1500	8
1501–2000	3
2001–2500	1
2501–3000	1
	25

Check Points 12.2

1. a. $\dfrac{10+20+30+40+50}{5} = \dfrac{150}{5} = 30$

 b. $\dfrac{3+10+10+10+117}{5} = \dfrac{150}{5} = 30$

2.

x	f	xf
30	3	$30 \cdot 3 = 90$
33	4	$33 \cdot 4 = 132$
40	4	$40 \cdot 4 = 160$
50	1	$50 \cdot 1 = 50$
	12	$\sum xf = 432$

$\text{Mean} = \dfrac{\sum xf}{n} = \dfrac{432}{12} = 36$

3. a. First arrange the data items from smallest to largest: 25, 28, <u>35</u>, 40, 42
  The number of data items is odd, so the median is the middle number. The median is 35.

 b. First arrange the data items from smallest to largest: 61, 72, <u>79</u>, <u>85</u>, 87, 93
  The number of data items is even, so the median is the mean of the two middle data items.
  The median is $\dfrac{79+85}{2} = \dfrac{164}{2} = 82$.

4. The data items are arranged from smallest to largest with $n = 19,$ which gives $\dfrac{n+1}{2} = \dfrac{19+1}{2} = \dfrac{20}{2} = 10$

    The median is in the 10th position, which means the median is 5.

5. The eating times from smallest to largest are 1:06, 1:09, 1:14, 1:21, 1:22, 1:25, 1:29, 1:29, 1:34, 1:34, 1:36, 1:45, 1:46, 1:49, 1:54, 1:57, 2:10, 2:15.

    There are 18 data items so $n = 18,$ which gives $\dfrac{n+1}{2} = \dfrac{18+1}{2} = \dfrac{19}{2} = 9.5$ position

    The median is the mean of the data items in positions 9 and 10.
    Both the 9th and 10th positions are 1:34.
    Thus, the median is 1 hour, 34 minutes.

6. The total frequency is $1+1+1+3+1+2+2+2+1+2+1+1 = 18,$ therefore $n = 18$

    The median's position is $\dfrac{n+1}{2} = \dfrac{18+1}{2} = \dfrac{19}{2} = 9.5$.

    Therefore, the median is the mean of the data items in positions 9 and 10.
    Counting through the frequency row identifies that the 9th data item is 54 and the 10th data item is 55.

    Thus, the median is $\dfrac{54+55}{2} = \dfrac{109}{2} = 54.5$.

7. **a.** $\text{Mean} = \dfrac{\$0 + \$19.6 + \$21.0 + \$23.9 + \$24.7 + \$25.1}{6} = \$19.05 \text{ million}$

    b.   Position of mean: $\dfrac{n+1}{2} = \dfrac{6+1}{2} = 3.5 \text{ position}$

    The median is the mean of the data items in positions 3 and 4.

    Thus, the median is $\dfrac{\$21.0 + \$23.9}{2} = \$22.45 \text{ million }$.

    c.   The mean is so much greater than the median because one data item (\$0) is much smaller than the others.

8. The number 8 occurs more often than any other. The mode is 8.

9. $\text{Midrange} = \dfrac{\$83,623,776 + \$152,389,371}{2} = \$118,006,573.50$

10. **a.** $\text{Mean} = \dfrac{173 + 191 + 182 + 190 + 172 + 147 + 146 + 138 + 175 + 136 + 179 + 153 + 107 + 195 + 135 + 140 + 138}{17}$

    $= \dfrac{2697}{17} = 158.6 \text{ calories}$

    b.   Order the data items: 107, 135, 136, 138, 138, 140, 146, 147, <u>153</u>, 172, 173, 175, 179, 182, 190, 191, 195
    The number of data items is odd, so the median is the middle number. The median is 153 calories.

    c.   The number 138 occurs more often than any other. The mode is 138 calories.

    d. $\text{Midrange} = \dfrac{107 + 195}{2} = \dfrac{302}{2} = 151 \text{ calories}$

Exercise Set 12.2

1. $\dfrac{7+4+3+2+8+5+1+3}{8} = \dfrac{33}{8} = 4.125$

2. $\dfrac{11+6+4+0+2+1+12+0+0}{9} = \dfrac{36}{9} = 4$

3. $\dfrac{91+95+99+97+93+95}{6} = \dfrac{570}{6} = 95$

4. $\dfrac{100+100+90+30+70+100}{6} = \dfrac{490}{6} \approx 81.67$

5. $\dfrac{100+40+70+40+60}{5} = \dfrac{310}{5} = 62$

6. $\dfrac{1+3+5+10+8+5+6+8}{8} = \dfrac{46}{8} = 5.75$

7. $\dfrac{1.6+3.8+5.0+2.7+4.2+4.2+3.2+4.7+3.6+2.5+2.5}{11} = \dfrac{38}{11} \approx 3.45$

8. $\dfrac{1.4+2.1+1.6+3.0+1.4+2.2+1.4+9.0+9.0+1.8}{10} = \dfrac{32.9}{10} = 3.29$

9.

x	f	xf
1	1	$1 \cdot 1 = 1$
2	3	$2 \cdot 3 = 6$
3	4	$3 \cdot 4 = 12$
4	4	$4 \cdot 4 = 16$
5	6	$5 \cdot 6 = 30$
6	5	$6 \cdot 5 = 30$
7	3	$7 \cdot 3 = 21$
8	2	$8 \cdot 2 = 16$
28		$\sum xf = 132$

$\text{Mean} = \dfrac{\sum xf}{n} = \dfrac{132}{28} \approx 4.71$

10.

x	f	xf
1	2	$1 \cdot 2 = 2$
2	4	$2 \cdot 4 = 8$
3	5	$3 \cdot 5 = 15$
4	7	$4 \cdot 7 = 28$
5	6	$5 \cdot 6 = 30$
6	4	$6 \cdot 4 = 24$
7	3	$7 \cdot 3 = 21$
31		$\sum xf = 128$

$\text{Mean} = \dfrac{\sum xf}{n} = \dfrac{128}{31} \approx 4.13$

11.

x	f	xf
1	1	$1 \cdot 1 = 1$
2	1	$2 \cdot 1 = 2$
3	2	$3 \cdot 2 = 6$
4	5	$4 \cdot 5 = 20$
5	7	$5 \cdot 7 = 35$
6	9	$6 \cdot 9 = 54$
7	8	$7 \cdot 8 = 56$
8	6	$8 \cdot 6 = 48$
9	4	$9 \cdot 4 = 36$
10	3	$10 \cdot 3 = 30$
	46	$\sum xf = 288$

$$\text{Mean} = \frac{\sum xf}{n} = \frac{288}{46} \approx 6.26$$

12.

x	f	xf
1	3	$1 \cdot 3 = 3$
2	4	$2 \cdot 4 = 8$
3	6	$3 \cdot 6 = 18$
4	8	$4 \cdot 8 = 32$
5	9	$5 \cdot 9 = 45$
6	7	$6 \cdot 7 = 42$
7	5	$7 \cdot 5 = 35$
8	2	$8 \cdot 2 = 16$
9	1	$9 \cdot 1 = 9$
10	1	$10 \cdot 1 = 10$
	46	$\sum xf = 218$

$$\text{Mean} = \frac{\sum xf}{n} = \frac{218}{46} \approx 4.74$$

13. First arrange the data items from smallest to largest: 1, 2, 3, 3, 4, 5, 7, 8
The number of data items is even, so the median is the mean of the two middle data items. The median is 3.5.

14. First arrange the data items from smallest to largest: 0, 0, 0, 1, 2, 4, 6, 11, 12
The number of data items is odd, so the median is the middle number.
The median is 2.

15. First arrange the data items from smallest to largest: 91, 93, 95, 95, 97, 99
The number of data items is even, so the median is the mean of the two middle data items.
$$\text{Median} = \frac{95 + 95}{2} = 95$$

16. First arrange the data items from smallest to largest: 30, 70, 90, 100, 100, 100
The number of data items is even, so the median is the mean of the two middle data items.
$$\text{Median} = \frac{90 + 100}{2} = 95$$

17. First arrange the data items from smallest to largest: 40, 40, 60, 70, 100
The number of data items is odd, so the median is the middle number. The median is 60.

18. First arrange the data items from smallest to largest: 1, 3, 5, 5, 6, 8, 8, 10
The number of data items is even, so the median is the mean of the two middle data items.
$$\text{Median} = \frac{5 + 6}{2} = 5.5$$

19. First arrange the data items from smallest to largest: 1.6, 2.5, 2.5, 2.7, 3.2, 3.6, 3.8, 4.2, 4.2, 4.7, 5.0
The number of data items is odd, so the median is the middle number. The median is 3.6.

20. First arrange the data items from smallest to largest:
1.4, 1.4, 1.4, 1.6, 1.8, 2.1, 2.2, 3.0, 9.0, 9.0
The number of data items is even, so the median is the mean of the two middle data items.
$$\text{Median} = \frac{1.8 + 2.1}{2} = 1.95$$

21. $n = 28$
$$\frac{n+1}{2} = \frac{28+1}{2} = \frac{29}{2} = 14.5$$
The median is in the 14.5 position, which means the median is the mean of the data items in positions 14 and 15. Counting down the frequency column, the 14th and 15th data items are both 5.
$$\text{Median} = \frac{5+5}{2} = 5$$

22. $n = 31$
$$\frac{n+1}{2} = \frac{31+1}{2} = \frac{32}{2} = 16$$
The median is in the 16th position. Counting down the frequency column, the 16th data item is 4. The median is 4.

23. $n = 46$
$$\frac{n+1}{2} = \frac{46+1}{2} = 23.5$$
The median is in the 23.5 position, which means the median is the mean of the data items in positions 23 and 24. Counting down the frequency column, the 23rd and 24th data items are both 6.
$$\text{Median} = \frac{6+6}{2} = 6$$

24. $n = 46$
$$\frac{n+1}{2} = \frac{46+1}{2} = 23.5$$
The median is in the 23.5 position, which means the median is the mean of the data items in positions 23 and 24. Counting down the frequency column, the 23rd and 24th data items are both 5.
$$\text{Median} = \frac{5+5}{2} = 5$$

25. The mode is 3.

26. The mode is 0.

27. The mode is 95.

28. The mode is 100.

29. The mode is 40.

30. The modes are 5 and 8 (bimodal).

31. The modes are 2.5 and 4.2 (bimodal).

32. The mode is 1.4.

33. The mode is 5.

34. The mode is 4.

35. The mode is 6.

36. The mode is 5.

37. lowest data value = 1, highest data value = 8

$$\text{Midrange} = \frac{1+8}{2} = 4.5$$

38. lowest data value = 0, highest data value = 12

$$\text{Midrange} = \frac{0+12}{2} = 6$$

39. lowest data value = 91, highest data value = 99

$$\text{Midrange} = \frac{91+99}{2} = 95$$

40. lowest data value = 30, highest data value = 100

$$\text{Midrange} = \frac{30+100}{2} = 65$$

41. lowest data value = 40, highest data value = 100

$$\text{Midrange} = \frac{40+100}{2} = 70$$

42. lowest data value = 1, highest data value = 10

$$\text{Midrange} = \frac{1+10}{2} = 5.5$$

43. lowest data value = 1.6, highest data value = 5.0

$$\text{Midrange} = \frac{1.6+5.0}{2} = 3.3$$

44. lowest data value = 1.4, highest data value = 9.0

$$\text{Midrange} = \frac{1.4+9.0}{2} = 5.2$$

45. $\text{Midrange} = \dfrac{1+8}{2} = 4.5$

46. $\text{Midrange} = \dfrac{1+7}{2} = 4$

47. $\text{Midrange} = \dfrac{1+10}{2} = 5.5$

48. $\text{Midrange} = \dfrac{1+10}{2} = 5.5$

49.

x	f	xf
10	1	10
20	2	40
30	4	120
40	2	80
50	1	50
	10	$\sum xf = 300$

$$\text{Mean} = \frac{\sum xf}{n} = \frac{300}{10} = 30$$

The median is the mean of the 5th and 6th data items. Since these items are both 30, the median is 30. The mode is 30 (it has the highest frequency).

$$\text{Midrange} = \frac{10+50}{2} = 30$$

50.

x	f	xf
10	5	50
20	3	60
30	2	60
40	1	40
50	1	50
	12	$\sum xf = 260$

$$\text{Mean} = \frac{\sum xf}{n} = \frac{260}{12} \approx 21.7$$

The median is the mean of the 6th and 7th data items. Since these items are both 20, the median is 20. The mode is 10 (it has the highest frequency).

$$\text{Midrange} = \frac{10+50}{2} = 30$$

51.

x	f	xf
10	2	20
11	2	22
12	3	36
13	4	52
14	1	14
15	2	30
	14	$\sum xf = 174$

$$\text{Mean} = \frac{\sum xf}{n} = \frac{174}{14} \approx 12.4$$

The median is the mean of the 7th and 8th data items. $\text{Median} = \frac{12+13}{2} = 12.5$

The mode is 13 (it has the highest frequency).

$$\text{Midrange} = \frac{10+15}{2} = 12.5$$

52.

x	f	xf
10	1	10
11	2	22
12	4	48
13	5	65
14	2	28
15	2	30
	16	$\sum xf = 203$

$$\text{Mean} = \frac{\sum xf}{n} = \frac{203}{16} \approx 12.7$$

The median is the mean of the 8th and 9th data items. Since these items are both 13, the median is 13. The mode is 13 (it has the highest frequency).

$$\text{Midrange} = \frac{10+15}{2} = 12.5$$

53. The data items are 21, 24, 25, 30, 31, 31, 33, 42, 45

$$\text{Mean} = \frac{21+24+25+30+31+31+33+42+45}{9} = \frac{282}{9} \approx 31.3$$

The median is the 5th data item, or 31.
The mode is 31.

$$\text{Midrange} = \frac{21+45}{2} = 33$$

54. The data items are 28, 32, 34, 34, 39, 40, 41, 45, 47

$$\text{Mean} = \frac{28+32+34+34+39+40+41+45+47}{9} = \frac{340}{9} \approx 37.8$$

The median is the 5th data item, or 39.
The mode is 34.

$$\text{Midrange} = \frac{28+47}{2} = 37.5$$

55. **a.** $\text{Mean} = \dfrac{\$14,458}{30} \approx \$481.9 \text{ million}$

b. The median is the mean of the 15th and 16th data items. $\text{Median} = \dfrac{\$406+\$401}{2} = \$403.5 \text{ million}$

c. The mode is \$406 million.

d. $\text{Midrange} = \dfrac{\$277+\$1500}{2} = \$888.5 \text{ million}$

56. **a.** $\text{Mean} = \dfrac{\$5819}{30} \approx \$194.0 \text{ million}$

b. The median is the mean of the 15th and 16th data items. $\text{Median} = \dfrac{\$184+\$181}{2} = \$182.5 \text{ million}$

c. The modes are \$196 million, \$186 million, \$174 million, and \$160 million.

d. $\text{Midrange} = \dfrac{\$139+\$375}{2} = \$257 \text{ million}$

57.

x	f	xf
2	12	$2 \cdot 12 = 24$
7	16	$7 \cdot 16 = 112$
12	16	$12 \cdot 16 = 192$
17	16	$17 \cdot 16 = 272$
22	10	$22 \cdot 10 = 220$
27	11	$27 \cdot 11 = 297$
32	4	$32 \cdot 4 = 128$
37	3	$37 \cdot 3 = 111$
42	3	$42 \cdot 3 = 126$
47	3	$47 \cdot 3 = 141$
	94	$\sum xf = 1623$

a. Mean $= \dfrac{\sum xf}{n} = \dfrac{1623}{94} \approx 17.27$

b. The median is 17 because the 47th and 48th data items both are 17.

c. The modes are 7, 12, and 17.

d. Midrange $= \dfrac{47+2}{2} = \dfrac{49}{2} = 24.5$

58. Mean $= \dfrac{1 \cdot 150 + 2 \cdot 155 + 2 \cdot 160 + 4 \cdot 165 + 6 \cdot 170 + 8 \cdot 175 + 5 \cdot 180 + 4 \cdot 185 + 2 \cdot 190 + 3 \cdot 195 + 1 \cdot 200 + 2 \cdot 205}{40} = 176.875$ lb

59. $n = 40$, $\dfrac{n+1}{2} = \dfrac{40+1}{2} = \dfrac{41}{2} = 20.5$

The median is in the 20.5 position, which means the median is the mean of the data items in positions 20 and 21.

Median $= \dfrac{175+175}{2} = 175$ lb

60. The modal weight is 175 lb.

61. Midrange $= \dfrac{150+205}{2} = 177.5$ lb

62. a.

Words per Minute	Number of People
600	1
650	2
700	2
750	2
800	3
850	3
900	3
950	2
1000	4
1050	1
1100	1
	24

$$\text{Mean} = \frac{1 \cdot 600 + 2 \cdot 650 + 2 \cdot 700 + 2 \cdot 750 + 3 \cdot 800 + 3 \cdot 850 + 3 \cdot 900 + 2 \cdot 950 + 4 \cdot 1000 + 1 \cdot 1050 + 1 \cdot 1100}{24}$$

≈ 854 words per minute

$\text{Median} = \dfrac{850 + 850}{2} = 850$ words per minute

$\text{Mode} = 1000$ words per minute

$\text{Midrange} = \dfrac{600 + 1100}{2} = 850$ words per minute

b. Mode

c. Answers will vary.

63. Find the weighted mean by treating the number of credits as the "frequency."

Course	Grade	Value (x)	Credits (f)	xf
Sociology	A	4	3	$4 \cdot 3 = 12$
Biology	C	2	3.5	$2 \cdot 3.5 = 7$
Music	B	3	1	$3 \cdot 1 = 3$
Math	B	3	4	$3 \cdot 4 = 12$
English	C	2	3	$2 \cdot 3 = 6$
			14.5	$\sum xf = 40$

$$\text{Mean} = \frac{\sum xf}{n} = \frac{40}{14.5} \approx 2.76$$

73. makes sense

74. does not make sense; Explanations will vary. Sample explanation: The extreme value makes the team's mean height greater than its median height.

75. makes sense

76. does not make sense; Explanations will vary. Sample explanation: The instructors might use different measures of central tendency to determine the student's final course grade.

77. Answers will vary. Sample answers:

   a.   75, 80, 80, 90, 91, 94

   b.   50, 80, 80, 85, 90, 95

   c.   70, 75, 80, 85, 90, 100

   d.   75, 80, 85, 90, 95, 95

   e.   75, 80, 85, 85, 90, 95

   f.   68, 70, 72, 72, 74, 76

78. All 30 students had the same grade.

Check Points 12.3

1. $\text{Range} = 11 - 2 = 9$

2. $\text{Mean} = \dfrac{2+4+7+11}{4} = \dfrac{24}{4} = 6$

Data item	Deviation: Data item – mean
2	$2 - 6 = -4$
4	$4 - 6 = -2$
7	$7 - 6 = 1$
11	$11 - 6 = 5$

3. $\text{Mean} = \dfrac{2+4+7+11}{4} = \dfrac{24}{4} = 6$

Data item	Deviation: Data item – mean	$(\text{Deviation})^2$: $(\text{Data item–mean})^2$
2	$2 - 6 = -4$	$(-4)^2 = 16$
4	$4 - 6 = -2$	$(-2)^2 = 4$
7	$7 - 6 = 1$	$1^2 = 1$
11	$11 - 6 = 5$	$5^2 = 25$
		$\sum (\text{data item–mean})^2 = 46$

$\text{Standard deviation} = \sqrt{\dfrac{46}{4-1}} = \sqrt{\dfrac{46}{3}} \approx 3.92$

4. *Sample A*

$$\text{Mean} = \frac{73+75+77+79+81+83}{6} = \frac{468}{6} = 78$$

Data item	Deviation: Data item − mean	(Deviation)^2: (Data item−mean)^2
73	$73 - 78 = -5$	$(-5)^2 = 25$
75	$75 - 78 = -3$	$(-3)^2 = 9$
77	$77 - 78 = -1$	$(-1)^2 = 1$
79	$79 - 78 = 1$	$1^2 = 1$
81	$81 - 78 = 3$	$3^2 = 9$
83	$83 - 78 = 5$	$5^2 = 25$

$$\sum (\text{data item−mean})^2 = 70$$

$$\text{Standard deviation} = \sqrt{\frac{70}{6-1}} = \sqrt{\frac{70}{5}} \approx 3.74$$

Sample B

$$\text{Mean} = \frac{40+44+92+94+98+100}{6} = \frac{468}{6} = 78$$

Data item	Deviation: Data item − mean	(Deviation)^2: (Data item−mean)^2
40	$40 - 78 = -38$	$(-38)^2 = 1444$
44	$44 - 78 = -34$	$(-34)^2 = 1156$
92	$92 - 78 = 14$	$14^2 = 196$
94	$94 - 78 = 16$	$16^2 = 256$
98	$98 - 78 = 20$	$20^2 = 400$
100	$100 - 78 = 22$	$22^2 = 484$

$$\sum (\text{data item−mean})^2 = 3936$$

$$\text{Standard deviation} = \sqrt{\frac{3936}{6-1}} = \sqrt{\frac{3936}{5}} \approx 28.06$$

5. a. Stocks had a greater return on investment.

b. Stocks have the greater risk. The high standard deviation indicates that stocks are more likely to lose money.

Exercise Set 12.3

1. Range $= 5 - 1 = 4$

2. Range $= 20 - 16 = 4$

3. Range $= 15 - 7 = 8$

4. Range $= 17 - 11 = 6$

5. Range $= 5 - 3 = 2$

6. Range $= 5 - 3 = 2$

7. a.

Data item	Deviation: Data item – mean
3	$3 - 12 = -9$
5	$5 - 12 = -7$
7	$7 - 12 = -5$
12	$12 - 12 = 0$
18	$18 - 12 = 6$
27	$27 - 12 = 15$

   b. $-9 - 7 - 5 + 0 + 6 + 15 = 0$

8. a.

Data item	Deviation: Data item – mean
84	$84 - 91 = -7$
88	$88 - 91 = -3$
90	$90 - 91 = -1$
95	$95 - 91 = 4$
98	$98 - 91 = 7$

   b. $-7 - 3 - 1 + 4 + 7 = 0$

9. a.

Data item	Deviation: Data item – mean
29	$29 - 49 = -20$
38	$38 - 49 = -11$
48	$48 - 49 = -1$
49	$49 - 49 = 0$
53	$53 - 49 = 4$
77	$77 - 49 = 28$

   b. $-20 - 11 - 1 + 0 + 4 + 28 = 0$

10. a.

Data item	Deviation: Data item – mean
60	$60 - 65 = -5$
60	$60 - 65 = -5$
62	$62 - 65 = -3$
65	$65 - 65 = 0$
65	$65 - 65 = 0$
65	$65 - 65 = 0$
66	$66 - 65 = 1$
67	$67 - 65 = 2$
70	$70 - 65 = 5$
70	$70 - 65 = 5$

   b. $-5 - 5 - 3 + 0 + 0 + 0 + 1 + 2 + 5 + 5 = 0$

11. a. Mean $= \dfrac{85 + 95 + 90 + 85 + 100}{5} = 91$

b.

Data item	Deviation: Data item – mean
85	$85 - 91 = -6$
95	$95 - 91 = 4$
90	$90 - 91 = -1$
85	$85 - 91 = -6$
100	$100 - 91 = 9$

c. $-6 + 4 - 1 - 6 + 9 = 0$

12. a. Mean $= \dfrac{94 + 62 + 88 + 85 + 91}{5} = 84$

b.

Data item	Deviation: Data item – mean
94	$94 - 84 = 10$
62	$62 - 84 = -22$
88	$88 - 84 = 4$
85	$85 - 84 = 1$
91	$91 - 84 = 7$

c. $10 - 22 + 4 + 1 + 7 = 0$

13. a. Mean $= \dfrac{146 + 153 + 155 + 160 + 161}{5} = 155$

b.

Data item	Deviation: Data item – mean
146	$146 - 155 = -9$
153	$153 - 155 = -2$
155	$155 - 155 = 0$
160	$160 - 155 = 5$
161	$161 - 155 = 6$

c. $-9 - 2 + 0 + 5 + 6 = 0$

14. a. Mean $= \dfrac{150 + 132 + 144 + 122}{4} = 137$

b.

Data item	Deviation: Data item – mean
150	$150 - 137 = 13$
132	$132 - 137 = -5$
144	$144 - 137 = 7$
122	$122 - 137 = -15$

c. $13 - 5 + 7 - 15 = 0$

15. a. Mean $= \dfrac{2.25 + 3.50 + 2.75 + 3.10 + 1.90}{5} = 2.70$

b.

Data item	Deviation: Data item – mean
2.25	$2.25 - 2.70 = -0.45$
3.50	$3.50 - 2.70 = 0.80$
2.75	$2.75 - 2.70 = 0.05$
3.10	$3.10 - 2.70 = 0.40$
1.90	$1.90 - 2.70 = -0.80$

c. $-0.45 + 0.80 + 0.05 + 0.40 - 0.80 = 0$

16. a. Mean $= \dfrac{0.35 + 0.37 + 0.41 + 0.39 + 0.43}{5} = 0.39$

b.

Data item	Deviation: Data item – mean
0.35	$0.35 - 0.39 = -0.04$
0.37	$0.37 - 0.39 = -0.02$
0.41	$0.41 - 0.39 = 0.02$
0.39	$0.39 - 0.39 = 0$
0.43	$0.43 - 0.39 = 0.04$

c. $-0.04 - 0.02 + 0.02 + 0 + 0.04 = 0$

17. Mean $= \dfrac{1 + 2 + 3 + 4 + 5}{5} = 3$

Data item	Deviation: Data item – mean	$(\text{Deviation})^2$: $(\text{Data item–mean})^2$
1	$1 - 3 = -2$	$(-2)^2 = 4$
2	$2 - 3 = -1$	$(-1)^2 = 1$
3	$3 - 3 = 0$	$0^2 = 0$
4	$4 - 3 = 1$	$1^2 = 1$
5	$5 - 3 = 2$	$2^2 = 4$

$$\sum(\text{data item–mean})^2 = 10$$

Standard deviation $= \sqrt{\dfrac{10}{5-1}} = \sqrt{\dfrac{10}{4}} \approx 1.58$

18. Mean $= \dfrac{16+17+18+19+20}{5} = 18$

Data item	Deviation: Data item – mean	(Deviation)^2 : (Data item–mean)^2
16	$16 - 18 = -2$	$(-2)^2 = 4$
17	$17 - 18 = -1$	$(-1)^2 = 1$
18	$18 - 18 = 0$	$0^2 = 0$
19	$19 - 18 = 1$	$1^2 = 1$
20	$20 - 18 = 2$	$2^2 = 4$

$$\sum (\text{data item–mean})^2 = 10$$

Standard deviation $= \sqrt{\dfrac{10}{5-1}} = \sqrt{\dfrac{10}{4}} \approx 1.58$

19. Mean $= \dfrac{7+9+9+15}{4} = 10$

Data item	Deviation: Data item – mean	(Deviation)^2 : (Data item–mean)^2
7	$7 - 10 = -3$	$(-3)^2 = 9$
9	$9 - 10 = -1$	$(-1)^2 = 1$
9	$9 - 10 = -1$	$(-1)^2 = 1$
15	$15 - 10 = 5$	$5^2 = 25$

$$\sum (\text{data item–mean})^2 = 36$$

Standard deviation $= \sqrt{\dfrac{36}{4-1}} = \sqrt{\dfrac{36}{3}} \approx 3.46$

20. Mean $= \dfrac{11+13+14+15+17}{5} = 14$

Data item	Deviation: Data item – mean	(Deviation)^2 : (Data item–mean)^2
11	$11 - 14 = -3$	$(-3)^2 = 9$
13	$13 - 14 = -1$	$(-1)^2 = 1$
14	$14 - 14 = 0$	$0^2 = 0$
15	$15 - 14 = 1$	$1^2 = 1$
17	$17 - 14 = 3$	$3^2 = 9$

$$\sum (\text{data item–mean})^2 = 20$$

Standard deviation $= \sqrt{\dfrac{20}{5-1}} = \sqrt{\dfrac{20}{4}} \approx 2.24$

21. $\text{Mean} = \dfrac{3+3+4+4+5+5}{6} = 4$

Data item	Deviation: Data item – mean	$(\text{Deviation})^2$: $(\text{Data item–mean})^2$
3	$3 - 4 = -1$	$(-1)^2 = 1$
3	$3 - 4 = -1$	$(-1)^2 = 1$
4	$4 - 4 = 0$	$0^2 = 0$
4	$4 - 4 = 0$	$0^2 = 0$
5	$5 - 4 = 1$	$1^2 = 1$
5	$5 - 4 = 1$	$1^2 = 1$

$$\sum (\text{data item–mean})^2 = 4$$

$$\text{Standard deviation} = \sqrt{\dfrac{4}{6-1}} = \sqrt{\dfrac{4}{5}} \approx 0.89$$

22. $\text{Mean} = \dfrac{3+3+3+4+5+5+5}{7} = 4$

Data item	Deviation: Data item – mean	$(\text{Deviation})^2$: $(\text{Data item–mean})^2$
3	$3 - 4 = -1$	$(-1)^2 = 1$
3	$3 - 4 = -1$	$(-1)^2 = 1$
3	$3 - 4 = -1$	$(-1)^2 = 1$
4	$4 - 4 = 0$	$0^2 = 0$
5	$5 - 4 = 1$	$1^2 = 1$
5	$5 - 4 = 1$	$1^2 = 1$
5	$5 - 4 = 1$	$1^2 = 1$

$$\sum (\text{data item–mean})^2 = 6$$

$$\text{Standard deviation} = \sqrt{\dfrac{6}{7-1}} = \sqrt{\dfrac{6}{6}} = 1$$

23. Mean $= \dfrac{1+1+1+4+7+7+7}{7} = 4$

Data item	Deviation: Data item – mean	(Deviation)^2 : (Data item–mean)^2
1	$1 - 4 = -3$	$(-3)^2 = 9$
1	$1 - 4 = -3$	$(-3)^2 = 9$
1	$1 - 4 = -3$	$(-3)^2 = 9$
4	$4 - 4 = 0$	$0^2 = 0$
7	$7 - 4 = 3$	$3^2 = 9$
7	$7 - 4 = 3$	$3^2 = 9$
7	$7 - 4 = 3$	$3^2 = 9$

$$\sum (\text{data item–mean})^2 = 54$$

Standard deviation $= \sqrt{\dfrac{54}{7-1}} = \sqrt{\dfrac{54}{6}} = 3$

24. Mean $= \dfrac{6+6+6+6+7+7+7+4+8+3}{10} = 6$

Data item	Deviation: Data item – mean	(Deviation)^2 : (Data item–mean)^2
6	$6 - 6 = 0$	$0^2 = 0$
6	$6 - 6 = 0$	$0^2 = 0$
6	$6 - 6 = 0$	$0^2 = 0$
6	$6 - 6 = 0$	$0^2 = 0$
7	$7 - 6 = 1$	$1^2 = 1$
7	$7 - 6 = 1$	$1^2 = 1$
7	$7 - 6 = 1$	$1^2 = 1$
4	$4 - 6 = -2$	$(-2)^2 = 4$
8	$8 - 6 = 2$	$2^2 = 4$
3	$3 - 6 = -3$	$(-3)^2 = 9$

$$\sum (\text{data item–mean})^2 = 20$$

Standard deviation $= \sqrt{\dfrac{20}{10-1}} = \sqrt{\dfrac{20}{9}} \approx 1.49$

25. Mean $= \dfrac{9+5+9+5+9+5+9+5}{8} = 7$

Data item	Deviation: Data item – mean	(Deviation)^2: (Data item–mean)^2
9	$9 - 7 = 2$	$2^2 = 4$
5	$5 - 7 = -2$	$(-2)^2 = 4$
9	$9 - 7 = 2$	$2^2 = 4$
5	$5 - 7 = -2$	$(-2)^2 = 4$
9	$9 - 7 = 2$	$2^2 = 4$
5	$5 - 7 = -2$	$(-2)^2 = 4$
9	$9 - 7 = 2$	$2^2 = 4$
5	$5 - 7 = -2$	$(-2)^2 = 4$
		$\sum$ (data item–mean)$^2 = 32$

Standard deviation $= \sqrt{\dfrac{32}{8-1}} = \sqrt{\dfrac{32}{7}} \approx 2.14$

26. Mean $= \dfrac{6+10+6+10+6+10+6+10}{8} = 8$

Data item	Deviation: Data item – mean	(Deviation)^2: (Data item–mean)^2
6	$6 - 8 = -2$	$(-2)^2 = 4$
10	$10 - 8 = 2$	$2^2 = 4$
6	$6 - 8 = -2$	$(-2)^2 = 4$
10	$10 - 8 = 2$	$2^2 = 4$
6	$6 - 8 = -2$	$(-2)^2 = 4$
10	$10 - 8 = 2$	$2^2 = 4$
6	$6 - 8 = -2$	$(-2)^2 = 4$
10	$10 - 8 = 2$	$2^2 = 4$
		$\sum$ (data item–mean)$^2 = 32$

Standard deviation $= \sqrt{\dfrac{32}{8-1}} = \sqrt{\dfrac{32}{7}} \approx 2.14$

27. *Sample A*

$$\text{Mean} = \frac{6+8+10+12+14+16+18}{7} = 12$$

Range = 18 – 6 = 12

Data item	Deviation: Data item – mean	$(\text{Deviation})^2$: $(\text{Data item–mean})^2$
6	6 – 12 = –6	$(-6)^2 = 36$
8	8 – 12 = –4	$(-4)^2 = 16$
10	10 – 12 = –2	$(-2)^2 = 4$
12	12 – 12 = 0	$0^2 = 0$
14	14 – 12 = 2	$2^2 = 4$
16	16 – 12 = 4	$4^2 = 16$
18	18 – 12 = 6	$6^2 = 36$

$$\sum (\text{data item–mean})^2 = 112$$

$$\text{Standard deviation} = \sqrt{\frac{112}{7-1}} = \sqrt{\frac{112}{6}} \approx 4.32$$

Sample B

$$\text{Mean} = \frac{6+7+8+12+16+17+18}{7} = 12$$

Range = 18 – 6 = 12

Data item	Deviation: Data item – mean	$(\text{Deviation})^2$: $(\text{Data item–mean})^2$
6	6 – 12 = –6	$(-6)^2 = 36$
7	7 – 12 = –5	$(-5)^2 = 25$
8	8 – 12 = –4	$(-4)^2 = 16$
12	12 – 12 = 0	$0^2 = 0$
16	16 – 12 = 4	$4^2 = 16$
17	17 – 12 = 5	$5^2 = 25$
18	18 – 12 = 6	$6^2 = 36$

$$\sum (\text{data item–mean})^2 = 154$$

$$\text{Standard deviation} = \sqrt{\frac{154}{7-1}} = \sqrt{\frac{154}{6}} \approx 5.07$$

Sample C

Mean $= \dfrac{6+6+6+12+18+18+18}{7} = 12$

Range $= 18 - 6 = 12$

Data item	Deviation: Data item – mean	$(\text{Deviation})^2$: $(\text{Data item–mean})^2$
6	$6 - 12 = -6$	$(-6)^2 = 36$
6	$6 - 12 = -6$	$(-6)^2 = 36$
6	$6 - 12 = -6$	$(-6)^2 = 36$
12	$12 - 12 = 0$	$0^2 = 0$
18	$18 - 12 = 6$	$6^2 = 36$
18	$18 - 12 = 6$	$6^2 = 36$
18	$18 - 12 = 6$	$6^2 = 36$

$\sum (\text{data item–mean})^2 = 216$

Standard deviation $= \sqrt{\dfrac{216}{7-1}} = \sqrt{\dfrac{216}{6}} = 6$

The samples have the same mean and range, but different standard deviations.

28. *Sample A*

Mean $= \dfrac{8+10+12+14+16+18+20}{7} = 14$

Range $= 20 - 8 = 12$

Data item	Deviation: Data item – mean	$(\text{Deviation})^2$: $(\text{Data item–mean})^2$
8	$8 - 14 = -6$	$(-6)^2 = 36$
10	$10 - 14 = -4$	$(-4)^2 = 16$
12	$12 - 14 = -2$	$(-2)^2 = 4$
14	$14 - 14 = 0$	$0^2 = 0$
16	$16 - 14 = 2$	$2^2 = 4$
18	$18 - 14 = 4$	$4^2 = 16$
20	$20 - 14 = 6$	$6^2 = 36$

$\sum (\text{data item–mean})^2 = 112$

Standard deviation $= \sqrt{\dfrac{112}{7-1}} = \sqrt{\dfrac{112}{6}} \approx 4.32$

Sample B

$\text{Mean} = \dfrac{8+9+10+14+18+19+20}{7} = 14$

$\text{Range} = 20 - 8 = 12$

Data item	Deviation: Data item – mean	$(\text{Deviation})^2$: $(\text{Data item–mean})^2$
8	$8 - 14 = -6$	$(-6)^2 = 36$
9	$9 - 14 = -5$	$(-5)^2 = 25$
10	$10 - 14 = -4$	$(-4)^2 = 16$
14	$14 - 14 = 0$	$0^2 = 0$
18	$18 - 14 = 4$	$4^2 = 16$
19	$19 - 14 = 5$	$5^2 = 25$
20	$20 - 14 = 6$	$6^2 = 36$

$$\sum (\text{data item–mean})^2 = 154$$

$\text{Standard deviation} = \sqrt{\dfrac{154}{7-1}} = \sqrt{\dfrac{154}{6}} \approx 5.07$

Sample C

$\text{Mean} = \dfrac{8+8+8+14+20+20+20}{7} = 14$

$\text{Range} = 20 - 8 = 12$

Data item	Deviation: Data item – mean	$(\text{Deviation})^2$: $(\text{Data item–mean})^2$
8	$8 - 14 = -6$	$(-6)^2 = 36$
8	$8 - 14 = -6$	$(-6)^2 = 36$
8	$8 - 14 = -6$	$(-6)^2 = 36$
14	$14 - 14 = 0$	$0^2 = 0$
20	$20 - 14 = 6$	$6^2 = 36$
20	$20 - 14 = 6$	$6^2 = 36$
20	$20 - 14 = 6$	$6^2 = 36$

$$\sum (\text{data item–mean})^2 = 216$$

$\text{Standard deviation} = \sqrt{\dfrac{216}{7-1}} = \sqrt{\dfrac{216}{6}} = 6$

The samples have the same mean and range, but different standard deviations.

29. Mean $= \dfrac{9+9+9+9+9+9+9}{7} = \dfrac{63}{7} = 9$

Data item	Deviation: Data item – mean	(Deviation)^2: (Data item–mean)^2
9	$9 - 9 = 0$	$(0)^2 = 0$
9	$9 - 9 = 0$	$(0)^2 = 0$
9	$9 - 9 = 0$	$(0)^2 = 0$
9	$9 - 9 = 0$	$(0)^2 = 0$
9	$9 - 9 = 0$	$(0)^2 = 0$
9	$9 - 9 = 0$	$(0)^2 = 0$
9	$9 - 9 = 0$	$(0)^2 = 0$

$$\sum (\text{data item} - \text{mean})^2 = 0$$

Standard deviation $= \sqrt{\dfrac{0}{7-1}} = \sqrt{\dfrac{0}{6}} = 0$

30. Mean $= \dfrac{8+8+9+9+9+10+10}{7} = \dfrac{63}{7} = 9$

Data item	Deviation: Data item – mean	(Deviation)^2: (Data item–mean)^2
8	$8 - 9 = -1$	$(-1)^2 = 1$
8	$8 - 9 = -1$	$(-1)^2 = 1$
9	$9 - 9 = 0$	$(0)^2 = 0$
9	$9 - 9 = 0$	$(0)^2 = 0$
9	$9 - 9 = 0$	$(0)^2 = 0$
10	$10 - 9 = 1$	$(-1)^2 = 1$
10	$10 - 9 = 1$	$(-1)^2 = 1$

$$\sum (\text{data item} - \text{mean})^2 = 4$$

Standard deviation $= \sqrt{\dfrac{4}{7-1}} = \sqrt{\dfrac{4}{6}} \approx 0.82$

31. Mean $= \dfrac{8+8+8+9+10+10+10}{7} = \dfrac{63}{7} = 9$

Data item	Deviation: Data item – mean	(Deviation)^2 : (Data item–mean)^2
8	$8-9=-1$	$(-1)^2 = 1$
8	$8-9=-1$	$(-1)^2 = 1$
8	$8-9=-1$	$(-1)^2 = 1$
9	$9-9=0$	$(0)^2 = 0$
10	$10-9=1$	$(-1)^2 = 1$
10	$10-9=1$	$(-1)^2 = 1$
10	$10-9=1$	$(-1)^2 = 1$

$$\sum (\text{data item} - \text{mean})^2 = 6$$

Standard deviation $= \sqrt{\dfrac{6}{7-1}} = \sqrt{\dfrac{6}{6}} = 1$

32. Mean $= \dfrac{6+6+6+9+12+12+12}{7} = \dfrac{63}{7} = 9$

Data item	Deviation: Data item – mean	(Deviation)^2 : (Data item–mean)^2
6	$6-9=-3$	$(-3)^2 = 9$
6	$6-9=-3$	$(-3)^2 = 9$
6	$6-9=-3$	$(-3)^2 = 9$
9	$9-9=0$	$(0)^2 = 0$
12	$12-9=3$	$(3)^2 = 9$
12	$12-9=3$	$(3)^2 = 9$
12	$12-9=3$	$(3)^2 = 9$

$$\sum (\text{data item} - \text{mean})^2 = 54$$

Standard deviation $= \sqrt{\dfrac{54}{7-1}} = \sqrt{\dfrac{54}{6}} = 3$

33. $\text{Mean} = \dfrac{5+10+15+20+25}{5} = \dfrac{75}{5} = 15$

Data item	Deviation: Data item – mean	(Deviation)^2 : (Data item–mean)^2
5	$5 - 15 = -10$	$(-10)^2 = 100$
10	$10 - 15 = -5$	$(-5)^2 = 25$
15	$15 - 15 = 0$	$(0)^2 = 0$
20	$20 - 15 = 5$	$(5)^2 = 25$
25	$25 - 15 = 10$	$(10)^2 = 100$

$$\sum (\text{data item} - \text{mean})^2 = 250$$

$\text{Standard deviation} = \sqrt{\dfrac{250}{5-1}} = \sqrt{\dfrac{250}{4}} \approx 7.91$

34. $\text{Mean} = \dfrac{4+8+12+16+20}{5} = \dfrac{60}{5} = 12$

Data item	Deviation: Data item – mean	(Deviation)^2 : (Data item–mean)^2
4	$4 - 12 = -8$	$(-8)^2 = 64$
8	$8 - 12 = -4$	$(-4)^2 = 16$
12	$12 - 12 = 0$	$(0)^2 = 0$
16	$16 - 12 = 4$	$(4)^2 = 16$
20	$20 - 12 = 8$	$(8)^2 = 64$

$$\sum (\text{data item} - \text{mean})^2 = 160$$

$\text{Standard deviation} = \sqrt{\dfrac{160}{5-1}} = \sqrt{\dfrac{160}{4}} \approx 6.32$

35. Mean $= \dfrac{17+18+18+18+19+19+20+20+21+22}{10} = \dfrac{192}{10} = 19.2$

Data item	Deviation: Data item − mean	(Deviation)^2 : (Data item–mean)^2
17	$17 - 19.2 = -2.2$	$(-2.2)^2 = 4.84$
18	$18 - 19.2 = -2.2$	$(-1.2)^2 = 1.44$
18	$18 - 19.2 = -2.2$	$(-1.2)^2 = 1.44$
18	$18 - 19.2 = -2.2$	$(-1.2)^2 = 1.44$
19	$19 - 19.2 = -0.2$	$(-0.2)^2 = 0.04$
19	$19 - 19.2 = -0.2$	$(-0.2)^2 = 0.04$
20	$20 - 19.2 = 0.8$	$(0.8)^2 = 0.64$
20	$20 - 19.2 = 0.8$	$(0.8)^2 = 0.64$
21	$21 - 19.2 = 1.8$	$(1.8)^2 = 3.24$
22	$22 - 19.2 = 2.8$	$(2.8)^2 = 7.84$

$$\sum (\text{data item} - \text{mean})^2 = 21.6$$

Standard deviation $= \sqrt{\dfrac{21.6}{10-1}} = \sqrt{\dfrac{21.6}{9}} \approx 1.55$

36. Mean $= \dfrac{13+13+13+14+15+18+20+20+23+24}{10} = \dfrac{173}{10} = 17.3$

Data item	Deviation: Data item − mean	(Deviation)^2 : (Data item–mean)^2
13	$13 - 17.3 = -4.3$	$(-4.3)^2 = 18.49$
13	$13 - 17.3 = -4.3$	$(-4.3)^2 = 18.49$
13	$13 - 17.3 = -4.3$	$(-4.3)^2 = 18.49$
14	$14 - 17.3 = -3.3$	$(-3.3)^2 = 10.89$
15	$15 - 17.3 = -2.3$	$(-2.3)^2 = 5.29$
18	$18 - 17.3 = 0.7$	$(0.7)^2 = 0.49$
20	$20 - 17.3 = 2.7$	$(2.7)^2 = 7.29$
20	$20 - 17.3 = 2.7$	$(2.7)^2 = 7.29$
23	$23 - 17.3 = 5.7$	$(5.7)^2 = 32.49$
24	$24 - 17.3 = 6.7$	$(6.7)^2 = 44.89$

$$\sum (\text{data item} - \text{mean})^2 = 164.1$$

Standard deviation $= \sqrt{\dfrac{164.1}{10-1}} = \sqrt{\dfrac{164.1}{9}} \approx 4.27$

37. a. The male artists' data set has the greater mean. This can be seen without calculating by observing that at each rank, the male artist had more platinum albums than the corresponding female artist.

b. Mean (male artists) $= \dfrac{385}{5} = 77;$ Mean (female artists) $= \dfrac{285}{5} = 57$

c. The male artists' data set has the greater standard deviation. This can be seen without calculating by observing that the male artists' data set data has a greater spread.

d. Standard deviation (male artists) $= \sqrt{\dfrac{1586}{5-1}} = \sqrt{\dfrac{1586}{4}} \approx 19.91$

Standard deviation (female artists) $= \sqrt{\dfrac{140}{5-1}} = \sqrt{\dfrac{140}{4}} \approx 5.92$

38. a. The ages of the last six presidents has the greater standard deviation. This can be seen without calculating by observing that the ages for the last six presidents include ages which are both higher and lower than age of the first six presidents

b. Standard deviation (first six presidents) $= \sqrt{\dfrac{12.8334}{6-1}} = \sqrt{\dfrac{12.8334}{5}} \approx 1.60$

Standard deviation (last six presidents) $= \sqrt{\dfrac{431.3333}{6-1}} = \sqrt{\dfrac{431.3333}{5}} \approx 9.29$

47. makes sense

48. makes sense

49. makes sense

50. makes sense

53. a is the best approximation

54 Original data:

Mean $= \dfrac{0+1+3+4+4+6}{6} = \dfrac{18}{6} = 3$

Standard deviation $= \sqrt{\dfrac{24}{6-1}} = \sqrt{\dfrac{24}{5}} \approx 2.19$

Adjusted data:

Mean $= \dfrac{2+3+5+6+6+8}{6} = \dfrac{30}{6} = 5$

Standard deviation $= \sqrt{\dfrac{24}{6-1}} = \sqrt{\dfrac{24}{5}} \approx 2.19$

Adding 2 to each data item raises the mean by 2, but does not affect the standard deviation.

Check Points 12.4

1. **a.**   Height = mean + 3·standard deviation
               $= 65 + 3 \cdot 3.5 = 75.5$ in.

    b.   Height = mean − 2·standard deviation
               $= 65 - 2 \cdot 3.5 = 58$ in.

2. **a.**   The 68-95-99.7 Rule states that approximately 95% of the data items fall within 2 standard deviations of the mean. The figure shows that 95% of male adults have heights between 62 inches and 78 inches.

    b.   The 68-95-99.7 Rule states that approximately 95% of the data items fall within 2 standard deviations of the mean. Since the mean is 70 inches, the figure shows that half of the 95%, or 47.5% of male adults have heights between 70 inches and 78 inches.

    c.   The 68-95-99.7 Rule states that approximately 68% of the data items fall within 1 standard deviation of the mean, thus 32% of the data falls outside this range. Half of the 32%, or 16% of male adults will have heights above 74 inches.

3. **a.** $z_{342} = \dfrac{\text{data item} - \text{mean}}{\text{standard deviation}} = \dfrac{342 - 336}{3} = \dfrac{6}{3} = 2$

    b. $z_{336} = \dfrac{\text{data item} - \text{mean}}{\text{standard deviation}} = \dfrac{336 - 336}{3} = \dfrac{0}{3} = 0$

    c. $z_{333} = \dfrac{\text{data item} - \text{mean}}{\text{standard deviation}} = \dfrac{333 - 336}{3} = \dfrac{-3}{3} = -1$

4. Find the z-score for each test taken.
    SAT: $z_{550} = \dfrac{\text{data item} - \text{mean}}{\text{standard deviation}} = \dfrac{550 - 500}{100} = \dfrac{50}{100} = 0.5$
    ACT: $z_{24} = \dfrac{\text{data item} - \text{mean}}{\text{standard deviation}} = \dfrac{24 - 18}{6} = \dfrac{6}{6} = 1$
    You scored better on the ACT test because the score is 1 standard deviation above the mean. The SAT score is only half a standard deviation above the mean.

5. **a.**   Score = mean − 2.25·standard deviation $= 100 - 2.25(16) = 64$

    b.   Score = mean + 1.75·standard deviation $= 100 + 1.75(16) = 128$

6. This means that 75% of the scores on the SAT are less than this student's score.

7. **a.**   The sample size is $n = 2513$. The margin of error is $\pm \dfrac{1}{\sqrt{n}} \times 100\% = \pm \dfrac{1}{\sqrt{2513}} \times 100\% \approx \pm 0.020 \times 100\% = \pm 2.0\%.$

    b.   There is a 95% probability that the true population percentage lies between
               the sample percent $- \dfrac{1}{\sqrt{n}} \times 100\% = 36\% - 2.0\% = 34\%$ and the sample percent $+ \dfrac{1}{\sqrt{n}} \times 100\% = 36\% + 2.0\% = 38\%.$
               We can be 95% confident that between 34% and 38% of Americans read more than ten books per year.

    c.   Sample answer: Some people may be embarrassed to admit that they read few or no books in a year.

Exercise Set 12.4

1. Score = $100 + 1 \cdot 20 = 100 + 20 = 120$

2. Score = $100 + 2 \cdot 20 = 100 + 40 = 140$

3. Score = $100 + 3 \cdot 20 = 100 + 60 = 160$

4. Score = $100 + 1.5(20) = 100 + 30 = 130$

5. Score = $100 + 2.5(20) = 100 + 50 = 150$

6. Score = $100 - 1 \cdot 20 = 100 - 20 = 80$

7. Score = $100 - 2 \cdot 20 = 100 - 40 = 60$

8. Score = $100 - 3 \cdot 20 = 100 - 60 = 40$

9. Score = $100 - 0.5(20) = 100 - 10 = 90$

10. Score = $100 - 2.5(20) = 100 - 50 = 50$

11. $16,500 is 1 standard deviation below the mean and $17,500 is 1 standard deviation above the mean. The Rule and the figure indicate that 68% of the buyers paid between $16,500 and $17,500.

12. $16,000 is 2 standard deviations below the mean and $18,000 is 2 standard deviations above the mean. The Rule and the figure indicate that 95% of the buyers paid between $16,000 and $18,000.

13. $17,500 is 1 standard deviation above the mean. 68% of the buyers paid between $16,500 and $17,500. Because of symmetry, the percent that paid between $17,000 and $17,500 is $\frac{1}{2}(68\%) = 34\%$.

14. $18,000 is 2 standard deviations above the mean. 95% of the buyers paid between $16,000 and $18,000. Because of symmetry, the percent that paid between $17,000 and $18,000 is $\frac{1}{2}(95\%) = 47.5\%$.

15. $16,000 is 2 standard deviations below the mean. 95% of the buyers paid between $16,000 and $18,000. Because of symmetry, the percent that paid between $16,000 and $17,000 is $\frac{1}{2}(95\%) = 47.5\%$.

16. $16,500 is 1 standard deviation below the mean. 68% of the buyers paid between $16,500 and $17,500. Because of symmetry, the percent that paid between $16,500 and $17,000 is $\frac{1}{2}(68\%) = 34\%$.

17. $15,500 is 3 standard deviations below the mean. 99.7% of the buyers paid between $15,500 and $18,500. Because of symmetry, the percent that paid between $15,500 and $17,000 is

    $\frac{1}{2}(99.7\%) = 49.85\%$.

18. $18,500 is 3 standard deviations above the mean. 99.7% of the buyers paid between $15,500 and $18,500. Because of symmetry, the percent that paid between $17,000 and $18,500 is

    $\frac{1}{2}(99.7\%) = 49.85\%$.

19. $17,500 is 1 standard deviation above the mean. Since 68% of the data items fall within 1 standard deviation of the mean, $100\% - 68\% = 32\%$ fall farther than 1 standard deviation from the mean. Because of symmetry, the percent that paid more

    than $17,500 is $\frac{1}{2}(32\%) = 16\%$.

20. $18,000 is 2 standard deviations above the mean. Since 95% of the data items fall within 2 standard deviations of the mean, $100\% - 95\% = 5\%$ fall farther than 2 standard deviations from the mean. Because of symmetry, the percent that paid more

    than $18,000 is $\frac{1}{2}(5\%) = 2.5\%$.

21. $16,000 is 2 standard deviations below the mean. Since 95% of the data items fall within 2 standard deviations of the mean, $100\% - 95\% = 5\%$ fall farther than 2 standard deviations from the mean. Because of symmetry, the percent that paid less than

    $16,000 is $\frac{1}{2}(5\%) = 2.5\%$.

22. $16,500 is 1 standard deviation below the mean. Since 68% of the data items fall within 1 standard deviation of the mean, $100\% - 68\% = 32\%$ fall farther than 1 standard deviation from the mean. Because of symmetry, the percent that paid less than $16,500 is

    $\frac{1}{2}(32\%) = 16\%$.

23. The 68-95-99.7 Rule states that approximately 95% of the data items fall within 2 standard deviations of the mean.
    95% of people will have IQs between 68 and 132.

24. The 68-95-99.7 Rule states that approximately 68% of the data items fall within 1 standard deviation of the mean.
68% of people will have IQs between 84 and 116.

25. The 68-95-99.7 Rule states that approximately 95% of the data items fall within 2 standard deviations of the mean.
Half of the 95%, or 47.5% of people will have IQs between 68 and 100.

26. The 68-95-99.7 Rule states that approximately 68% of the data items fall within 1 standard deviation of the mean.
Half of the 68%, or 34% of people will have IQs between 68 and 100.

27. The 68-95-99.7 Rule states that approximately 68% of the data items fall within 1 standard deviation of the mean.
Thus, 100% – 68% = 32% will fall outside this range. Half of the 32%, or 16% of people will have IQs above 116.

28. The 68-95-99.7 Rule states that approximately 95% of the data items fall within 2 standard deviations of the mean.
Thus, 100% – 95% = 5% will fall outside this range. Half of the 5%, or 2.5% of people will have IQs above 132.

29. The 68-95-99.7 Rule states that approximately 95% of the data items fall within 2 standard deviations of the mean.
Thus, 100% – 95% = 5% will fall outside this range. Half of the 5%, or 2.5% of people will have IQs below 68.

30. The 68-95-99.7 Rule states that approximately 68% of the data items fall within 1 standard deviation of the mean.
Thus, 100% – 68% = 32% will fall outside this range. Half of the 32%, or 16% of people will have IQs below 84.

31. The 68-95-99.7 Rule states that approximately 99.7% of the data items fall within 3 standard deviations of the mean.
Thus, 100% – 99.7% = 0.3% will fall outside this range. Half of the 0.3%, or 0.15% of people will have IQs above 148.

32. The 68-95-99.7 Rule states that approximately 99.7% of the data items fall within 3 standard deviations of the mean.
Thus, 100% – 99.7% = 0.3% will fall outside this range. Half of the 0.3%, or 0.15% of people will have IQs below 52.

33. $z_{68} = \dfrac{68-60}{8} = \dfrac{8}{8} = 1$

34. $z_{76} = \dfrac{76-60}{8} = \dfrac{16}{8} = 2$

35. $z_{84} = \dfrac{84-60}{8} = \dfrac{24}{8} = 3$

36. $z_{92} = \dfrac{92-60}{8} = \dfrac{32}{8} = 4$

37. $z_{64} = \dfrac{64-60}{8} = \dfrac{4}{8} = 0.5$

38. $z_{72} = \dfrac{72-60}{8} = \dfrac{12}{8} = 1.5$

39. $z_{74} = \dfrac{74-60}{8} = \dfrac{14}{8} = 1.75$

40. $z_{78} = \dfrac{78-60}{8} = \dfrac{18}{8} = 2.25$

41. $z_{60} = \dfrac{60-60}{8} = \dfrac{0}{8} = 0$

42. $z_{100} = \dfrac{100-60}{8} = \dfrac{40}{8} = 5$

43. $z_{52} = \dfrac{52-60}{8} = \dfrac{-8}{8} = -1$

44. $z_{44} = \dfrac{44-60}{8} = \dfrac{-16}{8} = -2$

45. $z_{48} = \dfrac{48-60}{8} = \dfrac{-12}{8} = -1.5$

46. $z_{40} = \dfrac{40-60}{8} = \dfrac{-20}{8} = -2.5$

47. $z_{34} = \dfrac{34-60}{8} = \dfrac{-26}{8} = -3.25$

48. $z_{30} = \dfrac{30-60}{8} = \dfrac{-30}{8} = -3.75$

49. $z = \dfrac{\text{data item} - \text{mean}}{\text{standard deviation}} = \dfrac{17-11}{4} = 1.5$

50. $z = \dfrac{\text{data item} - \text{mean}}{\text{standard deviation}} = \dfrac{18-11}{4} = 1.75$

51. $z = \dfrac{\text{data item} - \text{mean}}{\text{standard deviation}} = \dfrac{20-11}{4} = 2.25$

52. $z = \dfrac{\text{data item} - \text{mean}}{\text{standard deviation}} = \dfrac{12-11}{4} = 0.25$

53. $z = \dfrac{\text{data item} - \text{mean}}{\text{standard deviation}} = \dfrac{6-11}{4} = -1.25$

54. $z = \dfrac{\text{data item} - \text{mean}}{\text{standard deviation}} = \dfrac{8-11}{4} = -0.75$

55. $z = \dfrac{\text{data item} - \text{mean}}{\text{standard deviation}} = \dfrac{5-11}{4} = -1.5$

56. $z = \dfrac{\text{data item} - \text{mean}}{\text{standard deviation}} = \dfrac{1-11}{4} = -2.5$

57. z-score of 128 on the Stanford-Binet:

$z = \dfrac{\text{data item} - \text{mean}}{\text{standard deviation}} = \dfrac{128-100}{16} = 1.75$

z-score of 127 on the Wechsler:

$z = \dfrac{\text{data item} - \text{mean}}{\text{standard deviation}} = \dfrac{127-100}{15} = 1.8$

The person who scores 127 on the Wechsler has the higher IQ.

58. z-score of 150 on the Stanford-Binet:

$z = \dfrac{\text{data item} - \text{mean}}{\text{standard deviation}} = \dfrac{150-100}{16} = 3.125$

z-score of 148 on the Wechsler:

$z = \dfrac{\text{data item} - \text{mean}}{\text{standard deviation}} = \dfrac{148-100}{15} = 3.2$

The person who scores 148 on the Wechsler has the higher IQ.

59. $2 \cdot 50 = 100$
The data item is 100 units above the mean.
$400 + 100 = 500$

60. $3 \cdot 50 = 150$
The data item is 150 units above the mean.
$400 + 150 = 550$

61. $1.5(50) = 75$
The data item is 75 units above the mean.
$400 + 75 = 475$

62. $2.5(50) = 125$
The data item is 125 units above the mean.
$400 + 125 = 525$

63. $-3 \cdot 50 = -150$
The data item is 150 units below the mean.
$400 - 150 = 250$

64. $-2 \cdot 50 = -100$
The data item is 100 units below the mean.
$400 - 100 = 300$

65. $-2.5(50) = -125$
The data item is 125 units below the mean.
$400 - 125 = 275$

66. $-1.5(50) = -75$
The data item is 75 units below the mean.
$400 - 75 = 325$

67. a. $\text{margin of error} = \pm \dfrac{1}{\sqrt{1023}} \times 100\%$

$\approx \pm 0.031 \times 100\%$

$= \pm 3.1\%$

b. $25\% - 3.1\% = 21.9\%$
$25\% + 3.1\% = 28.1\%$
We can be 95% confident that between 21.9% and 28.1% of high school students have information technology as their career choice.

68. a. $\text{margin of error} = \pm \dfrac{1}{\sqrt{2774}} \times 100\%$

$\approx \pm 0.019 \times 100\%$

$= \pm 1.9\%$

b. $79\% - 1.9\% = 77.1\%$
$79\% + 1.9\% = 80.9\%$
We can be 95% confident that for between 77.1% and 80.9% of college students a "green" company would have an impact on their decision.

69. a. $\text{margin of error} = \pm \dfrac{1}{\sqrt{4000}} \times 100\%$

$\approx \pm 0.016 \times 100\%$

$= \pm 1.6\%$

b. $60.2\% - 1.6\% = 58.6\%$
$60.2\% + 1.6\% = 61.8\%$
We can be 95% confident that between 58.6% and 61.8% of all TV households watched the final episode of $M*A*S*H$.

70. a.　margin of error $= \pm \dfrac{1}{\sqrt{4000}} \times 100\%$

$\approx \pm 0.016 \times 100\%$

$= \pm 1.6\%$

b.　$51.1\% - 1.6\% = 49.5\%$
$51.1\% + 1.6\% = 52.7\%$
We can be 95% confident that between 49.5% and 52.7% of all TV households watched *Roots*, Part 8.

71.　new margin of error $= \pm \dfrac{1}{\sqrt{5000}} \times 100\%$

$\approx \pm 0.014 \times 100\%$

$= \pm 1.4\%$

improvement $= 1.6\% - 1.4\% = 0.2\%$

72.　new margin of error $= \pm \dfrac{1}{\sqrt{10,000}} \times 100\%$

$= \pm 0.010 \times 100\%$

$= \pm 1.0\%$

improvement $= 1.4\% - 1.0\% = 0.4\%$

73. a.　The graph is skewed to the right.

b.

x	f	xf
1	3	$1 \cdot 3 = 3$
2	9	$2 \cdot 9 = 18$
3	8	$3 \cdot 8 = 24$
4	2	$4 \cdot 2 = 8$
5	7	$5 \cdot 7 = 35$
6	9	$6 \cdot 9 = 54$
7	5	$7 \cdot 5 = 35$
8	4	$8 \cdot 4 = 32$
9	1	$9 \cdot 1 = 9$
10	1	$10 \cdot 1 = 10$
12	1	$123 \cdot 1 = 12$
29	1	$29 \cdot 1 = 29$
	51	$\sum xf = 269$

$\text{Mean} = \dfrac{\sum xf}{n} = \dfrac{269}{51} \approx 5.3$

The mean rate is 5.3 murders per 100,000 residents.

c.　The median is in the 26th position. The median rate is 5 murders per 100,000 residents.

d.　Yes, these rates are consistent with the graph. The mean is greater than the median, which is expected with a distribution that is skewed to the right.

e.　$z_{29} = \dfrac{29 - 5.3}{4.2} \approx 5.6$

Yes, this is unusually high. For a normal distribution, almost 100% of the z-scores are between -3 and 3.

74. a.　The median is in the 26th position. The median rate is 5 murders per 100,000 residents.

b.　The first quartile is in the $0.25(51) = 12.75$ position, which means it is the mean of the data items in positions 12 and 13.

first quartile $= \dfrac{2 + 3}{2} = 2.5$

c.　The third quartile is in the $0.75(51) = 38.25$ position, which means it is the mean of the data items in positions 38 and 39.

third quartile $= \dfrac{6 + 7}{2} = 6.5$

d.　Plot points.

e.　Box-and-whisker plot:

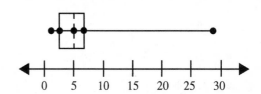

f.　The box-and-whisker plot indicates that the distribution is skewed to the right.

g.　yes

87.　does not make sense; Explanations will vary. Sample explanation: The standard deviation is too big for this case.

88.　makes sense

89.　does not make sense; Explanations will vary. Sample explanation: The margin of error is approximately $\pm 2.9\%$. So we are 95% confident that between 48.1% and 53.9% of voters will vote for candidate A which does not mean they will definitely win.

90.　makes sense

Check Points 12.5

1. $z_{83.60} = \dfrac{\text{data item} - \text{mean}}{\text{standard deviation}} = \dfrac{83.60 - 62}{18} = 1.2$
A z-score of 1.2 corresponds to a percentile of 88.49. Thus, 88.49% of plans have charges less than $83.60.

2. $z_{69.9} = \dfrac{\text{data item} - \text{mean}}{\text{standard deviation}} = \dfrac{69.9 - 65}{3.5} = 1.4$
A z-score of 1.4 corresponds to a percentile of 91.93. Thus, 100% − 91.92% = 8.08% of women have heights greater than 69.9 inches.

3. $z_{11} = \dfrac{\text{data item} - \text{mean}}{\text{standard deviation}} = \dfrac{11 - 14}{2.5} = -1.2$ which corresponds to a percentile of 11.51.
$z_{18} = \dfrac{\text{data item} - \text{mean}}{\text{standard deviation}} = \dfrac{18 - 14}{2.5} = 1.6$ which corresponds to a percentile of 94.52.
Thus, 94.52% − 11.51% = 83.01% of refrigerators have lives between 11 and 18 years.

Exercise Set 12.5

1. a. 72.57%

   b. 100% − 72.57% = 27.43%

2. a. 78.81%

   b. 100% − 78.81% = 21.19%

3. a. 88.49%

   b. 100% − 88.49% = 11.51%

4. a. 91.92%

   b. 100% − 91.92% = 8.08%

5. a. 24.20%

   b. 100% − 24.20% = 75.8%

6. a. 34.46%

   b. 100% − 34.46% = 65.54%

7. a. 11.51%

   b. 100% − 11.51% = 88.49%

8. a. 3.59%

   b. 100% − 3.59% = 96.41%

9. $z = 0.2 \rightarrow 57.93\%$
$z = 1.4 \rightarrow 91.92\%$
91.92% − 57.93% = 33.99%

10. $z = 0.3 \rightarrow 61.79\%$
$z = 2.1 \rightarrow 98.21\%$
98.21% − 61.79% = 36.42%

11. $z = 1 \rightarrow 84.13\%$
$z = 3 \rightarrow 99.87\%$
99.87% − 84.13% = 15.74%

12. $z = 2 \rightarrow 97.72\%$
$z = 3 \rightarrow 99.87\%$
99.87% − 97.72% = 2.15%

13. $z = -1.5 \rightarrow 6.68\%$
$z = 1.5 \rightarrow 93.32\%$
93.32% − 6.68% = 86.64%

14. $z = -1.2 \rightarrow 11.51\%$
$z = 1.2 \rightarrow 88.49\%$
88.49% − 11.51% = 76.98%

15. $z = -2 \rightarrow 2.28\%$
$z = -0.5 \rightarrow 30.85\%$
30.85% − 2.28% = 28.57%

16. $z = -2.2 \rightarrow 1.39\%$
$z = -0.3 \rightarrow 38.21\%$
38.21% − 1.39% = 36.82%

17. $z_{142} = \dfrac{\text{data item} - \text{mean}}{\text{standard deviation}} = \dfrac{142 - 121}{15} = 1.4$
A z-score of 1.4 corresponds to a percentile of 91.92. Thus, 91.92% of people have blood pressure below 142

18. $z_{148} = \dfrac{\text{data item} - \text{mean}}{\text{standard deviation}} = \dfrac{148 - 121}{15} = 1.8$
A z-score of 1.8 corresponds to a percentile of 96.41. Thus, 96.41% of people have blood pressure below 148

19. $z_{130} = \dfrac{\text{data item} - \text{mean}}{\text{standard deviation}} = \dfrac{130 - 121}{15} = 0.6$
A z-score of 0.6 corresponds to a percentile of 72.57. Thus, 100% − 72.97% = 27.43% of people have blood pressure above 130.

20. $z_{133} = \dfrac{\text{data item} - \text{mean}}{\text{standard deviation}} = \dfrac{133 - 121}{15} = 0.8$
A z-score of 0.8 corresponds to a percentile of 78.81. Thus, 100% − 78.81% = 21.19% of people have blood pressure above 133.

21. $z_{103} = \dfrac{\text{data item} - \text{mean}}{\text{standard deviation}} = \dfrac{103 - 121}{15} = -1.2$

A z-score of -1.2 corresponds to a percentile of 11.51. Thus, $100\% - 11.51\% = 88.49\%$ of people have blood pressure above 103.

22. $z_{100} = \dfrac{\text{data item} - \text{mean}}{\text{standard deviation}} = \dfrac{100 - 121}{15} = -1.4$

A z-score of -1.4 corresponds to a percentile of 8.08. Thus, $100\% - 8.08\% = 91.92\%$ of people have blood pressure above 100.

23. $z_{142} = \dfrac{\text{data item} - \text{mean}}{\text{standard deviation}} = \dfrac{142 - 121}{15} = 1.4$

A z-score of 1.4 corresponds to a percentile of 91.92.

$z_{154} = \dfrac{\text{data item} - \text{mean}}{\text{standard deviation}} = \dfrac{154 - 121}{15} = 2.2$

A z-score of 2.2 corresponds to a percentile of 98.61. Thus, $98.61\% - 91.92\% = 6.69\%$ of people have blood pressure between 142 and 154.

24. $z_{145} = \dfrac{\text{data item} - \text{mean}}{\text{standard deviation}} = \dfrac{145 - 121}{15} = 1.6$

A z-score of 1.6 corresponds to a percentile of 94.52.

$z_{157} = \dfrac{\text{data item} - \text{mean}}{\text{standard deviation}} = \dfrac{157 - 121}{15} = 2.4$

A z-score of 2.4 corresponds to a percentile of 99.18. Thus, $99.18\% - 94.52\% = 4.66\%$ of people have blood pressure between 145 and 157.

25. $z_{112} = \dfrac{\text{data item} - \text{mean}}{\text{standard deviation}} = \dfrac{112 - 121}{15} = -0.6$

A z-score of -0.6 corresponds to a percentile of 27.43.

$z_{130} = \dfrac{\text{data item} - \text{mean}}{\text{standard deviation}} = \dfrac{130 - 121}{15} = 0.6$

A z-score of 0.6 corresponds to a percentile of 72.57. Thus, $72.57\% - 27.43\% = 45.14\%$ of people have blood pressure between 112 and 130.

26. $z_{109} = \dfrac{\text{data item} - \text{mean}}{\text{standard deviation}} = \dfrac{109 - 121}{15} = -0.8$

A z-score of -0.8 corresponds to a percentile of 21.19.

$z_{133} = \dfrac{\text{data item} - \text{mean}}{\text{standard deviation}} = \dfrac{133 - 121}{15} = 0.8$

A z-score of 0.8 corresponds to a percentile of 78.81. Thus, $78.81\% - 21.19\% = 57.62\%$ of people have blood pressure between 109 and 133.

27. $z_{25.8} = \dfrac{25.8 - 22.5}{2.2} = 1.5$

$z = 1.5 \rightarrow 93.32\%$
$100\% - 93.32\% = 6.68\%$ weigh more than 25.8 pounds.

28. $z_{23.6} = \dfrac{23.6 - 22.5}{2.2} = 0.5$

$z = 0.5 \rightarrow 69.15\%$
$100\% - 69.15\% = 30.85\%$ weigh more than 23.6 pounds.

29. $z_{19.2} = \dfrac{19.2 - 22.5}{2.2} = -1.5$

$z = -1.5 \rightarrow 6.68\%$

$z_{21.4} = \dfrac{21.4 - 22.5}{2.2} = -0.5$

$z = -0.5 \rightarrow 30.85\%$
$30.85\% - 6.68\% = 24.17\%$ weigh between 19.2 and 21.4 pounds.

30. $z_{18.1} = \dfrac{18.1 - 22.5}{2.2} = -2$

$z = -2 \rightarrow 2.28\%$

$z_{19.2} = \dfrac{19.2 - 22.5}{2.2} = -1.5$

$z = -1.5 \rightarrow 6.68\%$
$6.68\% - 2.28\% = 4.4\%$ weigh between 18.1 and 19.2 pounds.

31. The 77th percentile means that 77% of U.S. drivers are younger than 55.

32. The 60th percentile means that 60% of U.S. drivers are younger than 45.

33. The 14th percentile means that 14% of U.S. drivers are younger than 25. So $100\% - 14\% = 86\%$ which are at least 25.

34. The 37th percentile means that 37% of U.S. drivers are younger than 35. So $100\% - 37\% = 63\%$ which are at least 35.

35. 88% are younger than 65 and 98% are younger than 75. So $98\% - 88\% = 10\%$ which are at least 65 and younger than 75.

36. 5% are younger than 20 and 88% are younger than 65. So $88\% - 5\% = 83\%$ which are at least 20 and younger than 65.

39. does not make sense; Explanations will vary. Sample explanation: Percentiles are always positive.

40. makes sense

41. makes sense

42. makes sense

44. $\dfrac{1}{400} = 0.0025 = 0.25\%$

A z-score of -2.8 has 0.26% of the data items below it. So find the height corresponding to $z = -2.8$.
$69 - 2.8(2.5) = 62$ inches
The woman is 62 inches tall.

45. A z-score of 1.3 has 90.32% of the data items below it, and 9.68% above it. So find the score corresponding to $z = 1.3$.
$500 + 1.3(100) = 630$
The cutoff score is 630.

Check Points 12.6

1. 0.51 would indicate a moderate correlation between the two.

2.

x	y	xy	x^2	y^2
8	2.2	17.6	64	4.84
15	2.3	34.5	225	5.29
18	3.8	68.4	324	14.44
31	2.8	86.8	961	7.84
31	3.5	108.5	961	12.25
32	2.7	86.4	1024	7.29
32	5.0	160	1024	25
44	6.5	286	1936	42.25
58	4.5	261	3364	20.25
90	11.0	990	8100	121

$\sum x = 359 \quad \sum y = 44.3 \quad \sum xy = 2099.2 \quad \sum x^2 = 17{,}983 \quad \sum y^2 = 260.45$

$\left(\sum x\right)^2 = (359)^2 = 128{,}881$ and $\left(\sum y\right)^2 = (44.3)^2 = 1962.49$

$r = \dfrac{10(2099.2) - (359)(44.3)}{\sqrt{10(17{,}983) - 128{,}881}\sqrt{10(260.45) - 1962.49}} = \dfrac{5088.3}{\sqrt{50949}\sqrt{642.01}} \approx 0.89$

This value for r is fairly close to 1 and indicates a moderately strong positive correlation. This means the higher the rate of firearm ownership, the higher the rate of deaths.

3. $m = \dfrac{10(2099.2) - (359)(44.3)}{10(17{,}983) - 128{,}881} = \dfrac{5088.3}{50949} \approx 0.1$

$b = \dfrac{44.3 - (0.1)(359)}{10} = \dfrac{8.4}{10} \approx 0.8$

The equation of the regression line is $y = 0.1x + 0.8$.

The predicted rate in a country with 80 firearms per 100 persons can be found by substituting 80 for x.
$y = 0.1x + 0.8$

$= 0.1(80) + 0.8$

$= 8.8$

The death rate would be 8.8 per 100,000 people.

4. Yes, $|r| = 0.89$. Since $0.89 > 0.632$ and 0.765 (using table 12.16), we may conclude that a correlation does exist.

Exercise Set 12.6

1. There appears to be a positive correlation.

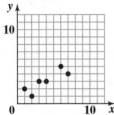

2. There appears to be a positive correlation.

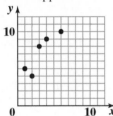

3. There appears to be a negative correlation.

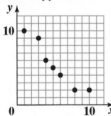

4. There does not appear to be a correlation.

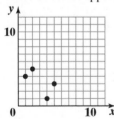

5. There appears to be a positive correlation.

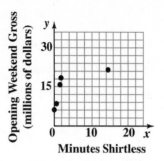

6. There appears to be a negative correlation.

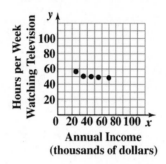

7. There appears to be a positive correlation.

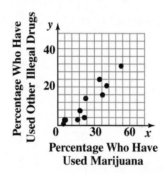

8. There appears to be a negative correlation.

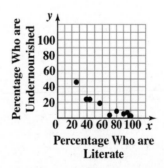

9. False; the correlation is negative.

10. False; there is a negative correlation.

11. True

12. False; correlation does not indicate causality.

13. True

14. False; there are 5 births per woman in Vietnam.

15. False; see for example, Syria and Vietnam.

16. False; Kenya has the greatest number of births per woman, but it does not have the smallest percentage of women using contraceptives.

17. True

18. False; Each of the over 75 points represent a country.

19. False; Generally speaking, as per capita income rises, the percentage of people who call themselves "happy" rises.

20. False; Several countries with low per capital income report relatively high levels of "happiness".

21. True

22. True

23. False; The lowest the lowest level was reported by the Ukraine, yet several countries have lower per capita income (points to the left).

24. False; The highest per capita income is in the U.S., yet several countries have higher percentages of people calling themselves "happy" (points above).

25. False; The correlation is positive, but not that strong..

26. False; The correlation is positive.

27. a

28. b

29. d

30. e

31.

x	y	xy	x^2	y^2
1	2	2	1	4
6	5	30	36	25
4	3	12	16	9
3	3	9	9	9
7	4	28	49	16
2	1	2	4	1

$$\sum x = 23 \quad \sum y = 18 \quad \sum xy = 83 \quad \sum x^2 = 115 \quad \sum y^2 = 64$$

$$\left(\sum x\right)^2 = (23)^2 = 529 \text{ and } \left(\sum y\right)^2 = (18)^2 = 324$$

$$r = \frac{6(83) - (23)(18)}{\sqrt{6(115) - 529}\sqrt{6(64) - (324)}}$$

$$= \frac{84}{\sqrt{161}\sqrt{60}}$$

$$\approx 0.85$$

32.

x	y	xy	x^2	y^2
2	4	8	4	16
1	5	5	1	25
6	10	60	36	100
3	8	24	9	64
4	9	36	16	81

$\sum x = 16$ $\sum y = 36$ $\sum xy = 133$ $\sum x^2 = 66$ $\sum y^2 = 286$

$\left(\sum x\right)^2 = (16)^2 = 256$ and $\left(\sum y\right)^2 = (36)^2 = 1296$

$r = \dfrac{5(133) - (16)(36)}{\sqrt{5(66) - 256}\sqrt{5(286) - 1296}}$

$= \dfrac{89}{\sqrt{74}\sqrt{134}}$

≈ 0.89

33.

x	y	xy	x^2	y^2
8	2	16	64	4
6	4	24	36	16
1	10	10	1	100
5	5	25	25	25
4	6	24	16	36
10	2	20	100	4
3	9	27	9	81

$\sum x = 37$ $\sum y = 38$ $\sum xy = 146$ $\sum x^2 = 251$ $\sum y^2 = 266$

$\left(\sum x\right)^2 = (37)^2 = 1369$ and $\left(\sum y\right)^2 = (38)^2 = 1444$

$r = \dfrac{7(146) - (37)(38)}{\sqrt{7(251) - 1369}\sqrt{7(266) - 1444}}$

$= \dfrac{-384}{\sqrt{388}\sqrt{418}}$

≈ -0.95

34.

x	y	xy	x^2	y^2
4	1	4	16	1
5	3	15	25	9
2	5	10	4	25
1	4	4	1	16

$\sum x = 12$ $\sum y = 13$ $\sum xy = 33$ $\sum x^2 = 46$ $\sum y^2 = 51$

$\left(\sum x\right)^2 = (12)^2 = 144$ and $\left(\sum y\right)^2 = (13)^2 = 169$

$r = \dfrac{4(33) - (12)(13)}{\sqrt{4(46) - 144}\sqrt{4(51) - 169}}$

$= \dfrac{-24}{\sqrt{40}\sqrt{35}}$

≈ -0.64

35. a.

x	y	xy	x²	y²
0	6.1	0	0	37.21
0.8	8.3	6.64	0.64	68.89
1.6	15.6	24.96	2.56	243.36
1.8	18.1	32.58	3.24	327.61
14.6	21.6	315.36	213.16	466.56

$\sum x = 18.8$ $\sum y = 69.7$ $\sum xy = 379.54$ $\sum x^2 = 219.6$ $\sum y^2 = 1143.63$

$\left(\sum x\right)^2 = (18.8)^2 = 353.44$ and $\left(\sum y\right)^2 = (69.7)^2 = 4858.09$

$r = \dfrac{5(379.54) - (18.8)(69.7)}{\sqrt{5(219.6) - 353.44}\sqrt{5(1143.63) - 4858.09}}$

$= \dfrac{587.34}{\sqrt{744.56}\sqrt{860.06}}$

≈ 0.73

b. $m = \dfrac{5(379.54) - (18.8)(69.7)}{5(219.6) - 353.44} = \dfrac{587.34}{744.56} \approx 0.79$

$b = \dfrac{69.7 - 0.79(18.8)}{5} = \dfrac{-174.95}{5} \approx 10.97$

$y = mx + b$

$y = 0.79x + 10.97$

c. $y = 0.79x + 10.97$

$y = 0.79(20) + 10.97$

$= 26.77$

≈ 26.8

We can anticipate that a McConaughey film in which he appears shirtless for 20 minutes will gross $26.8 million in the film's opening weekend.

36. a.

x	y	xy	x²	y²
25	56.3	1407.5	625	3169.69
35	51.0	1785.0	1225	2601.00
45	50.5	2272.5	2025	2550.25
55	49.7	2733.5	3025	2470.09
70	48.7	3409.0	4900	2371.69

$\sum x = 230$ $\sum y = 256.2$ $\sum xy = 11607.5$ $\sum x^2 = 11800$ $\sum y^2 = 13,162.72$

$\left(\sum x\right)^2 = (230)^2 = 52,900$ and $\left(\sum y\right)^2 = (256.2)^2 = 65,638.44$

$r = \dfrac{5(11,607.5) - (230)(256.2)}{\sqrt{5(11,800) - 52,900}\sqrt{5(13,162.72) - 65,638.44}}$

$= \dfrac{-888.5}{\sqrt{6100}\sqrt{175.16}}$

≈ -0.86

b. $m = \dfrac{5(11,607.5)-(230)(256.2)}{5(11,800)-52,900} = \dfrac{-888.5}{6100} \approx -0.15$

$b = \dfrac{256.2-(-0.1457)(230)}{5} = \dfrac{289.711}{5} \approx 57.94$

$y = mx + b$

$y = -0.15x + 57.94$

c. $y = -0.15x + 57.94$

$y = -0.15(100) + 57.94$

$= 42.94$

≈ 42.9

We can anticipate that a person earning $100 thousand per year will watch 42.9 hours of television per week.

37. a.

x	y	xy	x^2	y^2
22	4	88	484	16
17	3	51	289	9
40	21	840	1600	441
5	1	5	25	1
37	16	592	1369	256
19	8	152	361	64
23	14	322	529	196
6	3	18	36	9
7	3	21	49	9
53	31	1643	2809	961
34	24	816	1156	576

$\sum x = 263 \qquad \sum y = 128 \qquad \sum xy = 4548 \qquad \sum x^2 = 8707 \qquad \sum y^2 = 2538$

$\left(\sum x\right)^2 = (263)^2 = 69,169$ and $\left(\sum y\right)^2 = (128)^2 = 16,384$

$r = \dfrac{11(4548)-(263)(128)}{\sqrt{11(8707)-69,169}\sqrt{11(2538)-16,384}}$

$= \dfrac{16,364}{\sqrt{26,608}\sqrt{11,534}}$

≈ 0.93

b. $m = \dfrac{11(4548)-(263)(128)}{11(8707)-69,169} = \dfrac{16,364}{26,608} \approx 0.62$

$b = \dfrac{128-0.6150(263)}{11} = \dfrac{-33.745}{11} \approx -3.07$

$y = mx + b$

$y = 0.62x - 3.07$

c. $y = 0.62x - 3.07$

$y = 0.62(10) - 3.07$

$= 3.13$

≈ 3

We can anticipate that a country where 10% of teenagers have used marijuana will have 3% of teenagers using other illegal drugs.

38. a.

x	y	xy	x^2	y^2
100	2	200	10000	4
71	4	284	5041	16
36	46	1656	1296	2116
96	7	672	9216	49
98	2	196	9604	4
80	9	720	6400	81
91	6	546	8281	36
50	24	1200	2500	576
99	3	297	9801	9
53	24	1272	2809	576
67	19	1273	4489	361

$$\sum x = 841 \quad \sum y = 146 \quad \sum xy = 8316 \quad \sum x^2 = 69,437 \quad \sum y^2 = 3828$$

$$\left(\sum x\right)^2 = (841)^2 = 707,281 \text{ and } \left(\sum y\right)^2 = (146)^2 = 21,316$$

$$r = \frac{11(8316) - (841)(146)}{\sqrt{11(69,437) - 707,281}\sqrt{11(3828) - 21,316}}$$

$$= \frac{-31,310}{\sqrt{56,526}\sqrt{20,792}}$$

$$\approx -0.91$$

b. $m = \dfrac{11(8316) - (841)(146)}{11(69,437) - 707,281} = \dfrac{-31,310}{56,526} \approx -0.55$

$b = \dfrac{146 - (-0.5539)(841)}{11} = \dfrac{611.8299}{11} \approx 55.62$

$y = mx + b$

$y = -0.55x + 55.62$

c. $y = -0.55x + 55.62$

$y = -0.55(60) + 55.62$

$= 22.62$

≈ 23

We can anticipate that a country where 60% of people are literate will have 23% of people undernourished.

39. $|r| = 0.5$

Since $0.5 > 0.444$, conclude that a correlation does exist.

40. $|r| = 0.4$

Since $0.4 > 0.381$, conclude that a correlation does exist.

41. $|r| = 0.5$

Since $0.5 < 0.576$, conclude that a correlation does not exist.

42. $|r| = 0.04$

Since $0.04 < 0.423$, conclude that a correlation does not exist.

43. $|r| = 0.351$

Since $0.351 > 0.232$, conclude that a correlation does exist.

44. $|r| = 0.37$

Since $0.37 > 0.325$, conclude that a correlation does exist.

45. $|r| = 0.37$

Since $0.37 < 0.444$, conclude that a correlation does not exist.

46. $|r| = 0.73$

Since $0.73 > 0.602$, conclude that a correlation does exist.

58. does not make sense; Explanations will vary. Sample explanation: The use of other drugs might lead to people using marijuana.

59. does not make sense; Explanations will vary. Sample explanation: Increasing literacy does not necessarily decrease undernourishment.

60. does not make sense; Explanations will vary. Sample explanation: The correlation coefficient and the slope of the regression line must have the same signs.

61. does not make sense; Explanations will vary. Sample explanation: The correlation would be higher for identical twins reared together.

Chapter 12 Review Exercises

1. a

2.

Time Spent on Homework (in hours)	Number of students
6	1
7	3
8	3
9	2
10	1
	10

3.

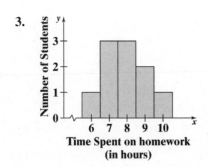

4.

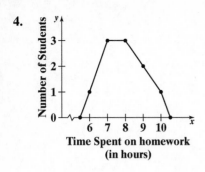

5.

Grades	Number of students
0–39	19
40–49	8
50–59	6
60–69	6
70–79	5
80–89	3
90–100	3
	50

6.

Stems	Leaves
1	3 4 1 3 7 8
2	4 9 6 9 2 7
3	4 9 6 5 1 1 1
4	4 0 2 7 9 1 2 5
5	7 9 6 4 0 1
6	3 3 7 0 8 9
7	2 3 4 0 5
8	7 1 6
9	5 1 0

7. The sizes of the barrels are not scaled proportionally in terms of the data they represent.

8. Mean $= \dfrac{84+90+95+89+98}{5}$

$\qquad = \dfrac{456}{5}$

$\qquad = 91.2$

9. Mean $= \dfrac{33+27+9+10+6+7+11+23+27}{9}$

$\qquad = \dfrac{153}{9}$

$\qquad = 17$

10. Mean $= \dfrac{1\cdot 2 + 2\cdot 4 + 3\cdot 3 + 4\cdot 1}{10}$

$= \dfrac{2+8+9+4}{10}$

$= \dfrac{23}{10}$

$= 2.3$

11. First arrange the data items from smallest to largest.
6, 7, 9, 10, 11, 23, 27, 27, 33
There is an odd number of data items, so the median is the middle number. The median is 11.

12. First arrange the data items from smallest to largest.
16, 22, 28, 28, 34
There is an odd number of data items, so the median is the middle number. The median is 28.

13. The median is the value in the $\dfrac{n+1}{2} = \dfrac{10+1}{2} = \dfrac{11}{2} = 5.5$ position, which means the median is the mean of the 5th and 6th values. The 5th and 6th values are both 2, therefore the median is 2.

14. The number 27 occurs most frequently, so the mode is 27.

15. Bimodal; 585 and 587 each occur twice.

16. The number 2 occurs most frequently, so the mode is 2.

17. lowest data value = 84, highest data value = 98
Midrange $= \dfrac{84+98}{2} = \dfrac{182}{2} = 91$

18. lowest data value = 6, highest data value = 33
Midrange $= \dfrac{6+33}{2} = \dfrac{39}{2} = 19.5$

19. lowest data value = 1, highest data value = 4
Midrange $= \dfrac{1+4}{2} = \dfrac{5}{2} = 2.5$

21. a.

Age at first inauguration	Number of Presidents
42	1
43	1
44	0
45	0
46	2
47	2
48	1
49	2
50	1
51	5
52	2
53	0
54	5
55	4
56	3
57	4
58	1
59	0
60	1
61	3
62	1
63	0
64	2
65	1
66	0
67	0
68	1
69	1
	44

b.

$$\text{Mean} = \frac{\left(\begin{array}{l}42\cdot1+43\cdot1+46\cdot2+47\cdot2+48\cdot1+49\cdot2+50\cdot1+51\cdot5+52\cdot2+54\cdot5+55\cdot4\\ +56\cdot3+57\cdot4+58\cdot1+60\cdot1+61\cdot3+62\cdot1+64\cdot2+65\cdot1+68\cdot1+69\cdot1\end{array}\right)}{44} = \frac{2405}{44} \approx 54.66 \text{ years}$$

The median is the value in the $\dfrac{n+1}{2} = \dfrac{44+1}{2} = \dfrac{45}{2} = 22.5$ position, which means the median is the mean of the data in positions 22 and 23.

$$\text{Median} = \frac{54+55}{2} = 54.5 \text{ years}$$

The model ages are 51 and 54 years (bimodal).

$$\text{Midrange} = \frac{42+69}{2} = 55.5 \text{ years}$$

22. Range = $34 - 16 = 18$

23. Range = $783 - 219 = 564$

24. a.

Data item	Deviation: Data item – mean
29	$29 - 35 = -6$
9	$9 - 35 = -26$
8	$8 - 35 = -27$
22	$22 - 35 = -13$
46	$46 - 35 = 11$
51	$51 - 35 = 16$
48	$48 - 35 = 13$
42	$42 - 35 = 7$
53	$53 - 35 = 18$
42	$42 - 35 = 7$

b. $-6 - 26 - 27 - 13 + 11 + 16 + 13 + 7 + 18 + 7 = 0$

25. a. $\text{Mean} = \dfrac{36 + 26 + 24 + 90 + 74}{5} = \dfrac{250}{5} = 50$

b.

Data item	Deviation: Data item – mean
36	$36 - 50 = -14$
26	$26 - 50 = -24$
24	$24 - 50 = -26$
90	$90 - 50 = 40$
74	$74 - 50 = 24$

c. $-14 - 24 - 26 + 40 + 24 = 0$

26. $\text{Mean} = \dfrac{3 + 3 + 5 + 8 + 10 + 13}{6} = \dfrac{42}{6} = 7$

Data item	Deviation: Data item – mean	$(\text{Deviation})^2$: $(\text{Data item–mean})^2$
3	$3 - 7 = -4$	$(-4)^2 = 16$
3	$3 - 7 = -4$	$(-4)^2 = 16$
5	$5 - 7 = -2$	$(-2)^2 = 4$
8	$8 - 7 = 1$	$1^2 = 1$
10	$10 - 7 = 3$	$3^2 = 9$
13	$13 - 7 = 6$	$6^2 = 36$

$$\sum (\text{data item–mean})^2 = 82$$

$$\text{Standard deviation} = \sqrt{\dfrac{82}{6-1}} = \sqrt{\dfrac{82}{5}} \approx 4.05$$

27. Mean $= \dfrac{20 + 27 + 23 + 26 + 28 + 32 + 33 + 35}{8} = \dfrac{224}{8} = 28$

Data item	Deviation: Data item − mean	(Deviation)^2: (Data item−mean)^2
20	$20 - 28 = -8$	$(-8)^2 = 64$
27	$27 - 28 = -1$	$(-1)^2 = 1$
23	$23 - 28 = -5$	$(-5)^2 = 25$
26	$26 - 28 = -2$	$(-2)^2 = 4$
28	$28 - 28 = 0$	$0^2 = 0$
32	$32 - 28 = 4$	$4^2 = 16$
33	$33 - 28 = 5$	$5^2 = 25$
35	$35 - 28 = 7$	$7^2 = 49$

$$\sum (\text{data item−mean})^2 = 184$$

Standard deviation $= \sqrt{\dfrac{184}{8-1}} = \sqrt{\dfrac{184}{7}} \approx 5.13$

28. Mean $= \dfrac{10 + 30 + 37 + 40 + 43 + 44 + 45 + 69 + 86 + 86}{10} = \dfrac{490}{10} = 49$

Range $= 86 - 10 = 76$

Data item	Deviation: Data item − mean	(Deviation)^2: (Data item−mean)^2
10	$10 - 49 = -39$	$(-39)^2 = 1521$
30	$30 - 49 = -19$	$(-19)^2 = 361$
37	$37 - 49 = -12$	$(-12)^2 = 144$
40	$40 - 49 = -9$	$(-9)^2 = 81$
43	$43 - 49 = -6$	$(-6)^2 = 36$
44	$44 - 49 = -5$	$(-5)^2 = 25$
45	$45 - 49 = -4$	$(-4)^2 = 16$
69	$69 - 49 = 20$	$20^2 = 400$
86	$86 - 49 = 37$	$37^2 = 1369$
86	$86 - 49 = 37$	$37^2 = 1369$

$$\sum (\text{data item−mean})^2 = 5322$$

Standard deviation $= \sqrt{\dfrac{5322}{10-1}} = \sqrt{\dfrac{5322}{9}} \approx 24.32$

29. Set A:

$$\text{Mean} = \frac{80+80+80+80}{4} = \frac{320}{4} = 80$$

Data item	Deviation: Data item – mean	(Deviation)^2 : (Data item–mean)^2
80	$80 - 80 = 0$	$0^2 = 0$
80	$80 - 80 = 0$	$0^2 = 0$
80	$80 - 80 = 0$	$0^2 = 0$
80	$80 - 80 = 0$	$0^2 = 0$

$$\sum(\text{data item–mean})^2 = 0$$

$$\text{Standard deviation} = \sqrt{\frac{0}{4-1}} = \sqrt{\frac{0}{3}} = 0$$

Set B:

$$\text{Mean} = \frac{70+70+90+90}{4} = \frac{320}{4} = 80$$

Data item	Deviation: Data item – mean	(Deviation)^2 : (Data item–mean)^2
70	$70 - 80 = -10$	$(-10)^2 = 100$
70	$70 - 80 = -10$	$(-10)^2 = 100$
90	$90 - 80 = 10$	$10^2 = 100$
90	$90 - 80 = 10$	$10^2 = 100$

$$\sum(\text{data item–mean})^2 = 400$$

$$\text{Standard deviation} = \sqrt{\frac{400}{4-1}} = \sqrt{\frac{400}{3}} \approx 11.55$$

Written descriptions of the similarities and differences between the two sets of data will vary.

30. Answers will vary.

31. $70 + 2 \cdot 8 = 70 + 16 = 86$

32. $70 + 3.5(8) = 70 + 28 = 98$

33. $70 - 1.25(8) = 70 - 10 = 60$

34. 64 is one standard deviation below the mean and 72 is one standard deviation above the mean, so 68% of the people in the retirement community are between 64 and 72 years old.

35. 60 is two standard deviations below the mean and 76 is two standard deviations above the mean, so 95% of the people in the retirement community are between 60 and 76 years old.

36. 68 is the mean and 72 is one standard deviation above the mean, so half of 68%, or 34% of the people in the retirement community are between 68 and 72 years old.

37. 56 is three standard deviations below the mean and 80 is three standard deviations above the mean, so 99.7% of the people in the retirement community are between 56 and 80 years old.

38. 72 is one standard deviation above the mean, so 16% of the people in the retirement community are over 72 years old. (Note: 100% – 68% = 32%, half of 32% is 16%).

39. 72 is one standard deviation above the mean, so 84% of the people in the retirement community are under 72 years old. (Note: Question #41 showed that 16% is above 72, 100% – 16% = 84%)

40. 76 is two standard deviations above the mean, so 2.5% of the people in the retirement community are over 76 years old. (Note: 100% – 95% = 5%, half of 5% is 2.5%).

41. $z_{50} = \dfrac{50-50}{5} = \dfrac{0}{5} = 0$

42. $z_{60} = \dfrac{60-50}{5} = \dfrac{10}{5} = 2$

43. $z_{58} = \dfrac{58-50}{5} = \dfrac{8}{5} = 1.6$

44. $z_{35} = \dfrac{35-50}{5} = \dfrac{-15}{5} = -3$

45. $z_{44} = \dfrac{44-50}{5} = \dfrac{-6}{5} = -1.2$

46. vocabulary test: $z_{60} = \dfrac{60-50}{5} = \dfrac{10}{5} = 2$

grammar test: $z_{80} = \dfrac{80-72}{6} = \dfrac{8}{6} \approx 1.3$

The student scored better on the vocabulary test because it has a higher z-score.

47. $1.5(4000) = 6000$
$32{,}000 + 6000 = 38{,}000$ miles

48. $2.25(4000) = 9000$
$32{,}000 + 9000 = 41{,}000$ miles

49. $-2.5(4000) = -10{,}000$
$32{,}000 - 10{,}000 = 22{,}000$ miles

50. a. margin of error $= \pm \dfrac{1}{\sqrt{2281}}$

$\approx \pm 0.021$

$\approx \pm 2.1\%$

b. $31\% - 2.1\% = 28.9\%$
$31\% + 2.1\% = 33.1\%$
We can be 95% confident that between 28.9% and 33.1% of American adults would be willing to sacrifice a percentage of their salary to work for an environmentally friendly company.

51. a. The graph is skewed to the right.

b.

x	f	xf
1	36	$1 \cdot 36 = 36$
2	34	$2 \cdot 34 = 68$
3	18	$3 \cdot 18 = 54$
4	9	$4 \cdot 9 = 36$
5	2	$5 \cdot 2 = 10$
6	1	$6 \cdot 1 = 6$
	100	$\sum xf = 210$

$$\text{Mean} = \frac{\sum xf}{n} = \frac{210}{100} = 2.1 \text{ syllables}$$

The median is the mean of the 50th and 51st positions. Since these data items are both 2, the median is 2 syllables. The mode is 1 syllable.

c. Yes, these measures of central tendency are consistent with the graph. The mean is greater than the median, which is expected with a distribution that is skewed to the right.

52. $z_{221} = \dfrac{221 - 200}{15} = \dfrac{21}{15} = 1.4$

$z = 1.4 \rightarrow 91.92\%$

91.92% have cholesterol less than 221.

53. $z_{173} = \dfrac{173 - 200}{15} = \dfrac{-27}{15} = -1.8$

$z = -1.8 \rightarrow 3.59\%$

$100\% - 3.59\% = 96.41\%$ have cholesterol greater than 173.

54. $z_{173} = \dfrac{173 - 200}{15} = \dfrac{-27}{15} = -1.8$

and $z = -1.8 \rightarrow 3.59\%$

$z_{221} = \dfrac{221 - 200}{15} = \dfrac{21}{15} = 1.4$

and $z = 1.4 \rightarrow 91.92\%$

$91.92\% - 3.59\% = 88.33\%$ have cholesterol between 173 and 221.

55. $z_{164} = \dfrac{164 - 200}{15} = \dfrac{-36}{15} = -2.4$

and $z = -2.4 \rightarrow 0.82\%$

$z_{182} = \dfrac{182 - 200}{15} = \dfrac{-18}{15} = -1.2$

and $z = -1.2 \rightarrow 11.51\%$

$11.51\% - 0.82\% = 10.69\%$ have cholesterol between 164 and 182.

56. 75%

57. $100\% - 86\% = 14\%$

58. $86\% - 75\% = 11\%$

59. There appears to be a positive correlation.

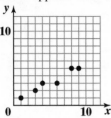

60. There appears to be a negative correlation.

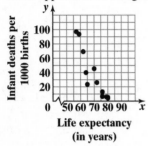

61. False; the correlation is only moderate.

62. True

63. False

64. False; data points that are vertically aligned dispute this statement.

65. True

66. False; there is a moderate negative correlation.

67. True

68. c

69. a.

x	y	xy	x^2	y^2
1	1	1	1	1
3	2	6	9	4
4	3	12	16	9
6	3	18	36	9
8	5	40	64	25
9	5	45	81	25

$$\sum x = 31 \qquad \sum y = 19 \qquad \sum xy = 122 \qquad \sum x^2 = 207 \qquad \sum y^2 = 73$$

$$\left(\sum x\right)^2 = (31)^2 = 961 \text{ and } \left(\sum y\right)^2 = (19)^2 = 361$$

$$r = \frac{6(122) - (31)(19)}{\sqrt{6(207) - 961}\sqrt{6(73) - 361}} = \frac{143}{\sqrt{281}\sqrt{77}} \approx 0.972$$

b. $m = \dfrac{6(122) - (31)(19)}{6(207) - 961} = \dfrac{143}{281} \approx 0.509$

   $b = \dfrac{19 - (0.509)(31)}{6} = \dfrac{3.221}{6} \approx 0.537$

   $y = 0.509x + 0.537$

70. a.

x	y	xy	x^2	y^2
22	26	1	1	1
32	32	6	9	4
42	34	12	16	9
52	39	18	36	9
62	44	45	81	25

$\sum x = 210 \qquad \sum y = 175 \qquad \sum xy = 7780 \qquad \sum x^2 = 9820 \qquad \sum y^2 = 6313$

$\left(\sum x\right)^2 = (210)^2 = 44{,}100$ and $\left(\sum y\right)^2 = (175)^2 = 30{,}625$

$r = \dfrac{5(7780) - (210)(175)}{\sqrt{5(9820) - 44{,}100}\,\sqrt{5(6313) - 30{,}625}} = \dfrac{2150}{\sqrt{5000}\,\sqrt{940}} \approx 0.99$

   b.   There is a correlation.

Chapter 12 Test

1. d

2.

Score	Frequency
3	1
4	2
5	3
6	2
7	2
8	3
9	2
10	1
	16

3.

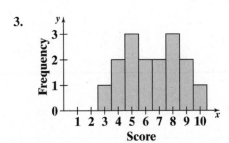

4.

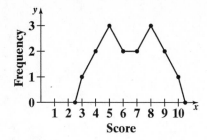

5.

Class	Frequency
40–49	3
50–59	6
60–69	6
70–79	7
80–89	6
90–99	2
	30

6.

Stems	Leaves
4	1 8 6
5	9 1 0 5 0 0
6	2 3 7 0 1 1
7	9 3 1 5 8 9 1
8	8 9 9 1 3 0
9	0 3

7. The roofline gives the impression that the percentage of home schooled students grew at the same rate each year between the years shown. This may be misleading if the growth rate was not constant from year to year.

8. $\text{Mean} = \dfrac{3+6+2+1+7+3}{6} = \dfrac{22}{6} \approx 3.67$

9. First arrange the numbers from smallest to largest.
1, 2, 3, 3, 6, 7
There is an even number of data items, so the median is the mean of the middle two data values.
$\text{Median} = \dfrac{3+3}{2} = \dfrac{6}{2} = 3$

10. lowest data value = 1
highest data value = 7
$\text{Midrange} = \dfrac{1+7}{2} = \dfrac{8}{2} = 4$

11.

Data item	Deviation: Data item – mean	(Deviation)^2: (Data item–mean)^2
3	$3 - 3.7 = -0.7$	$(-0.7)^2 = 0.49$
6	$6 - 3.7 = 2.3$	$(2.3)^2 = 5.29$
2	$2 - 3.7 = -1.7$	$(-1.7)^2 = 2.89$
1	$1 - 3.7 = -2.7$	$(-2.7)^2 = 7.29$
7	$7 - 3.7 = 3.3$	$(3.3)^2 = 10.89$
3	$3 - 3.7 = -0.7$	$(-0.7)^2 = 0.49$

$$\sum (\text{data item–mean})^2 = 27.34$$

$$\text{Standard deviation} = \sqrt{\frac{27.34}{6-1}} = \sqrt{\frac{27.34}{5}} \approx 2.34$$

12. $\text{Mean} = \dfrac{1\cdot 3 + 2\cdot 5 + 3\cdot 2 + 4\cdot 2}{12}$

$\qquad\quad = \dfrac{3 + 10 + 6 + 8}{12}$

$\qquad\quad = \dfrac{27}{12}$

$\qquad\quad = 2.25$

13. The median is in the $\dfrac{n+1}{2} = \dfrac{12+1}{2} = \dfrac{13}{2} = 6.5$ position, which means the median is the mean of the values in the 6th and 7th positions.

$\text{Median} = \dfrac{2+2}{2} = \dfrac{4}{2} = 2$

14. Mode = 2

15. Answers will vary.

16. $7 + 1(5.3) = 12.3$

68% of the data values are within 1 standard deviation of the mean. Because of symmetry, $\dfrac{1}{2}(68\%) = 34\%$ of college freshmen study between 7 and 12.3 hours per week.

17. $7 + 2(5.3) = 17.6$

95% of the data values are within 2 standard deviations of the mean. $100\% - 95\% = 5\%$ of the values are farther than 2 standard deviations from the mean. Because of symmetry, $\dfrac{1}{2}(5\%) = 2.5\%$ of college freshmen study more than 17.6 hours per week.

18. student: $z_{120} = \dfrac{120 - 100}{10} = \dfrac{20}{10} = 2$

professor: $z_{128} = \dfrac{128 - 100}{15} = \dfrac{28}{15} \approx 1.9$

The student scored better, because the student's z-score is higher.

19. $z_{88} = \dfrac{88-74}{10} = \dfrac{14}{10} = 1.4$

$z = 1.4 \rightarrow 91.92\%$

$100\% - 91.92\% = 8.08\%$ of the scores are above 88.

20. $49\% - 8\% = 41\%$

21. a. margin of error $= \pm \dfrac{1}{\sqrt{n}}$

$= \pm \dfrac{1}{\sqrt{100}}$

$= \pm 0.1$

$= \pm 10\%$

b. We can be 95% confident that between 50% and 70% of all students are very satisfied with their professors.

22. There appears to be a strong negative correlation.

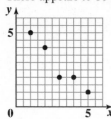

23. False; Though the data shows that there is a <u>correlation</u>, it does not prove <u>causation</u>.

24. False

25. True

26. Answers will vary.

Chapter 13
Mathematical Systems

Check Points 13.1

1. $O + O = E$. This means that the sum of two odd numbers is an even number.

2. No, the set is not closed under addition. Example: $2 + 2 = 4$; 4 is not an element of the set.

3. Yes, the natural numbers are closed under multiplication.

4. No, the natural numbers are not closed under division. Example: 2 divided by 3 is not a natural number.

5. We must show that $(1 \oplus 3) \oplus 2 = 1 \oplus (3 \oplus 2)$.
$$(1 \oplus 3) \oplus 2 = 1 \oplus (3 \oplus 2)$$
$$0 \oplus 2 = 1 \oplus 1$$
$$2 = 2$$

6. The identity element is g, because it does not change anything.

7. The inverse is –12. (because $12 + (-12) = 0$)

8. The inverse is $\dfrac{1}{12}$. (because $12 \cdot \dfrac{1}{12} = 1$)

9. **a.** The identity element is k, because it does not change anything.

   b. The inverse of j is l because $j \circ l = k$
   The inverse of k is k because $k \circ k = k$
   The inverse of l is j because $l \circ j = k$
   The inverse of m is m because $m \circ m = k$

Exercise Set 13.1

1. $\{e, a, b, c\}$

2. The binary operation is $\circ$.

3. $a \circ b = c$

4. $c \circ a = b$

5. $b \circ c = a$

6. $c \circ b = a$

7. $e \circ e = e$

8. $e \circ a = a$

9. $b \circ e = b$

10. $c \circ e = c$

11. $a \circ a = e$

12. $(b \circ b) \circ c = e \circ c = c$

13. $(c \circ c) \circ a = e \circ a = a$

14. Yes. The answer to any possible combination of two elements of the set is an element that is in the set.

15. No. For example, $4 + 1 = 5$, and 5 is not in the set.

16. No. For example, $5 + 1 = 6$, and 6 is not in the set.

17. Yes. The answer to any possible combination of two elements of the set is an element that is in the set.

18. Yes. The answer to any possible combination of two elements of the set is an element that is in the set.

19. No. For example, $1 - 2 = -1$, and -1 is not in the set.

20. No. For example, $1 \div 2 = \dfrac{1}{2}$, and $\dfrac{1}{2}$ is not in the set.

21. No, the system is not closed under $*$. $b * a = c$, and c is not in the set.

22. No, the system is not closed under $*$. $d * f = g$, and g is not in the set.

23. $2 \oplus 4 = 1$
$4 \oplus 2 = 1$
So $2 \oplus 4 = 4 \oplus 2$

24. $3 \oplus 4 = 2$
$4 \oplus 3 = 2$
So $3 \oplus 4 = 4 \oplus 3$

25. $4 \oplus 1 = 0$
$1 \oplus 4 = 0$
So $4 \oplus 1 = 1 \oplus 4$

26. $2 \oplus 3 = 0$

$3 \oplus 2 = 0$

So $2 \oplus 3 = 3 \oplus 2$

27. The Commutative Property; since table entries are mirror images of each other across the main diagonal, $\oplus$ is commutative.

28. $(3 \oplus 2) \oplus 4 = 0 \oplus 4 = 4$

$3 \oplus (2 \oplus 4) = 3 \oplus 1 = 4$

$(3 \oplus 2) \oplus 4 = 3 \oplus (2 \oplus 4)$

29. $(4 \oplus 3) \oplus 2 = 2 \oplus 2 = 4$

$4 \oplus (3 \oplus 2) = 4 \oplus 0 = 4$

$(4 \oplus 3) \oplus 2 = 4 \oplus (3 \oplus 2)$

30. $(2 \oplus 2) \oplus 3 = 4 \oplus 3 = 2$

$2 \oplus (2 \oplus 3) = 2 \oplus 0 = 2$

$(2 \oplus 2) \oplus 3 = 2 \oplus (2 \oplus 3)$

31. $(4 \oplus 4) \oplus 2 = 3 \oplus 2 = 0$

$4 \oplus (4 \oplus 2) = 4 \oplus 1 = 0$

$(4 \oplus 4) \oplus 2 = 4 \oplus (4 \oplus 2)$

32. The Associative Property

33. a. $(b \circ c) \circ b = c \circ b = b$

b. $b \circ (c \circ b) = b \circ b = a$

c. No. $(b \circ c) \circ b \neq b \circ (c \circ b)$

When the grouping changed, the answer changed.

34. a. $(b \circ b) \circ c = b \circ c = a$

b. $b \circ (b \circ c) = b \circ a = b$

c. No. $(b \circ b) \circ c \neq b \circ (b \circ c)$

When the grouping changed, the answer changed.

35. Answers will vary. Sample answer:

$(5 - 2) - 1 = 3 - 1 = 2$ but $5 - (2 - 1) = 5 - 1 = 4$

36. Answers will vary. Sample answer:

$(16 \div 4) \div 2 = 4 \div 2 = 2$ but

$16 \div (4 \div 2) = 16 \div 2 = 8$

37. $29 + (-29) = 0$

-29 is the inverse of 29 under the operation of addition.

38. $43 + (-43) = 0$

-43 is the inverse of 43 under the operation of addition.

39. $29 \cdot \dfrac{1}{29} = 1$

$\dfrac{1}{29}$ is the inverse of 29 under the operation of multiplication.

40. $43 \cdot \dfrac{1}{43} = 1$

$\dfrac{1}{43}$ is the inverse of 43 under the operation of multiplication.

41. $a \circ a = a$

42. $a \circ b = b$

43. $a \circ c = c$

44. $a \circ d = d$

45. $a \circ e = e$

46. $b \circ a = b$

47. $c \circ a = c$

48. $d \circ a = d$

49. $e \circ a = e$

50. a is the identity element under the operation $\circ$.

51. a

52. e

53. d

54. c

55. b

56. The elements are inverses of each other under the operation $\circ$.

57. 0 is the identity element.

58. $0 \circ 0 = 0$
0 is the inverse for 0.

59. $1 \oplus 4 = 0$
4 is the inverse for 1.

60. $2 \circ 3 = 0$
3 is the inverse for 2.

61. $3 \oplus 2 = 0$
2 is the inverse for 3.

62. $4 \circ 1 = 0$
1 is the inverse for 4.

63. a. d is the identity element.

b.

element	inverse
a	none
b	none
c	none
d	d

64. a. c is the identity element.

b.

element	inverse
a	none
b	none
c	c
d	e
e	d

65. a. $e \triangle (c \square d) = (e \triangle c) \square (e \triangle d)$

$e \triangle a = d \square c$

$a = a$

b. distributive property

66. a. $c \triangle (d \square e) = (c \triangle d) \square (c \triangle e)$

$c \triangle c = b \square d$

$e = e$

b. distributive property

67. $c \triangle [c \square (c \triangle c)] = c \triangle [c \square e]$

$= c \triangle b$

$= c$

68. $d \triangle [d \square (d \triangle d)] = d \triangle [d \square e]$

$= d \triangle c$

$= b$

69. $x \square d = e$ is true if $x = b$.

70. $x \square d = a$ is true if $x = c$.

71. $x \triangle (e \square c) = d$
$x \triangle b = d$ is true if $x = d$.

72. $x \triangle (e \square d) = b$
$x \triangle c = b$ is true if $x = d$.

73. The mathematical system shows all possible starting and ending positions for the four-way switch. The 25 entries in the table represent the final position of the switch for each starting position (shown in the left column) and number of clockwise turns (shown across the top).

74. The mathematical system shows the ending position relative to the starting position after the person completes a command shown in the left column followed by a command in the top row.

75–80.

$\times$	E	O
E	E	E
O	E	O

75. Yes. The answer to any possible combination of two elements of the set is an element that is in the set.

76. $E \times O = E$ and $O \times E = E$

77. $(O \times E) \times O = E$ and $O \times (E \times O) = E$

78. O is the identity element.

79. E does not have an inverse.

80. $O \circ O = O$; O is the inverse of O.

88. makes sense

89. does not make sense; Explanations will vary. Sample explanation: The given expression tells us that the system does not satisfy the commutative property.

90. does not make sense; Explanations will vary. Sample explanation: The most efficient way is to see if the part of the table above the main diagonal is symmetrical (mirror image) to the part below.

91. does not make sense; Explanations will vary. Sample explanation: The presence of an identity element does not necessarily mean that each element has an inverse. For example, multiplication has the identity element of 1, but notice that 0 does not have an inverse.

93. a. $\begin{bmatrix} 2 & 3 \\ 4 & 7 \end{bmatrix} \times \begin{bmatrix} 0 & 1 \\ 5 & 6 \end{bmatrix}$

$= \begin{bmatrix} 2 \cdot 0 + 3 \cdot 5 & 2 \cdot 1 + 3 \cdot 6 \\ 4 \cdot 0 + 7 \cdot 5 & 4 \cdot 1 + 7 \cdot 6 \end{bmatrix}$

$= \begin{bmatrix} 0 + 15 & 2 + 18 \\ 0 + 35 & 4 + 42 \end{bmatrix}$

$= \begin{bmatrix} 15 & 20 \\ 35 & 46 \end{bmatrix}$

b. $\begin{bmatrix} 0 & 1 \\ 5 & 6 \end{bmatrix} \times \begin{bmatrix} 2 & 3 \\ 4 & 7 \end{bmatrix}$

$= \begin{bmatrix} 0 \cdot 2 + 1 \cdot 4 & 0 \cdot 3 + 1 \cdot 7 \\ 5 \cdot 2 + 6 \cdot 4 & 5 \cdot 3 + 6 \cdot 7 \end{bmatrix}$

$= \begin{bmatrix} 0 + 4 & 0 + 7 \\ 10 + 24 & 15 + 42 \end{bmatrix}$

$= \begin{bmatrix} 4 & 7 \\ 34 & 57 \end{bmatrix}$

c. Matrix multiplication is not commutative.

Check Points 13.2

1. a. 1. The set is closed under the binary operation because the entries in the body of the table are all elements of the set.

2. Associative Property: For example,
$(O \circ E) \circ O = O \circ (E \circ O)$
$O \circ O = O \circ O$
$E = E$
and
$(E \circ O) \circ O = E \circ (O \circ O)$
$O \circ O = E \circ E$
$E = E$

3. E is the identity element.

4.
element	inverse
E	E
O	O

Each element has an inverse.
Since the system meets the four requirements, the system is a group.

b. The Commutative Property holds for this group (as can be seen by the symmetry along the diagonal from the upper left to lower right). Therefore, this system is a commutative group.

2. a. $(8 + 5) + 11 = 8 + (5 + 11)$
$1 + 11 = 8 + 4$
$0 = 0$

b. Locating 9 on the left and 4 across the top indicates that $9 + 4 = 1$.
Locating 4 on the left and 9 across the top indicates that $4 + 9 = 1$.

3. a. true; $61 \equiv 5 \pmod 7$ because
$61 \div 7 = 8$, remainder 5.

b. true; $36 \equiv 0 \pmod 6$ because
$36 \div 6 = 6$, remainder 0.

c. false; $57 \equiv 2 \pmod{11}$ because
$57 \div 11 = 5$, remainder 2 (not 3).

4. a. $(1 + 3)(\bmod 5) \equiv 4(\bmod 5)$

b. $(5 + 4)(\bmod 7) \equiv 9(\bmod 7) \equiv 2(\bmod 7)$

c. $(8 + 10)(\bmod 13) \equiv 18(\bmod 13) \equiv 5(\bmod 13)$

5. $97 \equiv 6(\bmod 7)$ thus, the desired day of the week is 6 days past Wednesday, or Tuesday.

Exercise Set 13.2

1. 8-fold rotational symmetry.

2. 5-fold rotational symmetry.

3. 18-fold rotational symmetry.

4. 4-fold rotational symmetry.

5. For any 2 elements in the set, the result is also in the set.

6. $(p \circ s) \circ t = p \circ (s \circ t)$
$t \circ t = p \circ q$
$e = e$

7. $(r \circ t) \circ q = r \circ (t \circ q)$
$p \circ q = r \circ r$
$e = e$

8. The Associative Property.

9. e is the identity element.

10. $e \circ e = e$

e is the inverse of e.

11. $p \circ q = e$

q is the inverse of p.

12. $q \circ p = e$

p is the inverse of q.

13. $r \circ r = e$

r is the inverse of r.

14. $s \circ s = e$

s is the inverse of s.

15. $t \circ t = e$

t is the inverse of t.

16. This mathematical system is a group.

17. $r \circ p = t$

18. $p \circ r = s$

19. The system is not a commutative group.

20. The natural numbers do not have an identity element under addition.

21. Most elements do not have an inverse. For example, no natural number will satisfy the expression $2 \times ? = 1$.

22. The system lacks the associative property. For example, $10 - (5 - 2) \neq (10 - 5) - 2$

23. a.

+	0	1	2	3	4	5
0	0	1	2	3	4	5
1	1	2	3	4	5	0
2	2	3	4	5	0	1
3	3	4	5	0	1	2
4	4	5	0	1	2	3
5	5	0	1	2	3	4

b. 1. The set is closed under the operation of clock addition because the entries in the body of the table are all elements of the set.

2. Associative Property: For example,
$(2 + 3) + 4 = 2 + (3 + 4)$
$5 + 4 = 2 + 1$
$3 = 3$
and
$(3 + 4) + 0 = 3 + (4 + 0)$
$1 + 0 = 3 + 4$
$1 = 1$

3. 0 is the identity element.

4.

element	inverse
0	0
1	5
2	4
3	3
4	2
5	1

Each element has an inverse.

5. The table is symmetric, so the Commutative Property holds. Therefore, this system is a commutative group.

24. a.

+	0	1	2	3	4	5	6
0	0	1	2	3	4	5	6
1	1	2	3	4	5	6	0
2	2	3	4	5	6	0	1
3	3	4	5	6	0	1	2
4	4	5	6	0	1	2	3
5	5	6	0	1	2	3	4
6	6	0	1	2	3	4	5

b. 1. The set is closed under the operation of clock addition because the entries in the body of the table are all elements of the set.

2. Associative Property: For example,
$(2+4)+6 = 2+(4+6)$
$6+6 = 2+3$
$5 = 5$
and
$(1+3)+5 = 1+(3+5)$
$4+5 = 1+1$
$2 = 2$

3. 0 is the identity element.

4.

element	inverse
0	0
1	6
2	5
3	4
4	3
5	2
6	1

Each element has an inverse.

5. The table is symmetric, so the Commutative Property holds. Therefore, this system is a commutative group.

25. $7 \equiv 2 \pmod 5$
$7 \div 5 = 1$, remainder 2
True

26. $8 \equiv 3 \pmod 5$
$8 \div 5 = 1$, remainder 3
True

27. $41 \equiv 6 \pmod 7$
$41 \div 7 = 5$, remainder 6
True

28. $77 \equiv 5 \pmod{12}$
$77 \div 12 = 6$, remainder 5
True

29. $84 \equiv 1 \pmod 7$
$84 \div 7 = 12$, remainder 0
False
A true statement is $84 \equiv 0 \pmod 7$

30. $21 \equiv 5 \pmod 7$
$21 \div 7 = 3$, remainder 0
False
A true statement is $21 \equiv 0 \pmod 7$

31. $23 \equiv 2 \pmod 4$
$23 \div 4 = 5$, remainder 3
False
A true statement is $23 \equiv 3 \pmod 4$

32. $29 \equiv 3 \pmod 4$
$29 \div 4 = 7$, remainder 1
False
A true statement is $29 \equiv 1 \pmod 4$

33. $55 \equiv 0 \pmod{11}$
$55 \div 11 = 5$, remainder 0
True

34. $75 \equiv 0 \pmod{25}$
$75 \div 25 = 3$, remainder 0
True

35. $(3+2) \pmod 6$
$3+2 = 5$, $5 < 6$
$3+2 \equiv 5 \pmod 6$

36. $(3+4) \pmod 8$
$3+4 = 7$, $7 < 8$
$3+4 \equiv 7 \pmod 8$

37. $(4+5) \pmod 6$
$4+5 = 9$, $9 > 6$
$9 \div 6 = 1$, remainder 3
$4+5 \equiv 3 \pmod 6$

38. $(5+6) \pmod 8$
$5+6 = 11$, $11 > 8$
$11 \div 8 = 1$, remainder 3
$5+6 \equiv 3 \pmod 8$

39. $(6+5) \pmod 7$
$6+5 = 11$, $11 > 7$
$11 \div 7 = 1$, remainder 4
$6+5 \equiv 4 \pmod 7$

40. $(8+7)\,(\bmod\,9)$

$8+7=15,\ 15>9$

$15\div 9=1,\ \text{remainder } 6$

$8+7=6\,(\bmod\,9)$

41. $(49+49)\,(\bmod\,5)$

$49+49=98,\ 98>50$

$98\div 50=1,\ \text{remainder } 48$

$49+49\equiv 48\,(\bmod\,50)$

42. $(75+75)\,(\bmod\,100)$

$75+75=150,\ 150>100$

$150\div 100=1,\ \text{remainder } 50$

$75+75\equiv 50\,(\bmod\,100)$

43. $(5\times 7)\,(\bmod\,12)\equiv 35\,(\bmod\,12)$
$$\equiv 11\,(\bmod\,12)$$

44. $(6\times 5)\,(\bmod\,8)\equiv 30\,(\bmod\,8)$
$$\equiv 6\,(\bmod\,8)$$

45. a. $\big[3\times(4+5)\big](\bmod\,7)\equiv 27\,(\bmod\,7)$
$$\equiv 6\,(\bmod\,7)$$

b. $\big[(3\times 4)+(3\times 5)\big](\bmod\,7)\equiv 27\,(\bmod\,7)$
$$\equiv 6\,(\bmod\,7)$$

c. distributive property

46. a. $\big[5\times(3+7)\big](\bmod\,9)\equiv 50\,(\bmod\,9)$
$$\equiv 5\,(\bmod\,9)$$

b. $\big[(5\times 3)+(5\times 7)\big](\bmod\,9)\equiv 50\,(\bmod\,9)$
$$\equiv 5\,(\bmod\,9)$$

c. distributive property

47. $3x\equiv 1\,(\bmod\,5)$ is true for $x=2$.

$3(2)\equiv 1\,(\bmod\,5)$

$6\equiv 1\,(\bmod\,5)$

48. $3x\equiv 2\,(\bmod\,7)$ is true for $x=3$.

$3(3)\equiv 2\,(\bmod\,7)$

$9\equiv 2\,(\bmod\,7)$

49. $3x\equiv 3\,(\bmod\,6)$ is true for $x=1$, 3, and 5.

$3(1)\equiv 3\,(\bmod\,6)$

$3\equiv 3\,(\bmod\,6)$

$3(3)\equiv 3\,(\bmod\,6)$

$9\equiv 3\,(\bmod\,6)$

$3(5)\equiv 3\,(\bmod\,6)$

$15\equiv 3\,(\bmod\,6)$

50. $2x\equiv 0\,(\bmod\,12)$ is true for $x=0$ and 6.

$2(0)\equiv 0\,(\bmod\,12)$

$0\equiv 0\,(\bmod\,12)$

$2(6)\equiv 0\,(\bmod\,12)$

$12\equiv 0\,(\bmod\,12)$

51. $4x\equiv 5\,(\bmod\,8)$ is false for all values of x.
No replacements exist.

52. $4x\equiv 1\,(\bmod\,6)$ is false for all values of x.
No replacements exist.

53. $(1200+0600)\,(\bmod\,2400)$

$1200+0600=1800,\ 1800<2400$

$1200+0600\equiv 1800\,(\bmod\,2400)$

54. $(1300+1900)\,(\bmod\,2400)$

$1300+1900=3200,\ 3200>2400$

$3200\div 2400=1,\ \text{remainder } 800$

$1300+1900\equiv 0800\,(\bmod\,2400)$

55. $(0830+1550)\,(\bmod\,2400)$

$0830+1550=2380,$

$23\text{ hr }80\text{ min}\equiv 24\text{ hr }20\text{ min}$

$2420\equiv 0020\,(\bmod\,2400)$

56. $(1315+0945)\,(\bmod\,2400)$

$1315+0945=2260,$

$22\text{ hr }60\text{ min}\equiv 23\text{ hr }0\text{ min}$

$2300\equiv 2300\,(\bmod\,2400)$

57. $67\div 7=9,\ \text{remainder } 4$

$67\equiv 4\,(\bmod\,7)$

Thus, the desired day of the week is 4 days past Wednesday, or Sunday.

58. $147 \div 7 = 21$, remainder 0

$147 \equiv 0 \pmod 7$

Thus, the desired day of the week is 0 days past Tuesday, or Tuesday.

59. *Beam me up*

Code:	9	12	8	20	7	20	12	7	1	23
Add 20:	29	32	28	40	27	40	32	27	21	43
Mod 27:	2	5	1	13	0	13	5	0	21	16
Letter:	B	E	A	M	_	M	E	_	U	P

60. $0 + 2(1) + 3(3) + 4(1) + 5(4) + 6(3) + 7(2) + 8(4) + 9(3) = 126$

Since $126 \equiv 5 \pmod{11}$ and the last digit is 5, the number is a valid ISBN.

61. $0 + 2(1) + 3(3) + 4(2) + 5(1) + 6(9) + 7(1) + 8(4) + 9(1) = 126$

Since $126 \equiv 5 \pmod{11}$ and the last digit is 5, the number is a valid ISBN.

62. $3 + 2(4) + 3(1) + 4(6) + 5(1) + 6(0) + 7(9) + 8(2) + 9(7) = 185$

Since $185 \equiv 9 \pmod{11}$ and the last digit is 4, the number is a not a valid ISBN.

63. $2 + 2(4) + 3(1) + 4(9) + 5(7) + 6(1) + 7(3) + 8(2) + 9(9) = 208$

Since $208 \equiv 10 \pmod{11}$ and the last digit is 0, the number is a not a valid ISBN.

64. $3 + 2(4) + 3(9) + 4(2) + 5(1) + 6(6) + 7(6) + 8(2) + 9(7) = 208$

Since $208 \equiv 10 \pmod{11}$ and the last digit is X, the number is a valid ISBN.

65. $0 + 2(1) + 3(3) + 4(2) + 5(2) + 6(5) + 7(9) + 8(8) + 9(0) = 186$

Since $186 \equiv 10 \pmod{11}$ and the last digit is X, the number is a valid ISBN.

66. $\left[3(0 + 2 + 8 + 2 + 1 + 9) + (1 + 1 + 9 + 9 + 0 + 4)\right] = 90$

Since $90 \equiv 0 \pmod{10}$ the number is a valid universal product number.

67. $\left[3(2 + 2 + 9 + 1 + 3 + 4) + (5 + 9 + 8 + 7 + 9 + 9)\right] = 110$

Since $110 \equiv 0 \pmod{10}$ the number is a valid universal product number.

68. $\left[3(0 + 2 + 4 + 6 + 8 + 0) + (1 + 3 + 5 + 7 + 9 + 1)\right] = 86$

Since $86 \equiv 6 \pmod{10}$ the number is not a valid universal product number.

69. $\left[3(0 + 4 + 0 + 1 + 5 + 9) + (6 + 2 + 0 + 1 + 8 + 7)\right] = 81$

Since $81 \equiv 1 \pmod{10}$ the number is not a valid universal product number.

77. makes sense

78. does not make sense; Explanations will vary. Sample explanation: To be a group, the system must satisfy the associative property.

79. does not make sense; Explanations will vary. Sample explanation: The system meets all the requirements of a group.

80. does not make sense; Explanations will vary. Sample explanation: To work with modulo 4, you should use the set $\{0,1,2,3\}$.

81. E(conditional): $p \rightarrow q$

C(converse): $q \rightarrow p$

I(inverse): $\sim p \rightarrow \sim q$

CP(contrapositive): $\sim q \rightarrow \sim p$

a. C followed by CP changes $q \rightarrow p$ to $\sim p \rightarrow \sim q$, which is inverse, I. C followed by I changes $q \rightarrow p$ to $\sim q \rightarrow \sim p$ which is the contrapositive, CP.

b.

$\circ$	E	C	I	CP
E	E	C	I	CP
C	C	E	CP	I
I	I	CP	E	C
CP	CP	I	C	E

c. 1. Closure. The mathematical system is closed since every entry of the table in part **b** is an element of the set $\{E, C, I, CP\}$.

2. Associative. Examples may vary.

$(C \circ I) \circ CP = CP \circ CP = E$

$C \circ (I \circ CP) = C \circ C = E$

Thus, $(C \circ I) \circ CP = C \circ (I \circ CP)$.

$(CP \circ I) \circ C = C \circ C = E$

$CP \circ (I \circ C) = CP \circ CP = E$

Thus, $(CP \circ I) \circ C = CP \circ (I \circ C)$

3. Identity. E is the identity element, since E does not change the conditional statement.

4. Inverse.

$E \circ E = E, C \circ C = E,$

$I \circ I = E,$ and $CP \circ CP = E,$

so each element has an inverse. Actually, each element is its own inverse.

Thus this is a group. To show that the group is commutative, note that the parts of the table above and below the main diagonal (upper left to lower right) are mirror images.

82. Example involving associative property:

$(2 \circ 3) \circ 5 \neq 2 \circ (3 \circ 5)$

$(2 - 3 + 2 \cdot 3) \circ 5 \neq 2 \circ (3 - 5 + 3 \cdot 5)$

$5 \circ 5 \neq 2 \circ 13$

$5 - 5 + 5 \cdot 5 \neq 2 - 13 + 2 \cdot 13$

$25 \neq 15$

Since the associative property is not satisfied, the mathematical system is not a group.

83. Answers will vary. Sample answer:

+	0
0	0

84. $99,999,999 \div 24 = 4,166,666$, remainder 15

$99,999,999 = 15 \pmod{24}$

It will be 15 hours past 5:00 P.M., or 8:00 A.M.

85. a. $(3-6)(\bmod 7) \equiv 4$

b. $(2-4)(\bmod 5) \equiv 3$

Chapter 13 Review Exercises

1. $\{e, c, f, r\}$

2. Yes. Any possible combination of two elements of the set is an element of the set.

3. $c \circ f = r$

4. $r \circ r = f$

5. $e \circ c = c$

6. $c \circ r = e$
$r \circ c = e$

7. $f \circ r = c$
$r \circ f = c$

8. $f \circ e = f$
$e \circ f = f$

9. The Commutative Property

10. Since the table entries are symmetric about the main diagonal, the operation is commutative.

11. $(c \circ r) \circ f = e \circ f = f$
$c \circ (r \circ f) = c \circ c = f$

12. $(r \circ e) \circ c = r \circ c = e$
$r \circ (e \circ c) = r \circ c = e$

13. The Associative Property

14. e is the identity element.

15. $e \circ e = e$
e is the inverse for e.

16. $c \circ r = e$
r is the inverse for c.

17. $f \circ f = e$
f is the inverse for f.

18. $r \circ c = e$
c is the inverse for r.

19. No. $1 + 1 = 2$, and 2 is not in the set.

20. Yes. Any possible combination of two elements of the set is an element of the set.

21. No. For example, $1 \div 2 = \dfrac{1}{2}$, and $\dfrac{1}{2}$ is not in the set.

22. $123 + (-123) = 0$
-123 is the additive inverse of 123.

23. $123 \cdot \dfrac{1}{123} = 1$
$\dfrac{1}{123}$ is the multiplicative inverse of 123.

24. a.

$\circ$	0	1	2	3	4
0	0	1	2	3	4
1	1	1	2	3	4
2	2	2	2	3	4
3	3	3	3	3	4
4	4	4	4	4	4

b. Zero is the identity element.

c. No. There is no element in the set such that $2 \circ ? = 0$.

25. 3-fold rotational symmetry

26. 18-fold rotational symmetry

27. a.

+	0	1	2	3	4
0	0	1	2	3	4
1	1	2	3	4	0
2	2	3	4	0	1
3	3	4	0	1	2
4	4	0	1	2	3

b. 1. The set is closed under the operation of clock addition because the entries in the body of the table are all elements of the set.

    2. Associative Property: For example,
$$(1+2)+3 = 1+(2+3)$$
$$3+3 = 1+0$$
$$1 = 1$$

    3. 0 is the identity element.

    4.

element	inverse
0	0
1	4
2	3
3	2
4	1

    Each element has an inverse.

    5. The table is symmetric, so the Commutative Property holds. Therefore, this system is a commutative group.

28. $17 \equiv 2 \ (\text{mod} \ 8)$

$17 \div 8 = 2$, remainder 1

False

A true statement is $17 \equiv 1 \ (\text{mod} \ 8)$.

29. $37 \equiv 3 \ (\text{mod} \ 5)$

$37 \div 5 = 7$, remainder 2

False

A true statement is $37 \equiv 2 \ (\text{mod} \ 5)$.

30. $60 \equiv 0 \ (\text{mod} \ 10)$

$60 \div 10 = 6$, remainder 0

True

31. $(4+3) \ (\text{mod} \ 6)$

$4+3 = 7, \ 7 > 6$

$7 \div 6 = 1$, remainder 1

$4+3 \equiv 1 (\text{mod} \ 6)$

32. $(7+7) \ (\text{mod} \ 8)$

$7+7 = 14, \ 14 > 8$

$14 \div 8 = 1$, remainder 6

$7+7 \equiv 6 (\text{mod} \ 8)$

33. $(4+3) \ (\text{mod} \ 9)$

$4+3 = 7, \ 7 < 9$

$4+3 = 7 (\text{mod} \ 9)$

34. $(3+18) \ (\text{mod} \ 20)$

$3+18 = 21, \ 21 > 20$

$21 \div 20 = 1$, remainder 1

$3+18 \equiv 1 \ (\text{mod} \ 20)$

Chapter 13 Test

1. Yes. Any possible combination of two elements of the set is an element of the set.

2. $z \circ y = x$

$y \circ z = x$

This illustrates the Commutative Property.

3. $(x \circ z) \circ z = z \circ z = y$

$x \circ (z \circ z) = x \circ y = y$

This illustrates the Associative Property.

4. x is the identity element.

5.

element	inverse
x	x
y	z
z	y

6. No. For example, $1 + 1 = 2$, and 2 is not in the set.

7. $5 \cdot \dfrac{1}{5} = 1$

$\dfrac{1}{5}$ is the multiplicative inverse of 5.

8. 6-fold rotational symmetry; Since it takes 6 equal turns to restore the design to its original position and each of these turns is a design that is identical to the original, the design has 6-fold rotational symmetry.

9.

+	0	1	2	3
0	0	1	2	3
1	1	2	3	0
2	2	3	0	1
3	3	0	1	2

10. 1. The set is closed under the operation of clock addition because the entries in the body of the table are all elements of the set.

    2. Associative Property:
        For example,
$$(1+2)+3 = 1+(2+3)$$
$$3+3 = 1+1$$
$$2 = 2$$

    3. 0 is the identity element.

    4.

element	inverse
0	0
1	3
2	2
3	1

Each element has an inverse.

    5. The table is symmetric, so the Commutative Property holds. Therefore, this system is a commutative group.

11. $39 \equiv 3 \ (\mathrm{mod}\, 6)$

$39 \div 6 = 6$, remainder 3

True

12. $14 \equiv 2 \ (\mathrm{mod}\, 7)$

$14 \div 7 = 2$, remainder 0

False

A true statement is $14 \equiv 0 \ (\mathrm{mod}\, 7)$

13. $(9+1) \ (\mathrm{mod}\, 11)$

$9+1 = 10, \ 10 < 11$

$9+1 \equiv 10 \ (\mathrm{mod}\, 11)$

14. $(9+6) \ (\mathrm{mod}\, 10)$

$9+6 = 15, \ 15 > 10$

$15 \div 10 = 1$, remainder 5

$9+6 \equiv 5 \ (\mathrm{mod}\, 10)$

Chapter 14
Voting and Apportionment

Check Points 14.1

1. **a.** We find the number of people who voted in the election by adding the numbers in the row labeled Number of Votes: 2100 + 1305 + 765 + 40 = 4210. Thus, 4210 people voted in the election.

   b. We find how many people selected the candidates in the order B, S, A, C by referring to the fourth column of letters in the preference table. Above this column is the number 40. Thus, 40 people voted in the order B, S, A, C.

   c. We find the number of people who selected S as their first choice by reading across the row that says First Choice: 2100 + 765 = 2865. Thus, 2865 students selected S (Samir) as their first choice for student body president.

2. The candidate with the most first-place votes is the winner. When using Table 14.2, it is only necessary to look at the row which indicates the number of first-place votes. This indicates that A (Antonio) gets 130 first-place votes, C (Carmen) gets 150 first-place votes, and D (Donna) gets 120 + 100 = 220 first-place votes. Thus Donna is declared the winner using the plurality method.

3. Because there are four candidates, a first-place vote is worth 4 points, a second-place vote is worth 3 points, a third-place vote is worth 2 points, and a fourth-place vote is worth 1 point. We show the points produced by the votes in the preference table.

Number of Votes	130	120	100	150
First Choice: 4 points	A: $130 \times 4 = 520$ pts	D: $120 \times 4 = 480$ pts	D: $100 \times 4 = 400$ pts	C: $150 \times 4 = 600$ pts
Second Choice: 3 points	B: $130 \times 3 = 390$ pts	B: $120 \times 3 = 360$ pts	B: $100 \times 3 = 300$ pts	B: $150 \times 3 = 450$ pts
Third Choice: 2 points	C: $130 \times 2 = 260$ pts	C: $120 \times 2 = 240$ pts	A: $100 \times 2 = 200$ pts	A: $150 \times 2 = 300$ pts
Fourth Choice: 1 point	D: $130 \times 1 = 130$ pts	A: $120 \times 1 = 120$ pts	C: $100 \times 1 = 100$ pts	D: $150 \times 1 = 150$ pts

Now we read down each column and total the points for each candidate separately.

A gets 520 + 120 + 200 + 300 = 1140 points
B gets 390 + 360 + 300 + 450 = 1500 points
C gets 260 + 240 + 100 + 600 = 1200 points
D gets 130 + 480 + 400 + 150 = 1160 points

Because B (Bob) has received the most points, he is the winner and the new mayor of Smallville.

4. There are 130 + 120 + 100 + 150, or 500, people voting. In order to receive a majority, a candidate must receive more than 50% of the votes, meaning more than 250 votes. The number of first-place votes for each candidate is
   A (Antonio) = 130   B (Bob) = 0   C (Carmen) = 150   D (Donna) = 220

We see that no candidate receives a majority of first-place votes. Because Bob received the fewest first-place votes, he is eliminated in the next round. We construct a new preference table in which B is removed. Each candidate below B moves up one place, while the positions of candidates above B remain unchanged.

Number of Votes	130	120	100	150
First Choice	A	D	D	C
Second Choice	C	C	A	A
Third Choice	D	A	C	D

The number of first-place votes for each candidate is now A (Antonio) = 130; C (Carmen) = 150; D (Donna) = 220

No candidate receives a majority of first-place votes. Because Antonio received the fewest first-place votes, he is eliminated in the next round.

Number of Votes	130	120	100	150
First Choice	C	D	D	C
Second Choice	D	C	C	D

The number of first-place votes for each candidate is now C (Carmen) = 280; D (Donna) = 220

Because Carmen has received the majority of first-place votes, she is the winner and the new mayor of Smallville.

5.

A vs. B

130	120	100	150
A	D	D	C
B	B	B	B
C	C	A	A
D	A	C	D

130 voters prefer A to B.
120 + 100 + 150 = 370 voters prefer B to A.

Conclusion: B wins this comparison and gets one point.

A vs. C

130	120	100	150
A	D	D	C
B	B	B	B
C	C	A	A
D	A	C	D

130 + 100 = 230 voters prefer A to C.
120 + 150 = 270 voters prefer C to A.

Conclusion: C wins this comparison and gets one point.

A vs. D

130	120	100	150
A	D	D	C
B	B	B	B
C	C	A	A
D	A	C	D

130 + 150 = 280 voters prefer A to D.
120 + 100 = 220 voters prefer D to A.

Conclusion: A wins this comparison and gets one point.

B vs. C

130	120	100	150
A	D	D	C
B	B	B	B
C	C	A	A
D	A	C	D

130 + 120 + 100 = 350 voters prefer B to C.
150 voters prefer C to B.

Conclusion: B wins this comparison and gets one point.

	B vs. D			
	130	120	100	150
	A	**D**	**D**	C
	B	*B*	*B*	**B**
	C	C	A	A
	D	A	C	*D*

130 + 150 = 280 voters prefer B to D.
120 + 100 = 220 voters prefer D to B.

Conclusion: B wins this comparison and gets one point.

	C vs. D			
	130	120	100	150
	A	**D**	**D**	C
	B	B	B	B
	C	*C*	A	A
	D	A	*C*	*D*

130 + 150 = 280 voters prefer C to D.
120 + 100 = 220 voters prefer D to C.

Conclusion: C wins this comparison and gets one point.

We now use each of the six conclusions and add points for the six comparisons.

    A gets 1 point.
    B gets 1 + 1 + 1 = 3 points.
    C gets 1 + 1 = 2 points.

After all comparisons have been made, the candidate receiving the most points is B (Bob). He is the winner and the new mayor of Smallville.

Exercise Set 14.1

1.

Number of Votes	7	5	4
First Choice	A	B	C
Second Choice	B	C	B
Third Choice	C	A	A

2.

Number of Votes	8	6	2
First Choice	A	B	C
Second Choice	B	C	B
Third Choice	C	A	A

3.

Number of Votes	5	1	4	2
First Choice	A	B	C	C
Second Choice	B	D	B	B
Third Choice	C	C	D	A
Fourth Choice	D	A	A	D

4.

Number of Votes	4	1	5	2
First Choice	A	B	C	C
Second Choice	B	D	B	B
Third Choice	C	C	A	D
Fourth Choice	D	A	D	A

5. **a.** $14 + 8 + 3 + 1 = 26$

   b. 8

   c. $14 + 8 = 22$

   d. 3

6. **a.** $70 + 30 + 10 + 5 = 115$

   b. 10

   c. $30 + 10 = 40$

   d. $70 + 10 = 80$

7. "Musical" received 12 first-place votes, "comedy" received 10 first-place votes, and "drama" received 8 first-place votes, so the type of play selected is a musical.

8. New York received 14 first-place votes, San Francisco received 16 first-place votes, and Chicago received 4 first-place votes, so the city selected is San Francisco.

9. Darwin received 30 first-place votes, Einstein received 22 first-place votes, Freud received 20 first-place votes, and Hawking received 14 first-place votes, so the professor declared chair is Darwin.

10. Disney received 10 first-place votes, Ford received 30 first-place votes, Gates received 24 first-place votes, and Sarnoff received 18 first-place votes, so the professor declared president is Ford.

11.

Number of Votes	10	6	6	4	2	2
First Choice: 3 points	M: $10 \times 3 = 30$	C: $6 \times 3 = 18$	D: $6 \times 3 = 18$	C: $4 \times 3 = 12$	D: $2 \times 3 = 6$	M: $2 \times 3 = 6$
Second Choice: 2 points	C: $10 \times 2 = 20$	M: $6 \times 2 = 12$	C: $6 \times 2 = 12$	D: $4 \times 2 = 8$	M: $2 \times 2 = 4$	D: $2 \times 2 = 4$
Third Choice: 1 point	D: $10 \times 1 = 10$	D: $6 \times 1 = 6$	M: $6 \times 1 = 6$	M: $4 \times 1 = 4$	C: $2 \times 1 = 2$	C: $2 \times 1 = 2$

C gets $20 + 18 + 12 + 12 + 2 + 2 = 66$ points.
D gets $10 + 6 + 18 + 8 + 6 + 4 = 52$ points.
M gets $30 + 12 + 6 + 4 + 4 + 6 = 62$ points.

C (Comedy) receives the most points, and is selected.

12.

Number of Votes	16	8	6	4
First Choice: 3 points	S: $16 \times 3 = 48$	N: $8 \times 3 = 24$	N: $6 \times 3 = 18$	C: $4 \times 3 = 12$
Second Choice: 2 points	N: $16 \times 2 = 32$	S: $8 \times 2 = 16$	C: $6 \times 2 = 12$	N: $4 \times 2 = 8$
Third Choice: 1 point	C: $16 \times 1 = 16$	C: $8 \times 1 = 8$	S: $6 \times 1 = 6$	S: $4 \times 1 = 4$

N gets $32 + 24 + 18 + 8 = 82$ points
S gets $48 + 16 + 6 + 4 = 74$ points
C gets $16 + 8 + 12 + 12 = 48$ points

N (New York) receives the most points and is selected.

13.

Number of Votes	30	22	20	12	2
First Choice: 4 points	D: $30 \times 4 = 120$	E: $22 \times 4 = 88$	F: $20 \times 4 = 80$	H: $12 \times 4 = 48$	H: $2 \times 4 = 8$
Second Choice: 3 points	H: $30 \times 3 = 90$	F: $22 \times 3 = 66$	E: $20 \times 3 = 60$	E: $12 \times 3 = 36$	F: $2 \times 3 = 6$
Third Choice: 2 points	F: $30 \times 2 = 60$	H: $22 \times 2 = 44$	H: $20 \times 2 = 40$	F: $12 \times 2 = 24$	D: $2 \times 2 = 4$
Fourth Choice: 1 point	E: $30 \times 1 = 30$	D: $22 \times 1 = 22$	D: $20 \times 1 = 20$	D: $12 \times 1 = 12$	E: $2 \times 1 = 2$

D gets $120 + 22 + 20 + 12 + 4 = 178$ points.
E gets $30 + 88 + 60 + 36 + 2 = 216$ points.
F gets $60 + 66 + 80 + 24 + 6 = 236$ points.
H gets $90 + 44 + 40 + 48 + 8 = 230$ points.

F (Freud) receives the most points and is declared the new division chair.

14.

Number of Votes	30	22	18	10	2
First Choice: 4 points	F: $30 \times 4 = 120$	G: $22 \times 4 = 88$	S: $18 \times 4 = 72$	D: $10 \times 4 = 40$	G: $2 \times 4 = 8$
Second Choice: 3 points	D: $30 \times 3 = 90$	D: $22 \times 3 = 66$	G: $18 \times 3 = 54$	S: $10 \times 3 = 30$	S: $2 \times 3 = 6$
Third Choice: 2 points	G: $30 \times 2 = 60$	S: $22 \times 2 = 44$	D: $18 \times 2 = 36$	G: $10 \times 2 = 20$	D: $2 \times 2 = 4$
Fourth Choice: 1 point	S: $30 \times 1 = 30$	F: $22 \times 1 = 22$	F: $18 \times 1 = 18$	F: $10 \times 1 = 10$	F: $2 \times 1 = 2$

D gets $90 + 66 + 36 + 40 + 4 = 236$ points.
F gets $120 + 22 + 18 + 10 + 2 = 172$ points.
G gets $60 + 88 + 54 + 20 + 8 = 230$ points.
S gets $30 + 44 + 72 + 30 + 6 = 182$ points.

D (Disney) receives the most points, and is declared the new president.

15. There are 30 people voting, so the winner needs more than 15 votes for a majority.
The number of first-place votes for each candidate is

C (Comedy) = 10   D (Drama) = 8   M (Musical) = 12

No candidate has a majority. Drama received the fewest first-place votes, so we eliminate it in the next round.

Number of Votes	10	6	6	4	2	2
First Choice	M	C	C	C	M	M
Second Choice	C	M	M	M	C	C

The number of first-place votes for each candidate is now

C (Comedy) = 16   M (Musical) = 14

C (Comedy) has 16 votes, which is a majority, so "Comedy" is selected.

16. There are 34 people voting, so the winner needs more than 17 votes for a majority. The number of first-place votes for each candidate is

N (New York) = 14   S (San Francisco) = 16   C (Chicago) = 4

No candidate has a majority. Chicago received the fewest first-place votes, so we eliminate it in the next round.

Number of Votes	16	8	6	4
First Choice	S	N	N	N
Second Choice	N	S	S	S

The number of first-place votes for each candidate is now

N (New York) = 18   S (San Francisco) = 16

N (New York) has 18 votes, which is a majority, so New York is selected.

17. There are 86 people voting, so the winner needs more than 43 votes for a majority. The number of first-place votes for each candidate is

D (Darwin) = 30   E (Einstein) = 22
F (Freud) = 20   H (Hawking) = 14

No candidate has a majority. Hawking received the fewest first-place votes, so we eliminate him in the next round.

Number of Votes	30	22	20	12	2
First Choice	D	E	F	E	F
Second Choice	F	F	E	F	D
Third Choice	E	D	D	D	E

The number of first-place votes for each candidate is now

D (Darwin) = 30 E (Einstein) = 34 F (Freud) = 22

No candidate has a majority. Freud received the fewest first-place votes, so we eliminate him in the next round:

Number of Votes	30	22	20	12	2
First Choice	D	E	E	E	D
Second Choice	E	D	D	D	E

The number of first-place votes for each candidate is now

D (Darwin) = 32 E (Einstein) = 54

E (Einstein) has 54 votes, which is a majority, so Einstein is declared the new division chair.

18. There are 82 people voting, so the winner needs more than 41 votes for a majority. The number of first-place votes for each candidate is

    D (Disney) = 10   F (Ford) = 30
    G (Gates) = 24   S (Sarnoff) = 18

    No candidate has a majority. Disney received the fewest first-place votes, so we eliminate him in the next round.

Number of Votes	30	22	18	10	2
First Choice	F	G	S	S	G
Second Choice	G	S	G	G	S
Third Choice	S	F	F	F	F

    The number of first-place votes for each candidate is now F (Ford) = 30; G (Gates) = 24; S (Sarnoff) = 28

    No candidate has a majority. Gates received the fewest first-place votes, so we eliminate him in the next round.

Number of Votes	30	22	18	10	2
First Place	F	S	S	S	S
Second Place	S	F	F	F	F

    The number of first-place votes for each candidate is now F (Ford) = 30; S (Sarnoff) = 52

    S (Sarnoff) has 52 votes, which is a majority, so Sarnoff is declared the new president.

19. With $n = 5$, there are $\dfrac{5(5-1)}{2} = 10$ comparisons.

20. With $n = 6$, there are $\dfrac{6(6-1)}{2} = 15$ comparisons.

21. With $n = 8$, there are $\dfrac{8(8-1)}{2} = 28$ comparisons.

22. With $n = 9$, there are $\dfrac{9(9-1)}{2} = 36$ comparisons.

23.

10	6	6	4	2	2
M	C	D	C	D	M
C	M	C	D	M	D
D	D	M	M	C	C

C vs. D
10 + 6 + 4 = 20 voters prefer C to D.
6 + 2 + 2 = 10 voters prefer D to C.
C wins this comparison and gets one point.

D vs. M
6 + 4 + 2 = 12 voters prefer D to M.
10 + 6 + 2 = 18 voters prefer M to D.
M wins this comparison and gets one point.

C vs. M
6 + 6 + 4 = 16 voters prefer C to M.
10 + 2 + 2 = 14 voters prefer M to C.
C wins this comparison and gets one point

Adding points for the three comparisons:
C gets 1 + 1 = 2 points.
D gets 0 points.
M gets 1 point.

C (Comedy) receives the most points, so a comedy is selected.

24.

16	8	6	4
S	N	N	C
N	S	C	N
C	C	S	S

N vs. S
$8 + 6 + 4 = 18$ voters prefer N to S.
16 voters prefer S to N.
N wins this comparison and gets one point.

S vs. C
$16 + 8 = 24$ voters prefer S to C.
$6 + 4 = 10$ voters prefer C to S.
S wins this comparison and gets one point.

N vs. C
$16 + 8 + 6 = 30$ voters prefer N to C.
4 voters prefer C to N.
N wins this comparison and gets one point.

Adding points for the three comparisons:
N gets $1 + 1 = 2$ points.
S gets 1 point.
C gets 0 points.

N (New York) receives the most points, so New York is selected.

25.

30	22	20	12	2
D	E	F	H	H
H	F	E	E	F
F	H	H	F	D
E	D	D	D	E

D vs. E
$30 + 2 = 32$ voters prefer D to E.
$22 + 20 + 12 = 54$ voters prefer E to D.
E wins the comparison and gets one point

D vs. H
30 voters prefer D to H.
$22 + 20 + 12 + 2 = 56$ voters prefer H to D.
H wins this comparison and gets one point.

E vs. H
$22 + 20 = 42$ voters prefer E to H.
$30 + 12 + 2 = 44$ voters prefer H to E.
H wins this comparison and gets one point.

D vs. F
30 voters prefer D to F.
$22 + 20 + 12 + 2 = 56$ voters prefer F to D.
F wins this comparison and gets one point.

E vs. F
$22 + 12 = 34$ voters prefer E to F.
$30 + 20 + 2 = 52$ voters prefer F to E.
F wins this comparison and gets one point

F vs. H
$22 + 20 = 42$ voters prefer F to H.
$30 + 12 + 2 = 44$ voters prefer H to F.
H wins this comparison and gets one point.

Adding points for the six comparisons:
D gets 0 points.
E gets 1 point.
F gets $1 + 1 = 2$ points.
H gets $1 + 1 + 1 = 3$ points.

H (Hawking) receives the most points, so Hawking is declared the new division chair.

26.

30	22	18	10	2
F	G	S	D	G
D	D	G	S	S
G	S	D	G	D
S	F	F	F	F

D vs. F
22 + 18 + 10 + 2 = 52 voters prefer D to F.
30 voters prefer F to D.
D wins this comparison and gets one point.

D vs. G
30 + 10 = 40 voters prefer D to G.
22 + 18 + 2 = 42 voters prefer G to D.
G wins this comparison and gets one point.

D vs. S
30 + 22 + 10 = 62 voters prefer D to S.
18 + 2 = 20 voters prefer S to D.
D wins this comparison and gets one point

F vs. G
30 voters prefer F to G.
22 + 18 + 10 + 2 = 52 voters prefer G to F.
G wins this comparison and gets one point

F vs. S
30 voters prefer F to S.
22 + 18 + 10 + 2 = 52 voters prefer S to F.
S wins this comparison and gets one point.

G vs. S
30 + 22 + 2 = 54 voters prefer G to S.
18 + 10 = 28 voters prefer S to G.
G wins this comparison and gets one point.

Adding points for the three comparisons:
D gets 1 + 1 = 2 points.
F gets 0 points.
G gets 1 + 1 + 1 = 3 points.
S gets 1 point.

G (Gates) receives the most points, so Gates is declared the new president.

27. A received 34 first-place votes, B received 30 first-place votes, C received 6 first-place votes, and D received 2 first-place votes, so A is the winner.

28.

Number of Votes	34	30	6	2
First Choice: 4 points	A: $34 \times 4 = 136$	B: $30 \times 4 = 120$	C: $6 \times 4 = 24$	D: $2 \times 4 = 8$
Second Choice: 3 points	B: $34 \times 3 = 102$	C: $30 \times 3 = 90$	D: $6 \times 3 = 18$	B: $2 \times 3 = 6$
Third Choice: 2 points	C: $34 \times 2 = 68$	D: $30 \times 2 = 60$	B: $6 \times 2 = 12$	C: $2 \times 2 = 4$
Fourth Choice: 1 point	D: $34 \times 1 = 34$	A: $30 \times 1 = 30$	A: $6 \times 1 = 6$	A: $2 \times 1 = 2$

A gets $136 + 30 + 6 + 2 = 174$ points.
B gets 102 + 120 + 12 + 6 = 240 points.
C gets 68 + 90 + 24 + 4 = 186 points.
D gets 34 + 60 + 18 + 8 = 120 points.

B receives the most points and is the winner.

29. There are 72 people voting, so the winner needs more than 36 votes for a majority. The number of first-place votes for each candidate is: A = 34;   B = 30;   C = 6;   D = 2

No candidate has a majority. D received the fewest first-place votes, so we eliminate it in the next round.

Number of Voters	34	30	6	2
First Choice	A	B	C	B
Second Choice	B	C	B	C
Third Choice	C	A	A	A

The number of first-place votes for each candidate is now A = 34;   B = 32;   C = 6

No candidate has a majority. C received the fewest first-place votes, so we eliminate it in the next round.

Number of Voters	34	30	6	2
First Choice	A	B	B	B
Second Choice	B	A	A	A

The number of first-place votes for each candidate is now A = 34;   B = 38

B has 38 votes, which is a majority, so B is selected.

30.

34	30	6	2
A	B	C	D
B	C	D	B
C	D	B	C
D	A	A	A

A vs. B
34 voters prefer A to B.
30 + 6 + 2 = 38 voters prefer B to A.
B wins this comparison and gets one point.

A vs. D
34 voters prefer A to D.
30 + 6 + 2 = 38 voters prefer D to A.
D wins this comparison and gets one point.

B vs. D
34 + 30 = 64 voters prefer B to D.
6 + 2 = 8 voters prefer D to B.
B wins this comparison and gets one point

A vs. C
34 voters prefer A to C.
30 + 6 + 2 = 38 voters prefer C to A.
C wins this comparison and gets one point.

B vs. C
34 + 30 + 2 = 66 voters prefer B to C.
6 voters prefer C to B.
B wins this comparison and gets one point.

C vs. D
34 + 30 + 6 = 70 voters prefer C to D.
2 voters prefer D to C.
C wins this comparison and gets one point.

Adding points for the six comparisons:
A gets 0 points.
B gets 1 + 1 + 1 = 3 points.
C gets 1 + 1 = 2 points.
D gets 1 point.

B receives the most points, so B is the winner.

31.

Number of Votes	5	5	4	3	3	2
First choice: 5 points	C: $5 \times 5 = 25$	S: $5 \times 5 = 25$	C: $4 \times 5 = 20$	W: $3 \times 5 = 15$	W: $3 \times 5 = 15$	P: $2 \times 5 = 10$
Second choice: 4 points	R: $5 \times 4 = 20$	R: $5 \times 4 = 20$	P: $4 \times 4 = 16$	P: $3 \times 4 = 12$	R: $3 \times 4 = 12$	S: $2 \times 4 = 8$
Third choice: 3 points	P: $5 \times 3 = 15$	W: $5 \times 3 = 15$	R: $4 \times 3 = 12$	R: $3 \times 3 = 9$	S: $3 \times 3 = 9$	C: $2 \times 3 = 6$
Fourth choice: 2 points	W: $5 \times 2 = 10$	P: $5 \times 2 = 10$	S: $4 \times 2 = 8$	S: $3 \times 2 = 6$	C: $3 \times 2 = 6$	R: $2 \times 2 = 4$
Fifth choice: 1 point	S: $5 \times 1 = 5$	C: $5 \times 1 = 5$	W: $4 \times 1 = 4$	C: $3 \times 1 = 3$	P: $3 \times 1 = 3$	W: $2 \times 1 = 2$

C gets $25 + 5 + 20 + 3 + 6 + 6 = 65$ points.
P gets $15 + 10 + 16 + 12 + 3 + 10 = 66$ points.
R gets $20 + 20 + 12 + 9 + 12 + 4 = 77$ points.
S gets $5 + 25 + 8 + 6 + 9 + 8 = 61$ points.
W gets $10 + 15 + 4 + 15 + 15 + 2 = 61$ points.

R (Rent) receives the most points and is selected.

32. C received 9 first-place votes, P received 2 first-place votes, R received 0 first-place votes, S received 5 first-place votes, and W received 6 first-place votes, so C (Cabaret) is the winner.

33.

5	5	4	3	3	2
C	S	C	W	W	P
R	R	P	P	R	S
P	W	R	R	S	C
W	P	S	S	C	R
S	C	W	C	P	W

C vs. P
$5 + 4 + 3 = 12$ voters prefer C to P.
$5 + 3 + 2 = 10$ voters prefer P to C.
C wins this comparison and gets one point.

C vs. R
$5 + 4 + 2 = 11$ voters prefer C to R.
$5 + 3 + 3 = 11$ voters prefer R to C.
C and R are tied. Each gets $\frac{1}{2}$ point.

C vs. S
$5 + 4 = 9$ voters prefer C to S.
$5 + 3 + 3 + 2 = 13$ voters prefer S to C.
S wins this comparison and gets one point.

C vs. W
$5 + 4 + 2 = 11$ voters prefer C to W.
$5 + 3 + 3 = 11$ voters prefer W to C.
C and W are tied. Each gets $\frac{1}{2}$ point.

P vs. R
$4 + 3 + 2 = 9$ voters prefer P to R.
$5 + 5 + 3 = 13$ voters prefer R to P.
R wins this comparison and gets one point.

P vs. S
$5 + 4 + 3 + 2 = 14$ voters prefer P to S.
$5 + 3 = 8$ voters prefer S to P.
P wins this comparison and gets one point.

P vs. W

$5 + 4 + 2 = 11$ voters prefer P to W.

$5 + 3 + 3 = 11$ voters prefer W to P.

P and W are tied. Each gets $\frac{1}{2}$ point.

R vs. W

$5 + 5 + 4 + 2 = 16$ voters prefer R to W.

$3 + 3 = 6$ voters prefer W to R.

R wins this comparison and gets one point.

R vs. S

$5 + 4 + 3 + 3 = 15$ voters prefer R to S.

$5 + 2 = 7$ voters prefer S to R.

R wins this comparison and gets one point.

S vs. W

$5 + 4 + 2 = 11$ voters prefer S to W.

$5 + 3 + 3 = 11$ voters prefer W to S.

S and W are tied. Each gets $\frac{1}{2}$ point.

Adding points for 10 comparisons:

C gets $1 + \frac{1}{2} + \frac{1}{2} = 2$ points.

P gets $1 + \frac{1}{2} = 1\frac{1}{2}$ points.

R gets $\frac{1}{2} + 1 + 1 + 1 = 3\frac{1}{2}$ points.

S gets $1 + \frac{1}{2} = 1\frac{1}{2}$ points.

W gets $\frac{1}{2} + \frac{1}{2} + \frac{1}{2} = 1\frac{1}{2}$ points.

R (Rent) receives the most points, so Rent is the winner.

34. There are 22 people voting, so the winner needs more than 11 votes for a majority. The number of first-place votes for each candidate is

$C = 9$ $P = 2$ $R = 0$ $S = 5$ $W = 6$

No candidate has a majority. R received the fewest first-place votes, so we eliminate it in the next round.

Number of Votes	5	5	4	3	3	2
First Choice	C	S	C	W	W	P
Second Choice	P	W	P	P	S	S
Third Choice	W	P	S	S	C	C
Fourth Choice	S	C	W	C	P	W

The number of first-place votes for each candidate is now

$C = 9$ $P = 2$ $S = 5$ $W = 6$

No candidate has a majority. P received the fewest first-place votes, so we eliminate it in the next round.

Number of Votes	5	5	4	3	3	2
First Choice	C	S	C	W	W	S
Second Choice	W	W	S	S	S	C
Third Choice	S	C	W	C	C	W

The number of first-place votes for each candidate is now

$C = 9$ $S = 7$ $W = 6$

No candidate has a majority. W received the fewest first-place votes, so we eliminate it in the next round.

Number of Votes	5	5	4	3	3	2
First Choice	C	S	C	S	S	S
Second Choice	S	C	S	C	C	C

The number of first-place votes for each candidate is now
$$C = 9 \qquad S = 13$$

S (Sweeney Todd) has 13 votes, which is a majority, so Sweeney Todd is selected.

35. a.

Number of Votes	5	5	3	3	3	2
First Choice: 5 points	A: $5 \times 5 = 25$	C: $5 \times 5 = 25$	D: $3 \times 5 = 15$	A: $3 \times 5 = 15$	B: $3 \times 5 = 15$	D: $2 \times 5 = 10$
Second Choice: 4 points	B: $5 \times 4 = 20$	E: $5 \times 4 = 20$	C: $3 \times 4 = 12$	D: $3 \times 4 = 12$	E: $3 \times 4 = 12$	C: $2 \times 4 = 8$
Third Choice: 3 points	C: $5 \times 3 = 15$	D: $5 \times 3 = 15$	B: $3 \times 3 = 9$	B: $3 \times 3 = 9$	A: $3 \times 3 = 9$	B: $2 \times 3 = 6$
Fourth Choice: 2 points	D: $5 \times 2 = 10$	A: $5 \times 2 = 10$	E: $3 \times 2 = 6$	C: $3 \times 2 = 6$	C: $3 \times 2 = 6$	A: $2 \times 2 = 4$
Fifth Choice: 1 point	E: $5 \times 1 = 5$	B: $5 \times 1 = 5$	A: $3 \times 1 = 3$	E: $3 \times 1 = 3$	D: $3 \times 1 = 3$	E: $2 \times 1 = 2$

A gets $25 + 10 + 3 + 15 + 9 + 4 = 66$ points.
B gets $20 + 5 + 9 + 9 + 15 + 6 = 64$ points.
C gets $15 + 25 + 12 + 6 + 6 + 8 = 72$ points.
D gets $10 + 15 + 15 + 12 + 3 + 10 = 65$ points.
E gets $5 + 20 + 6 + 3 + 12 + 2 = 48$ points.

C receives the most points and is the winner.

b.

Number of Votes	5	5	3	3	3	2
First Choice: 4 points	A: $5 \times 4 = 20$	C: $5 \times 4 = 20$	D: $3 \times 4 = 12$	A: $3 \times 4 = 12$	B: $3 \times 4 = 12$	D: $2 \times 4 = 8$
Second Choice: 3 points	B: $5 \times 3 = 15$	D: $5 \times 3 = 15$	C: $3 \times 3 = 9$	D: $3 \times 3 = 9$	A: $3 \times 3 = 9$	C: $2 \times 3 = 6$
Third Choice: 2 points	C: $5 \times 2 = 10$	A: $5 \times 2 = 10$	B: $3 \times 2 = 6$	B: $3 \times 2 = 6$	C: $3 \times 2 = 6$	B: $2 \times 2 = 4$
Fourth Choice: 1 points	D: $5 \times 1 = 5$	B: $5 \times 1 = 5$	A: $3 \times 1 = 3$	C: $3 \times 1 = 3$	D: $3 \times 1 = 3$	A: $2 \times 1 = 2$

A gets $20 + 10 + 3 + 12 + 9 + 2 = 56$ points.
B gets $15 + 5 + 6 + 6 + 12 + 4 = 48$ points.
C gets $10 + 20 + 9 + 3 + 6 + 6 = 54$ points.
D gets $5 + 15 + 12 + 9 + 3 + 8 = 52$ points.

A receives the most points and is the winner.

36. a.

5	5	3	3	3	2
A	C	D	A	B	D
B	E	C	D	E	C
C	D	B	B	A	B
D	A	E	C	C	A
E	B	A	E	D	E

A vs. B
$5 + 5 + 3 = 13$ voters prefer A to B.
$3 + 3 + 2 = 8$ voters prefer B to A.
A wins this comparison and gets one point.

A vs. C
$5 + 3 + 3 = 11$ voters prefer A to C.
$5 + 3 + 2 = 10$ voters prefer C to A.
A wins this comparison and gets one point.

A vs. D
$5 + 3 + 3 = 11$ voters prefer A to D.
$5 + 3 + 2 = 10$ voters prefer D to A.
A wins this comparison and gets one point.

A vs. E
$5 + 3 + 2 = 10$ voters prefer A to E.
$5 + 3 + 3 = 11$ voters prefer E to A.
E wins this comparison and gets one point.

B vs. C
$5 + 3 + 3 = 11$ voters prefer B to C.
$5 + 3 + 2 = 10$ voters prefer C to B.
B wins this comparison and gets one point.

B vs. D
$5 + 3 = 8$ voters prefer B to D.
$5 + 3 + 3 + 2 = 13$ voters prefer D to B.
D wins this comparison and gets one point.

B vs. E
$5 + 3 + 3 + 3 + 2 = 16$ voters prefer B to E.
5 voters prefer E to B.
B wins this comparison and gets one point.

C vs. D
$5 + 5 + 3 = 13$ voters prefer C to D.
$3 + 3 + 2 = 8$ voters prefer D to C.
C wins this comparison and gets one point.

C vs. E
$5 + 5 + 3 + 3 + 2 = 18$ voters prefer C to E.
3 voters prefer E to C.
C wins this comparison and gets one point.

D vs. E
$5 + 3 + 3 + 2 = 13$ voters prefer D to E.
$5 + 3 = 8$ voters prefer E to D.
D wins this comparison and gets one point.

Adding points for the ten comparisons:
A gets $1 + 1 + 1 = 3$ points.
B gets $1 + 1 = 2$ points.
C gets $1 + 1 = 2$ points.
D gets $1 + 1 = 2$ points.
E gets 1 point.

A receives the most points, so A is declared the new division chair.

b.

Number of Votes	5	5	3	3	3	2
First Choice	A	C	D	A	B	D
Second Choice	B	D	C	D	A	C
Third Choice	C	A	B	B	C	B
Fourth Choice	D	B	A	C	D	A

A vs. B
$5 + 5 + 3 = 13$ voters prefer A to B.
$3 + 3 + 2 = 8$ voters prefer B to A.
A wins this comparison and gets one point.

A vs. C
$5 + 3 + 3 = 11$ voters prefer A to C.
$5 + 3 + 2 = 10$ voters prefer C to A.
A wins this comparison and gets one point.

A vs. D
$5 + 3 + 3 = 11$ voters prefer A to D.
$5 + 3 + 2 = 10$ voters prefer D to A.
A wins this comparison and gets one point.

B vs. C
$5 + 3 + 3 = 11$ voters prefer B to C.
$5 + 3 + 2 = 10$ voters prefer C to B.
B wins this comparison and gets one point.

B vs. D
$5 + 3 = 8$ voters prefer B to D.
$5 + 3 + 3 + 2 = 13$ voters prefer D to B.
D wins this comparison and gets one point.

C vs. D
$5 + 5 + 3 = 13$ voters prefer C to D.
$3 + 3 + 2 = 8$ voters prefer D to C.
C wins this comparison and gets one point.

Adding points for the six comparisons:
A gets $1 + 1 + 1 = 3$ points.
B gets 1 point.
C gets 1 point.
D gets 1 point.

A receives the most points, so A is declared the new division chair.

37. First use the plurality method: C receives 12,000 first-place votes, and A receives 12,000 first-place votes. This results in a tie, so we use the Borda count method.

Number of Votes	12,000	7500	4500
First Choice: 3 points	C: $12{,}000 \times 3 = 36{,}000$	A: $7500 \times 3 = 22{,}500$	A: $4500 \times 3 = 13{,}500$
Second Choice: 2 points	B: $12{,}000 \times 2 = 24{,}000$	B: $7500 \times 2 = 15{,}000$	C: $4500 \times 3 = 9000$
Third Choice: 1 points	A: $12{,}000 \times 1 = 12{,}000$	C: $7500 \times 1 = 7500$	B: $4500 \times 1 = 4500$

A gets $12{,}000 + 22{,}500 + 13{,}500 = 48{,}000$ points.
B gets $24{,}000 + 15{,}000 + 4500 = 43{,}500$ points.
C gets $36{,}000 + 7500 + 9000 = 52{,}500$ points.
C receives the most points and is the winner.

38. First use the pairwise comparison method.

60,000	40,000	40,000	20,000	20,000
A	C	B	A	C
B	A	C	C	B
C	B	A	B	A

A vs. B
$60{,}000 + 40{,}000 + 20{,}000 = 120{,}000$ voters prefer A to B.
$40{,}000 + 20{,}000 = 60{,}000$ voters prefer B to A.
A wins this comparison and gets one point.

A vs. C
$60{,}000 + 20{,}000 = 80{,}000$ voters prefer A to C.
$40{,}000 + 40{,}000 + 20{,}000 = 100{,}000$ voters prefer C to A.
C wins this comparison and gets one point.

B vs. C
$60{,}000 + 40{,}000 = 100{,}000$ voters prefer B to C.
$40{,}000 + 20{,}000 + 20{,}000 = 80{,}000$ voters prefer C to B.
B wins this comparison and gets one point.

Adding points for the three comparisons:
A gets 1 point.
B gets 1 point.
C gets 1 point.

We have a tie. We next try the Borda count method.

Number of Votes	60,000	40,000	40,000	20,000	20,000
First Choice: 3 points	A: 60,000 × 3 = 180,000	C: 40,000 × 3 = 120,000	B: 40,000 × 3 = 120,000	A: 20,000 × 3 = 60,000	C: 20,000 × 3 = 60,000
Second Choice: 2 points	B: 60,000 × 2 = 120,000	A: 40,000 × 2 = 80,000	C: 40,000 × 2 = 80,000	C: 20,000 × 2 = 40,000	B: 20,000 × 2 = 40,000
Third Choice: 1 point	C: 60,000 × 1 = 60,000	B: 40,000 × 1 = 40,000	A: 40,000 × 1 = 40,000	B: 20,000 × 1 = 20,000	A: 20,000 × 1 = 20,000

A gets 180,000 + 80,000 + 40,000 + 60,000 + 20,000 = 380,000 points.
B gets 120,000 + 40,000 + 120,000 + 20,000 + 40,000 = 340,000 points.
C gets 60,000 + 120,000 + 80,000 + 40,000 + 60,000 = 360,000 points.

A receives the most points, so A becomes the new mayor.

49. does not make sense; Explanations will vary. Sample explanation: A candidate with a majority must win using the plurality method.

50. does not make sense; Explanations will vary. Sample explanation: A candidate with a majority must win using the plurality-with-elimination method.

51. makes sense

52. makes sense

Check Points 14.2

1. **a.** There are 14 first-place votes. A candidate with more than half of these receives a majority. The first-choice row shows that candidate A received 8 first-place votes. Thus, candidate A has a majority of first-place votes.

   b. Using the Borda count method with four candidates, a first-place vote is worth 4 points, a second-place vote is worth 3 points, a third-place vote is worth 2 points, and a fourth-place vote is worth 1 point.

Number of Votes	6	4	2	2
First Choice: 4 points	A: 6 × 4 = 24 pts	B: 4 × 4 = 16 pts	B: 2 × 4 = 8 pts	A: 2 × 4 = 8 pts
Second Choice: 3 points	B: 6 × 3 = 18 pts	C: 4 × 3 = 12 pts	D: 2 × 3 = 6 pts	B: 2 × 3 = 6 pts
Third Choice: 2 points	C: 6 × 2 = 12 pts	D: 4 × 2 = 8 pts	C: 2 × 2 = 4 pts	D: 2 × 2 = 4 pts
Fourth Choice: 1 point	D: 6 × 1 = 6 pts	A: 4 × 1 = 4 pts	A: 2 × 1 = 2 pts	C: 2 × 1 = 2 pts

Now we read down the columns and total the points for each candidate.
A gets 24 + 4 + 2 + 8 = 38 points.
B gets 18 + 16 + 8 + 6 = 48 points.
C gets 12 + 12 + 4 + 2 = 30 points.
D gets 6 + 8 + 6 + 4 = 24 points.

Because candidate B has received the most points, candidate B is declared the new principal using the Borda count method.

2. **a.** We begin by comparing A and B. A is favored over B in column 1, giving A 3 votes. B is favored over A in columns 2 and 3, giving B 2 + 2, or 4, votes. Thus, B is favored when compared to A.

   Now we compare B to C. B is favored over C in columns 1 and 2, giving B 3 + 2, or 5, votes. C is favored over B in column 3, giving C 2 votes. Thus, B is favored when compared to C.

   We see that B is favored over both A and C using a head-to-head comparison.

b. Using the plurality method, the brand with the most first-place votes is the winner. In the row indicating first choice, A received 3 votes, B received 2 votes, and C received 2 votes. A wins using the plurality method.

3. a. There are 120 people voting. No candidate initially receives more than 60 votes. Because C receives the fewest first-place votes, C is eliminated in the next round. The new preference table is

Number of Votes	42	34	28	16
First Choice	A	A	B	B
Second Choice	B	B	A	A

Because A has received a majority of first-place votes, A is the winner of the straw poll.

b. No candidate initially receives more than 60 votes. Because B receives the fewest first-place votes, B is eliminated in the next round. The new preference table is

Number of Votes	54	34	28	4
First Choice	A	C	C	A
Second Choice	C	A	A	C

Because C has received a majority of first-place votes, C is the winner of the second election.

c. A won the first election. A then gained additional support with the 12 voters who changed their ballots to make A their first choice. A lost the second election. This violates the monotonicity criterion.

4. a. Because there are 4 candidates, $n = 4$ and the number of comparisons we must make is

$$\frac{n(n-1)}{2} = \frac{4(4-1)}{2} = \frac{4 \cdot 3}{2} = \frac{12}{2} = 6 .$$

The following table shows the results of these 6 comparisons.

Comparison	Vote Results	Conclusion
A vs. B	270 voters prefer A to B. 90 voters prefer B to A.	A wins and gets 1 point.
A vs. C	270 voters prefer A to C. 90 voters prefer C to A.	A wins and gets 1 point.
A vs. D	150 voters prefer A to D. 210 voters prefer D to A.	D wins and gets 1 point.
B vs. C	180 voters prefer B to C. 180 voters prefer C to B.	B and C tie. Each gets $\frac{1}{2}$ point.
B vs. D	240 voters prefer B to D. 120 voters prefer D to B.	B wins and gets 1 point.
C vs. D	240 voters prefer C to D. 120 voters prefer D to C.	C wins and gets 1 point.

Thus A gets 2 points, B gets $1\frac{1}{2}$ points, C gets $1\frac{1}{2}$ points, and D gets 1 point. Therefore A is the winner.

b. After B and C withdraw, there is a new preference table:

Number of Votes	150	90	90	30
First Choice	A	D	D	D
Second Choice	D	A	A	A

Using the pairwise comparison test with 2 candidates, there is only one comparison to make namely A vs. D.

150 voters prefer A to D, and 210 voters prefer D to A. D gets 1 point, A gets 0 points, and D wins the election.

    c.   The first election count produced A as the winner. The removal of B and C from the ballots produced D as the winner. This violates the irrelevant alternatives criterion.

Exercise Set 14.2

1. a.   D has 300 first-place votes, which is more than half of the 570 total votes, so D has a majority of first-place votes.

    b.

Number of Votes	300	120	90	60
First Choice: 4 points	D: $300 \times 4 = 1200$	C: $120 \times 4 = 480$	C: $90 \times 4 = 360$	A: $60 \times 4 = 240$
Second Choice: 3 points	A: $300 \times 3 = 900$	A: $120 \times 3 = 360$	A: $90 \times 3 = 270$	D: $60 \times 3 = 180$
Third Choice: 2 points	B: $300 \times 2 = 600$	B: $120 \times 2 = 240$	D: $90 \times 2 = 180$	B: $60 \times 2 = 120$
Fourth Choice: 1 point	C: $300 \times 1 = 300$	D: $120 \times 1 = 120$	B: $90 \times 1 = 90$	C: $60 \times 1 = 60$

A gets $900 + 360 + 270 + 240 = 1770$ points.
B gets $600 + 240 + 90 + 120 = 1050$ points.
C gets $300 + 480 + 360 + 60 = 1200$ points.
D gets $1200 + 120 + 180 + 180 = 1680$ points.

A receives the most points, so A is the chosen design.

    c.   No. D receives a majority of first-place votes, but A is chosen by the Borda count method.

2. a.   A has 27 first-place votes, which is more than half of the 53 total votes, so A has a majority of first-place votes.

    b.

Number of Votes	27	24	2
First Choice: 3 points	A: $27 \times 3 = 81$	B: $24 \times 3 = 72$	C: $2 \times 3 = 6$
Second Choice: 2 points	C: $27 \times 2 = 54$	C: $24 \times 2 = 48$	B: $2 \times 2 = 4$
Third Choice: 1 point	B: $27 \times 1 = 27$	A: $24 \times 1 = 24$	A: $2 \times 1 = 2$

A gets $81 + 24 + 2 = 107$ points.
B gets $27 + 72 + 4 = 103$ points.
C gets $54 + 48 + 6 = 108$ points.

C receives the most points, so C is the winner.

    c.   No. A receives the majority of first-place votes, but C is chosen by the Borda count method.

3. a.   A is favored over R in columns 1 and 3, giving A $12 + 4$, or 16, votes. R is favored over A in columns 2 and 4, giving R $9 + 4$, or 13, votes. Thus, A is favored when compared to R.

          A is favored over V in columns 1 and 4, giving A $12 + 4$, or 16, votes. V is favored over A in columns 2 and 3, giving V $9 + 4$, or 13, votes. Thus, A is favored when compared to V.

          We see that A is favored over the other two cities using a head-to-head comparison.

    b.   A gets 12 first-place votes, V gets 13 first-place votes, and R gets 4 first-place votes, so V wins using the plurality method.

    c.   No. A wins the head-to-head comparison, but V wins the election.

4. a. B is favored over A in columns 2 and 3, giving B 19 + 5, or 24, votes. A is favored over B in column 1, giving A 20 votes. Thus, B is favored when compared to A.

B is favored over C in columns 1 and 2, giving B 20 + 19, or 39, votes. C is favored over B in column 3, giving C 5 votes. Thus, B is favored when compared to C. We see that B is favored over the other two cities using a head-to-head comparison.

b. A gets 20 first-place votes, B gets 19 first-place votes, and C gets 5 first-place votes, so A wins using the plurality method.

c. No. B wins the head-to-head comparison, but A wins the election.

5. a. A is favored over B in columns 1 and 4, giving A 120 + 30, or 150, votes. B is favored over A in columns 2, 3, and 5, giving B 60 + 30 + 30, or 120 votes. Thus, A is favored when compared to B.

A is favored over C in columns 1 and 3, giving A 120 + 30, or 150 votes. C is favored over A in columns 2, 4, and 5, giving C 60 + 30 + 30, or 120, votes. Thus, A is favored when compared to C.

We see that A is favored over the other two options using a head-to-head comparison.

b.

Number of Votes	120	60	30	30	30
First Choice: 3 points	A: $120 \times 3 = 360$	C: $60 \times 3 = 180$	B: $30 \times 3 = 90$	C: $30 \times 3 = 90$	B: $30 \times 3 = 90$
Second Choice: 2 points	C: $120 \times 2 = 240$	B: $60 \times 2 = 120$	A: $30 \times 2 = 60$	A: $30 \times 2 = 60$	C: $30 \times 2 = 60$
Third Choice: 1 point	B: $120 \times 1 = 120$	A: $60 \times 1 = 60$	C: $30 \times 1 = 30$	B: $30 \times 1 = 30$	A: $30 \times 1 = 30$

A gets 360 + 60 + 60 + 60 + 30 = 570 points.
B gets 120 + 120 + 90 + 30 + 90 = 450 points.
C gets 240 + 180 + 30 + 90 + 60 = 600 points.

C receives the most points, so C is the winner.

c. No. A wins the head-to-head comparison, but C wins the election.

6. a. C is favored over A in column 1, giving C 200 votes. A is favored over C in columns 2 and 3, giving A 80 + 80, or 160, votes. Thus, C is favored when compared to A. C is favored over B in column 1, giving C 200 votes. B is favored over C in columns 2 and 3, giving B 80 + 80, or 160, votes. Thus, C is favored when compared with B.

We see that C is favored over the other two options using a head-to-head comparison.

b.

Number of Votes	200	80	80
First Choice: 3 points	C: $200 \times 3 = 600$	B: $80 \times 3 = 240$	A: $80 \times 3 = 240$
Second Choice: 2 points	A: $200 \times 2 = 400$	A: $80 \times 2 = 160$	B: $80 \times 2 = 160$
Third Choice: 1 point	B: $200 \times 1 = 200$	C: $80 \times 1 = 80$	C: $80 \times 1 = 80$

A gets 400 + 160 + 240 = 800 points.
B gets 200 + 240 + 160 = 600 points.
C gets 600 + 80 + 80 = 760 points.

A receives the most points, so A is the favored option.

c. No. C wins the head-to-head comparison, but A wins the election.

7. a.   There are 29 people voting. No one receives the 15 first-place votes needed for a majority.
B receives the fewest first-place votes and is eliminated in the next round.

Number of Votes	18	11
First Choice	C	A
Second Choice	A	C

C receives the majority of first-place votes, so C is the winner.

b.   With the voting change, a new preference table results.

Number of Votes	14	8	7
First Choice	C	B	A
Second Choice	A	C	B
Third Choice	B	A	C

No one receives a majority of first-place votes. A receives the fewest first-place votes, and is eliminated in the next round.

Number of Votes	14	15
First Choice	C	B
Second Choice	B	C

B receives the majority of first-place votes, so B is the winner.

c.   No. C wins the straw vote, and the only change increases the number of first-place votes for C, but B wins the election.

8. a.   There are 42 people voting. No one receives the 22 first-place votes needed for a majority.
B receives the fewest first-place votes and is eliminated in the next round.

Number of Votes	26	16
First Choice	C	A
Second Choice	A	C

C receives the majority of first-place votes, so C is the winner.

b.   With the voting change, a new preference table results.

Number of Votes	20	12	10
First Choice	C	B	A
Second Choice	A	C	B
Third Choice	B	A	C

No one receives a majority of first-place votes. A receives the fewest first-place votes, and is eliminated in the next round.

Number of Votes	20	22
First Choice	C	B
Second Choice	B	C

B receives the majority of first-place votes, so B is the winner.

c.   No. C wins the straw vote, and the only change increases the number of first-place votes for C, but B wins the election.

9. a.   There are 3 candidates, so $n = 3$ and the number of comparisons we must make is $\frac{n(n-1)}{2} = \frac{3(2)}{2} = 3$.

Comparison	Vote Results	Conclusion
H vs. L	10 voters prefer H to L. 13 voters prefer L to H.	L wins and gets one point.
H vs. S	10 voters prefer H to S. 13 voters prefer S to H.	S wins and gets one point.
L vs. S	8 voters prefer L to S. 15 voters prefer S to L.	S wins and gets one point.

Thus, L gets 1 point and S gets 2 points. Therefore, S is the winner when candidates H and L are included.

b.   New preference table:

Number of Votes	15	8
First Choice	S	L
Second Choice	L	S

With only two candidates, we can only make one comparison. We see that S wins, defeating L by 15 votes to 8 votes. Thus S gets 1 point, L gets 0 points, and S is the winner.

c.   Yes. S wins whether or not H withdraws.

10. a.   There are 3 candidates, so $n = 3$ and the number of comparisons we must make is $\frac{n(n-1)}{2} = \frac{3(2)}{2} = 3$.

Comparison	Vote Results	Conclusion
G vs. S	14 voters prefer G to S. 12 voters prefer S to G.	G wins and gets one point.
G vs. R	18 voters prefer G to R. 8 voters prefer R to G.	G wins and gets one point.
S vs. R	12 voters prefer S to R. 14 voters prefer R to S.	R wins and gets one point.

Thus G gets 2 points and R gets 1 point. Therefore, G is the winner when candidates S and R are included.

b.   New preference table:

Number of Votes	18	8
First Choice	G	R
Second Choice	R	G

With only two candidates, we can only make one comparison. We see that G wins, defeating R by 18 votes to 8 votes. Thus, G gets 1 point, R gets 0 points, and G is the winner.

c.   Yes. G is the winner whether or not S withdraws.

11. a.

Number of Votes	20	16	10	4
First Choice: 4 points	D: $20 \times 4 = 80$	C: $16 \times 4 = 64$	C: $10 \times 4 = 40$	A: $4 \times 4 = 16$
Second Choice: 3 points	A: $20 \times 3 = 60$	A: $16 \times 3 = 48$	B: $10 \times 3 = 30$	B: $4 \times 3 = 12$
Third Choice: 2 points	B: $20 \times 2 = 40$	B: $16 \times 2 = 32$	D: $10 \times 2 = 20$	D: $4 \times 2 = 8$
Fourth Choice: 1 point	C: $20 \times 1 = 20$	D: $16 \times 1 = 16$	A: $10 \times 1 = 10$	C: $4 \times 1 = 4$

A gets $60 + 48 + 10 + 16 = 134$ points.
B gets $40 + 32 + 30 + 12 = 114$ points.
C gets $20 + 64 + 40 + 4 = 128$ points.
D gets $80 + 16 + 20 + 8 = 124$ points.

A receives the most points, so A is the winner.

b. No. A has only 4 first-place votes, out of 50 total votes. C has 26 first-place votes, which is a majority, but A wins the election.

12. a.

Number of Votes	20	15	3	1
First Choice: 4 points	A: $20 \times 4 = 80$	B: $15 \times 4 = 60$	C: $3 \times 4 = 12$	D: $1 \times 4 = 4$
Second Choice: 3 points	B: $20 \times 3 = 60$	C: $15 \times 3 = 45$	D: $3 \times 3 = 9$	B: $1 \times 3 = 3$
Third Choice: 2 points	C: $20 \times 2 = 40$	D: $15 \times 2 = 30$	B: $3 \times 2 = 6$	C: $1 \times 2 = 2$
Fourth Choice: 1 point	D: $20 \times 1 = 20$	A: $15 \times 1 = 15$	A: $3 \times 1 = 3$	A: $1 \times 1 = 1$

A gets $80 + 15 + 3 + 1 = 99$ points.
B gets $60 + 60 + 6 + 3 = 129$ points.
C gets $40 + 45 + 12 + 2 = 99$ points.
D gets $20 + 30 + 9 + 4 = 63$ points.

B receives the most points, so B is the winner.

b. No. A receives 20 first-place votes out of 39 total votes, which is a majority, but B wins the election.

13. a. There are 70 people voting. No one receives the 36 first-place votes needed for a majority. B receives the fewest first-place votes and is eliminated in the next round.

Number of Votes	24	20	10	8	8
First Choice	D	C	A	A	C
Second Choice	A	A	D	C	D
Third Choice	C	D	C	D	A

No one receives a majority of first-place votes. A receives the fewest first-place votes and is eliminated in the next round.

Number of Votes	34	36
First Choice	D	C
Second Choice	C	D

C receives 36 first-place votes, which is a majority, so C is the winner.

b. No. When compared individually to B, A wins with 60 votes to 10. Compared with C, A wins with 42 votes to 28. Compared with D, A wins with 38 votes to 32. So A is favored in all head-to-head contests but C wins the election.

14. a. There are 51 people voting. No one receives the 26 first-place votes needed for a majority. B and D tie for the fewest first-place votes, so both are eliminated in the next round.

Number of Votes	22	29
First Choice	A	C
Second Choice	C	A

C has a majority of first-place votes, so C is the winner.

b. No. D wins the head-to-head comparison against A, B, and C, but C wins using the plurality-with-elimination method.

15. a.

Number of Votes	14	8	4
First Choice: 4 points	A: $14 \times 4 = 56$	B: $8 \times 4 = 32$	D: $4 \times 4 = 16$
Second Choice: 3 points	B: $14 \times 3 = 42$	D: $8 \times 3 = 24$	A: $4 \times 3 = 12$
Third Choice: 2 points	C: $14 \times 2 = 28$	C: $8 \times 2 = 16$	C: $4 \times 2 = 8$
Fourth Choice: 1 point	D: $14 \times 1 = 14$	A: $8 \times 1 = 8$	B: $4 \times 1 = 4$

A gets $56 + 8 + 12 = 76$ points.
B gets $42 + 32 + 4 = 78$ points.
C gets $28 + 16 + 8 = 52$ points.
D gets $14 + 24 + 16 = 54$ points.

B receives the most points, so B is the winner.

b. No. A receives the majority of first-place votes, but B wins the election.

c. No. A wins all head-to-head comparisons, but B wins the election.

d. Using the Borda count method with C removed:

Number of Votes	14	8	4
First Choice: 3 points	A: $14 \times 3 = 42$	B: $8 \times 3 = 24$	D: $4 \times 3 = 12$
Second Choice: 2 points	B: $14 \times 2 = 28$	D: $8 \times 2 = 16$	A: $4 \times 2 = 8$
Third Choice: 1 point	D: $14 \times 1 = 14$	A: $8 \times 1 = 8$	B: $4 \times 1 = 4$

A gets $42 + 8 + 8 = 58$ points.
B gets $28 + 24 + 4 = 56$ points.
D gets $14 + 16 + 12 = 42$ points.

A receives the most points, and wins the election.

The irrelevant alternatives criterion is not satisfied. Candidate C's dropping out changed the outcome of the election.

16. a. There are 42 people voting. No one receives the 22 first-place votes needed for a majority. D receives the fewest first-place votes and is eliminated in the next round.

Number of Votes	14	12	16
First Choice	A	B	C
Second Choice	B	A	B
Third Choice	C	C	A

No one receives a majority of first-place votes. B receives the fewest first-place votes and is eliminated in the next round.

Number of Votes	26	16
First Choice	A	C
Second Choice	C	A

A receives 26 first-place votes, which is a majority, so A is the winner.

b. New preference table:

Number of Votes	14	12	10	6
First Choice	A	B	C	A
Second Choice	B	A	B	D
Third Choice	C	C	A	C
Fourth Choice	D	D	D	B

No one receives a majority of first-place votes.
D receives the fewest first-place votes and is eliminated in the next round.

Number of Votes	14	12	10	6
First Choice	A	B	C	A
Second Choice	B	A	B	C
Third Choice	C	C	A	B

No one receives a majority of first-place votes.
C receives the fewest first-place votes and is eliminated in the next round.

Number of Votes	14	12	10	6
First Choice	A	B	B	A
Second Choice	B	A	A	B

The above table is equivalent to the following table.

Number of Votes	20	22
First Choice	A	B
Second Choice	B	A

B receives 22 first-place votes, which is a majority, so B is the winner. The monotonicity criterion is not satisfied because the only change gave A more first-place votes, but resulted in A's losing the election.

17. a.

Number of Votes	16	14	12	4	2
First Choice: 5 points	A: $16 \times 5 = 80$	D: $14 \times 5 = 70$	D: $12 \times 5 = 60$	C: $4 \times 5 = 20$	E: $2 \times 5 = 10$
Second Choice: 4 points	B: $16 \times 4 = 64$	B: $14 \times 4 = 56$	B: $12 \times 4 = 48$	A: $4 \times 4 = 16$	A: $2 \times 4 = 8$
Third Choice: 3 points	C: $16 \times 3 = 48$	A: $14 \times 3 = 42$	E: $12 \times 3 = 36$	B: $4 \times 3 = 12$	D: $2 \times 3 = 6$
Fourth Choice: 2 points	D: $16 \times 2 = 32$	C: $14 \times 2 = 28$	C: $12 \times 2 = 24$	D: $4 \times 2 = 8$	B: $2 \times 2 = 4$
Fifth Choice: 1 point	E: $16 \times 1 = 16$	E: $14 \times 1 = 14$	A: $12 \times 1 = 12$	E: $4 \times 1 = 4$	C: $2 \times 1 = 2$

A gets $80 + 42 + 12 + 16 + 8 = 158$ points.
B gets $64 + 56 + 48 + 12 + 4 = 184$ points.
C gets $48 + 28 + 24 + 20 + 2 = 122$ points.
D gets $32 + 70 + 60 + 8 + 6 = 176$ points.
E gets $16 + 14 + 36 + 4 + 10 = 80$ points.

B receives the most points, so B is the winner.

b. No. D gets a majority of first-place votes, but B wins the election.

c. No. D wins all head-to-head comparisons, but B wins the election.

18. a. There are 5 candidates, so the number of pairwise comparisons is $\frac{n(n-1)}{2} = \frac{5(5-1)}{2} = \frac{5(4)}{2} = 10$.

Comparison	Vote Results	Conclusion
A vs. B	14 voters prefer A to B. 18 voters prefer B to A.	B wins and gets 1 point.
A vs. C	28 voters prefer A to C. 4 voters prefer C to A.	A wins and gets 1 point.
A vs. D	28 voters prefer A to D. 4 voters prefer D to A.	A wins and gets 1 point.
A vs. E	28 voters prefer A to E. 4 voters prefer E to A.	A wins and gets 1 point.
B vs. C	14 voters prefer B to C. 18 voters prefer C to B.	C wins and gets 1 point.
B vs. D	18 voters prefer B to D. 14 voters prefer D to B.	B wins and gets 1 point.
B vs. E	16 voters prefer B to E. 16 voters prefer E to B.	B and E tie. Each gets $\frac{1}{2}$ point.
C vs. D	18 voters prefer C to D. 14 voters prefer D to C.	C wins and gets 1 point.
C vs. E	16 voters prefer C to E. 16 voters prefer E to C.	C and E tie. Each gets $\frac{1}{2}$ point.
D vs. E	26 voters prefer D to E. 6 voters prefer E to D.	D wins and gets 1 point.

Thus A gets 3 points, B gets $2\frac{1}{2}$ points, C gets $2\frac{1}{2}$ points, D gets 1 point, and E gets 1 point. Therefore, A is the winner.

b. After eliminating C, we have 4 candidates, and need 6 comparisons.

Comparison	Vote Results	Conclusion
A vs. B	14 voters prefer A to B. 18 voters prefer B to A.	B wins and gets 1 point.
A vs. D	28 voters prefer A to D. 4 voters prefer D to A.	A wins and gets 1 point.
A vs. E	28 voters prefer A to E. 4 voters prefer E to A.	A wins and gets 1 point.
B vs. D	18 voters prefer B to D. 14 voters prefer D to B.	B wins and gets 1 point.
B vs. E	16 voters prefer B to E. 16 voters prefer E to B.	B and E tie. Each gets $\frac{1}{2}$ point.
D vs. E	26 voters prefer D to E. 6 voters prefer E to D.	D wins and gets 1 point.

Thus A gets 2 points, B gets $2\frac{1}{2}$ points, D gets 1 point, and E gets $\frac{1}{2}$ point. Therefore, B is the winner.

The irrelevant alternatives criterion is not satisfied, since removing one candidate changed the outcome of the election.

19. a. A receives the most first-place votes, and is the winner.

b. Yes. A has a majority of the first-place votes, and wins.

c. Yes. A wins in comparisons to B and C.

d. New preference table:

Number of Votes	7	3	2
First Choice	A	B	A
Second Choice	B	C	C
Third Choice	C	A	B

A has the majority of first-place votes, and wins using the plurality method.

e. Yes. A still receives the most first-place votes, and wins.

f. No. The fact that all four criteria are satisfied in a particular case does not mean that the method used always satisfies all four criteria.

28. makes sense

29. makes sense

30. does not make sense; Explanations will vary. Sample explanation: In a reelection, the supporters of the former loser(s) may come out in larger numbers.

31. does not make sense; Explanations will vary. Sample explanation: The majority criterion could be violated. For instance, suppose candidate A is the first choice of 51% of voters and is approved by 60% of voters, yet candidate B is the first choice of 49% of voters and is approved by 70% of voters.

Check Points 14.3

1. **a.** Standard divisor = $\dfrac{\text{total population}}{\text{number of allocated items}} = \dfrac{10,000}{200} = 50$

   b. Standard quota for state A = $\dfrac{\text{population of state A}}{\text{standard divisor}} = \dfrac{1112}{50} = 22.24$

   Standard quota for state B = $\dfrac{\text{population of state B}}{\text{standard divisor}} = \dfrac{1118}{50} = 22.36$

   Standard quota for state C = $\dfrac{\text{population of state C}}{\text{standard divisor}} = \dfrac{1320}{50} = 26.4$

   Standard quota for state D = $\dfrac{\text{population of state D}}{\text{standard divisor}} = \dfrac{1515}{50} = 30.3$

   Standard quota for state E = $\dfrac{\text{population of state E}}{\text{standard divisor}} = \dfrac{4935}{50} = 98.7$

Table 14.27		Population of Amador by State				
State	A	B	C	D	E	Total
Population (in thousands)	1112	1118	1320	1515	4935	10,000
Standard quota	22.24	22.36	26.4	30.3	98.7	200

2.

State	Population (in thousands)	Standard Quota	Lower Quota	Fractional Part	Surplus	Final Apportionment
A	1112	22.24	22	0.24		22
B	1118	22.36	22	0.36		22
C	1320	26.4	26	0.4 (next largest)	1	27
D	1515	30.3	30	0.3		30
E	4935	98.7	98	0.7 (largest)	1	99
Total	10,000	200	198			200

3.

State	Population (in thousands)	Modified Quota (using $d = 49.3$)	Modified Lower Quota	Final Apportionment
A	1112	22.56	22	22
B	1118	22.68	22	22
C	1320	26.77	26	26
D	1515	30.73	30	30
E	4935	100.10	100	100
Total	10,000		200	200

4.

State	Population (in thousands)	Modified Quota (using $d = 50.5$)	Modified Upper Quota
A	1112	22.02	23
B	1118	22.14	23
C	1320	26.14	27
D	1515	30	30
E	4935	97.72	98
Total	10,000		201

This sum should be 200, not 201.

State	Population (in thousands)	Modified Quota (using $d = 50.6$)	Modified Upper Quota	Final Apportionment
A	1112	21.98	22	22
B	1118	22.09	23	23
C	1320	26.09	27	27
D	1515	29.94	30	30
E	4935	97.53	98	98
Total	10,000		200	200

5.

State	Population (in thousands)	Modified Quota (using $d = 49.8$)	Modified Rounded Quota
A	1112	22.33	22
B	1118	22.45	22
C	1320	26.51	27
D	1515	30.42	30
E	4935	99.10	99
Total	10,000		200

Exercise Set 14.3

1. a. Standard divisor $= \frac{1600}{80} = 20$. There are 20,000 people for each seat in congress.

b–c. State	A	B	C	D
Standard quota	$\frac{138}{20} = 6.9$	$\frac{266}{20} = 13.3$	$\frac{534}{20} = 26.7$	$\frac{662}{20} = 33.1$
Lower quota	6	13	26	33
Upper Quota	7	14	27	34

2. a. Standard divisor $= \frac{1600}{200} = 8$. There are 8000 people for each seat in congress.

b–c. State	A	B	C	D
Standard quota	$\frac{138}{8} = 17.25$	$\frac{266}{8} = 33.25$	$\frac{534}{8} = 66.75$	$\frac{662}{8} = 82.75$
Lower quota	17	33	66	82
Upper Quota	18	34	67	83

3.

State	Population (in thousands)	Standard Quota	Lower Quota	Fractional Part	Surplus	Final Apportionment
A	138	6.9	6	0.9	1	7
B	266	13.3	13	0.3		13
C	534	26.7	26	0.7	1	27
D	662	33.1	33	0.1		33
Total	1600	80	78			80

4.

State	Population (in thousands)	Standard Quota	Lower Quota	Fractional Part	Surplus	Final Apportionment
A	138	17.25	17	0.25		17
B	266	33.25	33	0.25		33
C	534	66.75	66	0.75	1	67
D	662	82.75	82	0.75	1	83
Total	1600	200	198			200

5.

School	Enrollment	Standard Quota	Lower Quota	Fractional Part	Surplus	Final Apportionment
Humanities	1050	30.26	30	0.26		30
Social Science	1410	40.63	40	0.63	1	41
Engineering	1830	52.74	52	0.74	1	53
Business	2540	73.20	73	0.20		73
Education	3580	103.17	103	0.17		103
Total	10,410	300	298			300

We use $\frac{10,410}{300} = 34.7$ as the standard divisor.

6.

School	Enrollment	Standard Quota	Lower Quota	Fractional Part	Surplus	Final Apportionment
Liberal Arts	1180	32.60	32	0.60		32
Education	1290	35.64	35	0.64	1	36
Business	2140	59.12	59	0.12		59
Engineering	2930	80.94	80	0.94	1	81
Sciences	3320	91.71	91	0.71	1	92
Total	10,860	300.01	297			300

We use $\frac{10,860}{300} = 36.2$ as the standard divisor.

7.

State	Population	Modified Quota ($d = 32{,}920$)	Modified Lower Quota	Final Apportionment
A	126,316	3.84	3	3
B	196,492	5.97	5	5
C	425,264	12.92	12	12
D	526,664	15.998	15	15
E	725,264	22.03	22	22
Total	2,000,000		57	57

	Modified Quota	Modified	Final

8.

State	Population	($d = 7.82$)	Lower Quota	Apportionment
A	424	54.22	54	54
B	664	84.91	84	84
C	892	114.07	114	114
D	1162	148.59	148	148
Total	3142		400	400

9. There are 15,000 patients. The standard divisor is $\frac{15,000}{150}$, or 100. Try a modified divisor of 98.

Clinic	Average Weekly Patient Load	Modified Quota	Modified Lower Quota	Final Apportionment
A	1714	17.49	17	17
B	5460	55.71	55	55
C	2440	24.90	24	24
D	5386	54.96	54	54
Total	15,000		150	150

10. There are 2914 patients. The standard divisor is $\frac{2914}{70}$, or 41.63. Try a modified divisor of 39.8.

Clinic	Average Weekly Patient Load	Modified Quota	Modified Lower Quota	Final Apportionment
A	316	7.94	7	7
B	598	15.03	15	15
C	396	9.95	9	9
D	692	17.39	17	17
E	426	10.70	10	10
F	486	12.21	12	12
Total	2914		70	70

11.

Precinct	Crimes	Modified Quota ($d = 16$)	Modified Upper Quota	Final Apportionment
A	446	27.88	28	28
B	526	32.88	33	33
C	835	52.19	53	53
D	227	14.19	15	15
E	338	21.13	22	22
F	456	28.5	29	29
Total	2828		180	180

12.

Person	Contribution	Modified Quota ($d = 108$)	Modified Upper Quota	Final Apportionment
A	2013	18.64	19	19
B	187	1.73	2	2
C	290	2.69	3	3
D	3862	35.76	36	36
Total	6352		60	60

13. There is a total of $2025 to be invested. The standard divisor is $\frac{2025}{30}$, or 67.5. Try a modified divisor of 72.

Person	Amount	Modified Quota	Modified Upper Quota	Final Apportionment
A	795	11.04	12	12
B	705	9.79	10	10
C	525	7.29	8	8
Total	2025		30	30

14. There are 15,000 patients. The standard divisor is $\frac{15,000}{150}$, or 100. Try a modified divisor of 101.2.

Clinic	Average Weekly Patient Load	Modified Quota	Modified Upper Quota	Final Apportionment
A	1714	16.94	17	17
B	5460	53.95	54	54
C	2440	24.11	25	25
D	5386	53.22	54	54
Total	15,000		150	150

15.

Course	Enrollment	Modified Quota ($d = 29.6$)	Modified Rounded Quota	Final Apportionment
Introductory Algebra	130	4.39	4	4
Intermediate Algebra	282	9.53	10	10
Liberal Arts Math	188	6.35	6	6
Total	600		20	20

16.

State	Population (in thousands)	Modified Quota ($d = 9.98$)	Modified Rounded Quota	Final Apportionment
A	424	42.48	42	42
B	664	66.53	67	67
C	892	89.38	89	89
D	1162	116.43	116	116
Total	3142		314	314

17. The total number of passengers is 11,060. The standard divisor is $\frac{11,060}{200}$ or 55.3. Try a modified divisor of 55.5.

Route	Average Number of Passengers	Modified Quota	Modified Rounded Quota	Final Apportionment
A	1087	19.59	20	20
B	1323	23.84	24	24
C	1592	28.68	29	29
D	1596	28.76	29	29
E	5462	98.41	98	98
Total	11,060		200	200

18. The total number of crimes is 2828. The standard divisor is $\frac{2828}{180}$, or 15.71. Try a modified divisor of 15.7.

Precinct	Crimes	Modified Quota	Modified Rounded Quota	Final Apportionment
A	446	28.41	28	28
B	526	33.50	34	34
C	835	53.18	53	53
D	227	14.46	14	14
E	338	21.53	22	22
E	456	29.04	29	29
Total	2828		180	180

19. The total number of patients is 2000. The standard divisor is $\frac{2000}{250}$, or 8. Use Hamilton's method.

Shift	Average Number of Patients	Standard Quota	Lower Quota	Fractional Part	Surplus	Final Apportionment
A	453	56.625	56	0.625	1	57
B	650	81.25	81	0.25		81
C	547	68.375	68	0.375		68
D	350	43.75	43	0.75	1	44
Total	2000	250	248			250

20. Try a modified divisor of 7.93. Use Jefferson's method.

Shift	Average Number of Patients	Modified Quota	Modified Lower Quota	Final Apportionment
A	453	57.12	57	57
B	650	81.97	81	81
C	547	68.98	68	68
D	350	44.14	44	44
Total	2000		250	250

21. Try a modified divisor of 8.06. Use Adams' method.

Shift	Average Number of Patients	Modified Quota	Modified Upper Quota	Final Apportionment
A	453	56.20	57	57
B	650	80.65	81	81
C	547	67.87	68	68
D	350	43.42	44	44
Total	2000		250	250

22. Try a modified divisor of 8. Use Webster's method.

Shift	Average Number of Patients	Modified Quota	Modified Rounded Quota	Final Apportionment
A	453	56.625	57	57
B	650	81.25	81	81
C	547	68.375	68	68
D	350	43.75	44	44
Total	2000		250	250

23. The total population is 3,615,920. The standard divisor is $\frac{3,615,920}{105}$, or 34,437.333. Use Hamilton's method.

State	Population	Standard Quota	Lower Quota	Fractional Part	Surplus	Final Apportionment
Connecticut	236,841	6.88	6	0.88	1	7
Delaware	55,540	1.61	1	0.61	1	2
Georgia	70,835	2.06	2	0.06		2
Kentucky	68,705	1.995	1	0.995	1	2
Maryland	278,514	8.09	8	0.09		8
Massachusetts	475,327	13.80	13	0.80	1	14
New Hampshire	141,822	4.12	4	0.12		4
New Jersey	179,570	5.21	5	0.21		5
New York	331,589	9.63	9	0.63	1	10
North Carolina	353,523	10.27	10	0.27		10
Pennsylvania	432,879	12.57	12	0.57	1	13
Rhode Island	68,446	1.99	1	0.99	1	2
South Carolina	206,236	5.99	5	0.99	1	6
Vermont	85,533	2.48	2	0.48		2
Virginia	630,560	18.31	18	0.31		18
Total	3,615,920	105.005	97			105

24. Use Jefferson's method with $d = 33,000$.

State	Population	Modified Quota	Modified Lower Quota	Final Apportionment
Connecticut	236,841	7.18	7	7
Delaware	55,540	1.68	1	1
Georgia	70,835	2.15	2	2
Kentucky	68,705	2.08	2	2
Maryland	278,514	8.44	8	8
Massachusetts	475,327	14.40	14	14
New Hampshire	141,822	4.30	4	4
New Jersey	179,570	5.44	5	5
New York	331,589	10.05	10	10
North Carolina	353,523	10.71	10	10
Pennsylvania	432,879	13.12	13	13
Rhode Island	68,446	2.07	2	2
South Carolina	206,236	6.25	6	6
Vermont	85,533	2.59	2	2
Virginia	630,560	19.11	19	19
Total	3,615,920		105	105

25. Use Adams' method with $d = 36,100$.

State	Population	Modified Quota	Modified Upper Quota	Final Apportionment
Connecticut	236,841	6.56	7	7
Delaware	55,540	1.54	2	2
Georgia	70,835	1.96	2	2
Kentucky	68,705	1.90	2	2
Maryland	278,514	7.72	8	8
Massachusetts	475,327	13.17	14	14
New Hampshire	141,822	3.93	4	4
New Jersey	179,570	4.97	5	5
New York	331,589	9.19	10	10
North Carolina	353,523	9.79	10	10
Pennsylvania	432,879	11.99	12	12
Rhode Island	68,446	1.90	2	2
South Carolina	206,236	5.71	6	6
Vermont	85,533	2.37	3	3
Virginia	630,560	17.47	18	18
Total	3,615,920		105	105

26. Use Webster's method with $d = 34,500$.

State	Population	Modified Quota	Modified Rounded Quota	Final Apportionment
Connecticut	236,841	6.86	7	7
Delaware	55,540	1.61	2	2
Georgia	70,835	2.05	2	2
Kentucky	68,705	1.99	2	2
Maryland	278,514	8.07	8	8
Massachusetts	475,327	13.78	14	14
New Hampshire	141,822	4.11	4	4
New Jersey	179,570	5.20	5	5
New York	331,589	9.61	10	10
North Carolina	353,523	10.25	10	10
Pennsylvania	432,879	12.55	13	13
Rhode Island	68,446	1.98	2	2
South Carolina	206,236	5.98	6	6
Vermont	85,533	2.48	2	2
Virginia	630,560	18.28	18	18
Total	3,615,920		105	105

42. makes sense

43. does not make sense; Explanations will vary. Sample explanation: For the U.S. Senate, each state is allocated two representatives.

44. does not make sense; Explanations will vary. Sample explanation: These two methods are of similar difficulty.

45. does not make sense; Explanations will vary. Sample explanation: These data indicate an apportionment that match the upper quota and thus do not violate the quota rule.

46. Rearranging the formula standard quota = $\frac{\text{population of a group}}{\text{standard divisor}}$, we find that standard divisor = $\frac{\text{population of a group}}{\text{standard quota}}$, so for

Alabama, the standard divisor is $\frac{1,262,505}{7.671}$, or 164,581.5409. By rearranging the formula standard divisor =

$\frac{\text{total population}}{\text{number of allocated items}}$, we find that total population = (standard divisor)(number of allocated items). So for the U.S., the total population is (164,581.5409)(300), or 49,374,462.26. The nearest whole number is 49,374,462.

Check Points 14.4

1. We begin with 99 seats in the Congress.

First we compute the standard divisor: Standard divisor = $\dfrac{\text{total population}}{\text{number of allocated items}} = \dfrac{20,000}{99} = 202.02$

Using this value, make a table showing apportionment using Hamilton's method.

State	Population	Standard Quota	Lower Quota	Fractional Part	Surplus Seats	Final Apportionment
A	2060	10.20	10	0.20		10
B	2080	10.30	10	0.30	1	11
C	7730	38.26	38	0.26		38
D	8130	40.24	40	0.24		40
Total	20,000	99	98			99

Now let's see what happens with 100 seats in Congress.

First we compute the standard divisor: Standard divisor $\dfrac{\text{total population}}{\text{number of allocated items}} = \dfrac{20,000}{100} = 200$.

Using this value, make a table showing apportionment using Hamilton's method.

State	Population	Standard Quota	Lower Quota	Fractional Part	Surplus Seats	Final Apportionment
A	2060	10.3	10	0.3		10
B	2080	10.4	10	0.4		10
C	7730	38.65	38	0.65	1	39
D	8130	40.65	40	0.65	1	41
Total	20,000	100	98			100

The final apportionments are summarized in the following table.

State	Apportionment with 99 seats	Apportionment with 100 seats
A	10	10
B	11	10
C	38	39
D	40	41

When the number of seats increased from 99 to 100, B's apportionment decreased from 11 to 10.

2. a. We use Hamilton's method to find the apportionment for each state with its original population. First we compute the standard divisor.

$$\text{Standard divisor} = \frac{\text{total population}}{\text{number of allocated items}} = \frac{200,000}{100} = 2000$$

Using this value, we show the apportionment in the following table.

State	Original Population	Standard Quota	Lower Quota	Fractional Part	Surplus Seats	Final Apportionment
A	19,110	9.56	9	0.56	1	10
B	39,090	19.55	19	0.55		19
C	141,800	70.9	70	0.9	1	71
Total	200,000	100.01	98			100

b. The fraction for percent increase is the amount of increase divided by the original amount. The percent increase in the population of each state is determined as follows.

State A: $\dfrac{19,302-19,110}{19,110} = \dfrac{192}{19,110} \approx 0.01005 = 1.005\%$

State B: $\dfrac{39,480-39,090}{39,090} = \dfrac{390}{39,090} \approx 0.00998 = 0.998\%$

State A is increasing at a rate of 1.005%. This is faster than State B, which is increasing at a rate of 0.998%.

c. We use Hamilton's method to find the apportionment for each state with its new population. First we compute the standard divisor.

$$\text{Standard divisor} = \frac{\text{total population}}{\text{number of allocated items}} = \frac{200,582}{100} = 2005.82$$

Using this value, we show the apportionment in the following table.

State	New Population	Standard Quota	Lower Quota	Fractional Part	Surplus Seats	Final Apportionment
A	19,302	9.62	9	0.62		9
B	39,480	19.68	19	0.68	1	20
C	141,800	70.69	70	0.69	1	71
Total	200,582	99.99	98			100

The final apportionments are summarized in the following table.

State	Growth Rate	Original Apportionment	New Apportionment
A	1.005%	10	9
B	0.998%	19	20
C	0%	71	71

State A loses a seat to State B, even though the population of State A is increasing at a faster rate. This is an example of the population paradox.

3. a. We use Hamilton's method to find the apportionment for each school. First we compute the standard divisor.

$$\text{Standard divisor} = \frac{\text{total population}}{\text{number of allocated items}} = \frac{12,000}{100} = 120$$

Using this value, we show the apportionment in the following table.

School	Enrollment	Standard Quota	Lower Quota	Fractional Part	Surplus	Final Apportionment
East High	2574	21.45	21	0.45		21
West High	9426	78.55	78	0.55	1	79
Total	12,000	100	99			100

b. Again we use Hamilton's method.

$$\text{Standard divisor} = \frac{\text{total population}}{\text{number of allocated items}} = \frac{12,750}{106} = 120.28$$

Using this value, we show the apportionment in the following table

School	Enrollment	Standard Quota	Lower Quota	Fractional Part	Surplus	Final Apportionment
East High	2574	21.40	21	0.40	1	22
West High	9426	78.37	78	0.37		78
North High	750	6.24	6	0.24		6
Total	12,750	106.01	105			106

West High has lost a counselor to East High.

Exercise Set 14.4

1. a. The standard divisor is $\frac{1800}{30}$, or 60.

Course	Enrollment	Standard Quota	Lower Quota	Fractional Part	Surplus	Final Apportionment
College Algebra	978	16.30	16	0.30		16
Statistics	500	8.33	8	0.33		8
Liberal Arts Math	322	5.37	5	0.37	1	6
Total	1800	30	29			30

b. The standard divisor is $\frac{1800}{31}$, or 58.06.

Course	Enrollment	Standard Quota	Lower Quota	Fractional Part	Surplus	Final Apportionment
College Algebra	978	16.84	16	0.84	1	17
Statistics	500	8.61	8	0.61	1	9
Liberal Arts Math	322	5.55	5	0.55		5
Total	1800	31	29			31

Liberal Arts Math loses a teaching assistant when the total number of teaching assistants is raised from 30 to 31. This is an example of the Alabama paradox.

2. a. The standard divisor is $\frac{14,250}{57} = 250$.

School	Enrollment	Standard Quota	Lower Quota	Fractional Part	Surplus	Final Apportionment
A	5040	20.16	20	0.16		20
B	4560	18.24	18	0.24		18
C	4040	16.16	16	0.16		16
D	610	2.44	2	0.44	1	3
Total	14,250	57	56			57

b. The standard divisor is $\frac{14,250}{58} = 245.69$.

School	Enrollment	Standard Quota	Lower Quota	Fractional Part	Surplus	Final Apportionment
A	5040	20.51	20	0.51	1	21
B	4560	18.56	18	0.56	1	19
C	4040	16.44	16	0.44		16
D	610	2.48	2	0.48		2
Total	14,250	57.99	56			58

D loses one laptop when the total number of laptops is increased from 57 to 58. This is an example of the Alabama paradox.

3. Standard divisor with 40 seats: $\frac{20,000}{40} = 500$. Use Hamilton's method.

State	Population	Standard Quota	Lower Quota	Fractional Part	Surplus	Final Apportionment
A	680	1.36	1	0.36	1	2
B	9150	18.30	18	0.30		18
C	10,170	20.34	20	0.34		20
Total	20,000	40	39			40

Standard divisor with 41 seats: $\frac{20,000}{41} = 487.8$. Use Hamilton's method.

State	Population	Standard Quota	Lower Quota	Fractional Part	Surplus	Final Apportionment
A	680	1.39	1	0.39		1
B	9150	18.76	18	0.76	1	19
C	10,170	20.85	20	0.85	1	21
Total	20,000	41	39			41

State A loses a seat when the total number of seats increases from 40 to 41.

4. Standard divisor with 24 seats: $\frac{3760}{24} = 156.7$. Use Hamilton's method.

State	Population (in thousands)	Standard Quota	Lower Quota	Fractional Part	Surplus	Final Apportionment
A	530	3.38	3	0.38	1	4
B	990	6.32	6	0.32		6
C	2240	14.30	14	0.30		14
Total	3760	24	23			24

Standard divisor with 25 seats: $\frac{3760}{25} = 150.4$. Use Hamilton's method.

State	Population (in thousands)	Standard Quota	Lower Quota	Fractional Part	Surplus	Final Apportionment
A	530	3.52	3	0.52		3
B	990	6.58	6	0.58	1	7
C	2240	14.89	14	0.89	1	15
Total	3760	25	23			25

A loses a seat when the total number of seats increases from 24 to 25.

5. a. Standard divisor: $\frac{3760}{24} = 156.7$. Use Hamilton's method.

State	Original Population	Standard Quota	Lower Quota	Fractional Part	Surplus	Final Apportionment
A	530	3.38	3	0.38	1	4
B	990	6.32	6	0.32		6
C	2240	14.30	14	0.30		14
Total	3760	24	23			24

b. Percent increase for state A: $\dfrac{680 - 530}{530} \approx 0.283 = 28.3\%$

Percent increase for state B: $\dfrac{1250 - 990}{990} \approx 0.263 = 26.3\%$

Percent increase for state C: $\dfrac{2570 - 2240}{2240} \approx 0.147 = 14.7\%$

c. Standard divisor: $\frac{4500}{24} = 187.5$. Use Hamilton's method.

State	New Population	Standard Quota	Lower Quota	Fractional Part	Surplus	Final Apportionment
A	680	3.63	3	0.63		3
B	1250	6.67	6	0.67	1	7
C	2570	13.71	13	0.71	1	14
Total	4500	24.01	22			24

A loses a seat while B gains, even though A has a faster increasing population. The population paradox does occur.

6. a. Standard divisor: $\frac{20,000}{200} = 100$.

State	Original Population	Standard Quota	Lower Quota	Fractional Part	Surplus	Final Apportionment
A	2224	22.24	22	0.24		22
B	2236	22.36	22	0.36		22
C	2640	26.40	26	0.40	1	27
D	3030	30.30	30	0.30		30
E	9870	98.70	98	0.70	1	99
Total	20,000	200	198			200

b. State A: $\dfrac{2424 - 2224}{2224} \approx 0.090 = 9.0\%$

State B: $\dfrac{2436 - 2236}{2236} \approx 0.089 = 8.9\%$

State C: $\dfrac{2740 - 2640}{2640} \approx 0.038 = 3.8\%$

State D: $\dfrac{3130 - 3030}{3030} \approx 0.033 = 3.3\%$

State E: $\dfrac{10,070 - 9870}{9870} \approx 0.020 = 2.0\%$

c. Standard divisor: $\dfrac{20,800}{200} = 104$

State	New Population	Standard Quota	Lower Quota	Fractional Part	Surplus	Final Apportionment
A	2424	23.31	23	0.31		23
B	2436	23.42	23	0.42	1	24
C	2740	26.35	26	0.35		26
D	3130	30.10	30	0.10		30
E	10,070	96.83	96	0.83	1	97
Total	20,800	200.01	198			200

State A has a larger percent population change than state B, but B gains more seats. This is a paradoxical result, but it is not technically an instance of the population paradox, since no state actually loses seats to another state with a lower percent population change. Notice also that state C has a larger percent population change than state D, but C loses a seat while D remains unchanged. If C lost a seat and D gained one, that would be an example of the population paradox.

7. Original standard divisor: $\dfrac{8880}{40} = 222$

District	Original Population	Standard Quota	Lower Quota	Fractional Part	Surplus	Final Apportionment
A	1188	5.35	5	0.35		5
B	1424	6.41	6	0.41		6
C	2538	11.43	11	0.43	1	12
D	3730	16.80	16	0.80	1	17
Total	8880	39.99	38			40

New standard divisor: $\dfrac{9000}{40} = 225$

District	New Population	Standard Quota	Lower Quota	Fractional Part	Surplus	Final Apportionment
A	1188	5.28	5	0.28		5
B	1420	6.311	6	0.311	1	7
C	2544	11.307	11	0.307		11
D	3848	17.10	17	0.10		17
Total	9000	39.998	39			40

Percent increase by state:

A: 0% (no change)   B: $\dfrac{1420 - 1424}{1424} \approx -0.0028 = -0.28\%$

C: $\dfrac{2544 - 2538}{2538} \approx 0.0024 = 0.24\%$ D: $\dfrac{3848 - 3730}{3730} \approx 0.032 = 3.2\%$

C loses a truck to B even though C increased in population faster than B. This shows the population paradox occurs.

8. Original standard divisor: $\dfrac{9000}{50} = 180$

District	Original Population	Standard Quota	Lower Quota	Fractional Part	Surplus	Final Apportionment
A	780	4.33	4	0.33		4
B	1500	8.33	8	0.33		8
C	1730	9.61	9	0.61	1	10
D	2040	11.33	11	0.33		11
E	2950	16.39	16	0.39	1	17
Total	9000	49.99	48			50

New standard divisor: $\dfrac{9090}{50} = 181.8$

District	New Population	Standard Quota	Lower Quota	Fractional Part	Surplus	Final Apportionment
A	780	4.29	4	0.29	1	5
B	1500	8.25	8	0.25		8
C	1810	9.96	9	0.96	1	10
D	2040	11.22	11	0.22		11
E	2960	16.28	16	0.28		16
Total	9090	50	48			50

Percent increase by state: A, B, D: 0% (no change)

C: $\dfrac{1810-1730}{1730} \approx 0.046 = 4.6\%$ E: $\dfrac{2960-2950}{2950} \approx 0.0034 = 0.34\%$

E loses a truck to A even though E has a faster population increase. This shows that the population paradox occurs.

9. a. Standard divisor: $\dfrac{10,000}{100} = 100$

Branch	Employees	Standard Quota	Lower Quota	Fractional Part	Surplus	Final Apportionment
A	1045	10.45	10	0.45		10
B	8955	89.55	89	0.55	1	90
Total	10,000	100	99			100

b. New standard divisor: $\dfrac{10,525}{105} = 100.238$

Branch	Employees	Standard Quota	Lower Quota	Fractional Part	Surplus	Final Apportionment
A	1045	10.43	10	0.43	1	11
B	8955	89.34	89	0.34		89
C	525	5.24	5	0.24		5
Total	10,525	105.01	104			105

Branch B loses a promotion when branch C is added. This means the new-states paradox has occurred.

10. a. Standard divisor: $\dfrac{3000}{60} = 50$

Branch	Employees	Standard Quota	Lower Quota	Fractional Part	Surplus	Final Apportionment
A	209	4.18	4	0.18		4
B	769	15.38	15	0.38		15
C	2022	40.44	40	0.44	1	41
Total	3000	60	59			60

b. New standard divisor: $\dfrac{3260}{65} = 50.15$

Branch	Employees	Standard Quota	Lower Quota	Fractional Part	Surplus	Final Apportionment
A	209	4.17	4	0.17		4
B	769	15.33	15	0.33	1	16
C	2022	40.32	40	0.32		40
D	260	5.18	5	0.18		5
Total	3260	65	64			65

Branch C loses a promotion when branch D is added. This means the new-states paradox has occurred.

11. a. Standard divisor: $\dfrac{9450 + 90{,}550}{100} = 1000$

State	Population	Standard Quota	Lower Quota	Fractional Part	Surplus	Final Apportionment
A	9450	9.45	9	0.45		9
B	90,550	90.55	90	0.55	1	91
Total	100,000	100	99			100

b. New standard divisor: $\dfrac{100{,}000 + 10{,}400}{110} = 1003.64$

State	Population	Standard Quota	Lower Quota	Fractional Part	Surplus	Final Apportionment
A	9450	9.42	9	0.42	1	10
B	90,550	90.22	90	0.22		90
C	10,400	10.36	10	0.36		10
Total	110,400	110	109			110

State B loses a seat when state C is added.

12. a. Standard divisor: $\dfrac{99{,}000 + 214{,}000 + 487{,}000}{50} = 16{,}000$

State	Population	Standard Quota	Lower Quota	Fractional Part	Surplus	Final Apportionment
A	99,000	6.19	6	0.19		6
B	214,000	13.38	13	0.38		13
C	487,000	30.44	30	0.44	1	31
Total	800,000	50.01	49			50

b. New standard divisor: $\dfrac{800{,}000+116{,}000}{57}=16{,}070.175$

State	Population	Standard Quota	Lower Quota	Fractional Part	Surplus	Final Apportionment
A	99,000	6.16	6	0.16		6
B	214,000	13.32	13	0.32	1	14
C	487,000	30.30	30	0.30		30
D	116,000	7.22	7	0.22		7
Total	916,000	57	56			57

State C loses a seat when State D is added.

13. a.

State	Population	Modified Quota	Modified Lower Quota	Final Apportionment
A	99,000	6.39	6	6
B	214,000	13.81	13	13
C	487,000	31.42	31	31
Total	800,000		50	50

b.

State	Population	Modified Quota	Modified Lower Quota	Final Apportionment
A	99,000	6.39	6	6
B	214,000	13.81	13	13
C	487,000	31.42	31	37
D	116,000	7.48	7	7
Total	916,000		57	57

The new-states paradox does not occur. As long as the modified divisor, d, remains the same, adding a new state cannot change the number of seats held by existing states.

18. makes sense

19. makes sense

20. does not make sense; Explanations will vary. Sample explanation: Balinski and Young's theorem deals with apportionment methods, not voting methods.

21. does not make sense; Explanations will vary. Sample explanation: Mathematicians (Balinski and Young) have proved this to be impossible.

Chapter 14 Review Exercises

1.

Number of Votes	4	3	3	2
First Choice	A	B	C	C
Second Choice	B	D	B	B
Third Choice	C	C	D	A
Fourth Choice	D	A	A	D

2. $9 + 5 + 4 + 2 + 2 + 1 = 23$

3. 4

4. $9 + 5 + 2 = 16$

5. $9 + 5 = 14$

6. M receives 12 first-choice votes, compared to 10 for C and 2 for D, so M (Musical) is selected.

7.

Number of Votes	10	8	4	2
First Choice: 3 points	C: $10 \times 3 = 30$	M: $8 \times 3 = 24$	M: $4 \times 3 = 12$	D: $2 \times 3 = 6$
Second Choice: 2 points	D: $10 \times 2 = 20$	C: $8 \times 2 = 16$	D: $4 \times 2 = 8$	M: $2 \times 2 = 4$
Third Choice: 1 point	M: $10 \times 1 = 10$	D: $8 \times 1 = 8$	C: $4 \times 1 = 4$	C: $2 \times 1 = 2$

C gets $30 + 16 + 4 + 2 = 52$ points.
D gets $20 + 8 + 8 + 6 = 42$ points.
M gets $10 + 24 + 12 + 4 = 50$ points.

C (Comedy) gets the most points and is chosen.

8. There are 24 voters, so 13 votes are needed for a majority. None of the candidates has 13 first-place votes. D has the fewest first-place votes and is eliminated in the next round.

Number of Votes	10	14
First Choice	C	M
Second Choice	M	C

M (Musical) has 14 first-place votes, a majority, so a musical is selected.

9. There are 3 choices so we make $\frac{3(3-1)}{2} = 3$ comparisons.

Comparison	Vote Results	Conclusion
C vs. D	18 voters prefer C to D. 6 voters prefer D to C.	C wins and gets 1 point.
C vs. M	10 voters prefer C to M. 14 voters prefer M to C.	M wins and gets 1 point.
D vs. M	12 voters prefer D to M. 12 voters prefer M to D.	D and M tie. Each gets $\frac{1}{2}$ point.

C gets 1 point, D gets $\frac{1}{2}$ point, and M gets $1\frac{1}{2}$ points. So M (Musical) wins, and is selected.

10. A receives 40 first-place votes, compared to 30 for B, 6 for C, and 2 for D. So A wins.

11.

Number of Votes	40	30	6	2
First Choice: 4 points	A: 40 × 4 = 160	B: 30 × 4 = 120	C: 6 × 4 = 24	D: 2 × 4 = 8
Second Choice: 3 points	B: 40 × 3 = 120	C: 30 × 3 = 90	D: 6 × 3 = 18	B: 2 × 3 = 6
Third Choice: 2 points	C: 40 × 2 = 80	D: 30 × 2 = 60	B: 6 × 2 = 12	C: 2 × 2 = 4
Fourth Choice: 1 point	D: 40 × 1 = 40	A: 30 × 1 = 30	A: 6 × 1 = 6	A: 2 × 1 = 2

A gets 160 + 30 + 6 + 2 = 198 points.
B gets 120 + 120 + 12 + 6 = 258 points.
C gets 80 + 90 + 24 + 4 = 198 points.
D gets 40 + 60 + 18 + 8 = 126 points.

B receives the most points, and wins.

12. There are 78 voters, so 40 first-place votes are needed for a majority. A has 40 first-place votes, and wins.

13. There are 4 candidates, so $\frac{4(4-1)}{2} = 6$ comparisons are needed.

Comparison	Vote Results	Conclusion
A vs. B	40 voters prefer A to B. 38 voters prefer B to A.	A wins and gets 1 point.
A vs. C	40 voters prefer A to C. 38 voters prefer C to A.	A wins and gets 1 point.
A vs. D	40 voters prefer A to D. 38 voters prefer D to A.	A wins and gets 1 point.
B vs. C	72 voters prefer B to C. 6 voters prefer C to B.	B wins and gets 1 point.
B vs. D	70 voters prefer B to D. 8 voters prefer D to B.	B wins and gets 1 point.
C vs. D	76 voters prefer C to D. 2 voters prefer D to C.	C wins and gets 1 point.

A gets 3 points, B gets 2 points, C gets 1 point, and D gets 0 points. So A wins.

14.

Number of Votes	1500	600	300
First Choice: 4 points	A: 1500 × 4 = 6000	B: 600 × 4 = 2400	C: 300 × 4 = 1200
Second Choice: 3 points	B: 1500 × 3 = 4500	D: 600 × 3 = 1800	B: 300 × 3 = 900
Third Choice: 2 points	C: 1500 × 2 = 3000	C: 600 × 2 = 1200	D: 300 × 2 = 600
Fourth Choice: 1 point	D: 1500 × 1 = 1500	A: 600 × 1 = 600	A: 300 × 1 = 300

A gets 6000 + 600 + 300 = 6900 points.
B gets 4500 + 2400 + 900 = 7800 points.
C gets 3000 + 1200 + 1200 = 5400 points.
D gets 1500 + 1800 + 600 = 3900 points.

B receives the most points, and wins.

15. A has a majority of first-place votes. In Exercise 14, B wins and so the majority criterion is not satisfied.

16. A is favored above all others using a head-to-head comparison. This is automatically true, since A has a majority of first-place votes. In Exercise 14, B wins and so the head-to-head criterion is not satisfied.

17. There are 2500 voters. 1251 first-place votes are needed for a majority. B has 1500 first-place votes, and is the winner.

18. B is favored above all others using a head-to-head comparison. This is automatically true, since B has a majority of first-place votes. In Exercise 17, B wins and so the head-to-head criterion is satisfied.

19. A receives 180 first-place votes, compared with 100 for B, 30 for C, and 40 for D. Therefore A wins.

20.

Number of Votes	180	100	40	30
First Choice: 4 points	A: $180 \times 4 = 720$	B: $100 \times 4 = 400$	D: $40 \times 4 = 160$	C: $30 \times 4 = 120$
Second Choice: 3 points	B: $180 \times 3 = 540$	D: $100 \times 3 = 300$	B: $40 \times 3 = 120$	B: $30 \times 3 = 90$
Third Choice: 2 points	C: $180 \times 2 = 360$	A: $100 \times 2 = 200$	C: $40 \times 2 = 80$	A: $30 \times 2 = 60$
Fourth Choice: 1 point	D: $180 \times 1 = 180$	C: $100 \times 1 = 100$	A: $40 \times 1 = 40$	D: $30 \times 1 = 30$

A gets $720 + 200 + 40 + 60 = 1020$ points.
B gets $540 + 400 + 120 + 90 = 1150$ points.
C gets $360 + 100 + 80 + 120 = 660$ points.
D gets $180 + 300 + 160 + 30 = 670$ points.

B gets the most points, and wins.

21. There are 350 voters. 176 first-place votes are needed for a majority. A has 180 votes, a majority, and wins.

22. There are 4 candidates, and therefore $\frac{4(4-1)}{2} = 6$ comparisons.

Comparison	Vote Results	Conclusion
A vs. B	180 voters prefer A to B. 170 voters prefer B to A.	A wins and gets 1 point.
A vs. C	280 voters prefer A to C. 70 voters prefer C to A.	A wins and gets 1 point.
A vs. D	210 voters prefer A to D. 140 voters prefer D to A.	A wins and gets 1 point.
B vs. C	320 voters prefer B to C. 30 voters prefer C to B.	B wins and gets 1 point.
B vs. D	310 voters prefer B to D. 40 voters prefer D to B.	B wins and gets 1 point.
C vs. D	210 voters prefer C to D. 140 voters prefer D to C.	C wins and gets 1 point.

A gets 3 points, B gets 2 points, C gets 1 point, and D gets 0 points. Therefore A wins.

23. A has a majority of first-place votes. Based on Exercises 19–22, only the Borda count method violates the majority criterion. B wins by the Borda count method.

24. There are 1450 voters. 726 first-place votes are needed for a majority. No candidate has a majority. A has the fewest first-place votes and is eliminated in the next round.

Number of Votes	900	550
First Choice	B	C
Second Choice	C	B

B has the majority of first-place votes, and wins.

25. There is a new preference table:

Number of Votes	700	400	350
First Choice	B	A	C
Second Choice	C	B	A
Third Choice	A	C	B

No candidate has a majority of first-place votes. C has the fewest first-place votes, and is eliminated in the next round.

Number of Votes	700	750
First Choice	B	A
Second Choice	A	B

A has a majority of first-place votes, and wins. This does not satisfy the monotonicity criterion, since the only change gave B more first-place votes, but after the change B lost the election.

26. A has 400 first-place votes, compared to 200 for B and 250 for C. Therefore A wins.

27.
Number of Votes	400	450
First Choice	A	C
Second Choice	C	A

C has the majority of first-place votes, and wins this election. The irrelevant alternatives criterion is not satisfied, because removing B changes the winner from A to C.

28.
Number of Votes	400	250	200
First Choice: 3 points	A: $400 \times 3 = 1200$	C: $250 \times 3 = 750$	B: $200 \times 3 = 600$
Second Choice: 2 points	B: $400 \times 2 = 800$	B: $250 \times 2 = 500$	C: $200 \times 2 = 400$
Third Choice: 1 point	C: $400 \times 1 = 400$	A: $250 \times 1 = 250$	A: $200 \times 1 = 200$

A gets $1200 + 250 + 200 = 1650$ points.
B gets $800 + 500 + 600 = 1900$ points.
C gets $400 + 750 + 400 = 1550$ points.

B gets the most points, and wins.

29.
Number of Votes	400	450
First Choice: 2 points	A: $400 \times 2 = 800$	B: $450 \times 2 = 900$
Second Choice: 1 point	B: $400 \times 1 = 400$	A: $450 \times 1 = 450$

A gets $800 + 450 = 1250$ points.
B gets $400 + 900 = 1300$ points.

B still gets the most points, and wins. The same thing happens if A drops out instead of C, and so the irrelevant alternatives criterion is satisfied.

30. $\dfrac{275 + 392 + 611 + 724}{40} = \dfrac{2002}{40} = 50.05$

31. With a standard divisor of 50.05:

Clinic	A	B	C	D
Average weekly patient load	275	392	611	724
Standard Quota	5.49	7.83	12.21	14.47

32. Using the results of Exercise 31:

Clinic	Standard Quota	Lower Quota	Upper Quota
A	5.49	5	6
B	7.83	7	8
C	12.21	12	13
D	14.47	14	15

33.

Clinic	Standard Quota	Lower Quota	Fractional Part	Surplus	Final Apportionment
A	5.49	5	0.49	1	6
B	7.83	7	0.83	1	8
C	12.21	12	0.21		12
D	14.47	14	0.47		14
Total	40	38			40

34.

Clinic	Average Weekly Patient Load	Modified Quota ($d = 48$)	Modified Lower Quota	Final Apportionment
A	275	5.73	5	5
B	392	8.17	8	8
C	611	12.73	12	12
D	724	15.08	15	15
Total	2002		40	40

35.

Clinic	Average Weekly Patient Load	Modified Quota ($d = 52$)	Modified Upper Quota	Final Apportionment
A	275	5.29	6	6
B	392	7.54	8	8
C	611	11.75	12	12
D	724	13.92	14	14
Total	2002		40	40

36.

Clinic	Average Weekly Patient Load	Modified Quota ($d = 49.95$)	Modified Rounded Quota	Final Apportionment
A	275	5.51	6	6
B	392	7.85	8	8
C	611	12.23	12	12
D	724	14.49	14	14
Total	2002		40	40

37. Standard divisor: $\dfrac{3320+10,060+15,020+19,600}{200} = \dfrac{48,000}{200} = 240$

State	Population	Standard Quota	Lower Quota	Fractional Part	Surplus	Final Apportionment
A	3320	13.83	13	0.83	1	14
B	10,060	41.92	41	0.92	1	42
C	15,020	62.58	62	0.58		62
D	19,600	81.67	81	0.67	1	82
Total	48,000	200	197			200

38. Try modified divisor $d = 238$.

State	Population	Modified Quota	Modified Lower Quota	Final Apportionment
A	3320	13.95	13	13
B	10,060	42.27	42	42
C	15,020	63.11	63	63
D	19,600	82.35	82	82
Total	48,000		200	200

39. Try modified divisor $d = 242$.

State	Population	Modified Quota	Modified Upper Quota	Final Apportionment
A	3320	13.72	14	14
B	10,060	41.57	42	42
C	15,020	62.07	63	63
D	19,600	80.99	81	81
Total	48,000		200	200

40. Try modified divisor $d = 240.4$.

State	Population	Modified Quota	Modified Rounded Quota	Final Apportionment
A	3320	13.81	14	14
B	10,060	41.85	42	42
C	15,020	62.48	62	62
D	19,600	81.53	82	82
Total	48,000		200	200

41. a. Standard divisor: $\dfrac{7500}{150} = 50$

School	Enrollment	Standard Quota	Lower Quota	Fractional Part	Surplus	Final Apportionment
A	370	7.4	7	0.4	1	8
B	3365	67.3	67	0.3		67
C	3765	75.3	75	0.3		75
Total	7500	150	149			150

b. Standard divisor: $\dfrac{7500}{151} = 49.67$

School	Enrollment	Standard Quota	Lower Quota	Fractional Part	Surplus	Final Apportionment
A	370	7.45	7	0.45		7
B	3365	67.75	67	0.75	1	68
C	3765	75.80	75	0.80	1	76
Total	7500	151	149			151

The Alabama paradox occurs. A loses a laptop when the overall number of laptops changes from 150 to 151.

42. a. Standard divisor: $\dfrac{200,000}{100} = 2000$

School	Original Population	Standard Quota	Lower Quota	Fractional Part	Surplus	Final Apportionment
A	143,796	71.90	71	0.90	1	72
B	41,090	20.55	20	0.55		20
C	15,114	7.56	7	0.56	1	8
Total	200,000	100.01	98			100

b. Percent increase of B: $\dfrac{41,420 - 41,090}{41,090} \approx 0.0080 = 0.8\%$

Percent increase of C: $\dfrac{15,304 - 15,114}{15,114} \approx 0.0126 \approx 1.3\%$

c. Standard divisor: $\dfrac{200,520}{100} = 2005.2$

School	New Population	Standard Quota	Lower Quota	Fractional Part	Surplus	Final Apportionment
A	143,796	71.71	71	0.71	1	72
B	41,420	20.66	20	0.66	1	21
C	15,304	7.63	7	0.63		7
Total	200,520	100	98			100

The population paradox occurs. C loses a seat to B, even though C is growing faster.

43. a. Standard divisor: $\dfrac{1650}{33} = 50$

Branch	Employees	Standard Quota	Lower Quota	Fractional Part	Surplus	Final Apportionment
A	372	7.44	7	0.44		7
B	1278	25.56	25	0.56	1	26
Total	1650	33	32			33

b. Standard divisor: $\dfrac{2005}{40} = 50.125$

Branch	Employees	Standard Quota	Lower Quota	Fractional Part	Surplus	Final Apportionment
A	372	7.42	7	0.42		7
B	1278	25.50	25	0.50	1	26
C	355	7.08	7	0.08		7
Total	2005	40	39			40

The new-states paradox does not occur. Neither branch A nor branch B loses any promotions.

44. False. Answers will vary.

Chapter 14 Test

1. $1200 + 900 + 900 + 600 = 3600$

2. 600

3. $900 + 600 = 1500$

4. $900 + 600 = 1500$

5. A received 1200 first-place votes, B received 1500, and C received 900. Therefore B wins.

6.

Number of Votes	1200	900	900	600
First Choice: 3 points	A: $1200 \times 3 = 3600$	C: $900 \times 3 = 2700$	B: $900 \times 3 = 2700$	B: $600 \times 3 = 1800$
Second Choice: 2 points	B: $1200 \times 2 = 2400$	A: $900 \times 2 = 1800$	C: $900 \times 2 = 1800$	A: $600 \times 2 = 1200$
Third Choice: 1 point	C: $1200 \times 1 = 1200$	B: $900 \times 1 = 900$	A: $900 \times 1 = 900$	C: $600 \times 1 = 600$

A gets $3600 + 1800 + 900 + 1200 = 7500$ points.
B gets $2400 + 900 + 2700 + 1800 = 7800$ points.
C gets $1200 + 2700 + 1800 + 600 = 6300$ points.

B receives the most points and is the winner.

7. There are 3600 voters. 1801 first-place votes are needed for a majority. No candidate has a majority. C receives the fewest first-place votes and is eliminated in the next round.

Number of Votes	2100	1500
First Choice	A	B
Second Choice	B	A

A receives the majority of first-place votes, and wins.

8. There are 3 candidates. The number of comparisons is $\frac{3(3-1)}{2}$, or 3.

Comparison	Vote Results	Conclusion
A vs. B	2100 voters prefer A to B. 1500 voters prefer B to A.	A wins and gets 1 point.
A vs. C	1800 voters prefer A to C. 1800 voters prefer C to A.	A and C tie. Each gets $\frac{1}{2}$ point.
B vs. C	2700 voters prefer B to C. 900 voters prefer C to B.	B wins and gets 1 point.

A gets $1\frac{1}{2}$ points, B gets 1 point, and C gets $\frac{1}{2}$ point. Therefore A wins.

9.

Number of Votes	240	160	60
First Choice: 4 points	A: $240 \times 4 = 960$	C: $160 \times 4 = 640$	D: $60 \times 4 = 240$
Second Choice: 3 points	B: $240 \times 3 = 720$	B: $160 \times 3 = 480$	A: $60 \times 3 = 180$
Third Choice: 2 points	C: $240 \times 2 = 480$	D: $160 \times 2 = 320$	C: $60 \times 2 = 120$
Fourth Choice: 1 point	D: $240 \times 1 = 240$	A: $160 \times 1 = 160$	B: $60 \times 1 = 60$

A gets $960 + 160 + 180 = 1300$ points.
B gets $720 + 480 + 60 = 1260$ points.
C gets $480 + 640 + 120 = 1240$ points.
D gets $240 + 320 + 240 = 800$ points.

A gets the most points, and wins.

10. A has the majority of first-place votes. Based on Exercise 9, the majority criterion is satisfied.

11. A has 1500 first-place votes, whereas B and C have 1000 each. Therefore A wins.

12. B is favored when compared to A, by 2000 votes to 1500. B is favored when compared to C, by 2500 votes to 1000. So B is favored in each head-to-head comparison. Based on Exercise 11, the head-to-head criterion is not satisfied, because A wins the election.

13. There are 210 voters. 106 votes are needed for a majority. No candidate has a majority. B receives the fewest first-place votes and is eliminated in the next round.

Number of Votes	130	80
First Choice	C	A
Second Choice	A	C

C receives a majority of votes, and wins.

14. New preference table:

Number of Votes	100	60	50
First Choice	C	B	A
Second Choice	A	C	B
Third Choice	B	A	C

No candidate has a majority. A has the fewest first-place votes and is eliminated in the next round.

Number of Votes	100	110
First Choice	C	B
Second Choice	B	C

B has the majority of first-place votes, and wins. The monotonicity criterion is not satisfied, because the only change gave more first-place votes to C, but C lost the second election.

15. B has 90 first-place votes, C has 75, and A has 45. Therefore B wins. If C drops out, there is a new preference table:

Number of Votes	90	120
First Choice	B	A
Second Choice	A	B

A has a majority of first-place votes, and wins. This changed outcome shows that the irrelevant alternatives criterion is not satisfied.

16. $\dfrac{119+165+216}{10} = \dfrac{500}{10} = 50$

17. A: $\dfrac{119}{50} = 2.38$ \qquad B: $\dfrac{165}{50} = 3.3$ \qquad C: $\dfrac{216}{50} = 4.32$

18. A: 2, 3; B: 3, 4; C: 4, 5

19.

Clinic	Average Weekly Patient Load	Standard Quota	Lower Quota	Fractional Part	Surplus	Final Apportionment
A	119	2.38	2	0.38	1	3
B	165	3.3	3	0.3		3
C	216	4.32	4	0.32		4
Total	500	10	9			10

20.

Clinic	Average Weekly Patient Load	Modified Quota ($d = 42$)	Modified Lower Quota	Final Apportionment
A	119	2.83	2	2
B	165	3.93	3	3
C	216	5.14	5	5
Total	500		10	10

21.

Clinic	Average Weekly Patient Load	Modified Quota ($d = 56$)	Modified Upper Quota	Final Apportionment
A	119	2.13	3	3
B	165	2.95	3	3
C	216	3.86	4	4
Total	500		10	10

22.

Clinic	Average Weekly Patient Load	Modified Quota ($d = 47.7$)	Modified Rounded Quota	Final Apportionment
A	119	2.49	2	2
B	165	3.46	3	3
C	216	4.52	5	5
Total	500		10	10

23. New standard divisor: $\dfrac{500}{11} = 45.45$

Clinic	Average Weekly Patient Load	Standard Quota	Lower Quota	Fractional Part	Surplus	Final Apportionment
A	119	2.62	2	0.62		2
B	165	3.63	3	0.63	1	4
C	216	4.75	4	0.75	1	5
Total	500	11	9			11

The Alabama paradox occurs. Clinic A loses one doctor when the total number of doctors is raised from 10 to 11.

24. New standard divisor: $\dfrac{500+110}{12} = \dfrac{610}{12} = 50.83$

Clinic	Average Weekly Patient Load	Standard Quota	Lower Quota	Fractional Part	Surplus	Final Apportionment
A	119	2.34	2	0.34	1	3
B	165	3.25	3	0.25		3
C	216	4.25	4	0.25		4
D	110	2.16	2	0.16		2
Total	610	12	11			12

The new-states paradox does not occur. No clinic loses doctors when a new clinic is added.

25. Answers will vary.

Check Points 15.1

1. Graphs (a) and (b) both have vertices *A, B, C, D,* and *E.* Also, both graphs have edges *AB, AC, BD, BE, CD, CE,* and *DE.*

   Because the two graphs have the same number of vertices connected to each other in the same way, they are the same. In fact, graph (b) is just graph (a) rotated clockwise and bent out of shape.

2. Draw points for the five land masses and label them *N, S, A, B,* and *C.*

   There is one bridge that connects North Metroville to Island *A,* so one edge is drawn connecting vertex *N* to vertex *A.* Similarly, one edge connects vertex *A* with vertex *B,* and one edge connects vertex *B* with vertex *C.* Since there are two bridges connecting Island *C* to South Metroville, two edges connect vertex *C* with vertex *S.*

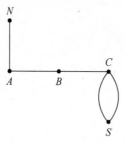

3. We use the abbreviations for the states to label the vertices: ID for Idaho, MT for Montana, WY for Wyoming, UT for Utah, and CO for Colorado. The precise placement of these vertices is not important.

   Whenever two states share a common border, we connect the respective vertices with an edge. For example, Idaho shares a common border with Montana, with Wyoming, and with Utah. Continuing in this manner, we obtain the following graph.

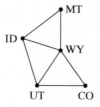

4. We use the letters in Figure 15.13 to label each vertex. Only one door connects the outside, *E,* with room *B,* so we draw one edge from vertex *E* to vertex *B.* Two doors connect the outside, *E,* to room *D,* so we draw two edges from *E* to *D.* Counting doors between the rooms, we complete the following graph.

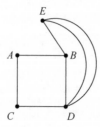

5. We label each of the corners and intersections with an upper-case letter and use points to represent the corners and street intersections. Now we are ready to draw the edges that represent the streets the security guard has to walk. Each street only needs to be walked once, so we draw one edge to represent each street. This results in the following graph.

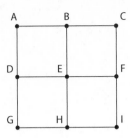

6. We systematically list which pairs of vertices are adjacent, working alphabetically. Thus, the adjacent vertices are *A* and *B*, *A* and *C*, *A* and *D*, *A* and *E*, *B* and *C*, and *E* and *E*.

Exercise Set 15.1

1. There are six edges attached to the Pittsburgh vertex, so Pittsburgh plays six games during the week. One edge connects the Pittsburgh vertex to the St. Louis vertex, so one game is against St. Louis. One edge connects the Pittsburgh vertex to Chicago, so one game is against Chicago. Two edges connect the Pittsburgh vertex to the Philadelphia vertex, so two games are against Philadelphia. Two edges connect the Pittsburgh vertex to the Montreal vertex, so two games are against Montreal.

2. There are five edges attached to the Montreal vertex, so Montreal plays five games during the week. One edge connects the Montreal vertex to the Philadelphia vertex, so one game is against Philadelphia. One edge connects the Montreal vertex to the St. Louis vertex, so one game is against St. Louis. Two edges connect the Montreal vertex to the Pittsburgh vertex, so two games are against Pittsburgh. One edge connects the Montreal vertex to the New York vertex, so one game is against New York.

3. No. Montreal is farther north than New York but is drawn lower on the graph. However, the graph is not drawn incorrectly. Only the games between teams are important, and these are represented by the edges. Geographic position is not relevant.

4. No. Chicago is west of New York, but not farther south. On the graph, Chicago's position appears to be southwest of New York's. However, the graph is not drawn incorrectly. Only the games between teams are important, and these are represented by the edges. Geographic position is not relevant.

5. Possible answers:

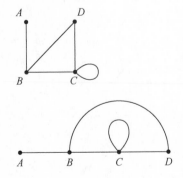

6. Possible answers:

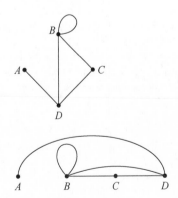

7. Both graphs have vertices *A*, *B*, *C*, and *D* and edges *AB*, *AC*, *AD*, and *BD*. The two graphs have the same number of vertices connected in the same way, so they are the same.

    Possible answer:

8. Both graphs have vertices *A*, *B*, *C*, and *D* and edges *AB*, *AC*, *BC*, and *BD*. The two graphs have the same number of vertices connected in the same way, so they are the same.
    Possible answer:

9. We label each student's vertex with the first letter of his or her name. An edge connecting two vertices represents a friendship prior to forming the homework group. The following graph results.

    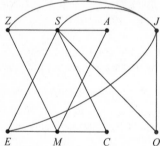

10. Use vertices to represent the three committees. The Preserving Open Space and Fund Raising Committees have two members in common (B and D), the Fund Raising and Wetlands Protection Committees have two members in common (C and D), and the Preserving Open Space and Wetlands Protection Committees have one member in Common (D).

    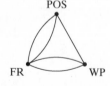

11. Label one vertex *N*, for North Gothamville. Label another *S*, for South Gothamville. Label the islands, from left to right, *A, B,* and *C*. Label three vertices accordingly. Use edges to represent bridges. The following graph results.

    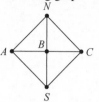

12. Label one vertex *N*, for North Wisdomville. Label another *S*, for South Wisdomville. Label the islands, from left to right, *A, B,* and *C*. Label three vertices accordingly. Use edges to represent bridges. The following graph results.

    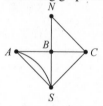

13. We use the abbreviations WA, OR, ID, MT, and WY to label the vertices representing Washington, Oregon, Idaho, Montana, and Wyoming. The following graph results.

    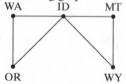

14. We use the abbreviations WA, OR, CA, AZ, NV, and ID to label the vertices representing Washington, Oregon, California, Arizona, Nevada, and Idaho. The following graph results.

    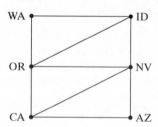

628

15.
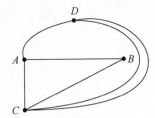

16.
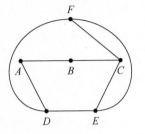

17.
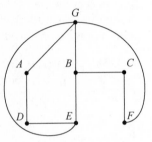

18.
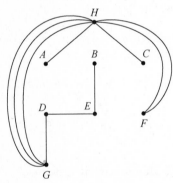

19.
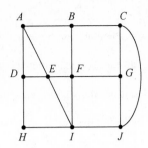

20.
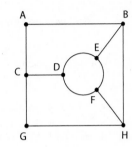

21.
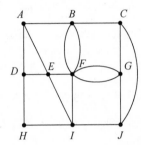

22.
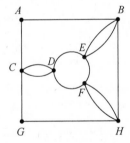

23. The degree of a vertex is the number of edges at that vertex. Thus, vertex *A* has degree 2, vertex *B* has degree 2, vertex *C* has degree 3, vertex *D* has degree 3, vertex *E* has degree 3, and vertex *F* has degree 1. (The loop at *E* counts for 2.)

24. Vertices *A* and *B* each have 2 edges, an even number, attached to them, so *A* and *B* are even vertices. Vertices *C*, *D*, and *E* each have 3 edges attached to them, and vertex *F* has 1 edge attached to it. Since these are all odd numbers, *C*, *D*, *E*, and *F* are odd vertices.

25. Vertices *B* and *C* each have an edge connecting to *A*, so *B* and *C* are adjacent to *A*.

26. Vertices *C*, *E*, and *F* are each connected to vertex *D* by an edge, so *C*, *E*, and *F* are adjacent to *D*.

27. Starting at vertex *A*, we proceed to vertex *C*, then vertex *D*. This is one path from *A* to *D*. For a second path, start at vertex *A*, then proceed to vertex *B*, then *C*, then *D*.

28. Starting at vertex B, we proceed to vertex A, then vertex C, then vertex D. This is one path from B to D. For a second path, start at vertex B, then proceed to vertex C, then D.

29. The edges not included are the edge connecting A to C, and the edge connecting D to F.

30. The edges not included are the edges connecting B to C, and the edge connecting D to F.

31. While edge CD is included, the graph is connected. If we remove CD, the graph will be disconnected. Thus, CD is a bridge.

32. While edge DE is included, the graph is connected. If we remove DE, the graph will be disconnected. Thus, DE is a bridge.

33. Edge DF is also a bridge. With it, the graph is connected. If DF is removed, vertex F stands alone, so the graph is disconnected.

34. Vertex A has 2 attached edges, so A has degree 2. Vertex B has 2 attached edges, so B has degree 2. Vertex C has 5 attached edges (counting the loop twice), so C has degree 5. Vertex D has 3 attached edges, so D has degree 3. Vertex E has 1 attached edge, so E has degree 1. Vertex F has 3 attached edges, so F has degree 3. Vertex G has 2 attached edges, so G has degree 2. Vertex H has 2 attached edges, so H has degree 2. Vertex I has 2 attached edges, so I has degree 2.

35. Vertices A, B, G, H, and I each have two attached edges, which is an even number of edges. Thus A, B, G, H, and I are even vertices. Vertex C has five attached edges, vertex E has one, and vertices D and F have three. These are odd numbers of edges. Thus C, E, D, and F are odd vertices.

36. Vertex E has an edge connecting to vertex D. Thus D is adjacent to E.

37. Vertex F has edges connecting to vertices D, G, and I. Thus D, G, and I are adjacent to F.

38. Begin at vertex A. Proceed to vertex C, next along the loop back to vertex C, next to vertex D, and finally to vertex F. This is one path. For another, begin at A, then proceed to B, then C, then D, then F.

39. Begin at vertex B. Proceed to vertex C, then vertex D, then vertex F. This is one path from B to F. For a second path, begin at B, then proceed to A, then C, then D, then F.

40. Begin at vertex F. Proceed to vertex I, then vertex H, then vertex G, and finally to vertex F. This is a circuit. (The counterclockwise order also works.)

41. Begin at vertex G. proceed to vertex F, then vertex I, then vertex H, then vertex G. This is a circuit. (The counterclockwise order also works.)

42. Begin at vertex H. Proceed to vertex I, then vertex F, then vertex D, then vertex E.

43. Begin at vertex A. Proceed to vertex B, then vertex C, then around the loop to C again, then vertex D, then vertex F, then vertex G, then vertex H, then vertex I.

44. A, C, D, E, D requires that the edge DE be traversed twice. This is not allowed within a path.

45. G, F, D, E, D requires that edge DE be traversed twice. This is not allowed within a path.

46. A, C, D, G is not a path because no edge connects vertices D and G.

47. H, I, F, E is not a path because no edge connects vertices F and E.

48. Edge *CD* is a bridge. When it is removed, the following graph results.

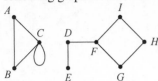

Edge *DE* is a bridge. When it is removed, the following graph results.

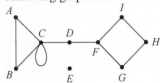

Edge *DF* is a bridge. When it is removed, the following graph results.

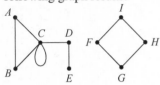

49. Possible answer:

Each vertex has degree 2.

50. Possible answer:

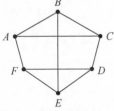

Each vertex has degree 3.

51. Possible answer:

Vertex *A* has degree 1, and the rest have degree 3.

52. Possible answer:

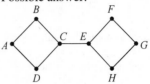

CE is the bridge.

66. does not make sense; Explanations will vary. Sample explanation: Identical graphs do not necessarily look alike.

67. makes sense

68. makes sense

69. does not make sense; Explanations will vary. Sample explanation: All circuits are paths.

71. Use vertices to represent the six members.

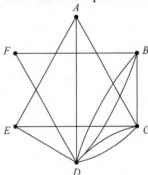

72. The sum of the degree of the vertices is twice the number of edges.

Check Points 15.2

1. We use trial and error to find one such path. The following figure shows a result.

    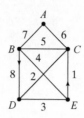

    Using vertex letters to name the path, we write *E, C, D, E, B, C, A, B, D*.

2. We use trial and error to find an Euler circuit that starts at *G*. The following figure shows a result.

    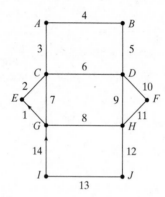

    Using vertex letters to name the circuit, we write *G, E, C, A, B, D, C, G, H, D, F, H, J, I, G*.

3. **a.** A walk through every room and the outside, using each door exactly once, means that we are looking for an Euler path or Euler circuit on the graph in Figure 15.34(b). This graph has exactly two odd vertices, namely *B* and *E*. By Euler's theorem, the graph has at least one Euler path, but no Euler circuit. It is possible to walk through every room and the outside, using each door exactly once. It is not possible to begin and end the walk in the same place.

    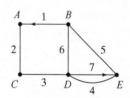

    b. Euler's theorem tells us that a possible Euler path must start at one of the odd vertices and end at the other. We use trial and error to find such a path, starting at vertex *B* (room *B* in the floor plan), and ending at vertex *E* (outside in the floor plan). Possible paths follow.

    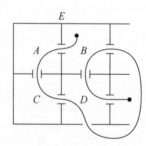

4. The graph has no odd vertices, so we can begin at any vertex. We choose vertex C as the starting point. From C we can travel to A, B, or D. We choose to travel to D.

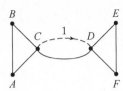

Now the remaining edge CD is a bridge, so we must travel to either E or F. We choose F.

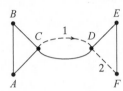

We have no choices for our next three steps, which are bridges. We must travel to E, then D, then C.

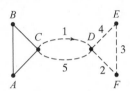

From C, we may travel to either A or B. We choose B. Then we must travel to A, then back to C.

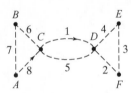

The above figure shows the completed Euler circuit. Written using the letters of the vertices, the path is C, D, F, E, D, C, B, A, C.

Exercise Set 15.2

1.

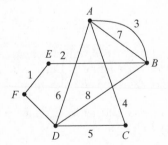

This path does not include edge FD, so it is neither an Euler path nor an Euler circuit.

2.

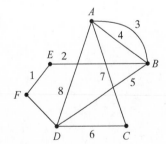

This path does not include edge FD, so it is neither an Euler path nor an Euler circuit.

3.

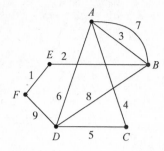

This path travels through each edge of the graph once, and only once. It begins and ends at *F*. Therefore, it is an Euler circuit.

4.

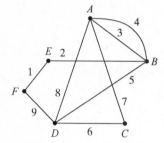

This path travels through each edge of the graph once, and only once. It begins and ends with *F*. Therefore, it is an Euler circuit.

5.

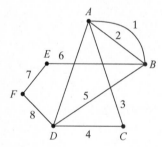

This path does not include edge *AD*, so it is neither an Euler path nor an Euler circuit.

6.

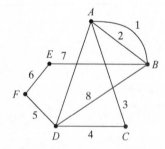

This path does not include edge *AD*, so it is neither an Euler path nor an Euler circuit.

7. a. There are exactly two odd vertices, namely *A* and *B*, so by Euler's theorem there is at least one Euler path.

b.

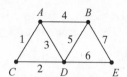

This path begins at *A* and ends at *B*.

8. a. There are exactly two odd vertices, namely *A* and *C*, so by Euler's theorem there is at least one Euler path.

b.

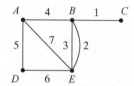

This path begins at *C* and ends at *A*.

9. a. There are no odd vertices, so by Euler's theorem, there is at least one Euler circuit.

b.

This circuit begins and ends at *C*.

10. a. There are no odd vertices, so by Euler's theorem, there is at least one Euler circuit.

b.

This circuit begins and ends at *B*.

11. There are more than two odd vertices, namely *B, D, G,* and *K*. Therefore by Euler's theorem, there are no Euler paths and no Euler circuits.

12. There are more than two odd vertices, namely *B, C, E, I, H, L, N,* and *O*. Therefore by Euler's theorem, there are no Euler paths and no Euler circuits.

13. Since the graph has no odd vertices, it must have an Euler circuit, by Euler's theorem.

14. Since the graph has no odd vertices, it must have an Euler circuit, by Euler's theorem.

15. Since the graph has exactly two odd vertices, it has an Euler path, but no Euler circuit, by Euler's theorem.

16. Since the graph has exactly two odd vertices, it has an Euler path, but no Euler circuit, by Euler's theorem.

17. Since the graph has more than two odd vertices, it has neither an Euler path nor an Euler circuit, by Euler's theorem.

18. Since the graph has more than two odd vertices, it has neither an Euler path nor an Euler circuit, by Euler's theorem.

19. a. All vertices are even, so there must be an Euler circuit.

   b.
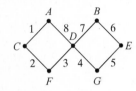

20. a. All vertices are even, so there must be an Euler circuit.

   b.
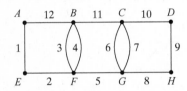

21. a. There are exactly two odd vertices, so there must be an Euler path.

   b.
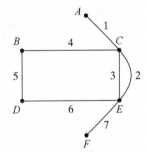

22. a. There are exactly two odd vertices, so there must be an Euler path.

   b.
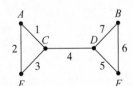

23. a. There are more than two odd vertices, so there is neither an Euler path nor an Euler circuit.

24. a. There are more than two odd vertices, so there is neither an Euler path nor an Euler circuit.

25. a. There are exactly two odd vertices, so there is an Euler path.

   b.
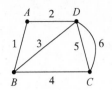

26. a. There are exactly two odd vertices, so there is an Euler path.

   b.
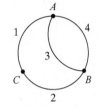

27. a. There are no odd vertices, so there is an Euler circuit.

   b.

28. a. There are no odd vertices, so there is an Euler circuit.

   b.
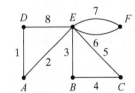

29. a. There are more than two odd vertices, so there is neither an Euler path nor an Euler circuit.

30. a. There are more than two odd vertices, so there is neither an Euler path nor an Euler circuit.

31. a. There are exactly two odd vertices, so there is an Euler path.

b.

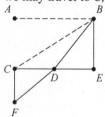

32. a. There are exactly two odd vertices, so there is an Euler path.

b.

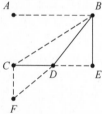

33. The two odd vertices in the graph are *A* and *C*. We start with *A*, so we must progress next to *B*. From *B*, we may travel to *C*, *D*, or *E*. We choose *C*.

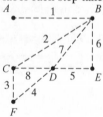

Next we travel to *F*, then *D*, then *E*.

Finally we travel to *B*, then *D*, and last, to *C*. We label each step taken.

34. The two odd vertices in the graph are *A* and *B*. We start with *B* and progress to *A*, then *D*, then *E*.

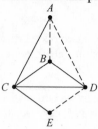

From *E*, we travel to *C*, then *D*, then *B*, then *C*, and last, to *A*. We label each step taken.

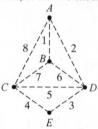

35. The two odd vertices in the graph are *A* and *C*. We start with *A*, then travel to *B*, *C*, and *E*.

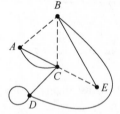

We continue on to *B*, *D*, *D*, *C*, *A*, and *C*. We label each step taken.

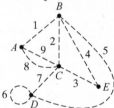

36. The two odd vertices in the graph are *A* and *B*. We start with *B*, then travel to *D*, *F*, *E*, *C*, and *A*.

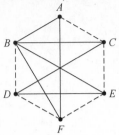

We continue on to *B*, then *C*, *D*, *E*, *B*, *F*, and *A*. We label each step taken.

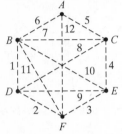

37. We begin with *A*, and travel to *D*, *H*, *G*, *F*, *E*, *B*, and *C*.

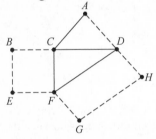

We continue on to *F*, *D*, *C*, and back to *A*. We label each step.

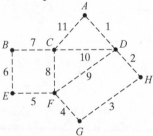

38. We begin with *B*, and travel to *A*, *D*, *J*, *K*, *L*, *G*, and *C*.

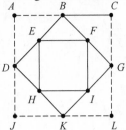

We continue on to *B*, *E*, *D*, *H*, *K*, *I*, *G*, *F*, *I*, *H*, *E*, *F*, and back to *B*. We label each step.

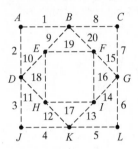

39. We begin with *A*, and travel to *C*, *G*, *K*, *H*, *I*, *L*, *J*, *F*, *B*, *E*, and *D*.

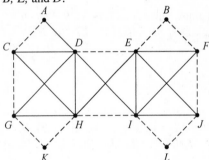

We continue on to *C*, *H*, *G*, *D*, *H*, *E*, *F*, *I*, *J*, *E*, *I*, *D*, and back to *A*. We label each step.

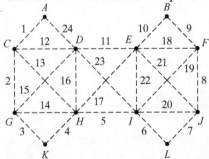

40. We begin with *A*, and travel to *F, J, K, L, M, N, I, E, D, C,* and *B*.

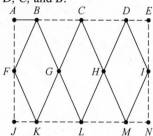

We continue on to *F, K, G, L, H, M, I, D, H, C, G, B,* and back to *A*. We label each step.

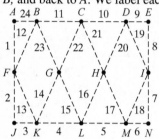

41. **a.** Remove *FG*.

    b. Sample Euler circuit: *EC, CB, BD, DF, FA, AD, DG, GH, HC, CG, GB, BH, HE*

42. **a.** Remove *JB*.

    b. Sample Euler circuit: *AB, BC, CD, DE, EF, FO, ON, NM, MI, IN, NE, EG, GD, DM, ML, LK, KH, HC, CL, LH, HB, BK, KJ, JA*

43. **a.** Remove *BA* and *FJ*.

    b. Sample Euler circuit: *CA, AD, DI, IH, HG, GF, FC, CD, DE, EH, HJ, JG, GB, BC*

44. **a.** Remove *AC* and *BF*.

    b. Sample Euler circuit: *DA, AB, BE, EF, FK, KL, LR, RQ, QV, VU, UX, XW, WT, TS, SN, NM, MG, GH, HC, CD, DE, EJ, JK, KQ, QP, PJ, JI, IO, OP, PU, UT, TO, ON, NH, HI, ID*

45. The graph that models the neighborhood has no odd vertices, so an Euler circuit exists with any vertex, including *B*, as the starting point.

46.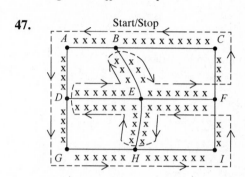

47.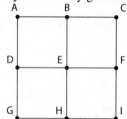

48. First we draw a graph that models the streets walked by the security guard.

    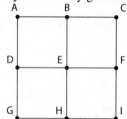

    The graph has more than two odd vertices, namely *B, D, F,* and *H*. Therefore there is no route the security guard can take in order to walk each street exactly once.

49. **a.**

    b. There are exactly two odd vertices, namely *E* and *B*. Therefore the guard should begin at one of these vertices and end at the other.

50. a.

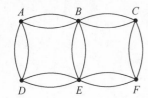

b. The graph depicts an Euler circuit, since each vertex is even. Therefore the carrier can park at any intersection and deliver all the mail without retracing the side of any street.

c.

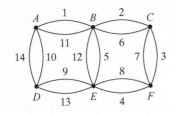

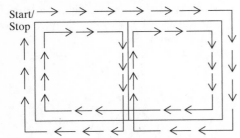

51. a. Label the vertices *N* for North Bank, *S* for South Bank, and *A* and *B* for the two islands. Draw edges to represent bridges.

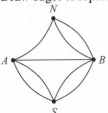

b. The graph has exactly two odd vertices, *N* and *B*, so residents can walk across all the bridges without crossing the same bridge twice.

c.

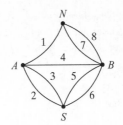

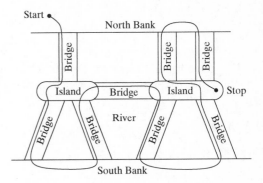

52. a. Label the vertices *N* for North Bank, *S* for South Bank, and *A* and *B* for the two islands. Draw edges to represent bridges.

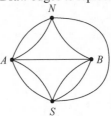

b. The graph has exactly two odd vertices, *A* and *S*, so residents can walk across all the bridges without crossing the same bridge twice.

c.

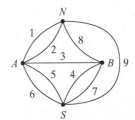

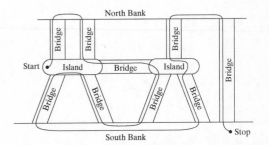

53. Use NJ to label the New Jersey vertex, M for Manhattan, SI for Staten Island, and LI for Long Island. Each edge represents a bridge.

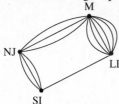

There are exactly two odd vertices, M and LI, so the graph has an Euler path. Therefore it is possible to visit each location, using each bridge or tunnel exactly once.

54. a.

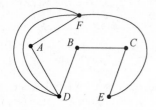

b. There are no odd vertices, so the graph has an Euler circuit. Therefore, it is possible to walk through each room and the outside, using each door exactly once.

c.

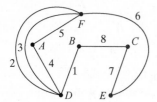

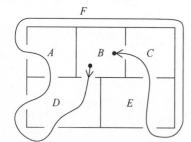

55. a.

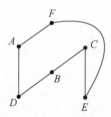

b. There are no odd vertices, so the graph has an Euler circuit. Therefore, it is possible to walk through each room and the outside, using each door exactly once.

c.

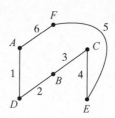

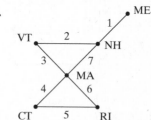

56. There are exactly two odd vertices on the graph, so an Euler path exists, by Euler's theorem. Thus, we can travel each border exactly once while visiting these states.

57.

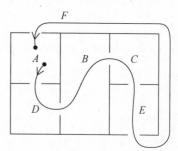

58.

59. a.

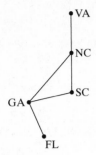

b. There are more than two odd vertices, so no Euler path exists. Therefore it is not possible to travel through these states, crossing each border exactly once.

d. For the same reason as in (b), this is not possible.

60. a.

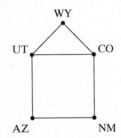

b. There are exactly two odd vertices, so there is an Euler path. Therefore it is possible to travel through these states, crossing each border exactly once.

c.

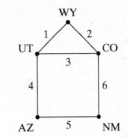

d. Because there are two odd vertices, there is no Euler circuit. Hence the trip cannot start and end in the same state.

69. makes sense

70. does not make sense; Explanations will vary. Sample explanation: Euler's Theorem tells us whether or not Euler paths or Euler circuits exist, but not how to find them.

71. does not make sense; Explanations will vary. Sample explanation: Fleury's Algorithm is used to find Euler paths or Euler circuits, not to determine if they exist.

72. does not make sense; Explanations will vary. Sample explanation: The driver must find an Euler Circuit.

Check Points 15.3

1. a. A Hamilton path must pass through each vertex exactly once. The graph has many Hamilton paths. An example of such a path is *E, C, D, G, B, A, F*.

   b. A Hamilton circuit must pass through every vertex exactly once and begin and end at the same vertex. The graph has many Hamilton circuits. An example of such a circuit is *E, C, D, G, B, F, A, E*.

2. In each case, we use the expression $(n - 1)!$. For three vertices, substitute 3 for n in the expression. For six and ten vertices, substitute 6 and 10, respectively, for n.

   a. A complete graph with three vertices has $(3 - 1)! = 2! = 2 \cdot 1 = 2$ Hamilton circuits.

   b. A complete graph with six vertices has $(6 - 1)! = 5! = 5 \cdot 4 \cdot 3 \cdot 2 \cdot 1 = 120$ Hamilton circuits.

   c. A complete graph with ten vertices has $(10 - 1)! = 9! = 9 \cdot 8 \cdot 7 \cdot 6 \cdot 5 \cdot 4 \cdot 3 \cdot 2 \cdot 1 = 362{,}880$ Hamilton circuits.

3. The trip described by the Hamilton circuit *A, C, B, D, A* involves the sum of four costs:

$124 + $126 + $155 + $157 = $562.

Here, $124 is the cost of the trip from *A* to *C*; $126 is the cost from *C* to *B*; $155 is the cost from *B* to *D*; and $157 is the cost from *D* to *A*. The total cost of the trip is $562.

4. The graph has four vertices. Thus, using $(n - 1)!$, there are $(4 - 1)! = 3! = 6$ possible Hamilton circuits. The 6 possible Hamilton circuits and their costs are shown.

Hamilton Circuit	Sum of the Weights of the Edges	=	Total Cost
A, B, C, D, A	20 + 15 + 50 + 30	=	$115
A, B, D, C, A	20 + 10 + 50 + 70	=	$150
A, C, B, D, A	70 + 15 + 10 + 30	=	$125
A, C, D, B, A	70 + 50 + 10 + 20	=	$150
A, D, B, C, A	30 + 10 + 15 + 70	=	$125
A, D, C, B, A	30 + 50 + 15 + 20	=	$115

The two Hamilton circuits having the lowest cost of $115 are *A, B, C, D, A* and *A, D, C, B, A*.

5. The Nearest Neighbor method is carried out as follows:

- Start at *A*.

- Choose the edge with the smallest weight: 13. Move along this edge to *B*.

- From *B*, choose the edge with the smallest weight that does not lead to *A*: 5. Move along this edge to *C*.

- From *C*, choose the edge with the smallest weight that does not lead to a city already visited: 12. Move along this edge to *D*.

- From *D*, the only choice is to fly to *E*, the only city not yet visited: 154.

- From *E*, close the circuit and return home to *A*: 14.

An approximate solution is the Hamilton circuit *A, B, C, D, E, A*. The total weight is $13 + 5 + 12 + 154 + 14 = 198$.

Exercise Set 15.3

1. One such path is *A, G, C, F, E, D, B*.

2. One such path is *G, A, D, B, F, C, E*.

3. One such circuit is *A, B, G, C, F, E, D, A*.

4. One such circuit is *A, G, C, B, F, E, D, A*.

5. One such path is *A, F, G, E, C, B, D*.

6. One such path is *A, F, D, B, C, E, G*.

7. One such circuit is *A, B, C, E, G, F, D, A*.

8. One such circuit is *F, G, E, C, B, A, D, F*.

9. a. This graph is not complete. For example, no edge connects *A* and *B*. Therefore it may not have Hamilton circuits.

10. a. This graph is not complete. For example, no edge connects *B* and *G*. Therefore it may not have Hamilton circuits.

11. a. This graph is complete: there is an edge between each pair of vertices. Therefore it must have Hamilton circuits.

b. There are 6 vertices, so the number of Hamilton circuits is $(6 - 1)! = 5! = 120$.

12. a. This graph is complete: there is an edge between each pair of vertices. Therefore it must have Hamilton circuits.

b. There are 7 vertices, so the number of Hamilton circuits is $(7 - 1)! = 6! = 720$.

13. a. This graph is not complete. For example, no edge connects *G* and *F*. Therefore it may not have Hamilton circuits.

14. a. This graph is not complete. For example, no edge connects *A* and *K*. Therefore it may not have Hamilton circuits.

15. $(3 - 1)! = 2! = 2$

16. $(4 - 1)! = 3! = 6$

17. $(12 - 1)! = 11! = 39,916,800$

18. $(13 - 1)! = 12! = 479,001,600$

19. 11

20. 7

21. $9 + 8 + 11 + 6 + 2 = 36$

22. $9 + 7 + 4 + 11 + 10 = 41$

23. $9 + 7 + 6 + 11 + 3 = 36$

24. $9 + 5 + 11 + 4 + 2 = 31$

25. $40 + 24 + 10 + 14 = 88$

26. $40 + 12 + 10 + 20 = 82$

27. $20 + 24 + 12 + 14 = 70$

28. $20 + 10 + 12 + 40 = 82$

29. $14 + 12 + 24 + 20 = 70$

30. $14 + 10 + 24 + 40 = 88$

31. On a complete graph with four vertices, there are 6 distinct Hamilton circuits. These are listed in Exercises 25–30. We have already computed the weight of each possible Hamilton circuit, as required by the Brute Force Method. The optimal solutions have the smallest weight, 70. They are *A, C, B, D, A*, and *A, D, B, C, A*.

32. Starting from *A*, the edge with smallest weight is *AD*, with weight 14. Therefore proceed to *D*. From *D*, the edge having smallest weight and not returning to *A* is *DC*, with weight 10. The only edge from *C* which does not lead to a previously visited vertex is *CB*, with weight 24. Last, return to *A*. Edge *BA* has weight 40. The total weight of this Hamilton circuit is $14 + 10 + 24 + 40 = 88$.

33. Starting from *B*, the edge with smallest weight is *BD*, with weight 12. Therefore, proceed to *D*. From *D*, the edge having smallest weight and not leading back to *B* is *DC*, with weight 10. From *C*, our only choice is *CA*, with weight 20. From *A*, return to *B*. Edge *AB* has weight 40. The total weight of the Hamilton circuit is $12 + 10 + 20 + 40 = 82$.

34. Starting from *C*, the edge with smallest weight is *CD*, with weight 10. Therefore proceed to *D*. From *D*, the edge having smallest weight and not leading back to *C* is *DB*, with weight 12. From *B*, our only choice is edge *BA*, with weight 40. From *A*, we return to *C*. Edge *AC* has weight 20. The total weight of this Hamilton circuit is $10 + 12 + 40 + 20 = 82$.

35. a. Add *AB*
Number of Hamilton circuits: $(4-1)!=3!=6$

    b. Sample Hamilton circuit: *AD, DB, BC, CA*
Sample Hamilton circuit: *CA, AB, BD, DC*

    c. Remove *CD*

    d. Sample Euler circuit: *AC, CB, BD, DA*

36. a. Add *CD*
Number of Hamilton circuits: $(4-1)!=3!=6$

    b. Sample Hamilton circuit: *CA, AD, DB, BC*
Sample Hamilton circuit: *CA, AB, BD, DC*

    c. Remove *AB*

    d. Sample Euler circuit: *AC, CB, BD, DA*

37. a. Add *AB, AC, BC,* and *DE*
Number of Hamilton circuits: $(5-1)!=4!=24$

    b. Sample Hamilton circuit: *AB, BC, CE, ED, DA*
Sample Hamilton circuit: *AB, BC, CD, DE, EA*

    c. Remove *BD* and *BE*

    d. Sample Euler circuit: *AE, EC, CD, DA*

38. a. Add *AD, AE, BC, BD,* and *DE*
Number of Hamilton circuits: $(5-1)!=4!=24$

    b. Sample Hamilton circuit: *AB, BC, CE, ED, DA*
Sample Hamilton circuit: *AB, BC, CD, DE, EA*

    c. Remove *CD*

    d. Sample Euler circuit: *AB, BE, EC, CA*

39.

Hamilton Circuit	Sum of the Weights of the Edges	=	Total Weight
A, B, C, D, E, A	500 + 305 + 320 + 302 + 205	=	1632
A, B, C, E, D, A	500 + 305 + 165 + 302 + 185	=	1457
A, B, D, C, E, A	500 + 360 + 320 + 165 + 205	=	1550
A, B, D, E, C, A	500 + 360 + 302 + 165 + 200	=	1527
A, B, E, C, D, A	500 + 340 + 165 + 320 + 185	=	1510
A, B, E, D, C, A	500 + 340 + 302 + 320 + 200	=	1662
A, C, B, D, E, A	200 + 305 + 360 + 302 + 205	=	1372
A, C, B, E, D, A	200 + 305 + 340 + 302 + 185	=	1332
A, C, D, B, E, A	200 + 320 + 360 + 340 + 205	=	1425
A, C, E, B, D, A	200 + 165 + 340 + 360 + 185	=	1250
A, D, B, C, E, A	185 + 360 + 305 + 165 + 205	=	1220
A, D, C, B, E, A	185 + 320 + 305 + 340 + 205	=	1355

Using the Brute Force method, we compute the sum of the weights of the edges for each possible Hamilton circuit, as in the table above. The smallest weight sum is 1220, representing a total cost of $1220 for airfare. This results from the Hamilton circuit *A, D, B, C, E, A.* Thus, the sales director should fly to the cities in this order.

40. Starting from *A*, the edge with smallest weight is *AD*, with weight 185. Proceed to edge *D*. From *D*, the edge having smallest weight and not leading back to *A* is *DE*, with weight 302. From *E*, the edge with smallest weight and not leading back to *A* or *D* is *EC*, with weight 165. From *C*, the only option is *CB*, with weight 305. From *B*, return to *A*. Edge *BA* has weight 500. The total weight for this Hamilton circuit is 185 + 302 + 165 + 305 + 500 = 1457, meaning the cost is $1457.

41.

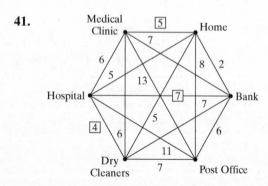

42. There are six vertices; so there are $(6 - 1)! = 5! = 120$ possible routes.

43. $2 + 6 + 7 + 4 + 6 + 5 = 30$

44. Start at Home. The shortest distance is 2, to the Bank. From the Bank, the shortest distance to another errand is 6, to the Post Office. From there, the shortest distance to an undone errand is 7, to the Dry Cleaners. From there, the shortest distance to an undone errand is 4, to the Hospital. The only errand remaining is the Medical Center, at a distance of 6 from the Hospital. The return Home from the Medical Center is a distance of 5. This is the same route found in Exercise 43.

45. Label the vertices *H* for Home, *B* for Bank, *P* for Post Office, and *M* for Market.

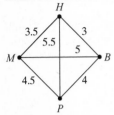

46. The distances are the same in both directions, so we only need to check half the possible Hamilton circuits. There are $(4 - 1)! = 3! = 6$ Hamilton circuits.

Hamilton Circuit	Sum of the Weights of the Edges	=	Total Distance
H, B, P, M, H	$3 + 4 + 4.5 + 3.5$	=	15
H, B, M, P, H	$3 + 5 + 4.5 + 5.5$	=	18
H, P, B, M, H	$5.5 + 4 + 5 + 3.5$	=	18

The minimum distance is 15 miles, along the route *H, B, P, M, H*.

47. From Home, the closest errand is the Bank, 3 miles away. From the Bank, the closest remaining errand is the Post Office, 4 miles away. From the Post Office, the last remaining errand is the Market, 4.5 miles away. From the Market, Home is 3.5 miles away. The total distance for this Hamilton circuit is $3 + 4 + 4.5 + 3.5 = 15$ miles. This is the same route found in Exercise 46.

60. does not make sense; Explanations will vary. Sample explanation: No graph has exactly 25 Hamilton circuits. A complete graph with 5 vertices would have $4! = 24$ Hamilton circuits and a complete graph with 6 vertices would have $5! = 120$ Hamilton circuits.

61. does not make sense; Explanations will vary. Sample explanation: Even the fastest existing super computer could not do that task in one evening.

62. does not make sense; Explanations will vary. Sample explanation: Though the traveling salesperson problem is not solved which means city planners are not able to be sure they find the *most* efficient routes; there are many methods that give city planners ways of improving efficiency of routes.

63. makes sense

64. $120 = 5! = (6 - 1)!$. Therefore, the graph has 6 vertices.

Check Points 15.4

1. The graph in Figure 15.51(c) is a tree. It is connected and has no circuits. There is only one path joining any two vertices. Every edge is a bridge; if removed, each edge would create a disconnected graph. Finally, the graph has 7 vertices and 7 – 1, or 6, edges.

   The graph in Figure 15.51(a) is not a tree because it is disconnected. There are 7 vertices and only 5 edges, not the 6 edges required for a tree.

   The graph in Figure 15.51(b) is not a tree because it has a circuit, namely A, B, C, D, A. There are 7 vertices and 7 edges, not the 6 edges required for a tree.

2. A spanning tree must contain all six vertices shown in the connected graph in Figure 15.55. The spanning tree must have one edge less than it has vertices, so it must have five edges. The graph in Figure 15.55 has eight edges, so we must remove three edges. We elect to remove the edges of the circuit C, D, E, C. This leaves us the following spanning tree.

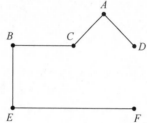

3. Step 1. Find the edge with the smallest weight. This is edge DE; mark it.

   Step 2. Find the next-smallest edge in the graph. This is edge DC; mark it.

   Step 3. Find the next-smallest edge in the graph that does not create a circuit. This is edge DA; mark it.

   Step 4. Find the next-smallest edge in the graph that does not create a circuit. This is AB; mark it.

   The resulting minimum spanning tree is complete. It contains all 5 vertices of the graph, and has 5 – 1, or 4, edges. Its total weight is 12 + 14 + 21 + 22 = 69. It is shown below.

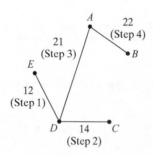

Exercise Set 15.4

1. Yes, this graph is a tree. It has 3 edges on 4 vertices, is connected, and has no circuits. Every edge is a bridge.

2. Yes, this graph is a tree. It has 5 edges on 6 vertices, is connected, and has no circuits. Every edge is a bridge.

3. No, this graph is not a tree. It is disconnected.

4. No, this graph is not a tree. It is disconnected.

5. Yes, this graph is a tree. It has 3 edges on 4 vertices, is connected, and has no circuits. Every edge is a bridge.

6. Yes, this graph is a tree. It has 3 edges on 4 vertices, is connected, and has no circuits. Every edge is a bridge.

7. No, this graph is not a tree. It has a circuit.

8. No, this graph is not a tree. It has a circuit.

9. Yes, this graph is a tree. It has 6 edges on 7 vertices, is connected, and has no circuits. Every edge is a bridge.

10. Yes, this graph is a tree. It has 8 edges on 9 vertices, is connected, and has no circuits. Every edge is a bridge.

11. i; If the graph contained any circuits, some points would have more than one path joining them.

12. i; Since every edge is a bridge, there are no circuits.

13. ii; A tree with n vertices must have $n - 1$ edges.

14. ii; A tree with n vertices must have $n - 1$ edges.

15. iii

16. iii

17.

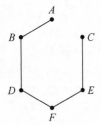

18.

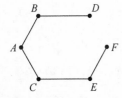

19.

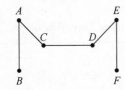

20.

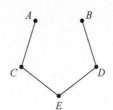

21.

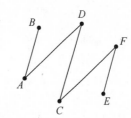

22.

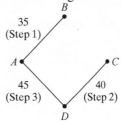

23. Kruskal's algorithm results in the following figure.

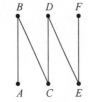

This minimum spanning tree has weight
$35 + 40 + 45 = 120$.

24. Kruskal's algorithm results in the following figure.

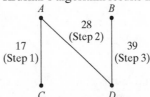

This minimum spanning tree has weight
$17 + 28 + 39 = 84$.

25. Kruskal's algorithm results in the following figure.

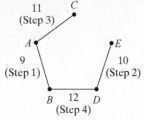

This minimum spanning tree has weight
9 + 10 + 11 + 12 = 42.

26. Kruskal's algorithm results in the following figure.

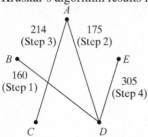

This minimum spanning tree has weight
160 + 175 + 214 + 305 = 854.

27. Kruskal's algorithm results in the following figure.

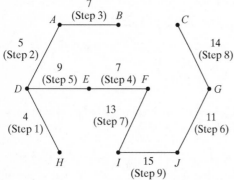

This minimum spanning tree has weight
4 + 5 + 7 + 7 + 9 + 11 + 13 + 14 + 15 = 85.

28. Kruskal's algorithm results in the following figure.

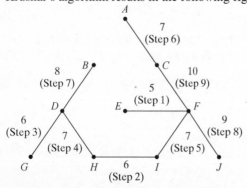

This minimum spanning tree has weight
5 + 6 + 6 + 7 + 7 + 7 + 8 + 9 + 10 = 65.

29. Kruskal's algorithm results in the following figure.

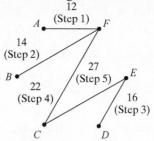

This minimum spanning tree has weight
12 + 14 + 16 + 22 + 27 = 91.

30. Kruskal's algorithm results in the following figure.

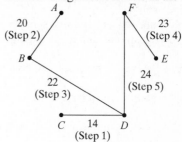

This minimum spanning tree has weight
14 + 20 + 22 + 23 + 24 = 103.

31. Sample Spanning Tree: *AB, AC, CD*
Sample Spanning Tree: *AB, BC, CD*
Sample Spanning Tree: *AB, AD, CD*
Sample Spanning Tree: *AB, AD, BC*

32. Sample Spanning Tree: *AB, BC, CD, DE*
Sample Spanning Tree: *AC, BC, BE, DE*
Sample Spanning Tree: *AB, BE, CD, DE*
Sample Spanning Tree: *AC, CD, BE, DE*

33. Maximum Spanning Tree: *AE, BC, CD, CE*
Total weight is $\underset{AE}{15} + \underset{BC}{14} + \underset{CD}{18} + \underset{CE}{17} = 64$

34. Maximum Spanning Tree: *AE, BE, CD, CE*
Total weight is $\underset{AE}{315} + \underset{BE}{375} + \underset{CD}{425} + \underset{CE}{405} = 1520$

35. Sample Maximum Spanning Tree: *AE, BC, BE, CF, DE, EH, FG, FJ, HI*
Total weight is
$\underset{AE}{10} + \underset{BC}{16} + \underset{BE}{15} + \underset{CF}{17} + \underset{DE}{9} + \underset{EH}{17} + \underset{FG}{16} + \underset{FJ}{19} + \underset{HI}{22} = 141$

36. Sample Maximum Spanning Tree: *AB, BC, CE, CF, DE, EH, EI, FJ, GH*
Total weight is
$\underset{AB}{11} + \underset{BC}{12} + \underset{CE}{12} + \underset{CF}{10} + \underset{DE}{11} + \underset{EH}{9} + \underset{EI}{10} + \underset{FJ}{9} + \underset{GH}{8} = 92$

37.

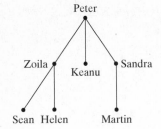

38.

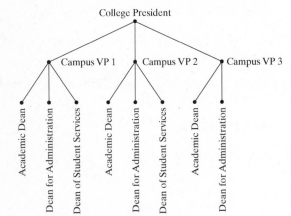

39. a.

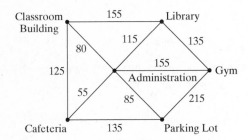

b. Kruskal's algorithm is shown in the figure.

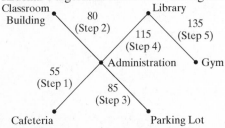

The total length of the sidewalks that need to be sheltered by awnings is
$55 + 80 + 85 + 115 + 135 = 470$ feet.

40. a.

b. Kruskal's algorithm is shown in the figure.

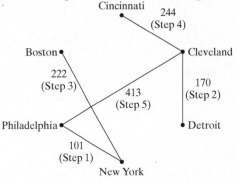

The total length of cable needed is
$101 + 170 + 222 + 244 + 413 = 1150$ miles.

41. Kruskal's algorithm is shown in the figure.

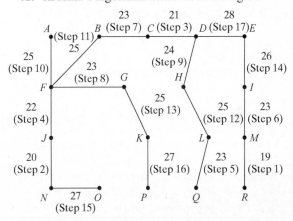

The smallest number of feet of underground pipes is
$19 + 20 + 21 + 22 + 23 + 23 + 23 + 23 + 24 + 25 +$
$25 + 25 + 25 + 26 + 27 + 27 + 28 = 406$ feet.

42. Kruskal's algorithm is shown in the figure.

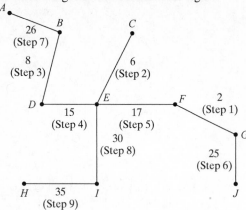

The minimum mileage for the bike trail is
$2 + 6 + 8 + 15 + 17 + 25 + 26 + 30 + 35 = 164$
miles.

52. does not make sense; Explanations will vary. Sample explanation: A tree has *one fewer* edge than it has vertices.

53. does not make sense; Explanations will vary. Sample explanation: You want a minimum *circuit*.

54. makes sense

55. makes sense

56. The graph has 6 vertices and 6 edges. A spanning tree on 6 vertices has 5 edges. Only three edges are able to be removed without a disconnected graph resulting. These are *BC*, *BF*, and *CF*. The result of removing any one of these edges is a spanning tree.

Chapter 15 Review Exercises

1. Each graph has 5 vertices, *A, B, C, D,* and *E*. Each has one edge connecting *A* and *B*, one connecting *A* and *C*, one connecting *A* and *D*, one connecting *A* and *E*, and one connecting *B* and *C*. Both graphs have the same number of vertices, and these vertices are connected in the same ways. A third way to draw the same graph is

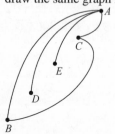

2. *A*: 5 (A loop adds degree 2.); *B*: 4; *C*: 5; *D*: 4; *E*: 2

3. Even: *B, D, E*; odd: *A, C*

4. *B, C,* and *E*

5. Possible answer: *E, D, B, A* and *E, C, A*

6. Possible answer: *E, D, C, E*

7. Yes. A path can be found from any vertex to any other vertex.

8. No. There is no edge which can be removed to leave a disconnected graph.

9. *AD, DE,* and *DF*

10.

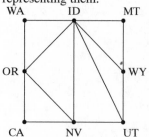

11. Use the states' abbreviations to label the vertices representing them.

WA   ID   MT
OR   WY
CA   NV   UT

12.

G
A   B   C
D   E   F

13. a. Neither. There are more than two odd vertices.

14. a. Euler circuit: there are no odd vertices.

b.
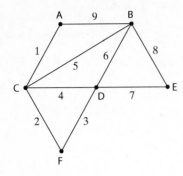

15. a. Euler path: there are exactly two odd vertices.

b.
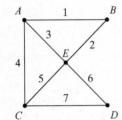

16. There are exactly two odd vertices, *G* and *I*. We start at *G* and continue to *D, A, B, C, F, I, H,* and *E*.

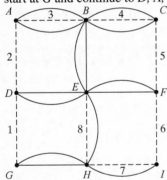

We continue erasing edges as we go, till we have completed an Euler path ending at *I*.

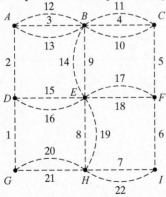

17. We may begin anywhere, since there are no odd vertices. We erase edges as we go, till we have the Euler circuit. We begin at *A*.

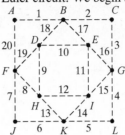

18. a. Yes, they would. The graph has exactly two odd vertices, so there is an Euler path.

b.
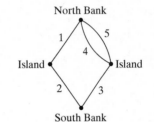

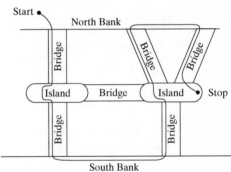

c. No; there is no such path. Since the graph has odd vertices, it does not have an Euler circuit.

19. Yes, it is possible. There are exactly two odd vertices, and therefore there is an Euler path (but no Euler circuit).

20. a. Yes it is possible. There are no odd vertices, so there is an Euler circuit.

b.

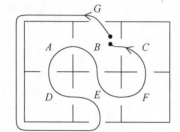

21. a.

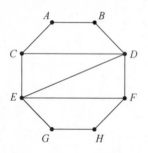

b. Yes. There are exactly two odd vertices C and F, so there is an Euler path.

c. The guard should begin at C and end at F, or vice versa.

22. A, E, C, B, D, A

23. D, B, A, E, C, D

24. a. No, because this is not a complete graph. It may not have Hamilton circuits.

25. a. Yes, because this is a complete graph.

b. $(4-1)! = 3! = 6$

26. a. No, because this is not a complete graph. It may not have Hamilton circuits.

27. a. Yes, because this is a complete graph.

b. $(5-1)! = 4! = 24$

28.

A, B, C, D, A:	$4+6+5+4$	$= 19$
A, B, D, C, A:	$4+7+5+2$	$= 18$
A, C, B, D, A:	$2+6+7+4$	$= 19$
A, C, D, B, A:	$2+5+7+4$	$= 18$
A, D, B, C, A:	$4+7+6+2$	$= 19$
A, D, C, B, A:	$4+5+6+4$	$= 19$

29. These are the only possible Hamilton circuits on a graph with 4 vertices. The lowest weight, 18, occurs on the circuits A, B, D, C, A and A, C, D, B, A. These are the optimal solutions.

30. Start with A. Then edge AC has the smallest weight, 2, of all edges starting at A. Proceed to C. From C, edge CD has the smallest weight, 5, of edges not returning to A. From D, we must travel DB, with weight 7, to B. We return to A along BA, with weight 4. The total weight of this Hamilton circuit is $2+5+7+4 = 18$.

31. Start with A. Of all paths leading from A, the path with smallest weight is AB, with weight 4. Proceed to B. The path with smallest weight leading from B, but not to A, is BE, with weight 6. The path with smallest weight leading from E, but not to A or B, is ED, with weight 4. From D, we proceed along DC, with weight 3, to C, the only remaining vertex. We then return to A along CA, with weight 7. The total weight is $4+6+4+3+7 = 24$.

32.

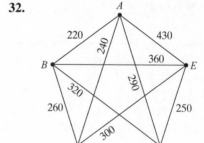

33. Start at *A*. The lowest cost from *A*, $220, is on edge *AB*. From *B*, the lowest cost other than returning to *A* is $260, on edge *BC*. From *C*, the lowest cost to a new city is $180, on edge *CD*. From *D*, the salesman must fly to *E* for $250, then return to *A* for $430. The total cost of this circuit is
$220 + 260 + 180 + 250 + 430 = \$1340$.

34. Yes. It is connected, has no circuits, has 6 edges on 7 vertices, and each edge is a bridge.

35. No. It has a circuit.

36. No. It is disconnected.

37.

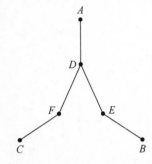

38.

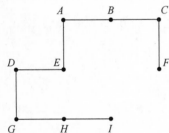

39. Kruskal's algorithm is demonstrated in the figure.

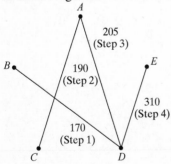

The total weight is
$170 + 190 + 205 + 310 = 875$.

40. Kruskal's algorithm is demonstrated in the figure.

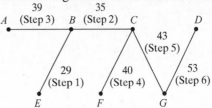

The total weight is
$29 + 35 + 39 + 40 + 43 + 53 = 239$.

41. The figure demonstrates Kruskal's algorithm and the layout of the cable system.

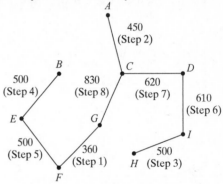

The smallest length of cable needed is
$360 + 450 + 500 + 500 + 500 + 610 + 620 + 830 = 4370$ miles.

Chapter 15 Test

1. *A*: 2; *B*: 2; *C*: 4; *D*: 3; *E*: 2; *F*: 1

2. *A, D, E* and *A, B, C, E*

3. *B, A, D, E, C, B*

4. *CF*

5.

Netherlands
Belgium
Luxembourg
France
Germany
Switzerland
Austria

6. a.   Euler path: there are exactly two odd vertices.

b.

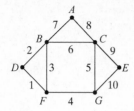

7. a.   Neither: there are more than two odd vertices.

b.   N/A

8. a.   Euler circuit: there are no odd vertices.

b.

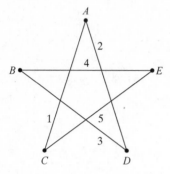

9.   We begin at *A*, then proceed to *E, I, H*, and so on, erasing edges once they have been crossed. The result is shown in the figure.

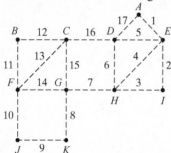

10. a.

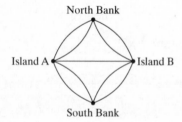

b.   Yes: there are exactly two odd vertices.

c.   It should begin at one of the islands, and end at the other island.

11. a.

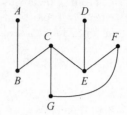

b.   No: there are more than two odd vertices.

12. a.   Let vertices represent intersections, and let edges represent streets.

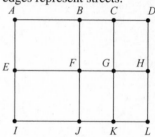

b.   No: there are more than two odd vertices.

13.   A, B, C, D, G, F, E, A and A, F, G, D, C, B, E, A.

14. $(5 - 1)! = 4! = 24$

15.

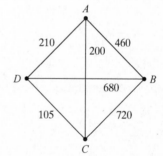

16.

Hamilton Circuit	Sum of the Weights of the Edges	=	Total Cost
A, B, C, D, A	460 + 720 + 105 + 210	=	$1495
A, B, D, C, A	460 + 680 + 105 + 200	=	$1445
A, C, B, D, A	200 + 720 + 680 + 210	=	$1810
A, C, D, B, A	200 + 105 + 680 + 460	=	$1445
A, D, B, C, A	210 + 680 + 720 + 200	=	$1810
A, D, C, B, A	210 + 105 + 720 + 460	=	$1495

The optimal route is *A, B, D, C, A* or *A, C, D, B, A*. The total cost for this route is $1445.

17. Starting from *A*, the edge with smallest weight is *AE*, with weight 5. Proceed to *E*. From *E*, the edge with smallest weight, and not leading back to *A*, is *ED*, with weight 8. From *D*, the edge with smallest weight, and to a new vertex, is *DC*, with weight 4. From *C*, only *B* remains. Edge *CB* has weight 5. Return to *A* by edge *BA*, with weight 11. The total weight of this Hamilton circuit is
$5 + 8 + 4 + 5 + 11 = 33$.

18. No; it has a circuit, namely *C, D, E, C*.

19.

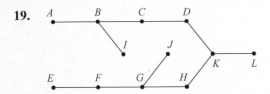

20. Kruskal's algorithm is shown in the figure.

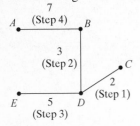

The total weight of the minimum spanning tree is $2 + 3 + 5 + 7 = 17$.